We are The Seriou
of Great Brit

- *Especially wanted are good quality mint or used collections of pre QEII.*
- *Specialized collections of all GB apart from Decimal Machins*
- *National and International Exhibits Especially Silver medal and above*
- *Better Pre QEII First Day Covers (sorry we do not require QEII FDC)*
- *QEII Errors that are listed in this catalogue*
- *Specialist collections of Line-engraved especially "old time lots"*
- *Any Stamp in Fine Condition with a value in this catalogue of a £1000 or more*

Est. 1975

MARK BLOXHAM
STAMPS LTD

Proud

PTS

Member

W: www.philatelic.co.uk   T: +44 (0)1661 871953   E: mark@philatelic.co.uk

SG2263Var 2002
Teddy Bear ERROR Value
and Queens Head at LEFT
U/M with PTS Cert

2002 1st Bear pulling Potted Topiary Tree (Moving Home). Variety Queens Head and Value at left hand side instead of right hand due to mis-perforation Error. SG2263Var U/M

Please contact us for more details

Est. 1975

MARK BLOXHAM
STAMPS LTD

Proud

PTS

Member

W: www.philatelic.co.uk   T: +44 (0)1661 871953   E: mark@philatelic.co.uk

Stanley Gibbons

Great Britain
CONCISE
Stamp Catalogue

2018 edition

STANLEY GIBBONS LTD
London and Ringwood

By Appointment to
Her Majesty The Queen
Philatelists
Stanley Gibbons Ltd
London

Published by *Stanley Gibbons Publications*
Editorial, Sales Offices and Distribution Centre:
7 Parkside, Christchurch Road, Ringwood,
Hants BH24 3SH

First Edition —	May 1986	18th Edition —	April 2003
Second Edition —	May 1987	19th Edition —	April 2004
Third Edition —	May 1988	20th Edition —	May 2005
Fourth Edition —	May 1989	21st Edition —	April 2006
Fifth Edition —	May 1990	22nd Edition —	April 2007
Sixth Edition —	May 1991	23rd Edition —	April 2008
Seventh Edition —	May 1992	24th Edition —	April 2009
Eighth Edition —	April 1993	24th Edition —	reprinted June 2009
Ninth Edition —	April 1994	25th Edition —	May 2010
Tenth Edition —	April 1995	26th Edition —	April 2011
11th Edition —	April 1996	27th Edition —	April 2012
12th Edition —	April 1997	28th Edition —	April 2013
13th Edition —	April 1998	29th Edition —	April 2014
14th Edition —	April 1999	30th Edition —	May 2015
15th Edition —	May 2000	31st Edition —	May 2016
16th Edition —	April 2001	32nd Edition —	June 2017
17th Edition —	April 2002	33rd Edition —	May 2018

Contents

Are You THINKING of SELLING?

This is

HOW THE STAMP TRADE WORKS

Philatelic Expert Lets You into his *Selling Secrets* so you can benefit from a *totally different* (and New) Selling Experience

by Andrew McGavin

1 **If You want to learn** how the stamp trade works, please read on… When I was 15, I did. I wondered if there was some secret source of supply? So, I bought my 1st stamp mixture, (wholesale I thought), broke it into 50 smaller units, advertised it in Stamp Magazine 'Classifieds', and waited for the orders to roll in… I'm still waiting, 48 years later !...

Wrong Offer ✗ *Wrong Price* ✗
Wrong Place ✗

(naïve seller ✔ = 😞 me but I was only 15 at the time!)

2 **Three years later,** attending my first public stamp auctions I wondered how some bidders seemed to buy everything, paying the highest price? It didn't occur to me that they were probably Auction Bidding Agents, paid by absent (dealer) bidders to represent them. I wondered why two collectors sitting side by side muttered to each other **"he's a dealer"** as if that justified him paying the highest price…

…but did it really? What was the real reason? How could a Dealer pay a higher price than a Collector? It doesn't make sense, does it? Collectors are customers. Customers usually pay the highest price, unless… for a Collector, this was…

Wrong Presentation ✗ *Wrong Place* ✗
therefore Wrong Price ✗

3 **Fast-forward 48 years later** to a British Empire collection, lot #1 in an International Stamp Auction – Estimated at £3,000, but we were the highest bidder at £21,000 – **YES** – some 7×higher. Including Buyer's Premium in the extraordinary sum of £4,788 we actually paid GBP£25,788= upon a £3,000 estimate… **however,** we broke it down into sets, singles, mini-collections etc. We made a profit. Some might say it found its price. Others may say:

Wrong Estimate ✗ *Wrong Presentation* ✗
Wrong Structure ✗ *Wrong Protection of Price* ✗

– Lucky for the seller that 2 well-healed bidders saw the potential value that day or it could have been given away… the seller could easily have lost out couldn't he? or she?

So, by un-peeling the layers of obfuscation, hopefully we can all agree:

The Secret is Simple –

Plus the 3 Philatelic 'P's –

Presentation ✔ Place ✔ and Price ✔

4 **Understanding the problem…** I always remember the car trade had their own little 'bible' – Glass's Guide. I've no idea, I've not even looked - in this internet-dominated world, it may even have disappeared. Well, there's an insider Stamp Trade publication for Stamp Dealers called "The Philatelic Exporter". There's nothing that special about it – and you won't learn much or find massively reduced prices by subscribing – **BUT** – it is a forum, a paper focal point, a last 'bastion' in this on-line transparent world that we inhabit… whereby dealers (and auctioneers) can try and communicate with each other. I publish my own articles there…

Recently I discussed the outcome of my 10 years' simple research, asking dealers and auctioneers **'what is your biggest problem?'**

To a man, (why are we almost all men), they replied – **"my biggest problem is stock, if I can get more of the right stock I can sell it easily"**

Strange that, nobody ever asked me the same question back – because my answer would have been entirely different (and I don't treat it as a problem) – **I seek to satisfy collectors**

This is the reason why my company has such massive advertising. This is the reason why we spend up to 8% of turnover – up to £200,000 per annum in marketing costs. (Most dealers don't even sell £200K per annum).

About The Author ❭ Andrew found his Father's stamps at the age of 10. A year later at Senior School he immediately joined the School Stamp Club. He 'specialised'(!) in British, but soon was interested in Queen Victoria which he could not afford. The 2nd to last boy wearing short trousers in his school year, he religiously bought Post Office New Issues on Tuesdays with his pocket money. He soon found that he enjoyed swapping / trading stamps as much as collecting them. Aged 19, eschewing University he quickly found a philatelic career in London, leading to creating his own companies in stamps. Andrew has authored many internationally published Stamp 'Tips' articles, appearing on Local Radio and National TV promoting Philately with Alan Titchmarsh. Andrew's area of expertise is unusual – in so far as his grounding in collecting and wide philatelic knowledge has given him a deep understanding of Philately. He has studied Philately for the past 45 years, in combination with Commerce and Marketing Expertise, enabling him to create synergies in 'lifetime' interlinked Stamp Selling Systems, selling unit-priced stamps through to handling collections & Rarities up to £700,000 each. Today Andrew is fortunate to be co-owner with his Wife, of Universal Philatelic Auctions (aka UPA) – the Largest No Buyer's Premium Reducing-Estimate System Stamp Auction in the World, creating records selling stamps to 2,261 different bidders from 54 different countries in his latest auction. Andrew stopped collecting stamps aged 18 reasoning that his enjoyment of stamps would be in handling them and selling them…

5 **Why is that?** Because, as the world revolved **the Stamp Market, imperceptibly** *Changed*, **and incrementally – Massively**

So, although few will tell you this, it's clearly evident that the problem for most Sellers of Stamps today is no longer absent stock – but absent collectors in the place they choose to sell their stamps in. Simply put, other Dealers, Auctions, Stamp Fairs have not invested in marketing to have a strong Customer-core. To be fair, this is not true of all – but it is true of most – so that our nearest competitor 'Apex' had 800 bidders in a recent auction. In my most recent 20,000+ lot UPA 68th Auction we had 2,184 different bidders from 58 different countries, 95% of whom were Collectors. Some other well-advertised auctions only have 200 bidders (a high percentage of whom are dealers – so that, essentially they are Dealer-dominated auctions) – so that when you sell through them – you're paying up to 18% (including VAT) seller's commission and the buyer is paying up to 25% **and** more in Buyer's Premium, credit card fees, on-line bidding fee, delivery and insurance etc… **AND all of that so that your stamps may be sold, wait for it – TO DEALERS (and some collectors),** but Dealers, that naturally must make a profit to survive…

6 **Now, let's examine the cost implications – Example:** Your stamp collection sells in public auction for £800. Upon a 25% buyer's premium, the dealer pays £1,000 and it could be more. He breaks it into £2,000+ selling price (much lower and he'll go out of business). The auction charges you a seller's commission of up to 18% (VAT included) upon the £800 sale price. This is GBP£144. Therefore you receive approaching £656 – which is approximately 33% of the dealer's £2,000+/- retail selling price - **BUT… now that we have identified the problem…**

Isn't the Solution Staring us Right in The Face ?

7 **Why Pay an Auction to Sell to Dealers: Sell to Collectors instead ?** In our example with buyer's premium, sellers commission, lotting fees, extra credit card charges, VAT and even insurance - you're already being charged in different ways up to 40% of the selling price to sell, possibly or probably, **to the wrong person.**

Why not direct that 40% cost you're paying to sell to Collectors instead? Sounds good, so why hasn't this been done before ?

8 **Truth is, it *Has* been done before…** Sometimes the 'old' ways are the best ways aren't they? But in today's enthusiasm to obscure the obvious so that money may be taken, almost surreptitiously, in numerous different ways, (without us apparently noticing until we see the cheque in our pocket) – the transparent 'seller pays' has been deliberately 'obscured' – so much so that, **amazingly,** the latest 2017 European Auction Selling Legislation just introduced – now requires auctions that charge 'buyer's premiums' **to warn the buyer in advance.** Just imagine going into the petrol station, and being warned that the price you're paying to put fuel in you tank is not the real price, you have to pay a premium! Obviously, there would be an uproar…

9 **How can you cut out the middleman and sell to Collectors instead?** Well, I can think of two ways. 1). **DIY** - Do It Yourself selling on eBay. That may be fine for lower grade material – but, would you risk auctioning relatively unprotected rare material on eBay ? We don't and we're professionals, so we should know what we're doing. Or 2). Cut out the extra middle-man. **Use my company UPA, which reaches collectors instead.** Here's how it works: Continuing from our previous **Example**:

The auction sold your stamps to a dealer for £1,000 – but You received circa £656

UPA sells them to collectors for you for up to £2,000 – even after 40% commission you receive up to £1,200. Up to £544 more. Now that's amazing, isn't it? 🏆

10 **Sounds Good Andrew, but Can You 'Deliver'?** Obviously, nothing is as simple as that, and as we auction stamps to collectors some collections may 'break' to the example £2,000+/- but the stamps may be sold for more or less – especially as we reserve all lots at 20% below, (Estimate £2,000 = £1,600 reserve) and not everything sells first or even 2nd time so prices may come down… Naturally, it's not that straightforward for a dealer either – he may sell at a discount to 'move' stock **OR**, like many dealers he may be sitting on the same unsold stamps, that you see time and time again, in dealer's stocks years later and still at the same unattractive prices…

So, I think it is more reasonable for you to expect up to 36% to 50% more, indirectly or directly via my **Collector's Secret Weapon:** Universal Philatelic Auctions, which moves material more quickly, by incrementally reducing estimate (and reserve) price in a structured selling system…

11 **Q.)** **What is the Collector's 'Secret Weapon'?**

A.) **It's called the Unique UPA Reducing Estimate System…** ★★
This is a rather long explanation, I don't want to bore you, but 18 years ago, when my wife and I set up Universal Philatelic Auctions I detected that the stamp trade's biggest problem then was not what sold – **but what didn't sell…** So, because I didn't want to try to keep on offering the same either unsaleable or overpriced stock I created the unique UPA Reducing Estimate (and reserve) Selling System. Simply put, if a lot doesn't sell in the 1st auction we reduce the estimate (and reserve) by 11% and unlike other dealers and auctions **WE TELL YOU – 'US'** = once unsold. If unsold after the following auction we **reduce by a further 12%** and **WE TELL YOU 'US2'**, if unsold after a 3rd UPA auction we reduce by a further 13% and **WE TELL YOU 'US3'** and so on till the lot finds its price, is sold or virtually given away… ✓

12 **Any Scientist will tell you** that combinations of ingredients can produce powerful results. So we created the unique combination of my UPA Reducing Estimate System, married (in stone), with UPA's fair 'NO BUYER'S Premium' policy, PLUS each lot carries my total 'no quibble' guarantee – this formula is the reason why within the span of 4 auctions (one year)… 90%-95% of lots broken from a collection have sold. This Unique Philatelic Selling System **Formula** is the reason why we are the largest stamp auction in the UK today with 2,184 different bidders in my recent auction. 🧠

In Hindsight Dealers warned me 18 years ago that my idea wouldn't work. 18 years later I think I've proven that it does. (Reader: Please Request a complimentary UPA catalogue – using the contact details further below)

13 **OK, Cut to the Chase Andrew, what's the offer?** All of my Selling Systems are based upon **selling to Collectors Globally,** so that 95% of stamps sold by UPA are

ATTENTION OWNERS OF LARGE/ VALUABLE COLLECTIONS –

sold directly to Collectors. If you wish to benefit by up to 50% or more, depending upon your circumstance and type of material, by cutting out the middleman – then this offer may be for you. Generally 'time' is the enemy in our lives, and for most dealers not being able to sell stock. Now is the time to let 'time' do the 'heavy-lifting' and consider making 'time' work for you, so that at UPA you can make time your friend. 👍

14 AND the SMALL PRINT? Some lots are too small in value for us to offer this system. Other lots may not be suited to selling in this manner (e.g. surplus mint British decimal stamps best used for postage) – especially if the market is heavily compromised by stock overhang in specific areas. Some Collectors will not wish to use time and systems to leverage price, others will want to agree a specific price and know that they are paid precisely this amount. No client is treated like a number and no client is forced like a square peg into a round hole. ☀

15 OK, What Do I Do Next?

a). You contact UPA to discuss with Andrew or a highly-qualified Auction Valuer/Describer what you have to dispose of and your options bearing in mind your specific interests / requirements

b). If you wish, get a 2nd opinion, but investigate what type of auction / dealer you are dealing with. Is it a Dealer's auction with relatively few collectors? Can you see where / how the Dealer sells? If you can't easily see any pricelists or high quality selling catalogues – that Dealer may sell your stamps to other dealers…

c). Finally you ask U P A to collect your stamps, insure in transit for an estimated replacement retail value…☎ 💻 🚚

16 What Happens then? A member of my Team telephones/e-mails you to confirm safe receipt. 'Overnight' valuations, unless simple, are rare. Valuing stamp collections that have taken tens of years to create takes time. Depending upon your priorities / timescale I, or an experienced member of my Team will contact you to discuss your requirements and the options available to you for the sale

SCOTTISH & NORTH CONTACT

COTSWOLDS MIDLANDS & SOUTH CONTACT

Contact UPA: 01451 861 111

of your collection. Provided only that you feel well-informed and comfortable do we agree strategy 🖩 🤝

17 How Strong is the Stamp and Cover Market? Everybody knows that the strongest areas are GB and British Empire. Post-Independence / QEII material sells but if hinged at considerable discount. Mint hinged material pre 1952 is regarded as the industry 'norm' and therefore desirable – but <u>genuine</u> never-hinged commands a premium. Europe sells but at reduced levels, Americas is good, as generally is Asia but the 'heat' has come off China which is still good – and Russia which can still be good. East Europe is weaker. Overall, Rarities throughout can command their own price levels and real Postal History has good demand.

18 What Should I Do Next? Discuss your collection with U P A. Contact Andrew or an experienced member of his Team now… 💻 ☎

19 Guarantee: I want You to be absolutely Sure So If You're not sure we'll transport and return your stamps for FREE up to £200 in actual shipping cost at our expense. It sounds generous (and it is), but it's far less than the cost of driving 100+ miles each way and 3 to 6 hours in your home valuing your stamps 😊

20 My Double Cast Iron Guarantee: We can do a better job valuing your stamps in our office than in your home. If you don't agree I'll pay you an extra £50 for you to pay somebody trusted to open the boxes and put your albums back, in the same place, on the shelf they came from. 😊😊

21 Act NOW: Contact Andrew or an experienced member of his Team using the on-line selling form at our website, by fax, telephone or by mail. We'll work harder for you not to regret the decision to sell all or part of your collection…☎ 💻

Andrew McGavin, Philatelic Expert, Author, Managing Director
Universal Philatelic Auctions UPA

Request Your Next FREE Catalogue NOW

Preface

The primary aim of the Stanley Gibbons Catalogue, ever since it was first published in 1865 has been to provide collectors with the information they need in a form which they find most convenient. As time goes by, both of these are subject to gradual change; collecting interests expand, decline and then grow in other areas, so it is important that the catalogue reflects those changes. As for the form in which the catalogue is presented, it is inevitable that the time will come when most collectors prefer to access their information electronically, but for the time being, we are certain that the majority still wish their catalogue to be published in book form and there is no doubt that the preferred option is for a traditional casebound book, a book with hard covers, which will cope with the rigours of regular use and lie flat on the desk when being referred to – which is why this is the first edition of the *Great Britain Concise Catalogue* which has been published entirely in casebound form.

Editorial developments

Going back to the changing needs of collectors, it has become clear that there are more useful ways of utilising the space devoted in the past to illustrating the first day of issue postmarks for every commemorative set, so these have been removed from this edition. Further space has been saved by removing repetitive footnotes and replacing them with single notes, covering a number of issues. Another feature which has become increasingly repetitive is the notation of colours used in the production of modern stamps. These days, whether the issue is litho or gravure printed, most commemorative sets use the same four 'process' colours, with an occasional fifth on top. For this edition these colours have been replaced by a description of what the stamp depicts in an effort to aid identification, while the set heading incorporates a new |MULTI|COLOUR| note, designed to provide the necessary information in an abbreviated form.

It should not be assumed however, that this edition has been all about saving space; there are several areas in which information has been expanded as well. Our colleague, David Smythe, has undertaken the revision and expansion of the design index for commemorative and pictorial stamps. This has been a painstaking process, begun in last year's *Concise* and now further expanded for 2018 to make it much easier to find odd single stamps within the listings.

Probably the most important additions to this catalogue over the past three years have been the tables compiled by John M Deering for the 'Security' Machin definitives, and for Post & Go stamps. 2017 saw the extension and development of the 'ROYALMAIL' Security backing papers, used for self-adhesive sheet, business sheet and booklet stamps. The resulting differences are now incorporated into John's tables, although, since the backing is not a part of the stamp itself, they do not impact on the main listings.

One thing which certainly has affected the listings is that the 'U' section of Security Machins has been renumbered to remove all the suffix letters for basic stamps, while, in an effort to minimise the number of future changes, 'blank' numbers have been left for future issues. A complete listing of the number changes is included in the Machin section of this catalogue.

Returning to John Deering's tables, those following the Post & Go stamps, listing stamps dispensed at exhibitions and museums have now been given prices. These have been provided at the request of collectors and represent the prices you might expect to pay for collectors' strips obtained from these sources.

There are also new tables in the booklets section, combining, for relevant stamp books, details of year codes on the stamps with the different types of backing paper reported at the time of going to press. Helpful explanatory notes and prices are, naturally, included.

Elsewhere, of course, new discoveries have been added to the listings and new notes provided, as necessary for the guidance of collectors.

In the Regional Issues, the stamps with values in the revised typeface, introduced for the £1.17 and £1.40 stamps in 2017 and now extended to the 1st and 2nd class stamps and the new values for 2018, are now listed as separate sets.

Prices

We cannot of course, close without saying something about the price changes to this edition, which in terms of sheer numbers are undoubtedly more extensive than they have been in any edition of this catalogue for a number of years.

The most extensive and noticeable changes affect the commemorative stamps of the present reign, where there has been a distinct softening of the market in recent years. In view of this catalogue's importance as a source of information, it would be irresponsible not to have reflected this development in the prices quoted.

The process has been carried out with great care and does not represent a wholesale reduction. There are a great many prices that are unchanged and, indeed, quite a few which have been increased, even within the period in question, while most of the adjustments to the pre-1952 section of the catalogue are in an upward direction.

Whether or not you view this year's price changes in a positive light, one thing which we are sure you will view positively is the lower retail price for this edition, which we hope will encourage all collectors of Great Britain stamps to bring themselves up to date with the latest issues, discoveries, information and market prices.

HUGH JEFFERIES
VINCE CORDELL

May 2018

Features of this Catalogue

The Concise Catalogue, now in its 33rd year of publication, has established itself as an essential guide for the "one-country" collector of Great Britain. As the popularity of Great Britain stamps continues to grow — the Concise Catalogue supplies the information you need to enhance your collection.

✦ All issues from the Penny Black of 1840 to 1 April 2018 including Regional, Postage Due, Official and Postal Fiscal stamps.

✦ All different stamp designs are illustrated.

✦ Every basic stamp listed, including those with different watermarks or perforations and those showing graphite lines or phosphor bands.

✦ Unmounted mint and mounted mint prices quoted for 1887 "Jubilee" series and all King Edward VII and King George V issues, apart from the Departmental Officials.

✦ Missing colours, missing embossing, watermark errors, imperforate errors and phosphor omitted varieties from those stamps normally issued with phosphor bands.

✦ Booklet panes listed up to 1952, including inverted watermark varieties.

✦ Gutter Pairs and "Traffic light" Gutter Pairs listed in mint sets.

✦ First Day Covers for Special Issues from 1924 and for King Edward VIII and King George VI definitives. For the present reign the coverage also extends to Prestige Booklet panes and Regionals. All British Post Office special First Day of Issue postmarks are priced on cover.

✦ Post Office Picture Cards (PHQ cards) are priced as sets, both mint and used with First Day of Issue postmarks.

✦ Presentation, Collector and Gift Packs, including the scarce versions with foreign inscriptions.

✦ Quick-reference diagrams for listed Machin decimal booklet panes.

✦ Design Index for Commemorative and Special Stamps after the Philatelic Information Section.

✦ Machin and commemorative underprints given separate catalogue numbers.

✦ Post Office Yearbooks.

✦ Royal Mail Postage Labels priced in mint or used sets and on British Post Office First Day Covers.

✦ Royal Mail Post & Go stamps; with notes on machine types, errors, date codes and special inscriptions.

✦ Notes on Postage Due bisects based on research by Mr. P. Frost.

✦ Wartime issues for the Channel Islands.

✦ Separate section for Post Office Stamp Booklets with dated editions of King George VI and Queen Elizabeth listed separately.

✦ Post Office Label Sheets, popularly known as 'Generic Smilers'.

✦ Specimen overprints up to 1952.

✦ Helpful introductory section providing definitions and guidance for the collector and including all watermark illustrations shown together to assist identification.

✦ Addresses for specialist philatelic societies covering Great Britain stamps.

✦ Post Office Telegraph Stamps

✦ The following have been added to this edition: 87c, 95, 218a, 218aw, 243, 267a, 267aw, 400Wk

We would like to thank all those who have assisted in the compilation of this catalogue. Special thanks for amendments to this edition are due to Rowan Baker, David Brooker, Gary Burgess, Ian de la Rue Browne, Keith Emerson, Ron Grierson, John Horsey, Peter Jones, Ian Lasok-Smith, Ken Law, Brian Lingard, Peter McCulloch, Alan Mitchell, Robert Oliver, John Peart, Ian Pooley, Michael Round, Kevin Samuels, Ian Shaw, David Smythe, Bruce Stewart, Julian Tremayne, Brian Wenden, Peter Wess, Judy Wieland

Great Britain Philatelic Societies

The Great Britain Philatelic Society.
Hon. Membership Secretary: Victoria Lajer,
Stanley Gibbons Ltd., 399 Strand, London WC2R 0LX

The Modern British Philatelic Circle. Hon. Membership Secretary: A. J. Wilkins, 3 Buttermere Close, Brierley Hill, West Midlands, DY5 3SD.

The Great Britain Collectors' Club.
Secretary: Mr S. McGill, 10309 Brookhollow Circle, Highlands Ranch, CO 80129, USA

Stanley Gibbons Holdings Plc

Stanley Gibbons Limited,
Stanley Gibbons Auctions
399 Strand, London WC2R 0LX
Tel: +44 (0)207 836 8444
Fax: +44 (0)207 836 7342
E-mail: help@stanleygibbons.com
Website: www.stanleygibbons.com
for all departments, Auction and
Specialist Stamp Departments.
Open Monday–Friday 9.30 a.m. to 5
p.m.
Shop. Open Monday–Friday 9 a.m.
to 5.30 p.m. and Saturday 9.30 a.m.
to 5.30 p.m.

Stanley Gibbons Publications
Gibbons Stamp Monthly and
Philatelic Exporter
7 Parkside, Christchurch Road,
Ringwood, Hampshire BH24 3SH.
Tel: +44 (0)1425 472363
Fax: +44 (0)1425 470247
E-mail: help@stanleygibbons.com
Publications Mail Order.
FREEPHONE 0800 611622
Monday–Friday 8.30 a.m. to 5 p.m.

Stanley Gibbons (Jersey) Limited
18 Hill Street, St Helier, Jersey,
Channel Islands JE2 4UA.
Tel: +44 (0)1534 766711
Fax: +44 (0)1534 766177
E-mail: investment@stanleygibbons.
com

Stanley Gibbons (Asia) Limited
Room 618, 6/F
100 Queen's Road,
Central,
Hong Kong
Tel: +852 3180 93708
E-mail: elee@stanleygibbons.com

Stanley Gibbons Publications
Overseas Representation
Stanley Gibbons Publications
are represented overseas by the
following

Australia *Renniks Publications*
Pty Ltd
Unit 3 37-39 Green Street,
Banksmeadow, NSW 2019,
Australia
Tel: +612 9695 7055
Website: www.renniks.com

Canada *Unitrade Associates*
99 Floral Parkway, Toronto,
Ontario M6L 2C4, Canada
Tel: +1 416 242 5900
Website: www.unitradeassoc.com

Germany *Schaubek Verlag Leipzig*
Am Glaeschen 23, D-04420
Markranstaedt, Germany
Tel: +49 34 205 67823
Website: www.schaubek.de

Italy *Ernesto Marini S.R.L.*
V. Struppa, 300, Genova, 16165,
Italy
Tel: +3901 0247-3530
Website: www.ernestomarini.it

Japan *Japan Philatelic*
PO Box 2, Suginami-Minami,
Tokyo 168-8081,
Japan
Tel: +81 3330 41641
Website: www.yushu.co.jp

Netherlands also covers Belgium
Denmark, Finland & France
Uitgeverij Davo BV
PO Box 411, Ak Deventer, 7400
Netherlands
Tel. I 315 7050 2700
Website: www.davo.nl

New Zealand *House of Stamps*
PO Box 12, Paraparaumu,
New Zealand
Tel: +61 6364 8270
Website: www.houseofstamps.co.nz

New Zealand *Philatelic Distributors*
PO Box 863
15 Mount Edgecumbe Street
New Plymouth 4615, New Zealand
Tel: +6 46 758 65 68
Website: www.stampcollecta.com

Norway *Skanfil A/S*
Spanav. 52 / Boks 2030
N-5504 Haugesund, Norway
Tel: +47-52703940
E-mail: magne@skanfil.no

Singapore *C S Philatelic Agency*
Peninsula Shopping Centre #04-29
3 Coleman Street, 179804, Singapore
Tel: +65 6337-1859
Website: www.cs.com.sg

South Africa *Peter Bale Philatelics*
P O Box 3719, Honeydew,
2040, South Africa
Tel: +27 11 462 2463
Tel: +27 82 330 3925
E-mail: balep@iafrica.com

Sweden *Chr Winther Sorensen AB*
Box 43, S-310 20 Knaered, Sweden
Tel: +46 43050743
Website: www.collectia.se

Prices

The prices quoted in this catalogue are the estimated selling prices of Stanley Gibbons Ltd at the time of publication. They are, *unless it is specifically stated otherwise*, for examples in fine condition for the issue concerned. Superb examples are worth more; those of a lower quality considerably less.

All prices are subject to change without prior notice and Stanley Gibbons Ltd may from time to time offer stamps below catalogue price. Individual low value stamps sold at 399, Strand are liable to an additional handling charge. Purchasers of new issues are asked to note that the prices charged for them contain an element for the service rendered and so may exceed the prices shown when the stamps are subsequently catalogued.

No guarantee is given to supply all stamps priced, since it is not possible to keep every catalogued item in stock.

Quotation of prices

The prices in the left-hand column are for unused stamps and those in the right-hand column are for used.

A dagger (†) denotes that the item listed does not exist in that condition and a blank, or dash, that it exists, or may exist, but no market price is known.

Prices are expressed in pounds and pence sterling. One pound comprises 100 pence (£1 = 100p).

The method of notation is as follows: pence in numerals (e.g. 5 denotes five pence); pounds and pence up to £100, in numerals (e.g. 4·25 denotes four pounds and twenty-five pence); prices above £100 expressed in whole pounds with the "£" sign shown.

Unused and Used stamps

The prices for unused stamps of Queen Victoria issued before 1887 are for lightly hinged examples. Unused stamps of the 1887 "Jubilee" issue and from the reigns of King Edward VII and King George V are priced in both unmounted and mounted condition. The only exception is the Departmental Officials, which are priced unused, used and used on cover. Unused prices for King Edward VIII to Queen Elizabeth II issues are for unmounted mint (though when not available, mounted mint stamps are often supplied at a lower price). Prices for used stamps are for fine postally used examples, usually cancelled by a clear operational circular datestamp.

Prices quoted for bisects on cover or on large piece are for those dated during the period officially authorised.

Minimum price

The minimum price quoted is 10 pence. For individual stamps, prices between 10 pence and 95 pence are provided as a guide for catalogue users. The lowest price *charged* for individual stamps or sets purchased from Stanley Gibbons Ltd is £1.

Set prices

Set prices are generally for one of each value, excluding shades and varieties, but including major colour changes.

Where there are alternative shades, etc., the cheapest is usually included. The number of stamps in the set is always stated for clarity.

The mint and used prices for sets containing *se-tenant* pieces are based on the prices quoted for such combinations, and not on those for individual stamps.

Gutter Pairs

These, and traffic light gutter pairs, are priced as complete sets.

Used on Cover prices

To assist collectors, cover prices are quoted in a third column for postage and Official stamps issued in the reign of Queen Victoria and in boxed notes for the 1887 "Jubilee" issue and for King Edward VII stamps.

The cover should be of non-philatelic origin, bearing the correct postal rate for the period and distance involved and cancelled with the markings normal to the offices concerned. Purely philatelic items have a cover value only slightly greater than the catalogue value for the corresponding used stamps. This applies generally to those high-value stamps used philatelically rather than in the normal course of commerce.

Oversized covers, difficult to accommodate on an album page, should be reckoned as worth little more than the corresponding value of the used stamps. The condition of a cover affects its value. Except for "wreck covers", serious damage or soiling reduces the value where the postal markings and stamps are ordinary ones. Conversely, visual appeal adds to the value and this can include freshness of appearance, important addresses, old-fashioned but legible handwriting, historic town-names, etc. The prices quoted are a base on which further value would be added to take account of the cover's postal historical importance in demonstrating such things as unusual, scarce or emergency cancels, interesting routes, significant postal markings, combination usage, the development of postal rates, and so on.

However, it should also be noted that multiples of some stamps are frequently more commonly found on cover than single usages and in such cases the cover might be worth less than the price quoted.

First Day Cover prices

Prices are quoted for commemorative first day covers from 1924 British Empire Exhibition pair onwards. These prices are for special covers (from 1937) franked with complete sets and cancelled by ordinary operational postmarks to the end of 1962 or the various standard "First Day of Issue" markings from 1963.

Prices are provided for King Edward VIII and King George VI definitives on plain covers with operational postmarks of the first day of issue. For some values special covers also exist and these are worth more than the prices quoted.

The Philatelic Bureau and other special "First Day of Issue" postmarks provided by the Post Office since 1963 are listed under each issue. Prices quoted are for these postmarks used on illustrated covers (from 1964 those produced by the Post Office), franked with complete sets.

The British Post Office did not introduce special First Day of Issue postmarks for definitive issues until the first instalment of the Machin £sd series, issued 5 June 1967, although "First Day" treatment had been provided for some Regional stamps from 8 June 1964 onwards. Prices for the First Day Covers from 1952 to 1966, showing definitive stamps are for the stamps indicated, used on illustrated envelopes and postmarked with operational cancellations.

From 1967 onwards the prices quoted are for stamps as indicated, used on illustrated envelopes and postmarked with special First Day of Issue handstamps. Other definitives issued during this period were not accepted for "First Day" treatment by the British Post Office.

Guarantee

All stamps are guaranteed genuine originals in the following terms:

If not as described, and returned by the purchaser, we undertake to refund the price paid to us in the original transaction. If any stamp is certified as genuine by the Expert Committee of the Royal Philatelic Society, London, or by B.P.A. Expertising Ltd, the purchaser shall not be entitled to make any claim against us for any error, omission or mistake in such certificate.

Consumers' statutory rights are not affected by the above guarantee.

The recognised Expert Committees in this country are those of the Royal Philatelic Society, 41 Devonshire Place, London W1G 6JY, and B.P.A. Expertising Ltd, P.O. Box 1141, Guildford, Surrey GU5 0WR. They do not undertake valuations under any circumstances and fees are payable for their services.

Contacting the Catalogue Editor

The Editor is always interested in hearing from people who have new information which will improve or correct the Catalogue. As a general rule he must see and examine the actual stamps before they can be considered for listing; photographs or scans are insufficent evidence, although an initial email to the editor *hjefferies@stanleygibbons.com* will determine whether or not an item is likely to be of interest.

Submissions should be made in writing to the Catalogue Editor, Stanley Gibbons Publications. The cost of return postage for items submitted is appreciated, and this should include the registration fee if required.

Where information is solicited purely for the benefit of the enquirer, the editor cannot undertake to reply if the answer is already contained in these published notes or if return postage is omitted. Written or email communications are greatly preferred to enquiries by telephone and the editor regrets that he or his staff cannot see personal callers without a prior appointment being made. Correspondence may be subject to delay during the production period of each new edition.

Please note that the following classes of material are outside the scope of this Catalogue:

(a) Non-postal revenue or fiscal stamps.
(b) Postage stamps used fiscally.
(c) Local carriage labels and private local issues.
(d) Punctured postage stamps (perfins).
(e) Bogus or phantom stamps.
(f) Railway or airline letter fee stamps, bus or road transport company labels.
(g) Postal stationery cut-outs.
(h) All types of non-postal labels and souvenirs.

(i) Documentary labels for the postal service, e.g. registration, recorded delivery, airmail etiquettes, etc.
(j) Privately applied embellishments to official issues and privately commissioned items generally.
(k) Stamps for training postal staff.

> **We regret we do not give opinions as to the genuineness of stamps, nor do we identify stamps or number them by our Catalogue.**

General Abbreviations

Alph	Alphabet
Anniv	Anniversary
Brt	Bright (colour)
C.	Overprinted in carmine
Des	Designer; designed
Dp	Deep (colour)
Eng	Engraver; engraved
Horiz	Horizontal; horizontally
Imp, Imperf	Imperforate
Inscr	Inscribed
L	Left
Litho	Lithographed
Lt	Light (colour)
mm	Millimetres
MS	Miniature sheet
Opt(d)	Overprint(ed)
P, Perf	Perforated
Photo	Photogravure
Pl	Plate
Pr	Pair
Ptd	Printed
Ptg	Printing
PVA	Polyvinyl alcohol (gum)
R	Right
R.	Row
Recess	Recess-printed
T	Type
Typo	Typographed (Letterpress)
Un	Unused
Us	Used
Vert	Vertical; vertically
W or wmk	Watermark
Wmk s	Watermark sideways

(†) = Does not exist.

(—) (or blank price column) = Exists, or may exist, but no market price is known.

/ between colours means "on" and the colour following is that of the paper on which the stamp is printed.

Printers

B.W.	Bradbury Wilkinson & Co, Ltd.
Cartor	Cartor S.A., La Loupe, France
D.L.R.	De La Rue & Co, Ltd, London, and (from 1961) Bogota, Colombia. De La Rue Security Print (*formerly Harrison & Sons Ltd*) from 8 September 1997.
Enschedé	Joh. Enschedé en Zonen, Haarlem, Netherlands.
Harrison	Harrison & Sons, Ltd, High Wycombe.
ISP	International Security Printers (Walsall and/ or Cartor
J.W.	John Waddington Security Print, Ltd, Leeds.
P.B.	Perkins Bacon Ltd, London.
Questa	Questa Colour Security Printers, Ltd.
Waterlow	Waterlow & Sons, Ltd, London.
Walsall	Walsall Security Printers, Ltd.

Philatelic information

Catalogue Numbers

The catalogue number appears in the extreme left column. The boldface Type numbers in the next column are merely cross-reference to illustrations. Catalogue numbers in the *Gibbons Stamp Monthly* Supplements are provisional only and may need to be altered when the lists are consolidated.

Our Catalogue numbers are universally recognised in specifying stamps and as a hallmark of status.

Inverted and other watermark varieties incorporate "Wi", etc., within the number. Other items which appear in this Catalogue but not *Part 1 (British Commonwealth) Catalogue*, incorporate "Ea", etc.

Catalogue Illustrations

Stamps and first day postmarks are illustrated at three-quarters linear size. Stamps not illustrated are the same size and format as the value shown, unless otherwise indicated. Overprints, surcharges and watermarks are normally actual size. Illustrations of varieties are often enlarged to show the detail. Illustrations of miniature sheets have their dimensions, in millimetres, stated with the width given first.

Designers

Designers' names are quoted where known, though space precludes naming every individual concerned in the production of a set. In particular, photographers supplying material are usually named only when they also make an active contribution in the design stage; posed photographs of reigning monarchs are, however, an exception to this rule.

Printing Errors

Errors in printing are of major interest to this Catalogue. Authenticated items meriting consideration would include: background, centre or frame inverted or omitted; centre or subject transposed; error of colour; error or omission of value; double prints and impressions; printed both sides; and so on. Designs *tête-bêche*, whether intentionally or by accident, are listable. Colours only partially omitted are not listed. However, stamps with embossing, phosphor or both omitted and stamps printed on the gummed side are included.

Printing technology has radically improved over the years, during which time gravure and lithography have become predominant. Varieties nowadays are more in the nature of flaws which are almost always outside the scope of this book.

In no catalogue, however, do we list such items as: dry prints, kiss prints, doctor-blade flaws, colour shifts or registration flaws (unless they lead to the complete omission of a colour from an individual stamp), lithographic ring flaws, and so on. Neither do we recognise fortuitous happenings like paper creases or confetti flaws.

Paper Types

All stamps listed are deemed to be on "ordinary" paper of the wove type and white in colour; only departures from this are normally mentioned.

A coloured paper is one that is coloured right through (front and back of the stamp). In the Catalogue the colour of the paper is given in *italics*, thus:

purple/*yellow* = purple design on yellow paper.

Papers have been made specially white in recent years by, for example, a very heavy coating of chalk. We do not classify shades of whiteness of paper as distinct varieties. The availability of many postage stamps for revenue purposes made necessary some safeguard against the illegitimate re-use of stamps with removable cancellations. This was at first secured by using fugitive inks and later by printing on chalky (chalk-surfaced) paper, both of which made it difficult to remove any form of obliteration without also damaging the stamp design. Stamps which exist on both ordinary and chalk-surfaced papers are separately listed.

The "traditional" method of identifying chalk-surfaced papers has been that, when touched with a silver wire, a black mark is left on the paper, and the listings in this catalogue are based on that test. However, the test itself is now largely discredited, for, although the mark can be removed by a soft rubber, some damage to the stamp will result from its use.

The difference between chalk-surfaced and pre-war ordinary papers is fairly clear: chalk-surfaced papers being smoother to the touch and showing a characteristic sheen when light is reflected off their surface. Under good magnification tiny bubbles or pock marks can be seen on the surface of the stamp and at the tips of the perforations the surfacing appears "broken". Traces of paper fibres are evident on the surface of ordinary paper and the ink shows a degree of absorption into it.

Initial chalk-surfaced paper printings by De La Rue had a thinner coating than subsequently became the norm. The characteristics described above are less pronounced in these printings.

Perforation Measurement

The gauge of a perforation is the number of holes in a length of 2 cm.

The Gibbons *Instanta* gauge is the standard for measuring perforations. The stamp is viewed against a dark background with the transparent gauge put on top of it. Though the gauge measures to decimal accuracy, perforations read from it are generally quoted in the Catalogue to the nearest half. For example:

Just over perf 12¾ to just under 13¼ .... = perf 13
Perf 13¼ exactly, rounded up .... = perf 13½
Just over perf 13¼ to just under 13¾ .... = perf 13½
Perf 13¾ exactly, rounded up .... = perf 14

However, where classification depends on it, actual quarter-perforations are quoted. Perforations are usually abbreviated (and spoken) as follows, though sometimes they may be spelt out for clarity.

P 14: perforated alike on all sides (read: "perf 14").

P 14 x 15: the first figure refers to top and bottom, the second to left and right sides (read: "perf 14 by 15"). This is a compound perforation.

Such headings as "P 13 x 14 (vert) and P 14 x 13 (horiz)" indicate which perforations apply to which stamp format— vertical or horizontal.

From 1992 onwards most definitive and greetings stamps from both sheets and booklets occur with a large elliptical (oval) hole inserted in each line of vertical perforations as a security measure. The £10 definitive, No. 1658, is unique in having two such holes in the horizontal perforations.

Stamps which have the elliptical perforations hole towards the top in error are normally outside the scope of this catalogue, but in 2013 a booklet was issued in which the entire print run contained Machin stamps in this format. These are listed as U3073 and U3076.

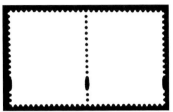

Elliptical Perforations

Perforation Errors

Authenticated errors, where a stamp normally perforated is accidentally issued imperforate, are listed provided no traces of perforations (blind holes or indentations) remain. They must be provided as pairs, both stamps wholly imperforate, and are only priced in that form.

Numerous part-perforated stamps arose from the introduction of the Jumelle Press. This had a rotary perforator with rows of pins on one drum engaging with holes on another. Engagement is only gradual when the perforating unit is started up or stopped, giving rise to perforations "fading out", a variety mentioned above as not listed.

Stamps from the Jumelle printings sometimes occur imperforate between stamp and sheet margin. Such errors are not listed in this catalogue, but are covered by the volumes of the *Great Britain Specialised Catalogue*.

Pairs described as "imperforate between" have the line of perforations between the two stamps omitted.

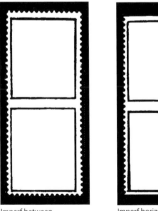
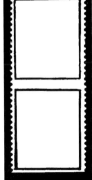

Imperf between (vertical pair)

Imperf horizontally (vertical pair)

Imperf between (horiz pair): a horizontal pair of stamps with perfs all around the edges but none between the stamps.

Imperf between (vert pair): a vertical pair of stamps with perfs all around the edges but none between the stamps. Where several of the rows have escaped perforation the resulting varieties are listable. Thus:

Imperf vert (horiz pair): a horizontal pair of stamps perforated at top and bottom; all three vertical directions are imperf—the two outer edges and between the stamps.

Imperf horiz (vert pair): a vertical pair perforated at left and right edges; all three horizontal directions are imperf—the top, bottom and between the stamps.

Varieties of double, misplaced or partial perforation caused by error or machine malfunction are not listable, neither are freaks, such as perforations placed diagonally from paper folds, nor missing holes caused by broken pins.

Phosphor Issues

Machines which sort mail electronically were introduced progressively and the British Post Office issued the first stamps specially marked for electronic sorting in 1957. This first issue had easily visible graphite lines printed on the back beneath the gum (see Nos. 561/6). They were issued in the Southampton area where the experiment was carried out.

The graphite lines were replaced by phosphor bands, activated by ultraviolet light. The bands are printed on the front of the stamps and show as a matt surface against the usual smooth or shiny appearance of the untreated surface of the paper. The bands show clearly in the top or bottom horizontal margins of the sheet.

The first phosphor issues appeared in 1959 (see Nos. 599/609) and these stamps also had graphite lines on the back. Further details will be found in the listings above No. 599 and 619. From 1962 onwards most commemoratives were issued in versions with or without bands. From 1967 all commemorative stamps had phosphor bands, but from 1972 they were replaced by "all-over" phosphor covering the entire area of the stamp.

After a considerable period of development a special paper was produced in which the phosphor had been incorporated into the coating. From 15 August 1979 to April 1996 phosphorised paper was accepted for use generally, replacing phosphor bands on most issues for all values except the second class letter rate. Phosphorised paper can only be identified by ultraviolet light. The Stanley Gibbons Ultraviolet Lamp is firmly recommended for use in identifying the phosphor stamps listed in this Catalogue. *Warning*. Never stare at the lighted lamp but follow the manufacturer's instructions. Phosphor bands were reintroduced for all issues from April 1996.

During the years 1967 to 1972, when all issues, except the high values, should have shown phosphor bands, a number of stamps appeared with them omitted in error. These varieties are listed in this Catalogue. Stamps with "all-over" phosphor omitted can only be detected by the use of an ultraviolet lamp and these varieties are listed in the Stanley Gibbons *Great Britain Specialised Catalogue*. Note that prices are for unmounted mint examples only. Varieties such as double or misplaced bands are not listed in this Catalogue.

Gum Description

All stamps listed are assumed to have gum of some kind and original gum (o.g.) means that which was present on the stamp as issued to the public. Deleterious climates and the presence of certain chemicals can cause gum to crack and, with early stamps, even make the paper deteriorate. Unscrupulous fakers are adept in removing it and regumming the stamp to meet the unreasoning demand

Multi-value Coil Strip

often made for "full o.g." "unmounted" or "never hinged, mint" (NHM) in cases where such a thing is virtually impossible.

The gum normally used on stamps has been gum arabic until the late 1960's when synthetic adhesives were introduced. Harrison and Sons Ltd for instance used *polyvinyl alcohol*, known to philatelists as PVA (see note above SG723).

From 1993 many stamps have been issued with self-adhesive gum. Unused prices are for such stamps with backing paper attached, as issued. Initially such stamps were issued with a water-soluble layer of gum allowing used examples to be "soaked off", but with the 2008 Christmas issue, most self-adhesive stamps are issued without the water-soluble layer of gum, preventing their removal from paper without damage. It is recommended that used stamps from this later period be collected "on piece".

Colour Identification

The 200 colours most used for stamp identification are given in the Stanley Gibbons Stamp Colour Key. The Catalogue has used the Colour Key as a standard for describing new issues for some years. The names are also introduced as lists are rewritten, though exceptions are made for those early issues where traditional names have become universally established.

In compound colour names the second is the predominant one, thus:

orange-red = a red tending towards orange.

red-orange = an orange containing more red than usual.

When comparing actual stamps with colour samples in the Colour Key, view in a good north daylight (or its best substitute: fluorescent "colour-matching" light). Sunshine is not recommended. Choose a solid portion of the stamp design; if available, marginal markings such as solid bars of colour or colour check dots are helpful. Shading lines in the design can be misleading as they appear lighter than solid colour. Furthermore, the listings refer to colours as issued: they may deteriorate into something different through the passage of time.

Shades are particularly significant when they can be linked to specific printings. In general, shades need to be quite marked to fall within the scope of this Catalogue.

Modern colour printing by lithography is prone to marked differences of shade, even within a single run, and variations can occur within the same sheet. Such shades are not listed.

Royal Mail Colour Descriptions

In recent years Royal Mail has introduced its own colour descriptions of definitive stamps, describing, for example, the £1.05 stamp (SG 2935) as 'Gooseberry green' and incorporating this in the sheet margin of the stamp. We do not use these descriptions because they are, in many cases, unfamiliar to collectors and, should a listable change in shade occur in a later printing, we would expect that the sheet margin would continue to bear the original Royal Mail colour description.

Errors of Colour

Major colour errors in stamps or overprints which qualify for listing are: wrong colours; albinos (colourless impressions), where these have Expert Committee certificates; colours completely omitted, but only on unused stamps (if found on used stamps the information is usually footnoted) and with good credentials, missing colours being frequently faked.

Colours only partially omitted are not recognised. Colour shifts, however spectacular, are not listed.

Booklet Stamps

Single stamps from booklets are listed if they are distinguishable in some way (such as watermark or phosphor bands) from similar sheet stamps. Single booklet stamps whose only distinguishing feature is that they are imperforate on one or two adjacent sides are omitted

Booklet panes are listed where they contain stamps of different denominations *se-tenant*, where stamp-size printed labels are included, or where such panes

Booklet Pane with Printed Labels

Se-tenant Pane of Four

are otherwise identifiable. Booklet panes are placed in the listing under the lowest denomination present.

Booklet panes containing single values issued up to 1952 are also listed in this catalogue. Users should note that prices are for panes with the binding margin intact and full perforations on the other three sides.

In the listing of complete booklets the numbers and prefix letters are the same as used in the Stanley Gibbons *Great Britain Specialised Catalogue*.

Coil Stamps

Stamps only issued in coil form are given full listing. If stamps are issued in both sheets and coils, the coil stamps are listed separately only where there is some feature (e.g. watermark sideways or gum change) by which single stamps can be distinguished. Coil strips containing different values *se-tenant* are also listed.

Coil join pairs are generally too random and easily faked to permit listing; similarly ignored are coil stamps which have accidentally suffered an extra row of perforations from the claw mechanism in a malfunctioning vending machine.

Gutter pair

Gutter Pairs

In 1988 the recess-printed Castle high value definitives were issued in sheets containing four panes separated by a gutter margin. All modern Great Britain commemoratives and special stamps are produced in sheets containing two panes separated by a blank horizontal or vertical margin known as a gutter. This feature first made its appearance on some supplies of the 1972 Royal Silver Wedding 3p and marked the introduction of Harrison & Sons' new "Jumelle" stamp-printing press. There are advantages for both the printer and the Post Office in such a layout which has been used for most commemorative issues since 1974.

Traffic Light Gutter Pair

The term "gutter pair" is used for a pair of stamps separated by part of the blank gutter margin as illustrated above. Most printers include some form of colour check device on the sheet margins, in addition to the cylinder or plate numbers. Harrison & Sons use round "dabs", or spots of colour, resembling traffic lights. For the period from the 1972 Royal Silver Wedding until the end of 1979 these colour dabs appeared in the gutter margin. There was always one

example to every double-pane sheet of stamps. They can also be found in the high value Machin issue printed in photogravure. Gutter pairs showing these "traffic lights" are priced in complete sets in this catalogue.

From the 2004 Entente Cordiale set, Walsall reintroduced traffic lights in the gutters of certain sets. Where these extend over more than one section of gutter margin on any value, they are priced in blocks rather than pairs.

Miniature Sheets

A miniature sheet contains a single stamp or set with wide inscribed or decorated margins. The stamps often also exist in normal sheet format. This Catalogue lists, with **MS** prefix, complete miniature sheets which have been issued by the Post Office and which are valid for postal purposes.

Stamps from miniature sheets, not also available in normal sheet format, are not individually listed or priced in this catalogue.

Where such stamps have also appeared in a booklet, and the booklet pane differs in layout or design to the miniature sheet (e.g. "Britain Alone" (2nd issue), Nos. 3082/5) these stamps are listed separately, but if the booklet pane is the same as the miniature sheet (e.g. "Astronomy" , Nos. **MS**2315/a) they are only listed as complete miniature sheets or booklet panes.

Miniature Sheet containing a set of stamps

Se-tenant Combinations

Se-tenant means "joined together". Some sets include stamps of different design arranged *se-tenant* as blocks or strips and, in mint condition, these are usually collected unsevered as issued. The set prices quoted in this catalogue refer to the unsevered combination plus singles of any other values in the set.

Presentation and Souvenir Packs

Special Packs comprising slip-in cards with printed commemorative inscriptions and notes on the back and with protective covering, were introduced in 1964 for the Shakespeare issue. Definitive issues first appeared in Presentation Packs in 1960. Notes will be found in the listings to describe souvenir books issued on special occasions.

Issues of 1968–1969 (British Paintings to the Prince of Wales Investiture) were also issued in packs with text in German for sale through the Post Office's German Agency and these are also included.

Collectors packs, first called gift packs, containing commemoratives issued in the preceding 12 months, first appeared in 1967. These are listed and priced.

It should be noted that prices given for presentation packs are for items as originally sold, including any additional inserts, such as questionnaire forms and publicity material.

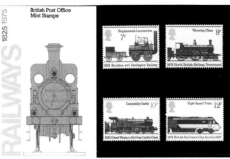

13 August 1975 Public Railways Presentation Pack

Yearbooks

Special Post Office Yearbooks were first available in 1984. They contain all of the commemorative issues for one year in a hardbound book, illustrated in colour complete with slip case. These are listed and priced.

Commemorative First Day Covers

Until 1963 the Post Office did not provide any special first day of issue postmark facilities for collectors. Several philatelic organisations and stamp dealers did produce pictorial covers for the various commemorative issues and collectors serviced these to receive ordinary operational postmarks. Occasionally a special handstamp was produced which coincided with a new stamp issue, or relevant slogan postmarks, like the 1953 "Long Live the Queen" type, were in general use at the time.

On 21 March 1963 the Post Office installed special posting boxes at 11 main post offices so that collectors could obtain "uniformly high standard" impressions, from normal operational postmarks, for their first day covers. From 7 May 1963 special "First Day of Issue" slogans (Type A) were applied to mail posted in these special boxes, whose number had, by then, risen to 30. The Philatelic Bureau accepted orders by post for such covers from the issue of 16 May 1963 onwards.

The slogan type was replaced on 23 April 1964 by "First Day of Issue" handstamps (Type B). These were, initially, of considerable size, but were later replaced by smaller versions (Type C) which remained in use at nearly 200 principal offices until the Christmas issue of 2 November 1998. From 1970 the Bureau postmarks as Type C were inscribed "British Philatelic Bureau".

Since 1972 the Post Office has provided for virtually all issues an additional "alternative" pictorial "First Day of Issue" cancellation, at a location connected with the issue. Being available from the Bureau, these cancellations are listed in this catalogue.

From 12 January 1999 (Millennium Inventors' Tale issue) the "alternative" pictorial postmark has been applied to all covers posted in special first day boxes throughout the country, replacing the local, non-pictorial, cancels. A bilingual version is used when the "alternative" office is in Wales. For collectors who prefer plain postmarks a non-pictorial version of the "alternative" postmark is available from Royal Mail Special Handstamp Centres.

"First Day of Issue" postmarks of standard or pictorial type have occasionally been provided on a "one-off" basis for places linked to particular stamp issues, eg Weymouth for the 1975 Sailing set. Such postmarks, which are not available from the Bureau, are footnoted only.

Royal Mail established Special Handstamp Centres in

1990 where all sponsored special handstamps and many "First Day of Issue" postmarks are now applied.

Pictorial local "First Day of Issue" postmarks were in use between 1988 and 1998 applied to covers posted in first day boxes and sent to main offices or Special Handstamp Centres. These included Birmingham (1993–98), Durham (1988–98), City of London (1989–98), London (1993–98), Newcastle upon Tyne (1992–94), and St Albans (1995–98). Different designs were used at the Glasgow Handstamp Centre for various places, 1993–98. As these postmarks were not available from the Bureau they are not included in this catalogue.

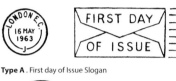

Type A. First day of Issue Slogan

Type B. Large Handstamp

Type C. Small Handstamp

Type D. Maltese Cross

Type E

Type F. £ Sign

Type G. Three Lions

Type H. Four Castles

Type I. Windsor Keep

Type J. Millennium
(2000 issues are inscr "Beyond 2000")

Type K. Arms of Post Office

Illustrations shown at 60 percent.

First day cover prices for modern issues are based on those with a Philatelic Bureau (later, "Tallents House") postmark.

Post Office Label Sheets

This catalogue lists complete "Generic Smilers" sheets in a section following the booklet listings. "Personalised" and "Corporate" sheets are not listed, neither are identifiable single stamps from label sheets.

No Value Indicated Stamps

From 22 August 1989 various definitive and special stamps appeared inscribed "2nd", "1st" or "E" instead of a face value. These were sold at the current minimum rates for these services which were as follows:

Inland Postage Rate	2nd Class	1st Class
5 September 1988	14p.	19p.
2 October 1989	15p.	20p.
17 September 1990	17p.	22p.
16 September 1991	18p.	24p.
1 November 1993	19p.	25p.
8 July 1996	20p.	26p.
26 April 1999	19p.	26p.
17 April 2000	19p.	27p.
8 May 2003	20p.	28p.
1 April 2004	21p.	28p.
7 April 2005	21p.	30p.
3 April 2006	23p.	32p.
2 April 2007	24p.	34p.
7 April 2008	27p.	36p.
6 April 2009	30p.	39p.
6 April 2010	32p.	41p.
4 April 2011	36p.	46p.
30 April 2012	50p.	60p.
31 March 2014	53p.	62p.
30 March 2015	54p	63p
29 March 2016	55p	64p
27 March 2017	56p.	65p.
26 March 2018	58p.	67p.

European Airmail Rate

26 April 1999	30p.
25 October 1999	34p.
27 April 2000	36p.
2 July 2001	37p.
27 March 2003	38p.
1 April 2004	40p.

From June 2004, European Airmail rate stamps reverted to showing a face value.

From 21 August 2006 "Large" letters were charged at a higher rate following the introduction of "Pricing in Proportion". Rates as follows:

Inland Postage Rate	2nd Class Large	1st Class Large
21 August 2006	37p.	44p.
2 April 2007	40p.	48p.
7 April 2008	42p.	52p.
6 April 2009	47p.	61p.
6 April 2010	51p.	66p.
4 April 2011	58p.	75p.
30 April 2012	69p.	90p.
31 March 2014	73p.	93p.
30 March 2015	74p	95p
29 March 2016	75p	96p
27 March 2017	76p.	98p.
26 March 2018	79p.	£1.01

PHQ Card cancelled
on First Day of Issue

PHQ Cards

From 1973 the Post Office produced sets of picture cards to accompany commemorative issues which can be sent through the post as postcards. Each card shows an enlarged colour reproduction of one stamp, initially of a single value from one set and subsequently of all values.

The Post Office gives each card a "PHQ" serial number, hence the term. The cards are usually on sale shortly before the date of issue of the stamps, but there is no officially designated "first day". Cards are priced in fine mint condition for complete sets as issued. Used prices are for cards franked with the stamp affixed, on the obverse, as illustrated; the stamp being cancelled with an official postmark for first day of issue, or reverse.

Watermark Types

Stamps are on unwatermarked paper except where the heading to the set states otherwise.

AS DESCRIBED (Read through front of stamp)		AS SEEN DURING WATERMARK DETECTION (Stamp face down and back examined)
GvR	Normal	ЯvⱯ
ЯʌⱯ	Inverted	ⱯʌЯ
ЯvⱯ	Reversed	GvR
ⱯʌЯ	Inverted and reversed	ЯʌⱯ
GvR	Sideways	ЯvⱯ
ЯvⱯ	Sideways inverted	ⱯʌЯ
ⱯʌЯ	Sideways reversed	GvR
ⱯʌЯ	Sideways inverted and reversed	GvR

Watermarks are detected for Catalogue description by one of four methods: (1) holding stamps to the light; (2) laying stamps face down on a dark background; (3) by use of the Morley-Bright Detector, which works by revealing the thinning of the paper at the watermark; or (4) by the more complex electric watermark detectors such as the Stanley Gibbons Detectamark Spectrum.

The diagram above shows how watermark position is described in the Catalogue. Watermarks are usually impressed so that they read normally when looked through from the printed side. However, since philatelists customarily detect watermarks by looking at the back of the stamp, the watermark diagram also makes clear what is actually seen. Note that "G v R" is only an example and illustrations of the different watermarks employed are shown in the listings. The illustrations are actual size and shown in normal positions (from the front of the stamps).

Watermark Errors and Varieties

Watermark errors are recognised as of major importance. They comprise stamps showing the wrong watermark devices or stamps printed on paper with the wrong watermark. Stamps printed on paper showing broken or deformed bits on the dandy roll, are not listable.

Underprints

From 1982 various values appeared with underprints, printed on the reverse, in blue, over the gum. These were usually from special stamp booklets, sold at a discount by the Post Office, but in 1985 surplus stocks of such underprinted paper were used for other purposes.

In this Catalogue stamps showing underprints are priced mint only. Used examples can be obtained, but care has to be taken in floating the stamps since the devices were printed on top of the gum and will be removed as the gum dissolves.

General Types of watermark as seen through the front of the stamp

Underprint Types

1 Star with central dot   **2** Double-lined Star   **3** Double-lined "D"

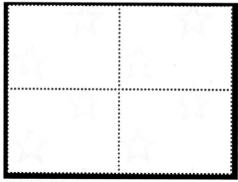

4 Multiple double lined stars

5 Multiple double-lined "D"
(Types **4/5** are shown ¾ actual size)

Note: Types 4/5 are arranged in a random pattern so that the stamps from the same sheet or booklet pane will show the underprint in a slightly different position to the above. Stamps, when inspected, should be placed the correct way up, face down, when comparing with the illustrations.

Specimen Stamps

From 1847 stamps have been overprinted "SPECIMEN" for a variety of purposes, including the provision of samples to postmasters, as a security overprint on printers' or official reference copies and, from 1859, on examples of current British stamps sent to the International Bureau of the Univeral Postal Union for distribution to member nations.

Numerous styles were employed for these "Specimen" overprints, which are now listed in this catalogue up to the end of the reign of King George VI. The different types are illustrated here. Note that for ease of reference type numbers are the same as those given in the *Stanley Gibbons Great Britain Specialised Catalogue* and "missing" type numbers may have been used on stamps outside the scope of this catalogue or may refer to "Cancelled" overprints, which are, likewise, not listed here.

SPECIMEN
1

SPECIMEN
2

SPECIMEN
4

SPECIMEN
5

SPECIMEN
6

SPECIMEN
7

SPECIMEN
8

SPECIMEN
9

SPECIMEN
10

SPECIMEN
11

SPECIMEN
12

SPECIMEN
13

SPECIMEN
15

SPECIMEN
16

SPECIMEN
17

SPECIMEN
22

SPECIMEN
23

SPECIMEN
26

SPECIMEN
29

SPECIMEN
30

SPECIMEN
31

SPECIMEN
32

"Specimen" stamps are listed with details of the types of "Specimen" overprints found. The different types are not listed here and where more than one type was used the price given is for the cheapest version. Imperforate overprints are also not listed, unless the stamp was normally issued in that form.

More detailed listings will be found in Volumes 1 and 2 of the *Great Britain Specialised Catalogue*.

This index gives an easy reference to the inscriptions and designs of the Special Stamps 1953 to March 2018. Where a complete set shares an inscription or type of design, then only the catalogue number of the first stamp is given in addition to separate entries for stamps depicting popular thematic subjects. Paintings, inventions, etc., are indexed under the name of the artist or inventor, where this is shown on the stamp.

Miniature Sheet Design Index

Stanley Gibbons receives, on a regular basis, enquiries concerning the allocation of SG Numbers to some of individual stamps included in Miniature Sheets. Stamps which are available from more than one source, usually from counter sheets in addition to the Miniature sheet, are allocated numbers.

From this flow of enquiries a decision was made, as part of the review of the design index, to include a new section identifying all the Miniature Sheets issued for GB. These are listed numerically by SG Number, alphabetically by title of sheet and finally (alphabetically) by the individual stamps printed within the MS.

In future editions of the catalogue the induvial stamp listing will be expanded to include more detailed identification by thematic elements.

Numerically by SG Number

UNITED KINGDOM OF GREAT BRITAIN AND IRELAND

Queen Victoria

20 June 1837–22 January 1901

PARLIAMENTARY ENVELOPES. When the Uniform Penny Postage was introduced on 10 January 1840 the free franking privileges of Members of Parliament were abolished. During the same month, special envelopes were introduced for mail posted from the Houses of Parliament and these remained in use until the introduction of stamps and the Mulready stationery in May 1840. Envelopes are priced in used condition only.

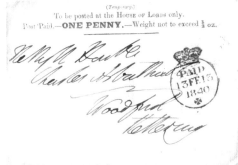

Inscribed	*Houses of Parliament* in black (16 Jan 1840)		
PE2	1d. envelope	*from*	£18000
PE3	2d. envelope	*from*	£45000
PE4	4d. envelope	*from*	

Inscribed	*House of Lords* in vermilion (Jan 1840)		
PE5	1d. envelope	*from*	£25000
PE8	2d. envelope		

Inscribed	*House of Commons* in black (Jan 1840)		
PE9	1d. envelope	*from*	£6000

MULREADY ENVELOPES AND LETTER SHEETS, so called from the name of the designer, William Mulready, were issued concurrently with the first British adhesive stamps.

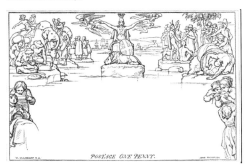

A large number of letter sheets and much smaller quantity of envelopes were sold by businesses, advertising to promote their services.

Letter sheets
ME1	1d. black	£350	£550
	a. With advertisements printed inside	£750	£850
	s. "Specimen", Type 2	*From* £7500	
ME3	2d. blue	£425	£2400
	a. With advertisements printed inside	*From*	£3200
	s. "Specimen", Type 2	*From* £7750	

Envelopes
ME2	1d. black	£350	£550
	a. With advertisements printed inside	£2500	£4000
	s. "Specimen", Type 2	*From* £7000	
ME4	2d. blue	£450	£2500
	a. With advertisements printed inside	*From*	£3500
	s. "Specimen", Type 2	£7000	

LINE-ENGRAVED ISSUES
GENERAL NOTES

Brief notes on some aspects of the line-engraved stamps follow, but for further information and a full specialist treatment of these issues collectors are recommended to consult Volume 1 of the Stanley Gibbons *Great Britain Specialised Catalogue.*

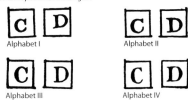

Typical Corner Letters of the four Alphabets

Alphabets. Four different styles were used for the corner letters on stamps prior to the issue with letters in all four corners, these being known to collectors as:

Alphabet I. Used for all plates made from 1840 to the end of 1851. Letters small.

Alphabet II. Plates from 1852 to mid-1855. Letters larger, heavier and broader.

Alphabet III. Plates from mid-1855 to end of period. Letters tall and more slender.

Alphabet IV. 1861. 1d. Die II, Plates 50 and 51 only. Letters were hand-engraved instead of being punched on the plate. They are therefore inconsistent in shape and size but generally larger and outstanding.

While the general descriptions and the illustrations of typical letters given above may be of some assistance, only long experience and published aids can enable every stamp to be allocated to its particular Alphabet without hesitation, as certain letters in each are similar to those in one of the others.

Blued Paper. The blueing of the paper of the earlier issues is believed to be due to the presence of prussiate of potash in the printing ink, or in the paper, which, under certain conditions, tended to colour the paper when the sheets were damped for printing. An alternative term is *bleuté* paper.

Corner Letters. The corner letters on the early British stamps were intended as a safeguard against forgery, each stamp in the sheet having a different combination of letters. Taking the first 1d. stamp, printed in 20 horizontal rows of 12, as an example, the lettering is as follows:

Row 1.   A A, A B, A C, etc. to A L.

Row 2.   B A, B B, B C, etc. to B L.

and so on to

Row 20   T A, T B, T C, etc. to T L.

On the stamps with four corner letters, those in the upper corners are in the reverse positions to those in the lower corners.
Thus in a sheet of 240 (12×20) the sequence is:

```
        A A   B A   C A        L A
Row 1.                    etc. to
        A A   A B   A C        A L
        A B   B B   C B        L B
Row 2.                    etc. to
        B A   B B   B C        B L
        and so on to
        A T   B T   C T        L T
Row 20.                   etc. to
        T A   T B   T C        T L
```

Placing letters in all four corners was not only an added precaution against forgery but was meant to deter unmarked parts of used stamps being pieced together and passed off as an unused whole.

Dies. The first die of the 1d. was used for making the original die of the 2d., both the No Lines and White Lines issues. In 1855 the 1d. Die I was amended by retouching the head and deepening the lines on a transferred impression of the original. This later version, known to collectors as Die II, was used for making the dies for the 1d. and 2d. with letters in all four corners and also for the 1½d.

The two dies are illustrated above No. 17 in the catalogue.

Double letter

Guide line in corner

Guide line through value

Double Corner Letters. These are due to the workman placing his letter-punch in the wrong position at the first attempt, when lettering the plate, and then correcting the mistake; or to a slight shifting of the punch when struck. If a wrong letter was struck in the first instance, traces of a wrong letter may appear in a corner in addition to the correct one. A typical example is illustrated.

Guide Lines and Dots. When laying down the impressions of the design on the early plates, fine vertical and horizontal guide lines were marked on the plates to assist the operative. These were usually removed from the gutter margins, but could not be removed from the stamp impression without damage to the plate, so that in such cases they appear on the printed stamps, sometimes in the corners, sometimes through "POSTAGE" or the value. Typical examples are illustrated.

Guide dots or cuts were similarly made to indicate the spacing of the guide lines. These too sometimes appear on the stamps.

Ivory Head

"Ivory Head". The so-called "ivory head" variety is one in which the Queen's Head shows white on the back of the stamp. It arises from the comparative absence of ink in the head portion of the design, with consequent absence of blueing. (See "Blued Paper", on page 1).

Line-engraving. In this context "line-engraved" is synonymous with recess-printing, in which the engraver cuts recesses in a plate and printing (the coloured areas) is from these recesses. "Line-engraved" is the traditional philatelic description for these stamps; other equivalent terms found are "engraving in *taille-douce*" (French) or "in *intaglio*" (Italian).

Plates. Until the introduction of the stamps with letters in all four corners, the number of the plate was not indicated in the design of the stamp, but was printed on the sheet margin. By long study of identifiable blocks and the minor variation in the design, coupled with the position of the corner letters, philatelists are now able to allot many of these stamps to their respective plates. Specialist collectors often endeavour to obtain examples of a given stamp printed from its different plates and our catalogue accordingly reflects this depth of detail.

Maltese Cross   Type of Town postmark

Type of Penny Post cancellation

Example of 1844 type postmark

Postmarks. The so-called "Maltese Cross" design was the first employed for obliterating British postage stamps and was in use from 1840 to 1844. Being hand-cut, the obliterating stamps varied greatly in detail and some distinctive types can be allotted to particular towns or offices. Local types, such as those used at Manchester, Norwich, Leeds, etc., are keenly sought. A red ink was first employed, but was superseded by black, after some earlier experiments, in February 1841. Maltese Cross obliterations in other colours are rare.

Obliterations of this type, numbered 1 to 12 in the centre, were used at the London Chief Office in 1843 and 1844.

Some straight-line cancellations were in use in 1840 at the Penny Post receiving offices, the adhesives then being obliterated at the Head Office. They are nevertheless known, with or without Maltese Cross, on the early postage stamps.

In 1842 some offices in south west England used dated postmarks in place of the Maltese Cross, usually on the back of the letter since they were not originally intended as obliterators. These town postmarks have likewise been found on adhesives.

In 1844 the Maltese Cross design was superseded by numbered obliterators of varied type, one of which is illustrated. They are naturally comparatively scarce on the first 1d. and 2d. stamps.

Like the Maltese Cross they are found in various colours, some of which are rare.

Re-entry

"Union Jack" re-entry

Re-entries. Re-entries on the plate show as a doubling of part of the design of the stamp generally at top or bottom. Many re-entries are very slight while others are most marked. A typical one is illustrated.

The *"Union Jack"* re-entry, so-called owing to the effect of the re-entry on the appearance of the corner stars (see illustration) occurs on stamp L K of Plate 75 of the 1d. red, Die I.

T A (T L)   M A (M L)
Varieties of Large Crown Watermark

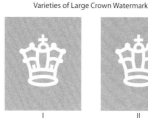

I   II
Two states of Large Crown Watermark

Watermarks. Two watermark varieties, as illustrated, consisting of crowns of entirely different shape, are found in sheets of the Large Crown paper and fall on stamps lettered M A and T A (or M L and T L when the paper is printed on the wrong side). Both varieties are found on the 1d. rose-red of 1857, while the M A (M L) variety comes also on some plates of the 1d. of 1864 (Nos. 43, 44) up to about Plate 96. On the 2d. the T A (T L) variety is known on plates 8 and 9, and the M A (M L) on later prints of plate 9. These varieties may exist inverted, or inverted reversed on stamps lettered A A and A L and H A and H L, and some are known.

In 1861 a minor alteration was made in the Large Crown watermark by the removal of the two vertical strokes, representing *fleurs-de-lis*, which projected upwards from the uppermost of the three horizontal curves at the base of the Crown. Hence two states are distinguishable, as illustrated.

CONDITION–IMPERFORATE LINE-ENGRAVED ISSUES

The prices quoted for the 1840 and 1841 imperforate Line engraved issues are for "fine" examples. As condition is most important in assessing the value of a stamp, the following definitions will assist collectors in the evaluation of individual examples.

Four main factors are relevant when considering quality.

(a) Impression. This should be clean and the surface free of any rubbing or unnatural blurring which would detract from the appearance.

(b) Margins. This is perhaps the most difficult factor to evaluate. Stamps described as "fine", the standard adopted in this catalogue for pricing purposes, should have margins of the recognised width, defined as approximately one half of the distance between two adjoining unsevered stamps. Stamps described as "very fine" or "superb" should have margins which are proportionately larger than those of a "fine" stamp. Examples with close margins should not, generally, be classified as "fine".

(c) Cancellation. On a "fine" stamp this should be reasonably clear and not noticeably smudged. A stamp described as "superb" should have a neat cancellation, preferably centrally placed or to the right.

(d) Appearance. Stamps, at the prices quoted, should always be without any tears, creases, bends or thins and should not be toned on either the front or back. Stamps with such defects are worth only a proportion of the catalogue price.

Average

Fine

Very Fine

Superb

The actual size illustrations of 1840 1d. blacks show the various grades of quality. When comparing these illustrations it should be assumed that they are all from the same plate and that they are free of any hidden defects.

PRINTERS. Nos. 1/53a were recess-printed by Perkins, Bacon & Petch, known from 1852 as Perkins, Bacon & Co.

STAMPS ON COVER. Prices are quoted, for those Victorian and Edwardian issues usually found used on cover. In general these prices refer to single examples of the cheapest versions of each basic stamp, with other shades, plates or varieties, together with unusual frankings and postmarks, being worth more. However multiples of some stamps may be more common than single usages and in this case the covers might be worth considerably less than the price quoted.

1

1a

2 Small Crown

(Eng Charles and Frederick Heath)

1840 (6 May). Letters in lower corners. *Wmk* Small Crown, *W* **2**. *Imperf.*

			Unused	Used	Used on cover
1	**1**	1d. intense black	£17500	£525	
2		1d. black	£12500	£375	£750
		Wi. Watermark inverted	£50000	£2500	
3		1d. grey-black (worn plate)	£16500	£500	
4	**1a**	2d. deep full blue	£45000	£1200	
5		2d. blue	£38000	£950	£2500
		Wi. Watermark inverted	£90000	£6250	
6		2d. pale blue	£48000	£1000	

The 1d. stamp in black was printed from Plates 1 to 11. Plate 1 exists in two states (known to collectors as 1a and 1b), the latter being the result of extensive repairs.

Repairs were also made to plates 2, 5, 6, 8, 9, 10 and 11, and certain impressions exist in two or more states.

The so-called "Royal reprint" of the 1d. black was made in 1864, from Plate 66, Die II, on paper with Large Crown watermark, inverted. A printing was also made in carmine, on paper with the same watermark, upright.

For 1d. black with "VR" in upper corners see No. V1 under Official Stamps.

The 2d. stamps were printed from Plates 1 and 2.

Plates of 1d. black

	Unused	Used	Used on cover
1a	£18500	£375	£1000
1b	£12500	£375	£750
2	£12500	£375	£750
3	£20000	£500	£900
4	£13000	£400	£800
5	£12500	£375	£775
6	£13500	£375	£775
7	£13500	£400	£825
8	£16500	£525	£1000
9	£21000	£625	£1200
10	£26500	£950	£3500
11	£23000	£4600	£16000

Varieties of 1d. black

			Unused	Used
a.	On *bleuté* paper (Plates 1 to 8)	from		£775
b.	Double letter in corner	from	£13000	£400
bb.	Re-entry	from	£13500	£450
bc.	"PB" re-entry (Plate 5, 3rd state)		—	£10500
c.	Guide line in corner		£13000	£400
cc.	Large letters in each corner (E J, I L, J C and P A) (Plate 1b)	from	£13500	£550
d.	Guide line through value		£13000	£450
g.	Obliterated by Maltese Cross			
	In red		—	£425
	In black		—	£375
	In blue		—	£12000
	In magenta		—	£3000
	In yellow		—	—
	In violet		—	£12000
h.	Obliterated by Maltese Cross with number in centre	from	—	£20000
i.	Obliterated "Penny Post" in black (without Maltese Cross)	from	—	£5500
j.	Obliterated by town postmark (without Maltese Cross)			
	In black	from	—	£17500
	In yellow	from	—	£60000
	In red	from	—	£18500
k.	Obliterated by 1844 type postmark in black	from	—	£1800

OFFICIAL STAMP

In 1840 the 1d. black (Type **1**), with "V R" in the upper corners, was prepared for official use, but was never issued for postal purposes. Obliterated specimens are those which were used for experimental trials of obliterating inks, or those that passed through the post by oversight.

V **1**

1840. Prepared for use but not issued; *V R* in upper corners. *Imperf.*

			Unused	Used
V1	V **1**	1d. black	£32000	£35000

Plates of 2d. blue

Plate		Unused	Used	Used on cover
1	Shades from	£38000	£950	£2750
2	Shades from	£48000	£1100	£3250

Varieties of 2d. blue

		Unused	Used
a.	Double letter in corner	—	£1000
aa.	Re-entry	—	£1100
b.	Guide line in corner	—	£975
c.	Guide line through value	—	£975
e.	Obliterated by Maltese Cross		
	In red	—	£1200
	In black	—	£950
	In blue	—	£15000
	In magenta	—	£12000

			Unused	Used
f.	Obliterated by Maltese Cross with number in centre..*from*		—	£18000
g.	Obliterated "Penny Post" in black (without Maltese Cross)..*from*		—	£16000
h.	Obliterated by town postmark (without Maltese Cross) in black..................................*from*		—	£10000
i.	Obliterated by 1844 type postmark			
	In black..*from*		—	£2500
	In blue...*from*		—	£18000

1841 (10 Feb). Printed from 'black' plates. *Wmk W* **2**. Paper more or less blued. *Imperf.*

			Unused	Used	Used on cover
7	**1**	1d. red-brown (*shades*).................	£2700	£130	£240
		a. "PB" re-entry (Plate 5, 3rd state)...	—	£2600	
		Wi. Watermark inverted (Plates 1b, 8 and 10)...................*from*	—	£3250	

The first printings of the 1d. in red-brown were made from Plates 1b, 2, 5 and 8 to 11 used for the 1d. black.

1d. red-brown from "black" plates

Plate	Unused	Used	Used on cover
1b..........................	£23000	£375	£650
2..............................	£25000	£325	£550
5..............................	£12000	£200	£400
8..............................	£13000	£190	£350
9..............................	£6500	£190	£325
10............................	£2800	£190	£325
11............................	£11500	£190	£350

1841 (late Feb). Plate 12 onwards. *Wmk W* **2**. Paper more or less blued. *Imperf.*

			Unused	Used	Used on cover
8	**1**	1d. red-brown................................	£600	35·00	45·00
		s. Optd "SPECIMEN" (1)...............	£3500		
		Wi. Watermark inverted..................	£5000	£400	
8a		1d. red-brown on very blue paper	£700	35·00	
9		1d. pale red-brown (worn plates)	£675	45·00	
10		1d. deep red-brown.........................	£900	50·00	
11		1d. lake-red.....................................	£5250	£850	
12		1d. orange-brown............................	£2000	£275	

Error. No letter "A" in right lower corner (Stamp B (A), Plate 77)

12a	**1**	1d. red-brown...............................	—	£26000

The error "No letter A in right corner" was due to the omission to insert this letter on stamp B A of Plate 77. The error was discovered some months after the plate was registered and was then corrected.

There are innumerable variations in the colour shade of the 1d. "red" and those given in the above list represent colour groups each covering a wide range.

Varieties of 1d. red-brown, etc.

		Un	Used
b.	Major re-entry from..	—	90·00
c.	Double letter in corner from...........................	—	40·00
d.	Double Star (Plate 75) "Union Jack" re-entry..	£34000	£3000
e.	Guide line in corner..	—	35·00
f.	Guide line through value.................................	—	40·00
g.	Thick outer frame to stamp..............................	—	38·00
h.	Ivory head..	£600	38·00
i.	Treasury roulette..	£85000	£7200
j.	Left corner letter "S" inverted (Plates 78, 105, 107)...*from*	—	£160
k.	P converted to R (Plates 30/1, 33, 83, 86).......*from*	—	80·00
l.	Obliterated by Maltese Cross		
	In red...	—	£4800
	In black...	—	65·00
	In blue..	—	£675
m.	Obliterated by Maltese Cross with number in centre		
	No. 1	—	£180
	No. 2	—	£180
	No. 3	—	£225
	No. 4	—	£600
	No. 5	—	£180
	No. 6	—	£160
	No. 7	—	£160
	No. 8	—	£160
	No. 9	—	£180
	No. 10	—	£320
	No. 11	—	£350
	No. 12	—	£350
n.	Obliterated "Penny Post" in black (without Maltese Cross)...	—	£1100
o.	Obliterated by town postmark (without Maltese Cross)		
	In black...*from*	—	£825
	In blue...*from*	—	£2700
	In green...*from*	—	£5500

			Un	Used
	In yellow..*from*		—	£15000
	In red...*from*		—	£15000
p.	Obliterated by 1844 type postmark			
	In blue...*from*		—	£250
	In red...*from*		—	£9750
	In green..*from*		—	£3250
	In violet...*from*		—	£4000
	In black...*from*		—	35·00
	In olive-yellow/brown............................*from*		—	£2000

Stamps with thick outer frame to the design are from plates on which the frame-lines have been straightened or recut, particularly Plates 76 and 90.

For "Union Jack" re-entry see General Notes to Line-engraved Issues.

In "P converted to R" the corner letter "R" is formed from the "P", the distinctive long tail having been hand-cut.

KEY TO LINE-ENGRAVED ISSUES

SG Nos.	Description	Date	Wmk	Perf	Die	Alphabet
	THE IMPERFORATE ISSUES					
1/3	1d. black	6.5.40	SC	Imp	I	I
4/6	2d. no lines	8.5.40	SC	Imp	I	I
	PAPER MORE OR LESS BLUED					
7	1d. red-brown	Feb 1841	SC	Imp	I	I
8/12	1d. red-brown	Feb 1841	SC	Imp	I	I
8/12	1d. red-brown	6.2.52	SC	Imp	I	II
13/15	2d. white lines	13.3.41	SC	Imp	I	I
	THE PERFORATED ISSUES ONE PENNY VALUE					
16a	1d. red-brown	1848	SC	Roul	I	I
16b	1d. red-brown	1850	SC	16	I	I
16c	1d. red-brown	1853	SC	16	I	II
17/18	1d. red-brown	Feb 1854	SC	16	I	II
22	1d. red-brown	Jan 1855	SC	14	I	II
24/5	1d. red-brown	28.2.55	SC	14	II	II
21	1d. red-brown	1.3.55	SC	16	II	II
26	1d. red-brown	15.5.55	LC	16	II	II
29/33	1d. red-brown	Aug 1855	LC	14	II	III
	NEW COLOURS ON WHITE PAPER					
37/41	1d. rose-red	Nov 1856	LC	14	II	III
36	1d. rose-red	26.12.57	LC	16	II	III
42	1d. rose-red	1861	LC	14	II	IV
	TWO PENCE VALUE					
19, 20	2d. blue	1.3.54	SC	16	I	I
23	2d. blue	22.2.55	SC	16	I	I
23a	2d. blue	5.7.55	SC	14	I	II
20a	2d. blue	18.8.55	SC	16	I	II
27	2d. blue	20.7.55	LC	16	I	II
34	2d. blue	20.7.55	LC	14	I	II
35	2d. blue	2.7.57	LC	14	I	III
36a	2d. blue	1.2.58	LC	16	I	III
	LETTERS IN ALL FOUR CORNERS					
48/9	½d. rose-red	1.10.70	W 9	14	—	
43/4	1d. rose-red	1.4.64	LC	14	II	
53a	1½d. rosy mauve	1860	LC	14	II	
51/3	1½d. rose-red	1.10.70	LC	14	II	
45	2d. blue	July 1858	LC	14	I	
46/7	2d. thinner lines	7.7.69	LC	14	II	

Watermarks: SC = Small Crown, T **2**. LC = Large Crown, T **4**.
Dies: See notes above No. 17 in the catalogue.
Alphabets: See General Notes to this section.

3 White lines added

1841 (13 Mar)–**51**. White lines added. *Wmk W* **2**. Paper more or less blued. *Imperf.*

			Unused	Used	Used on cover
13	**3**	2d. pale blue.................................	£9500	£110	
14		2d. blue...	£6250	90·00	£350
		s. Optd "SPECIMEN" (1)...............	£9000		
		Wi. Watermark inverted.................	£24000	£875	
15		2d. deep full blue.........................	£8500	£110	
15aa		2d. violet-blue (1851)....................	£28000	£1800	

The 2d. stamp with white lines was printed from Plates 3 and 4.

No. 15aa came from Plate 4 and the quoted price is for examples on thicker, lavender tinted paper.

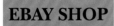

Plates of 2d. blue

Plate		Unused	Used
3 shades.....*from*		£6250	£100
4 shades.....*from*		£6250	90·00

Varieties of 2d. blue

			Unused	Used
a.	Guide line in corner		—	£110
b.	Guide line through value		£6750	£110
bb.	Double letter in corner		—	£120
be	Re-entry		£8250	£200
c.	Ivory head		£6250	£100
e.	Obliterated by Maltese Cross			
	In red		—	—
	In black		—	£275
	In blue		—	£5000
f.	Obliterated by Maltese Cross with number in centre			
	No. 1		—	£700
	No. 2		—	£700
	No. 3		—	£700
	No. 4		—	£700
	No. 5		—	£850
	No. 6		—	£700
	No. 7		—	£1200
	No. 8		—	£1000
	No. 9		—	£1200
	No. 10		—	£1500
	No. 11		—	£850
	No. 12		—	£550
g.	Obliterated by town postmark (without Maltese Cross)			
	In black	*from*	—	£3500
	In blue	*from*	—	£4500
h.	Obliterated by 1844 type postmark			
	In black	*from*	—	90·00
	In blue	*from*	—	£1000
	In red	*from*	—	£28000
	In green	*from*	—	£9000

1841 (Apr). Trial printing (unissued) on Dickinson silk-thread paper. No wmk. *Imperf.*

16	**1**	1d. red-brown (Plate 11)	£7750

Eight sheets were printed on this paper, six being gummed, two ungummed, but we have only seen examples without gum.

1848. Wmk W **2**. Rouletted approx 11½ by Henry Archer.

16a	**1**	1d. red-brown (Plates 70, 71)	£25000

1850. *Wmk W* **2**. *P* 16 by Henry Archer.

			Un	Used	Used on cover
16b	**1**	1d. red-brown (Alphabet 1) (from Plates 90–101, 105, 107, 108, 116) *from*	£3500	£625	£2000
		bWi. Watermark inverted	—	£3750	

1853. *Wmk W* **2**. Government Trial Perforation.

16c	**1**	1d. red-brown (P 16) (Alphabet II) (on cover)	

SEPARATION TRIALS. Although the various trials of machines for rouletting and perforating were unofficial, Archer had the consent of the authorities in making his experiments, and sheets so experimented upon were afterwards used by the Post Office.

As Archer ended his experiments in 1850 and plates with corner letters of Alphabet II did not come into issue until 1852, perforated stamps with corner letters of Alphabet I may safely be assumed to be Archer productions, if genuine.

The Government trial perforation is believed to have been done on Archer's machines after they had been purchased in 1853. As Alphabet II was by that time in use, the trials can be distinguished from the perforated stamps listed below by being dated prior to 24 February 1854, the date when the perforated stamps were officially issued.

Die I, Alphabet I, stamps from plates 74 and 113 perforated 14 have been recorded for many years, but it is now generally recognised that the type of comb machine used, producing one extension hole in the side margins, cannot be contemporary with other trials of this period.

Die I   Die II   **4** Large Crown

Die I: The features of the portrait are lightly shaded and consequently lack emphasis.

Die II: (Die I retouched): The lines of the features have been deepened and appear stronger. The eye is deeply shaded and made more lifelike. The nostril and lips are more clearly defined, the latter appearing much thicker. A strong downward stroke of colour marks the corner of the mouth. There is a deep indentation of colour between lower lip and chin. The band running from the back of the ear to the chignon has a bolder horizontal line below it than in Die I.

1854–57. Paper more or less blued.

(a) Wmk Small Crown, W **2**. *P* 16.

			Unused	Used	Used on cover
17	**1**	1d. red-brown (Die I) (24.2.54)	£375	35·00	60·00
		a. Imperf three sides (horiz pair)	†	£7500	
		Wi. Watermark inverted	—	£200	
18		1d. yellow-brown (Die I)	£450	50·00	
19	**3**	2d. deep blue (Plate 4) (12.3.54)	£4700	£100	£200
		a. Imperf three sides (horiz pair)	†		
		s. Optd "SPECIMEN" (2)	£2000		
		Wi. Watermark inverted	—	£325	
20		2d. pale blue (Plate 4)	£5500	£110	
20a		2d. blue (Plate 5) (18.8.55)	£10000	£350	£550
		aWi. Watermark inverted	—	£900	
21	**1**	1d. red-brown (Die II) (22.2.55)	£550	65·00	£110
		a. Imperf (Plates 2, 14)			
		Wi. Watermark inverted	—	£1750	£260

(b) Wmk Small Crown, W **2**. *P* 14.

22	**1**	1d. red-brown (Die I) (1.55)	£1000	90·00	£160
		Wi. Watermark inverted	—	£300	
23	**3**	2d. blue (Plate 4) (22.2.55)	£13000	£225	£375
		s. Optd "SPECIMEN" (2)	£1700		
		Wi. Watermark inverted	£18500	£650	
23a		2d. blue (Plate 5) (4.7.55)	£14000	£350	£525
		b. Imperf (Plate 5)	—		
		aWi. Watermark inverted	—	£750	
24	**1**	1d. red-brown (Die II) (27.2.55)	£700	70·00	£110
		Wi. Watermark inverted	£2400	£350	
24a		1d. deep red-brown (very blue paper) (Die II)	£850	£110	
25		1d. orange-brown (Die II)	£1900	£170	

(c) Wmk Large Crown, W **4**. *P* 16.

26	**1**	1d. red-brown (Die II) (15.5.55)	£2500	£130	£240
		a. Imperf (Plate 7)			
		Wi. Watermark inverted	—	£450	
27	**3**	2d. blue (Plate 5) (20.7.55)	£18500	£450	£575
		a. Imperf	—	£12000	
		Wi. Watermark inverted	—	£1000	

(d) Wmk Large Crown, W **4**. *P* 14.

29	**1**	1d. red-brown (Die II) (6.55)	£240	22·00	40·00
		a. Imperf (shades) (Plates 22, 24, 25, 32, 43)	£4000	£3500	
		s. Optd "SPECIMEN" (2)	£700		
		Wi. Watermark inverted	£1000	£150	
30		1d. brick-red (Die II)	£375	45·00	
31		1d. plum (Die II) (2.56)	£3800	£900	
32		1d. brown-rose (Die II)	£375	55·00	
33		1d. orange-brown (Die II) (3.57)	£725	60·00	
34	**3**	2d. blue (Plate 5) (20.7.55)	£2850	70·00	£200
		Wi. Watermark inverted	—	£325	
35		2d. blue (Plate 6) (2.7.57)	£3400	70·00	£200
		a. Imperf	—	£12000	
		b. Imperf horiz (vert pair)	†	—	
		Wi. Watermark inverted	—	£325	

*17/35a **For well-centred, lightly used +125%**

1856–58. *Wmk Large Crown, W* **4**. Paper no longer blued.

(a) P 16.

36	**1**	1d. rose-red (Die II) (26.12.57)	£2750	80·00	£160
		Wi. Watermark inverted	—	£475	
36a	**3**	2d. blue (Plate 6) (1.2.58)	£14500	£375	£550
		aWi. Watermark inverted	—	£1000	

(b) Die II. P 14.

37	**1**	1d. red-brown (11.56)	£2400	£375	£1100

BILL BARRELL LTD

'Concise' and to the point - GB stamps at fair prices. Fine stocks of
fine GB stamps, mint, used, on cover, officials, telegraphs etc.
Enquiries and wants list welcome.

SG14. Fine
mint 1841 2d
blue.

SG166a. Error
imperf with cert.

SG8. Very fine
used.

SG16b. Archer
experimental,
very fine used.

SG266. Very fine used.

SG137. Fine used.

SG438. Superb used.

SG183. Very
fine used.

SG110. Fine
mint.

SG2. pl.10.
Very fine used.

PO Box 10494, Grantham, Lincolnshire,
NG31 0HS, United Kingdom
01476 594698

e-mail: bill@barrell.co.uk *website*: www.barrell.co.uk

38	1d. pale red (9.4.57)	£100	35·00	
	a. Imperf	£4800	£3600	
	s. Optd "SPECIMEN" (6, 7, 10)	£200		
39	1d. pale rose (3.57)	£110	35·00	
40	1d. rose-red (9.57)	50·00	12·00	23·00
	a. Imperf	£5000	£3800	
	b. Imperf vert (horiz pair)	†	—	
	Wi. Watermark inverted	£180	85·00	
41	1d. deep rose-red (7.57)	£160	20·00	

1861. Letters engraved on plate instead of punched (Alphabet IV).

42	**1**	1d. rose-red (Die II) (Plates 50 and 51)	£250	40·00	70·00
		a. Imperf	—	£5750	
		Wi. Watermark inverted	£750	£200	

*36/42a **For well-centred, lightly used +125%**

The original die (Die I) was used to provide roller dies for the laying down of all the line-engraved stamps from 1840 to 1855. In that year a new master die was laid down (by means of a Die I roller die) and the impression was retouched by hand engraving by William Humphrys. This retouched die, always known to philatelists as Die II, was from that time used for preparing all new roller dies.

One Penny. The numbering of the 1d. plates recommenced at 1 on the introduction of Die II. Plates 1 to 21 were Alphabet II from which a scarce plum shade exists. Corner letters of Alphabet III appear on Plate 22 and onwards. As an experiment, the corner letters were engraved by hand on Plates 50 and 51 in 1856, instead of being punched (Alphabet IV), but punching was again resorted to from Plate 52 onwards. Plates 50 and 51 were not put into use until 1861.

Two Pence. Unlike the 1d. the old sequence of plate numbers continued. Plates 3 and 4 of the 2d. had corner letters of Alphabet I, Plate 5 Alphabet II and Plate 6 Alphabet III. In Plate 6 the white lines are thinner than before.

In both values, varieties may be found as described in the preceding issues – ivory heads, inverted watermarks, re-entries, and double letters in corners.

The change of perforation from 16 to 14 was decided upon late in 1854 since the closer holes of the former gauge tended to cause the sheets of stamps to break up when handled, but for a time both gauges were in concurrent use. Owing to faulty alignment of the impressions on the plates and to shrinkage of the paper when dampened, badly perforated stamps are plentiful in the line-engraved issues.

5

6

Showing position of the plate number on the 1d. and 2d. values. (Plate 170 shown)

1864–79. Letters in all four corners. *Wmk* Large Crown, *W* **4**. Die II. *P* **14**.

			Unused	Used*	Used on cover
43	**5**	1d. rose-red (1.4.64)	27·00	2·75	8·00
		s. Optd "SPECIMEN" (1, 6, 8, 9) .... *from*	£225		
44		1d. lake-red	27·00	2·75	
		a. Imperf .... *from*	£8500	£4500	
		Wi. Watermark inverted .... *from*	£110	35·00	

*43/4a **For well-centred, lightly used +125%**

The following plate numbers are known imperf (No. 44a); 72, 79, 80, 81, 82, 83, 84, 85, 86, 87, 88, 90, 91, 92, 93, 96, 97, 98, 100, 101, 102, 103, 104, 105, 107, 108, 109, 112, 113, 114, 116, 117, 120, 121, 122, 136, 137, 142, 146, 148, 158, 162, 164, 166, 171, 174, 191 and 202.

The numbering of this series of 1d. red plates follows after that of the previous 1d. stamp, last printed from Plate 68.

Plates 69, 70, 75, 126 and 128 were prepared for this issue but rejected owing to defects, and stamps from these plates do not exist, so that specimens which appear to be from these plates (like many of those which optimistic collectors believe to be from Plate 77) bear other plate numbers. Owing to faulty engraving or printing it is not always easy to identify the plate number. Plate 77 was also rejected but some stamps printed from it were used. One specimen is in the Tapling Collection and six or seven others are known. Plates 226 to 228 were made but not used.

Specimens from most of the plates are known with inverted watermark. The variety of watermark described in the General Notes to this section occurs on stamp M A (or M L) on plates up to about 96 (Prices from £120 used).

Re-entries in this issue are few, the best being on stamps M K and T K of Plate 71 and on S L and T L, Plate 83.

Plate	Un	Used	Plate	Un	Used
71	55·00	4·00	150	27·00	2·75
72	60·00	5·00	151	80·00	11·00
73	60·00	4·00	152	80·00	7·50
74	60·00	2·75	153	£140	11·00
76	55·00	2·75	154	70·00	2·75
77	—	£600000	155	70·00	3·00
78	£130	2·75	156	65·00	2·75
79	48·00	2·75	157	70·00	2·75
80	65·00	2·75	158	48·00	2·75
81	65·00	3·00	159	48·00	2·75
82	£130	5·00	160	48·00	2·75
83	£155	9·00	161	80·00	9·00
84	80·00	3·00	162	70·00	9·00
85	60·00	4·00	163	70·00	4·00
86	70·00	5·00	164	70·00	4·00
87	48·00	2·75	165	65·00	2·75
88	£190	9·50	166	65·00	7·00
89	60·00	2·75	167	65·00	10·00
90	60·00	2·75	168	70·00	10·00
91	75·00	7·00	169	80·00	9·00
92	55·00	2·75	170	55·00	2·75
93	70·00	2·75	171	27·00	2·75
94	65·00	6·00	172	48·00	2·75
95	60·00	2·75	173	95·00	11·00
96	65·00	2·75	174	50·00	2·75
97	60·00	4·50	175	80·00	4·50
98	70·00	7·00	176	80·00	3·00
99	75·00	6·00	177	60·00	2·75
100	80·00	3·00	178	80·00	4·50
101	80·00	11·00	179	70·00	3·00
102	65·00	2·75	180	80·00	6·50
103	70·00	4·50	181	65·00	2·75
104	£100	6·00	182	£130	6·50
105	£130	9·00	183	75·00	4·00
106	75·00	2·75	184	48·00	3·00
107	80·00	9·00	185	70·00	4·00
108	£110	3·00	186	90·00	3·00
109	£120	4·50	187	70·00	2·75
110	80·00	11·00	188	95·00	12·00
111	70·00	3·00	189	95·00	8·50
112	90·00	3·00	190	70·00	7·00
113	70·00	15·00	191	48·00	9·00
114	£325	15·00	192	70·00	2·75
115	£130	3·00	193	48·00	2·75
116	£100	11·00	194	70·00	10·00
117	65·00	2·75	195	70·00	10·00
118	70·00	2·75	196	70·00	6·50
119	65·00	2·75	197	75·00	11·00
120	27·00	2·75	198	60·00	7·00
121	60·00	11·00	199	75·00	7·00
122	27·00	2·75	200	80·00	2·75
123	60·00	2·75	201	48·00	6·00
124	42·00	2·75	202	80·00	10·00
125	60·00	2·75	203	48·00	20·00
127	75·00	3·00	204	75·00	3·00
129	60·00	10·00	205	75·00	4·00
130	75·00	3·00	206	75·00	11·00
131	85·00	20·00	207	80·00	11·00
132	£190	27·00	208	75·00	18·00
133	£160	11·00	209	65·00	10·00
134	27·00	2·75	210	90·00	15·00
135	£130	30·00	211	95·00	25·00
136	£130	24·00	212	80·00	13·00
137	42·00	3·00	213	80·00	13·00
138	32·00	2·75	214	90·00	23·00
139	80·00	20·00	215	90·00	23·00
140	32·00	2·75	216	95·00	23·00
141	£100	11·00	217	95·00	9·00
142	95·00	30·00	218	90·00	10·00
143	80·00	17·00	219	£130	85·00
144	£130	25·00	220	60·00	9·00
145	48·00	3·00	221	95·00	20·00
146	60·00	7·00	222	£110	50·00
147	70·00	4·00	223	£130	75·00
148	60·00	4·00	224	£165	65·00
149	60·00	7·00	225	£3200	£800

1858-76 *Wmk* Large Crown. Die II. *P.* 14

			Un	Used*	Used on cover
45	**6**	2d. blue (thick lines) (7.58)	£350	15·00	50·00
		a. Imperf (Plate 9)		£13000	
		s. Optd "SPECIMEN" (1, 7)	£650		
		Wi. Watermark inverted	£1700	£240	
		Plate			
		7	£2000	65·00	
		8	£1850	45·00	
		9	£350	15·00	
		12	£3000	£140	
46		2d. blue (thin lines) (1.7.69)	£375	27·00	75·00

	s. Optd "SPECIMEN" (pl. 14, 15) (6, 8, 9, 10)		£250		
	Wi. Watermark inverted		£2250	£300	
47	2d. deep blue (thin lines)		£375	30·00	
	a. Imperf (Plate 13)		£12000		
	Plate				
	13		£375	30·00	
	14		£500	38·00	
	15		£525	38·00	

*45/7 **For well-centred, lightly used +125%**

Plates 10 and 11 of the 2d. were prepared but rejected. Plates 13 to 15 were laid down from a new roller impression on which the white lines were thinner.

There are some marked re-entries and repairs, particularly on Plates 7, 8, 9 and 12.

Stamps with inverted watermark may be found and also the T A (T L) and M A (M L) watermark varieties (see General Notes to this section).

Though the paper is normally white, some printings showed blueing and stamps showing the "ivory head" may therefore be found.

7

Showing the plate number (9)

9

1870 (1 Oct)-**79**. *Wmk W* **9,** extending over three stamps. *P* **14**.

			Unused	*Used**	*Used on cover*
48	7	½d. rose-red	£110	30·00	70·00
49		½d. rose	£110	30·00	
		a. Imperf (Plates 1, 4, 5, 6, 8, 14) ...*from*	£4500	£3200	
		s. Optd "SPECIMEN" (various plates) (2, 8, 9, 10)	£225		
		Wi. Watermark inverted	£450	£150	
		Wj. Watermark reversed	£450	£150	
		Wk. Watermark inverted and reversed	£300	£100	
		Plate			
		1	£325	£100	
		3	£240	55·00	
		4	£150	50·00	
		5	£110	30·00	
		6	£120	30·00	
		8	£600	£120	
		9	£6000	£850	
		10	£130	30·00	
		11	£120	30·00	
		12	£120	30·00	
		13	£120	30·00	
		14	£120	30·00	
		15	£175	50·00	
		19	£300	65·00	
		20	£350	85·00	

*48/9a **For well-centred, lightly used +200%**

The ½d. was printed in sheets of 480 (24×20) so that the check letters run from

A A   A X
to
T A   T X

Plates 2, 7, 16, 17 and 18 were not completed while Plates 21 and 22, though made, were not used.

Owing to the method of perforating, the outer side of stamps in either the A or X row (ie the left or right side of the sheet) is imperf.

Stamps may be found with watermark inverted or reversed, or without watermark, the latter due to misplacement of the paper when printing.

8

Position of plate number

1870 (1 Oct)-**74**. *Wmk W* **4**. *P* **14**.

			Unused	*Used**	*Used on cover*
51	8	1½d. rose-red	£500	75·00	£275

	s. Optd "SPECIMEN" (pl. 1) (2, 6)		£550		
	sa. Optd "SPECIMEN" (pl. 3) (8, 9, 10)		£300		
52	1½d. lake-red		£600	75·00	
	a. Imperf (Plates 1 and 3)....*from*	£10000		†	
	Wi. Watermark inverted		£3000	£500	
	Plate				
	1		£725	£110	
	3		£500	75·00	
	Error of lettering. OP–PC for CP–PC (Plate 1)				
53	8	1½d. rose-red	£30000	£2000	£7500
	Prepared for use in 1860, but not issued; blued paper.				
53a	8	1½d. rosy mauve (Plate 1)	£8500	—	
	b. Error of lettering, OP–PC for CP–PC	—	†	
	s. Optd "SPECIMEN" (2, 6)	£2250		

*51/3 **For well-centred, lightly used +125%**

Owing to a proposed change in the postal rates, 1½d. stamps were first printed in 1860, in rosy mauve, No. 53a, but the change was not approved and the greater part of the stock was destroyed, although three or four postally used examples have been recorded.

In 1870 a 1½d. stamp was required and was issued in rose-red. Plate 1 did not have the plate number in the design of the stamps, but on stamps from Plate 3 the number will be found in the frame as shown above. Plate 2 was defective and was not used.

The error of lettering OP–PC on Plate 1 was apparently not noticed by the printer, and therefore not corrected.

EMBOSSED ISSUES

Volume 1 of the Stanley Gibbons Great Britain Specialised Catalogue gives further detailed information on the embossed issues.

PRICES. The prices quoted are for cut-square stamps with average to fine embossing. Stamps with exceptionally clear embossing are worth more.

10   **11**   **12**

13

Position of die number

(Primary die engraved at the Royal Mint by William Wyon. Stamps printed at Somerset House.)

1847–54. *Imperf* (For paper and watermark see footnote).

			Unused	*Used*	*Used on cover*
54	10	1s. pale green (11.9.47)	£24000	£1000	£1900
		s. Optd "SPECIMEN" (red opt)	£3000		
		sa. Optd "SPECIMEN" (black opt) (1, 2)	£2800		
55		1s. green	£24000	£1000	
56		1s. deep green	£28500	£1200	
		Die 1 (1847)	£24000	£1000	
		Die 2 (1854)	£26500	£1100	
57	11	10d. brown (6.11.48)	£11500	£1500	£3200
		s. Optd "SPECIMEN" (1, 2)	£3000		
		Die 1 (1848)	£12000	£1500	
		Die 2 (1850)	£11500	£1500	
		Die 3 (1853)	£11500	£1500	
		Die 4 (1854)	£13000	£1750	
58	12	6d. mauve (watermark reversed) (1.3.54)	£19500	£1000	
		s. Optd "SPECIMEN" (1, 2)	£3900		
59		6d. dull lilac	£19500	£1000	£1900
60		6d. purple (watermark upright)	£19500	£1000	
		Wi. Watermark inverted	£19500	£1000	
		Wk. Watermark inverted and reversed	£19500	£1000	
61		6d. violet	£32000	£4000	

The 1s. and 10d. are on "Dickinson" paper with "silk" threads. The 6d. is on paper watermarked V R in single-lined letters, W 13, which may be found in four ways—upright, inverted, upright reversed, and inverted reversed. In this listing the reversed watermark is taken to be 'normal'. **Collectors are reminded that Types 10/12 were also used to print postal stationery. 6d. stamps without watermark and 10d. and 1s. stamps without "silk" threads come from this source and should not be confused with the adhesives, Nos. 54/61.**

The die numbers are indicated on the base of the bust. Only Die 1 (1 *W W*) of the 6d. was used for the adhesive stamps. The 10d. is from Die 1 (W.W.1 on stamps), and Dies 2 to 4 (2W.W., 3W.W. and 4W.W.) but the number and letters on stamps from Die 1 are seldom clear and many specimens are known without any trace of them. Because of this the stamp was previously listed as "No die number" has been deleted. That they are from Die 1 is proved by the existence of blocks showing stamps with and without the die number. The 1s. is from Dies 1 and 2 (W.W.1, W.W.2).

The normal arrangement of the "silk" threads in the paper was in pairs running down each vertical row of the sheets, the space between the threads of each pair being approximately 5 mm and between pairs of threads 20 mm. Varieties due to misplacement of the paper in printing show a single thread on the first stamp from the sheet margin and two threads 20 mm apart on the other stamps of the row. Faulty manufacture is the cause of stamps with a single thread in the middle.

Through bad spacing of the impressions, which were handstruck, all values may be found with two impressions more or less overlapping. Owing to the small margin allowed for variation of spacing, specimens with good margins on all sides are not common.

Double impressions are known of all values.

Later printings of the 6d. had the gum tinted green to enable the printer to distinguish the gummed side of the paper.

SURFACE-PRINTED ISSUES

GENERAL NOTES

Volume 1 of the Stanley Gibbons *Great Britain Specialised Catalogue* gives further detailed information on the surface-printed issues.

"Abnormals". The majority of the great rarities in the surface printed group of issues are the so-called "abnormals", whose existence is due to the practice of printing six sheets from every plate as soon as made, one of which was kept for record purposes at Somerset House, while the others were perforated and usually issued. If such plates were not used for general production or if, before they came into full use, a change of watermark or colour took place, the six sheets originally printed would differ from the main issue in plate, colour or watermark and, if issued would be extremely rare.

The abnormal stamps of this class listed in this Catalogue and distinguished, where not priced, by an asterisk (*) are:

No.	
78	3d. Plate 3 (with white dots)
152	4d. vermilion, Plate 16
153	4d. sage-green, Plate 17
109	6d. mauve, Plate 10
124/*a*	6d. pale chestnut and 6d. chestnut, Plate 12
145	6d. pale buff, Plate 13
88	9d. Plate 3 (hair lines)
98	9d. Plate 5 (see footnote to No. 98)
113	10d. Plate 2
91	1s. Plate 3 ("Plate 2")
148/50	1s. green, Plate 14
120	2s. blue, Plate 3

Those which may have been issued, but of which no specimens are known, are 2½d. wmk Anchor, Plates 4 and 5; 3d. wmk Emblems, Plate 5; 3d. wmk Spray, Plate 21, 6d. wmk Spray, Plate 18; 8d. orange, Plate 2; 1s. wmk Emblems, Plate 5; 5s. wmk Maltese Cross, Plate 4.

The 10d. Plate 1, wmk Emblems (No. 99), is sometimes reckoned among the abnormals, but was an error, due to the use of the wrong paper.

Corner Letters. With the exception of the 4d., 6d. and 1s. of 1855–57 the ½d., 1½d., 2d. and 5d. of 1880, the 1d. lilac of 1881 and the £5 (which had letters in lower corners only, and in the reverse order to the normal), all the surface-printed stamps issued prior to 1887 had letters in all four corners, as in the later line-engraved stamps. The arrangement is the same, the letters running in sequence right across and down the sheets, whether there were divided into panes or not. The corner letters existing naturally depend on the number of stamps in the sheet and their arrangement.

Imprimaturs and Imperforate Stamps. The Post Office retained in their records (now in the National Postal Museum) one imperforate sheet from each plate, known as the Imprimatur (or officially approved) sheet. Some stamps were removed from time to time for presentation purposes and have come on to the market, but these imperforates are not listed as they were not issued. Full details can be found in Volume 1 of the *Great Britain Specialised Catalogue*.

However, other imperforate stamps are known to have been issued and these are listed where it has been possible to prove that they do not come from the Imprimatur sheets. It is therefore advisable to purchase these items only when accompanied by an Expert Committee certificate of genuineness.

Plate Numbers. All stamps from No. 75 to No. 163 bear in their designs either the plate number or, in one or two earlier instances, some other indication by which one plate can be distinguished from another. With the aid of these and of the corner letters it is thus possible to "reconstruct" a sheet of stamps from any plate of any issue or denomination.

Surface-printing. In this context the traditional designation "surface-

printing" is synonymous with letterpress—the printers' term—as meaning printing from (the surface of) raised type while philatelists often use the expression 'Typo(graphy)', although this is beginning to fall out of favour. It is also called relief printing, as the image is in relief (in French, *en épargne*), unwanted parts of the design having been cut away. Duplicate impressions can be electrotyped or stereotyped from an original die, the resulting clichés being locked together to form the printing plate.

Wing Margins. As the vertical gutters (spaces) between the panes, into which sheets of stamps of most values were divided until the introduction of the Imperial Crown watermark, were perforated through the centre with a single row of holes, instead of each vertical row of stamps on the inner side of the panes having its own line of perforation as is usual, a proportion of the stamps in each sheet have what is called a "wing margin" about 5 mm wide on one or other side.

The stamps with "wing margins" are the watermark Emblems and Spray of Rose series (3d., 6d., 9d., 10d., 1s. and 2s.) with letters D, E, H or I in the south-east corner, and the watermark Garter series (4d. and 8d.) with letters F or G in the south-east corner. Knowledge of this lettering will enable collectors to guard against stamps with wing margin cut down and re-perforated, but note that wing margin stamps of Nos. 62 to 73 are also to be found re-perforated.

PRINTERS. The issues of Queen Victoria, Nos. 62/214, were typo by Thomas De La Rue & Co.

PERFORATIONS. All the surface-printed issues of Queen Victoria are perf 14, with the exception of Nos. 126/9.

KEY TO SURFACE-PRINTED ISSUES 1855–83

SG Nos.	*Description*	*Watermark*	*Date of Issue*
	NO CORNER LETTERS		
62	4d. carmine	Small Garter	31.7.55
63/5	4d. carmine	Medium Garter	25.2.56
66/a	4d. carmine	Large Garter	Jan 1857
69/70	6d. lilac	Emblems	21.10.56
71/3	1s. green	Emblems	1.11.56
	SMALL WHITE CORNER LETTERS		
75/7	3d. carmine	Emblems	1.5.62
78	3d. carmine (dots)	Emblems	Aug 1862
79/82	4d. red	Large Garter	15.1.62
83/5	6d. lilac	Emblems	1.12.62
86/8	9d. bistre	Emblems	15.1.62
89/91	1s. green	Emblems	1.12.62
	LARGE WHITE CORNER LETTERS		
92	3d. rose	Emblems	1.3.65
102/3	3d. rose	Spray	July 1867
93/4	4d. vermilion	Large Garter	4.7.65
96/7	6d. lilac	Emblems	7.3.65
104/7	6d. lilac	Spray	21.6.67
108/9	6d. lilac	Spray	8.3.69
122/4	6d. chestnut	Spray	12.4.72
125	6d. grey	Spray	24.4.73
98	9d. straw	Emblems	30.10.65
110/11	9d. straw	Spray	3.10.67
99	10d. brown	Emblems	11.11.67
112/14	10d. brown	Spray	1.7.67
101	1s. green	Emblems	19.1.65
115/17	1s. green	Spray	13.7.67
118/20b	2s. blue	Spray	1.7.67
121	2s. brown	Spray	27.2.80
126/7	5s. rose	Cross	1.7.67
128	10s. grey	Cross	26.9.78
129	£1 brown-lilac	Cross	26.9.78
130, 134	5s. rose	Anchor	25.11.82
131, 135	10s. grey-green	Anchor	Feb 1883
132, 136	£1 brown-lilac	Anchor	Dec 1882
133, 137	£5 orange	Anchor	21.3.82
	LARGE COLOURED CORNER LETTERS		
138/9	2½d. rosy mauve	Anchor	1.7.75
141	2½d. rosy mauve	Orb	1.5.76
142	2½d. blue	Orb	5-2.80
157	2½d. blue	Crown	23.3.81
143/4	3d. rose	Spray	5.7.73
158	3d. rose	Crown	Jan 1881
159	3d. on 3d. lilac	Crown	1.1.83
152	4d. vermilion	Large Garter	1.3.76
153	4d. sage-green	Large Garter	12.3.77
154	4d. brown	Large Garter	15.8.80
160	4d. brown	Crown	9.12.80
145	6d. buff	Spray	15.3.73
146/7	6d. grey	Spray	20.3.74
161	6d. grey	Crown	1.1.81
162	6d. on 6d. lilac	Crown	1.1.83
156a	8d. purple-brown	Large Garter	July 1876
156	8d. orange	Large Garter	11.9.76
148/50	1s. green	Spray	1.9.73
151	1s. brown	Spray	14.10.80
163	1s. brown	Crown	24.5.81

Watermarks:	Anchor	W **40, 47**
	Cross	W **39**
	Crown	W **49**

Fine Stamps of Great Britain
ANDREW VAUGHAN PHILATELICS

Emblems .... W **20**
Large Garter .... W **17**
Medium Garter .... W **16**
Orb .... W **48**
Small Garter .... W **15**
Spray .... W **33**

14   **15** Small Garter

16 Medium Garter   **17** Large Garter

1855–57. No corner letters.

(a) Wmk Small Garter, W **15.** *Highly glazed, deeply blued paper*
(31 July 1855)

			Unused	Used*	Used on cover
62	**14**	4d. carmine (*shades*)	£8500	£450	£780
		a. Paper slightly blued	£9000	£450	
		b. White paper	£20000	£1100	
		s. Optd "SPECIMEN" (2, 3)	£1200		
		Wi. Watermark inverted	£11000	£1200	

(b) Wmk Medium Garter, W **16.**
(i) Thick, blued highly glazed paper 25 February 1856.

63	**14**	4d. carmine (*shades*)	£14000	£575	£1100
		a. White paper	£12000		
		s. Optd "SPECIMEN" (2)	£1100		
		Wi. Watermark inverted	—	£1250	

(ii) Ordinary thin white paper – September 1856

64	**14**	4d. pale carmine	£13000	£500	£1000
		a. Stamp printed double	†	—	
		s. Optd "SPECIMEN" (2)	£1100		
		Wi. Watermark inverted	£17000	£1200	

(iii) Ordinary white paper, specially prepared ink – 1 November 1856

65	**14**	4d. rose or deep rose	£13000	£525	£1000
		s. Optd "SPECIMEN" (4)	£1850		
		Wi. Watermark inverted	†		

(c) Wmk Large Garter, W **17.** *Ordinary white paper – January* 1857.

66	**14**	4d. rose-carmine	£2100	£150	£225
		a. Rose.	£1750	£150	
		aWi. Watermark inverted	£4800	£400	
		aWj. Watermark inverted and			
		reversed			
		b. Thick glazed paper	£6500	£375	
		bWi. Watermark inverted			
		s. Optd "SPECIMEN" (2, 7)	£450		

***62/6b** For well-centred, lightly used* +125%

18   **19**

20 Emblems wmk
(normal)

20a Watermark error,
three roses and
shamrock

20b Watermark error,
three roses and thistle

(d) Wmk Emblems, W **20.**

			Unused	Used*	Used on cover
68	**18**	6d. lilac	£1350	£110	£240
69	**18**	6d. deep lilac (21.10.56)	£1800	£175	
		s. Optd "SPECIMEN" (2, 4, 7, 8)	£600		
70		6d. pale lilac	£1350	£125	£240
		a. Azure paper	£9000	£950	
		b. Thick paper	£4000	£425	
		c. Error. Watermark W **20a**			
		Wi. Watermark inverted	£3000	£400	
		Wj. Watermark reversed		£475	
		Wk. Watermark inverted and			
		reversed			
71	**19**	1s. deep green (1.11.56)	£5750	£550	
		s. Optd "SPECIMEN" (2, 4, 7)	£975		
72		1s. green	£3250	£350	£425
73		1s. pale green	£3250	£350	
		a. Azure paper	—	£2000	
		b. Thick paper	—	£400	
		c. Imperf		†	—
		Wi. Watermark inverted	—	£700	
		Wj. Watermark reversed	—	£1400	
		Wk. Watermark inverted and			
		reversed			

***69/73b** For well-centred, lightly used* +125%

21   **22**

23   **24**   **25** Plate 2

A. White dots added   B. Hair lines

1862–64. A small uncoloured letter in each corner, the 4d. wmk Large
Garter, W **17**, the others Emblems, W **20**.

			Unused	Used*	Used on cover
75	**21**	3d. deep carmine-rose (Plate 2)			
		(1.5.62)	£4800	£575	
		s. Optd "SPECIMEN" (2, 5, 6, 8)	£500		
76		3d. bright carmine-rose	£2700	£350	£600
		a. Error. Watermark W **20b**			
		(stamp TF)		£9000	
		Wi. Watermark inverted	—	£1200	
77		3d. pale carmine-rose	£2700	£350	
		b. Thick paper	£4000	£475	
		Wj. Watermark reversed			
78		3d. rose (with white dots, Type A,			
		Plate 3) (9.63)	£45000	£17000	
		a. Imperf (Plate 3)	£6750		
		s. Optd "SPECIMEN" (2)	£2000		
79	**22**	4d. bright red (Plate 3) (15.1.62)	£2200	£170	
		s. Optd "SPECIMEN" (2, 5, 6, 8)	£425		
80		4d. pale red	£2000	£140	£300
		Wi. Watermark inverted	—	£375	
81		4d. bright red (Hair lines, Type B,			
		Plate 4) (16.10.63)	£2300	£185	
		s. Optd "SPECIMEN" (2)	£500		
82		4d. pale red (Hair lines, Type B,			
		Plate 4)	£2100	£150	£300
		a. Imperf (Plate 4)	£2750		
		Wi. Watermark inverted	£6700	£375	
83	**23**	6d. deep lilac (Plate 3) (1.12.62)	£2800	£160	
84		6d. lilac	£2250	£140	£225
		a. Azure paper	—	£1400	
		b. Thick paper	—	£375	
		c. Error. Shamrock missing from			
		wmk (stamp TF)		£4000	
		d. Error. Watermark W **20b**			
		(stamp TF)	—	£8000	
		e. Hyphen omitted (KA)*		£7750	
		s. Optd "SPECIMEN" (2, 5, 8)	£600		
		Wi. Watermark inverted	£8250	£450	

Whatever your budget
or collecting interests

you will find a range of the
highest quality material for the
discerning collector.

Stanley Gibbons, a name synonymous with quality.

Ever since the birth of our hobby
Stanley Gibbons has been at the
forefront of GB philately and we invite
collectors access to one of the finest
GB stocks in the world by registering for
our renowned free monthly brochure.

STANLEY GIBBONS
LONDON 1856

BY APPOINTMENT TO
HER MAJESTY THE QUEEN
PHILATELISTS
STANLEY GIBBONS LTD
LONDON

Email gb@stanleygibbons.com or phone 020 7557 4464

STANLEY GIBBONS 399 STRAND LONDON WC2R 0LX | WWW.STANLEYGIBBONS.COM

Fine Stamps and Postal History

Visit our website to view hundreds of fine GB items:

www.andrewglajer.co.uk

Andrew G Lajer Ltd
sales@andrewglajer.co.uk / T: 01189 344151
The Old Post Office, Davis Way, Hurst, Berkshire, RG10 0TR

		Wj. Watermark reversed	£550		
		Wk. Watermark inverted and			
		reversed............................	£12000		
85		6d. lilac (Hair lines, Plate 4) (20.4.64)	£3000	£250	£350
		a. Imperf (watermark inverted)...	£3250		
		Eb. Imperf and watermark			
		upright..................................	£3500		
		c. Thick paper	£4000	£280	
		d. Error. Watermark *W* **20b**			
		(stamp TF)..............................			
		s. Optd "SPECIMEN" (2)..................	£600		
		Wi. Watermark inverted..................	£8250	£475	
		Wj. Watermark reversed			
		Wk. Watermark inverted and			
		reversed			
86	**24**	9d. bistre (Plate 2) (15.1.62)............	£5800	£575	£1200
		s. Optd "SPECIMEN" (2, 6)	£750		
		Wi. Watermark inverted..................	£10000	£700	
		Wj. Watermark reversed	—	£850	
		Wk. Watermark inverted and			
		reversed			
87		9d. straw	£4000	£475	£1000
		a. On azure paper...........................			
		b. Thick paper	£6000	£550	
		c. Error. Shamrock missing from			
		wmk (stamp TF).........................		†	
		d. Error. Watermark *W* **20b**			
		(stamp TF).............................	†	—	
		Wi. Watermark inverted..................	£6800	£650	
88		9d. bistre (Hair lines, Plate 3) (5.62)	£32000	£13500	
89	**25**	1s. deep green (Plate No. 1 =			
		Plate 2) (1.12.62)........................	£4800	£500	
90		1s. green (Plate No. 1 = Plate 2).....	£3200	£300	£450
		a. "K" in lower left corner in			
		white circle (stamp KD).............	£20000	£2750	
		awi. Watermark inverted..................	—	£4250	
		ab. "K" normal (stamp KD)...............	—	£2200	
		b. On azure paper........................			
		c. Error. Watermark *W* **20b**			
		(stamp TF).............................	—	£375	
		da. Thick paper, "K" in circle as No.			
		90a	—	£3750	
		s. Optd "SPECIMEN" (2, 5, 8)..........	£550		
		Wi. Watermark inverted..................		£450	
		Wj. Watermark reversed			
		Wk. Watermark inverted and			
		reversed	—	£475	
91		1s. deep green (Plate No. 2 =			
		Plate 3)	£35000		
		a. Imperf	£7250		
		as. Optd "SPECIMEN" (2).................	£4200		
		*a*Wi. Watermark inverted..................	£7250		

*75/91 **For well-centred, lightly used** +125%

The 3d. as Type **21**, but with network background in the spandrels, was never issued. Optd "SPECIMEN" *price* £800.

The plates of this issue may be distinguished as follows:

3d.	Plate 2	No white dots.
	Plate 3	White dots as illustration A.
4d.	Plate 3	No hair lines. Roman I next to lower corner letters.
	Plate 4	Hair lines in corners. (Illustration B.). Roman II.
6d.	Plate 3	No hair lines.
	Plate 4	Hair lines in corners.
9d.	Plate 2	No hair lines.
	Plate 3	Hair lines in corners. Beware of faked lines.
1s.	Plate 2	Numbered 1 on stamps.
	Plate 3	Numbered 2 on stamps and with hair lines.

*One used example on piece has been recorded, cancelled by a Glasgow Duplex postmark dated 06.1.1863.

The 9d. on azure paper (No. 87a) is very rare, only one confirmed example being known.

The variety "K" in circle, No. 90a, is believed to be due to a damaged letter having been cut out and replaced. It is probable that the punch was driven in too deeply, causing the flange to penetrate the surface, producing an indentation showing as an uncoloured circle.

The watermark variety "three roses and a shamrock" illustrated in W **20a** was evidently due to the substitution of an extra rose for the thistle in a faulty watermark bit. It is found on stamp TA of Plate 4 of the 3d., Plates 1 (No. 70c), 3, 5 and 6 of the 6d., Plate 4 of the 9d. and Plate 4 of the 1s.

Similar problems occurred on stamp TF of the 6d. and 9d. Here the shamrock emblem became detached and used examples are known showing it omitted. It was replaced by a third rose (*W* **20b**) and this variety exists on the 6d. (Nos. 84/5 and 97) and 9d. (Nos. 87 and 98).

26	27

---

28 (with hyphen) **28a** (without hyphen)

29	30	31

1865–67. Large uncoloured corner letters. *Wmk* Large Garter (4d.); others Emblems.

			Unused	Used*	Used on cover
92	**26**	3d. rose (Plate 4) (1.3.65).................	£2500	£250	£500
		a. Error. Watermark *W* **20a**	£6500	£1250	
		b. Thick paper	£3500	£325	
		s. Optd "SPECIMEN" (2)...................	£4500		
		Wi. Watermark inverted..................	—	£600	
		Wj. Watermark reversed			
		Wk. Watermark inverted and			
		reversed			
93	**27**	4d. dull vermilion (4.7.65)................	£650	90·00	
		s. Optd "SPECIMEN" (pl. 14) (8)......	£525		
94		4d. vermilion...............................	£575	75·00	£140
		a. Imperf (Plates 11, 12)................	£8500		
		Wi. Watermark inverted..................	£575	75·00	
95		4d. deep vermilion	£650	90·00	
		Plate			
		7 (1865)	£650	£130	
		8 (1866)	£600	90·00	
		9 (1867)	£600	90·00	
		10 (1868)	£825	£150	
		11 (1869)	£625	90·00	
		12 (1870)	£575	75·00	
		13 (1872)	£650	75·00	
		14 (1873)	£775	£110	
96	**28**	6d. dp lilac (with hyphen) (7.3.65)...	£1900	£200	
		s. Optd "SPECIMEN" (pl. 5) (2)........	£4750		
97		6d. lilac (with hyphen)	£1200	£140	£225
		a. Thick paper	£1600	£175	
		b. Stamp doubly printed (Plate 6)	—	£15000	
		c. Error. Watermark *W* **20a**			
		(Pl 5, 6) .... *from*	—	£2400	
		d. Error. Watermark *W* **20b** (Plate 5)			
		e. Imperf (Plate 5)			
		Wi. Watermark inverted..................	—	£250	
		Wj. Watermark reversed			
		Wk. Watermark inverted and			
		reversed.	†	—	
		Plate			
		5 (1865)	£1150	£140	
		6 (1867)	£3800	£250	
98	**29**	9d. straw (Plate 4) (25.10.65)..........	£4800	£600	£1400
		a. Thick paper	£5800	£850	
		b. Error. Watermark *W* **20a**	—	£2500	
		c. Error. Watermark *W* **20b**			
		(stamp TF)..............................	£13000		
		s. Optd "SPECIMEN" (2)...................	£925		
		Wi. Watermark inverted..................	—	£1650	
99	**30**	10d. red-brown (Plate 1) (11.11.67)	*	£55000	
101	**31**	1s. green (Plate 4) (19.1.65)	£2850	£275	£450
		a. Error. Watermark *W* **20a**	—	£1700	
		ab. Error. Watermark *W* **20b**			
		b. Thick paper	£3500	£380	
		c. Imperf between (vertical pair)....	—	£16000	
		s. Optd "SPECIMEN" (2)..................	£650		
		Wi. Watermark inverted..................	—	£650	
		Wia. Imperf watermark inverted			
		Wk. Watermark inverted and			
		reversed	—	£650	

*92/101c **For well-centred, lightly used** +100%

From mid-1866 to about the end of 1871 4d. stamps of this issue appeared generally with watermark inverted.

Unused examples of No. 98 from Plate 5 exist, but this was never put to press and all evidence points to such stamps originating from a portion of the Imprimatur sheet which was perforated by De La Rue in 1887 for insertion in albums to be presented to members of the Stamp Committee (*Price* £20000 *unused*).

The 10d. stamps, No. 99, were printed in error on paper watermarked "Emblems" instead of on "Spray of Rose".

No. 95 is vacant.

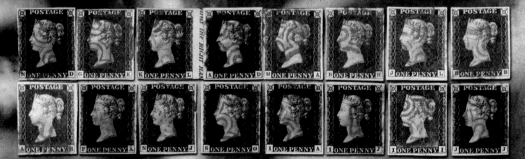

32

33 Spray of Rose

34

1867–80 *Wmk* Spray of Rose. *W* **33**.

			Unused	Used*	Used on cover
102	**26**	3d. deep rose (12.7.67)	£800	£100	
103		3d. rose	£525	60·00	£110
		a. Imperf (Plates 5, 6) ....*from*	£11000		
		s. Optd "SPECIMEN" (pl. 5) (8)	£275		
		sa. Optd "SPECIMEN" (pl. 6) (2, 8) ..	£300		
		sb. Optd "SPECIMEN" (pl. 7) (2, 6) ..	£300		
		sc. Optd "SPECIMEN" (pl. 8) (8)	£300		
		sd. Optd "SPECIMEN" (pl. 10) (2, 8, 9)	£270		
		Wi. Watermark inverted	£2250	£300	
		Plate			
		4 (1867)	£1850	£300	
		5 (1868)	£525	70·00	
		6 (1870)	£550	70·00	
		7 (1871)	£650	70·00	
		8 (1872)	£625	60·00	
		9 (1872)	£625	70·00	
		10 (1873)	£875	£150	
104	**28**	6d. lilac (with hyphen) (Plate 6) (21.6.67)	£1900	£175	£250
		a. Imperf		£6000	
		Wi. Watermark inverted	—	£350	
105		6d. deep lilac (with hyphen) (Plate 6)	£1900	£175	
106		6d. purple (with hyphen) (Plate 6)	£1900	£200	
107		6d. bright violet (with hyphen) (Plate 6) (22.7.68)	£1800	£200	
108	**28a**	6d. dull violet (without hyphen) (Plate 8) (8.3.69)	£1250	£190	
		s. Optd "SPECIMEN" (pl. 8) (1, 8) ..	£350		
		Wi. Watermark inverted	—	£275	
109		6d. mauve (without hyphen)	£700	90·00	£140
		a. Imperf (Plate Nos. 8 and 9)	£12000	£5000	
		s. Optd "SPECIMEN" (pl. 9) (6, 8) ..	£350		
		Wi. Watermark inverted	—	£250	
		Plate			
		8 (1869, mauve)	£800	£140	
		9 (1870, mauve)	£700	90·00	
		10 (1869, mauve)	*	£37500	
110	**29**	9d. straw (Plate No. 4) (3.10.67)	£2500	£325	£525
		s. Optd "SPECIMEN" (2, 8, 9, 10, 11)	£425		
		Wi. Watermark inverted	—	£650	
111		9d. pale straw (Plate No. 4)	£2400	£300	
		a. Imperf (Plate 4)	£22000		
112	**30**	10d. red-brown (1.7.67)	£3600	£400	£850
		s. Optd "SPECIMEN" (2, 5, 6, 8, 9, 10, 11)	£500		
		Wi. Watermark inverted	—	£1000	
113		10d. pale red-brown	£3600	£400	
114		10d. deep red-brown	£5000	£600	
		a. Imperf (Plate 1)	£17000		
		Plate			
		1 (1867)	£3600	£400	
		2 (1867)	£55000	£17000	
115	**31**	1s. deep green (13.7.67)	£1300	70·00	
117		1s. green	£800	45·00	90·00
		a. Imperf between (horiz pair) (Pl 7)			
		b. Imperf (Plate 4)	£10000	£6500	
		s. Optd "SPECIMEN" (pl. 4) (1, 8, 9)	£400		
		sa. Optd "SPECIMEN" (pl. 5) (2, 6, 8, 9)	£425		
		sb. Optd "SPECIMEN" (pl. 6) (8, 9) ..	£425		
		sc. Optd "SPECIMEN" (pl. 7) (9)	£400		
		Wi. Watermark inverted	£2400	£180	
		Plate			
		4 (1867)	£975	65·00	
		5 (1871)	£800	45·00	
		6 (1871)	£1200	45·00	
		7 (1873)	£1400	90·00	
118	**32**	2s. dull blue (1.7.67)	£4200	£225	£825
		s. Optd "SPECIMEN" (2, 5, 8, 9, 10, 11)	£600		
		Wi. Watermark inverted	—	£950	
119		2s. deep blue	£5000	£240	
		a. Imperf (Plate 1)	£23000		

			Unused	Used*	Used on cover
120		2s. pale blue	£5000	£275	
		aa. Imperf (Plate 1)	£22000		
120a		2s. cobalt	£25000	£3000	
120b		2s. milky blue	£24000	£2000	
		Plate			
		1 (1867)	£4200	£225	
		3 (1868)	*	£16500	
121		2s. brown (Plate No. 1) (27.2.80)	£30000	£4250	
		a. Imperf	£30000		
		b. No watermark	†	—	
		s. Optd "SPECIMEN" (9)	£3800		
		Wi. Watermark inverted	—	£6000	

*102/21 **For well-centred, lightly used** +75%

Examples of the 1s. from Plates 5 and 6 without watermark are postal forgeries used at the Stock Exchange Post Office in the early 1870s. (*Prices from £850*)

1872–73. Uncoloured letters in corners. *Wmk* Spray, *W* **33**.

			Unused	Used*	Used on cover
122	**34**	6d. deep chestnut (Plate 11) (12.4.72)	£1300	£125	
		s. Optd "SPECIMEN" (2, 6, 8)	£325		
122a		6d. chestnut (Plate 11) (22.5.72)	£800	65·00	£150
		Wi. Watermark inverted	—	£325	
122b		6d. pale chestnut (Plate 11) (1872)	£700	65·00	
123		6d. pale buff (18.10.72)	£1100	£125	£250
		Wi. Watermark inverted	—	£375	
		Plate			
		11 (1872, pale buff)	£1100	£125	
		12 (1872, pale buff)	£3400	£350	
124		6d. chestnut (Plate 12) (1872)	*	£3800	
124a		6d. pale chestnut (Plate 12) (1872)	*	£3500	
125		6d. grey (Plate No. 12) (24.4.73)	£1900	£300	£375
		a. Imperf	£15000		
		s. Optd "SPECIMEN" (6, 8, 9)	£375		
		Wi. Watermark inverted	£6250	—	

*122/5 **For well-centred, lightly used** +50%

35

36

37

38

39 Maltese Cross

40 Large Anchor

1867–83. Uncoloured letters in corners.

(a) Wmk Maltese Cross, W **39**. *P* 15½×15.

			Unused	Used*
126	**35**	5s. rose (1.7.67)	£11000	£675
		s. Optd "SPECIMEN" (2, 6)	£1100	
127		5s. pale rose	£11000	£675
		a. Imperf (Plate 1)	£18000	
		s. Optd "SPECIMEN" (pl. 2) (8, 9)	£1750	
		Plate		
		1 (1867)	£11000	£675
		2 (1874)	£18000	£1500
128	**36**	10s. greenish grey (Plate 1) (26.9.78)	£60000	£3200
		s. Optd "SPECIMEN" (8, 9)	£4250	
129	**37**	£1 brown-lilac (Plate 1) (26.9.78)	£90000	£4500
		s. Optd "SPECIMEN" (9)	£6250	

(b) Wmk Large Anchor, W **40**. *P* 14.

(i) Blued paper.

			Unused	Used*
130	**35**	5s. rose (Plate 4) (25.11.82)	£42000	£4800
		s. Optd "SPECIMEN" (9)	£5250	
		Wi. Watermark inverted	—	£18000
131	**36**	10s. grey-green (Plate 1) (2.83)	£135000	£5200
		s. Optd "SPECIMEN" (9)	£10000	
132	**37**	£1 brown-lilac (Plate 1) (12.82)	£175000	£10000
		s. Optd "SPECIMEN" (9)	£12500	
133	**38**	£5 orange (Plate 1) (21.3.82)	£70000	£15000
		s. Optd "SPECIMEN" (9, 11)	£3500	

(ii) White paper.

			Unused	Used*
134	**35**	5s. rose (Plate 4)	£35000	£4200
135	**36**	10s. greenish grey (Plate 1)	£160000	£4500
136	**37**	£1 brown-lilac (Plate 1)	£200000	£9000
		s. Optd "SPECIMEN" (6, 9)	£11500	
137	**38**	£5 orange (Plate 1)	£14500	£4750
		s. Optd "SPECIMEN" (9, 11, 16)	£4500	

*126/37 **For well-centred, lightly used +75%**

41 **42** **43**

44 **45** **46**

47 Small Anchor **48** Orb

1873–80. Large coloured letters in the corners.

(a) Wmk Small Anchor, W **47**.

			Unused	Used*	Used on cover
138	**41**	2½d. rosy mauve (*blued paper*) (1.7.75)	£875	£190	
		a. Imperf			
		s. Optd "SPECIMEN" (pl. 1) (8)	£350		
		Wi. Watermark inverted	£3000	£350	
		Plate			
		1 (*blued paper*) (1875)	£875	£190	
		2 (*blued paper*) (1875)	£8000	£1650	
		3 (*blued paper*) (1875)	—	£5750	
139		2½d. rosy mauve (*white paper*)	£675	£120	£180
		Wi. Watermark inverted	£2750	£250	
		Plate			
		1 (*white paper*) (1875)	£675	£120	
		2 (*white paper*) (1875)	£675	£120	
		3 (*white paper*) (1875)	£1000	£175	
		Error of Lettering L H—F L *for* L H—H L (*Plate 2*).			
140	**41**	2½d. rosy mauve	£34000	£2750	

(b) Wmk Orb, W **48**.

			Unused	Used*	Used on cover
141	**41**	2½d. rosy mauve (1.5.76)	£525	85·00	£125
		s. Optd "SPECIMEN" (pl. 3) (10)	£4200		
		sa. Optd "SPECIMEN" (pl. 5) (9)	£220		
		sb. Optd "SPECIMEN" (pl. 6) (8, 9)	£220		
		sc. Optd "SPECIMEN" (pl. 7) (9)	£220		
		sd. Optd "SPECIMEN" (pl. 10) (9)	£220		
		se. Optd "SPECIMEN" (pl. 16) (9)	£220		
		Wi. Watermark inverted	£1900	£225	
		Plate			
		3 (1876)	£1350	£150	
		4 (1876)	£525	85·00	
		5 (1876)	£525	85·00	
		6 (1876)	£525	85·00	
		7 (1877)	£525	85·00	
		8 (1877)	£525	85·00	
		9 (1877)	£525	85·00	
		10 (1878)	£550	85·00	
		11 (1878)	£525	85·00	
		12 (1878)	£525	85·00	
		13 (1878)	£525	85·00	
		14 (1879)	£525	85·00	
		15 (1879)	£525	85·00	
		16 (1879)	£525	85·00	
		17 (1880)	£1700	£300	
142	**41**	2½d. blue (5.2.80)	£575	55·00	90·00
		s. Optd "SPECIMEN" (pl. 17) (9)	£160		
		Wi. Watermark inverted	£2100	£275	
		Plate			
		17 (1880)	£575	75·00	
		18 (1880)	£575	55·00	
		19 (1880)	£575	55·00	
		20 (1880)	£575	55·00	

(c) Wmk Spray, W **33**.

			Unused	Used*	Used on cover
143	**42**	3d. rose (5.7.73)	£450	80·00	£120
		s. Optd "SPECIMEN" (pl. 14) (2)	£350		
		sa. Optd "SPECIMEN" (pl. 17) (8, 9)	£250		
		sb. Optd "SPECIMEN" (pl. 18) (8, 9, 10)	£250		
		sc. Optd "SPECIMEN" (pl. 19) (9, 10)	£250		
		Wi. Watermark inverted	£1650	£350	
144		3d. pale rose	£450	80·00	
		Plate			
		11 (1873)	£450	80·00	
		12 (1873)	£525	80·00	
		14 (1874)	£525	80·00	
		15 (1874)	£450	80·00	
		16 (1875)	£450	80·00	
		17 (1875)	£525	80·00	
		18 (1875)	£525	80·00	
		19 (1876)	£450	80·00	
		20 (1879)	£850	£140	
145	**43**	6d. pale buff (Plate 13) (15.3.73)	*	£25000	
146		6d. deep grey (20.3.74)	£600	£120	£150
		s. Optd "SPECIMEN" (pl. 14) (8, 10)	£300		
		sa. Optd "SPECIMEN" (pl. 15) (8, 9)	£300		
		sb. Optd "SPECIMEN" (pl. 16) (9)	£300		
147		6d. grey	£500	90·00	
		Wi. Watermark inverted	£1800	£350	
		13 (1874)	£500	90·00	
		14 (1875)	£500	90·00	
		15 (1876)	£500	90·00	
		16 (1878)	£500	90·00	
		17 (1880)	£500	£180	
148	**44**	1s. deep green (1.9.73)	£1100	£225	
150		1s. green	£650	£160	£240
		s. Optd "SPECIMEN" (pl. 11) (8)	£450		
		sa. Optd "SPECIMEN" (pl. 12) (8, 9, 10)	£350		
		sb. Optd "SPECIMEN" (pl. 13) (9)	£350		
		Wi. Watermark inverted	£2400	£400	
		Plate			
		8 (1873)	£825	£175	
		9 (1874)	£825	£175	
		10 (1874)	£775	£200	
		11 (1875)	£775	£175	
		12 (1875)	£650	£160	
		13 (1876)	£650	£160	
		14 (—)*	*	£40000	
151		1s. orange-brown (Plate 13) (14.10.80)	£4750	£700	£1800
		s. Optd "SPECIMEN" (9)	£550		
		Wi. Watermark inverted	£11000	£1800	

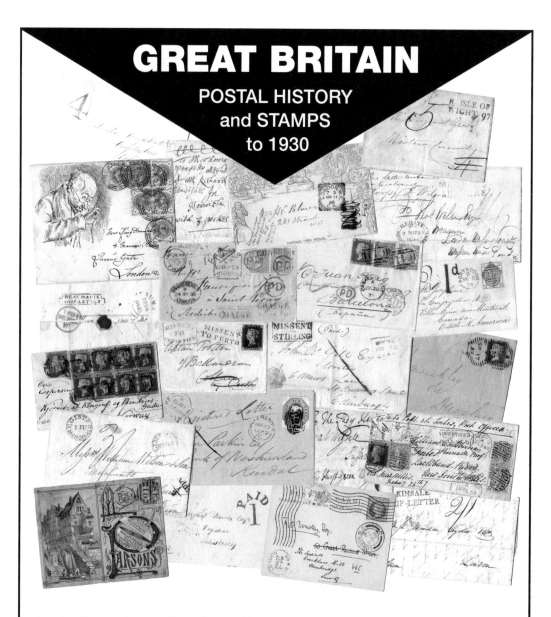

(d) Wmk Large Garter, W 17.

			Unused	Used*	Used on cover
152	**45**	4d. vermilion (1.3.76)	£3200	£525	£1100
		s. Optd "SPECIMEN" (pl. 15) (9)	£400		
		Wi. Watermark inverted	—	£1000	
		Plate			
		15 (1876)	£3200	£525	
		16 (1877)	*	£35000	
153		4d. sage-green (12.3.77)	£1400	£300	£600
		s. Optd "SPECIMEN" (pl. 15) (9)	£350		
		sa. Optd "SPECIMEN" (pl. 16) (9)	£350		
		Wi. Watermark inverted	£3000	£625	
		Plate			
		15 (1877)	£1600	£325	
		16 (1877)	£1400	£300	
		17 (1877)	*	£20000	
154		4d. grey-brown (Plate 17) (15.8.80)	£2800	£550	£1700
		a. Imperf	£22000		
		s. Optd "SPECIMEN" (9)	£350		
		Wi. Watermark inverted	—	£1200	
156	**46**	8d. orange (Plate 1) (11.9.76)	£1850	£350	£625
		s. Optd "SPECIMEN" (8, 9)	£350		
		Wi. Watermark inverted	—	£900	

*138/56 **For well-centred, lightly used +100%**

1876 (July). *Prepared for use but not issued.*

156a	**46**	8d. purple-brown (Plate 1)	£9750		
		s. Optd "SPECIMEN" (8, 9)	£6000		

KEY TO SURFACE-PRINTED ISSUES
1880–1900

Note that the £5 value used with the above series is listed as Nos. 133 and 137.

49 Imperial Crown   **(50)**

1880–83. *Wmk Imperial Crown, W* **49**.

			Unused	Used*	Used on cover
157	**41**	2½d. blue (23.3.81)	£450	35·00	55·00
		s. Optd "SPECIMEN" (pl. 23) (9)	£175		
		Wi. Watermark inverted	—	£550	
		Plate			
		21 (1881)	£500	45·00	
		22 (1881)	£450	45·00	
		23 (1881)	£450	35·00	
158	**42**	3d. rose (3.81)	£500	£100	£175
		s. Optd "SPECIMEN" (pl. 21) (9)	£250		
		Wi. Watermark inverted	—	£580	
		Plate			
		20 (1881)	£900	£150	
		21 (1881)	£500	£100	
159	**50**	3d. on 3d lilac (C.) (Plate 21) (1.1.83)	£650	£160	£450
		s. Optd "SPECIMEN" (9)	£300		
		Wi. Watermark inverted			
160	**45**	4d. grey-brown (8.12.80)	£450	75·00	£190
		s. Optd "SPECIMEN" (pl. 17) (9)	£250		
		sa. Optd "SPECIMEN" (pl. 18) (9)	£275		
		Wi. Watermark inverted	—	£650	
		Plate			
		17 (1880)	£475	80·00	
		18 (1882)	£450	75·00	
161	**43**	6d. grey (1.1.81)	£400	80·00	£120
		s. Optd "SPECIMEN" (pl. 18) (9)	£275		
		Wi. Watermark inverted	—	£650	
		Plate			
		17 (1881)	£425	80·00	
		18 (1882)	£400	80·00	
162	**50**	6d. on 6d lilac (C.) (Plate 18) (1.1.83)	£675	£150	£425
		a. Slanting dots (various)...*from*	£1800	£450	
		b. Optd double	—	£12500	
		s. Optd "SPECIMEN" (9)	£300		
		Wi. Watermark inverted	£3500	£850	
163	**44**	1s. orange-brown (24.5.81)	£750	£170	£550
		s. Optd "SPECIMEN" (pl. 13) (9)	£350		
		sa. Optd "SPECIMEN" (pl. 14) (9)	£350		
		Wi. Watermark inverted	£3250	£950	
		Plate			
		13 (1881)	£875	£170	
		14 (1881)	£750	£170	

*157/63 **For well-centred, lightly used +75%**

The 1s. plate 14 (line perf 14) exists in purple but was not issued in this shade (*Price* £15000 *unused*). Examples were included in a few of the Souvenir Albums prepared for members of the "Stamp Committee of 1884''.

52   **53**

54   **55**   **56**

1880–81. *Wmk Imperial Crown, W* **49**.

			Unused	Used*	Used on cover
164	**52**	½d. deep green (14.10.80)	55·00	22·00	30·00
		a. Imperf	£5000		
		b. No watermark	£10000		
		s. Optd "SPECIMEN" (9)	60·00		
		Wi. Watermark inverted	£2400	£575	
165		½d. pale green	55·00	22·00	
166	**53**	1d. Venetian red (1.1.80)	35·00	15·00	30·00
		a. Imperf	£5800		
		b. Error. *Wmk* **48**	†	£27000	
		s. Optd "SPECIMEN" (9)	£100		
		Wi. Watermark inverted	—	£350	
167	**54**	1½d. Venetian red (14.10.80)	£250	60·00	£160
		s. Optd "SPECIMEN" (9)	80·00		
		Wi. Watermark inverted	†	—	
168	**55**	2d. pale rose (8.12.80)	£340	£120	£300
		s. Optd "SPECIMEN" (9)	£110		
		Wi. Watermark inverted	£3000	£850	
168a		2d. deep rose	£360	£120	
169	**56**	5d. indigo (15.3.81)	£725	£175	£325
		a. Imperf	£6750	£4500	
		s. Optd "SPECIMEN" (9, 12, 13)	£160		
		Wi. Watermark inverted	—	£4800	

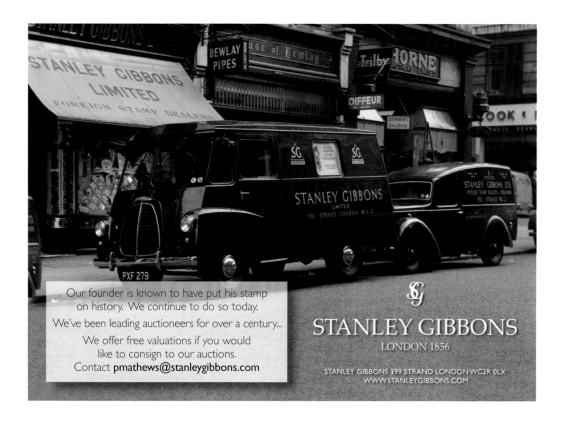

Set of 5 .... £1275 £350
*164/9 **For well-centred, lightly used +75%**
Two used examples of the 1d. value have been reported on the Orb (fiscal) watermark.

57	Die I	Die II

1881. *Wmk* Imperial Crown, *W* **49**.

(a) 14 *dots in each corner, Die I (12 July)*
170	**57**	1d. lilac...............................	£225	45·00	60·00
		s. Optd "SPECIMEN" (9).............	70·00		
		Wi. Watermark inverted............	—	£600	
171		1d. pale lilac............................	£225	45·00	

(b) 16 *dots in each corner, Die II (13 December)*.
172	**57**	1d. lilac....................................	2·75	2·20	4·00
		s. Optd "SPECIMEN" (9, 12)......	60·00		
		Wi. Watermark inverted............	60·00	35·00	
172a		1d. bluish lilac.........................	£475	£150	
173		1d. deep purple.......................	2·75	2·20	
		a. Printed both sides...............	£900	†	
		b. Frame broken at bottom..	£975	£350	
		c. Printed on gummed side..	£900	†	
		d. Imperf three sides (pair)...	£8250	†	
		e. Printed both sides but impression on back inverted..................................	£1000	†	
		f. No watermark.......................	£8000	†	
		g. Blued paper........................	—		
174		1d. mauve.................................	2·75	1·70	
		a. Imperf (pair)........................	£7500		

*170/4 **For well-centred, lightly used +50%**
1d. stamps with the words "PEARS SOAP" printed on the back in orange, blue or mauve *price from* £550, *unused*.

The variety "frame broken at bottom" (No. 173b) shows a white space just inside the bottom frame-line from between the "N" and "E" of "ONE" to below the first "N" of "PENNY", breaking the pearls and cutting into the lower part of the oval below "PEN".

58	**59**

60

1883–84. *Coloured letters* in the corners. *Wmk* Large Anchor, *W* **40**.

(a) Blued paper.
			Unused	Used*
175	**58**	2s.6d. lilac (2.7.83)	£6750	£1500
		s. Optd "SPECIMEN" (9).............	£625	
176	**59**	5s. rose (1.4.84).....................	£18000	£4000
		s. Optd "SPECIMEN" (9, 11).......	£1600	
177	**60**	10s. ultramarine (1.4.84)...........	£40000	£8250
		s. Optd "SPECIMEN" (9).............	£2850	
177a		10s. cobalt (5.84)..................	£62000	£13500
		s. Optd "SPECIMEN" (9).............	£5500	

(b) White paper.
178	**58**	2s.6d. lilac..............................	£600	£160
		s. Optd "SPECIMEN" (9, 11, 12, 13)..........	£425	
179		2s.6d. deep lilac.....................	£825	£225
		a. On blued paper..................	£9000	£3600
		Wi. Watermark inverted............	—	£11500
180	**59**	5s. rose...................................	£1100	£250
		Wi. Watermark inverted............	†	£12500
181		5s. crimson............................	£975	£250
		s. Optd "SPECIMEN" (9, 11, 12, 13)..........	£450	
182	**60**	10s. cobalt..............................	£42000	£8250
		s. Optd "SPECIMEN" (9).............	£3400	

183		10s. ultramarine......................	£2250	£525
		s. Optd "SPECIMEN" (9, 11, 13).........	£550	
183a		10s. pale ultramarine.............	£2500	£550

*175/83a **For well-centred, lightly used +50%**
For No. 180 perf 12 see second note below No. 196.

61

Broken frames, Plate 2

1884 (1 Apr). *Wmk* Three Imperial Crowns, *W* **49**.
185	**61**	£1 brown-lilac..........................	£32000	£3000
		a. Frame broken......................	£60000	£5000
		s. Optd "SPECIMEN" (9, 11, 12).......	£2800	
		Wi. Watermark inverted............	—	£38000

1888 (Feb). *Wmk* Three Orbs, *W* **48**.
186	**61**	£1 brown-lilac..........................	£72000	£4500
		a. Frame broken......................	£150000	£9000
		s. Optd "SPECIMEN" (11)...........	£6800	

*185/6a **For well-centred, lightly used +50%**
The broken-frame varieties, Nos. 185a and 186a, are on Plate 2 stamps JC and TA, as illustrated. See also No. 212a.

62	**63**	**64**

65	**66**

1883 (1 Aug). (9d.) or **1884** (1 Apr) (others). *Wmk* Imperial Crown, *W* **49** (sideways on horiz designs).
187	**52**	½d. slate-blue.........................	35·00	10·00	20·00
		a. Imperf..................................	£3750		
		s. Optd "SPECIMEN" (9).............	50·00		
		Wi. Watermark inverted............	£3000	£350	
188	**62**	1½d. lilac.................................	£125	45·00	£120
		a. Imperf..................................	£3750		
		s. Optd "SPECIMEN" (9).............	85·00		
		Wi. Watermark inverted............	£3000	£280	
189	**63**	2d. lilac....................................	£230	80·00	£150
		a. Imperf..................................	£4800		
		s. Optd "SPECIMEN" (9).............	85·00		
		Wi. Watermark sideways inverted..............................	£3000	£280	
190	**64**	2½d. lilac.................................	95·00	20·00	30·00
		a. Imperf..................................	£4800		
		s. Optd "SPECIMEN" (9).............	85·00		
		Wi. Watermark sideways inverted..............................	£600		
191	**65**	3d. lilac....................................	£280	£100	£180
		a. Imperf..................................	£4800		
		s. Optd "SPECIMEN" (9).............	85·00		
		Wi. Watermark inverted............	†	£1200	
192	**66**	4d. dull green..........................	£580	£210	£350
		a. Imperf..................................	£4800		
		s. Optd "SPECIMEN" (9).............	£190		
193	**62**	5d. dull green..........................	£580	£210	£350
		a. Imperf..................................	£5500		
		s. Optd "SPECIMEN" (9).............	£190		
194	**63**	6d. dull green..........................	£625	£240	£380
		a. Imperf..................................	£5750		
		s. Optd "SPECIMEN" (9).............	£220		
		Wi. Watermark sideways inverted..............................	£1400		

			Unmtd Mint	Mtd Mint	Used*
195	**64**	9d. dull green (1.8.83)	£1250	£480	£4750
		s. Optd "SPECIMEN" (9)	£425		
		Wi. Watermark sideways inverted	£2000	£775	
196	**65**	1s. dull green	£1600	£325	£625
		a. Imperf	£8750		
		s. Optd "SPECIMEN" (9)	£375		
		Wi. Watermark-inverted			
Set of 10			£5000	£1600	

*187/96 **For well-centred, lightly used +100%***

The normal sideways watermark shows the top of the crown pointing to the right *as seen from the back of the stamp*.

The above prices are for stamps in the true dull green colour. Stamps which have been soaked, causing the colour to run, are virtually worthless.

Stamps of the above set and No. 180 are also found perf 12; these are official perforations, but were never issued. A second variety of the 5d. is known with a line instead of a stop under the "d" in the value; this was never issued and is therefore only known unused (*Price* £38,000).

71		**72**		**73**	
74		**75**		**76**	
77		**78**		**79**	
80		**81**		**82**	

Die I   Die II

Die I: Square dots to right of "d".
Die II: Thin vertical lines to right of "d".

1½d. Deformed leaf
(Duty plate 4, R. 19/1)

1887 (1 Jan)–**92**. *Jubilee* issue. New types. The bicoloured stamps have the value tablets, or the frames including the value tablets, in the second colour. *Wmk* Imperial Crown, *W* **49** (Three Crowns on £1).

			Unmtd Mint	Mtd Mint	Used*
197	**71**	½d. vermilion	2·50	1·75	1·20
		a. Printed on gummed side	£4500	£3500	
		b. Printed both sides			

		c. Doubly printed	—	£32000	
		d. Imperf (showing bottom margins)	6500	£5000	
		s. Optd "SPECIMEN" (9, 10, 12)		35·00	
		Wi. Watermark inverted	90·00	60·00	60·00
197e		½d. orange-vermilion	2·50	1·75	1·20
198	**72**	1½d. dull purple and pale green	25·00	18·00	8·00
		a. Purple part of design double	—	—	£9000
		b. Deformed leaf		£800	£450
		s. Optd "SPECIMEN" (6, 9, 12)		55·00	
		Wi. Watermark inverted	£1600	£1200	£500
199	**73**	2d. green and scarlet	£550	£425	£260
200		2d. grey-green and carmine	50·00	35·00	15·00
		s. Optd "SPECIMEN" (9, 10, 12)		60·00	
		Wi. Watermark inverted	£1600	£1200	£525
201	**74**	2½d. purple/blue	45·00	25·00	5·00
		a. Printed on gummed side	£18000	£15000	
		b. Imperf three sides	—	£9500	
		c. Imperf	—	£12000	
		Ed. Missing "d" in value	†	†	£9500
		s. Optd "SPECIMEN" (6, 9, 12, 13)		75·00	
		Wi. Watermark inverted	£4500	£3500	£1400
202	**75**	3d. purple/yellow	45·00	25·00	5·00
		a. Imperf (wmk inverted)	—	£11000	
		s. Optd "SPECIMEN" (6, 9, 12)		60·00	
		Wi. Watermark inverted	—	—	£725
203		3d. deep purple/yellow	60·00	30·00	5·00
204		3d. purple/orange (1890)	£1300	£800	
205	**76**	4d. green and purple-brown	60·00	40·00	18·00
		aa. Imperf	—	£12000	
		s. Optd "SPECIMEN" (6, 9, 10, 12)		60·00	
		Wi. Watermark inverted	£1600	£1200	£650
205a		4d. green and deep brown	60·00	40·00	18·00
206	**77**	4½d. green and carmine (15.9.92)	17·00	11·00	45·00
		s. Optd "SPECIMEN" (9, 13)	£500	£400	
		Wi. Watermark inverted			
206a		4½d. green and deep bright carmine	£1000	£750	£650
207	**78**	5d. dull purple and blue (Die I)	£1100	£800	£120
		s. Optd "SPECIMEN" (9, 12)	£160	£110	
207a		5d. dull purple and blue (Die II) (1888)	60·00	42·00	15·00
		s. Optd "SPECIMEN" (9, 12)	90·00	65·00	
		Wi. Watermark inverted		£17000	£1250
208	**79**	6d. purple/rose-red	60·00	40·00	15·00
		s. Optd "SPECIMEN" (9, 10, 12)		65·00	
		Wi. Watermark inverted	£10000	£7500	£2000
208a		6d. deep purple/rose-red	60·00	40·00	15·00
209	**80**	9d. dull purple and blue	£110	75·00	48·00
		s. Optd "SPECIMEN" (6, 9, 12)	£100	70·00	
		Wi. Watermark inverted	£11000	£8000	£2800
210	**81**	10d. dull purple and carmine (shades) (24.2.90)	90·00	60·00	45·00
		aa. Imperf	—	£17500	
		s. Optd "SPECIMEN" (9, 13, 15)	£150	£110	
		Wi. Watermark inverted	£13000	£9500	£3000
210a		10d. dull purple and deep dull carmine	£800	£625	£250
210b		10d. dull purple and scarlet	£170	95·00	65·00
211	**82**	1s. dull green	£375	£275	80·00
		s. Optd "SPECIMEN" (9, 10, 12)	£100	75·00	
		Wi. Watermark inverted	£2200	£1700	£975
212	**61**	£1 green (28.1.91)	£7500	£4000	£800
		a. Frame broken	£16500	£8500	£2000
		s. Optd "SPECIMEN" (9, 11, 13, 15, 16)		£1100	
		Wi. Watermark inverted	—	£110000	£13000

*197/212a **For well-centred, lightly used +50%***

The broken-frame varieties, No. 212a, are on Plate 2 stamps JC or TA, as illustrated above No. 185.

½d. stamps with "PEARS SOAP" printed on the back in orange, blue or mauve, *price from* £525 *each*.

No used price is quoted for No. 204 as it is not possible to authenticate the paper colour on stamps in used condition.

1900. *Colours changed. Wmk* Imperial Crown, *W* **49**.

			Unmtd Mint	Mtd Mint	Used*
213	**71**	½d. blue-green (17.4)	2·50	2·00	2·25
		a. Printed on gummed side	—	—	†
		b. Imperf	£9500	£7500	
		s. Optd "SPECIMEN" (11, 15)		£650	
		Wi. Watermark inverted	£125	75·00	95·00
214	**82**	1s. green and carmine (11.7)	£100	65·00	£140
		s. Optd "SPECIMEN" (15)		£950	
		Wi. Watermark inverted	£2600	£1900	£1100
Set of 14				£950	£650	£380

*213/14 **For well-centred, lightly used +50%***

The ½d. No. 213, in bright blue, is a colour changeling caused by a constituent of the ink used for some months in 1900.

Looking for that
Elusive Stamp?

Get in touch with our team

Great Britain Department: email gb@stanleygibbons.com or phone 020 7557 4464
Commonwealth Department: email amansi@stanleygibbons.com or phone 020 7557 4455

BY APPOINTMENT TO
HER MAJESTY THE QUEEN
PHILATELISTS
STANLEY GIBBONS LTD
LONDON

STANLEY GIBBONS
LONDON 1856

STANLEY GIBBONS 399 STRAND LONDON WC2R 0LX | WWW.STANLEYGIBBONS.COM

USED ON COVER PRICES					
No. 197	£7	No. 205	£42	No. 209	£275
No. 198	£25	No. 206	£100	No. 210	£300
No. 200	£28	No. 207	£275	No. 211	£190
No. 201	£8	No. 207a	£50	No. 213	£6·50
No. 202	£38	No. 208	£95	No. 214	£1000

PRICES. Please note that, with the exception of Government Parcels stamps, the price columns in this section are for mounted mint, used and used on cover examples. Fot Government Parcels they are for mint and used only.

DEPARTMENTAL OFFICIALS

The following Official stamps were exclusively for the use of certain government departments. Until 1882 official mail used ordinary postage stamps purchased at post offices, the cash being refunded once a quarter. Later the government departments obtained Official stamps by requisition.

Official stamps may have been on sale to the public for a short time at Somerset House but they were not sold from post offices. The system of only supplying the Government departments with stamps was open to abuse so that all official stamps were withdrawn on 13 May 1904.

PRICES. Please note that the price columns in this section are for mounted mint, used and used on cover examples. For Government Parcels and Board of Education stamps, they are for mint and used only.

OVERPRINTS, PERFORATIONS, WATERMARKS. All official stamps were overprinted by Thomas De La Rue & Co. and are perf 14. Except for the 5s., and 10s. on Anchor, they are on Crown watermarked paper unless otherwise stated.

INLAND REVENUE

These stamps were used by revenue officials in the provinces, mail to and from Head Office passing without a stamp. The London Office used these stamps only for foreign mail.

I.R.   I. R.

OFFICIAL OFFICIAL

(O **1**)   (O **2**)

Optd with Types O **1** (½d. to 1s.) or O **2** (others).

1882–1901. *Stamps of* Queen Victoria.

(a) Issues of 1880–81

		Unused	*Used	Used on cover
O1	½d. deep green (1.11.82)	£135	60·00	£120
O2	½d. pale green	90·00	40·00	
	s. Optd "SPECIMEN" (9)	£325		
O3	1d. lilac (Die II) (1.10.82)	8·00	6·00	30·00
	a. Optd in blue-black	£300	£125	
	b. "OFFICIAL" omitted	—	£12500	
	c. Imperf	£4500		
	ca. Imperf, optd in blue-black	£4500		
	s. Optd "SPECIMEN" (9, 15)	£180		
	Wi. Watermark inverted	—	£2200	
O4	6d. grey (Plate 18) (3.11.82)	£575	£140	
	s. Optd "SPECIMEN" (9, 15)	£325		

No. O3 with the lines of the overprint transposed is an essay.

(b) Issues of 1884–88

		Unused	*Used	Used on cover
O5	½d. slate-blue (8.5.85)	85·00	35·00	£135
	s. Optd "SPECIMEN" (9)	£325		
O6	2½d. lilac (12.3.85)	£525	£180	£1400
	s. Optd "SPECIMEN" (9)	£325		
O7	1s. dull green (12.3.85)	£6000	£1900	
	s. Optd "SPECIMEN" (9)	£1250		
O8	5s. rose (*blued paper*) (*Wmk* Anchor) (12.3.85)	£17500	£6500	
	a. Raised stop after "R"	£18500	£7250	
	s. Optd "SPECIMEN" (9, 11)	£2750		
O9	5s. rose (*Wmk* Anchor) (3.90)	£12000	£2500	
	a. Raised stop after "R"	£14000	£3200	
	b. Optd in blue-black	£14000	£3200	
	s. Optd "SPECIMEN" (9, 11, 13, 16).	£1750		
O9c	10s. cobalt (*blued paper*) (*Wmk* Anchor) (12.3.85)	£38000	£9500	
	ca. Raised stop after "R"			
	cb. cobalt (*white paper*) (*Wmk* Anchor)	£22000	£7750	
	cs. Optd "SPECIMEN" (11)	£4500		
O9d	10s. ultramarine (*blued paper*) (*Wmk* Anchor) (12.3.85)	£25000	£7500	
	da Raised stop after "R"	£27000	£8500	
	ds. Optd "SPECIMEN" (10)	£3750		

O10	10s. ultramarine (*Wmk* Anchor) (3.90)	£11500	£3750	
	a. Raised stop after "R"	£12500	£4500	
	b. Optd in blue-black	£12500	£4500	
	s. Optd "SPECIMEN" (9, 10, 11, 16).	£2750		
O11	£1 brown-lilac (*Wmk* Crowns) (12.3.85)	£75000	£30000	
	a. Frame broken	£100000	—	
	s. Optd "SPECIMEN" (11)	£5500		
O12	£1 brown-lilac (*Wmk* Orbs) (3.90)..	£100000	£40000	
	a. Frame broken	£150000		
	b. Optd in blue-black	£160000		
	s. Optd "SPECIMEN" (9, 11)	£9500		

Nos. O3, O13, O15 and O16 may be found showing worn impressions of the overprints with thicker letters.

(c) Issues of 1887–92.

O13	½d. vermilion (15.5.88)	15·00	7·00	£110
	a. Without "I.R."	£7000		
	b. Imperf	£7000		
	c. Optd double (imperf)	£8000		
	s. Optd "SPECIMEN" (9, 15)	£120		
O14	2½d. purple/*blue* (2.92)	£175	30·00	£450
	s. Optd "SPECIMEN" (9, 13, 15)	£120		
O15	1s. dull green (9.89)	£1000	£375	£3750
	a. Optd in blue-black	£2250		
	s. Optd "SPECIMEN" (9, 15)	£260		
O16	£1 green (6.92)	£12500	£2500	
	a. No stop after "R"	—	£4000	
	b. Frame broken	£20000	£5250	
	s. Optd "SPECIMEN" (9, 10, 15)	£2250		

(d) Issues of 1887 and 1900.

O17	½d. blue-green (4.01)	20·00	15·00	£350
	s. Optd "SPECIMEN" (15)	£160		
O18	6d. purple/*rose-red* (1.7.01)	£500	£150	
	s. Optd "SPECIMEN" (15, 16)	£250		
O19	1s. green and carmine (12.01)	£4250	£1800	
	s. Optd "SPECIMEN" (15)	£1100		

*O1/19 **For well-centred, lightly used +35%**

OFFICE OF WORKS

These were issued to Head and Branch (local) offices in London and to Branch (local) offices at Birmingham, Bristol, Edinburgh, Glasgow, Leeds, Liverpool, Manchester and Southampton. The overprints on stamps of value 2d. and upwards were created later in 1902, the 2d. for registration fees and the rest for overseas mail.

O.W.

OFFICIAL

(O **3**)

Optd with Type O **3**

1896 (24 Mar)–**02.** Stamps of Queen Victoria.

		Unused	*Used	Used on Cover
O31	½d. vermilion	£350	£150	£800
	s. Optd "SPECIMEN" (9, 15)	£325		
O32	½d. blue-green (2.02)	£475	£225	
	s. Optd "SPECIMEN" (15)	£450		
O33	1d. lilac (Die II)	£500	£150	£1000
	s. Optd "SPECIMEN" (9, 15, 16)	£325		
O34	5d. dull purple and blue (II) (29.4.02)	£4000	£1400	
	s. Optd "SPECIMEN" (16)	£1250		
O35	10d. dull purple and carmine (28.5.02)	£7250	£2250	
	s. Optd "SPECIMEN" (16)	£2600		

ARMY

Letters to and from the War Office in London passed without postage. The overprinted stamps were distributed to District and Station Paymasters nationwide, including Cox and Co., the Army Agents, who were paymasters to the Household Division.

ARMY   ARMY

OFFICIAL OFFICIAL

(O **4**)   (O **5**)

1896 (1 Sept)–**01**. Stamps of Queen Victoria optd with Type O 4 (½d., 1d.) or O 5 (2½d., 6d.).

		Unused	*Used	Used on cover
O41	½d. vermilion	8·00	3·00	65·00
	a. "OFFICIAI" (R.13/7)	£300	£130	
	b. Lines of optd transposed	£4700		
	s. Optd "SPECIMEN" (9)	£225		
	Wi. Watermark inverted	£800	£375	
O42	½d. blue-green (6.00)	10·00	15·00	
	s. Optd "SPECIMEN" (15)	£325		
	Wi. Watermark inverted	£1000	£650	
O43	1d. lilac (Die II)	8·00	7·00	£110
	a. "OFFICIAI" (R.13/7)	£240	£150	
	s. Optd "SPECIMEN" (9)	£225		
O44	2½d. purple/*blue*	50·00	35·00	£775
	s. Optd "SPECIMEN" (9)	£225		
O45	6d. purple/*rose-red* (20.9.01)	£110	60·00	£1700
	s. Optd "SPECIMEN" (15)	£425		

Nos. O41a and O43a occur in sheets overprinted by Forme 1.

GOVERNMENT PARCELS

These stamps were issued to all departments, including Head Office, for use on parcels weighing over 3 lb. Below this weight government parcels were sent by letter post to avoid the 55% of the postage paid from accruing to the railway companies, as laid down by parcel-post regulations. Most government parcels stamps suffered heavy postmarks in use.

GOVT PARCEL8
(O **7**)
Optd as Type O 7

1883 (1 Aug)–**86**. Stamps of Queen Victoria.

O61	1½d. lilac (1.5.86)	£400	£100
	a. No dot under "T"	£775	£175
	b. Dot to left of "T"	£775	£175
	s. Optd "SPECIMEN" (9)	£220	
O62	6d. dull green (1.5.86)	£3500	£1400
	s. Optd "SPECIMEN" (9)	£300	
O63	9d. dull green	£2750	£1200
	s. Optd "SPECIMEN" (9)	£300	
O64	1s. orange-brown (watermark Crown, Pl 13)	£1750	£300
	a. No dot under "T"	£2750	£500
	b. Dot to left of "T"	£2750	£500
	s. Optd "SPECIMEN" (9)	£325	
O64c	1s. orange-brown (Pl 14)	£3500	£600
	ca. No dot under "T"	£4500	£850
	cb. Dot to left of "T"		

1887–90. Stamps of Queen Victoria.

O65	1½d. dull purple and pale green (29.10.87)	£160	28·00
	a. No dot under "T"	£260	75·00
	b. Dot to right of "T"	£260	75·00
	c. Dot to left of "T"	£260	75·00
	s. Optd "SPECIMEN" (9, 10, 13, 15)	£300	
O66	6d. purple/*rose-red* (19.12.87)	£275	75·00
	a. No dot under "T"	£375	£120
	b. Dot to right of "T"	£375	£120
	c. Dot to left of "T"	£375	£120
	s. Optd "SPECIMEN" (9, 13, 15)	£250	
O67	9d. dull purple and blue (21.8.88)	£425	£120
	a. Optd in blue-black		
	s. Optd "SPECIMEN" (9, 10, 13, 15)	£300	
	Wi. Watermark inverted		
O68	1s. dull green (25.3.90)	£700	£275
	a. No dot under "T"	£1000	£500
	b. Dot to right of "T"	£1000	£500
	c. Dot to left of "T"	£1000	£500
	d. Optd in blue-black		
	s. Optd "SPECIMEN" (9, 13, 15)	£300	

1891–1900. Stamps of Queen Victoria.

O69	1d. lilac (Die II) (18.6.97)	£100	30·00
	a. No dot under "T"	£160	75·00
	b. Dot to left of "T"	£160	75·00
	c. Optd inverted	£7500	£3500
	d. Optd inverted. Dot to left of "T"	£8500	£4500
	s. Optd "SPECIMEN" (15)	£450	
	Wi. Watermark inverted	—	£500
O70	2d. grey-green and carmine (24.10.91)	£250	50·00
	a. No dot under "T"	£400	£125
	b. Dot to left of "T"	£400	£125
	s. Optd "SPECIMEN" (9, 11, 13, 15)	£300	
O71	4½d. green and carmine (29.9.92)	£400	£275
	b. Dot to right of "T"		
	s. Optd "SPECIMEN" (9, 13, 15)	£300	
	Wi. Watermark inverted	—	£9000
O72	1s. green and carmine (11.00)	£650	£275
	a. Optd inverted	†	£17500
	s. Optd "SPECIMEN" (9)	£400	

*O61/72 **For well-centred lightly used +100%**

The "no dot under T" variety occurred on R.12/3 and 20/2. The "dot to left of T" comes four times in the sheet on R.2/7, 6/7, 7/9 and 12/9. The best example of the "dot to right of T" is on R.20/1. All three varieties were corrected around 1897.

BOARD OF EDUCATION

BOARD
OF
EDUCATION
(O **8**)
Optd with Type O 8

1902 (19 Feb). Stamps of Queen Victoria.

O81	5d. dull purple and blue (II)	£5750	£1500
	s. Optd "SPECIMEN" (15)	£1400	
O82	1s. green and carmine	£12000	£6000
	s. Optd "SPECIMEN" (15)	£3000	

POST OFFICE TELEGRAPH STAMPS

The telegraph system in the United Kingdom was originally operated by private companies, some of which issued their own stamps.

The Post Office took over the service in 1870, producing telegraph forms with impressed 1s. stationery dies and blank forms to which postage stamps were applied.

To assist in the separate accounting of revenues from the postal and telegraph services, special Post Office Telegraph stamps were issued from 1 February 1876 and from 1 May of that year the use of postage stamps to pre-pay telegraph services was prohibited.

Telegraph stamps were in use for little over five years, when it was decided to withdraw them and postage stamps were, once again, used for telegraph services.

PLATE NUMBERS Like the postage stamps of the period, all telegraph stamps showed their plate number within the design. These are listed under their respective values.

WATERMARKS To differentiate them from postage stamps, all telegraph stamps were in horizontal format and the watermarks appear sideways. Apart from the Shamrock watermark, W T **12**, all were as used for postage stamps of the period. For the purposes of this listing, watermark sideways refers to the top of the watermark device pointing to the right of the stamp *as viewed from the gummed side of the stamp*; watermark sideways inverted refers to the top of the device pointing to the left.

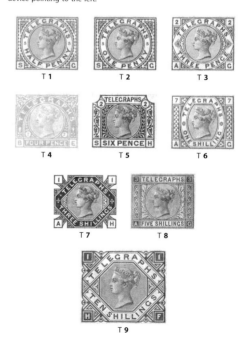

T **1**	T **2**	T **3**
T **4**	T **5**	T **6**
T **7**	T **8**	
	T **9**	

T **10**

T **11**

T **12**

1876 (1 February). Wmks as listed. *Perf* 15×15½ (5s., 10s., £5), *Perf* 14 (others).

T1	T **1**	½d. orange (W T **12**) (Plate 5) (1.4.80)..	30·00	35·00
		a. Imperf (vertical pair)............................	£2000	
		s. Optd "SPECIMEN" (9)...........................	65·00	
T2	T **2**	1d. red-brown (W T **12**).........................	30·00	28·00
		Wi. Watermark inverted	£300	£175
		s. Optd "SPECIMEN" (9, 10)	65·00	
		Plate 1..	30·00	28·00
		2..	35·00	28·00
		3..	35·00	28·00
T3	T **3**	3d. carmine (W **33** sideways)................	£100	60·00
		Wi. Watermark sideways inverted	£300	£280
		s. Optd "SPECIMEN" (9, 10)	80·00	
		Plate 1..	£100	75·00
		2..	£100	60·00
		3..	£125	90·00
T4		3d. carmine (W **49** sideways inverted) (6.6.81)............	£150	£120
		Plate 3..	£150	£120
		4 (watermark sideways)	£475	£250
		5. (watermark sideways)....................	£475	£250
T5	T **4**	4d. sage-green (W **17** sideways inverted) (Plate 1) (1.3.77).................	£150	£125
		a. Imperf (vertical pair)............................		
		wi. Watermark sideways..........................	—	—
		s. Optd "SPECIMEN" (9,11)......................	75·00	
T6	T **5**	6d. grey (W **33** sideways) (1.3.77)	£125	80·00
		s. Optd "SPECIMEN" (9,11)......................	75·00	
		Plate 1..	£125	80·00
		2..	£300	£160
T7		6d. grey (W **49** sideways inverted) (1.81)	£240	£150
		a. Imperf (vertical pair)............................		
T8	T **6**	1s. deep green (W **33** sideways)...........	£120	50·00
		Wi. Watermark sideways inverted	£500	
		Plate s. Optd "SPECIMEN" (9,10)	£110	
		1..	£180	65·00
		2..	£140	65·00
		3..	£140	55·00
		4..	£200	55·00
		5..	£120	50·00
		6..	£120	50·00
		7..	£350	55·00
		8..	£180	55·00
		9..	£180	55·00
		10...	£220	70·00
T9		1s. brown-orange (W **33** sideways) (10.80)................	£225	£150
		s. Optd "SPECIMEN" (9)...........................	£120	
		Plate 10..	£225	£150
		12...	£250	£190
T10		1s. brown-orange (W **49** sideways) (2.81?)................	£250	£200
		a. Imperf (vertical pair)............................		
		Wi. Watermark sideways inverted	£250	£200
		s. Optd "SPECIMEN" (12).........................	£300	
		Plate 11..	£250	£200
		12...	£550	£300
T11	T **7**	3s. slate-blue (W **33** sideways) (Plate 1) (1.3.77).................	£175	80·00
		Wi. Watermark sideways inverted	—	£500
		s. Optd "SPECIMEN" (8, 9, 11)...............	£120	
T12		3s. slate-blue (W **49** sideways inverted) (Plate 1) (8.81)	£6500	£3800
T13	T **8**	5s. rose (W **39**) (P15×15½).....................	£1100	£200
		s. Optd "SPECIMEN" (8, 9, 10)	£250	
		Plate 1..	£1100	£200
		2..	£2250	£375
T14		5s. rose (W **39**) (P. 14) (Plate 2) (1880)	£7000	£600
T15		5s. rose (W **40**) (P. 14) (Plate 3) (5.81).	£7000	£1100
		s. Optd "SPECIMEN" (9, 12).....................	£1000	
T16	T **9**	10s. grey-green (W **39**) (Plate 1) (13.77)..........................	£1750	£450
		s. Optd "SPECIMEN" (8, 9, 11)...............	£400	
T17	T **10**	£1 brown-lilac (W T **12** sideways ×3) (Plate 1) (1.3.77)...................	£8250	£950
		s. Optd "SPECIMEN" (8, 9, 11)...............	£900	
T18	T **11**	£5 orange (W T **12** sideways inverted ×3), (Plate 1) (1.3.77).................	£30000	£3200
		s. Optd "SPECIMEN" (8, 9, 11)...............	£2800	

*T1/18 **For well-centred lightly used + 75%**

Short reign.

Big achievements.

Despite only a short reign
Edward VII left a substantial philatelic legacy.

King Edward VII

22 January 1901 – 6 May 1910

PRINTINGS. Distinguishing De La Rue printings from the provisional printings of the same values made by Harrison & Sons Ltd. or at Somerset House may prove difficult in some cases. For very full guidance Volume 2 of the Stanley Gibbons *Great Britain Specialised Catalogue* should prove helpful.

Note that stamps perforated 15×14 must be Harrison; the 2½d., 3d. and 4d. in this perforation are useful reference material, their shades and appearance in most cases matching the Harrison perf 14 printings.

Except for the 6d. value, all stamps on chalk-surfaced paper were printed by De La Rue.

Of the stamps on ordinary paper, the De La Rue impressions are usually clearer and of a higher finish than those of the other printers. The shades are markedly different except in some printings of the 4d., 6d. and 7d. and in the 5s., 10s. and £1.

Used stamps in good, clean, unrubbed condition and with dated postmarks can form the basis of a useful reference collection, the dates often assisting in the assignment to the printers.

PRICES. For Nos. 215/456a prices are quoted for unmounted mint, mounted mint and used stamps.

USED STAMPS. For well-centred, lightly used examples of King Edward VII stamps, add the following percentages to the used prices quoted below:
De La Rue printings (Nos. 215/66)—3d. values + 35%, 4d. orange + 100%, 6d. + 75%, 7d. and 1s. + 25%, all other values + 50%. *Harrison printings* (Nos. 267/86)—all values and perforations + 75%. *Somerset House printings* (Nos. 287/320)—1s. values + 25%, all other values + 50%.

| 94 | 95 | 96 |

97

Deformed tablet (Pl. D4, R. 5/9)

(Des E. Fuchs)

1902 (1 Jan)-**10**. Printed by De La Rue & Co. *Wmk* Imperial Crown *W* **49** (½d. to 1s. Three Crowns on £1); Large Anchor, *W* **40** (2s.6d. to 10s.). Ordinary paper. *P* 14.

			Unmtd mint	Mtd mint	Used
215	**83**	½d. dull blue-green (1.1.02)	2·75	2·00	1·50
		s. Optd "SPECIMEN" (15)		£350	
		Wi. Watermark inverted	£3750	£2750	£2000
216		½d. blue-green	2·75	2·00	1·50
217		½d. pale yellowish green (26.11.04)	2·75	2·00	1·50
218		½d. yellowish green	2·75	2·00	1·50
		a. Pair. No. 218 plus St. Andrew's Cross label	£275	£175	£200
		aw. Pair. No. 218 Wi plus St. Andrew's Cross label	£275	£175	£200
		b. Booklet pane. No. 218×5 plus St. Andrew's Cross label	£975	£700	£550
		bw. Booklet pane. No. 218×5 plus St. Andrew's Cross label. Wmk inverted	£975	£700	£550
		c. Booklet pane. No. 218×6 (6.06)	£375	£275	£225
		cw. Booklet pane. No. 218×6. Wmk inverted	£375	£275	£225
		d. Doubly printed (bottom row on one pane) (Control H9)	£37500	£27500	
		s. Optd "SPECIMEN" (17, 22)		£275	
		Wi. Watermark inverted	22·00	12·00	9·00
219		1d. scarlet (1.1.02)	2·75	2·00	1·50
		a. Booklet pane. No. 219×6 (16.3.04)	£325	£250	£200
		aw. Booklet pane. No. 219×6. Wmk inverted	£325	£250	£200
		s. Optd "SPECIMEN" (15, 16, 17, 22)		£250	
220		1d. bright scarlet	2·75	2·00	1·50
		a. Imperf (pair)	†	£35000	
		Wi. Watermark inverted	8·00	4·00	4·00
221	**84**	1½d. dull purple and green (21.3.02)	95·00	50·00	24·00
		a. Deformed leaf		£825	£425
		s. Optd "SPECIMEN" (15)		£275	
222		1½d. slate-purple and green	95·00	50·00	24·00
		Wi. Watermark inverted	—	—	£900
223		1½d. pale dull purple and green (chalk-surfaced paper) (7.05)	75·00	45·00	24·00
		s. Optd "SPECIMEN" (17)		£700	

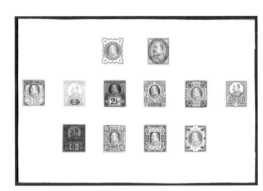

224		1½d. slate-purple and bluish green (*chalk-surfaced paper*)	75·00	45·00	22·00
225	**85**	2d. yellowish green and carmine-red (25.3.02)	£125	70·00	25·00
		s. Optd "SPECIMEN" (16)		£550	
		Wi. Watermark inverted	£28000		
226		2d. grey-green and carmine-red (1904)	£150	85·00	35·00
227		2d. pale grey-green and carmine-red (*chalk-surfaced paper*) (4.06)	80·00	45·00	32·00
		a. Deformed tablet		£1000	£750
		s. Optd "SPECIMEN" (17)		£700	
		Wi. Watermark inverted		£20000	
228		2d. pale grey-green and scarlet (*chalk-surfaced paper*) (1909)	80·00	45·00	32·00
229		2d. dull blue-green and carmine (*chalk-surfaced paper*) (1907)	£180	90·00	50·00
230	**86**	2½d. ultramarine (1.1.02)	34·00	20·00	15·00
		s. Optd "SPECIMEN" (15, 17)		£125	
231		2½d. pale ultramarine	34·00	20·00	15·00
		Wi. Watermark inverted	—	—	£4200
232	**87**	3d. dull purple/*orange-yellow* (20.3.02)	£100	50·00	18·00
		s. Optd "SPECIMEN" (15)		£350	
		Wi. Watermark inverted			
		a. *Chalk-surfaced paper* (3.06)	£450	£250	£100
232b		3d. deep purple/*orange-yellow*	90·00	45·00	18·00
232c		3d. pale reddish purple/*orange-yellow* (*chalk-surfaced paper*) (3.06)	£425	£225	85·00
		cs. Optd "SPECIMEN" (17)		£700	
233		3d. dull reddish purple/*yellow* (*lemon back*) (*chalk-surfaced paper*)	£425	£225	85·00
233b		3d. pale purple/*lemon* (*chalk-surfaced paper*)	85·00	45·00	20·00
234		3d. purple/*lemon* (*chalk-surfaced paper*)	85·00	45·00	20·00
235	**88**	4d. green and grey-brown (27.3.02)	£125	70·00	35·00
		s. Optd "SPECIMEN" (16)		£450	
		Wi. Watermark inverted			
236		4d. green and chocolate-brown	£125	70·00	35·00
		a. *Chalk-surfaced paper* (1.06)	75·00	40·00	20·00
		Wi. watermark inverted		£9500	
238		4d. deep green and chocolate-brown (*chalk-surfaced paper*) (1.06)	75·00	40·00	20·00
239		4d. brown-orange (1.11.09)	£300	£180	£140
		s. Optd "SPECIMEN" (17)		£700	
240		4d. pale orange (12.09)	45·00	20·00	18·00
241		4d. orange-red (12.09)	50·00	25·00	20·00
242	**89**	5d. dull purple and ultramarine (14.5.02)	£135	65·00	22·00
		aas. Optd "SPECIMEN" (16)		£350	
		a. *Chalk-surfaced paper* (5.06)	£120	60·00	22·00
243		5d. slate-purple and ultramarine (14.5.02)	£115	55·00	22·00
		a. slate-purple and ultramarine (*chalk-surfaced paper*) (5.06)	£115	55·00	22·00
		as. Optd "SPECIMEN" (17)		£700	
		Wi. Watermark inverted	£8000	£5500	
245	**83**	6d. pale dull purple (1.1.02)	85·00	45·00	22·00
		aas. Optd "SPECIMEN" (15)		£400	
		a. *Chalk-surfaced paper* (1.06)	85·00	45·00	22·00
246		6d. slate-purple	85·00	45·00	22·00
248		6d. dull purple (*chalk-surfaced paper*) (1.06)	85·00	45·00	22·00
		s. Optd "SPECIMEN" (17)		£700	
		Wi. Watermark inverted	—	—	£3500
249	**90**	7d. grey-black (4.5.10)	24·00	15·00	22·00
		s. Optd "SPECIMEN" (17)		£700	
249a		7d. deep grey-black	£170	£115	£100
250	**91**	9d. dull purple and ultramarine (7.4.02)	£275	£140	75·00
		aas. Optd "SPECIMEN" (16)		£450	
		a. *Chalk-surfaced paper* (6.05)	£250	£140	75·00
		aWi. Watermark inverted	—	—	£3500
251		9d. slate-purple and ultramarine	£275	£140	75·00
		a. *Chalk-surfaced paper* (6.05)	£225	£120	75·00
		as. Optd "SPECIMEN" (17)		£725	
254	**92**	10d. dull purple and carmine (3.7.02)	£300	£150	75·00
		aas. Optd "SPECIMEN" (16)		£500	
		a. No cross on crown	£775	£425	£300
		b. *Chalk-surfaced paper* (9.06)	£300	£140	75·00

255		10d. slate-purple and carmine (*chalk-surfaced paper*) (9.06)	£275	£140	75·00
		a. No cross on crown	£725	£450	£275
		as. Optd "SPECIMEN" (17)		£700	
256		10d. dull purple and scarlet (*chalk-surfaced paper*) (9.10)	£260	£140	75·00
		a. No cross on crown	£725	£425	£250
257	**93**	1s. dull green and carmine (24.3.02)	£225	£100	40·00
		aas. Optd "SPECIMEN" (16)		£400	
		a. *Chalk-surfaced paper* (9.05)	£225	£100	40·00
		as. Optd "SPECIMEN" (17)		£725	
259		1s. dull green and scarlet (*chalk-surfaced paper*) (9.10)	£225	£100	55·00
260	**94**	2s.6d. lilac (5.4.02)	£525	£280	£150
		s. Optd "SPECIMEN" (15, 16)		£400	
		Wi. Watermark inverted	£7500	£5000	£3500
261		2s.6d. pale dull purple (*chalk-surfaced paper*) (7.10.05)	£675	£350	£180
		s. Optd "SPECIMEN" (17)		£3250	
		Wi. Watermark inverted	£11000	£7500	£4250
262		2s.6d. dull purple (*chalk-surfaced paper*)	£600	£350	£180
263	**95**	5s. bright carmine (5.4.02)	£850	£450	£220
		s. Optd "SPECIMEN" (16, 17)		£400	
		Wi. Watermark inverted	—	£65000	£5750
264		5s. deep bright carmine	£900	£450	£220
265	**96**	10s. ultramarine (5.4.02)	£2000	£1000	£500
		s. Optd "SPECIMEN" (16, 17)		£500	
		Wi. Watermark inverted	—	£85000	£40000
266	**97**	£1 dull blue-green (16.6.02)	£3500	£2000	£825
		s. Optd "SPECIMEN" (16, 17)		£1400	
		Wi. Watermark inverted	—	£110000	£24000

USED ON COVER PRICES					
No. 215	£2.50	No. 217	£2.50	No. 21	£2.50
No. 222	£50	No. 225	£50	No. 230	£25
No. 232	£35	No. 236a	£45	No. 240	£40
No. 242	£50	No. 245	£60	No. 249	£200
No. 250	£250	No. 254	£225	No. 257	£175
No. 260	£1250	No. 263	£1850		

97a

1910 (May). Prepared for use, by De La Rue but not issued. *Wmk* Imperial Crown, W **49**. *P* 14.

266a	**97a**	2d. Tyrian plum	—	£115000	
		s. Optd "SPECIMEN" (17)		£62000	

One example of this stamp is known used, but it was never issued to the public.

1911. Printed by Harrison & Sons. Ordinary paper. *Wmk* Imperial Crown W **49**.

(a) P 14.

267	**83**	½d. dull yellow-green (3.5.11)	6·00	2·75	4·00
		a. Pair. No. 267 plus St. Andrew's Cross label	£400	£300	£300
		aw. Pair. No. 267Wi plus St. Andrew's Cross label	£400	£300	£300
		s. Optd "SPECIMEN" (22)		£325	
		Wi. Watermark inverted	£100	60·00	60·00
268		½d. dull green	6·00	3·00	4·00
269		½d. deep dull green	17·00	11·00	10·00
270		½d. pale bluish green	85·00	40·00	40·00
		a. Booklet pane. Five stamps plus St. Andrew's Cross label	£1250	£800	£650
		aw. Booklet pane. Five stamps plus St. Andrew's Cross label. Wmk inverted	£1250	£800	£650
		b. Booklet pane. No. 270×6.	£425	£325	£275
		bw. Booklet pane. No. 270×6. Wmk inverted	£425	£325	£275
		c. Watermark sideways	†	†	£35000
		d. Imperf (pair)	—	£40000	†
271		½d. bright green (fine impression) (6.11)	£425	£275	£170
272		1d. rose-red (3.5.11)	18·00	8·00	15·00
		a. No watermark (brick-red)	75·00	50·00	—
		b. Booklet pane. No. 272×6.	£325	£250	£200
		bw. Booklet pane. No. 272×6. Watermark inverted	£325	£250	£200
		s. Optd "SPECIMEN" (22)		£325	
		Wi. Watermark inverted	90·00	50·00	50·00
273		1d. deep rose-red	18·00	8·00	15·00

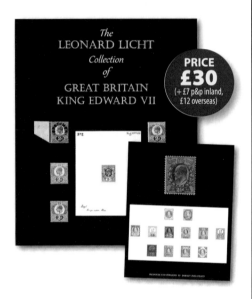

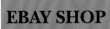
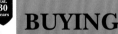

274		1d. rose-carmine........................	£100	55·00	50·00
275		1d. aniline pink (5.11)..............	£1250	£750	£400
275a		1d. aniline rose.....................	£300	£180	£140
276	86	2½d. bright blue (10.7.11)...........	£175	65·00	38·00
		Wi. Watermark inverted........	£2100	£1250	
277	87	3d. purple/lemon (12.9.11)......	£275	£150	£250
		s. Optd "SPECIMEN" (22)........		£300	
277a		3d. grey/lemon..................	£7000	£4500	
278	88	4d. bright orange (12.7.11)......	£225	£120	55·00
		s. Optd "SPECIMEN" (22)........		£240	
Set of 5			£575	£290	£290

(b) P 15×14.

279	83	½d. dull green (30.10.11).........	65·00	40·00	45·00
		Wi. Watermark inverted...........	†	†	£3500
279a		½d. deep dull green................	90·00	45·00	45·00
280		1d. rose-red (4.10.11)..............	80·00	45·00	25·00
281		1d. rose-carmine..................	35·00	15·00	15·00
		Wi. Watermark inverted...........	†	†	—
282		1d. pale rose-carmine............	40·00	22·00	15·00
283	86	2½d. bright blue (14.10.11).......	50·00	22·00	15·00
		s. Optd "SPECIMEN" (22)........		—	
284		2½d. dull blue....................	50·00	22·00	15·00
		Wi. Watermark inverted...........	—	—	£3000
285	87	3d. purple/lemon (22.9.11).......	80·00	45·00	15·00
285a		3d. grey/lemon..................	£4250	£3250	
286	88	4d. bright orange (11.11.11)......	60·00	30·00	15·00
Set of 5			£250	£130	90·00

USED ON COVER PRICES

No. 267	£4	No. 272	£18	No. 276	£55
No. 277	£550	No. 278	£175	No. 279	£100
No. 281	£30	No. 283	£35	No. 285	£40
No. 286	£65				

1911–13. Printed at Somerset House. Ordinary paper. *Wmk* as 1902–10. *P* 14.

287	84	1½d. reddish purple and bright green (13.7.11)......	90·00	45·00	38·00
288		1½d. dull purple and green........	60·00	30·00	30·00
289		1½d. slate-purple and green (1.12)......	65·00	30·00	30·00
290	85	2d. deep dull green and red (8.8.11)......	60·00	28·00	22·00
		a. Deformed tablet...............		£925	£550
		s. Optd "SPECIMEN" (22)........		£325	
291		2d. deep dull green and carmine......	70·00	30·00	25·00
292		2d. grey-green and bright carmine (carmine shows clearly on back) (11.3.12)..	55·00	28·00	28·00
293	89	5d. dull reddish purple and bright blue (7.8.11)......	60·00	30·00	22·00
		s. Optd "SPECIMEN" (2)...........		—	
294		5d. deep dull reddish purple and bright blue......	55·00	30·00	22·00
295	83	6d. royal purple (31.10.11)......	£110	50·00	90·00
296		6d. bright magenta (*chalk-surfaced paper*) (31.10.11).	£17500	£12500	
		s. Optd "SPECIMEN" (2)...........		£5750	
297		6d. dull purple........................	60·00	30·00	22·00
		s. Optd "SPECIMEN" (2)...........		£400	
298		6d. reddish purple (11.11).......	60·00	30·00	28·00
		a. No cross on crown (various shades)...................	£1800	£1200	
299		6d. very deep reddish purple (11.11)......	£120	55·00	45·00
300		6d. dark purple (3.12)..............	70·00	35·00	20·00
301		6d. dull purple "Dickinson" coated paper* (3.13)......	£425	£250	£190
303		6d. deep plum (*chalk-surfaced paper*) (7.13)......	60·00	30·00	75·00
		a. No cross on crown............	£1950	£1250	
305	90	7d. slate-grey (1.8.12).............	30·00	15·00	22·00
		s. Optd "SPECIMEN" (26)........		£350	
306	91	9d. reddish purple and light blue (24.7.11)......	£200	95·00	75·00
		s. Optd "SPECIMEN" (22)........		£450	
306a		9d. deep dull reddish purple and deep brt blue (9.11)..	£200	95·00	75·00
307		9d. dull reddish purple and blue (10.11)...........	£130	60·00	60·00
307a		9d. deep plum and blue (7.13)...........	£125	60·00	60·00
308		9d. slate-purple and cobalt-blue (3.12)...........	£350	£160	£110
309	92	10d. dull purple and scarlet (9.10.11)...........	£200	95·00	75·00
		s. Optd "SPECIMEN" (22)........		£375	
310		10d. dull reddish purple and aniline pink...................	£500	£275	£225

311		10d. dull reddish purple and carmine (5.12)......	£150	80·00	60·00
		a. No cross on crown..........	£2800	£1800	
312	93	1s. dark green and scarlet (13.7.11)......	£240	£120	60·00
		s. Optd "SPECIMEN" (22, 23, 26)......		£350	
313		1s. deep green and scarlet (9.10.11)......	£180	80·00	40·00
		Wi. Watermark inverted...........	£240	£150	†
314		1s. green and carmine (15.4.12)......	£140	60·00	35·00
315	94	2s.6d. dull greyish purple (15.9.11)......	£1750	£950	£450
		s. Optd "SPECIMEN" (22)........		£425	
316		2s.6d. dull reddish purple (11.11)......	£600	£300	£180
		Wi. Watermark inverted...........	†	†	—
317		2s.6d. dark purple (4.13)........	£650	£325	£190
318	95	5s. carmine (29.2.12)..............	£875	£425	£200
		s. Optd "SPECIMEN" (26)........		—	
319	96	10s. blue (14.1.12)...................	£2100	£1100	£600
320	97	£1 deep green (3.9.11).............	£3000	£2000	£750
		s. Optd "SPECIMEN" (22)........		£2200	

*No. 301 was on an experimental coated paper which does not respond to the silver test.

USED ON COVER PRICES

No. 288	£60	No. 305	£200	No. 316	£1700
No. 290	£55	No. 307	£190	No. 318	£1750
No. 293	£65	No. 311	£225		
No. 297	£90	No. 314	£200		

DEPARTMENTAL OFFICIALS

PRICES. Please note that, with the exception of Government Parcels Stamps, the price columns in this section are for mounted mint, used and used on cover examples. For Government Parcels Stamps they are for mint and used only.

INLAND REVENUE

These stamps were used by revenue officials in the provinces, mail to and from Head Office passing without a stamp. The London Office used these stamps only for foreign mail.

1902–04. Stamps of King Edward VII optd with type O **1** or O **2**. Ordinary paper.

			Unused	Used	Used on cover
O20		½d. blue-green (4.2.02)...................	32·00	4·50	£150
		s. Optd "SPECIMEN" (15).............	£425		
O21		1d. scarlet (4.2.02).......................	22·00	3·00	95·00
		s. Optd "SPECIMEN" (15).............	£425		
O22		2½d. ultramarine (19.2.02)............	£1000	£275	
		s. Optd "SPECIMEN" (15, 16).......	£580		
O23		6d. pale dull purple (14.3.04).........	£500000	£300000	
		s. Optd "SPECIMEN" (16).............	£45000		
O24		1s. dull green and carmine (29.4.02)......	£3750	£900	
		s. Optd "SPECIMEN" (16).............	£1200		
O25		5s. bright carmine (29.4.02).............	£45000	£11000	
		a. Raised stop after "R".................	£50000	£13000	
		s. Optd "SPECIMEN" (16).............	£8500		
O26		10s. ultramarine (29.4.02)............	£100000	£48000	
		a. Raised stop after "R".................	£125000	£48000	
		s. Optd "SPECIMEN" (16).............	£24000		
O27		£1 blue-green (29.4.02).................	£62500	£25000	
		s. Optd "SPECIMEN" (16).............	£16000		

Although an issue date of 4 February has long been recorded, the 1d. is not currently known used before 24 February and the ½d. before early March 1902.

OFFICE OF WORKS

These were issued to Head and Branch (local) offices in London and to Branch (local) offices at Birmingham, Bristol, Edinburgh, Glasgow, Leeds, Liverpool, Manchester and Southampton. The overprints on stamps of value 2d. and upwards were created later in 1902, the 2d. for registration fees and the rest for overseas mail.

1902 (11 Feb)–**03**. Stamps of King Edward VII optd with type O **3**. Ordinary paper.

O36		½d. blue-green (2.02)..........................	£575	£180	£2000
		s. Optd "SPECIMEN" (15)...................	£425		
O37		1d. scarlet...	£575	£180	£425
		s. Optd "SPECIMEN" (15)...................	£425		
O38		2d. yellowish green and carmine-red (27.4.02)......	£2000	£450	£3250
		s. Optd "SPECIMEN" (16)...................	£850		
O39		2½d. ultramarine (29.4.02)...................	£3500	£675	£4250
		s. Optd "SPECIMEN" (16)...................	£900		
O40		10d. dull purple and carmine (28.5.03).............................	£47500	£7000	

s. Optd "SPECIMEN" (16).................... £8000

*O31/40 **For well-centred, lightly used** +25%

ARMY

ARMY

OFFICIAL

(O **6**)

1902–03. Stamps of King Edward VII optd with Type O **4** (Nos. O48/**50**) or Type O **6** (O 52). Ordinary paper.

O48	½d. blue-green (11.2.02).....................	6·00	2·50 £100
	s. Optd "SPECIMEN" (15)..................	£350	
O49	1d. scarlet (11.2.02).........................	6·00	2·50 £100
	a. "ARMY" omitted	†	—
	s. Optd "SPECIMEN" (15)..................	£350	
O50	6d. pale dull purple (23.8.02)	£175	80·00
	s. Optd "SPECIMEN" (16)..................	£425	
O52	6d. pale dull purple (12.03).............	£3000	£1600

GOVERNMENT PARCELS

1902. Stamps of King Edward VII optd with type O **7**. Ordinary paper.

O74	1d. scarlet (30.10.02)	75·00	22·00
	s. Optd "SPECIMEN" (16).................	£350	
O75	2d. yellowish green and carmine-red		
	(29.4.02)	£225	60·00
	s. Optd "SPECIMEN" (16).................	£350	
O76	6d. pale dull purple (19.2.02)	£275	60·00
	a. Overprint double, one albino..................	£35000	
	s. Optd "SPECIMEN" (16).................	£350	
O77	9d. dull purple and ultramarine (28.8.02)....	£650	£175
	s. Optd "SPECIMEN" (16).................	£500	
O78	1s. dull green and carmine (17.12.02)	£1350	£300
	s. Optd "SPECIMEN" (16).................	£550	

BOARD OF EDUCATION

1902 (19 Feb)–**04**. Stamps of King Edward VII optd with type O **8**. Ordinary paper.

		Unused	*Used	Used on cover
O83	½d. blue-green	£180	45·00	£550
	s. Optd "SPECIMEN" (15)..................	£375		
O84	1d. scarlet	£180	45·00	£550
	s. Optd "SPECIMEN" (15)..................	£375		
O85	2½d. ultramarine......................................	£4850	£475	
	s. Optd "SPECIMEN" (15)..................	£1100		
O86	5d. dull purple and ultramarine			
	(6.2.04)...	£35000	£10000	
	s. Optd "SPECIMEN" (16).................	£7000		
O87	1s. dull green and carmine			
	(23.12.02)	£200000		
	s. Optd "SPECIMEN" (16).................	£38000		

ROYAL HOUSEHOLD

R.H.

OFFICIAL

(O **9**)

1902. Stamps of King Edward VII optd with Type O **9**. Ordinary paper.

		Unused	*Used	Used on cover
O91	½d. blue-green (29.4.02).....................	£375	£200	£1100
	s. Optd "SPECIMEN" (16)..................	£750		
O92	1d. scarlet (19.2.02).........................	£325	£175	£1000
	s. Optd "SPECIMEN" (15)..................	£750		

ADMIRALTY

ADMIRALTY   ADMIRALTY

OFFICIAL   OFFICIAL

(O **10**)   (O **11**)
(with different "M")

1903 (1 Apr). Stamps of King Edward VII optd with Type O **10**. Ordinary paper.

		Unused	*Used	Used on cover
O101	½d. blue-green	30·00	15·00	
	s. Optd "SPECIMEN" (16)...................	£400		
O102	1d. scarlet	20·00	10·00	£300
	s. Optd "SPECIMEN" (16)...................	£400		
O103	1½d. dull purple and green.................	£325	£150	
	s. Optd "SPECIMEN" (16)...................	£500		
O104	2d. yellowish green and carmine-			£160
	red..	£350		
	s. Optd "SPECIMEN" (16)...................	£500		
O105	2½d. ultramarine...........................	£475	£150	
	s. Optd "SPECIMEN" (16)...................	£500		
O106	3d. dull purple/*orange-yellow*...........	£425	£160	
	s. Optd "SPECIMEN" (16)...................	£500		

1903–04. Stamps of King Edward VII optd with Type O **11**. Ordinary paper.

		Unused	*Used	Used on cover
O107	½d. blue-green (9.03)	60·00	28·00	£500
	s. Optd "SPECIMEN" (16)...................	£400		
O108	1d. scarlet (12.03)	60·00	28·00	£160
	s. Optd "SPECIMEN" (16)...................	£400		
O109	1½d. dull purple and green (2.04).....	£1200	£650	
O110	2d. yellowish green and carmine-			
	red (3.04)...................................	£2700	£900	
	s. Optd "SPECIMEN" (16)...................	£750		
O111	2½d. ultramarine (3.04)	£2900	£950	
	s. Optd "SPECIMEN" (16)...................	£950		
O112	3d. dull purple/*orange-yellow*			
	(12.03).......................................	£2600	£400	
	s. Optd "SPECIMEN" (16)...................	£750		

Stamps of various issues perforated with a Crown and initials ("H.M.O.W.", "O.W.", "B.T." or "S.O.") or with initials only ("H.M.S.O." or "D.S.I.R.") have also been used for official purposes, but these are outside the scope of this catalogue.

Whatever your budget or collecting interests you will find a range of the highest quality material for the discerning collector.

Stanley Gibbons, a name synonymous with quality.

Ever since the birth of our hobby Stanley Gibbons has been at the forefront of GB philately and we invite collectors to access one of the finest GB stocks in the world by registering for our renowned free monthly brochure.

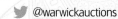

King George V

6 May 1910 – 20 January 1936

Further detailed information on the issues of King George V will be found in Volume 2 of the Stanley Gibbons *Great Britain Specialised Catalogue*.

PRINTERS. Types 98 to 102 were letterpress printed by Harrison & Sons Ltd, with the exception of certain preliminary printings made at Somerset House and distinguishable by the controls "A.11", "B.11" or "B.12" (the Harrison printings do not have a full stop after the letter). The booklet stamps, Nos. 334/7, and 344/5 were printed by Harrison only.

WATERMARK VARIETIES. Many British stamps to 1967 exist without watermark owing to misplacement of the paper, and with either inverted, reversed, or inverted and reversed watermarks. A proportion of the low-value stamps issued in booklets have the watermark inverted in the normal course of printing.

Low values with *watermark sideways* are normally from stamp rolls used on machines with sideways delivery or, from June 1940, certain booklets.

STAMPS WITHOUT WATERMARK. Stamps found without watermark, due to misplacement of the sheet in relation to the dandy roll, are not listed here but will be found in the *Great Britain Specialised Catalogue*.

The 1½d. and 5d. 1912–22, and ½d., 2d. and 2½d., 1924–26, listed here, are from whole sheets completely without watermark.

98	**99**	**100** Simple Cypher

For type difference with T **101/2** see notes below the latter.

Die A	Die B

Dies of Halfpenny

Die A. The three upper scales on the body of the right hand dolphin form a triangle; the centre jewel of the cross inside the crown is suggested by a comma.

Die B. The three upper scales are incomplete; the centre jewel is suggested by a crescent.

Die A	Die B

Dies of One Penny

Die A. The second line of shading on the ribbon to the right of the crown extends right across the wreath; the line nearest to the crown on the right hand ribbon shows as a short line at the bottom of the ribbon. Die B. The second line of shading is broken in the middle; the first line is little more than a dot.

(Des Bertram Mackennal and G. W. Eve. Head from photograph by W. and D. Downey. Die eng J. A. C. Harrison)

1911–12. *Wmk* Imperial Crown, W **49**. Perf 15×14.

321	**98**	½d. pale green (Die A)			
		(22.6.11)	10·00	5·00	4·00
322		½d. green (Die A) (22.6.11)	8·00	4·00	4·00
		a. Error. Perf 14 (8.11)	—	£20000	£1000
		s. Optd "SPECIMEN" (22)		£800	
		Wi. Watermark inverted	£20000	—	£2000
323		½d. bluish green (Die A)	£400	£300	£180
324		½d. yellow-green (Die B)	18·00	12·00	1·50
		a. booklet pane No. 324×6			
		(8.11)	£350	£250	£175
		aw. booklet pane No. 324×6,			
		watermark inverted	£275	£200	£140
		s. Optd "SPECIMEN" (22)		£350	
325		½d. bright green (Die B)	13·00	8·00	1·50
		a. Watermark sideways	—	—	£5500
		Wi. Watermark inverted	35·00	20·00	7·50
326		½d. bluish green (Die B)	£260	£160	£100
327	**99**	1d. carmine-red (Die A)			
		(22.6.11)	10·00	4·50	2·50
		c. Watermark sideways	†	†	£17000
		s. Optd "SPECIMEN" (22)		£550	
		Wi. Watermark inverted	£2200	£1500	£1250
328		1d. pale carmine (Die A)			
		(22.6.11)	25·00	14·00	3·00
		a. No cross on crown	£1250	£850	£500
329		1d. carmine (Die B)	15·00	10·00	3·00
		a. Booklet pane, No. 329×6			
		(8.11)	£350	£250	£175
		aw. Booklet pane, No. 329×6,			
		watermark inverted	£275	£200	£140
		s. Optd "SPECIMEN" (22)		£550	
		Wi. Watermark inverted	35·00	20·00	7·50
330		1d. pale carmine (Die B)	15·00	10·00	4·00
		a. No cross on crown	£1100	£800	£500
331		1d. rose-pink (Die B)	£225	£125	45·00
332		1d. scarlet (Die B) (6.12)	80·00	45·00	18·00
		a. Booklet pane, No. 332×6			
		(8.11)	£550	£400	£275
		aw. Booklet pane, No. 332×6,			
		watermark inverted	£550	£400	£275
		s. Optd "SPECIMEN" (22)		£750	
		Wi. Watermark inverted	80·00	45·00	18·00
333		1d. aniline scarlet (Die B)	£375	£240	£110
		a. Booklet pane, No. 333×6			
		(8.11)	£2000	£1500	£1100
		aw. Booklet pane, No. 333×6,			
		watermark inverted	£2000	£1500	£1100
		Wi. Watermark inverted	£375	£240	£110

For note on the aniline scarlet No. 333 see below No. 343.

1912 (20 Sept). Booklet stamps. Wmk Royal Cypher (Simple), W **100**. Perf 15×14.

334	**98**	½d. pale green (Die B)	90·00	45·00	40·00
335		½d. green (Die B)	90·00	45·00	40·00
		a. Booklet pane, No. 334 ×6			
		(9.12)	£500	£375	£260
		aw. Booklet pane, No. 334 ×6,			
		watermark inverted	£500	£375	£260
		s. Optd "SPECIMEN" (22, 26)		£300	
		Wi. Watermark inverted	90·00	45·00	40·00
		Wj. Watermark reversed	£1750	£1100	£800
		Wk. Watermark inverted and			
		reversed	£1600	£1100	£800
336	**99**	1d. scarlet (Die B)	40·00	30·00	30·00
		a. Booklet pane, No. 336×6			
		(9.12)	£400	£275	£190
		aw. Booklet pane, No. 336×6,			
		watermark inverted	£400	£275	£190
		s. Optd "SPECIMEN" (22, 26)		£325	
		Wi. Watermark inverted	40·00	30·00	30·00
		Wj. Watermark reversed	£1750	£1100	£800
		Wk. Watermark inverted and			
		reversed	—	—	£850
337		1d. bright scarlet (Die B)	40·00	30·00	30·00

101

102

103 Multiple Cypher

107

108

No. 357a

No. 357ab

No. 357ac

Type differences

½d. In T **98** the ornament above "P" of "HALFPENNY" has two thin lines of colour and the beard is undefined. In T **101** the ornament has one thick line and the beard is well defined.

1d. In T **99** the body of the lion is unshaded and in T **102** it is shaded.

1912 (1 Jan). *Wmk* Imperial Crown, W **49**. Perf 15×14.

338	**101**	½d. deep green	28·00	15·00	8·00
339		½d. green	15·00	8·00	4·00
		s. Optd "SPECIMEN" (26)		£325	
340		½d. yellow-green	15·00	8·00	4·00
		a. No cross on crown	£190	£100	55·00
		Wi. Watermark inverted	£1750	£1100	£650
341	**102**	1d. bright scarlet	10·00	5·00	2·00
		a. No cross on crown	£150	£110	55·00
		b. Printed double, one albino	£375	£275	
		Wi. Watermark inverted	£650	£425	£400
342		1d. scarlet	10·00	5·00	2·00
343		1d. aniline scarlet*	£275	£175	£100
		a. No cross on crown	£2000	£1400	

*Our prices for the aniline scarlet 1d. stamps, Nos. 333 and 343, are for the specimens in which the colour is suffused on the surface of the stamp and shows through clearly on the back. Specimens without these characteristics but which show "aniline" reactions under the quartz lamp are relatively common.

1912 (Aug). *Wmk* Royal Cypher (*Simple*), W **100**. Perf 15×14.

344	**101**	½d. green	14·00	7·00	3·00
		a. No cross on crown	£325	£225	£175
		s. Optd "SPECIMEN" (26)		£550	
		Wi. Watermark inverted	£600	£375	£275
		Wj. Watermark reversed	£600	£375	£275
		Wk. Watermark inverted and reversed	20·00	12·00	20·00
345	**102**	1d. scarlet	15·00	8·00	4·50
		a. No cross on crown	£175	£100	50·00
		Wi. Watermark inverted	28·00	18·00	25·00
		Wj. Watermark reversed	£200	£125	£125
		Wk. Watermark inverted and reversed	20·00	12·00	20·00

1912 (Sept). *Wmk* Royal Cypher (*Multiple*), W **103**. Perf 15×14.

346	**101**	½d. green (Oct)	20·00	12·00	8·00
		a. No cross on crown	£300	£200	£150
		b. Imperf	£250	£175	
		c. Watermark sideways	†	†	£4000
		d. Printed on gummed side	—	—	†
		Wi. Watermark inverted	20·00	12·00	20·00
		Wj. Watermark reversed	22·00	15·00	20·00
		Wk. Watermark inverted and reversed	£160	£100	£110
347		½d. yellow-green	20·00	15·00	8·00
348		½d. pale green	20·00	15·00	8·00
349	**102**	1d. bright scarlet	25·00	18·00	10·00
350		1d. scarlet	25·00	18·00	10·00
		a. No cross on crown	£225	£150	60·00
		b. Imperf	£225	£150	
		c. Watermark sideways	£325	£190	£220
		d. Watermark sideways. No cross on crown	£1200	£750	
		Wi. Watermark inverted	55·00	30·00	35·00
		Wj. Watermark reversed	55·00	30·00	35·00
		Wk. Watermark inverted and reversed	£1600	£1000	£650

104

105

106

Die I

Die II

Two Dies of the 2d.

Die I.—Inner frame-line at top and sides close to solid of background. Four complete lines of shading between top of head and oval frame-line. These four lines do not extend to the oval itself. White line round "TWO-PENCE" thin.

Die II.—Inner frame-line further from solid of background. Three lines between top of head and extending to the oval. White line round "TWOPENCE" thicker.

(Des Bertram Mackennal (heads) and G. W. Eve (frames). Coinage head (½, 1½, 2, 3 and 4d.); large medal head (1d., 2½d.); intermediate medal head (5d. to 1s.); small medal head used for fiscal stamps. Dies eng J. A. C. Harrison) (Letterpress by Harrison & Sons Ltd., except the 6d. printed by the Stamping Department of the Board of Inland Revenue, Somerset House. The latter also made printings of the following which can only be distinguished by the controls: ½d. B.13; 1½d. A.12; 2d. C.13; 2½d. A.12; 3d. A12, B.13, C.13; 4d. B.13; 5d. B.13; 7d. C.13; 8d. C.13; 9d. agate B.13; 10d. C.13; 1s. B.13)

1912–24. *Wmk* Royal Cypher (*Simple*), W **100**. Chalk-surfaced paper (6d.). Perf 15×14.

351	**105**	½d. green (16.1.13)	3·00	1·00	1·00
		a. Partial double print (half of bottom row) (Control G15)	—	£25000	
		b. Gummed both sides	£27500	—	—
		c. Booklet pane, No. 351×6 (A.13)	£140	£120	95·00
		cw. Booklet pane, No. 351×6, watermark inverted	£140	£100	70·00
		s. Optd "SPECIMEN" (23, 26)		£150	
		Wi. Watermark inverted	4·00	3·00	1·50
		Wj. Watermark reversed	80·00	55·00	60·00
		Wk. Watermark inverted and reversed	6·00	4·00	3·50
352		½d. bright green	3·00	1·00	1·00
353		½d. deep green	10·00	5·00	2·00
354		½d. yellow-green	10·00	6·00	3·00
355		½d. very yellow (Cyprus) green (1914)	£13000	£9000	†
356		½d. blue-green	60·00	40·00	25·00
357	**104**	1d. bright scarlet (8.10.12)	3·00	1·00	1·00
		a. "Q" for "O" (R. 1/4) (Control E14)	£240	£175	£175
		ab. "Q" for "O" (R. 4/11) (Control T22)	£450	£350	£190
		ac. Reversed "Q" for "O" (R. 15/9) (Control T22)	£400	£300	£240
		ad. Inverted "Q" for "O" (R. 20/3)	£500	£375	£240
		b. *Tête bêche* (pair)	—	£80000	†

Embassy Philatelists
POSTAL AUCTIONS

AUCTIONS HELD FIVE TIMES PER YEAR.....CATALOGUES SENT FREE ON REQUEST

(Pl.225)

(SG 177a)

(SG 173g)

(MAGENTA)

(SG 346c)

('CHROME')

('CAMBRIDGE')

		c. Booklet pane, No. 357 ×6 (4.13)	£175	£120	85·00
		cw. Booklet pane, No. 357 ×6, Wmk inverted	£175	£120	85·00
		s. Optd "SPECIMEN" (23, 26).		£200	
		Wi. Watermark inverted	4·00	2·00	1·00
		Wj. Watermark reversed	£145	95·00	£110
		Wk. Watermark inverted and reversed	6·00	3·00	3·00
358		1d. vermilion	9·00	5·00	2·50
359		1d. pale rose-red	30·00	20·00	5·00
360		1d. carmine-red	20·00	11·00	5·00
361		1d. scarlet-vermilion	£180	£125	50·00
		a. Printed on back	£450	£300	†
362	105	1½d. red-brown (15.10.12)	10·00	6·00	1·50
		a. "PENCF" (R. 15/12)	£400	£300	£250
		b. Booklet pane. Four stamps plus two printed labels (2.24)	£800	£600	£500
		bw. Booklet pane. Four stamps plus two printed labels, watermark inverted	£775	£600	£500
		c. Booklet pane, No. 362 ×6 (10.18)	£200	£150	£100
		cw. Booklet pane, No. 362 ×6, watermark inverted	£200	£150	£100
		s. Optd "SPECIMEN" (23, 26).		£125	
		Wi. Watermark inverted	9·00	5·00	2·00
		Wj. Watermark reversed	70·00	50·00	50·00
		Wk. Watermark inverted and reversed	15·00	8·00	8·00
363		1½d. chocolate-brown	20·00	11·00	2·00
		a. No watermark	£375	£240	£240
364		1½d. chestnut	5·00	3·00	1·00
		a. "PENCF" (R. 15/12)	£175	£125	£110
365		1½d. yellow-brown	30·00	20·00	16·00
366	106	2d. orange-yellow (Die I) (20.8.12)	14·00	8·00	3·00
367		2d. reddish orange (Die I) (11.13)	10·00	6·00	3·00
368		2d. orange (Die I)	8·00	4·00	3·00
		a. Booklet pane. No. 368 ×6 (7.20)	£425	£350	£300
		aw. Booklet pane. No. 368 ×6, watermark inverted	£275	£275	£225
		s. Optd "SPECIMEN" (26)		£250	
		Wi. Watermark inverted	22·00	12·00	12·00
		Wj. Watermark reversed	25·00	15·00	15·00
		Wk. Watermark inverted and reversed	18·00	10·00	10·00
369		2d. brt orange (Die I)	8·00	5·00	3·00
370		2d. orange (Die II) (9.21)	8·00	5·00	3·50
		a. Booklet pane. No. 370 ×6 (8.21)	£500	£350	£300
		aw. Booklet pane. No. 370 ×6, watermark inverted	£500	£350	£300
		s. Optd "SPECIMEN" (15, 23).		£800	
		Wi. Watermark inverted	60·00	40·00	40·00
		Wk. Watermark inverted and reversed	£200	£140	£130
371	104	2½d. cobalt-blue (18.10.12)	22·00	12·00	4·00
371a		2½d. bright blue (1914)	22·00	12·00	4·00
372		2½d. blue	22·00	12·00	4·00
		s. Optd "SPECIMEN" (15, 23, 26)		£120	
		Wi. Watermark inverted	£120	85·00	85·00
		Wj. Watermark reversed	£100	65·00	65·00
		Wk. Watermark inverted and reversed	45·00	28·00	28·00
373		2½d. indigo blue* (1920)	£5000	£3500	£2500
373a		2½d. dull Prussian blue* (12.20)	£1850	£1500	£850
374	106	3d. dull reddish violet (9.10.12)	22·00	12·00	3·00
375		3d. violet	15·00	8·00	3·00
		s. Optd "SPECIMEN" (15, 23, 26)		£250	
		Wi. Watermark inverted	£160	95·00	£110
		Wj. Watermark reversed	£850	£500	£500
		Wk. Watermark inverted and reversed	40·00	30·00	30·00
376		3d. bluish violet (11.13)	20·00	9·00	3·00
377		3d. pale violet	17·00	10·00	3·00
378		4d. deep grey-green (15.1.13)	75·00	45·00	25·00
379		4d. grey-green	25·00	15·00	2·00
		s. Optd "SPECIMEN" (15, 23, 26)		£125	
		Wi. Watermark inverted	50·00	30·00	30·00
		Wj. Watermark reversed	£550	£350	£350
		Wk. Watermark inverted and reversed	£140	90·00	£100
380		4d. pale grey-green	40·00	25·00	5·00
381	107	5d. brown (30.6.13)	25·00	15·00	5·00

		s. Optd "SPECIMEN" (15, 23, 26).		£250	
		Wi. Watermark inverted	£1800	£1200	£1100
		Wj. Watermark reversed	†	†	—
		Wk. Watermark inverted and reversed	£500	£400	£400
382		5d. yellow-brown	25·00	15·00	5·00
		a. No watermark	£2000	£1200	
383		5d. bistre-brown	£275	£185	75·00
384		6d. dull purple (1.8.13)	45·00	25·00	10·00
		s. Optd "SPECIMEN" (15, 23, 26).		£200	
385		6d. reddish purple (8.13)	30·00	15·00	7·00
		a. Perf 14 (9.20)	£150	90·00	£110
		Wi. Watermark inverted	85·00	50·00	60·00
		Wj. Watermark reversed	£5500	£4500	
		Wk. Watermark inverted and reversed	£150	£100	£100
386		6d. deep reddish purple	90·00	50·00	5·00
387		7d. olive (1.8.13)	35·00	20·00	10·00
		s. Optd "SPECIMEN" (26)		£200	
		Wi. Watermark inverted	85·00	50·00	60·00
		Wj. Watermark reversed	†	†	—
		Wk. Watermark inverted and reversed	£6000	£5000	
388		7d. bronze-green (1915)	£120	70·00	25·00
389		7d. sage-green (1917)	£120	70·00	18·00
390		8d. black/yellow (1.8.13)	55·00	32·00	11·00
		s. Optd "SPECIMEN" (26)		£250	
		Wi. Watermark inverted	£220	£150	£150
		Wj. Watermark reversed	£375	£250	£250
		Wk. Watermark inverted and reversed	£7000	£5500	
391		8d. black/yellow-buff (granite) (5.17)	60·00	40·00	15·00
392	108	9d. agate (30.6.13)	30·00	15·00	6·00
		a. Printed double, one albino		£425	
		s. Optd "SPECIMEN" (26)		£425	
		Wi. Watermark inverted	£240	£175	£175
		Wk. Watermark inverted and reversed	£240	£175	£175
393		9d. deep agate	45·00	25·00	6·00
393a		9d. olive-green (9.22)	£225	£110	30·00
		as. Optd "SPECIMEN" (15, 23).		£750	
		aWi. Watermark inverted	£1200	£900	£825
		aWk. Watermark inverted and reversed	£1500	£1100	£1000
393b		9d. pale olive-green	£250	£120	40·00
394		10d. turquoise-blue (1.8.13)	40·00	22·00	6·00
		s. Optd "SPECIMEN" (15, 23, 26)		£425	
		Wi. Watermark inverted	£4200	£3000	£2500
		Wk. Watermark inverted and reversed	£475	£325	£300
394a		10d. deep turquoise-blue	£150	90·00	30·00
395		1s. bistre (1.8.13)	40·00	20·00	4·00
		s. Optd "SPECIMEN" (15, 23, 26, 31).		£375	
		Wi. Watermark inverted	£350	£250	£225
		Wk. Watermark inverted and reversed	£120	70·00	70·00
396		1s. bistre-brown	55·00	35·00	12·00
Set of 15			£475	£250	95·00

Imperf stamps of this issue exist but may be war-time colour trials.

† The impression of No. 361a is set sideways and is very pale. Nos. 362a and 364a occur on Plates 12 and 29 and are known from Controls L18, M18, M19, O19 and Q21. The flaws were corrected by 1921.

* No. 373 comes from Control O20 and also exists on toned paper.

No. 373a comes from Control R21 and also exists on toned paper, but both are unlike the rare Prussian blue shade of the 1935 2½d. Jubilee Issue.

Examples of the 2d., T **106** which were in the hands of philatelists, are known bisected in Guernsey from 27 December 1940 to February 1941.

See also Nos. 418/29.

1913 (Aug). *Wmk Royal Cypher* (*Multiple*), W **103**. Perf 15×14.

397	105	½d. bright green	£250	£150	£180
		a. Watermark sideways	†	†	£18000
		Wi. Watermark inverted	£1200	£900	
398	104	1d. dull scarlet	£350	£225	£225
		Wi. Watermark inverted	£1600	£1100	

Both these stamps were originally issued in rolls only. Subsequently sheets were found, so that horizontal pairs and blocks are known but are of considerable rarity.

109

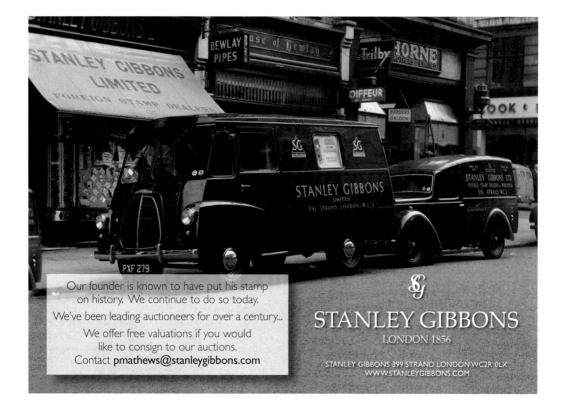

A   **110** Single Cypher

Note: All illustrations of re-entries on Nos. 399-417 are copyright GB Philatelic Publications Ltd and Bryan Kearsley and are reproduced with their permission.

Major Re-entries on 2s.6d.

No. 400a

Nos. 406/7a

No. 415b

No. 417a

(Des Bertram Mackennal. Dies eng J. A. C. Harrison. Recess)

High values, so-called "Sea Horses" design: T **109**. *Background around portrait consists of horizontal lines, Type A. Wmk Single Cypher, W* **110**. *P* 11×12.

1913 (30 June). Printed by Waterlow Bros & Layton.

399	**109**	2s.6d. deep sepia-brown	£850	£400	£200
		s. Optd "SPECIMEN" (23, 26).		£650	
400		2s.6d. sepia-brown	£600	£300	£150
		a. Re-entry (Plate 3, R. 2/1)	£2800	£1800	£800
		Wk. Watermark inverted and reversed	†	†	—
401		5s. rose-carmine	£1300	£625	£325
		s. Optd "SPECIMEN" (26)		£950	
402		10s. indigo-blue (1 Aug)	£2200	£1200	£475
		s. Optd "SPECIMEN" (23, 26, 29)		£1200	
403		£1 green (1 Aug)	£4800	£3500	£1400
		s. Optd "SPECIMEN" (23, 26).		£3250	
404		£1 dull blue-green (1 Aug)	£4800	£3500	£1600

399/404 **For well-centred, lightly used+35%*

1915 (Sept–Dec). Printed by De la Rue & Co.

405	**109**	2s.6d. deep yellow-brown (Oct)	£680	£375	£250
		Wi. Watermark inverted	£2400	£1500	
406		2s.6d. yellow-brown (inc. worn plates)	£550	£325	£225
		a. Re-entry (Plate 3, R. 2/1)	£3000	£2000	£950
		s. Optd "SPECIMEN" (23)		£1400	
		Wi. Watermark inverted	£1800	£1250	£875
		Wj. Watermark reversed	£1800	£1250	£1000
		Wk. Watermark inverted and reversed	£4750	£4000	
407		2s.6d. grey-brown (inc. worn plates)	£700	£400	£300
		a. Re-entry (Plate 3, R. 2/1)	£3000	£2000	£950
		Wi. Watermark inverted	£1800	£1250	£1000
		Wj. Watermark reversed	£1800	£1250	£1000
408		2s.6d. sepia (seal-brown)	£550	£325	£250
		Wi. Watermark inverted	£1800	£1250	£1000
		Wj. Watermark reversed	£1800	£1250	£1000
409		5s. bright carmine	£1100	£650	£400
		s. Optd "SPECIMEN" (23)		£1250	
		Wi. Watermark inverted	£6750	£4750	
		Wj. Watermark reversed	£6250	£4500	
		Wk. Watermark inverted and reversed	—	£18000	†
410		5s. pale carmine (worn plate)	£1400	£800	£500
411		10s. deep blue (Dec)	£5500	£3750	£1000
		s. Optd "SPECIMEN" (26)		£2800	
412		10s. blue	£4000	£3250	£875
		Wk. Watermark inverted and reversed	—	—	†
413		10s. pale blue	£4250	£3500	£875

405/13 **For well-centred, lightly used +45%*

No. 406/7 were produced from the original Waterlow plates as were all De La Rue 5s. and 10s. printings. Examples of No. 406/7, 410 and 411 occur showing degrees of plate wear. 412wi. one damaged mint example is recorded.

1918 (Dec)–**19**. Printed by Bradbury, Wilkinson & Co, Ltd.

413a	**109**	2s.6d. olive-brown	£350	£190	£100
		as. Optd "SPECIMEN" (15, 23, 26, 31, 32)		£1000	
414		2s.6d. chocolate-brown	£325	£160	75·00
415		2s.6d. reddish brown	£325	£160	75·00
415a		2s.6d. pale brown	£340	£175	85·00
		b. Major re-entry (Plate 3/5L, R. 1/2)	£1600	£1000	£500
416		5s. rose-red (1.19)	£475	£325	£135
		s. Optd "SPECIMEN" (15, 23, 26, 31, 32)		£1200	
417		10s. dull grey-blue (1.19)	£850	£475	£175
		a. Re-entry (Plate 1/3L, R. 1/1)	£2250	£1800	£1000
		s. Optd "SPECIMEN" (15, 23, 26, 31, 32)		£1400	

Set of 4 (inc. no. 403) £5800 £4000 £1500
413a/17 **For well-centred, lightly used +35%*

DISTINGUISHING PRINTINGS. Note that the £1 value was only printed by Waterlow.

Waterlow and De La Rue stamps measure exactly 22.1 mm vertically. In the De La Rue printings the gum is usually patchy and yellowish, and the colour of the stamp, particularly in the 5s., tends to show through the back. The holes of the perforation are smaller than those of the other two printers, but there is a thick perforation tooth at the top of each vertical side.

In the Bradbury Wilkinson printings the height of the stamp is 22.6 – 23.1 mm due to the use of curved plates. On most of the 22.6 mm high stamps a minute coloured guide dot appears in the margin just above the middle of the upper frame-line.

For (1934) re-engraved Waterlow printings see Nos. 450/2.

**UNITED KINGDOM OF GREAT BRITAIN
AND NORTHERN IRELAND**

111 Block Cypher

111a

The watermark Type **111a**, as compared with Type **111**, differs as follows: Closer spacing of horizontal rows (12½ mm instead of 14½ mm). Letters shorter and rounder. Watermark thicker. The dandy roll to produce watermark Type **111a** was provided by Somerset House in connection with experiments in paper composition undertaken during 1924–25. These resulted in a change from rag only paper to that made from a mixture including esparto and sulphite.

(Letterpress by Waterlow & Sons, Ltd (all values except 6d.) and later, 1934–35, by Harrison & Sons, Ltd (all values). Until 1934 the 6d. was printed at Somerset House where a printing of the 1½d. was also made in 1926 (identifiable only by control E.26). Printings by Harrisons in 1934–35 can be identified, when in mint condition, by the fact that the gum shows a streaky appearance vertically, the Waterlow gum being uniformly applied, but Harrisons also used up the balance of the Waterlow "smooth gum" paper)

1924 (Feb)–**26.** *Wmk Block Cypher, W* **111**. Perf 15×14.

418	**105**	½d. green.....................................	2·00	1·00	1·00
		a. Watermark sideways (5.24).................................	18·00	9·00	3·25
		aWi. Watermark sideways inverted.................................	£650	£450	
		b. Doubly printed.....................	£16000	£12000	†
		c. No watermark.....................	£6000	—	—
		d. Booklet pane. No. 418×6 (2.24)..................................	£120	85·00	60·00
		dw. Booklet pane. No. 418×6, watermark inverted..............	£120	85·00	60·00
		s. Optd "SPECIMEN" (15, 23, 30, 32).................................		90·00	
		Wi. Watermark inverted.............	7·00	3·50	1·00
419	**104**	1d. scarlet................................	2·00	1·00	1·00
		a. Watermark sideways...........	40·00	20·00	15·00
		b. Experimental paper, *W* **111a** (10.24).....................	40·00	22·00	
		c. Partial double print, one inverted.................................	—	—	
		d. Inverted "Q" for "O" (R. 20/3).................................	£850	£500	
		e. Booklet pane. No. 419×6 (2.24)..................................	£120	85·00	60·00
		ew. Booklet pane. No. 419×6, watermark inverted..............	£120	85·00	60·00
		s. Optd "SPECIMEN" (15, 23, 30, 32).................................		90·00	
		Wi. Watermark inverted.............	7·00	4·00	1·50
420	**105**	1½d. red-brown.......................	2·00	1·00	1·00
		a. *Tête-bêche* (pair)................	£750	£500	£800
		b. Watermark sideways (8.24)..................................	20·00	10·00	3·50
		bWi. Watermark sideways inverted.................................	—	£900	
		c. Printed on the gummed side.....................................	£1200	£750	
		d. Booklet pane. Four stamps plus two printed labels (3.24).............................	£300	£225	£190
		dw. Booklet pane. Four stamps plus two printed labels, watermark inverted.................	£300	£225	£190
		e. Booklet pane. No 420×6 (2.24)..................................	70·00	50·00	35·00
		ew. Booklet pane. No 420×6, watermark inverted..............	70·00	50·00	35·00
		f. Booklet pane. No 420×6, watermark sideways........	£14000	£10000	
		g. Experimental paper, *W* **111a** (10.24).....................	£160	£120	£120
		h. Double impression.............	—	—	†
		s. Optd "SPECIMEN" (15, 23, 30, 32).................................		90·00	
		Wi. Watermark inverted.............	3·50	2·00	1·00
421	**106**	2d. orange (Die II) (7.24)...........	4·00	2·50	2·50
		a. No watermark.....................	£2250	£1800	
		b. Watermark sideways (7.26)..................................	£210	£100	£100
		c. Partial double print............	—	£35000	†
422	**104**	2½d. blue (10.10.24)...............	10·00	5·00	3·00
		a. No watermark.....................	£3800	£2800	
		b. Watermark sideways.............	†	†	£18000
		s. Optd "SPECIMEN" (23, 32).		£550	
		Wi. Watermark inverted.............	£140	90·00	90·00
423	**106**	3d. violet (10.10.24)...............	20·00	10·00	2·50
		s. Optd "SPECIMEN" (23, 32).		£750	
		Wi. Watermark inverted.............	£140	90·00	90·00
424		4d. grey-green (10.10.24).........	28·00	12·00	2·50
		a. Printed on the gummed side	£6250	£4250	†
		s. Optd "SPECIMEN" (23, 32).		£650	
		Wi. Watermark inverted.............	£240	£150	£150
425	**107**	5d. brown (17.10.24)...............	40·00	20·00	3·00
		s. Optd "SPECIMEN" (23, 26, 32).................................		£140	
		Wi. Watermark inverted.............	£225	£150	£150
426		6d. reddish purple (*chalk-surfaced paper*) (9.24)..........	20·00	12·00	2·50
		Wi. Watermark inverted.............	90·00	60·00	60·00
		Wk. Watermark inverted and reversed...........................	£725	£450	£400
426a		6d. purple (6.26).....................	8·00	4·00	1·50
		as. Optd "SPECIMEN" (23, 26, 32).................................		£425	
		aWi. Watermark inverted.............	£140	90·00	90·00
427	**108**	9d. olive-green (11.11.24)........	40·00	12·00	3·50
		s. Optd "SPECIMEN" (23, 26, 32).................................		£140	
		Wi. Watermark inverted.............	£175	£120	£120
428		10d. turquoise-blue (28.11.24)..	85·00	40·00	40·00
		s. Optd "SPECIMEN" (23, 32).		£750	
		Wi. Watermark inverted.............	£3750	£2750	£2400
429		1s. bistre-brown (10.24)...........	50·00	22·00	3·00
		s. Optd "SPECIMEN" (23, 32).		£550	
		Wi. Watermark inverted.............	£600	£375	£375
Set of 12			£250	£110	60·00

There are numerous shades in this issue.

The 6d. on chalk-surfaced and ordinary papers was printed by both Somerset House and Harrisons. The Harrison printings have streaky gum, differ slightly in shade, and that on chalk-surfaced paper is printed in a highly fugitive ink. The prices quoted are for the commonest (Harrison) printing in each case.

112

Scratch across the Lion's nose
(left pane, R.1/1)

Tail to "N" of "EXHIBITION"
(Left pane, R.1/5)

(Des H. Nelson. Eng J. A. C. Harrison. Recess Waterlow)

1924–25. *British Empire Exhibition*. W **111**. Perf 14.

(a) Dated "1924" (23.4.24).

430	**112**	1d. scarlet......................................	12·00	10·00	11·00
		a. Scratch across the Lion's nose...	£225	£150	85·00
		b. Tail to "N" of EXHIBITION...	£225	£150	85·00
		s. Optd "SPECIMEN" (15, 23, 30)..		£1100	
431		1½d. brown.....................................	20·00	15·00	15·00
		s. Optd "SPECIMEN" (15, 23, 30).		£1100	
Set of 2			30·00	25·00	26·00
First Day Cover					£450

(b) Dated "1925" (9.5.25).

432	**112**	1d. scarlet................................	25·00	15·00	30·00
		s. Optd "SPECIMEN" (30).........		£1000	
433		1½d. brown................................	60·00	40·00	70·00
		s. Optd "SPECIMEN" (30).........		£1000	
Set of 2			80·00	55·00	£100
First Day Cover					£1700

113

114

115

118

119

120

116 St. George and the Dragon

121

122

117

Des J. Farleigh (T **113** and **115**), E. Linzell (T **114**) and H. Nelson (T **116**). Eng C. G. Lewis (T **113**), T. E. Storey (T **115**), both at the Royal Mint; J. A. C. Harrison, of Waterlow (T **114** and **116**). Letterpress by Waterlow from plates made at the Royal Mint, except T **116**, recess by Bradbury, Wilkinson from die and plate of their own manufacture

1929 (10 May). *Ninth U.P.U. Congress, London*.

(a) W **111**. *P* 15×14.

434	**113**	½d. green	3·00	2·25	2·25
		a. Watermark sideways	80·00	55·00	50·00
		b. Booklet pane. No. 434×6 (5.29)	£250	£200	£140
		bw. Booklet pane. No. 434×6, watermark inverted	£300	£225	£160
		Wi. Watermark inverted	35·00	15·00	12·00
435	**114**	1d. scarlet	3·00	2·25	2·25
		a. Watermark sideways	£140	95·00	90·00
		b. Booklet pane. No. 435×6 (5.29)	£250	£200	£140
		bw. Booklet pane. No. 435×6, watermark inverted	£300	£225	£160
		Wi. Watermark inverted	35·00	15·00	12·00
436		1½d. purple-brown	3·00	2·25	1·75
		a. Watermark sideways	90·00	60·00	55·00
		b. Booklet pane. Four stamps plus two printed labels	£500	£375	£325
		bw Booklet pane. Four stamps plus two printed labels, watermark inverted	£500	£375	£325
		c. Booklet pane. No. 436×6 (5.29)	85·00	60·00	42·00
		cw. Booklet pane. No. 436×6, watermark inverted	£110	80·00	60·00
		Wi. Watermark inverted	15·00	5·00	6·00
437	**115**	2½d. blue	28·00	10·00	10·00
		s. Optd "SPECIMEN" (32)		£3000	
		Wi. Watermark inverted	£3750	£2750	£1100

(b) W **117**. *P* 12.

438	**116**	£1 black	£1100	£750	£550
		s. Optd "SPECIMEN" (32, red opt)		£3000	
Set of 4 (to 2½d.)			35·00	15·00	14·50
First Day Cover (4 values)					£675
First Day Cover (5 values)					£14000

PRINTERS. All subsequent issues to No. 1919 were printed in photogravure by Harrison & Sons Ltd *except where otherwise stated.*

1934–36. W **111**. Perf 15×14.

439	**118**	½d. green (17.11.34)	1·00	50	50
		a. Watermark sideways	17·00	10·00	5·00
		aWi. Watermark sideways inverted	£600	£450	£150
		b. Imperf three sides	£7750	£5250	
		c. Booklet pane. No. 439×6 (1.35)	£120	85·00	60·00
		cw. Booklet pane. No. 439×6, watermark inverted	£130	95·00	65·00
		s. Optd "SPECIMEN" (23, 32)		£500	
		Wi. Watermark inverted	22·00	11·00	1·50
440	**119**	1d. scarlet (24.9.34)	1·00	50	50
		a. Imperf (pair)	£7000	£5000	
		b. Printed on gummed side	£1000	£750	
		c. Watermark sideways (30.4.35)	40·00	20·00	12·00
		cWi. Watermark sideways inverted	£190	£125	—
		d. Double impression	†	†	£24000
		e. Imperf between (pair)	£12500	£8500	
		f. Imperf (three sides) (pair)	£9500	£7000	
		g. Booklet pane. No. 440×6 (1.35)	£120	85·00	60·00
		gw. Booklet pane. No. 440×6, watermark inverted	£130	95·00	65·00
		s. Optd "SPECIMEN" (23, 32)		£600	
		Wi. Watermark inverted	20·00	9·00	3·00
441	**118**	1½d. red-brown (20.8.34)	1·00	50	50
		a. Imperf (pair)	£1700	£1250	
		b. Imperf (three sides) (lower stamp in vert pair)	£6750	£4800	
		c. Imperf between (horiz pair)			
		d. Watermark sideways	15·00	10·00	5·00
		dWi. Watermark sideways inverted			
		e. Booklet pane. Four stamps plus two printed labels (1.35)	£275	£200	£170
		ew. Booklet pane. Four stamps plus two printed labels, watermark inverted	£275	£200	£170
		f. Booklet pane. No. 441×6 (1.35)	42·00	30·00	21·00
		fw. Booklet pane. No. 441×6, watermark inverted	55·00	40·00	28·00
		s. Optd "SPECIMEN" (23, 32)		£650	
		Wi. Watermark inverted	8·00	4·00	1·00
442	**120**	2d. orange (19.1.35)	1·50	75	75
		a. Imperf (pair)	£7250	£5750	
		b. Watermark sideways (30.4.35)	£225	£125	90·00
		s. Optd "SPECIMEN" (30, 32)		—	
443	**119**	2½d. bright blue (18.3.35)	2·50	1·50	1·25
		s. Optd "SPECIMEN" (23)		£700	
444	**120**	3d. reddish violet (18.3.35)	3·00	1·50	1·25
		s. Optd "SPECIMEN" (23, 30)		£650	
		Wi. Watermark inverted	—	—	£9000
445		4d. deep grey-green (2.12.35)	4·00	2·00	1·25
		s. Optd "SPECIMEN" (23, 30)		£700	
		Wi. Watermark inverted	†	†	£9000
446	**121**	5d. yellow-brown (17.2.36)	13·00	6·50	2·75
		s. Optd "SPECIMEN" (23)		£650	
447	**122**	9d. deep olive-green (2.12.35)	20·00	12·00	2·25
		s. Optd "SPECIMEN" (23)		£650	
448		10d. turquoise-blue (24.2.36)	30·00	15·00	10·00
		s. Optd "SPECIMEN" (23, 32)		£700	
449		1s. bistre-brown (24.2.36)	40·00	15·00	1·25
		a. Double impression	—	—	†
		s. Optd "SPECIMEN" (23, 32)		£125	
Set of 11			95·00	50·00	20·00

Owing to the need for wider space for the perforations the size of the designs of the ½d. and 2d. were once, and the 1d. and 1½d. twice reduced from that of the first printings.

The format description, size in millimetres and SG catalogue number are given but further details will be found in the *Great Britain Specialised Catalogue*, Volume 2.

Description	Size	SG Nos.	Date of Issue
½d. intermediate format	18.4×22.2	—	19.11.34
½d. small format	17.9×21.7	439	14.2.35
1d. large format	18.7×22.5	—	24.9.34
1d. intermediate format	18.4×22.2	—	1934
1d. small format	17.9×21.7	440	8.2.35
1½d. large format	18.7×22.5	—	20.8.34
1½d. intermediate format	18.4×22.2	—	1934
1½d. small format	17.9×21.7	441	7.2.35
2d. intermediate format	18.4×22.2	—	21.1.35
2d. small format	18.15×21.7	442	1935

There are also numerous minor variations, due to the photographic element in the process.

Examples of 2d., T **120**, which were in the hands of philatelists are known bisected in Guernsey from 27 December 1940 to February 1941.

B   **123**

(Eng. J.A.C. Harrison. Recess Waterlow)

1934 (16 Oct). *T* **109** (re-engraved). Background around portrait consists of horizontal and diagonal lines, Type B. W **110**. Perf 11×12.

450	**109**	2s.6d. chocolate-brown	£150	80·00	40·00
		s. Optd "SPECIMEN" (23, 30).		£3250	
451		5s. bright rose-red	£400	£175	85·00
		s. Optd "SPECIMEN" (23, 30).		£3250	
452		10s. indigo	£500	£350	80·00
		s. Optd "SPECIMEN" (23, 30).		£3250	
Set of 3			£1000	£575	£190

There are numerous other minor differences in the design of this issue.

(Des B. Freedman)

1935 (7 May). *Silver Jubilee.* W **111**. Perf 15×14.

453	**123**	½d. green	1·00	1·00	1·00
		a. Booklet pane. No. 453×4 (5.35)	70·00	50·00	35·00
		aw. Booklet pane. No. 453×4, watermark inverted	80·00	60·00	42·00
		s. Optd "SPECIMEN" (23)		£1400	
		Wi. Watermark inverted	15·00	8·00	3·00
454		1d. scarlet	2·00	1·50	2·00
		a. Booklet pane. No. 454×4 (5.35)	60·00	45·00	32·00
		aw. Booklet pane. No. 454×4, watermark inverted	75·00	55·00	38·00
		s. Optd "SPECIMEN" (23)		£1400	
		Wi. Watermark inverted	15·00	8·00	4·00
455		1½d. red-brown	1·25	1·00	1·00
		a. Booklet pane. No. 455×4 (5.35)	25·00	18·00	13·00
		aw. Booklet pane. No. 455×4, watermark inverted	30·00	22·00	16·00
		s. Optd "SPECIMEN" (23)		£1400	
		Wi. Watermark inverted	5·00	3·00	1·50
456		2½d. blue	8·00	5·00	6·50
		s. Optd "SPECIMEN" (23)		£1750	
456a		2½d. Prussian blue	£18500	£13750	£15000
Set of 4			11·00	7·50	9·50
First Day Cover					£650

The 1d., 1½d. and 2½d. values differ from T **123** in the emblem in the panel at right.

Four sheets of No. 456a, printed in the wrong shade, were issued in error by the Post Office Stores Department on 25 June 1935. It is known that three of the sheets were sold from the sub-office at 134 Fore Street, Upper Edmonton, London, between that date and 4 July.

King Edward VIII

20 January – 10 December 1936

Further detailed information on the stamps of King Edward VIII will be found in Volume 2 of the Stanley Gibbons *Great Britain Specialised Catalogue*.

PRICES. From S.G. 457 prices quoted in the first column are for stamps in unmounted mint condition.

124   125

(Des H. Brown, adapted Harrison using a photo by Hugh Cecil)

1936. W **125**. Perf 15×14.

457	**124**	½d. green (1.9.36)	30	30
		a. Double impression.		
		b. Booklet pane. No. 457×6 (10.36)	30·00	
		bw. Booklet pane. No. 457×6, watermark inverted	45·00	
		s. Optd "SPECIMEN" (30, 32)	£775	
		Wi. Watermark inverted	10·00	5·00
458		1d. scarlet (14.9.36)	60	50
		a. Booklet pane. No. 458×6 (10.36)	25·00	
		aw. Booklet pane. No. 458×6, watermark inverted	40·00	
		s. Optd "SPECIMEN" (30, 32)	£775	
		Wi. Watermark inverted	9·00	5·00
459		1½d. red-brown (1.9.36)	30	30
		a. Booklet pane. Four stamps plus two printed labels (10.36)	£100	
		aw. Booklet pane. Four stamps plus two printed labels, watermark inverted	£100	
		b. Booklet pane. No. 459×6 (10.36)	15·00	
		bw. Booklet pane. No. 459×6, watermark inverted	15·00	
		c. Booklet pane. No. 459×2	30·00	
		cw. Booklet pane. No. 459×2, watermark inverted	30·00	
		d Imperf (pair)	£40000	
		s. Optd "SPECIMEN" (30, 32)	£775	
		Wi. Watermark inverted	1·00	1·00
460		2½d. bright blue (1.9.36)	30	85
		s. Optd "SPECIMEN" (30)	£850	
Set of 4			1·25	1·75

First Day Covers

1.9.36	½d., 1½d., 2½d. (457, 459/60)		£175
14.9.36	1d. (458)		£200

King George VI

11 December 1936 – 6 February 1952

Further detailed information on the stamps of King George VI will be found in Volume 2 of the Stanley Gibbons *Great Britain Specialised Catalogue*.

126 King George VI and Queen Elizabeth   **127**

Colon flaw (Cyl. 7 No dot, R. 10/1, later corrected)

(Des E. Dulac)

1937 (13 May). *Coronation.* W **127**. Perf 15×14.

461	**126**	1½d. maroon	30	30
		a. Colon flaw	70·00	
		s. Optd "SPECIMEN" (32)	£750	
First Day Cover				35·00

128   **129**   **130**

King George VI and National Emblems

(Des T **128/9**, E. Dulac (head) and E. Gill (frames). T **130**, E. Dulac (whole stamp))

1937–47. W **127**. Perf 15×14.

462	**128**	½d. green (10.5.37)	30	25
		a. Watermark sideways (1.38)	75	60
		ab. Booklet pane of 4 (6.40)	£110	
		b. Booklet pane. No 462×6 (8.37)	50·00	
		bw. Booklet pane. No 462×6. Watermark inverted	80·00	
		c. Booklet pane. No 462×2 (8.37)	£120	
		cw. Booklet pane. No 462×2. Watermark inverted	£120	
		s. Opt "SPECIMEN" (32)	10·00	60
		Wi. Watermark inverted	10·00	60
463		1d. scarlet (10.5.37)	30	25
		a. Watermark sideways (2.38)	20·00	9·00
		ab. Booklet pane of 4 (6.40)	£175	
		b. Booklet pane. No 463×6 (2.38)	65·00	
		bw. Booklet pane. No 463×6. Watermark inverted	£275	
		c. Booklet pane. No 463×2 (2.38)	£125	
		cw. Booklet pane. No 463×2. Watermark inverted	£125	
		s. Opt "SPECIMEN" (32)		
		Wi. Watermark inverted	40·00	3·00
464		1½d. red-brown (30.7.37)	30	25
		a. Watermark sideways (2.38)	1·25	1·25
		b. Booklet pane. Four stamps plus two printed labels (8.37)	£140	
		bw. Booklet pane. Four stamps plus two printed labels. Watermark inverted	£140	
		c. Booklet pane. No 464×6 (8.37)	60·00	

		cw. Booklet pane. No 464×6. Watermark inverted	£100	
		d. Booklet pane. No 464×2 (1.38)	35·00	
		dw. Booklet pane. No 464×2. Watermark inverted	50·00	
		e. Imperf three sides (pair)	£6500	
		s. Opt "SPECIMEN" (26)		
		Wi. Watermark inverted	15·00	1·25
465		2d. orange (31.1.38)	1·20	50
		a. Watermark sideways (2.38)	75·00	40·00
		b. Bisected (on cover)	†	50·00
		c. Booklet pane. No 465×6 (6.40)	£175	
		cw. Booklet pane. No 465×6. Watermark inverted	£425	
		s. Optd "SPECIMEN" (26)	£325	
		Wi. Watermark inverted	60·00	22·00
466		2½d. ultramarine (10.5.37)	40	25
		a. Watermark sideways (6.40)	75·00	35·00
		b. *Tête-bêche* (horiz pair)	£22000	
		c. Booklet pane. No 466×6 (6.40)	£150	
		cw. Booklet pane. No 466×6. Watermark inverted	£375	
		Wi. Watermark inverted	55·00	22·00
467		3d. violet (31.1.38)	5·00	1·00
		s. Optd "SPECIMEN" (26, 30)	£300	
468	**129**	4d. grey-green (21.11.38)	60	75
		a. Imperf (pair)	£9000	
		b. Imperf three sides (horiz pair)	£9500	
		s. Optd "SPECIMEN" (23)	£200	
469		5d. brown (21.11.38)	3·50	85
		a. Imperf (pair)	£8500	
		b. Imperf three sides (horiz pair)	£9000	
		s. Optd "SPECIMEN" (23)	£250	
470		6d. purple (30.1.39)	1·50	60
		s. Optd "SPECIMEN" (23)	£250	
471	**130**	7d. emerald-green (27.2.39)	5·00	60
		a. Imperf three sides (horiz pair)	£9000	
		s. Optd "SPECIMEN" (23)	£250	
472		8d. bright carmine (27.2.39)	7·50	80
		s. Optd "SPECIMEN" (23)	£250	
473		9d. deep olive-green (1.5.39)	6·50	80
		s. Optd "SPECIMEN" (23)	£250	
474		10d. turquoise-blue (1.5.39)	7·00	80
		aa. Imperf (pair)		
		aas. Optd "SPECIMEN" (23)	£250	
474*a*		11d. plum (29.12.47)	3·00	2·75
		as. Optd "SPECIMEN" (30)	£275	
475		1s. bistre-brown (1.5.39)	9·00	75
		s. Optd "SPECIMEN" (23, 33)	£160	
Set of 15			45·00	10·00

For later printings of the lower values in apparently lighter shades and different colours, see Nos. 485/90 and 503/8.

No. 465b was authorised for use in Guernsey from 27 December 1940 until February 1941.

Nos. 468b and 469b are perforated at foot only and each occurs in the same sheet as Nos. 468a and 469a.

No. 471a is also perforated at foot only, but occurs on the top row of a sheet.

First Day Covers

10.5.37	½d., 1d., 2½d. (462/3, 466)	45·00
30.7.37	1½d. (464)	45·00
31.1.38	2d., 3d. (465, 467)	£100
21.11.38	4d., 5d. (468/9)	65·00
30.1.39	6d. (470)	60·00
27.2.39	7d., 8d. (471/2)	85·00
1.5.39	9d., 10d., 1s. (473/4, 475)	£500
29.12.47	11d. (474a)	55·00

131   **132**

133

Mark in shield (R. 1/7)   Gashed diadem (R. 2/7)

Gashed crown (R. 5/5)   Broken stem (R. 1/4)

Blot on scroll   Scratch on scroll (R. 4/6)
(R. 2/5)

(Des E. Dulac (T **131**) and Hon. G. R. Bellew (T **132**).
Eng J. A. C. Harrison. Recess Waterlow)

1939–48. W **133**. Perf 14.

476	**131**	2s.6d. brown (4.9.39)	£100	8·00
		aa. Mark in shield	£190	85·00
		ab. Gashed diadem	£190	85·00
		ac. Gashed crown	£190	85·00
		as. Optd "SPECIMEN" (23)	£300	
476b		2s.6d. yellow-green (9.3.42)	15·00	1·50
		bs. Optd "SPECIMEN" (23)	£300	
477		5s. red (21.8.39)	20·00	2·00
		s. Optd "SPECIMEN" (23)	£300	
478	**132**	10s. dark blue (30.10.39)	£260	22·00
		aa. Broken stem	£275	80·00
		ab. Blot on scroll	£275	80·00
		ac. Scratch on scroll	£350	£100
		as. Optd "SPECIMEN" (23)	£500	
478b		10s. ultramarine (30.11.42)	45·00	5·00
		bs. Optd "SPECIMEN" (30)	£425	
478c		£1 brown (1.10.48)	25·00	26·00
		cs. Optd "SPECIMEN" (30)	—	
Set of 6			£425	60·00

First Day Covers

21.8.39	5s. (477)	£850
4.9.39	2s.6d. brown (476)	£1800
30.10.39	10s. dark blue (478)	£3250
9.3.42	2s.6d. yellow-green (476b)	£1750
30.11.42	10s. ultramarine (478b)	£3750
1.10.48	£1 (478c)	£325

The 10s. dark blue was pre-released in Northern Ireland on 3 October 1939.

134 Queen Victoria and
King George VI

(Des H. L. Palmer)

1940 (6 May). *Centenary of First Adhesive Postage Stamps.* W **127**. Perf 14½×14.

479	**134**	½d. green	30	75
		s. Optd "SPECIMEN" (23, 30)	—	
480		1d. scarlet	1·00	75
		s. Optd "SPECIMEN" (23, 30)	—	
481		1½d. red-brown	50	1·50
		s. Optd "SPECIMEN" (23, 30)	—	
482		2d. orange	1·00	75
		a. Bisected (on cover)	†	40·00
		s. Optd "SPECIMEN" (23, 30)	—	
483		2½d. ultramarine	2·25	50
		s. Optd "SPECIMEN" (23, 30)	—	
484		3d. violet	3·00	3·50
		s. Optd "SPECIMEN" (23, 30)	—	
Set of 6			8·75	5·25
First Day Cover				55·00

No. 482a was authorised for use on Guernsey from 27 December 1940 until February 1941.

1941–42. Head as Nos. 462/7, but with lighter background to provide a more economic use of the printing ink. W **127**. Perf 15×14.

485	**128**	½d. pale green (1.9.41)	30	30
		a. Tête-bêche (horiz pair)	£18000	
		b. Imperf (pair)	£8500	
		c. Booklet pane. No 485×6 (3.42)	30·00	
		cw. Ditto. Wmk inverted	45·00	
		d. Booklet pane. No 485×4 (1948)	—	
		e. Booklet pane. No 485×2 (12.47)	15·00	
		s. Optd "SPECIMEN" (23)	—	
		Wi. Watermark inverted	4·00	50
486		1d. pale scarlet (11.8.41)	30	30
		a. Watermark sideways (10.42)	5·00	4·50
		b. Imperf (pair)	£8000	
		c. Imperf three sides (horiz pair)	£8500	
		d. Booklet pane. No 486×4 (1948)	—	
		e. Booklet pane. No 486×2 (12.47)	40·00	
		s. Optd "SPECIMEN" (23)	—	
487		1½d. pale red-brown (28.9.42)	60	80
		a. Booklet pane. No 487×4 (1948)	—	
		b. Booklet pane. No 487×2 (12.47)	15·00	
		s. Optd "SPECIMEN" (23)	—	
488		2d. pale orange (6.10.41)	50	50
		a. Watermark sideways (6.42)	28·00	19·00
		b. Tête-bêche (horiz pair)	£18000	
		c. Imperf (pair)	£7500	
		d. Imperf pane*	£20000	
		e. Booklet pane. No 488×6 (3.42)	30·00	
		ew. Booklet pane. No 488×6. Watermark inverted	30·00	
		s. Optd "SPECIMEN" (23)	—	
		Wi. Watermark inverted	4·00	1·00
489		2½d. light ultramarine (21.7.41)	30	30
		a. Watermark sideways (8.42)	15·00	12·00
		b. Tête-bêche (horiz pair)	£18000	
		c. Imperf (pair)	£4800	
		d. Imperf pane*	£15000	
		e. Imperf three sides (horiz pair)	£7500	
		f. Booklet pane. No 489×6 (3.42)	20·00	
		fw. Booklet pane. No 489×6. Watermark inverted	20·00	
		s. Optd "SPECIMEN" (23)	—	
		Wi. Watermark inverted	1·50	1·00
490		3d. pale violet (3.11.41)	2·50	1·00
		s. Optd "SPECIMEN" (32)	—	
Set of 6			3·50	2·75

First Day Covers

21.7.41	2½d. (489)	45·00
11.8.41	1d. (486)	22·00
1.9.41	½d. (485)	22·00
6.10.41	2d. (488)	60·00
3.11.41	3d. (490)	£110
28.9.42	1½d. (487)	55·00

135   **136**

Extra porthole aft (Cyl.   Extra porthole fore   Seven berries (Cyl. 4
11 No dot, R. 16/1)   (Cyl. 8 Dot, R. 5/6)   No dot, R. 12/5)

(Des H. L. Palmer (T **135**) and R. Stone (T **136**))

1946 (11 June). *Peace.* W **127**. Perf 15×14.

491	**135**	2½d. ultramarine		20	20
		a. Extra porthole aft		95·00	
		b. Extra porthole fore		£120	
		s. Optd "SPECIMEN" (30)		—	
492	**136**	3d. violet		20	50
		a. Seven berries		35·00	
		s. Optd "SPECIMEN" (30)		—	
Set of 2				40	50
First Day Cover					65·00

137

138 King George VI and Queen Elizabeth

(Des G. Knipe and Joan Hassall from photographs by Dorothy Wilding)

1948 (26 Apr). *Royal Silver Wedding.* W **127**. Perf 15×14 (2½d.) or 14×15 (£1).

493	**137**	2½d. ultramarine		35	20
		s. Optd "SPECIMEN" (30)		—	
494	**138**	£1 blue		40·00	40·00
		s. Optd "SPECIMEN" (30)		—	
Set of 2				40·00	40·00
First Day Cover					£425

1948 (10 May). Stamps of 1d. and 2½d. showing seaweed-gathering were on sale at eight Head Post Offices in Great Britain, but were primarily for use in the Channel Islands and are listed there (see Nos. C1/2, after Royal Mail Post & Go Stamps).

139 Globe and Laurel Wreath

140 "Speed"

141 Olympic Symbol

142 Winged Victory

White blob on Lands End (Cyl. 3 No dot R. 7/3)

Spot below "9" (Cyl. 3 No dot R. 8/4)

Crown flaw (Cyl. 1 No dot, R. 20/2, later retouched)

(Des P. Metcalfe (T **139**), A. Games (T **140**), S. D. Scott (T **141**) and E. Dulac (T **142**))

1948 (29 July). *Olympic Games.* W **127**. Perf 15×14.

495	**139**	2½d. ultramarine		50	10
		s. Optd "SPECIMEN" (30)		£450	

496	**140**	3d. violet		50	50
		a. Crown flaw		75·00	
		s. Optd "SPECIMEN" (30)		£450	
497	**141**	6d. bright purple		3·25	75
		s. Optd "SPECIMEN" (30)		£450	
498	**142**	1s. brown		4·50	2·00
		a. White blob on Lands End		95·00	
		b. Spot below "9"		95·00	
		s. Optd "SPECIMEN" (30)		£450	
Set of 4				8·00	3·00
First Day Cover					45·00

143 Two Hemispheres

144 UPU Monument, Berne

145 Goddess Concordia, Globe and Points of Compass

146 Posthorn and Globe

Lake in Asia (Cyl. 3 Dot, R. 14/1)

Lake in India (Cyl. 2 No dot, R. 8/2)

Retouched background to "1/-" (R. 8/5)

(Des Mary Adshead (T **143**), P. Metcalfe (T **144**), H. Fleury (T **145**) and Hon. G. R. Bellew (T **146**))

1949 (10 Oct). *75th Anniv of Universal Postal Union.* W **127**. Perf 15×14.

499	**143**	2½d. ultramarine		25	10
		a. Lake in Asia		£145	
		b. Lake in India		£100	
		s. Optd "SPECIMEN" (31)		—	
500	**144**	3d. violet		25	50
		s. Optd "SPECIMEN" (31)		—	
501	**145**	6d. bright purple		50	75
		s. Optd "SPECIMEN" (31)		—	
502	**146**	1s. brown		1·00	1·25
		a. Retouched background to "1/-"		75·00	
		s. Optd "SPECIMEN" (31)		—	
Set of 4				1·50	2·50
First Day Cover					80·00

1950–52. 4d. as No. 468 and others as Nos. 485/**9**, but colours changed. W **127**. Perf 15×14.

503	**128**	½d. pale orange (3.5.51)		30	30
		a. Imperf (pair)		£7000	
		b. *Tête-bêche* (horiz pair)		£20000	
		c. Imperf pane*		£18000	
		d. Booklet pane. No 503×6 (5.51)		10·00	
		dw. Booklet pane. No 503×6. Watermark inverted		10·00	
		e. Booklet pane. No 503×4 (5.51)		15·00	
		ew. Booklet pane. No 503×4. Watermark inverted		15·00	
		f. Booklet pane. No 503×2 (5.51)		15·00	
		Wi. Watermark inverted		50	50
504		1d. light ultramarine (3.5.51)		30	30
		a. Watermark sideways (5.51)		1·10	1·25
		b. Imperf (pair)		£4800	
		c. Imperf three sides (horiz pair)		£6500	

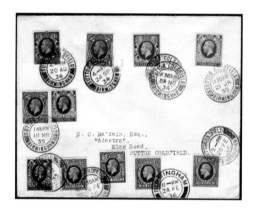

d.	Booklet pane. Three stamps plus three printed labels (3.52)	18·00	
dw.	Booklet pane. Three stamps plus three printed labels. Watermark inverted	18·00	
e.	Booklet pane. Three stamps plus three printed labels. Watermark inverted. Partial *tête-bêche* pane	£8500	
f.	Booklet pane. No 504×6 (1.53)	40·00	
fw.	Booklet pane. No 504×6. Watermark inverted	45·00	
g.	Booklet pane. No 504×4 (5.51)	20·00	
gw.	Ditto. Wmk inverted	35·00	
h.	Booklet pane. No 504×2 (5.51)	15·00	
Wi.	Watermark inverted	4·50	2·50

505	1½d. pale green (3.5.51)	65	60
a.	Watermark sideways (9.51)	3·25	5·00
b.	Booklet pane. No 505×6 (3.52)	30·00	
bw.	Booklet pane. No 505×6. Watermark inverted	40·00	
c.	Booklet pane. No 505×4 (5.51)	15·00	
cw.	Booklet pane. No 505×4. Watermark inverted	20·00	
d.	Booklet pane. No 505×2 (5.51)	15·00	
Wi.	Watermark inverted	6·00	1·00

506	2d. pale red-brown (3.5.51)	75	40
a.	Watermark sideways (5.51)	1·75	2·00
b.	*Tête-bêche* (horiz pair)	£18000	
c.	Imperf three sides (horiz pair)	£8000	
d.	Booklet pane. No 506×6 (5.51)	40·00	
dw.	Booklet pane. No 506×6. Watermark inverted	25·00	
Wi.	Watermark inverted	6·00	6·50

507	2½d. pale scarlet (3.5.51)	60	40
a.	Watermark sideways (5.51)	1·75	1·75
b.	*Tête-bêche* (horiz pair)		
c.	Booklet pane. No 507×6 (5.51)	8·00	
cw.	Booklet pane. No 507×6. Watermark inverted	10·00	
Wi.	Watermark inverted	2·00	1·25

508	**129**	4d. light ultramarine (2.10.50)	2·00	1·75
	a.	Double impression	†	£7000

Set of 6		4·00	3·25

* BOOKLET ERRORS. Those listed as "imperf panes" show one row of perforations either at the top or at the bottom of the pane of 6.
No. 504c is perforated at foot only and occurs in the same sheet as No. 504b.
No. 506c is also perforated at foot only.

First Day Covers

2.10.50	4d. (508)	£120
3.5.51	½d., 1d., 1½d., 2d., 2½d. (503/7)	55·00

147 HMS *Victory*

148 White Cliffs of Dover

149 St George and the Dragon

150 Royal Coat of Arms

(Des Mary Adshead (T **147/8**), P. Metcalfe (T **149/50**). Recess Waterlow)

1951 (3 May). W **133**. P 11×12.

509	**147**	2s.6d. yellow-green	7·50	1·00
	s.	Optd "SPECIMEN" (30)	£1000	
510	**148**	5s. red	35·00	1·00
	s.	Optd "SPECIMEN" (30)	£1000	
511	**149**	10s. ultramarine	15·00	7·50
	s.	Optd "SPECIMEN" (30)	£1000	
512	**150**	£1 brown	45·00	18·00
	s.	Optd "SPECIMEN" (30)	£1000	
Set of 4			£100	25·00
First Day Cover			£950	

151 "Commerce and Prosperity"

152 Festival Symbol

(Des E. Dulac (T **151**), A. Games (T **152**))

1951 (3 May). *Festival of Britain*. W **127**. P 15×14.

513	**151**	2½d. scarlet	20	15
514	**152**	4d. ultramarine	30	35
Set of 2			40	40
First Day Cover				38·00

Errors on stamps that make them...

LEGENDARY

BY APPOINTMENT TO
HER MAJESTY THE QUEEN
PHILATELISTS
STANLEY GIBBONS LTD
LONDON

STANLEY GIBBONS

LONDON 1856

Email gb@stanleygibbons.com or phone 020 7557 4464

STANLEY GIBBONS 399 STRAND LONDON WC2R 0LX | WWW.STANLEYGIBBONS.COM

Queen Elizabeth II

6 February 1952

Further detailed information on the stamps of Queen Elizabeth II will be found in Volumes 3, 4 and 5 of the Stanley Gibbons *Great Britain Specialised Catalogue*.

153 Tudor Crown　　　　**154**

155　　　　**156**　　　　**157**

158　　　　**159**　　　　**160**

Queen Elizabeth II and National Emblems

1½d. Extra white dot below "d" at left (Cyl. 13 dot, R.17/10

Two types of the 2½d.

Type I:— In the frontal cross of the diadem, the top line is only half the width of the cross.

Type II:— The top line extends to the full width of the cross and there are signs of strengthening in other parts of the diadem.

(Des Enid Marx (T **154**), M. Farrar-Bell (T **155/6**), G. Knipe (T **157**), Mary Adshead (T **158**), E. Dulac (T **159/60**). Portrait by Dorothy Wilding)

1952–54. W 153. Perf 15×14.

515	**154**	½d. orange-red (31.8.53)	25	15
		Wi. Watermark inverted (3.54)	2·00	2·00
516		1d. ultramarine (31.8.53)	30	20
		a. Booklet pane. Three stamps plus three printed labels	40·00	
		Wi. Watermark inverted (3.54)	6·00	3·00
517		1½d. green (5.12.52)	25	20
		a. Watermark sideways (15.10.54)	1·20	1·20
		b. Imperf pane*		
		c. Extra dot	28·00	
		Wi. Watermark inverted (5.53)	1·30	1·30

518		2d. red-brown (31.8.53)	30	20
		a. Watermark sideways (8.10.54)	2·00	2·00
		Wi. Watermark inverted (3.54)	30·00	22·00
519	**155**	2½d. carmine-red (Type I) (5.12.52)	30	15
		a. Watermark sideways (15.11.54)	12·00	12·00
		b. Type II (booklets) (5.53)	1·30	1·30
		bWi. Watermark inverted (5.53)	1·00	1·00
520		3d. deep lilac (18.1.54)	1·50	90
521	**156**	4d. ultramarine (2.11.53)	3·25	1·30
522	**157**	5d. brown (6.7.53)	1·00	3·50
523		6d. reddish purple (18.1.54)	4·00	1·00
		a. Imperf three sides (pair)	£3750	
524		7d. bright green (18.1.54)	9·50	5·50
525	**158**	8d. magenta (6.7.53)	1·25	85
526		9d. bronze-green (8.2.54)	23·00	4·75
527		10d. Prussian blue (8.2.54)	18·00	4·75
528		11d. brown-purple (8.2.54)	35·00	15·00
529	**159**	1s. bistre-brown (6.7.53)	80	50
530	**160**	1s.3d. green (2.11.53)	4·50	3·25
531		1s.6d. grey-blue (2.11.53)	14·00	3·75
Set of 17			£100	40·00

See also Nos. 540/56, 561/6, 570/94 and 599/618a.

* BOOKLET ERRORS. This pane of 6 stamps is completely imperf (see No. 540a, etc).

Stamps with *sideways watermark* come from left-side delivery coils and stamps with *inverted watermark* are from booklets.

For stamps as Types **154/5** and **157/60** with face values in decimal currency see Nos. 2031/3, 2258/9, **MS**2326, **MS**2367 and 2378/9.

First Day Covers

5.12.52	1½d., 2½d. (517, 519)	28·00
6.7.53	5d., 8d., 1s. (522, 525, 529)	60·00
31.8.53	½d., 1d., 2d. (515/16, 518)	60·00
2.11.53	4d., 1s.3d., 1s.6d. (521, 530/1)	£200
18.1.54	3d., 6d., 7d. (520, 523/4)	£125
8.2.54	9d., 10d., 11d. (526/8)	£250

161　　　　**162**

163　　　　**164**

(Des E. Fuller (2½d.), M. Goaman (4d.), E. Dulac (1s.3d.), M. Farrar-Bell (1s.6d.). Portrait (except 1s.3d.) by Dorothy Wilding)

1953 (3 June). *Coronation.* W **153**. Perf 15×14.

532	**161**	2½d. carmine-red	20	20
533	**162**	4d. ultramarine	80	40
534	**163**	1s.3d. deep yellow-green	3·00	1·00
535	**164**	1s.6d. deep grey-blue	6·50	2·00
Set of 4			10·00	3·50
First Day Cover				75·00

For a £1 value as Type **163** see Nos. **MS**2147 and 2380.

165 St Edward's Crown

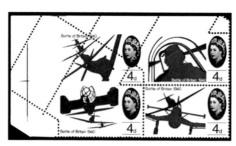

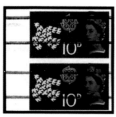

166 Carrickfergus Castle

167 Caernarvon Castle

168 Edinburgh Castle

169 Windsor Castle

(Des L. Lamb. Portrait by Dorothy Wilding. Recess Waterlow (until 31.12.57) and De La Rue (subsequently))

1955–58. W **165**. Perf 11×12.

536	**166**	2s.6d. black-brown (23.9.55)	15·00	2·00
		a. De La Rue printing (17.7.58)	30·00	2·50
		Wi. Watermark inverted	†	£3000
537	**167**	5s. rose-carmine (23.9.55)	40·00	4·00
		a. De La Rue printing (30.4.58)	65·00	10·00
538	**168**	10s. ultramarine (1.9.55)	90·00	14·00
		a. De La Rue printing. Dull ultramarine (25.4.58)	£225	22·00
539	**169**	£1 black (1.9.55)	£140	35·00
		a. De La Rue printing (28.4.58)	£350	65·00
Set of 4 (Nos. 536/9)			£250	50·00
Set of 4 (Nos. 536a/9a)			£600	90·00
First Day Cover (538/9)				£850
First Day Cover (536/7)				£650

See also Nos. 595/8a & 759/62.

On 1 January 1958, the contract for printing the high values, T **166** to **169**, was transferred to De La Rue & Co, Ltd. The work of the two printers is very similar, but the following notes will be helpful to those attempting to identify Waterlow and De La Rue stamps of the W **165** issue.

The De La Rue sheets are printed in pairs and have a -| or |-shaped guide-mark at the centre of one side-margin, opposite the middle row of perforations, indicating left and right-hand sheets respectively.

The Waterlow sheets have a small circle (sometimes crossed) instead of a "|-" and this is present in both side-margins opposite the 6th row of stamps, though one is sometimes trimmed off. Short dashes are also present in the perforation gutter between the marginal stamps marking the middle of the four sides and a cross is at the centre of the sheet. The four corners of the sheet have two lines forming a right-angle as trimming marks, but some are usually trimmed off. All these gutter marks and sheet trimming marks are absent in the De La Rue printings. De La Rue used the Waterlow die and no alterations were made to it, so that no difference exists in the design or its size, but the making of new plates at first resulted in slight but measurable variations in the width of the gutters between stamps, particularly the horizontal, as follows:

	Waterlow	De La Rue
Horiz gutters, mm	3.8 to 4.0	3.4 to 3.8

Later D.L.R. plates were however less distinguishable in this respect.

For a short time in 1959 the D.L.R. 2s.6d. appeared with one dot in the bottom margin below the first stamp. It is possible to sort singles with reasonable certainty by general characteristics. The individual lines of the D.L.R. impression are cleaner and devoid of the whiskers of colour of Waterlow's, and the whole impression lighter and softer.

Owing to the closer setting of the horizontal rows the strokes of the perforating comb are closer; this results in the topmost tooth on each side of De La Rue stamps being narrower than the corresponding teeth in Waterlow's which were more than normally broad.

Shades also help. The 2s.6d. D.L.R. is a warmer, more chocolate shade than the blackish brown of Waterlow; the 5s. a lighter red with less carmine than Waterlow's; the 10s. more blue and less ultramarine; the £1 less intense black.

The paper of D.L.R. printings is uniformly white, identical with that of Waterlow printings from February 1957 onwards, but earlier Waterlow printings are on paper which is creamy by comparison.

In this and later issues of T **166/9** the dates of issue given for changes of watermark or paper are those on which supplies were first sent by the Supplies Department to Postmasters.

A used example of No. 538a has been reported with watermark inverted.

1½d. Two white dots extending upwards from shamrock at left appearing as rabbit's ears. Occurs in booklets in position 2 or 5 in pane of 6

2½d. "Swan's head" flaw. Top of "2" is extended and curled. Occurs in booklets in positions 1 and 4 in pane of 6

1955–58. W **165**. Perf 15×14.

540	**154**	½d. orange-red (booklets 8.55, sheets 12.12.55)	20	15
		a. Part perf pane*	£5250	
		Wi. Watermark inverted (9.55)	45	40
541		1d. ultramarine (19.9.55)	30	15
		a. Booklet pane. Three stamps plus three printed labels	18·00	
		b. Tête-bêche (horiz pair)		
		Wi. Watermark inverted (9.55)	65	60
542		1½d. green (booklet 8.55, sheets 11.10.55)	25	30
		a. Watermark sideways (7.3.56)	35	70
		b. Tête-bêche (horiz pair)		
		c. Extra dot	28·00	
		d. "Rabbit's ears"	42·00	
		Wi. Watermark inverted (8.55)	75	70
543		2d. red-brown (6.9.55)	25	35
		aa. Imperf between (vert pair)	£4750	
		a. Watermark sideways (31.7.56)	55	70
		ab. Imperf between (horiz pair)	£4750	
		Wi. Watermark inverted (9.55)	11·00	9·00
543b		2d. light red-brown (17.10.56)	30	20
		ba. Tête-bêche (horiz pair)	—	
		bb. Part perf pane*	£6000	
		bc. Part perf pane*	£6000	
		bWi. Watermark inverted (1.57)	9·00	7·00
		a. Watermark sideways (5.3.57)	8·00	7·00
544	**155**	2½d. carmine-red (Type I) (28.9.55)	30	25
		a. Watermark sideways (Type I) (23.3.56)	1·50	1·80
		b. Type II (booklets 9.55, sheets 1957)	45	45
		ba. Tête-bêche (horiz pair)	—	
		bb. Imperf pane*	—	
		bc. Part perf pane*	£5250	
		bd. "Swan's head" flaw	95·00	
		bWi. Watermark inverted (9.55)	55	70
545		3d. deep lilac (17.7.56)	40	25
		aa. Tête-bêche (horiz pair)	£3000	
		a. Imperf three sides (pair)	£2750	
		b. Watermark sideways (22.11.57)	18·00	17·00
		Wi. Watermark inverted (1.10.57)	1·25	1·25
546	**156**	4d. ultramarine (14.11.55)	1·30	45
547	**157**	5d. brown (21.9.55)	6·00	6·00
548		6d. reddish purple (20.12.55)	4·50	1·20
		aa. Imperf three sides (pair)	£5250	
		a. Deep claret (8.5.58)	4·50	1·40
		ab. Imperf three sides (pair)	£5250	
549		7d. bright green (23.4.56)	50·00	10·00
550	**158**	8d. magenta (21.12.55)	7·00	1·30
551		9d. bronze-green (15.12.55)	20·00	2·75
552		10d. Prussian blue (22.9.55)	20·00	2·75
553		11d. purple-brown (28.10.55)	1·00	1·10
554	**159**	1s. bistre-brown (3.11.55)	22·00	65
555		1s.3d. green (27.3.56)	30·00	1·60
556	**160**	1s.6d. grey-blue (27.3.56)	23·00	1·60
Set of 18			£160	27·00

The dates given for Nos. 540/556 are those on which they were first issued by the Supplies Dept to postmasters.

In December 1956 a completely imperforate sheet of No. 543b was noticed by clerks in a Kent post office, one of whom purchased it against P.O. regulations. In view of this irregularity we do not consider it properly issued.

Types of 2½d. In this issue, in 1957, Type II formerly only found in stamps from booklets, began to replace Type I on sheet stamps.

*BOOKLET ERRORS. Those listed as "imperf panes" show one row of perforations either at top or bottom of the booklet pane; those as "part perf panes" have one row of 3 stamps imperf on three sides.

For Nos. 542 and 553 in Presentation Pack, see after No. 586.

170 Scout Badge and "Rolling Hitch"

171 "Scouts coming to Britain"

172 Globe within a Compass

(Des Mary Adshead (2½d.), P. Keely (4d.), W. H. Brown (1s.3d.))

1957 (1 Aug). *World Scout Jubilee Jamboree.* W **165**. Perf 15×14.

557	**170**	2½d. carmine-red	20	20
558	**171**	4d. ultramarine	50	50
559	**172**	1s.3d. green	3·00	2·00
Set of 3			3·50	2·50
First Day Cover				25·00

173

½d. to 1½d., 2½d., 3d. 2d. Graphite line arrangements (Stamps viewed from back)

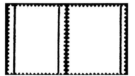

(Adapted F. Langfield)

1957 (12 Sept). *46th Inter-Parliamentary Union Conference.* W **165**. Perf 15×14.

560	**173**	4d. ultramarine	40	40
First Day Cover				£150

GRAPHITE-LINED ISSUES. These were used in connection with automatic sorting machinery, first introduced experimentally at Southampton. The graphite lines were printed in black on the back, beneath the gum; two lines per stamp, except for the 2d. In November 1959 phosphor bands were introduced (see notes after No. 598).

1d. Extra stop before "1d." at right. Occurs in sideways delivery coils (Roll No. 2). This was retouched on No. 571.

1d. Stop below "d" at left missing. Occurs on sideways delivery coils (Roll No. 3). The dot was added for No. 571.

1957 (19 Nov). Graphite-lined issue. Two graphite lines on the back, except 2d. value, which has one line. W **165**. Perf 15×14.

561	**154**	½d. orange-red	50	10
562		1d. ultramarine	70	60
		a. Extra stop	40·00	
		b. Stop omitted	40·00	
563		1½d. green	2·00	1·75
		a. Both lines at left	£1600	£600
564		2d. light red-brown	2·40	2·40
		a. Line at left	£700	£250
565	**155**	2½d. carmine-red (Type II)	8·50	7·00
566		3d. deep lilac	1·40	1·20
Set of 6			14·00	12·00
First Day Cover				90·00

No. 564a results from a misplacement of the line and horizontal pairs exist showing one stamp without line. No. 563a results from a similar misplacement. See also Nos. 587/94.

176 Welsh Dragon

177 Flag and Games Emblem

178 Welsh Dragon

3d. Short scale (Cyl. 2 Dot, R.1/1)   **3d.** Shoulder flaw (Cyl. 2 Dot, R. 12/2)

(Des R. Stone (3d.), W. H. Brown (6d.), P. Keely (1s.3d.))

1958 (18 July). *Sixth British Empire and Commonwealth Games,* Cardiff. W **165**. Perf 15×14.

567	**176**	3d. deep lilac	10	10
		a. Short scale	40·00	
		b. Shoulder flaw	40·00	
568	**177**	6d. reddish purple	30	30
569	**178**	1s.3d. green	1·00	1·00
Set of 3			1·20	1·20
First Day Cover				75·00

179 Multiple Crowns

½d. "d" at right joined to shamrock by white line. Occurs on vertical delivery coils (Roll No. 11).

1958–65. W **179**. Perf 15×14.

570	**154**	½d. orange-red (25.11.58)	10	10
		a. Watermark sideways (26.5.61)	75	75
		c. Part perf pane*	£4500	
		d. "d" joined to shamrock	30·00	
		Wi. Watermark inverted (11.58)	1·50	1·50
		k. Chalk-surfaced paper (15.7.63)	2·50	2·75
		kWi. Watermark inverted	2·75	3·00
		l. Booklet pane. No. 570a×4	7·50	
		m. Booklet pane. No. 570k×3 *se-tenant* with 574k	9·00	
		n. Booklet pane. No. 570a×2 *se-tenant* with 574l×2 (1.7.64)	2·25	
571		1d. ultramarine (booklets 11.58, sheets 24.3.59)	10	10
		aa. Imperf (vert pair from coil)	1·50	1·50
		a. Watermark sideways (26.5.61)	£5000	
		b. Part perf pane*	£6500	
		c. Imperf pane		
		d. *Tête-bêche* (horiz pair)		
		Wi. Watermark inverted (11.58)	50	50
		l. Booklet pane. No. 571a×4	12·00	
		m. Booklet pane. No. 571a×2 *se-tenant* with 575a×2 (1d. values at left) (16.8.65)	12·00	
		ma. Ditto. 1d. values at right	13·00	
572		1½d. green (booklets 12.58, sheets 30.8.60)	10	15
		a. Imperf three sides (horiz strip of 3)	£8500	
		b. Watermark sideways (26.5.61)	9·00	9·00
		c. *Tête-bêche* (horiz pair)		
		Wi. Watermark inverted (12.58)	1·50	1·25
		l. Booklet pane. No. 572b×4	40·00	
573		2d. light red-brown (4.12.58)	10	10
		a. Watermark sideways (3.4.59)	1·00	1·00
		Wi. Watermark inverted (10.4.61)	£140	70·00
574	**155**	2½d. carmine-red (Type II) (booklets 11.58, sheets 15.9.59)	10	20
		a. Imperf strip of 3	—	
		b. *Tête-bêche* (horiz pair)	—	
		c. Imperf pane*	—	
		ca. Part perf pane	£3750	
		d. "Swan's head" flaw	£100	

	Wi. Watermark inverted (Type II)		
	(11.58)	4·50	3·00
	e. Watermark sideways (Type I)		
	(10.11.60)	40	60
	ea. Imperf strip of 6		
	f. Type I (wmk upright) (4.10.61)	70	70
	k. Chalk-surfaced paper (Type II)		
	(15.7.63)	50	80
	kWi. Do. Watermark inverted (15.7.63) ..	75	1·30
	l. Watermark sideways (Type II)		
	(1.7.64)	70	1·30
575	3d. deep lilac (booklets 11.58, sheets		
	8.12.58)	20	15
	a. Watermark sideways (24.10.58)	50	55
	b. Imperf pane*	£4250	
	c. Part perf pane*	£4000	
	d. Phantom "R" (Cyl 41 no dot)	£375	
	Eda. Do. First retouch	30·00	
	Edb. Do. Second retouch	30·00	
	e. Phantom "R" (Cyl 37 no dot)	55·00	
	Eea. Do. Retouch	20·00	
	Wi. Watermark inverted (11.58)	50	55
	l. Booklet pane. No. 575a×4		
	(26.5.61)	3·25	
576 **156**	4d. ultramarine (29.10.58)	45	35
	a. Deep ultramarine†† (28.4.65)	15	15
	ab. Watermark sideways (31.5.65)	70	55
	ac. Imperf pane*	£5500	
	ad. Part perf pane*	£4500	
	ae. Double impression	—	
	al. Booklet pane. No. 576ab×4 (16.8.65)	3·25	
	aWi. Watermark inverted (21.6.65)	60	75
577	4½d. chestnut (9.2.59)	10	25
	Ea. Phantom frame	£100	
578 **157**	5d. brown (10.11.58)	30	40
579	6d. deep claret (23.12.58)	30	25
	a. Imperf three sides (pair)	£4000	
	b. Imperf (pair)	£4500	
580	7d. brt green (26.11.58)	50	45
581 **158**	8d. magenta (24.2.60)	60	40
582	9d. bronze-green (24.3.59)	60	40
583	10d. Prussian blue (18.11.58)	1·00	50
584 **159**	1s. bistre-brown (30.10.58)	75	30
585	1s.3d. green (17.6.59)	75	30
586 **160**	1s.6d. grey-blue (16.12.58)	5·00	40
Set of 17 (one of each value)		9·00	4·25
First Day Cover (577)			£250
*Presentation Pack***		£275	

*   BOOKLET ERROR. See note after No. 556.

** This was issued in 1960 and comprises Nos. 542, 553, 570/1 and
573/86. It exists in two forms: (a) inscribed "10s6d" for sale in the
U.K.; and (b) inscribed "$1.80" for sale in the U.S.A.

†† This "shade" was brought about by making more deeply etched
cylinders, resulting in apparent depth of colour in parts of the
design. There is no difference in the colour of the ink.

Sideways watermark. The 2d., 2½d., 3d. and 4d. come from coils
and the ½d., 1d., 1½d., 2½d., 3d. and 4d. come from booklets. In coil
stamps the sideways watermark shows the top of the watermark to
the left *as seen from the front of the stamp*. In the booklet stamps it
comes equally to the left or right.

Nos. 570k and 574k only come from 2s. "Holiday Resort"
experimental undated booklets issued in 1963, in which one page
contained 1 × 2½d. *se-tenant* with 3×½d. (See No. 570m).

No. 574l comes from coils, and the "Holiday Resort" experimental booklets dated
"1964" comprising four panes each containing two of these 2½d. stamps *se-tenant* vertically with two ½d. No. 570n. (See No. 570n).

2½d. imperf. No. 574a comes from a booklet with watermark
upright. No. 574da is from a coil with sideways watermark.

No. 574ca is partially perforated at top. Only one example has been
recorded, from which the top right stamp has been removed.

No. 574e comes from sheets bearing cylinder number 42 and is
also known on vertical delivery coils.

In 1964 No. 575 was printed from cylinder number 70 no dot and
dot on an experimental paper which is distinguishable by an additional
watermark letter "T" lying on its side, which occurs about four times in
the sheet, usually in the side margins, 48,000 sheets were issued.

No. 575 is known imperforate and *tête-bêche*. These came from
booklet sheets which were not issued (*price £70 per pair*).

Phantom "R" varieties

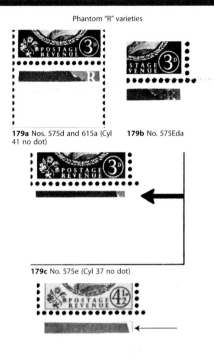

179a Nos. 575d and 615a (Cyl   **179b** No. 575Eda
41 no dot)

179c No. 575e (Cyl 37 no dot)

179d Phantom Frame variety Nos. 577Ea
and 616Eba

3d. An incomplete marginal rule revealed an "R" on cyls 37 and 41
no dot below R. 20/12. It is more noticeable on cyl 41 because of the
wider marginal rule. The "R" on cyl 41 was twice retouched, the first
being as illustrated here (No. 575Eda) and traces of the "R" can still be
seen in the second retouch.

No. 575d is best collected in a block of 4 or 6 with full margins in
order to be sure that it is not 615a with phosphor lines removed.

The retouch on cyl 37 is not easily identified: there is no trace of
the "R" but the general appearance of that part of the marginal rule is
uneven.

4½d. An incomplete marginal rule revealed a right-angled shaped
frame-line on cyl 8 no dot below R. 20/12. It occurs on ordinary and
phosphor.

DOLLIS HILL TRIAL STAMPS. From 1957 to 1972 trials were carried out
at the Post Office Research Station, Dollis Hill, London, to determine the
most efficient method of applying phosphor to stamps in connection with
automatic letter sorting. Stamps were frequently applied to "live" mail to
test sorting machinery.

The 2d. light red-brown and 3d. deep lilac stamps from these trials
exist on unwatermarked paper, *prices from £300* (2d.), *£350* (3d.), *mint
or used.*

WHITER PAPER. On 18 May 1962 the Post Office announced that a whiter
paper was being used for the current issue (including Nos. 595/8). This is
beyond the scope of this catalogue, but the whiter papers are listed in Vol.
3 of the Stanley Gibbons *Great Britain Specialised Catalogue*.

1958 (24 Nov)–**61**. Graphite-lined issue. Two graphite lines on the back,
except 2d. value, which has one line. *W* **179**. Perf 15×14.

587	**154**	½d. orange-red (15.6.59)	9·00	9·00
		Wi. Watermark inverted (4.8.59)	3·25	4·00
588		1d. ultramarine (18.12.58)	2·00	1·50
		a. Misplaced graphite lines (7.61)*	80	1·20
		b. Three graphite lines	65·00	60·00
		Wi. Watermark inverted (4.8.59)	1·50	2·00
589		1½d. green (4.8.59)	90·00	80·00
		Wi. Watermark inverted (4.8.59)	75·00	60·00
590		2d. light red-brown (24.11.58)	10·00	3·50
		a. One line at left	£975	
591	**155**	2½d. carmine-red (Type II) (9.6.59)	12·00	10·00
		Wi. Watermark inverted (21.8.59)	65·00	50·00
592		3d. deep lilac (24.11.58)	90	65
		a. Misplaced graphite lines (5.61)*	£550	£425
		b. One graphite line	£2500	—
		c. Three graphite lines	£150	£120
		Wi. Watermark inverted (4.8.59)	1·00	1·25
593	**156**	4d. ultramarine (29.4.59)	5·50	5·00
		a. Misplaced graphite lines (1961)*	£2400	

594		4½d. chestnut (3.6.59).....................................	6·50	5·00
Set of 8 (cheapest)			£110	70·00

Nos. 587/9 were only issued in booklets or coils (587/8).

* No. 588a (in coils), and Nos. 592a/c and 593a (all in sheets) result from the use of a residual stock of graphite-lined paper. As the use of graphite lines had ceased, the register of the lines in relation to the stamps was of no importance and numerous misplacements occurred – two lines close together, one line only, etc. No. 588a refers to two lines at left or right; No. 592a refers to stamps with two lines only at left and both clear of the perforations. No. 592b refers to stamps with a single line and Nos. 588b, 592c and 593a to stamps with two lines at left (with left line down perforations) and traces of a third line down the opposite perforations.

No. 592 Wi was included in 4s.6d. booklets, L15 and L16, dated April and June 1959. These represent production dates not issue dates.

(Recess D.L.R. (until 31.12.62), then B.W.)

1959–68. *W* **179.** Perf 11×12.

595	**166**	2s.6d. black-brown (22.7.59)...................	10·00	75
		Wi. Watermark inverted.............................	—	£3250
		a. B.W. printing (1.7.63).......................	35	40
		aWi. Watermark inverted..........................	£3250	£280
		k. Chalk-surfaced paper (30.5.68)........	50	1·50
596	**167**	5s. scarlet-vermilion (15.6.59)	45·00	2·00
		Wi. Watermark inverted.............................	£9000	£600
		a. B.W. ptg. *Red (shades)* (3.9.63).......	1·20	50
		ab. Printed on the gummed side...........	£1600	
		aWi. Watermark inverted..........................	£400	£300
597	**168**	10s. blue (21.7.59).................................	55·00	5·00
		a. B.W. ptg. *Bright ultramarine* (16.10.63).....................................	4·50	4·50
		aWi. Watermark inverted..........................	—	£3250
598	**169**	£1 black (23.6.59).................................	£120	12·00
		Wi. Watermark inverted.............................	—	£2500
		a. B.W. printing (14.11.63).....................	13·00	8·00
		aWi. Watermark inverted..........................	£15000	£3750
		k. Chalk-surfaced paper.........................	£5250	
Set of 4 (Nos. 595/8)			£195	17·00
Set of 4 (Nos. 595a/8a)			15·00	11·00
*Presentation Pack (1960)**			£1400	

The B.W. printings have a marginal Plate Number. They are generally more deeply engraved than the D.L.R. showing more of the Diadem detail and heavier lines on Her Majesty's face. The vertical perf is 11.9 to 12 against D.L.R. 11.8.

* This exists in three forms: (a) inscribed "$6.50" for sale in the U.S.A.; (b) without price for sale in the U.K.; (c) inscribed "£1 18s" for sale in the U.K.

See also Nos. 759/62.

PHOSPHOR BAND ISSUES. These are printed on the front and are wider than graphite lines. They are not easy to see but show as broad vertical bands at certain angles to the light.

Values representing the rate for printed papers (and when this was abolished in 1968 for second issue class mail) have one band and others two, three or four bands as stated, according to the size and format.

In the small size stamps the bands are on each side with the single band at left (*except where otherwise stated*). In the large size commemorative stamps the single band may be at left, centre or right, varying in different designs. The bands are vertical on both horizontal and vertical designs *except where otherwise stated*.

The phosphor was originally applied by letterpress but later usually by photogravure and sometimes using flexography, a relief printing process using rubber cylinders.

Three different types of phosphor have been used, distinguishable by the colour emitted under an ultra-violet lamp, the first being green, then blue and now violet. Different sized bands are also known. All these are fully listed in Vol. 3 of the Stanley Gibbons *Great Britain Specialised Catalogue*.

Varieties. Misplaced and missing phosphor bands are known but such varieties are beyond the scope of this Catalogue.

1959 (18 Nov). Phosphor-Graphite issue. Two phosphor bands on front and two graphite lines on back, except 2d. value, which has one band on front and one line on back. (a) *W* **165.** Perf 15×14.

599	**154**	½d. orange-red...................................	4·25	4·25
600		1d. ultramarine..................................	11·00	11·00
601		1½d. green..	4·50	4·50

(b) W **179.**

605	**154**	2d. light red-brown (1 band).................	6·00	4·25
		a. Error. *W* **165**	£200	£175
606	**155**	2½d. carmine-red (Type II).....................	22·00	18·00
607		3d. deep lilac....................................	12·00	8·00
608	**156**	4d. ultramarine..................................	20·00	16·00
609		4½d. chestnut.....................................	30·00	20·00
Set of 8			£100	80·00
Presentation Pack			£300	

Examples of the 2½d., No. 606, exist showing watermark W **165** in error. It is believed that phosphor-graphite stamps of this value with this watermark were not used by the public for postal purposes.

The Presentation Pack was issued in 1960 and comprises two each of Nos. 599/609. It exists in two forms: (a) inscribed "3s 8d" for sale in the U.K. and (b) inscribed "50c" for sale in the U.S.A.

1960 (22 June)–**67.** Phosphor issue. Two phosphor bands on front, except where otherwise stated. *W* **179.** Perf 15×14.

610	**154**	½d. orange-red....................................	10	15
		a. Watermark sideways (14.7.61).........	15·00	15·00
		b. "d" joined to shamrock....................	25·00	
		Wi. Watermark inverted (14.8.60)........	1·50	1·50
		l. Booklet pane. No. 610a×4.................	45·00	
611		1d. ultramarine..................................	10	10
		a. Watermark sideways (14.7.61).........	1·10	1·10
		Wi. Watermark inverted (14.8.60)........	65	65
		l. Booklet pane. No. 611a×4.................	10·00	
		m. Booklet pane. No. 611a×2 se-tenant with 615d×2† (16.8.65)........	18·00	
		ma. Booklet pane. No. 611a×2 se-tenant with 615dEa×2 (16.8.65)........	18·00	
		n. Booklet pane. No. 611a×2 se-tenant with 615b×2†† (11.67)........	10·00	
612		1½d. green..	15	15
		a. Watermark sideways (14.7.61).........	18·00	18·00
		Wi. Watermark inverted (14.8.60)........	25·00	22·00
		l. Booklet pane. No. 612a×4.................	50·00	
613		2d. light red-brown (1 band).................	22·00	22·00
613a		2d. light red-brown (2 bands) (4.10.61).......................................	10	15
		aa. Imperf three sides*** (pair)............	—	
		ab. Watermark sideways (6.4.67).........	1·00	1·00
614	**155**	2½d. carmine-red (Type II) (2 bands)*....	40	30
		Wi. Watermark inverted (14.8.60)........	£170	£140
614a		2½d. carmine-red (Type II) (1 band) (4.10.61).......................................	60	75
		aWi. Watermark inverted (3.62)............	50·00	42·00
614b		2½d. carmine-red (Type I) (1 band) (4.10.61).......................................	45·00	40·00
615		3d. deep lilac (2 bands).......................	60	55
		aa. Phantom "R" (Cyl 41 no dot)...........	55·00	
		Wi. Watermark inverted (14.8.60)........	50	90
		a. Imperf three sides (horiz pair)........	£2000	
		b. Watermark sideways (14.7.61).........	1·80	1·80
		l. Booklet pane. No. 615b×4.................	25·00	
615c		3d. deep lilac (1 band at right) (29.4.65).......................................	60	55
		cEa. Band at left..................................	60	70
		cWi. Watermark inverted (band at right) (2.67)................................	8·00	7·00
		cWia. Watermark inverted (band at left) (2.67)................................	80·00	80·00
		d. Watermark sideways (band at right) (16.8.65)...........................	5·50	5·00
		dEa. Watermark sideways (band at left)	5·50	5·00
		e. One centre band (8.12.66)...............	40	45
		eWi. Watermark inverted (8.67)............	4·00	4·00
		ea. Wmk sideways (19.6.67)..................	1·00	1·00
616	**156**	4d. ultramarine..................................	3·50	3·50
		a. Deep ultramarine (28.4.65).............	25	25
		aa. Part perf pane..............................	£5500	
		ab. Wmk sideways...............................	1·10	1·10
		aWi. Watermark inverted (21.6.65)........	75	75
		al. Booklet pane. No. 616ab×4..............	2·50	
616b		4½d. chestnut (13.9.61)........................	55	30
		Eba. Phantom frame............................	£100	
616c	**157**	5d. brown (9.6.67)..............................	55	35
617		6d. purple..	55	30
617a		7d. bright green (15.2.67).....................	70	50
617b	**158**	8d. magenta (28.6.67)..........................	70	55
617c		9d. bronze-green (29.12.66)...................	70	65
617d		10d. Prussian blue (30.12.66).................	1·00	1·00
617e	**159**	1s. bistre-brown (28.6.67)....................	1·00	35
618		1s.3d. green......................................	1·90	2·50
618a	**160**	1s.6d. grey-blue (12.12.66)...................	2·00	2·00
Set of 17 (one of each value)			10·50	8·00

The automatic facing equipment was brought into use on 6 July 1960 but the phosphor stamps may have been released a few days earlier.

The stamps with watermark sideways are from booklets except Nos. 613ab and 615ea which are from coils. No. 616ab comes from both booklets and coils.

No. 615a. See footnote after No. 586.

* No. 614 with two bands on the creamy paper was originally from cylinder 50 dot and no dot. When the change in postal rates took place in 1965 it was reissued from cylinder 57 dot and no dot on the whiter paper. Some of these latter were also released in error in districts of S.E. London in September 1964. The shade of the reissue is slightly more carmine.

*** This comes from the bottom row of a sheet which is imperf at bottom and both sides.

† Booklet pane No. 611m shows the 1d. stamps at left and No. 611ma the 1d. stamps at right.

†† Booklet pane No. 611n comes from 2s. booklets of January and March 1968. The two bands on the 3d. stamp were intentional because of the technical difficulties in producing one band and two band stamps se-tenant.

The Phosphor-Graphite stamps had the phosphor applied by letterpress but the Phosphor issue can be divided into those with the phosphor applied typographically and others where it was applied by photogravure. Moreover the photogravure form can be further divided into those which phosphoresce green and others which phosphoresce blue under ultra-violet light. From 1965 violet phosphorescence was introduced in place of the blue. All these are fully listed in Vol. 3 of the Stanley Gibbons *Great Britain Specialised Catalogue*.

Unlike previous one-banded phosphor stamps, No. 615c has a broad band extending over two stamps so that alternate stamps have the band at left or right (same prices either way). No. 615cWi comes from the 10s phosphor booklet of February 1967 and No. 615eWi comes from the 10s. phosphor booklets of August 1967 and February 1968.

Nos. 615a (Phantom "R") and 615Eba (Phantom frame), see illustrations following No. 586.

180 Postboy of 1660   **181** Posthorn of 1660

Broken mane (Cyl. 1 No dot, R. 17/2)

(Des R. Stone (3d.), Faith Jaques (1s.3d.))

1960 (7 July). *Tercentenary of Establishment of General Letter Office.* W **179** (sideways on 1s.3d.). Perf 15×14 (3d.) or 14×15 (1s.3d.).

619	**180**	3d. deep lilac	20	20
		a. Broken mane	70·00	
620	**181**	1s.3d. green	1.60	1.80
Set of 2			1.60	1.80
First Day Cover				50·00

182 Conference Emblem

(Des R. Stone (emblem, P. Rahikainen))

1960 (19 Sept). *First Anniversary of European Postal and Telecommunications Conference.* Chalk-surfaced paper. W **179**. Perf 15×14.

621	**182**	6d. bronze-green and purple	1·00	20
622		1s.6d. brown and blue	5·50	2·25
Set of 2			6·00	2·25
First Day Cover				50·00

SCREENS. Up to this point all photogravure stamps were printed in a 200 screen (200 dots per linear inch), but all later commemorative stamps are a finer 250 screen. Exceptionally No. 622 has a 200 screen for the portrait and a 250 screen for the background.

184 "Growth of Savings"

183 Thrift Plant   **185** Thrift Plant

(Des P. Gauld (2½d.), M. Goaman (others))

1961 (28 Aug). *Centenary of Post Office Savings Bank.* Chalk-surfaced paper. W **179** (sideways on 2½d.) Perf 14×15 (2½d.) or 15×14 (others).

A. "Timson" Machine

623A	**183**	2½d. black and red	10	10
		a. Black omitted	—	
624A	**184**	3d. orange-brown and violet	10	10
		a. Orange-brown omitted	£600	
		Eb. Perf through side sheet margin	35·00	38·00
625A	**185**	1s.6d. red and blue	1·00	1·20
Set of 3			1·00	1.20
First Day Cover				45·00

B. "Thrissell" Machine

623B	**183**	2½d. black and red	1·50	1·50
624B	**184**	3d. orange-brown and violet	30	30
		a. Orange-brown omitted	£1750	

2½d. TIMSON. Cyls 1E-1F. Deeply shaded portrait (brownish black).
2½d. THRISSELL. Cyls 1D-1B or 1D (dot)-1B (dot). Lighter portrait (grey-black).
3d. TIMSON. Cyls 3D-3E. Clear, well-defined portrait with deep shadows and bright highlights.
3d. THRISSELL. Cyls 3C-3B or 3C (dot)-3B (dot). Dull portrait, lacking in contrast.

Sheet marginal examples *without* single extension perf hole on the short side of the stamp are always "Timson", as are those with large punch-hole *not* coincident with printed three-sided box guide mark.

The 3d. "Timson" perforated completely through the right hand side margin comes from a relatively small part of the printing perforated on a sheet-fed machine.

Normally the "Timsons" were perforated in the reel, with three large punch-holes in both long margins and the perforations completely through both short margins. Only one punch-hole coincides with the guide-mark.

The "Thrissells" have one large punch-hole in one long margin, coinciding with guide-mark and one short margin imperf (except sometimes for encroachments).

186 C.E.P.T. Emblem   **187** Doves and Emblem

188 Doves and Emblem

(Des M. Goaman (doves T. Kurpershoek))

1961 (18 Sept). *European Postal and Telecommunications (C.E.P.T.) Conference, Torquay.* Chalk-surfaced paper. W **179**. Perf 15×14.

626	**186**	2d. orange, pink and brown	10	10
		a. Orange omitted	£15000	
		b. Pink omitted		
627	**187**	4d. buff, mauve and ultramarine	10	10
628	**188**	10d. turquoise, pale green and Prussian blue	20	20
		a. Pale green omitted	£24000	
		b. Turquoise omitted	7250	
Set of 3			30	30
First Day Cover				4·00

189 Hammer Beam Roof, Westminster Hall

190 Palace of Westminster

(Des Faith Jaques)

1961 (25 Sept). *Seventh Commonwealth Parliamentary Conference.* Chalk-surfaced paper. *W* **179** (sideways on 1s.3d.) Perf 15×14 (6d.) or 14×15 (1s.3d.).

629	**189**	6d. purple and gold	10	10
		a. Gold omitted	£2200	
630	**190**	1s.3d. green and blue	1·20	1·20
		a. Blue (Queen's head) omitted	£40000	
		b. Green omitted		
Set of 2			1·20	1·20
First Day Cover				25·00

191 "Units of Productivity"

192 "National Productivity"

193 "Unified Productivity"

3d. Lake in Scotland (Cyls. 2A-2B Dot, R. 1/3)

3d. Kent omitted (Cyls. 2C-2B No Dot, R. 18/2)

3d. Lake in Yorkshire (Cyls. 2C-2B Dot, R/19/1)

(Des D. Gentleman)

1962 (14 Nov). *National Productivity Year.* Chalk-surfaced paper. *W* **179** (inverted on 2½d. and 3d.). Perf 15×14.

631	**191**	2½d. myrtle-green and carmine-red (shades)	10	10
		Ea. Blackish olive and carmine-red	25	15
		p. One phosphor band. *Blackish olive and carmine-red*	60	50
632	**192**	3d. light blue and violet (shades)	25	25
		a. Light blue (Queen's head) omitted	£5750	
		b. Lake in Scotland	65·00	
		c. Kent omitted	70·00	
		d. Lake in Yorkshire	35·00	
		p. Three phosphor bands	1·50	80
633	**193**	1s.3d. carmine, light blue and deep green	80	80
		a. Light blue (Queen's head) omitted	£15000	
		p. Three phosphor bands	35·00	22·00
Set of 3 (Ordinary)			1·00	1·00
Set of 3 (Phosphor)			35·00	22·00
First Day Cover (Ordinary)				45·00
First Day Cover (Phosphor)				125·00

194 Campaign Emblem and Family

195 Children of Three Races

(Des M. Goaman)

1963 (21 Mar). *Freedom from Hunger.* Chalk-surfaced paper. *W* **179** (inverted). Perf 15×14.

634	**194**	2½d. crimson and pink	10	10
		p. One phosphor band	3·00	1·20
635	**195**	1s.3d. bistre-brown and yellow	1·00	1·00
		p. Three phosphor bands	30·00	23·00
Set of 2 (Ordinary)			1·00	1·00
Set of 2 (Phosphor)			30·00	23·00
First Day Cover (Ordinary)				25·00
First Day Cover (Phosphor)				40·00

196 "Paris Conference"

(Des R. Stone)

1963 (7 May). *Paris Postal Conference Centenary.* Chalk-surfaced paper. *W* **179** (inverted). Perf 15×14.

636	**196**	6d. green and mauve	20	20
		a. Green omitted	£5500	
		p. Three phosphor bands	3·00	2·75
First Day Cover (Ordinary)				7·50
First Day Cover (Phosphor)				30·00

197 Posy of Flowers

198 Woodland Life

"Caterpillar" flaw (Cyl. 3B Dot, R. 3/2)

(Des S. Scott (3d.), M. Goaman (4½d.))

1963 (16 May). *National Nature Week.* Chalk-surfaced paper. *W* **179**. Perf 15×14.

637	**197**	3d. yellow, green, brown and black	10	10
		a. "Caterpillar" flaw	75·00	
		p. Three phosphor bands	30	30
		pa. "Caterpillar" flaw	75·00	
638	**198**	4½d. black, blue, yellow, magenta and brown-red	15	15
		p. Three phosphor bands	1·40	1·40
Set of 2 (Ordinary)			20	20
Set of 2 (Phosphor)			1·50	1·50
First Day Cover (Ordinary)				12·00
First Day Cover (Phosphor)				35·00

Special First Day of Issue Postmark

	Ordinary	*Phosphor*
London E.C. (Type A)	12.00	35.00

This postmark was used on First Day Covers serviced by the Philatelic Bureau.

199 Rescue at Sea   **200** 19th-century Lifeboat

201 Lifeboatmen

(Des D. Gentleman)

1963 (31 May). *Ninth International Lifeboat Conference,* Edinburgh. Chalk-surfaced paper. *W* **179**. Perf 15×14.

639	**199**	2½d. blue, black and red	10	10
		p. One phosphor band	50	60
640	**200**	4d. red, yellow, brown, black and blue	20	20
		p. Three phosphor bands	50	60
641	**201**	1s.6d. sepia, yellow and grey-blue	1·50	1·50
		p. Three phosphor bands	48·00	28·00
Set of 3 (Ordinary)			1·50	1·50
Set of 3 (Phosphor)			48·00	28·00
First Day Cover (Ordinary)				20·00
First Day Cover (Phosphor)				55·00

Special First Day of Issue Postmark

		Ordinary Phosphor
London	65·00	80·00

This postmark was used on First Day Covers serviced by the Philatelic Bureau.

202 Red Cross   **203**

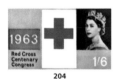

204

(Des H. Bartram)

1963 (15 Aug). *Red Cross Centenary Congress.* Chalk-surfaced paper. *W* **179**. Perf 15×14.

642	**202**	3d. red and deep lilac	25	25
		a. Red omitted	£16000	
		p. Three phosphor bands	1·10	1·00
		pa. Red omitted	—	
643	**203**	1s.3d. red, blue and grey	1·25	1·25
		p. Three phosphor bands	35·00	30·00
644	**204**	1s.6d. red, blue and bistre	1·25	1·25
		p. Three phosphor bands	35·00	27·00
Set of 3 (Ordinary)			2·50	2·50
Set of 3 (Phosphor)			65·00	55·00
First Day Cover (Ordinary)				20·00
First Day Cover (Phosphor)				60·00

Special First Day of Issue Postmark

1863 RED CROSS
CENTENARY
A CENTURY
OF SERVICE 1963

		Ordinary Phosphor
London E.C.	80·00	£110

This postmark was used on First Day Covers serviced by the Philatelic Bureau.

205 Commonwealth Cable

(Des P. Gauld)

1963 (3 Dec). *Opening of COMPAC* (Trans-Pacific Telephone Cable). Chalk-surfaced paper. *W* **179**. Perf 15×14.

645	**205**	1s.6d. blue and black	1·25	1·25
		a. Black omitted	£7000	
		p. Three phosphor bands	7·25	7·00
First Day Cover (Ordinary)				12·00
First Day Cover (Phosphor)				35·00

Special First Day of Issue Postmark

		Ordinary Phosphor
Philatelic Bureau, London E.C.1 (Type A)	12·00	35·00

PRESENTATION PACKS. Special Packs comprising slip-in cards with printed commemorative inscriptions and descriptive notes on the back and with protective covering, were introduced in 1964 with the Shakespeare issue. These are listed and priced. Issues of 1968-69 (British Paintings to the Prince of Wales Investiture) were also issued in packs with text in German for sale through the Post Office's German Agency and these are also quoted. Subsequently, however, the packs sold in Germany were identical with the normal English version with the addition of a separate printed insert card with German text. These, as also English packs with Japanese and Dutch printed cards for sale in Japan and the Netherlands respectively, are listed in Vols. 3 and 5 of the Stanley Gibbons *Great Britain Specialised Catalogue.*

206 Puck and Bottom (*A*   **207** Feste (*Twelfth Night*)
Midsummer Night's Dream)

208 Balcony Scene (*Romeo*   **209** Eve of Agincourt
and Juliet)   (*Henry V*)

210 Hamlet contemplating Yorick's Skull *Hamlet* and Queen Elizabeth II

(Des D. Gentleman. Photo Harrison & Sons (3d., 6d., 1s.3d., 1s.6d.). Des C. and R. Ironside. Recess B.W. (2s.6d.))

1964 (23 Apr). *Shakespeare Festival.* Chalk-surfaced paper. *W* **179**. Perf 11×12 (2s.6d.) or 15×14 (others).

646	**206**	3d. yellow-bistre, black and deep violet-blue (*shades*)	10	10
		p. Three phosphor bands	25	25
647	**207**	6d. yellow, orange, black and yellow-olive (*shades*)	20	20
		p. Three phosphor bands	75	75

648	**208**	1s.3d. cerise, blue-green, black and sepia (*shades*)...............	40	40
		Wi. Watermark inverted	£950	
		p. Three phosphor bands........................	2·00	2·00
		pWi. Watermark inverted	£400	
649	**209**	1s.6d. violet, turquoise, black and blue (*shades*)...............................	60	60
		Wi. Watermark inverted		£1300
		p. Three phosphor bands........................	2.50	2.50
650	**210**	2s.6d. deep slate-purple (*shades*)................	1·20	1·20
		Wi. Watermark inverted	£1000	
Set of 5 (Ordinary)...			2.00	2.00
Set of 4 (Phosphor)...			5·00	5·00
First Day Cover (Ordinary)				5·00
First Day Cover (Phosphor)				9·00
Presentation Pack (Ordinary)...			12·00	

The 3d. is known with yellow-bistre missing in the top two-thirds of the figures of Puck and Bottom. This occurred in the top row only of a sheet.

Special First Day of Issue Postmark

	Ordinary	*Phosphor*
Stratford-upon-Avon, Warwicks..	15·00	22·00

This postmark was used on First Day Covers serviced by the Philatelic Bureau, as well as on covers posted at Stratford P.O.

211 Flats near Richmond Park
Urban Development

212 Shipbuilding Yards, Belfast
Industrial Activity

213 Beddgelert Forest Park, Snowdonia *Forestry*

214 Nuclear Reactor, Dounreay
Technological Development

$2\frac{1}{2}d$

Short line under 2½d. (Cyl. 3D, various positions)

(Des D. Bailey)

1964 (1 July). *20th International Geographical Congress*, London. Chalk-surfaced paper. *W* **179**. Perf 15×14.

651	**211**	2½d. black, olive-yellow, olive-grey and turquoise-blue.......................	10	10
		a. Short line under 2½d.........................	14·00	
		p. One phosphor band............................	40	50
652	**212**	4d. orange-brown, red-brown, rose, black and violet..................................	30	30
		a. Violet (face value) omitted..................	275	
		c. Violet and red-brown (dock walls) omitted..	500	
		d. Red brown (dock walls) omitted.....	£850	
		Wi. Watermark inverted	£850	
		p. Three phosphor bands........................	1·20	1·20
653	**213**	8d. yellow-brown, emerald, green and black..	80	80
		a. Green (lawn) omitted...........................	£24000	
		Wi. Watermark inverted	£2200	
		p. Three phosphor bands........................	2·50	3·50
654	**214**	1s.6d. yellow-brown, pale pink, black and brown..	1.40	1.40
		Wi. Watermark inverted	55·00	
		p. Three phosphor bands........................	28·00	22·00
Set of 4 (Ordinary)...			2.00	2.00
Set of 4 (Phosphor)...			30·00	25·00
First Day Cover (Ordinary)				10·00
First Day Cover (Phosphor)				35·00
Presentation Pack (Ordinary)...			100.00	

A used example of the 4d. is known with the red-brown omitted.

Special First Day of Issue Postmark

	Ordinary	*Phosphor*
G.P.O. Philatelic Bureau, London E.C.1 (Type B).............	10·00	35·00

215 Spring Gentian   **216** Dog Rose

217 Honeysuckle   **218** Fringed Water Lily

Broken petal (Cyl. 3A Dot, R. 1/2)

Line through "INTER" (Cyl. 2A No dot, R. 1/1)

(Des M. and Sylvia Goaman)

1964 (5 Aug). *Tenth International Botanical Congress*, Edinburgh. Chalk-surfaced paper. *W* **179**. Perf 15×14.

655	**215**	3d. violet, blue and sage-green	25	25
		a. Blue omitted.......................................	£20000	
		b. Sage-green omitted..........................	£24000	
		c. Broken petal..	65·00	
		p. Three phosphor bands.......................	40	40
		pc. Broken petal.......................................	65·00	
656	**216**	6d. apple-green, rose, scarlet and green...	30	30
		p. Three phosphor bands.......................	2.50	2·75
657	**217**	9d. lemon, green, lake and rose-red.......	80	80
		a. Green (leaves) omitted.......................	£22000	
		b. Line through "INTER"...........................	65·00	
		Wi. Watermark inverted	75·00	
		p. Three phosphor bands.......................	4·50	4·50
		pb. Line through "INTER"..........................	65·00	
658	**218**	1s.3d. yellow, emerald, reddish violet and grey-green....................................	1·20	1·20
		a. Yellow (flowers) omitted...................	£45000	
		Wi. Watermark inverted	£2500	
		p. Three phosphor bands.......................	25·00	20·00
Set of 4 (Ordinary)...			2.00	2.00
Set of 4 (Phosphor)...			30·00	25·00
First Day Cover (Ordinary)				10·00
First Day Cover (Phosphor)				35·00
Presentation Pack (Ordinary)...			£125	

Unissued Goaman designs of the 3d and 9d values on perforated and gummed paper are known.

Special First Day of Issue Postmark

	Ordinary	*Phosphor*
G.P.O. Philatelic Bureau, London E.C.1 (Type B).............	10·00	35·00

219 Forth Road Bridge   **220** Forth Road and Railway Bridges

(Des A. Restall)

1964 (4 Sept). *Opening of Forth Road Bridge*. Chalk-surfaced paper. *W* **179**. Perf 15×14.

659	**219**	3d. black, blue and reddish violet.........	10	10
		p. Three phosphor bands.......................	50	50
660	**220**	6d. blackish lilac, light blue and carmine-red..	20	20
		a. Light blue omitted..............................	£6500	
		Wi. Watermark inverted	5·00	
		p. Three phosphor bands.......................	2.25	2.25
		pWi. Watermark inverted	£800	
Set of 2 (Ordinary)...			25	25
Set of 2 (Phosphor)...			2.50	2.50
First Day Cover (Ordinary)				3·00
First Day Cover (Phosphor)				10·00
Presentation Pack (Ordinary)...			£325	

	Ordinary	Phosphor
G.P.O. Philatelic Bureau, London E.C.1 (Type B)	15·00	20·00
North Queensferry, Fife	50·00	£130
South Queensferry, West Lothian	40·00	95·00

The Queensferry postmarks were applied to First Day Covers sent to a temporary Philatelic Bureau at Edinburgh.

221 Sir Winston Churchill

(Des D. Gentleman and Rosalind Dease, from photograph by Karsh)

1965 (8 July). *Churchill Commemoration.* Chalk-surfaced paper. *W* **179**. Perf 15×14.

I. "REMBRANDT" Machine

661	**221**	4d. black and olive-brown.......................	15	15
		Wi. Watermark inverted	3·00	
		p. Three phosphor bands	20	20

II. "TIMSON" Machine

661a	**221**	4d. black and olive-brown.......................	50	50

III. "L. & M. 4" Machine

662	–	1s.3d. black and grey	45	45
		Wi. Watermark inverted	£140	
		p. Three phosphor bands	1·00	1·00
Set of 2 (Ordinary)..			60	60
Set of 2 (Phosphor)..			1·10	1.10
First Day Cover (Ordinary)				4·75
First Day Cover (Phosphor)				5·00
Presentation Pack (Ordinary)...			40·00	

The 1s.3d. shows a closer view of Churchill's head.

Two examples of the 4d. value exist with the Queen's head omitted, one due to something adhering to the cylinder and the other due to a paper fold. The stamp also exists with Churchill's head omitted, also due to a paper fold.

4d. REMBRANDT, Cyls 1A-1B dot and no dot. Lack of shading detail on Churchill's portrait. Queen's portrait appears dull and coarse. This is a rotary machine which is sheet-fed.

4d. TIMSON. Cyls 5A-6B no dot. More detail on Churchill's portrait – furrow on forehead, his left eyebrow fully drawn and more shading on cheek. Queen's portrait lighter and sharper. This is a reel-fed two-colour 12-in. wide rotary machine and the differences in impressions are due to the greater pressure applied by this machine.

1s.3d. Cyls 1A-1B no dot. The "Linotype and Machinery No. 4" machine is an ordinary sheet-fed rotary press machine. Besides being used for printing the 1s.3d. stamps it was also employed for overprinting the phosphor bands on both values.

	Ordinary	Phosphor
G.P.O. Philatelic Bureau, London E.C.1 (Type B)	4.75	5.00

A First Day of Issue handstamp was provided at Bladon, Oxford, for this issue.

222 Simon de Montfort's Seal

223 Parliament Buildings
(after engraving by Hollar, 1647)

(Des S. Black (6d.), R. Guyatt (2s.6d.))

1965 (19 July). *700th Anniversary of Simon de Montfort's Parliament.* Chalk-surfaced paper. *W* **179**. Perf 15×14.

663	**222**	6d. olive-green.....................................	10	10
		p. Three phosphor bands.....................	50	50
664	**223**	2s.6d. black, grey and pale drab................	40	40
		Wi. Watermark inverted	60·00	
Set of 2 (Ordinary)..			40	40
First Day Cover (Ordinary)				6·00
First Day Cover (Phosphor)				15·00
Presentation Pack (Ordinary)...			65·00	

	Ordinary
G.P.O. Philatelic Bureau, London E.C.1 (Type B)	6·00

A First Day of Issue handstamp was provided at Evesham, Worcs, for this issue.

224 Bandsmen and Banner   **225** Three Salvationists

(Des M. Farrar-Bell (3d.), G. Trenaman (1s.6d.))

1965 (9 Aug). *Salvation Army Centenary.* Chalk-surfaced paper. *W* **179**. Perf 15×14.

665	**224**	3d. indigo, grey-blue, cerise, yellow and brown................................	10	10
		p. One phosphor band..........................	20	20
666	**225**	1s.6d. red, blue, yellow and brown............	60	60
		p. Three phosphor bands	90	90
Set of 2 (Ordinary)..			50	50
Set of 2 (Phosphor)..			1.00	1.00
First Day Cover (Ordinary)				10·00
First Day Cover (Phosphor)				22·00

The Philatelic Bureau did not provide First Day Cover services for Nos. 665/70.

226 Lister's Carbolic Spray   **227** Lister and Chemical Symbols

(Des P. Gauld (4d.), F. Ariss (1s.))

1965 (1 Sept). *Centenary of Joseph Lister's Discovery of Antiseptic Surgery.* Chalk-surfaced paper. *W* **179**. Perf 15×14.

667	**226**	4d. indigo, brown-red and grey-black.	10	10
		a. Brown-red (tube) omitted................	600	
		b. Indigo omitted................................	£7000	
		p. Three phosphor bands....................	25	25
		pa. Brown-red (tube) omitted..............	£6750	
668	**227**	1s. black, purple and new blue	40	40
		Wi. Watermark inverted	£675	
		p. Three phosphor bands	1·00	1·00
		pWi. Watermark inverted	£550	
Set of 2 (Ordinary)..			45	45
Set of 2 (Phosphor)..			1·10	1·10
First Day Cover (Ordinary)				5·00
First Day Cover (Phosphor)				9·00

228 Trinidad Carnival Dancers   **229** Canadian Folk-dancers

(Des D. Gentleman and Rosalind Dease)

1965 (1 Sept). *Commonwealth Arts Festival.* Chalk-surfaced paper. *W* **179**. Perf 15×14.

669	**228**	6d. black and orange..................................	10	10
		p. Three phosphor bands......................	40	40
670	**229**	1s.6d. black and light reddish violet	40	40
		p. Three phosphor bands......................	1·20	1·20
Set of 2 (Ordinary)..			45	45
Set of 2 (Phosphor)..			1·50	1·50
First Day Cover (Ordinary)				7·00
First Day Cover (Phosphor)				14·00

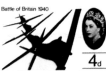 

230 Flight of Supermarine Spitfires   **231** Pilot in Hawker Hurricane Mk I

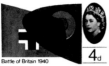

232 Wing-tips of Supermarine Spitfire and Messerschmitt Bf 109

233 Supermarine Spitfires attacking Heinkel He-111H Bomber

234 Supermarine Spitfire attacking Junkers Ju 87B "Stuka" Dive-bomber

235 Hawker Hurricanes Mk I over Wreck of Dornier Do-17Z Bomber

236 Anti-aircraft Artillery in Action

237 Air-battle over St Paul's Cathedral

(Des D. Gentleman and Rosalind Dease (4d.×6 and 1s.3d.), A. Restall (9d.))

1965 (13 Sept). *25th Anniv of Battle of Britain*. Chalk-surfaced paper. W **179**. Perf 15×14.

671	**230**	4d. yellow-olive and black		25	25
		a. Block of 6. Nos. 671/6		2·50	2·50
		p. Three phosphor bands		40	40
		pa. Block of 6. Nos. 671p/6p		3·75	3·75
672	**231**	4d. yellow-olive, olive-grey and black		25	25
		p. Three phosphor bands		40	40
673	**232**	4d. red, new blue, yellow-olive, olive-grey and black		25	25
		p. Three phosphor bands		40	40
674	**233**	4d. olive-grey, yellow-olive and black		25	25
		p. Three phosphor bands		40	40
675	**234**	4d. olive-grey, yellow-olive and black		25	25
		p. Three phosphor bands		40	40
676	**235**	4d. olive-grey, yellow-olive, new blue and black		25	25
		a. New blue omitted		†	£6500
		p. Three phosphor bands		40	40
677	**236**	9d. bluish violet, orange and slate purple		1·70	1·70
		Wi. Watermark inverted		£100	
		p. Three phosphor bands		2·00	2·00
6/8	**237**	1s.3d. Lt grey, dp grey, black, Lt blue and bright blue		1·70	1·70
		a. Face value omitted*		£1500	
		Wi. Watermark inverted		£190	
		p. Three phosphor bands		2·00	2·00
		pWi. Watermark inverted		5·00	
Set of 8 (Ordinary)				5·50	5·50
Set of 8 (Phosphor)				7·00	7·00
First Day Cover (Ordinary)					10·00
First Day Cover (Phosphor)					15·00
Presentation Pack (Ordinary)				40·00	

Nos. 671/6 were issued together *se-tenant* in blocks of 6 (3×2) within the sheet. No. 676a is only known commercially used on cover from Truro.

*No. 678a is caused by a 12 mm downward shift of black which resulted in the value being omitted from the top row of one sheet.

Special First Day of Issue Postmark

	Ordinary	Phosphor
G.P.O. Philatelic Bureau, London E.C.1 (Type C)	10·00	15·00

238 Tower and Georgian Buildings

239 Tower and "Nash" Terrace, Regent's Park

(Des C. Abbott)

1965 (8 Oct). *Opening of Post Office Tower*. Chalk-surfaced paper. W **179** (sideways on 3d.). Perf 14×15 (3d.) or 15×14 (1s.3d.).

679	**238**	3d. olive-yellow, new blue and bronze-green		10	10
		a. Olive-yellow (Tower) omitted		£6000	£2250
		p. One phosphor band at right		15	15
		pEa. Band at left		15	15
		pEb. Horiz pair. Nos. 679p/pEa		30	50
680	**239**	1s.3d. bronze-green, yellow-green and blue		20	20
		Wi. Watermark inverted		£175	
		p. Three phosphor bands		30	30
		pWi. Watermark inverted		£200	
Set of 2 (Ordinary)				25	25
Set of 2 (Phosphor)				40	40
First Day Cover (Ordinary)					2·50
First Day Cover (Phosphor)					4·75
Presentation Pack (Ordinary)				12·50	
Presentation Pack (Phosphor)				12·50	

The one phosphor band on No. 679p was produced by printing broad phosphor bands across alternate vertical perforations. Individual stamps show the band at right or left.

Special First Day of Issue Postmark

	Ordinary	Phosphor
G.P.O. Philatelic Bureau, London E.C.1 (Type C)	2·50	4·75

The Philatelic Bureau did not provide First Day Cover services for Nos. 681/4

240 U.N. Emblem

241 I.C.Y. Emblem

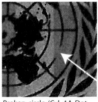

Broken circle (Cyl. 1A Dot, R. 11/4)

Lake in Russia (Cyl. 1A Dot, R. 19/3)

(Des J. Matthews)

1965 (25 Oct). *20th Anniv of U.N.O. and International Co-operation Year*. Chalk-surfaced paper. W **179**. Perf 15×14.

681	**240**	3d. black, yellow-orange and light blue		10	10
		a. Broken circle		65·00	
		b. Lake in Russia		65·00	
		p. One phosphor band		25	25
		pa. Broken circle		65·00	
		pb. Lake in Russia		65·00	
682	**241**	1s.6d. black, brt purple and light blue		35	35
		Wi. Watermark inverted			£2200
		p. Three phosphor bands		1·00	1·00
Set of 2 (Ordinary)				40	40
Set of 2 (Phosphor)				1·10	1·10
First Day Cover (Ordinary)					5·00
First Day Cover (Phosphor)					9·00

242 Telecommunications Network

243 Radio Waves and Switchboard

1s.6d. Red pin with arm (Cyl. 1D, R. 1/4)

(Des A. Restall)

1965 (15 Nov). *International Telecommunications Union Centenary.* Chalk-surfaced paper. *W* **179**. Perf 15×14.

683	**242**	9d. red, ultramarine, deep slate, violet, black and pink	20	20
		Wi. Watermark inverted	30·00	
		p. Three phosphor bands	75	75
		pWi. Watermark inverted	£110	
684	**243**	1s.6d. red, greenish blue, indigo, black and light pink	40	40
		a. Light pink omitted	£4000	£2500
		b. Red pin with arm	—	
		Wi. Watermark inverted	£300	
		p. Three phosphor bands	2.00	2.00
		pb. Red pin with arm	35·00	
Set of 2 (Ordinary)			50	50
Set of 2 (Phosphor)			2.50	2·50
First Day Cover (Ordinary)				8·00
First Day Cover (Phosphor)				13·00

Originally scheduled for issue on 17 May 1965, supplies from the Philatelic Bureau were sent in error to reach a dealer on that date and another dealer received his supply on 27 May.

244 Robert Burns (after Skirving chalk drawing)

245 Robert Burns (after Nasmyth portrait)

(Des G. Huntly)

1966 (25 Jan). *Burns Commemoration.* Chalk-surfaced paper. *W* **179**. Perf 15×14.

685	**244**	4d. black, dp violet-blue and new blue	10	10
		p. Three phosphor bands	20	20
686	**245**	1s.3d. black, slate-blue and yellow-orange	20	20
		p. Three phosphor bands	90	90
Set of 2 (Ordinary)			25	25
Set of 2 (Phosphor)			1·00	1·00
First Day Cover (Ordinary)				1·20
First Day Cover (Phosphor)				3·50
Presentation Pack (Ordinary)			40·00	

Special First Day of Issue Postmarks

	Ordinary	Phosphor
Alloway, Ayrshire	12·00	15·00
Ayr	12·00	15·00
Dumfries	12·00	15·00
Edinburgh	12·00	15·00
Glasgow	12·00	15·00
Kilmarnock, Ayrshire	12·00	15·00

A special Philatelic Bureau was set up in Edinburgh to deal with First Day Covers of this issue. The Bureau serviced covers to receive the above postmarks, and other versions were applied locally. The locally applied handstamps were 38-39 mm in diameter, the Bureau postmarks, applied by machine, 35 mm. The Ayr, Edinburgh, Glasgow and Kilmarnock postmarks are similar in design to that for Alloway. Similar handstamps were also provided at Greenock and Mauchline, but the Bureau did not provide a service for these.

246 Westminster Abbey   **247** Fan Vaulting, Henry VII Chapel

(Des Sheila Robinson. Photo Harrison (3d.). Des and eng Bradbury, Wilkinson. Recess (2s.6d.))

1966 (28 Feb). *900th Anniversary of Westminster Abbey.* Chalk-surfaced paper (3d.). *W* **179**. Perf 15×14 (3d.) or 11×12 (2s.6d.).

687	**246**	3d. black, red-brown and new blue	10	10
		p. One phosphor band	10	10
688	**247**	2s.6d. black	30	30
Set of 2			30	30
First Day Cover (Ordinary)				2·50
First Day Cover (Phosphor)				8·00
Presentation Pack (Ordinary)			40·00	

Special First Day of Issue Postmark

	Ordinary
G.P.O. Philatelic Bureau, London E.C.1 (Type B)	2.50

The Bureau did not provide a First Day Cover service for the 3d. phosphor stamp

248 View near Hassocks, Sussex

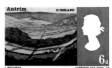

249 Antrim, Northern Ireland

250 Harlech Castle, Wales

251 Cairngorm Mountains Scotland

4d. Green flaw on tree trunk (Cyl. 1B Dot, R. 3/4)

6d. "AN" for "AND" (Cyl. 1A No dot, R. 10/3)

1s.3d. Broken "D" (Cyl. 2B, R. 14/2)

(Des L. Rosoman. Queen's portrait, adapted by D. Gentleman from coinage)

1966 (2 May). *Landscapes.* Chalk-surfaced paper. *W* **179**. Perf 15×14.

689	**248**	4d. black, yellow-green and new blue	10	10
		a. Green flaw	35·00	
		p. Three phosphor bands	10	10
		pa. Green flaw	35·00	
690	**249**	6d. black, emerald and new blue	10	10
		a. "AN" for "AND"	65·00	
		Wi. Watermark inverted	6·00	
		p. Three phosphor bands	10	10
		pa. "AN" for "AND"	65·00	
		pWi. Watermark inverted	£170	
691	**250**	1s.3d. black, greenish yellow and greenish blue	15	15
		a. Broken "D"	35·00	
		p. Three phosphor bands	15	15
		pa. Broken "D"	35·00	
692	**251**	1s.6d. black, orange and Prussian blue	15	15
		Wi. Watermark inverted	22·00	
		p. Three phosphor bands	15	15
Set of 4 (Ordinary)			40	40

Set of 4 (Phosphor)..		40	40
First Day Cover (Ordinary)			3·50
First Day Cover (Phosphor)			4·50

Blocks of four of Nos. 689 and 690 are known with the Queen's head and face value omitted on one stamp and a partial omission on the second, due to a paper fold (*Price per block.* £10000)

Special First Day of Issue Postmark

	Ordinary	*Phosphor*
G.P.O. Philatelic Bureau, London E.C.1 (Type B).............	3·50	4·50

First Day of Issue handstamps were provided at Lewes, Sussex; Coleraine, Co. Londonderry; Harlech, Merioneth and Grantown-on-Spey, Morayshire, for this issue.

252 Players with Ball   **253** Goalmouth Mêlée

254 Goalkeeper saving Goal

(Des D. Gentleman (4d.), W. Kempster (6d.), D. Caplan (1s.3d.). Queen's portrait adapted by D. Gentleman from coinage)

1966 (1 June). *World Cup Football Championship.* Chalk-surfaced paper. W **179** (sideways on 4d.). Perf 14×15 (4d.) or 15×14 (others).

693	**252**	4d. red, reddish purple, bright blue, flesh and black...................................	10	10
		p. Two phosphor bands...........................	10	10
694	**253**	6d. black, sepia, red, apple-green and blue...	10	10
		a. Black omitted	£200	
		b. Apple-green omitted...........................	£6000	
		c. Red omitted	£10000	
		Wi. Watermark inverted	5·00	
		p. Three phosphor bands........................	10	10
		pa. Black omitted	£2800	
695	**254**	1s.3d. black, blue, yellow, red and light yellow-olive..	15	15
		a. Blue omitted	£350	
		Wi. Watermark inverted	£150	
		p. Three phosphor bands........................	15	15
		pWi. Watermark inverted	2·00	

Set of 3 (Ordinary)..		30	30
Set of 3 (Phosphor)...		30	30
First Day Cover (Ordinary)			9·00
First Day Cover (Phosphor)			11·50
Presentation Pack (Ordinary).....................................		30·00	

Special First Day of Issue Postmark

	Ordinary	*Phosphor*
G.P.O. Philatelic Bureau, London E.C.1 (Type C).............	9·00	11·50

A First Day of Issue handstamp was provided at Wembley, Middx, for this issue.

255 Black-headed Gull   **256** Blue Tit

257 European Robin   **258** Blackbird

(Des J. Norris Wood)

1966 (8 Aug). *British Birds.* Chalk-surfaced paper. W **179**. Perf 15×14.

696	**255**	4d. grey, black, red, emerald-green, brt blue, greenish yellow and bistre..	10	10
		Wi. Watermark inverted	4·00	
		a. Block of 4. Nos. 696/9....................	40	40
		ab. Black (value), etc. omitted* (*block of four*)....................................	£20000	
		c. Black only omitted*............................	—	
		aWi. Watermark inverted (*block of four*)	18·00	
		p. Three phosphor bands........................	10	10
		pWi. Watermark inverted	20·00	
		pa. Block of 4. Nos. 696p/9p................	40	40
		paWi. Watermark inverted (*block of four*)	85·00	
697	**256**	4d. black, greenish yellow, grey, emerald-green, brt blue and bistre..	10	10
		b. Black "4d" only omitted....................	£2000	
		Wi. Watermark inverted	4·00	
		p. Three phosphor bands........................	10	10
		pWi. Watermark inverted	20·00	
698	**257**	4d. red, greenish yellow, black, grey, bistre, reddish brown and emerald-green...................................	10	10
		a. Black only omitted	£2000	
		Wi. Watermark inverted	4·00	
		p. Three phosphor bands........................	10	10
		pWi. Watermark inverted	20·00	
699	**258**	4d. black, reddish brown, greenish yellow, grey and bistre**..............	10	10
		b. Black "4d" only omitted***..............	£2000	
		Wi. Watermark inverted	4·00	
		p. Three phosphor bands........................	10	10
		pWi. Watermark inverted	20·00	

Set of 4 (Ordinary)..		40	40
Set of 4 (Phosphor)...		40	40
First Day Cover (Ordinary)			3·50
First Day Cover (Phosphor)			4·50
Presentation Pack (Ordinary).....................................		15·00	

Nos. 696/9 were issued together *se-tenant* in blocks of four within the sheet.

Nos. 697b and 699b are the result of a partial impression of the black, rendering the "4d" only omitted.

* In No. 696ab the blue, bistre and reddish brown are also omitted but in No. - 696c + 698c only the black is omitted.

** In No. 699 the black was printed over the bistre.

***A partial omission caused by a dry print affecting only the face value on the last column of the sheet.

Other colours omitted, and the stamps affected:

d.	Greenish yellow (Nos. 696/9)	£950
pd.	Greenish yellow (Nos. 696p/9p)	£2000
e.	Red (Nos. 696 and 698)	£1100
f.	Emerald-green (Nos. 696/8)	£200
pf.	Emerald-green (Nos. 696p/8p)	£200
g.	Bright blue (Nos. 696/7)	£700
pg.	Bright blue (Nos. 696p and 697p)	£5000
h.	Bistre (Nos. 696/9)	£200
ph.	Bistre (Nos. 696p/9p)	£2000
j.	Reddish brown (Nos. 698/9)	£125
pj.	Reddish brown (Nos. 698p and 699p)	£175

The prices quoted are for each stamp.

Special First Day of Issue Postmark

	Ordinary	*Phosphor*
G.P.O. Philatelic Bureau, London E.C.1 (Type C).............	3.50	4.50

259 Cup Winners

1966 (18 Aug). *England's World Cup Football Victory.* Chalk-surfaced paper. W **179** (sideways). Perf 14×15.

700	**259**	4d. red, reddish purple, bright blue, flesh and black..................................	10	10
First Day Cover...				7·50

These stamps were only put on sale at post offices in England, the Channel Islands and the Isle of Man, and at the Philatelic Bureau in London and also, on 22 August, in Edinburgh on the occasion of the opening of the Edinburgh Festival as well as at Army post offices at home and abroad.

The Philatelic Bureau did not service First Day Covers for this stamp, but a First Day of Issue handstamp was provided inscribed "Harrow & Wembley" to replace the "Wembley, Middx", postmark of the initial issue.

260 Jodrell Bank Radio Telescope

261 British Motor-cars

262 "SRN 6" Hovercraft

263 Windscale Reactor

6d. Broken "D"
(Cyl .1C, R. 19/6)

(Des D. and A. Gillespie (4d., 6d.), A. Restall (others))

1966 (19 Sept). *British Technology.* Chalk-surfaced paper. *W* **179**. Perf 15×14.

701	**260**	4d. black and lemon	10	10
		p. Three phosphor bands	10	10
702	**261**	6d. red, dp blue and orange	10	10
		a. Red (Mini-cars) omitted	£20000	—
		b. Deep blue (Jaguar & inscr) omitted	£17000	
		c. Broken "D"	35·00	
		p. Three phosphor bands	10	10
		pc. Broken "D"	35·00	
703	**262**	1s.3d. black, orange-red, slate and light greenish blue	15	15
		p. Three phosphor bands	20	20
704	**263**	1s.6d. black, yellow-green, bronze-green, lilac and deep blue	15	15
		p. Three phosphor bands	20	20
Set of 4 (Ordinary)			40	40
Set of 4 (Phosphor)			50	50
First Day Cover (Ordinary)				2·50
First Day Cover (Phosphor)				2·50
Presentation Pack (Ordinary)			20·00	

Special First Day of Issue Postmark

	Ordinary	*Phosphor*
G.P.O. Philatelic Bureau, Edinburgh 1 (Type C)	2·50	2·50

264   **265**

266   **267**

268   **269**

270 Norman Ship

271 Norman Horsemen attacking Harold's Troops

HARRISON AND SONS LTD
Club flaw (Cyl. 1A No dot, R. 7/2)

(All the above are scenes from the Bayeux Tapestry)

(Des D. Gentleman. Photo. Queen's head die-stamped (6d., 1s.3d.))

1966 (14 Oct). *900th Anniversary of Battle of Hastings.* Chalk-surfaced paper. *W* **179** (sideways on 1s.3d.). Perf 15×14.

705	**264**	4d. black, olive-green, bistre, deep blue, orange, magenta, green, blue and grey	10	10
		a. Strip of 6. Nos. 705/10	60	60
		ab. Imperforate strip of six	£3500	
		aWi. Strip of 6. Watermark inverted	45·00	
		Wi. Watermark inverted	7·00	
		p. Three phosphor bands	10	10
		pa. Strip of 6. Nos. 705p/10p	60	60
		pWi. Watermark inverted	3·00	
		paWi. Strip of 6. Watermark inverted	20·00	
706	**265**	4d. black, olive-green, bistre, deep blue, orange, magenta, green, blue and grey	10	10
		Wi. Watermark inverted	7·00	
		p. Three phosphor bands	10	10
		pWi. Watermark inverted	2·00	
707	**266**	4d. black, olive-green, bistre, deep blue, orange, magenta, green, blue and grey	10	10
		Wi. Watermark inverted	7·00	
		p. Three phosphor bands	10	10
		pWi. Watermark inverted	3·00	
708	**267**	4d. black, olive-green, bistre, deep blue, magenta, green, blue and grey	10	10
		Wi. Watermark inverted	7·00	
		p. Three phosphor bands	10	10
		pWi. Watermark inverted	3·00	
709	**268**	4d. black, olive-green, bistre, deep blue, orange, magenta, green, blue and grey	10	10
		Wi. Watermark inverted	7·00	
		p. Three phosphor bands	10	10
		pWi. Watermark inverted	3·00	
710	**269**	4d. black, olive-green, bistre, deep blue, orange, magenta, green, blue and grey	10	10
		Wi. Watermark inverted	7·00	
		p. Three phosphor bands	10	10
		pWi. Watermark inverted	3·00	
711	**270**	6d. black, olive-green, violet, blue, green and gold	10	10
		Wi. Watermark inverted	42·00	
		p. Three phosphor bands	10	10
		pWi. Watermark inverted	75·00	
712	**271**	1s.3d. black, lilac, bronze-green, rosine, bistre-brown and gold	20	30
		a. Lilac omitted	£5250	
		b. Club flaw	28·00	
		Wi. Watermark sideways inverted (top of crown pointing to right)*	50·00	
		p. Four phosphor bands	20	40
		pa. Lilac omitted	£1250	
		pb. Club flaw	28·00	
		pWi. Watermark sideways inverted (top of crown pointing to right)*	50·00	
Set of 8 (Ordinary)			85	1·00

Set of 8 (Phosphor)..	85	1·00
First Day Cover (Ordinary)		2·00
First Day Cover (Phosphor)		3·25
Presentation Pack (Ordinary).......................................	8·50	

Nos. 705/10 show battle scenes and they were issued together *se-tenant* in horizontal strips of six within the sheet.

* The normal sideways watermark shows the tops of the Crowns pointing to the left, as seen from the *back of the stamp*. Other colours omitted in the 4d. values and the stamps affected:

b. Olive-green (Nos. 705/10)	50·00	
pb. Olive-green (Nos. 705p/10p)	50·00	
c. Bistre (Nos. 705/10)	50·00	
pc. Bistre (Nos. 705p/10p)	50·00	
d. Deep blue (Nos. 705/10)	60·00	
pd. Deep blue (Nos. 705p/10p)............................	60·00	
e. Orange (Nos. 705/7 and 709/10)	50·00	
pe. Orange (Nos. 705p/7p and 709p/10p)	50·00	
f. Magenta (Nos. 705/10)	50·00	
pf. Magenta (Nos. 705p/10p)	50·00	
g. Green (Nos. 705/10)	45·00	
pg. Green (Nos. 705p/10p)	45·00	
h. Blue (Nos. 705/10)	35·00	
ph. Blue (Nos. 705p/10p)	50·00	
j. Grey (Nos. 705/10)	35·00	
pj. Grey (Nos. 705p/10p)	40·00	
pk. Magenta and green (Nos. 705p/10p).............	—	

The prices quoted are for each stamp.

Nos. 705 and 709, with grey and blue omitted, have been seen commercially used, posted from Middleton-in-Teesdale.

The 6d. phosphor is known in a yellowish gold as well as the reddish gold as used in the 1s.3d.

Three examples of No. 712 in a right-hand top corner block of 10 (2×5) are known with the Queen's head omitted as a result of a double paper fold prior to die-stamping. The perforation is normal. Of the other seven stamps, four have the Queen's head misplaced and three are normal.

MISSING GOLD HEADS. The 6d. and 1s.3d. were also issued with the die-stamped gold head omitted but as these can also be removed by chemical means we are not prepared to list them unless a way is found of distinguishing the genuine stamps from the fakes which will satisfy the Expert Committees.

The same remarks apply to Nos. 713/14.

Special First Day of Issue Postmark

	Ordinary	Phosphor
G.P.O. Philatelic Bureau, Edinburgh 1 (Type C)	2·00	3·25

A First Day of Issue handstamp was provided at Battle, Sussex, for this issue.

272 King of the Orient   **273** Snowman

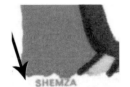

Missing "T" (Cyl. 1E No dot, R. 6/2)

(Des Tasveer Shemza (3d.), J. Berry (1s.6d.) (winners of children's design competition). Photo, Queen's head die-stamped)

1966 (1 Dec). *Christmas, Children's Paintings.* Chalk-surfaced paper. W **179** (sideways on 3d.). Perf 14×15.

713	**272**	3d. black, blue, green, yellow, red and gold	10	10
		a. Queen's head double*...........................	—	†
		ab. Queen's head double, one albino..	£500	
		b. Green omitted..................................		£4250
		c. Missing "T"	25·00	
		p. One phosphor band at right	10	10
		pEa. Band at left...	10	10
		pEb. Horiz pair. Nos. 713p/pEa.................	20	20

		pc. Missing "T"	45·00	
714	**273**	1s.6d. blue, red, pink, black and gold.......	10	10
		a. Pink (hat) omitted............................	£3800	
		Wi. Watermark inverted.........................	30·00	
		p. Two phosphor bands	10	10
		pWi. Watermark inverted.........................	90·00	
Set of 2 (Ordinary)..		20	20
Set of 2 (Phosphor)		20	20
First Day Cover (Ordinary)			70
First Day Cover (Phosphor)			70
Presentation Pack (Ordinary).......................................		10·00	

No. 713a refers to stamps showing two impressions, one directly below the other, both with embossing. Examples showing two partial strikes on opposite sides of the stamp, caused by a colour shift are common.

The single phosphor band on No. 713p was produced by printing broad phosphor bands across alternate perforations. Individual* show the band at right or left.

Special First Day of Issue Postmarks

	Ordinary	Phosphor
G.P.O. Philatelic Bureau, Edinburgh 1 (Type C)	70	70
Bethlehem, Llandeilo, Carms (Type C)............................	2·00	2·00

274 Sea Freight   **275** Air Freight

Broken undercarriage leg (Cyl. 2, No dot, R. 13/6)

(Des C. Abbott)

1967 (20 Feb). *European Free Trade Association (EFTA).* Chalk-surfaced paper. W **179**. Perf 15×14.

715	**274**	9d. deep blue, red, lilac, green, brown, new blue, yellow and black..	10	10
		a. Black (Queen's head, etc.), brown, new blue and yellow omitted.........	£1300	
		b. Lilac omitted....................................	£140	
		c. Green omitted..................................	£140	
		d. Brown (rail trucks) omitted..............	95·00	
		e. New blue omitted	£140	
		f. Yellow omitted.................................	£140	
		p. Three phosphor bands	10	10
		pb. Lilac omitted....................................	£225	
		pc. Green omitted..................................	£140	
		pd. Brown omitted.................................	95·00	
		pe. New blue omitted	£140	
		pf. Yellow omitted.................................	£180	
		pWi. Watermark inverted.........................	95·00	
716	**275**	1s.6d. violet, red, deep blue, brown, green, blue-grey, new blue, yellow and black............................	10	10
		a. Red omitted......................................	£550	
		b. Deep blue omitted............................	£550	
		c. Brown omitted..................................	£140	
		d. Blue-grey omitted	£140	
		e. New blue omitted	£140	
		f. Yellow omitted.................................	£140	
		g. Black omitted...................................	£3750	
		h. Broken undercarriage leg.................	40·00	
		Wi. Watermark inverted.........................	30·00	
		p. Three phosphor bands	10	10
		pa. Red omitted......................................		
		pb. Deep blue omitted............................	£140	£140
		pc. Brown omitted..................................	95·00	
		pd. Blue-grey omitted	£140	
		pf. New blue omitted	£140	
		ph. Broken undercarriage leg.................	40·00	
		pWi. Watermark inverted.........................	30·00	
Set of 2 (Ordinary)..			20	20
Set of 2 (Phosphor)			20	20

First Day Cover (Ordinary).. 5·00
First Day Cover (Phosphor)... 5·00
Presentation Pack (Ordinary).......................... 20·00

Special First Day of Issue Postmark

	Ordinary	Phosphor
G.P.O. Philatelic Bureau, Edinburgh 1 (Type C)............	5·00	5·00

276 Hawthorn and Bramble   **277** Larger Bindweed and Viper's Bugloss

278 Ox-eye Daisy, Coltsfoot and Buttercup   **279** Bluebell, Red Campion and Wood Anemone

280 Dog Violet   **281** Primroses

(Des Rev. W. Keble Martin (T **276**/**9**), Mary Grierson (others))

1967 (24 Apr). *British Wild Flowers*. Chalk-surfaced paper. W **179**. Perf 15×14.

717	**276**	4d. grey, lemon, myrtle-green, red, agate and slate-purple.....................	10	10
		a. Block of 4. Nos. 717/20.....................	40	40
		aWi. Block of 4. Watermark inverted	9·00	
		b. Grey double*....................................		
		c. Red omitted.....................................	£4000	
		f. Slate-purple omitted........................	£5500	
		Wi. Watermark inverted............................	2·00	
		p. Three phosphor bands.....................	10	10
		pa. Block of 4. Nos. 717p/20p................	40	40
		paWi. Block of 4. Watermark inverted	9·00	
		pd. Agate omitted.................................	£3500	
		pf. Slate-purple omitted........................	£500	
		pWi. Watermark inverted............................	2·00	
718	**277**	4d. grey, lemon, myrtle-green, red, agate and violet..............................	10	10
		b. Grey double*....................................		
		Wi. Watermark inverted............................	2·00	
		p. Three phosphor bands.....................	10	10
		pd. Agate omitted.................................	£3500	
		pe. Violet omitted.................................		
		pWi. Watermark inverted............................	2·00	
719	**278**	4d. grey, lemon, myrtle-green, red and agate.......................................	10	10
		b. Grey double*....................................		
		Wi. Watermark inverted............................	2·00	
		p. Three phosphor bands.....................	10	10
		pd. Agate omitted.................................	£3500	
		pWi. Watermark inverted............................	2·00	
720	**279**	4d. grey, lemon, myrtle-green, reddish purple, agate and violet	10	10
		c. Reddish purple omitted....................	£2000	
		d. Value omitted†................................	£9500	
		Wi. Watermark inverted............................	2·00	
		p. Three phosphor bands.....................	10	10
		pd. Agate omitted.................................	£3500	
		pe. Violet omitted.................................		
		pWi. Watermark inverted............................	2·00	
721	**280**	9d. lavender-grey, green, reddish violet and orange-yellow	15	15
		Wi. Watermark inverted............................	1·30	
		p. Three phosphor bands.....................	15	15
722	**281**	1s.9d. lavender-grey, green, greenish yellow and orange.............................	15	15
		p. Three phosphor bands.....................	15	15

Set of 6 (Ordinary)... 50   50
Set of 6 (Phosphor).. 50   50
First Day Cover (Ordinary)................................. 1·20

First Day Cover (Phosphor)... 7·00
Presentation Pack (Ordinary)............................ 20·00
Presentation Pack (Phosphor)........................... 20·00

Nos. 717/20 were issued together *se-tenant* in blocks of four within the sheet.

* The double impression of the grey printing affects the Queen's head, value and inscription.

† No. 720d was caused by something obscuring the face value on R14/6 during the printing of one sheet.

Special First Day of Issue Postmark

	Ordinary	Phosphor
G.P.O. Philatelic Bureau, Edinburgh 1 (Type C)............	1·20	7·00

PHOSPHOR BANDS. Issues from No. 723 are normally with phosphor bands only, except for the high values but most stamps have appeared with the phosphor bands omitted in error. Such varieties are listed under "Ey" numbers and are priced unused only. See also further notes after 1971–96 Decimal Machin issue.

PHOSPHORISED PAPER. Following the adoption of phosphor bands the Post Office started a series of experiments involving the addition of the phosphor to the paper coating before the stamps were printed. No. 743c was the first of these experiments to be issued for normal postal use. See also notes after 1971–96 Decimal Machin issue.

PVA GUM. Polyvinyl alcohol was introduced by Harrisons in place of gum arabic in 1968. As it is almost invisible a small amount of pale yellowish colouring was introduced to make it possible to check that the stamps had been gummed. Although this can be detected from gum arabic in unused stamps there is, of course, no means of detecting it in used examples. Where the two forms of gum exist on the same stamps, the PVA type are listed under "Ev" numbers, except in the case of the 1d. and 4d. (vermilion), both one centre band, which later appeared with gum arabic and these have "Eg" numbers. "Ev" and "Eg" numbers are priced unused only. All stamps printed from No. 763 onwards were issued with PVA gum only *except where otherwise stated*.

It should be further noted that gum arabic is shiny in appearance, and that, normally, PVA gum has a matt appearance. However, depending upon the qualities of the paper ingredients and the resultant absorption of the gum, occasionally, PVA gum has a shiny appearance. In such cases, especially in stamps from booklets, it is sometimes impossible to be absolutely sure which gum has been used except by testing the stamps chemically which destroys them. Therefore, whilst all gum arabic is shiny it does not follow that all shiny gum is gum arabic.

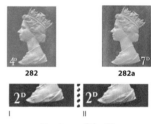

282   **282a**

I   II

Two types of the 2d.

I. Value spaced away from left side of stamp (cylinders 1 no dot and dot).

II. Value close to left side from new multipositive used for cylinders 5 no dot and dot onwards. The portrait appears in the centre, thus conforming to the other values.

Three types of the Machin head, known as Head A, B or C, are distinguished by specialists. These are illustrated in Vol. 3 of the *Great Britain Specialised Catalogue*.

(Des after plaster cast by Arnold Machin)

1967 (5 June)–**70**. Chalk-surfaced paper. Two phosphor bands except where otherwise stated. PVA gum except Nos. 725m, 728, 729, 731, 731Ea, 740, 742/Ea, 743/a and 744/Ea. No wmk. Perf 15×14.

723	**282**	½d. orange-brown (5.2.68).....................	10	10
		Ey. Phosphor omitted............................	30·00	
724		1d. light olive (*shades*) (2 bands) (5.2.68)...	10	10
		a. Imperf (coil strip)†............................	£3500	
		b. Part perf pane*................................	£5000	
		c. Imperf pane*....................................	£5750	
		d. Uncoated paper (1970)**...............	£150	
		Ey. Phosphor omitted............................	4·00	
		l. Booklet pane. No. 724×2 *se-tenant* with 730×2 (6.4.68).............	3·00	
		lEy. Booklet pane. Phosphor omitted.	90·00	
		m. Booklet pane. No. 724×4 *se-tenant* with 734×2 (6.1.69)..........	90	
		mEy. Booklet pane. Phosphor omitted.	£225	
		n. Booklet pane. No. 724×6, 734×3, 734Eb×3 & 735×3 *se-tenant* (1.12.69)..	8·50	
		na. Booklet pane. Uncoated paper**.	£925	
		nEy. Booklet pane. Phosphor omitted.	£225	

725		1d. yellowish olive (1 centre band)		
		(16.9.68)...............................	45	45
		Eg. Gum arabic (27.8.69)	1·00	
		l. Booklet pane. No. 725×4 se-		
		tenant with 732×2	4·00	
		lEy. Booklet pane. Phosphor omitted.	35·00	
		m. Coil strip. No. 728×2 se-tenant		
		with 729, 725Eg & 733Eg		
		(27.8.69)	1·90	
726		2d. lake-brown (Type I) (2 bands)		
		(5.2.68).................................	10	10
		Ey. Phosphor omitted	40·00	
727		2d. lake-brown (Type II) (2 bands)		
		(1969)...................................	10	10
		Ey. Phosphor omitted	2·00	
728		2d. lake-brown (Type II) (1 centre		
		band) (27.8.69)......................	35	40
729		3d. violet (shades) (1 centre band)		
		(8.8.67).................................	10	10
		a. Imperf (vert pair)	£950	
		Ey. Phosphor omitted	4·00	
		Ev. PVA gum (shades) (12.3.68)	1·00	
		Evy. Phosphor omitted	4·00	
730		3d. violet (2 bands) (6.4.68)	10	15
		a. Uncoated paper**	£6000	
731		4d. deep sepia (shades) (2 bands)	10	10
		Ey. Phosphor omitted	4·00	
		Ea. Deep olive-brown	1·00	1·00
		Eay. Phosphor omitted	6·00	
		b. Part perf pane*	£4000	
		Ev. PVA gum (shades) (22.1.68)	1·00	
		Evy. Phosphor omitted	4·00	
732		4d. deep olive-brown (shades) (1		
		centre band) (16.9.68).............	10	10
		a. Part perf pane*	£4250	
		l. Booklet pane. Two stamps plus		
		two printed labels	1·00	
		lEy. Booklet pane. Phosphor omitted.	45·00	
733		4d. bright vermilion (1 centre band)		
		(6.1.69).................................	10	10
		a. Tête-bêche (horiz pair)	£5000	
		b. Uncoated paper**	20·00	
		Ey. Phosphor omitted	4·00	
		l. Booklet pane. Two stamps plus		
		two printed labels (3.3.69)............	1·00	
		lEy. Booklet pane. Phosphor omitted.	75·00	
		Eg. Gum arabic (27.8.69)	1·00	
		Egy. Phosphor omitted	£1650	
734		4d. bright vermilion (1 band at left)		
		(6.1.69).................................	65	75
		a. Uncoated paper**	£475	
		Eb. One band at right (1.12.69)...........	1·00	1·00
		Eba. Ditto. Uncoated paper**	£425	
735		5d. royal blue (shades) (1.7.68)	10	10
		a. Imperf pane*	£3500	
		b. Part perf pane*	£2500	
		c. Imperf (pair)††	£275	
		d. Uncoated paper**	40·00	
		Ey. Phosphor omitted	6·50	
		Ee. Deep blue	1·00	1·00
		Eey. Phosphor omitted	6·00	
736		6d. brt reddish purple (shades)		
		(5.2.68).................................	10	10
		Ey. Phosphor omitted	35·00	
		Ea. Bright magenta	9·00	9·00
		Eb. Claret	1·25	1·25
		Eby. Phosphor omitted	45·00	
737	**282a**	7d. bright emerald (1.7.68)...............	25	25
		Ey. Phosphor omitted	£100	
738		8d. bright vermilion (1.7.68)...............	10	15
		Ey. Phosphor omitted	£450	
739		8d. light turquoise-blue (6.1.69)...........	25	25
		Ey. Phosphor omitted	80·00	
740		9d. myrtle-green (8.8.67)	10	1·50
		Ey. Phosphor omitted	60·00	
		Ev. PVA gum (29.11.68)	1·00	
		Evy. Phosphor omitted	85·00	
741	**282**	10d. drab (1.7.68)...............	25	25
		a. Uncoated paper**	85.00	
		Ey. Phosphor omitted	70·00	
742		1s. light bluish violet (shades).............	20	20
		Ey. Phosphor omitted	85·00	
		Ea. Pale bluish violet	1·00	1·00
		Ev. Ditto. PVA gum (26.4.68)	1·00	
		Evy. Phosphor omitted	12·00	
743		1s.6d. greenish blue and deep blue		
		(shades) (8.8.67)......................	25	25
		a. Greenish blue omitted	£160	
		Ey. Phosphor omitted	15·00	
		Ev. PVA gum (28.8.68)	1·00	
		Eva. Greenish blue omitted	£100	
		Evy. Phosphor omitted	22·00	

		Evb. Prussian blue and indigo...............	7.00	7.00
		Evby. Phosphor omitted	18·00	
		c. Phosphorised paper (Prussian		
		blue and indigo) (10.12.69).............	30	35
		ca. Prussian blue omitted	£450	
744		1s.9d. dull orange and black (shades).....	25	25
		Ey. Phosphor omitted	65·00	
		Ea. Bright orange and black	1·00	1·00
		Ev. PVA gum (bright orange and		
		black) (16.11.70)	2·50	
Set of 16 (one of each value and colour)			2·00	2·25
Presentation Pack (one of each value) (1968)			7·00	
Presentation Pack (German) (1969)			90.00	

* BOOKLET ERRORS. See note after No. 556.
** Uncoated paper. This does not respond to the chalky test, and may be further distinguished from the normal chalk-surfaced paper by the fibres which clearly show on the surface, resulting in the printing impression being rougher, and by the screening dots which are not so evident. The 1d., 4d. and 5d. come from the £1 "Stamps for Cooks" Booklet (1969); the 3d. and 10d. from sheets (1969). The 20p. and 50p. high values (Nos. 830/1) exist with similar errors.
† No. 724a occurs in a vertical strip of four, top stamp perforated on three sides, bottom stamp imperf three sides and the two middle stamps completely imperf.
†† No. 735c comes from the original state of cylinder 15 which is identifiable by the screening dots which extend through the gutters of the stamps and into the margins of the sheet. This must not be confused with imperforate stamps from cylinder 10, a large quantity of which was stolen from the printers early in 1970.

The 1d. with centre band and PVA gum (725) only came in the September 1968 10s. booklet (No. XP6). The 1d., 2d. and 4d. with centre band and gum arabic (725Eg, 728 and 733Eg respectively) only came in the coil strip (725m). The 3d. (No. 730) appeared in booklets on 6.4.68, from coils during Dec 68 and from sheets in Jan 1969. The 4d. with one side band at left (734) came from 10s. (band at left) and £1 (band at left or right) booklet se-tenant panes, and the 4d. with one side band at right (734Eb) came from the £1 booklet se-tenant panes only.

The 4d. (731) in shades of washed-out grey are colour changelings which we understand are caused by the concentrated solvents used in modern dry cleaning methods.

For decimal issue, see Nos. X841, etc.

First Day Covers

5.6 67	4d., 1s., 1s.9d. (731, 742, 744)		2.00
8.8.67	3d., 9d., 1s.6d. (729, 740, 743)		2.00
5.2.68	½d., 1d., 2d., 6d. (723/4, 726, 736)................................		2·25
1.7.68	5d., 7d., 8d., 10d. (735, 737/8, 741)		3·00

283 "Master Lambton" (Sir Thomas Lawrence)

284 "Mares and Foals in a Landscape" (George Stubbs)

285 "Children Coming Out of School" (L. S. Lowry)

(Des S. Rose)

1967 (10 July). *British Paintings* (1st series). Chalk-surfaced paper. Two phosphor bands. No wmk. Perf 14×15 (4d.) or 15×14 (others).

748	**283**	4d. rose-red, lemon, brown, black,		
		new blue and gold	10	10
		a. Gold (value and Queen's head)		
		omitted....................................	£275	
		b. New blue omitted....................................	£15000	
		Ey. Phosphor omitted	7·00	
749	**284**	9d. Venetian red, ochre, grey-black,		
		new-blue, greenish yellow and		
		black	10	10
		a. Black (Queen's head and value)		
		omitted....................................	£1000	
		ab. Black (Queen's head only) omitted ..	£2100	
		Ey. Phosphor omitted.........................	£500	
750	**285**	1s.6d. greenish yellow, grey, rose, new		
		blue, grey-black and gold...............	10	10
		a. Gold (Queen's head) omitted...............		
		b. New blue omitted................................	£275	

c. Grey (clouds and shading) omitted.	£150	
Ey. Phosphor omitted.....................................	£300	
Set of 3..	30	30
First Day Cover		1·00
Presentation Pack..	20·00	

Special First Day of Issue Postmark

G.P.O. Philatelic Bureau, Edinburgh 1 (Type C)..................................... 2·00
A First Day of Issue handstamp was provided at Bishop Auckland, Co. Durham, for this issue.

286 *Gipsy Moth IV*

(Des M. and Sylvia Goaman)

1967 (24 July). *Sir Francis Chichester's World Voyage*. Chalk-surfaced paper. Three phosphor bands. No wmk. Perf 15×14.

751	**286**	1s.9d. black, brown-red, light emerald and blue	10	10
		First Day Cover		40

Special First Day of Issue Postmarks

G.P.O. Philatelic Bureau, Edinburgh 1	2·50
Greenwich, London SE10...	2·50
Plymouth, Devon..	2·50

The Philatelic Bureau and Greenwich postmarks are similar in design to that for Plymouth. A First Day of Issue handstamp was provided at Chichester, Sussex for this issue.

287 Radar Screen   **288** *Penicillium notatum*

289 Vickers VC-10 Jet Engines   **290** Television Equipment

Broken scale (Cyl. 1c, R. 10/2)

(Des C. Abbott (4d., 1s.), Negus-Sharland team (others))

1967 (19 Sept). *British Discovery and Invention*. Chalk-surfaced paper. Three phosphor bands (4d.) or two phosphor bands (others). W **179** (sideways on 1s.9d.) Perf 14×15 (1s.9d.) or 15×14 (others).

752	**287**	4d. greenish yellow, black and vermilion.....................................	10	10
		a. Broken scale................................	45·00	
		Ey. Phosphor omitted	5·00	
753	**288**	1s. blue-green, lt greenish blue, slate-purple and bluish violet	10	10
		Wi. Watermark inverted......................	20·00	
		Ey. Phosphor omitted	10·00	
754	**289**	1s.6d. black, grey, royal blue, ochre and turquoise-blue.....................	10	10
		Wi. Watermark inverted......................	£240	
		Ey. Phosphor omitted	£525	
755	**290**	1s.9d. black, grey-blue, pale olive-grey, violet and orange.....................	10	10
		a. Pale olive-grey omitted.....		£4500
		b. Orange (Queen's head) omitted.....	£30000	
		Ey. Phosphor omitted	£525	
		Set of 4..	40	40

First Day Cover.. 70
Presentation Pack... 9.00

Special First of Issue Postmark

G.P.O. Philatelic Bureau, Edinburgh (Type C) 70

WATERMARK. All issues from this date are on unwatermarked paper *unless otherwise stated*

291 "The Adoration of the Shepherds" (School of Seville)   **292** "Madonna and Child" (Murillo)

293 "The Adoration of the Shepherds" (Louis le Nain)

(Des S. Rose)

1967 *Christmas, Paintings*. Chalk-surfaced paper. One phosphor band (3d.) or two phosphor bands (others). Perf 15×14 (1s.6d.) or 14×15 (others).

756	**291**	3d. olive-yellow, rose, blue, black and gold (27.11)	10	15
		a. Gold (value and Queen's head) omitted	£110	
		ab. Gold (Queen's head only) omitted	£2750	
		b. Printed on the gummed side..........	£625	
		c. Rose omitted	£3250	
		Ey. Phosphor omitted	1·00	
757	**292**	4d. bright purple, greenish yellow, new blue, grey-black and gold (18.10).....................................	10	15
		a. Gold (value and Queen's head) omitted	80·00	
		ab. Gold (Queen's head only) omitted	£4500	
		b. Gold ("4D" only) omitted..............	£2500	
		c. Greenish yellow (Child, robe and Madonna's face) omitted..................	£7500	
		d. Greenish yellow and gold omitted	£15000	
		Ey. Phosphor omitted	£125	
758	**293**	1s.6d. bright purple, bistre, lemon, black, orange-red, ultramarine and gold (27.11).....................................	15	15
		a. Gold (value and Queen's head) omitted	£15000	
		ab. Gold (value only) omitted..............	£3000	
		b. Ultramarine omitted	£750	
		c. Lemon omitted............................	£20000	
		Ey. Phosphor omitted	12·00	
		Set of 3..	30	30
		First Day Covers (2)		3.00

Distinct shades exist of the 3d. and 4d. values but are not listable as there are intermediate shades. For the 4d., stamps from one machine show a darker background and give the appearance of the yellow colour being omitted, but this is not so and these should not be confused with the true missing yellow No. 757c.

No. 757b comes from stamps in the first vertical row of a sheet.

The 3d. and 4d. values are known imperforate. They are of proof status.

Special First Day of Issue Postmarks

G.P.O. Philatelic Bureau, Edinburgh 1 (4d.) (18 Oct.) (Type C)........	1.00
G.P.O. Philatelic Bureau, Edinburgh 1 (3d., 1s.6d.) (27 Nov.) (Type C)	2·00
Bethlehem, Llandeilo, Carms (4d.) (18 Oct.) (Type C).............	2·00
Bethlehem, Llandeilo, Carms (3d., 1s.6d.) (27 Nov.) (Type C)........	3·00

Gift Pack 1967

1967 (27 Nov). Comprises Nos. 715p/22p and 748/58.
GP758c Gift Pack .... 2·25

(Recess Bradbury, Wilkinson)

1967–68. No wmk. White paper. Perf 11×12.

759	**166**	2s.6d. black-brown (1.7.68)	10	20
760	**167**	5s. red (10.4.68)	50	50
761	**168**	10s. bright ultramarine (10.4.68)	4.50	2·00
762	**169**	£1 black (4.12.67)	6·50	2·00
Set of 4			10·00	4·25

PVA GUM. All the following issues from this date have PVA gum except where footnotes state otherwise.

294 Tarr Steps, Exmoor

295 Aberfeldy Bridge

296 Menai Bridge

297 M4 Viaduct

(Des A. Restall (9d.), L. Rosoman (1s.6d.), J. Matthews (others))

1968 (29 Apr). *British Bridges*. Chalk-surfaced paper. Two phosphor bands. Perf 15×14.

763	**294**	4d. black, bluish violet, turquoise-blue and gold	10	10
		a. Printed on gummed side	35·00	
		Ey. Phosphor omitted	10.00	
764	**295**	9d. red-brown, myrtle-green, ultramarine, olive-brown, black and gold	10	15
		a. Gold (Queen's head) omitted	£225	
		b. Ultramarine omitted	†	£7000
		Ey. Phosphor omitted	15·00	
765	**296**	1s.6d. olive-brown, red-orange, brt green, turquoise-green and gold	15	20
		a. Gold (Queen's head) omitted	£375	
		b. Red-orange (rooftops) omitted	£375	
		Ey. Phosphor omitted	50·00	
766	**297**	1s.9d. olive-brown, greenish yellow, dull green, dp ultramarine and gold	15	25
		a. Gold (Queen's head) omitted	£325	
		Ey. Phosphor omitted	10·00	
		Eya. Gold (Queen's head) & Phosphor omitted	£3500	—
Set of 4			45	65
First Day Cover				90
Presentation Pack			5·25	

No. 764b is only known on First Day Covers posted from Canterbury, Kent, or the Philatelic Bureau, Edinburgh.

Used examples of the 1s.6d. and 1s.9d. are known with both the gold and the phosphor omitted.

Special First Day of Issue Postmarks

G.P.O. Philatelic Bureau, Edinburgh 1	2.25
Bridge, Canterbury, Kent	10·00
Aberfeldy, Perthshire (Type A) (9d. value only)	10·00
Menai Bridge, Anglesey (Type A) (1s.6d. value only)	10·00

The Bridge, Canterbury, postmark is similar in design to that for the Philatelic Bureau.

298 "TUC" and Trades Unionists

299 Mrs. Emmeline Pankhurst (statue)

300 Sopwith Camel and English Electric Lightning Fighters

301 Captain Cook's *Endeavour* and Signature

(Des D. Gentleman (4d.), C. Abbott (others))

1968 (29 May). *Anniversaries* (1st series). Events described on stamps. Chalk surfaced paper. Two phosphor bands. Perf 15×14.

767	**298**	4d. emerald, olive, blue and black	10	10
		Ey. Phosphor omitted	12·00	
768	**299**	9d. reddish violet, bluish grey and black	10	10
		Ey. Phosphor omitted	7·00	
769	**300**	1s. olive-brown, blue, red, slate-blue and black	15	20
		Ey. Phosphor omitted	10·00	
770	**301**	1s.9d. yellow-ochre and blackish brown	20	25
		Ey. Phosphor omitted	£190	
Set of 4			50	60
First Day Cover				2·50
Presentation Pack			5·00	

Special First Day of Issue Postmarks

G.P.O. Philatelic Bureau, Edinburgh 1 (Type C)	3·00
Manchester (4d. value only)	1·00
Aldeburgh, Suffolk (9d. value only)	2·00
Hendon, London NW4 (1s. value only)	3·00
Whitby, Yorkshire (1s.9d. value only)	4·00

The Philatelic Bureau postmark was used on sets of four, but the other postmarks were only available on single stamps.

302 "Queen Elizabeth I" (unknown artist)

303 "Pinkie" (Sir Thomas Lawrence)

304 "Ruins of St Mary Le Port" (John Piper)

305 "The Hay Wain" (John Constable)

(Des S. Rose)

1968 (12 Aug). *British Paintings* (2nd series). Queen's head embossed. Chalk-surfaced paper. Two phosphor bands. Perf 15×14 (1s.9d.) or 14×15 (others).

771	**302**	4d. black, vermilion, greenish yellow, grey and gold	10	10
		a. Gold (value and Queen's head) omitted	£300	
		b. Vermilion omitted*	£700	
		Ec. Embossing omitted	90·00	
		Ey. Phosphor omitted	1·50	
		Eya. Gold (value and Queen's head) and phosphor omitted	£4000	
772	**303**	1s. mauve, new blue, greenish yellow, black, magenta and gold	10	15
		a. Gold (value and Queen's head) omitted	£7500	
		Eb. Gold (value and Queen's head), embossing and phosphor omitted	£650	
		Ec. Embossing omitted		
		Ey. Phosphor omitted	7·00	
773	**304**	1s.6d. slate, orange, black, mauve, greenish yellow, ultramarine and gold	15	20
		a. Gold (value and Queen's head) omitted	£300	
		Eb. Embossing omitted	£300	
		Ey. Phosphor omitted	10·00	
774	**305**	1s.9d. greenish yellow, black, new blue, red and gold	15	20
		a. Gold (value and Queen's head) and embossing omitted	£900	
		b. Red omitted	£10000	
		Ec. Embossing omitted	£140	
		Ey. Phosphor omitted	20·00	
Set of 4			45	60

First Day Cover .... 1·00
Presentation Pack (P. O. Pack No. 1) .... 4·50
Presentation Pack (German) (P. O. Pack No. 1) .... 30·00
   No. 774a is only known with the phosphor also omitted.
* The effect of this is to leave the face and hands white and there is
more yellow and olive in the costume.
   The 4d. also exists with the value only omitted resulting from a
colour shift.

Special First Day of Issue Postmark

G.P.O. Philatelic Bureau, Edinburgh 1 (Type C) .... 2·00

Gift Pack 1968
1968 (16 Sept). Comprises Nos. 763/74.
GP774c Gift Pack .... 3·00
GP774d Gift Pack (German) .... 80·00

Collectors Pack 1968
1968 (16 Sept). Comprises Nos. 752/8 and 763/74.
CP774e Collectors Pack .... 2·50

306 Boy and Girl with Rocking Horse

307 Girl with Doll'sHouse

308 Boy with TrainSet

(Des Rosalind Dease. Head printed in gold and then embossed)

1968 (25 Nov). *Christmas*, Children's Toys. Chalk-surfaced paper. One
centre phosphor band (4d.) or two phosphor bands (others).
Perf 15×14 (4d.) or 14×15 (others).

775	**306**	4d. black, orange, vermilion, ultramarine, bistre and gold	10	10
		a. Gold omitted	£6000	
		b. Vermilion omitted*	£525	
		c. Ultramarine omitted	£500	
		d. Bistre omitted		
		e. Orange omitted	†	—
		Ef. Embossing omitted	6·00	
		Ey. Phosphor omitted	5·00	
		Eya. Embossing and phosphor omitted		
776	**307**	9d. yellow-olive, black, brown, yellow, magenta, orange, turquoise-green and gold	15	15
		a. Yellow omitted	£175	
		b. Turquoise-green (dress) omitted....	£22000	
		Ec. Embossing omitted	6·00	
		Ey. Phosphor omitted	10·00	
		Eya. Embossing and phosphor omitted	10·00	
777	**308**	1s.6d. ultramarine, yellow orange, bright purple, blue-green, black and gold	15	20
		Ea. Embossing omitted		
		Ey. Phosphor omitted	15·00	

Set of 3 .... 35 40
First Day Cover .... 1·00
Presentation Pack (P. O. Pack No. 4) .... 9·00
Presentation Pack (German) .... 30·00
* The effect of the missing vermilion is shown on the rocking horse,
saddle and faces which appear orange instead of red.
   A single used example of the 4d. exists with the bistre omitted.
   No. 775c is only known with phosphor also omitted.
   Two machines were used for printing for the 4d. value:
   Stamps from cylinders 1A-1B-2C-1D-1E in combination with 1F, 2F
or 3F (gold) were printed entirely on the Rembrandt sheet-fed machine.
They invariably have the Queen's head level with the top of the boy's
head and the sheets are perforated through the left side margin.
   Stamps from cylinders 2A-2B-3C-2D-2E in combination with 1F, 2F,
3F or 4F (gold) were printed on the reel-fed Thrissell machine in five
colours (its maximum colour capacity) and subsequently sheet-fed on
the Rembrandt machine for the Queen's head and the embossing. The
position of the Queen's head is generally lower than on the stamps
printed at one operation but it varies in different parts of the sheet
and is not, therefore, a sure indication for identifying single stamps.
Another small difference is that the boy's grey pullover is noticeably
"moth-eaten" in the Thrissell printings and is normal on the Rembrandt.
The Thrissell printings are perforated through the top margin.

Special First Day of Issue Postmarks

G.P.O. Philatelic Bureau, Edinburgh 1 (Type C) .... 1·00
Bethlehem, Llandeilo, Carms (Type C) .... 2·50

309 R.M.S. *Queen Elizabeth* 2

310 Elizabethan Galleon

311 East Indiaman

312 *Cutty Sark*

313 S.S. *Great Britain*

314 R.M.S. *Mauretania*

(Des D. Gentleman)

1969 (15 Jan). *British Ships*. Chalk-surfaced paper. Two vertical phosphor
bands at right (1s.), one horizontal phosphor band (5d.) or two
phosphor bands (9d.). Perf 15×14.

778	**309**	5d. black, grey, red and turquoise	10	10
		a. Black (Queen's head, value, hull and inscr) omitted	£3500	
		b. Grey (decks, etc.) omitted	£225	
		c. Red (inscription) omitted	£225	
		Ey. Phosphor omitted	5·00	
		Eya. Red and phosphor omitted	£190	
779	**310**	9d. red, blue, ochre, brown, black and grey	10	10
		a. Strip of 3. Nos. 779/81	40	50
		ab. Red and blue omitted	£3250	
		ac. Blue omitted	£3250	
		Ey. Phosphor omitted	12·00	
		Eya. Strip of 3. Nos. 779/81. Phosphor omitted	40·00	
780	**311**	9d. ochre, brown, black and grey	10	10
		Ey. Phosphor omitted	12·00	
781	**312**	9d. ochre, brown, black and grey	10	10
		Ey. Phosphor omitted	12·00	
782	**313**	1s. brown, black, grey, green and greenish yellow	15	15
		a. Pair. Nos. 782/3	50	60
		ab. Greenish yellow omitted	£4500	
		Ey. Phosphor omitted	28·00	
		Eya. Pair. Nos. 782/3. Phosphor omitted	65·00	
783	**314**	1s. red, black, brown, carmine and grey	15	15
		a. Carmine (hull overlay) omitted	£40000	
		b. Red (funnels) omitted	£30000	
		c. Carmine and red omitted	£30000	
		Ey. Phosphor omitted	30·00	

Set of 6 .... 80 1·00
First Day Cover .... 1·50
Presentation Pack (P. O. Pack No. 5) .... 3·00
Presentation Pack (German) (P. O. Pack No. 5) .... 38·00

The 9d. and 1s. values were arranged in horizontal strips of three and pairs respectively throughout the sheet. No. 779ab is known only with the phosphor also omitted.

Special First Day of Issue Postmark

G.P.O. Philatelic Bureau, Edinburgh 1 (Type C) .... 1·75

315 Concorde in Flight

316 Plan and Elevation Views

317 Concorde's Nose and Tail

(Des M. and Sylvia Goaman (4d.), D. Gentleman (9d., 1s.6d.))

1969 (3 Mar). *First Flight of Concorde.* Chalk-surfaced paper. Two phosphor bands. Perf 15×14.

784	**315**	4d. yellow-orange, violet, greenish blue, blue-green and pale green...	10	10
		a. Violet (value etc.) omitted.................	£750	
		b. Yellow-orange omitted.....................	£750	
		Ey. Phosphor omitted...........................	1·00	
		Eya. Yellow-orange and phosphor omitted...	£750	
785	**316**	9d. ultramarine, emerald, red and grey-blue..	15	15
		a. Face value and inscr omitted..........	—	
		Ey. Phosphor omitted...........................	£100	
786	**317**	1s.6d. deep blue, silver-grey and light blue..	15	15
		a. Silver-grey omitted...........................	£750	
		Ey. Phosphor omitted...........................	9·00	
Set of 3..			35	35
First Day Cover				4·00
Presentation Pack (P. O. Pack No. 6)			7.50	
Presentation Pack (German)........................			75·00	

No. 785a is caused by a colour shift of the grey-blue. On the only known example the top of the Queen's head appears across the perforations at foot. No. 786a affects the Queen's head which appears in the light blue colour.

Special First Day of Issue Postmarks

G.P.O Philatelic Bureau, Edinburgh (Type C) .... 4·00
Filton, Bristol (Type C) .... 12·00

318 Queen Elizabeth II
(See also Type **357**)

(Des after plaster cast by Arnold Machin. Recess Bradbury, Wilkinson)

1969 (5 Mar). Perf 12.

787	**318**	2s.6d. brown	20	20
788		5s. crimson-lake................................	85	25
789		10s. deep ultramarine	3·00	3·75
790		£1 bluish black..................................	1·75	75
Set of 4..			5·00	4·50
First Day Cover				6·50
Presentation Pack (P. O. Pack No. 7)			16·00	
Presentation Pack (German)........................			55·00	

Special First Day of Issue Postmarks

G.P.O. Philatelic Bureau (Type C) .... 12·00
Windsor, Berks (Type C).. 18·00

For decimal issue, see Nos. 829/31b and notes after No. 831b in Machin Decimal Definitives section.

319 Page from *Daily Mail,* and Vickers FB-27 Vimy Aircraft

320 Europa and CEPT Emblems

321 ILO Emblem

322 Flags of NATO Countries

323 Vickers FB-27 Vimy Aircraft and Globe showing Flight

(Des P. Sharland (5d., 1s., 1s.6d.), M. and Sylvia Goaman (9d., 1s.9d.))

1969 (2 Apr). *Anniversaries* (2nd series). Events described on stamps. Chalk-surfaced paper. Two phosphor bands. Perf 15×14.

791	**319**	5d. black, pale sage-green, chestnut and new blue..................................	10	10
		Ey. Phosphor omitted............................		
792	**320**	9d. pale turquoise, dp blue, lt emerald-green and black.................	10	15
		aEy. Phosphor omitted............................		
		a. Uncoated paper*..............................	£1800	
		Ey. Phosphor omitted............................	18·00	
793	**321**	1s. brt purple, dp blue and lilac...........	15	20
		Eya. Phosphor omitted............................	10·00	
794	**322**	1s.6d. red, royal blue, yellow-green, black, lemon and new blue	15	20
		e. Black omitted	£125	
		f. Yellow-green (from flags) omitted.	85·00	
		g. Lemon (from flags) omitted	†	£4500
		Ey. Phosphor omitted	9·00	
		Eya. Yellow-green and phosphor omitted	85·00	
795	**323**	1s.9d. yellow-olive, greenish yellow and pale turquoise-green.........................	25	30
		a. Uncoated paper*..............................	£275	
		Ey. Phosphor omitted	6·00	
Set of 5..			65	80
First Day Cover..				1·10
Presentation Pack (P. O. Pack No. 9)			4·50	
Presentation Pack (German).........................			50·00	

*Uncoated paper. The second note after No. 744 also applies here.
No. 794g is only known used on First Day Cover from Liverpool.
A trial of the 9d value in green and red is known.

Special First Day of Issue Postmarks

G.P.O. Philatelic Bureau, Edinburgh (Type C) .... 1·10

324 Durham Cathedral

325 York Minster

326 St Giles, Edinburgh

327 Canterbury Cathedral

328 St Paul's Cathedral

329 Liverpool Metropolitan Cathedral

(Des P. Gauld)

1969 (28 May). *British Architecture* (1st series). Cathedrals. Chalk-surfaced paper. Two phosphor bands. Perf 15×14.

796	**324**	5d. grey-black, orange, pale bluish violet and black................................	10	10
		a. Block of 4. Nos. 796/9......................	40	50
		ab. Block of 4. Uncoated paper†	£1000	
		b. Pale bluish violet omitted................	£12500	
797	**325**	5d. grey-black, pale bluish violet, new blue and black.............................	10	10
		b. Pale bluish violet omitted................	£12500	
798	**326**	5d. grey-black, purple, green and black...	10	10
		c. Green omitted*....................................	£100	
799	**327**	5d. grey-black, green, new blue and black...	10	10
800	**328**	9d. grey-black, ochre, pale drab, violet and black...	15	20
		a. Black (value) omitted.........................	£250	
		Ey. Phosphor omitted............................	45·00	
		Eya. Black and phosphor omitted.........	£325	
801	**329**	1s.6d. grey-black, pale turquoise, pale reddish violet, pale yellow-olive and black......................................	20	25
		a. Black (value) omitted.........................	£2750	
		b. Black (value) double..........................	£500	
		Ey. Phosphor omitted............................	20·00	
Set of 6..			70	85
First Day Cover				1·00
Presentation Pack (P. O. Pack No. 10)............................			5·50	
Presentation Pack (German)..			35·00	

*The missing green on the roof top is known on R. 2/5, R. 8/5 and R. 10/5 but all are from different sheets and it only occurred in part of the printing, being "probably caused by a batter on the impression cylinder". Examples are also known with the green partly omitted.

†Uncoated paper. The second note after No. 744 also applies here.

Nos. 796/9 were issued together *se-tenant* in blocks of four throughout the sheet.

Special First Day of Issue Postmark

G.P.O. Philatelic Bureau, Edinburgh (Type C) .... 1·00

330 The King's Gate, Caernarvon Castle

331 The Eagle Tower, Caernarvon Castle

332 Queen Eleanor's Gate, Caernarvon Castle

333 Celtic Cross, Margam Abbey

334 H.R.H. The Prince of Wales (after photograph by G. Argent)

(Des D. Gentleman)

1969 (1 July). *Investiture of H.R.H. The Prince of Wales.* Chalk-surfaced paper. Two phosphor bands. Perf 14×15.

802	**330**	5d. dp olive-grey, lt olive-grey, dp grey, light grey, red, pale turquoise-green, black and silver ..	10	10
		a. Strip of 3. Nos. 802/4......................	30	50
		b. Black (value and inscr) omitted......	£700	
		c. Red omitted*......................................	£1250	
		d. Deep grey omitted**........................	£500	
		e. Pale turquoise-green omitted	£1250	
		f. Light grey omitted..............................	£9500	
		Ey. Phosphor omitted............................	5·00	
		Eya. Strip of 3. Nos. 802/4. Phosphor omitted...	15·00	
803	**331**	5d. dp olive-grey, lt olive-grey, dp grey, light grey, red, pale turquoise-green, black and silver ..	10	10
		b. Black (value and inscr) omitted......	£700	
		c. Red omitted*......................................	£1250	
		d. Deep grey omitted**........................	£500	
		e. Pale turquoise-green omitted	£1250	
		f. Light grey (marks on walls, window frames, etc) omitted	£9500	—
		Ey. Phosphor omitted............................	5·00	
804	**332**	5d. dp olive-grey, lt olive-grey, dp grey, lt grey, red, pale turquoise-green, black and silver	10	10
		b. Black (value and inscr) omitted......	£700	
		c. Red omitted*......................................	£1250	
		d. Deep grey omitted**........................	£500	
		e. Pale turquoise-green omitted	£1250	
		f. Light grey omitted..............................	£9500	
		Ey. Phosphor omitted............................	5·00	
805	**333**	9d. dp grey, lt grey, black and gold.....	15	20
		Ey. Phosphor omitted............................	25·00	
806	**334**	1s. blackish yellow-olive and gold	15	20
		Ey. Phosphor omitted............................	18·00	
Set of 5..			55	80
First Day Cover				1·00
Presentation Pack† (P. O. Pack No. 11).........................			3·00	
Presentation Pack (German)..			35·00	

Nos. 802/4 were issued together *se-tenant* in strips of three throughout the sheet.

* The 5d. value is also known with the red misplaced downwards and where this occurs the red printing does not take very well on the silver background and in some cases is so faint it could be mistaken for a missing red. However, the red can be seen under a magnifying glass and caution should therefore be exercised when purchasing copies of Nos. 802/4c.
** The deep grey affects the dark portions of the windows and doors.
† In addition to the generally issued Presentation Pack a further pack in different colours and with all texts printed in both English and Welsh was made available exclusively through Education Authorities for free distribution to all schoolchildren in Wales and Monmouthshire (*Price £40*).

No. 803f is only known commercially used on cover.

Special First Day of Issue Postmarks

G.P.O. Philatelic Bureau, Edinburgh 1 (Type C)	1·00
Day of Investiture, Caernarvon..	1·50

335 Mahatma Gandhi

"Tooth" flaw (Cyl. 2A, R. 20/3)

(Des B. Mullick)

1969 (13 Aug). *Gandhi Centenary Year.* Chalk-surfaced paper. Two phosphor bands. Perf 15×14.

807	**335**	1s.6d. black, green, red-orange and grey	25	30
		a. "Tooth" flaw.................................	35·00	
		b. Printed on the gummed side..........	£1750	
		Ey. Phosphor omitted............................	4·00	
First Day Cover				3·25

Special First Day of Issue Postmark

G.P.O. Philatelic Bureau, Edinburgh (Type C) .... 3·25

Collectors Pack 1969

1969 (15 Sept). Comprises Nos. 775/86 and 791/807.

CP807*b* Collectors Pack .... 10·00

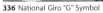

336 National Giro "G" Symbol

337 Telecommunications–
International Subscriber
Dialling

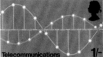

338 Telecommunications–
Pulse Code Modulation

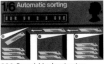

339 Postal Mechanisation–
Automatic Sorting

(Des D. Gentleman. Litho De La Rue)

1969 (1 Oct). *Post Office Technology Commemoration.* Chalk-surfaced paper. Two phosphor bands. Perf 13½×14.

808	**336**	5d. new blue, greenish blue, lavender and black..............	10	10
		Ey. Phosphor omitted	5·00	
809	**337**	9d. emerald, violet-blue and black	10	10
810	**338**	1s. emerald, lavender and black	15	15
		Ey. Phosphor omitted	£325	
811	**339**	1s.6d. bright purple, light blue, grey-blue and black	20	20
Set of 4..............			50	50
First Day Cover				75
Presentation Pack (P. O. Pack No. 13)............			5·00	

Special First Day of Issue Postmark

G.P.O.Philatelic Bureau, Edinburgh (Type C)............................ 75

340 Herald Angel

341 The Three Shepherds

342 The Three Kings

(Des F. Wegner. Queen's head (and stars 4d., 5d. and scrollwork 1s.6d.) printed in gold and then embossed)

1969 (26 Nov). *Christmas, Traditional Religious Themes.* Chalk-surfaced paper. Two phosphor bands (5d., 1s.6d.) or one centre band (4d.). Perf 15×14.

812	**340**	4d. vermilion, new blue, orange, brt purple, light green, bluish violet, blackish brown and gold	10	10
		a. Gold (Queen's head etc.) omitted..	£12000	
		Eb. Centre band 3½ mm	30	20
813	**341**	5d. magenta, light blue, royal blue, olive-brown, green, greenish yellow, red and gold	10	10
		a. Lt blue (sheep, etc.) omitted...........	£110	
		b. Red omitted*	£2200	
		c. Gold (Queen's head) omitted	£1200	
		d. Green omitted	£375	
		e. Olive-brown, red and gold omitted	£15000	
		Ef. Embossing omitted............................	25·00	
		Ey. Phosphor omitted	5·00	
814	**342**	1s.6d. greenish yellow, brt purple, bluish violet, orange, green, new blue and gold	15	15
		a. Gold (Queen's head etc.) omitted..	£150	
		b. Deep slate (value) omitted	£525	
		c. Greenish yellow omitted	£475	
		e. New blue omitted	£140	
		Ef. Embossing omitted............................	12·00	
		Ey. Phosphor omitted	6·00	
		Eya. Embossing and phosphor omitted	12·00	
Set of 3..............			30	30
First Day Cover				70
Presentation Pack (P. O. Pack No. 14)............			3·00	

* The effect of the missing red is shown on the hat, leggings and purse which appear as dull orange.

No. 812 has one centre band 8 mm. wide but this was of no practical use in the automatic facing machines and after about three-quarters of the stamps had been printed the remainder were printed with a 3½mm. band (No. 812Eb).

No. 813e was caused by a paper fold and also shows the phosphor omitted.

Used copies of the 5d. have been seen with the olive-brown or greenish yellow (tunic at left) omitted.

Special First Day of Issue Postmarks

P.O. Philatelic Bureau, Edinburgh (Type C)............................	70
Bethlehem, Llandeilo, Carms (Type C)..	1·00

343 Fife Harling

344 Cotswold Limestone

345 Welsh Stucco

346 Ulster Thatch

5d. Lemon omitted from left chimney (Cyl. 1H, R. 12/2)

(Des D. Gentleman (5d., 9d.), Sheila Robinson (1s., 1s.6d.))

1970 (11 Feb). *British Rural Architecture.* Chalk-surfaced paper. Two phosphor bands. Perf 15×14.

815	**343**	5d. grey, grey-black, black, lemon, greenish blue, orange-brown, ultramarine and green................	10	10
		a. Lemon omitted......................................	£160	
		b. Grey (Queen's head and cottage shading) omitted	—	
		c. Greenish blue (door) omitted..........	†	£4800
		d. Grey black (inscription & face value) omitted...................................	£20000	
		e. Grey black (face value only) omitted	£17000	
		f. Green omitted (cobblestones)		
		g. Lemon omitted from left chimney	35·00	
		Ey. Phosphor omitted	2·00	
816	**344**	9d. orange-brown, olive-yellow, bright green, black, grey-black and grey .	15	15
		Ey. Phosphor omitted	10·00	
817	**345**	1s. deep blue, reddish lilac, drab and new blue	15	15
		a. New blue omitted	£125	
		Ey. Phosphor omitted	15·00	
818	**346**	1s.6d. greenish yellow, black, turquoise-blue and lilac........................	20	25
		a. Turquoise-blue omitted	£17500	
		Ey. Phosphor omitted	5·00	
Set of 4..............			55	60
First Day Cover..............				85
Presentation Pack (P. O. Pack No. 15)..............			3.00	

Used examples of the 5d. exist, one of which is on piece, with the greenish blue colour omitted.

Special First Day of Issue Postmark

British Philatelic Bureau, Edinburgh (Type C) 85

347 Signing the Declaration of Arbroath

348 Florence Nightingale attending Patients

349 Signing of International Co-operative Alliance

350 Pilgrims and *Mayflower*

351 Sir William Herschel, Francis Baily, Sir John Herschel and Telescope

(Des F. Wegner (5d., 9d. and 1s.6d.), Marjorie Saynor (1s., 1s.9d.). Queen's head printed in gold and then embossed)

1970 (1 Apr). *Anniversaries* (3rd series). Events described on stamps. Chalk-surfaced paper. Two phosphor bands. Perf 15×14.

819	**347**	5d. black, yellow-olive, blue, emerald, greenish yellow, rose-red, gold and orange-red	10	10
		a. Gold (Queen's head) omitted	£3500	
		b. Emerald omitted	£475	
		Ey. Phosphor omitted	£375	
820	**348**	9d. ochre, deep blue, carmine, black, blue-green, yellow-olive, gold and blue	10	10
		a. Ochre omitted	£475	
		Eb. Embossing omitted	15·00	
		Ey. Phosphor omitted	5·00	
821	**349**	1s. green, greenish yellow, brown, black, cerise, gold and lt blue	15	15
		a. Gold (Queen's head) omitted	90·00	
		Eb. Green and embossing omitted	£150	
		c. Green omitted	£150	
		d. Brown omitted	£300	
		Ee. Embossing omitted	12·00	
		Ey. Phosphor omitted	5·00	
		Eya. Brown and phosphor omitted	£300	
		Eyb. Embossing and phosphor omitted	22·00	
822	**350**	1s.6d. greenish yellow, carmine, deep yellow-olive, emerald, black, blue, gold and sage-green	20	20
		a. Gold (Queen's head) omitted	£300	
		b. Emerald omitted	£150	
		Ec. Embossing omitted	6·00	
		Ey. Phosphor omitted	5·00	
823	**351**	1s.9d. black, slate, lemon, gold and bright purple	20	20
		a. Lemon (trousers and document) omitted	£10000	£6000
		Eb. Embossing omitted	75·00	
		Ey. Phosphor omitted	5·00	
		Set of 5	70	70
		First Day Cover		95
		Presentation Pack (P. O. Pack No. 16)	4·00	

No. 823a is known mint, or used on First Day Cover postmarked London WC.

352 "Mr. Pickwick and Sam Weller" (*Pickwick Papers*)

353 "Mr. and Mrs. Micawber" (*David Copperfield*)

354 "David Copperfield and Betsy Trotwood" (*David Copperfield*)

355 "Oliver asking for more" (*Oliver Twist*)

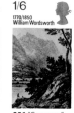

356 "Grasmere" (from engraving by J. Farrington, R.A.)

(Des Rosalind Dease. Queen's head printed in gold and then embossed)

1970 (3 June). *Literary Anniversaries* (1st series). Death Centenary of Charles Dickens (novelist) (5d.×4) and Birth Bicentenary of William Wordsworth (poet) (1s.6d.). Chalk-surfaced paper. Two phosphor bands. Perf 14×15.

824	**352**	5d. black, orange, silver, gold and magenta	10	10
		a. Block of 4. Nos. 824/7	40	60
		ab. Imperf (block of four)	£2250	
		ac. Silver (inscr) omitted (block of four)	—	
825	**353**	5d. black, magenta, silver, gold and orange	10	10
826	**354**	5d. black, light greenish blue, silver, gold and yellow-bistre	10	10
		b. Yellow-bistre (value) omitted	£8500	
827	**355**	5d. black, yellow-bistre, silver, gold and light greenish blue	10	10
		b. Yellow-bistre (background) omitted	£22000	
		c. Lt greenish blue (value) omitted*	£775	
		d. Lt greenish blue and silver (inscr at foot) omitted	£32000	
828	**356**	1s.6d. yellow-olive, black, silver, gold and bright blue	15	20
		a. Gold (Queen's head) omitted	£10000	
		b. Silver ("Grasmere") omitted	£250	
		c. Bright blue (face value) omitted	£20000	
		d. Bright blue and silver omitted	£25000	
		Ee. Embossing omitted	6·00	
		Ey. Phosphor omitted	5·00	
		Eya. Embossing and phosphor omitted	22·00	
		Set of 5	50	70
		First Day Cover		90
		Presentation Pack (P. O. Pack No. 17)	4·00	

Nos. 824/7 were issued together *se-tenant* in blocks of four throughout the sheet.
* No. 827c (unlike No. 826b) comes from a sheet on which the colour was only partially omitted so that, although No. 827 was completely without the light greenish blue colour, it was still partially present on No. 826.
Essays exist of Nos. 824/7 showing the Queen's head in silver and with different inscriptions. (*Price* £13000 *per block of 4*).

For Nos. 829/31*b* see Decimal Machin Definitives section.

358 Runners

359 Swimmers

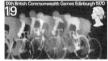

360 Cyclists

(Des A. Restall. Litho D.L.R.)

1970 (15 July). *Ninth British Commonwealth Games.* Chalk-surfaced paper. Two phosphor bands. Perf 13½×14.

832	**358**	5d. pink, emerald, greenish yellow and deep yellow-green	10	10
		a. Greenish yellow omitted	—	
		Ey. Phosphor omitted	£200	
833	**359**	1s.6d. light greenish blue, lilac, bistre-brown and Prussian blue	15	15
		Ey. Phosphor omitted	60·00	
834	**360**	1s.9d. yellow-orange, lilac, salmon and deep red-brown	15	15
Set of 3			45	45
First Day Cover				75
Presentation Pack (P. O. Pack No. 19)			3·00	

Special First Day of Issue Postmark

British Philatelic Bureau, Edinburgh (Type C) .... 1·00

Collectors Pack 1970

1970 Sept 14 Comprises Nos. 808/28 and 832/4.

CP834a	Collectors Pack	15·00

361 1d. Black (1840) **362** 1s. Green (1847) **363** 4d. Carmine (1855)

1840 first engraved issue 1847 first embossed issue 1855 first surface printed issue

(Des D. Gentleman)

1970 (18 Sept). *Philympia 70 Stamp Exhibition.* Chalk-surfaced paper. Two phosphor bands. Perf 14×14½.

835	**361**	5d. grey-black, brownish bistre, black and dull purple	10	10
		a. Dull purple (Queen's head) omitted	—	
		Ey. Phosphor omitted	5·00	
836	**362**	9d. light drab, bluish green, stone, black and dull purple	15	15
		Ey. Phosphor omitted	12·00	
837	**363**	1s.6d. carmine, light drab, black and dull purple	20	20
		Ey. Phosphor omitted	4·00	
Set of 3			40	40
First Day Cover				75
Presentation Pack (P. O. Pack No. 21)			3·00	

Special First Day of Issue Postmark

British Post Office Philatelic Bureau, Edinburgh (Type D) .... 1·00

364 Shepherds and Apparition of the Angel

365 Mary, Joseph and Christ in the Manger

366 The Wise Men bearing gifts

(Des Sally Stiff after De Lisle Psalter. Queen's head printed in gold and then embossed)

1970 (25 Nov). *Christmas,* Robert De Lisle Psalter. Chalk-surfaced paper. One centre phosphor band (4d.) or two phosphor bands (others). Perf 14×15.

838	**364**	4d. brown-red, turquoise-green, pale chestnut, brown, grey-black, gold and vermilion	10	10
		Ea. Embossing omitted	50·00	
		Ey. Phosphor omitted	60·00	
839	**365**	5d. emerald, gold, blue, brown-red, ochre, grey-black and violet	10	10
		a. Gold (Queen's head) omitted	†	£3500
		b. Emerald omitted	£140	
		c. Imperf (pair)	£400	
		d. Ochre omitted	£5500	†
		Ed. Embossing omitted	15·00	
		Ey. Phosphor omitted	5·00	
840	**366**	1s.6d. gold, grey-black, pale turquoise-green, salmon, ultramarine, ochre and yellow-green	15	15
		a. Salmon omitted	£220	
		b. Ochre omitted	£140	
		Ec. Embossing omitted	35·00	
		Ey. Phosphor omitted	5·00	
		Eya. Embossing and phosphor omitted		
Set of 3			30	30
First Day Cover				40
Presentation Pack (P. O. Pack No. 22)			4·00	

Special First Day of Issue Postmarks

British Post Office Philatelic Bureau, Edinburgh (Type D) 50
Bethlehem, Llandeilo, Carms .... 1·00

Nos. 841/880 are no longer used. For 1971-96 definitives in decimal currency with conventional perforations on all sides, see Nos. X841/1058 in the Decimal Machin Definitives section.

(New Currency. 100 new pence = £1)

368 *A Mountain Road*
(T. P. Flanagan)

369 *Deer's Meadow* (Tom Carr)

370 *Slieve na brock*
(Colin Middleton)

(Des Stuart Rose)

1971 (16 June). *Ulster 1971 Paintings.* |MULTI COLOUR| Chalk-surfaced paper.
Two phosphor bands. Perf 15×14.

881	**368**	3p. *A Mountain Road*		
		(T. P. Flanagan)	10	10
		Ey. Phosphor omitted	6·00	
		a. Venetian red omitted		—
882	**369**	7½p. *Deer's Meadow* (Tom Carr)	15	20
		a. Pale olive-grey omitted*	£380	
		Ey. Phosphor omitted	25·00	
883	**370**	9p. *Slieve na brock*		
		(Colin Middleton)	20	20
		a. Orange (*flowers*) omitted	£3500	
		Ey. Phosphor omitted	25·00	
Set of 3			40	45
First Day Cover				75
Presentation Pack (PO Pack No. 26a)			3·00	

* This only affects the boulder in the foreground, which appears
whitish and it only applied to some stamps in the sheet.

Special First Day of Issue Postmarks

British Post Office Philatelic Bureau, Edinburgh
(Type D, see Introduction) .... 1·10
Belfast .... 3·00
First Day of Issue handstamps, in the same design as that for
Belfast, were provided at Armagh, Ballymena, Coleraine, Cookstown,
Enniskillen, Londonderry, Newry, Omagh and Portadown for this issue.

371 John Keats (150th Death
Anniversary)

372 Thomas Gray (Death
Bicentenary)

373 Sir Walter Scott (Birth
Bicentenary)

(Des Rosalind Dease. Queen's head printed in gold and then embossed)

1971 (28 July). *Literary Anniversaries* (2nd series). |MULTI COLOUR| Chalk-surfaced
paper. Two phosphor bands. Perf 15×14.

884	**371**	3p. John Keats	10	10
		a. Gold (Queen's head) omitted	£275	
		Ey. Phosphor omitted	5·00	
885	**372**	5p. Thomas Gray	15	20
		a. Gold (Queen's head) omitted	£1200	
		Ey. Phosphor omitted	35·00	
886	**373**	7½p. Sir Walter Scott	20	20
		Eb. Embossing omitted	40·00	
		Ey. Phosphor omitted	25·00	
Set of 3			40	45
First Day Cover				75
Presentation Pack (PO Pack No. 32)			3·00	

Special First Day of Issue Postmarks

British Post Office Philatelic Bureau, Edinburgh
(Type D, see Introduction) .... 1·00
London EC .... 3·00

374 Servicemen and Nurse
of 1921

375 Roman Centurion

376 Rugby Football, 1871

(Des F. Wegner)

1971 (25 Aug). *Anniversaries* (4th series). Events described on stamps.
|MULTI COLOUR| Chalk-surfaced paper. Two phosphor bands. Perf 15×14.

887	**374**	3p. Servicemen and Nurse of 1921	10	10
		a. Deep blue omitted*	£950	
		b. Red-orange (nurse's cloak)		
		omitted	£850	
		c. Olive-brown (faces, etc.) omitted	£700	
		d. Black omitted		—
		e. Grey omitted		—
		f. Olive-green omitted		—
		Ey. Phosphor omitted	3·00	
888	**375**	7½p. Roman Centurion	15	20
		a. Grey omitted	£300	
		b. Ochre omitted		—
		Ey. Phosphor omitted	18·00	
889	**376**	9p. Rugby Football, 1871	20	20
		a. Olive-brown omitted	£325	
		b. New blue omitted	£9500	
		c. Myrtle-green omitted		£3000
		d. Lemon (jerseys) omitted		£3750
		Ey. Phosphor omitted	£450	
Set of 3			40	45
First Day Cover				1·00
Presentation Pack (PO Pack No. 32A)			3·00	

* The effect of the missing deep blue is shown on the sailor's
uniform, which appears as grey.

Special First Day of Issue Postmarks

British Post Office Philatelic Bureau, Edinburgh
(Type D, see Introduction) .... 1·10
Maidstone .... 5·00
Twickenham .... 5·00
York .... 5·00

377 Physical Sciences Building,
University College of Wales,
Aberystwyth

378 Faraday Building,
Southampton University

379 Engineering Department,
Leicester University

380 Hexagon Restaurant, Essex
University

(Des N. Jenkins)

1971 (22 Sept). *British Architecture* (2nd series). Modern University Buildings. |MULTI COLOUR Chalk-surfaced paper. Two phosphor bands. Perf 15×14.

890	**377**	3p. University College of Wales, Aberystwyth	10	10
		a. Lemon omitted	†	—
		b. Black (windows) omitted	£12500	
		Ey. Phosphor omitted	9·00	
891	**378**	5p. Southampton University	25	20
		Ey. Phosphor omitted	75·00	
892	**379**	7½p. Leicester University	20	30
		Ey. Phosphor omitted	15·00	
893	**380**	9p. Essex University	30	40
		a. Pale lilac omitted	†	
		Ey. Phosphor omitted	20·00	
Set of 4			55	75
First Day Cover				80
Presentation Pack (PO Pack No. 33)			5·00	

Mint examples of the 5p. exist with a larger 'P' following the face value.

No. 890a is only known used on commercial cover from Wantage.

No. 890b is only a partial omission with traces of black on the wall at the far right.

Special First Day of Issue Postmarks

British Post Office Philatelic Bureau, Edinburgh (Type D, see Introduction)	1·00
Aberystwyth	4·00
Colchester	4·00
Leicester	4·00
Southampton	4·00

Collectors Pack 1971

1971 (29 Sept). Comprises Nos. 835/40 and 881/93.

CP893a Collectors Pack	20·00

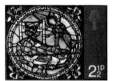 

381 Dream of the Wise Men   **382** Adoration of the Magi

383 Ride of the Magi

(Des Clarke-Clements-Hughes design team, from stained-glass windows, Canterbury Cathedral. Queen's head printed in gold and then embossed)

1971 (13 Oct). *Christmas, Stained-glass Windows*. |MULTI COLOUR Ordinary paper. One centre phosphor band (2½p.) or two phosphor bands (others). Perf 15×14.

894	**381**	2½p. Dream of the Wise Men	10	10
		a. Imperf (pair)	£550	
		Eb. Embossing omitted		
895	**382**	3p. Adoration of the Magi	10	10
		a. Gold (Queen's head) omitted	£2250	
		b. Carmine-rose omitted	£6250	
		c. Lemon (window panels) omitted	£250	
		d. New blue omitted	†	£7000
		e. Reddish violet (tunics etc) omitted	£8000	
		f. Carmine-rose and lemon omitted		£8000
		g. Reddish violet and embossing omitted		£5500
		Eh. Embossing omitted	15·00	
		Ey. Phosphor omitted	5·00	
		Eya. Embossing and phosphor omitted	£100	
896	**383**	7½p. Ride of the Magi	20	20
		a. Gold (Queen's head) omitted	£220	
		b. Lilac omitted	£1450	
		c. Emerald omitted	£750	
		d. Lemon omitted		£4500
		Ef. Embossing omitted	50·00	
		Ef. Embossing double	50·00	
		Ey. Phosphor omitted	12·00	
		Eya. Embossing and phosphor omitted	32·00	
Set of 3			35	35
First Day Cover				80
Presentation Pack (PO Pack No. 35)			2·25	

A used example of No. 894 has been reported with gold (Queen's head) omitted.

Special First Day of Issue Postmarks

British Post Office Philatelic Bureau, Edinburgh (Type D, see Introduction)	1·00
Bethlehem, Llandeilo, Carms	4·00
Canterbury	4·00

WHITE CHALK-SURFACED PAPER. From No. 897 all issues, with the exception of Nos. 904/8, were printed on fluorescent white paper, giving a stronger chalk reaction than the original cream paper.

384 Sir James Clark Ross   **385** Sir Martin Frobisher

386 Henry Hudson   **387** Robert Falcon Scott

(Des Marjorie Saynor. Queen's head printed in gold and then embossed)

1972 (16 Feb). *British Polar Explorers*. |MULTI COLOUR Two phosphor bands. Perf 14×15.

897	**384**	3p. Sir James Clark Ross	10	10
		a. Gold (Queen's head) omitted	£220	
		b. Slate-black (hair, etc.) omitted	£7500	
		c. Lemon omitted	£12000	
		Ed. Embossing omitted	45·00	
		Ee. Gold (Queen's head) and embossing omitted	£300	
		Ey. Phosphor omitted	5·00	
		Eya. Embossing and phosphor omitted	35·00	
898	**385**	5p. Sir Martin Frobisher	10	15
		a. Gold (Queen's head) omitted	£300	
		Eb. Embossing omitted	25·00	
		Ey. Phosphor omitted	12·00	
		Eya. Gold and phosphor omitted	£325	
		Eyb. Embossing and phosphor omitted		
899	**386**	7½p. Henry Hudson	10	15
		a. Gold (Queen's head) omitted	£400	
		Ey. Phosphor omitted	20·00	
900	**387**	9p. Robert Falcon Scott	20	25
		Ey. Phosphor omitted	£325	
Set of 4			45	60
First Day Cover				85
Presentation Pack (PO Pack No. 39)			4·00	

An example of the 3p. is known used on piece with the flesh colour omitted.

Special First Day of Issue Postmarks

Philatelic Bureau, Edinburgh	85
London WC	2·00

388 Statuette of Tutankhamun   **389** 19th-century Coastguard

390 Ralph Vaughan Williams and Score

(Des Rosalind Dease (3p.), F. Wegner (7½p.), C. Abbott (9p.). Queen's head printed in gold and then embossed (7½p., 9p.))

1972 (26 Apr). *Anniversaries* (5th series). Events described on stamps. |MULTI COLOUR| Two phosphor bands. Perf 15×14.

901	**388**	3p. Statuette of Tutankhamun	10	10
		a. Face value omitted	—	
902	**389**	7½p. 19th-century Coastguard	20	20
		Ea. Embossing omitted	£225	
		Ey. Phosphor omitted	£275	
903	**390**	9p. Ralph Vaughan Williams	20	25
		a. Gold (Queen's head) omitted	£3500	
		b. Brown (facial features) omitted	£4500	
		c. Deep slate omitted	—	
		Ed. Embossing omitted		
		Ey. Phosphor omitted	35·00	
	Set of 3		45	50
	First Day Cover			85
	Presentation Pack (PO Pack No. 40)		2·25	

391 St Andrew's, Greensted-juxta-Ongar, Essex

392 All Saints, Earls Barton, Northants

393 St Andrew's, Letheringsett, Norfolk

394 St Andrew's, Helpringham, Lincs

395 St Mary the Virgin, Huish Episcopi, Somerset

(Des R. Maddox. Queen's head printed in gold and then embossed)

1972 (21 June). *British Architecture* (3rd series). Village Churches. |MULTI COLOUR| Ordinary paper. Two phosphor bands. Perf 14×15.

904	**391**	3p. St Andrew's, Greensted-juxta-Ongar	10	10
		a. Gold (Queen's head) omitted	£250	
		b. Orange-vermilion omitted		£3500
		Ec. Embossing omitted	35·00	
		Ey. Phosphor omitted	8·00	
		Eya. Gold (Queen's head) and phosphor omitted	£350	
		Eyb. Embossing and phosphor omitted	22·00	
905	**392**	4p. All Saints, Earls Barton	10	10
		a. Gold (Queen's head) omitted	£6000	
		b. Violet-blue omitted	£300	
		Ec. Embossing omitted	12·00	
		Eya. Phosphor omitted	20·00	
		Eyb. Embossing and phosphor omitted		
906	**393**	5p. St Andrew's, Letheringsett	10	20
		a. Gold (Queen's head) omitted	£300	
		b. Red omitted	†	£3500

		Eb. Embossing omitted	50·00	
		Ey. Phosphor omitted	25·00	
907	**394**	7½p. St Andrew's, Helpringham	15	20
		Ey. Phosphor omitted	20·00	
		Eya. Embossing and phosphor omitted	50·00	
908	**395**	9p. St Mary the Virgin, Huish Episcopi	15	20
		Ea. Embossing omitted	22·00	
		Ey. Phosphor omitted	25·00	
	Set of 5		55	80
	First Day Cover			1·25
	Presentation Pack (PO Pack No. 41)		4·75	

Nos. 905a and 906a only exist with the phosphor omitted.

'Belgica 72' Souvenir Pack
1972 (24 June). Comprises Nos. 894/6 and 904/8.
CP908*b* Souvenir Pack .... 3·75

This pack was specially produced for sale at the 'Belgica '72' Stamp Exhibition, held in Brussels between 24 June and 9 July. It contains information on British stamps with a religious theme with text in English, French and Flemish, and was put on sale at Philatelic Bureaux in Britain on 26 June.

396 Microphones, 1924–69

397 Horn Loudspeaker

398 TV Camera, 1972

399 Oscillator and Spark Transmitter, 1897

(Des D. Gentleman)

1972 (13 Sept). *Broadcasting Anniversaries*. 75th Anniversary of Marconi and Kemp's Radio Experiments (9p.), and 50th Anniversary of Daily Broadcasting by the BBC (others). |MULTI COLOUR| Two phosphor bands. Perf 15×14.

909	**396**	3p. Microphones, 1924–69	10	10
		a. Greenish yellow (terminals) omitted	£4750	
910	**397**	5p. Horn Loudspeaker	10	10
		Ey. Phosphor omitted	6·00	
		Eya. Phosphor on back but omitted on front	45·00	
911	**398**	7½p. T.V. Camera, 1972	15	20
		a. Brownish slate (Queen's head) omitted	†	£3500
		Eya. Phosphor on back but omitted on front	45·00	
		Ey. Phosphor omitted	12·00	
912	**399**	9p. Oscillator and Spark Transmitter	15	20
		a. Brownish slate (Queen's head) omitted	£7500	
		Ey. Phosphor omitted	13·00	
	Set of 4		45	55
	First Day Cover			1·20
	Presentation Pack (PO Pack No. 43)		3·25	

In addition to the generally issued Presentation Pack a further pack exists inscribed '1922–1972'. This pack of stamps commemorating the 50th Anniversary of the BBC was specially produced as a memento of the occasion for the BBC staff. It was sent with the good wishes of the Chairman and Board of Governors, the Director-General and Board of Management. The pack contains Nos. 909/11 only (*Price* £35).

No. 911a is only found in First Day Covers posted from the Philatelic Bureau in Edinburgh.

400 Angel holding Trumpet

401 Angel playing Lute

402 Angel playing Harp

(Des Sally Stiff. Photo and embossing)

1972 (18 Oct). *Christmas, Angels.* |MULTI COLOUR One centre phosphor band (2½p.) or two phosphor bands (others). Perf 14×15.

913	**400**	2½p. Angel holding Trumpet	10	10
		a. Gold omitted	£1500	
		Eb. Embossing omitted	15·00	
		c. Deep grey omitted	£2800	
		Ey. Phosphor omitted	15·00	
914	**401**	3p. Angel playing Lute	10	10
		a. Red-brown omitted	£1100	
		b. Bright green omitted	£250	
		c. Bluish violet omitted	£300	
		d. Lavender omitted		
		e. Gold omitted	£1800	
		Ef. Embossing omitted	10·00	
		Ey. Phosphor omitted	8·00	
		Eya. Embossing and phosphor omitted	15·00	
915	**402**	7½p. Angel playing Harp	20	20
		a. Ochre omitted	£250	
		b. Blackish violet (*shadow*) omitted		
		Ec. Embossing omitted	20·00	
		Ey. Phosphor omitted	12·00	
		Eya. Embossing and phosphor omitted	30·00	
Set of 3			35	35
First Day Cover				85
Presentation Pack (PO Pack No. 44)			2·00	

The gold printing on the 3p. is from two cylinders: 1E and 1F. Examples have been seen with the gold of the 1F cylinder omitted, but these are difficult to detect on single stamps.

Special First Day of Issue Postmarks

Philatelic Bureau, Edinburgh		1·00
Bethlehem, Llandeilo, Carms		3·00

403 Queen Elizabeth and Duke of Edinburgh

404 'Europe'

(Des J. Matthews from photo by N. Parkinson)

1972 (20 Nov). *Royal Silver Wedding.* |MULTI COLOUR 'All-over' phosphor (3p.) or without phosphor (20p.). Perf 14×15.

I. 'Rembrandt' Machine

916	**403**	3p. Queen Elizabeth and Duke of Edinburgh	20	20
		a. Silver omitted	£700	
917		20p. Queen Elizabeth and the Duke of Edinburgh	60	60

II. 'Jumelle' Machine

918	**403**	3p. Queen Elizabeth and Duke of Edinburgh	50	50
Set of 2			75	75
Gutter Pair (No. 918)			1·50	
Traffic Light Gutter Pair			20·00	
First Day Cover				60
Presentation Pack (PO Pack No. 45)			2·00	
Presentation Pack (Japanese)			3·00	
Souvenir Book			1·20	

The souvenir book is a twelve-page booklet containing photographs of the Royal Wedding and other historic events of the royal family and accompanying information. The 3p. 'JUMELLE' has a lighter shade of the brownish black than the 3p. 'REMBRANDT'. It also has the brown cylinders less deeply etched, which can be distinguished in the Duke's face which is slightly lighter, and in the Queen's hair where the highlights are sharper.

3p. 'REMBRANDT'. Cyls. 3A-1B-11C no dot. Sheets of 100 (10×10).
3p. 'JUMELLE'. Cyls. 1A-1B-3C dot and no dot. Sheets of 100 (two panes 5×10, separated by gutter margin).

Special First Day of Issue Postmarks

Philatelic Bureau, Edinburgh		70
Windsor, Berks		2·50

Collectors Pack 1972
1972 (20 Nov). Comprises Nos. 897/917.

CP918a Collectors Pack		12·00

(Des P. Murdoch)

1973 (3 Jan). *Britain's Entry into European Communities.* |MULTI COLOUR Two phosphor bands. Perf 14×15.

919	**404**	3p. 'Europe' (lilac background)	10	10
920		5p. 'Europe' (new blue jigsaw pieces)	15	20
		a. Pair. Nos. 920/1	35	45
921		5p. 'Europe' (light emerald-green jigsaw pieces)	15	20
Set of 3			40	45
First Day Cover				70
Presentation Pack (PO Pack No. 48)			4·00	

Nos. 920/1 were printed horizontally *se-tenant* throughout the sheet.

Special First Day of Issue Postmark

Philatelic Bureau, Edinburgh		80

405 Oak Tree

(Des D. Gentleman)

1973 (28 Feb). *Tree Planting Year. British Trees* (1st issue). |MULTI COLOUR Two phosphor bands. Perf 15×14.

922	**405**	9p. Oak Tree	15	15
		a. Brownish black (value and inscr) omitted	£875	
		b. Brownish grey (Queen's head) omitted	£825	
		Ey. Phosphor omitted	90·00	
First Day Cover				40
Presentation Pack (PO Pack No. 49)			1·20	

See also No. 919.

Special First Day of Issue Postmark

Philatelic Bureau, Edinburgh		50

CHALK-SURFACED PAPER. The following issues are printed on chalk-surfaced paper but where 'all-over' phosphor has been applied there is no chalk reaction except in the sheet margins outside the phosphor area.

406 David Livingstone

407 Henry M Stanley

408 Sir Francis Drake   **409** Walter Raleigh

411   **412**   **413**

(T **411/13** show sketches of W G Grace by Harry Furniss)

(Des E. Ripley. Queen's head printed in gold and then embossed)

1973 (16 May). *County Cricket 1873–1973*. |MULTI COLOUR| 'All-over' phosphor. Perf 14×15.

928	**411**	3p. black, ochre and gold	10	10
		a. Gold (Queen's head) omitted	£6000	
		Eb. Embossing omitted	25·00	
929	**412**	7½p. black, light sage-green and gold	30	30
		Eb. Embossing omitted	35·00	
930	**413**	9p. black, cobalt and gold	40	40
		Eb. Embossing omitted	85·00	
Set of 3			75	75
First Day Cover				1·20
Presentation Pack (PO Pack No. 51)			3·25	
Souvenir Book			3·50	
PHQ Card (No. 928) (1)			35·00	150·00

Nos. 928/30 with two phosphor bands are known.

The souvenir book is a 24-page illustrated booklet containing a history of County Cricket with text by John Arlott.

The PHQ card did not become available until mid-July. The used price quoted is for an example used in July or August 1973.

Special First Day of Issue Postmarks

Philatelic Bureau, Edinburgh .... 1·40
Lords, London NW .... 3·00

410 Charles Sturt

(Des Marjorie Saynor. Queen's head printed in gold and then embossed)

1973 (18 Apr). *British Explorer*. |MULTI COLOUR| 'All-over' phosphor. Perf 14×15.

923	**406**	3p. David Livingstone	10	10
		a. Pair. Nos. 923/4	20	20
		b. Gold (Queen's head) omitted	£125	
		c. Turquoise-blue (background and inscr) omitted	£2500	
		d. Light orange-brown omitted	£1200	
		Ee. Embossing omitted	35·00	
924	**407**	3p. Henry M Stanley	10	10
		b. Gold (Queen's head) omitted	£125	
		c. Turquoise-blue (background and inscr) omitted	£2500	
		d. Light orange-brown omitted	£1200	
		Ee. Embossing omitted	35·00	
925	**408**	5p. Sir Francis Drake	20	20
		a. Gold (Queen's head) omitted	£275	
		b. Grey-black omitted	£3000	
		c. Sepia omitted	£6000	
		Ed. Embossing omitted	9·00	
926	**409**	7½p. Walter Raleigh	20	20
		a. Gold (Queen's head) omitted	£9000	
		b. Ultramarine (eyes) omitted	—	—
927	**410**	9p. Charles Sturt	20	20
		a. Gold (Queen's head) omitted	£250	
		b. Brown-grey printing double from .	£500	
		c. Grey-black omitted	£4000	
		d. Brown-red (rivers on map) omitted	£1200	
		Ee. Embossing omitted	40·00	
Set of 5			75	75
First Day Cover				90
Presentation Pack (PO Pack No. 50)			2·20	

Nos. 923/4 were issued horizontally *se-tenant* throughout the sheet.

Caution is needed when buying missing gold heads in this issue as they can be removed by using a hard eraser, etc., but this invariably affects the 'all-over' phosphor. Genuine examples have the phosphor intact. Used examples off cover cannot be distinguished as much of the phosphor is lost in the course of floating.

In the 5p. value the missing grey-black affects the doublet, which appears as brownish grey, and the lace ruff, which is entirely missing. The missing sepia affects only Drake's hair, which appears much lighter.

The double printing of the brown-grey (cylinder 1F) on the 9p., is a most unusual type of error to occur in a multicoloured photogravure issue. Two sheets are known and it is believed that they stuck to the cylinder and went through a second time. This would result in the following two sheets missing the colour but at the time of going to press this error has not been reported. The second print is slightly askew and more prominent in the top half of the sheets. Examples from the upper part of the sheet showing a clear double impression of the facial features are worth a substantial premium over the price quoted.

Special First Day of Issue Postmark

Philatelic Bureau, Edinburgh .... 1·00
First Day of Issue handstamps were provided at Blantyre, Glasgow, and Denbigh for this issue.

 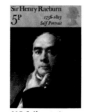

414 *Self-portrait* (Reynolds)   **415** *Self-portrait* (Raeburn)

416 *Nelly O'Brien* (Reynolds)   **417** *Rev. R. Walker* (The Skater) (Raeburn)

(Des S. Rose. Queen's head printed in gold and then embossed)

1973 (4 July). *British Paintings* (3rd series). 250th Birth Anniversary of Sir Joshua Reynolds and 150th Death Anniversary of Sir Henry Raeburn. |MULTI COLOUR| 'All-over' phosphor. Perf 14×15.

931	**414**	3p. *Self-portrait* (Reynolds)	10	10
		a. Gold (Queen's head) omitted	£160	
		Ec. Gold (Queen's head) and embossing omitted	£180	
932	**415**	5p. *Self-portrait* (Raeburn)	15	15
		a. Gold (Queen's head) omitted	£180	
		b. Greenish yellow omitted	£1200	
		Ec. Embossing omitted	30·00	
933	**416**	7½p. *Nelly O'Brien* (Reynolds)	15	15
		a. Gold (Queen's head) omitted	£250	
		b. Cinnamon omitted	£17500	
		Ec. Embossing omitted	25·00	
934	**417**	9p. *Rev. R. Walker (The Skater)* (Raeburn)	20	20
		b. Brownish rose omitted	£190	
		Ec. Embossing omitted	£150	

Set of 4	50	50
First Day Cover		80
Presentation Pack (PO Pack No. 52)	1·50	

Special First Day of Issue Postmark

Philatelic Bureau, Edinburgh	1·80

418 Court Masque Costumes

419 St Paul's Church, Covent Garden

420 Prince's Lodging, Newmarket

421 Court Masque Stage Scene

(Des Rosalind Dease. Litho and typo Bradbury Wilkinson)

1973 (15 Aug). *400th Birth Anniversary of Inigo Jones (architect and designer).* MULTICOLOUR 'All-over' phosphor. Perf 15×14.

935	**418**	3p. Court Masque Costumes	10	10
		a. Pair. Nos. 935/6	20	25
		ab. Face values omitted	£15000	
		Eac. Deep mauve ptg double (pair)	£5500	
		Ec. 9 mm phosphor band*	15·00	
936	**419**	3p. St Paul's Church, Covent Garden	10	10
937	**420**	5p. Prince's Lodging, Newmarket	15	
		a. Pair. Nos. 937/8	30	35
		Ec. 9 mm phosphor band*	18·00	
938	**421**	5p. Court Masque Stage Scene	15	
Set of 4			40	50
First Day Cover				70
Presentation Pack (PO Pack No. 53)			1·60	
PHQ Card (No. 936) (2)			95·00	95·00

The 3p. and 5p. values were printed horizontally *se-tenant* within the sheet.

No. 935ab is caused by the omission of virtually all the black printing from one horizontal row.

*On part of the printings for both values the 'all-over' phosphor band missed the first vertical row and a 9 mm phosphor band was applied to correct this.

Special First Day of Issue Postmark

Philatelic Bureau, Edinburgh	80

422 Palace of Westminster seen from Whitehall

423 Palace of Westminster seen from Millbank

(Des R. Downer. Recess and typo Bradbury Wilkinson)

1973 (12 Sept). *19th Commonwealth Parliamentary Conference.* MULTICOLOUR 'All-over' phosphor. Perf 15×14.

939	**422**	8p. Palace of Westminster seen from Whitehall	15	15
940	**423**	10p. Palace of Westminster seen from Millbank	20	20
Set of 2			30	30
First Day Cover				55
Presentation Pack (PO Pack No. 54)			1·50	
Souvenir Book			3·50	
PHQ Card (No. 939) (3)			18·00	70·00

The souvenir book is a twelve-page booklet containing a history of the Palace of Westminster.

Special First Day of Issue Postmark

Philatelic Bureau, Edinburgh	1·60

424 Princess Anne and Capt Mark Phillips

(Des C. Clements and E. Hughes from photo by Lord Lichfield)

1973 (14 Nov). *Royal Wedding.* 'All-over' phosphor. Perf 15×14.

941	**424**	3½p. Princess Anne and Capt Mark Phillips	10	10
		a. Imperf (horiz pair)	£7000	
942		20p. deep brown and silver	35	25
		a. Silver omitted	£7000	
Set of 2			40	30
Set of 2 Gutter Pairs			80	
Set of 2 Traffic Light Gutter Pairs			65·00	
First Day Cover				40
Presentation Pack (PO Pack No. 56)			1·20	
PHQ Card (No. 941) (4)			3·75	20·00

Special First Day of Issue Postmarks

Philatelic Bureau, Edinburgh	1·30
Westminster Abbey, London SW1	3·50
Windsor, Berks	3·50

425

426

427

428

429

430

(T **425/30** show scenes from the carol 'Good King Wenceslas')

(Des D. Gentleman)

1973 (28 Nov). *Christmas, Good King Wenceslas.* MULTICOLOUR One centre phosphor band (3p.) or 'All-over' phosphor (3½p.). Perf 15×14.

943	**425**	3p. King Wenceslas sees peasant	15	15
		a. Strip of 5. Nos. 943/7	90	1·10
		ab. Rosy mauve omitted (strip of 5)	£12000	
		b. Imperf (horiz strip of 5)	£5750	
		c. Black (face value) omitted*	£9500	
		Eg. Gum arabic	20	
		Ega. Strip of 5. Nos. 943Eg/7Eg	1·20	
		Egb. Imperf (strip of 5. Nos. 943 Eg/7Eg)	£5500	
944	**426**	3p. Page tells king about peasant	15	15
		Eg. Gum arabic	20	
945	**427**	3p. King and page set out	15	15
		Eg. Gum arabic	20	
946	**428**	3p. King encourages page	15	15
		Eg. Gum arabic	20	
947	**429**	3p. King and page give food to peasant	15	15
		Eg. Gum arabic	20	
948	**430**	3½p. Peasant, King and page	15	15
		a. Imperf (pair)	£475	
		b. Grey-black (value, inscr, etc.) omitted	£180	
		c. Salmon-pink omitted	£120	

d. Blue (leg, robes) omitted.................. £300
e. Rosy mauve (robe at right) omitted .. £160
f. Blue and rosy mauve omitted......... £600
g. Brt rose-red (King's robe) omitted.. £170
h. Red-brown (logs, basket, etc.)
omitted ....
i. Turquoise-green (leg, robe, etc.)
omitted £5250
j. Gold (background) omitted............. † —
Set of 6... 95 1·10
First Day Cover .... 1·20
Presentation Pack (PO Pack No. 57)...................... 1·80
The 3p. values depict the carol 'Good King Wenceslas' and were printed horizontally *se-tenant* within the sheet.
Examples of No. 948j are only known used on covers from Gloucester. The 3½p. has also been seen with the lavender-grey omitted used on piece.
No. 948h is only known used. The true error shows the pile of logs at night completely omitted.
The 3p. and 3½p. are normally with PVA gum with added dextrin, but the 3½p. also exists with normal PVA gum.
* No. 943c is known in a corner marginal strip of five showing a progressive dry print of black leaving a total omission on the first stamp. Adjacent similar strips of five all show traces of black.

Special First Day of Issue Postmark
Philatelic Bureau, Edinburgh.. 1·30
Bethlehem, Llandeilo, Carms... 2·75

Collectors Pack 1973
1973 (28 Nov). Comprises Nos. 919/48.
CP948k Collectors Pack... 11·50

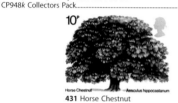

431 Horse Chestnut

(Des D. Gentleman)
1974 (27 Feb). *British Trees* (2nd issue). |MULTI COLOUR 'All-over' phosphor. Perf 15×14.
949   **431**   10p. Horse Chestnut........................ 20   15
Gutter Pair 40
Traffic Light Gutter Pair... 45·00
First Day Cover 40
Presentation Pack (PO Pack No. 59) .... 1·10
PHQ Card (5)... 80·00   80·00
The pack number is stated to be 58 on the reverse but the correct number is 59.

Special First Day of Issue Postmark
Philatelic Bureau, Edinburgh.. 50

432 First Motor Fire-engine, 1904

433 Prize-winning Fire-engine, 1863

434 First Steam Fire-engine, 1830   **435** Fire-engine, 1766

(Des D. Gentleman)
1974 (24 Apr). *Bicentenary of the Fire Prevention (Metropolis) Act.* |MULTI COLOUR 'All-over' phosphor. Perf 15×14.
950   **432**   3½p. First Motor Fire-engine, 1904 10   10
a. Imperf (pair)... £850
951   **433**   5½p. Prize-winning Fire-engine, 1863...... 10   10
952   **434**   8p. First Steam Fire-engine, 1830......... 15   20
953   **435**   10p. Fire-engine, 1766......................... 20   20
Set of 4... 50   55
Set of 4 Gutter Pairs .... 1·00
Set of 4 Traffic Light Gutter Pairs............................ 36·00
First Day Cover .... 1·10

Presentation Pack (PO Pack No. 60) .... 1·50
PHQ Card (No. 950) (6)............................ 65·00   70·00
The 3½p. exists with ordinary PVA gum.

Special First Day of Issue Postmark
Philatelic Bureau, Edinburgh.. 1·60

436 P & O Packet, *Peninsular*, 1888

437 Farman H.F. III Biplane, 1911

438 Airmail-blue Van and Postbox, 1930

439 Imperial Airways Short S.21 Flying Boat *Maia*, 1937

5½p. 'Bomb burst' damage to wheels at left (Cyl. 1C, R. 6/4)

(Des Rosalind Dease)
1974 (12 June). *Centenary of Universal Postal Union.* |MULTI COLOUR 'All-over' phosphor. Perf 15×14.
954   **436**   3½p. P & O Packet, *Peninsular*, 1888........ 10   10
955   **437**   5½p. Farman H.F. III Biplane, 1911.......... 10   10
a. 'Bomb burst'................................. 35·00
956   **438**   8p. Airmail-blue Van and Postbox,
1930.. 10   10
957   **439**   10p. Imperial Airways Short S.21 Flying
Boat *Maia*, 1937 15   15
Set of 4... 40   40
Set of 4 Gutter Pairs 80
Set of 4 Traffic Light Gutter Pairs............................ 28·00
First Day Cover 60
Presentation Pack (PO Pack No. 64) .... 2·00

Special First Day of Issue Postmark
Philatelic Bureau, Edinburgh.. 70

440 Robert the Bruce

441 Owain Glyndwr

442 Henry V

443 The Black Prince

(Des F. Wegner)
1974 (10 July). *Medieval Warriors.* |MULTI COLOUR 'All-over' phosphor. Perf 15×14.
958   **440**   4½p. Robert the Bruce....................... 10   10
959   **441**   5½p. Owain Glyndwr......................... 15   15
960   **442**   8p. Henry V.................................... 15   15
961   **443**   10p. The Black Prince...................... 15   15
Set of 4... 50   50
Set of 4 Gutter Pairs .... 1·00
Set of 4 Traffic Light Gutter Pairs............................ 40·00

First Day Cover .... 1·20
Presentation Pack (PO Pack No. 65) .... 1·60
PHQ Cards (set of 4) (7).. 12·00   30·00
Imperforate pairs of SG961 are known and thought to be of proof status (£700 *per pair*).

Special First Day of Issue Postmark

Philatelic Bureau, Edinburgh .... 1·75

444 Churchill in Royal Yacht Squadron Uniform

445 Prime Minister, 1940

446 Secretary for War and Air, 1919

447 War Correspondent, South Africa, 1899

(Des C. Clements and E. Hughes)

1974 (9 Oct). *Birth Centenary of Sir Winston Churchill.* MULTI COLOUR 'All-over' phosphor. Perf 14×15.

962	**444**	4½p. Churchill in Royal Yacht Squadron Uniform	10	10
963	**445**	5½p. Prime Minister, 1940	20	15
964	**446**	8p. Secretary for War and Air, 1919	30	30
965	**447**	10p. War Correspondent, South Africa, 1899	30	30
Set of 4			80	75
Set of 4 Gutter Pairs			1·60	
Set of 4 Traffic Light Gutter Pairs			22·00	
First Day Cover				80
Presentation Pack (PO Pack No. 66)			1·70	
Souvenir Book			1·50	
PHQ Card (No. 963) (8)			2·75	15·00

The souvenir book consists of an illustrated folder containing a biography of Sir Winston.

Nos. 962/5 come with PVA gum containing added dextrin, but the 8p. also exists with normal PVA.

Special First Day of Issue Postmark

Philatelic Bureau, Edinburgh .... 1·80
Blenheim, Woodstock, Oxford .... 4·00
House of Commons, London SW.. 4·00

448 Adoration of the Magi (York Minster, *circa* 1355)

449 The Nativity (St Helen's Church, Norwich, *circa* 1480)

450 Virgin and Child (Ottery St Mary Church, *circa* 1350)

451 Virgin and Child (Worcester Cathedral, *circa* 1224)

(Des Peter Hatch Partnership)

1974 (27 Nov). *Christmas, Church Roof Bosses.* MULTI COLOUR One phosphor band (3½p.) or 'All-over' phosphor (others). Perf 15×14.

966	**448**	3½p. York Minster	10	10

a. Light stone (background shading) omitted .... —
Ey. Phosphor omitted .... 12·00

967	**449**	4½p. St Helen's Church, Norwich	10	10
968	**450**	8p. Ottery St Mary Church	10	10
969	**451**	10p. Worcester Cathedral	15	15
Set of 4			40	40
Set of 4 Gutter Pairs			80	
Set of 4 Traffic Light Gutter Pairs			24·00	
First Day Cover				70
Presentation Pack (PO Pack No. 67)			1·50	

The phosphor band on the 3½p. was first applied down the centre of the stamp but during the printing this was deliberately placed to the right between the roof boss and the value; however, intermediate positions, due to shifts, are known.

Two used examples of the 3½p. have been reported with the light brown colour omitted.

Special First Day of Issue Postmarks

Philatelic Bureau, Edinburgh 80
Bethlehem, Llandeilo, Carms.. 1·75

Collectors Pack 1974
1974 (27 Nov). Comprises Nos. 949/69.
CP969a Collectors Pack .... 4·75

452 Invalid in Wheelchair

(Des P. Sharland)

1975 (22 Jan). *Health and Handicap Funds.* 'All-over' phosphor. Perf 15×14.

970	**452**	4½p. Invalid in Wheelchair	15	15
Gutter Pair			30	
Traffic Light Gutter Pair			2·25	
First Day Cover				30

Special First Day of Issue Postmark

Philatelic Bureau, Edinburgh 40

453 Peace - Burial at Sea

454 Snow Storm- Steam-boat off a Harbour's Mouth

455 The Arsenal, Venice

456 St Laurent

(Des S. Rose)

1975 (19 Feb). *Birth Bicentenary of J M W Turner* (*painter*). MULTI COLOUR 'All-over' phosphor. Perf 15×14.

971	**453**	4½p. Peace - Burial at Sea	10	10
972	**454**	5½p. Snow Storm-Steam-boat off a Harbour's Mouth	10	10
973	**455**	8p. The Arsenal, Venice	10	10
974	**456**	10p. St Laurent	15	15
Set of 4			40	40
Set of 4 Gutter Pairs			80	
Set of 4 Traffic Light Gutter Pairs			5·50	
First Day Cover				50
Presentation Pack (PO Pack No. 69)			1·50	
PHQ Card (No. 972) (9)			18·00	20·00

Special First Day of Issue Postmarks

London WC .... 1·50
Philatelic Bureau, Edinburgh 75

457 Charlotte Square, Edinburgh

458 The Rows, Chester

459 Royal Observatory, Greenwich

460 St George's Chapel, Windsor

461 National Theatre, London

(Des P. Gauld)

1975 (23 Apr). *European Architectural Heritage Year.* MULTI COLOUR 'All-over' phosphor. Perf 15×14.

975	**457**	7p. Charlotte Square, Edinburgh	10	10
		a. Pair. Nos. 975/6	20	20
976	**458**	7p. The Rows, Chester	10	10
977	**459**	8p. Royal Observatory, Greenwich	10	10
978	**460**	10p. St George's Chapel, Windsor	15	15
979	**461**	12p. National Theatre, London	20	20
Set of 5			60	60
Set of 5 Gutter Pairs			1·20	
Set of 5 Traffic Light Gutter Pairs			14·00	
First Day Cover				80
Presentation Pack (PO Pack No. 70)			1·50	
PHQ Cards (Nos. 975/7) (10)			4·75	10·00

Nos. 975/6 were printed horizontally *se-tenant* within the sheet.

Special First Day of Issue Postmark

Philatelic Bureau, Edinburgh .... 1·70

462 Sailing Dinghies

463 Racing Keel Yachts

464 Cruising Yachts

465 Multihulls

(Des A. Restall. Recess and photo)

1975 (11 June). *Sailing.* MULTI COLOUR 'All-over' phosphor. Perf 15×14.

980	**462**	7p. Sailing Dinghies	10	10
981	**463**	8p. Racing Keel Yachts	10	10
		a. Black omitted	£135	
982	**464**	10p. Cruising Yachts	15	15
983	**465**	12p. Multihulls	20	20
Set of 4			50	50
Set of 4 Gutter Pairs			1·00	
Set of 4 Traffic Light Gutter Pairs			17·50	
First Day Cover				70
Presentation Pack (PO Pack No. 71)			1·20	
PHQ Card (No. 981) (11)			2·75	8·00

On No. 981a the recess-printed black colour is completely omitted.

Special First Day of Issue Postmark

Philatelic Bureau, Edinburgh .... 1·20

A First Day of Issue handstamp was provided at Weymouth for this issue.

466 Stephenson's *Locomotion*, 1825

467 *Abbotsford*, 1876

468 *Caerphilly Castle*, 1923

469 High Speed Train, 1975

(Des B. Craker)

1975 (13 Aug). *150th Anniversary of Public Railways.* MULTI COLOUR 'All-over' phosphor. P 15×14.

984	**466**	7p. Stephenson's *Locomotion*, 1825......	10	10
985	**467**	8p. Abbotsford, 1876..........................	20	20
986	**468**	10p. *Caerphilly Castle*, 1923................	20	20
987	**469**	12p. High Speed Train, 1975.................	30	30
Set of 4			70	70
Set of 4 Gutter Pairs			1·40	
Set of 4 Traffic Light Gutter Pairs			7·50	
First Day Cover				90
Presentation Pack (PO Pack No. 72)			2·00	
Souvenir Book			1·60	
PHQ Cards (set of 4) (12)			30·00	30·00

The souvenir book is an eight-page booklet containing a history of the railways.

Special First Day of Issue Postmarks

Philatelic Bureau, Edinburgh	1·00
Darlington, Co. Durham	4·00
Shildon, Co. Durham	5·00
Stockton-on-Tees, Cleveland...	4·00

470 Palace of Westminster

(Des R. Downer)

1975 (3 Sept). *62nd Inter-Parliamentary Union Conference.* MULTI COLOUR 'All-over' phosphor. Perf 15×14.

988	**470**	12p. Palace of Westminster.......................	20	20
Gutter Pair			40	
Traffic Light Gutter Pair			2·25	
First Day Cover				30
Presentation Pack (PO Pack No. 74)			85	

Special First Day of Issue Postmark

Philatelic Bureau, Edinburgh 40

471 Emma and Mr Woodhouse (*Emma*)

472 Catherine Morland (*Northanger Abbey*)

473 Mr Darcy (*Pride and Prejudice*)

474 Mary and Henry Crawford (*Mansfield Park*)

(Des Barbara Brown)

1975 (22 Oct). *Birth Bicentenary of Jane Austen* (*novelist*). MULTI COLOUR 'All-over' phosphor. Perf 14×15.

989	**471**	8½p. Emma and Mr Woodhouse	10	10
990	**472**	10p. Catherine Morland	15	15
991	**473**	11p. Mr Darcy	15	15
992	**474**	13p. Mary and Henry Crawford	25	20
Set of 4			60	55
Set of 4 Gutter Pairs			1·20	
Set of 4 Traffic Light Gutter Pairs			7·00	
First Day Cover				75
Presentation Pack (PO Pack No. 75)			7·00	
PHQ Cards (set of 4) (13)			9·50	15·00

Special First Day of Issue Postmarks

Philatelic Bureau, Edinburgh	85
Steventon, Basingstoke, Hants	1·50

475 Angels with Harp and Lute   **476** Angel with Mandolin

477 Angel with Horn   **478** Angel with Trumpet

(Des R. Downer)

1975 (26 Nov). *Christmas, Angels.* MULTI COLOUR One phosphor band (6½p.), phosphor-inked background (8½p.), 'All-over' phosphor (others). Perf 15×14.

993	**475**	6½p. Angels with Harp and Lute	10	10
994	**476**	8½p. Angel with Mandolin	10	10
995	**477**	11p. Angel with Horn	20	15
996	**478**	13p. Angel with Trumpet	20	20
Set of 4			35	50
Set of 4 Gutter Pairs			1·10	
Set of 4 Traffic Light Gutter Pairs			5·00	
First Day Cover				50
Presentation Pack (PO Pack No. 76)			1·50	

The 6½p. exists with both ordinary PVA gum and PVA containing added dextrin.

Special First Day of Issue Postmarks

Philatelic Bureau, Edinburgh	60
Bethlehem, Llandeilo, Dyfed	1·00

Collectors Pack 1975

1975 (26 Nov). Comprises Nos. 970/96.

CP996a Collectors Pack	4·25

479 Housewife   **480** Policeman

481 District Nurse   **482** Industrialist

(Des P. Sharland)

1976 (10 Mar). *Telephone Centenary.* MULTI COLOUR 'All-over' phosphor. Perf 15×14.

997	**479**	8½p. Housewife	10	10
		a. Deep rose (vase and picture frame) omitted	£6750	
998	**480**	10p. Policeman	15	15
999	**481**	11p. District Nurse	15	15
1000	**482**	13p. Industrialist	25	20
Set of 4			60	55
Set of 4 Gutter Pairs			1·20	
Set of 4 Traffic Light Gutter Pairs			11·00	
First Day Cover				60
Presentation Pack (PO Pack No. 78)			1·40	

Special First Day of Issue Postmark

Philatelic Bureau, Edinburgh	70

483 Hewing Coal (Thomas Hepburn)   **484** Machinery (Robert Owen)

485 Chimney Cleaning (Lord Shaftesbury)   **486** Hands clutching Prison Bars (Elizabeth Fry)

(Des D. Gentleman)

1976 (28 Apr). *Social Reformers.* MULTI COLOUR 'All-over' phosphor. Perf 15×14.

1001	**483**	8½p. Hewing Coal (Thomas Hepburn)	10	10
1002	**484**	10p. Machinery (Robert Owen)	15	15
1003	**485**	11p. Chimney Cleaning (Lord Shaftesbury)	15	15
1004	**486**	13p. Hands clutching Prison Bars (Elizabeth Fry)	25	20
Set of 4			60	55
Set of 4 Gutter Pairs			1·20	
Set of 4 Traffic Light Gutter Pairs			5·00	
First Day Cover				60
Presentation Pack (PO Pack No. 79)			1·30	
PHQ Card (No. 1001) (14)			2·75	9·00

Special First Day of Issue Postmark

Philatelic Bureau, Edinburgh	70

487 Benjamin Franklin (bust by Jean-Jacques Caffieri)

(Des P. Sharland)

1976 (2 June). *Bicentenary of American Revolution.* MULTI COLOUR 'All-over' phosphor. Perf 14×15.

1005	**487**	11p. Benjamin Franklin	20	20
Gutter Pair			40	
Traffic Light Gutter Pair			2·25	
First Day Cover				50

Presentation Pack (PO Pack No. 80) 65
PHQ Card (15) .... 2·25   8·00

Special First Day of Issue Postmark

Philatelic Bureau, Edinburgh 60

488 'Elizabeth of Glamis'   **489** 'Grandpa Dickson'

490 'Rosa Mundi'   **491** 'Sweet Briar'

(Des Kristin Rosenberg)

1976 (30 June). *Centenary of Royal National Rose Society.* MULTI COLOUR 'All-over' phosphor. Perf 14×15.
1006	**488**	8½p. 'Elizabeth of Glamis'...............	10	10
1007	**489**	10p. 'Grandpa Dickson'.................	15	15
1008	**490**	11p. 'Rosa Mundi'......................	15	15
1009	**491**	13p. 'Sweet Briar'.....................	25	20
		a. Value omitted*..........................	—	

Set of 4... 60   55
Set of 4 Gutter Pairs... 1·20
Set of 4 Traffic Light Gutter Pairs.............................. 6·00
First Day Cover.. 60
Presentation Pack (PO Pack No. 81) .... 1·50
PHQ Cards (set of 4) (16).. 14·00   15·00

*During repairs to the cylinder the face value on R.1/9 was temporarily covered with copper. This covering was inadvertently left in place during printing, but the error was discovered before issue and most examples were removed from the sheets. Two mint and one used examples have so far been reported, but only one of the mint remains in private hands.

Special First Day of Issue Postmark

Philatelic Bureau, Edinburgh 70

492 Archdruid   **493** Morris Dancing

494 Scots Piper   **495** Welsh Harpist

(Des Marjorie Saynor)

1976 (4 Aug). *British Cultural Traditions.* MULTI COLOUR 'All-over' phosphor. Perf 14×15.
1010	**492**	8½p. Archdruid	10	10
1011	**493**	10p. Morris Dancing	15	15
1012	**494**	11p. Scots Piper	15	15
1013	**495**	13p. Welsh Harpist	25	20

Set of 4... 60   55
Set of 4 Gutter Pairs... 1·20
Set of 4 Traffic Light Gutter Pairs.............................. 6·00
First Day Cover.. 60
Presentation Pack (PO Pack No. 82) .... 1·30
PHQ Cards (set of 4) (17) .... 7·50   12·00

The 8½p. and 13p. commemorate the 800th anniversary of the Royal National Eisteddfod.

Special First Day of Issue Postmarks

Philatelic Bureau, Edinburgh 70
Cardigan, Dyfed .... 1·25

496 Woodcut from *The Canterbury Tales*   **497** Extract from *The Tretyse of Love*

498 Woodcut from *The Game and Playe of Chesse*   **499** Early Printing Press

(Des R. Gay. Queen's head printed in gold and then embossed)

1976 (29 Sept). *500th Anniversary of British Printing.* MULTI COLOUR 'All-over' phosphor. P 14×15.
1014	**496**	8½p. Woodcut from *The Canterbury Tales*	10	10
1015	**497**	10p. Extract from *The Tretyse of Love*......	15	15
1016	**498**	11p. Woodcut from *The Game and Playe of Chesse* ...	15	15
1017	**499**	13p. Early Printing Press..........................	25	25

Set of 4... 60   60
Set of 4 Gutter Pairs .... 1·20
Set of 4 Traffic Light Gutter Pairs.............................. 6·00
First Day Cover.. 65
Presentation Pack (PO Pack No. 83) .... 1·30
PHQ Cards (set of 4) (18) .... 6·00   9·00

Special First Day of Issue Postmarks

Philatelic Bureau, Edinburgh 75
London SW1 .... 1·00

500 Virgin and Child   **501** Angel with Crown

502 Angel appearing to Shepherds **503** The Three Kings

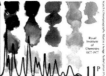
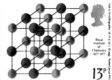

511 Starch - Chromatography **512** Salt - Crystallography

(Des Enid Marx)

1976 (24 Nov). *Christmas, English Medieval Embroidery.* |MULTI COLOUR| One phosphor band (6½p.) or 'All-over' phosphor (others). Perf 15×14.

1018	**500**	6½p. Virgin and Child	10	10
		a. Imperf (pair)	£750	
1019	**501**	8½p. Angel with Crown	15	15
1020	**502**	11p. Angel appearing to Shepherds	15	15
		a. Uncoated paper*	75·00	30·00
1021	**503**	13p. The Three Kings	20	20
Set of 4			55	55
Set of 4 Gutter Pairs			1·10	
Set of 4 Traffic Light Gutter Pairs			4·50	
First Day Cover				60
Presentation Pack (PO Pack No. 87)			1·40	
PHQ Cards (set of 4) (19)			1·80	5·00

*See footnote after No. 744.

Special First Day of Issue Postmarks

| Philatelic Bureau, Edinburgh | 70 |
| Bethlehem, Llandeilo, Dyfed | 1·25 |

Collectors Pack 1976
1976 (24 Nov). Comprises Nos. 997/1021.
CP1021*a* Collectors Pack................................ 5·50

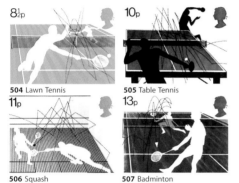

504 Lawn Tennis **505** Table Tennis

506 Squash **507** Badminton

(Des A. Restall)

1977 (12 Jan). *Racket Sports.* |MULTI COLOUR| Phosphorised paper. Perf 15×14.

1022	**504**	8½p. Lawn Tennis	10	10
		a. Imperf (horiz pair)	£2750	
1023	**505**	10p. Table Tennis	15	15
1024	**506**	11p. Squash	15	15
		a. Imperf (horiz pair)	£9000	
1025	**507**	13p. Badminton	20	20
Set of 4			55	55
Set of 4 Gutter Pairs			1·10	
Set of 4 Traffic Light Gutter Pairs			5·50	
First Day Cover				60
Presentation Pack (PO Pack No. 89)			1·50	
PHQ Cards (set of 4) (20)			3·40	8·00

The only known example of No. 1024a is cut close at left.

Special First Day of Issue Postmark

Philatelic Bureau, Edinburgh ....

For Nos. 1026/8 see Decimal Machin Definitives section

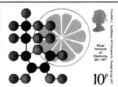

509 Steroids – Conformational Analysis **510** Vitamin C - Synthesis

(Des J. Karo)

1977 (2 Mar). *Royal Institute of Chemistry Centenary.* |MULTI COLOUR| 'All-over' phosphor. Perf 15×14.

1029	**509**	8½p. Steroids - Conformational Analysis	10	10
		a. Imperf (horiz pair)	£5000	
1030	**510**	10p. Vitamin C - Synthesis	15	15
1031	**511**	11p. Starch - Chromatography	15	15
1032	**512**	13p. Salt - Crystallography	20	20
Set of 4			55	55
Set of 4 Gutter Pairs			1·10	
Set of 4 Traffic Light Gutter Pairs			5·50	
First Day Cover				60
Presentation Pack (PO Pack No. 92)			1·50	
PHQ Cards (set of 4) (21)			3·40	8·00

Special First Day of Issue Postmark

Philatelic Bureau, Edinburgh 70

513 **514**

515 **516**

T **513/16** differ in the decorations of 'ER'.

(Des R. Guyatt)

1977 (11 May–15 June). *Silver Jubilee.* |MULTI COLOUR| 'All-over' phosphor. Perf 15×14.

1033	**513**	8½p. Pale turquoise-green background	10	10
		a. Imperf (pair)	£950	
1034		9p. Lavender background (15 June)	20	20
1035	**514**	10p. Ochre background	10	10
		a. Imperf (horiz pair)	£3000	
1036	**515**	11p. Rose-pink background	25	30
		a. Imperf (horiz pair)	£3000	
1037	**516**	13p. Bistre-yellow background	25	30
		a. Imperf (pair)	£2000	
Set of 5			80	85
Set of 5 Gutter Pairs			1·60	
Set of 5 Traffic Light Gutter Pairs			8·00	
First Day Covers (2)				90
Presentation Pack (Nos. 1033, 1035/7) (PO Pack No. 94)			1·00	
Souvenir Book			1·20	
PHQ Cards (set of 5) (22)			5·40	10·00

The Souvenir book is a 16-page booklet containing a history of the Queen's reign.

Special First Day of Issue Postmarks

Philatelic Bureau, Edinburgh (1033, 1035/7) (11 May)	50
Philatelic Bureau, Edinburgh (1034) (15 June)	50
Windsor, Berks (1033, 1035/7) (11 May)	1·00
Windsor, Berks (1034) (15 June)	50

517 'Gathering of Nations'

(Des P. Murdoch. Recess and photo)

1977 (8 June). *Commonwealth Heads of Government Meeting*, London. |MULTI COLOUR| 'All-over' phosphor. Perf 14×15.

1038	**517**	13p. 'Gathering of Nations'	20	
Gutter Pair			40	
Traffic Light Gutter Pair			1·75	
First Day Cover				40
Presentation Pack (PO Pack No. 95)			45	
PHQ Card (23)			1·20	1·50

Special First Day of Issue Postmarks

Philatelic Bureau, Edinburgh	45
London SW	55

518 Hedgehog

519 Brown Hare

520 Red Squirrel

521 Otter

522 Badger

(Des P. Oxenham)

1977 (5 Oct). *British Wildlife.* |MULTI COLOUR| 'All-over' phosphor. Perf 14×15.

1039	**518**	9p. Hedgehog	15	20
		a. Horiz strip of 5. Nos. 1039/43	70	95
		b. Imperf (vert pair)	£3000	
		c. Imperf (horiz pair. Nos. 1039/40)	£4750	
1040	**519**	9p. Brown Hare	15	20
1041	**520**	9p. Red Squirrel	15	20
1042	**521**	9p. Otter	15	20
1043	**522**	9p. Badger	15	20
Set of 5			70	95
Gutter Strip of 10			1·40	
Traffic Light Gutter Strip of 10			5·00	
First Day Cover				1·00
Presentation Pack (PO Pack No. 96)			1·00	
PHQ Cards (set of 5) (25)			1·50	2·50

Nos. 1039/43 were printed horizontally *se-tenant* within the sheet.

Special First Day of Issue Postmark

Philatelic Bureau, Edinburgh	1·10

523 'Three French Hens, Two Turtle Doves and a Partridge in a Pear Tree'

524 'Six Geese-a-laying, Five Gold Rings, Four Colly Birds'

525 'Eight Maids-a-milking, Seven Swans-a-swimming'

526 'Ten Pipers piping, Nine Drummers drumming'

527 'Twelve Lords a-leaping, Eleven Ladies dancing'

528 'A Partridge in a Pear Tree'

(Des D. Gentleman)

1977 (23 Nov). *Christmas, The Twelve Days of Christmas.* |MULTI COLOUR| One centre phosphor band (7p.) or 'All-over' phosphor (9p.). Perf 15×14.

1044	**523**	7p. 'Three French Hens, Two Turtle Doves and a Partridge in a Pear Tree'.	10	10
		a. Horiz strip of 5. Nos. 1044/8	50	50
		ab. Imperf (strip of 5. Nos. 1044/8)	£4500	
1045	**524**	7p. 'Six Geese-a-laying, Five Gold Rings, Four Colly Birds'	10	10
1046	**525**	7p. 'Eight Maids-a-milking, Seven Swans-a-swimming'	10	10
1047	**526**	7p. 'Ten Pipers piping, Nine Drummers drumming'	10	10
1048	**527**	7p. 'Twelve Lords a-leaping, Eleven Ladies dancing'	10	10
1049	**528**	9p. 'A Partridge in a Pear Tree'	10	20
		a. Imperf (pair)	£1800	
Set of 6			60	70
Set of 6 Gutter Pairs			1·20	
Traffic Light Gutter Pairs			3·75	
First Day Cover				75
Presentation Pack (PO Pack No. 97)			90	
PHQ Cards (set of 6) (26)			1·50	2·50

Nos. 1044/8 were printed horizontally *se-tenant* within the sheet.

Special First Day of Issue Postmarks

Philatelic Bureau, Edinburgh	75
Bethlehem, Llandeilo, Dyfed	80

Collectors Pack 1977

1977 (23 Nov). Comprises Nos. 1022/5 and 1029/49.

CP1049b Collectors Pack	3·75

529 Oil – North Sea

530 Coal – Modern Pithead Production Platform

531 Natural Gas – Flame Rising from Sea

532 Electricity – Nuclear Power Station and Uranium Atom

(Des P. Murdoch)

1978 (25 Jan). *Energy Resources.* |MULTI COLOUR| 'All-over' phosphor. Perf 14×15.

1050	**529**	9p. Oil	10	10
1051	**530**	10½p. Coal	15	15
1052	**531**	11p. Natural Gas	15	15
1053	**532**	13p. Electricity	20	20
Set of 4			55	55
Set of 4 Gutter Pairs			1·10	
Set of 4 Traffic Light Gutter Pairs			4·50	
First Day Cover				60
Presentation Pack (PO Pack No. 99)			85	
PHQ Cards (set of 4) (27)			1·50	2·50

Special First Day of Issue Postmark

Philatelic Bureau, Edinburgh 70

533 The Tower of London

534 Holyroodhouse

535 Caernarvon Castle

536 Hampton Court Palace

(Des R. Maddox (stamps), J. Matthews (miniature sheet))

1978 (1 Mar). *British Architecture* (4th series), Historic Buildings. |MULTI COLOUR| 'All-over' phosphor. Perf 15×14.

1054	**533**	9p. The Tower of London	10	10
1055	**534**	10½p. Holyroodhouse	15	15
1056	**535**	11p. Caernarvon Castle	15	15
1057	**536**	13p. Hampton Court Palace	20	20
Set of 4			55	55
Set of 4 Gutter Pairs			1·10	
Set of 4 Traffic Light Gutter Pairs			4·25	
First Day Cover				60
Presentation Pack (PO Pack No. 100)			75	
PHQ Cards (set of 4) (28)			1·50	2·50
MS1058 121×89 mm. Nos. 1054/7 (sold at 53½p.)			70	70
	a. Imperforate		£15000	
	b. Lt yellow-olive (Queen's head) omitted		£22000	
	c. Rose-red (Union Jack on 9p.) omitted		£7500	
	d. Orange-yellow omitted		£10000	
	e. New blue (Union Jack on 9p.) omitted			
First Day Cover				85

The premium on No. **MS**1058 was used to support the London 1980 International Stamp Exhibition. No. **MS**1058d is most noticeable on the 10½p. (spheres absent on towers) and around the roadway and arch on the 13p.

Special First Day of Issue Postmarks

Philatelic Bureau, Edinburgh (stamps)	80
Philatelic Bureau, Edinburgh (miniature sheet).	95
London EC (stamps)	90
London EC (miniature sheet)	1·00

537 State Coach

538 St Edward's Crown

539 The Sovereign's Orb

540 Imperial State Crown

(Des J. Matthews)

1978 (31 May). *25th Anniversary of Coronation.* |MULTI COLOUR| 'All-over' phosphor. Perf 14×15.

1059	**537**	9p. State Coach	15	20
1060	**538**	10½p. St Edward's Crown	20	20
1061	**539**	11p. The Sovereign's Orb	20	20
1062	**540**	13p. Imperial State Crown	25	25
Set of 4			70	75
Set of 4 Gutter Pairs			1·40	
Set of 4 Traffic Light Gutter Pairs			4·25	
First Day Cover				80
Presentation Pack (PO Pack No. 101)			85	
Souvenir Book			1·20	
PHQ Cards (set of 4) (29)			1·50	2·25

The souvenir book is a 16-page booklet illustrated with scenes from the Coronation.

Special First Day of Issue Postmarks

Philatelic Bureau, Edinburgh	85
London SW1	95

541 Shire Horse

542 Shetland Pony

543 Welsh Pony

544 Thoroughbred

(Des P. Oxenham)

1978 (5 July). *Horses.* |MULTI COLOUR| 'All-over' phosphor. Perf 15×14.

1063	**541**	9p. Shire Horse	10	10
		a. Imperf (vert pair)	—	
1064	**542**	10½p. Shetland Pony	15	15
1065	**543**	11p. Welsh Pony	15	15
1066	**544**	13p. Thoroughbred	20	20
Set of 4			55	55
Set of 4 Gutter Pairs			1·10	
Set of 4 Traffic Light Gutter Pairs			4·50	
First Day Cover				60
Presentation Pack (PO Pack No. 102)			75	
PHQ Cards (set of 4) (30)			1·00	1·80

Special First Day of Issue Postmarks

Philatelic Bureau, Edinburgh	65
Peterborough	75

545 'Penny-farthing' and 1884 Safety Bicycle

546 1920 Touring Bicycles

547 1978 Small-wheel Bicycles

548 1978 Road-racers

(Des F. Wegner)

1978 (2 Aug). *Centenaries of Cyclists' Touring Club and British Cycling Federation.* |MULTI COLOUR 'All-over' phosphor. Perf 15×14.

1067	**545**	9p. 'Penny-farthing' and 1884 Safety Bicycle	10	10
		a. Imperf (pair)	£675	
1068	**546**	10½p. 1920 Touring Bicycles	15	15
1069	**547**	11p. 1978 Small-wheel Bicycles	15	15
1070	**548**	13p. 1978 Road-racers	20	20
		a. Imperf (pair)	£2000	
Set of 4			55	55
Set of 4 Gutter Pairs			1·10	
Set of 4 Traffic Light Gutter Pairs			4·25	
First Day Cover				60
Presentation Pack (PO Pack No. 103)			75	
PHQ Cards (set of 4) (31)			1·00	1·80

Special First Day of Issue Postmarks

Philatelic Bureau, Edinburgh	65
Harrogate, North Yorkshire	75

549 Singing Carols round the Christmas Tree

550 The Waits

551 18th-century Carol Singers

552 'The Boar's Head Carol'

(Des Faith Jaques)

1978 (22 Nov). *Christmas, Carol singers.* |MULTI COLOUR One centre phosphor band (7p.) or 'All-over' phosphor (others). Perf 15×14.

1071	**549**	7p. Singing Carols round the Christmas Tree	10	10
		a. Imperf (pair)	£700	
1072	**550**	9p. The Waits	15	15
		a. Imperf (pair)	£2000	
1073	**551**	11p. 18th-century Carol Singers	15	15
		a. Imperf (horiz pair)	£2000	
1074	**552**	13p. 'The Boar's Head Carol'	20	20
Set of 4			55	55
Set of 4 Gutter Pairs			1·10	
Set of 4 Traffic Light Gutter Pairs			4·00	
First Day Cover				60
Presentation Pack (PO Pack No. 104)			75	
PHQ Cards (set of 4) (32)			1·00	1·80

Special First Day of Issue Postmarks

Philatelic Bureau, Edinburgh	65
Bethlehem, Llandeilo, Dyfed	70

Collectors Pack 1978

1978 (22 Nov). Comprises Nos. 1050/7 and 1059/74.

CP1074a	Collectors Pack	3·75

553 Old English Sheepdog

554 Welsh Springer Spaniel

555 West Highland Terrier

556 Irish Setter

(Des P. Barrett)

1979 (7 Feb). *Dogs.* |MULTI COLOUR 'All-over' phosphor. Perf 15×14.

1075	**553**	9p. Old English Sheepdog	10	10
1076	**554**	10½p. Welsh Springer Spaniel	15	15
1077	**555**	11p. West Highland Terrier	15	15
		a. Imperf (horiz pair)	£6750	
1078	**556**	13p. Irish Setter	20	20
Set of 4			55	55
Set of 4 Gutter Pairs			1·10	
Set of 4 Traffic Light Gutter Pairs			4·00	
First Day Cover				60
Presentation Pack (PO Pack No. 106)			70	
PHQ Cards (set of 4) (33)			80	1·50

Special First Day of Issue Postmarks

Philatelic Bureau, Edinburgh	65
London SW	75

557 Primroses

558 Daffodils

559 Bluebells

560 Snowdrops

(Des P. Newcombe)

1979 (21 Mar). *Spring Wild Flowers.* |MULTI COLOUR 'All-over' phosphor. Perf 14×15.

1079	**557**	9p. Primroses	10	10
		a. Imperf (vert pair)	£800	
1080	**558**	10½p. Daffodils	15	15
		a. Imperf (vert pair)	£3500	
1081	**559**	11p. Bluebells	15	15
		a. Imperf (horiz pair)	£3250	
1082	**560**	13p. Snowdrops	20	20
		a. Imperf (horiz pair)	£2500	
Set of 4			55	55
Set of 4 Gutter Pairs			1·10	
Set of 4 Traffic Light Gutter Pairs			4·00	
First Day Cover				60
Presentation Pack (PO Pack No. 107)			70	
PHQ Cards (set of 4) (34)			80	1·20

Special First Day of Issue Postmark

Philatelic Bureau, Edinburgh	65

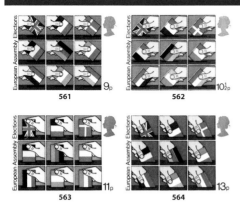

561   **562**

563   **564**

(Des S. Cliff)

1979 (9 May). *First Direct Elections to European Assembly.* |MULTI COLOUR (colours of backgrounds to flag panels given) Phosphorised paper. Perf 15×14.

1083	**561**	9p. dull ultramarine	10	10
1084	**562**	10½p. chestnut	15	15
1085	**563**	11p. grey-green	15	15
1086	**564**	13p. brown	20	20
Set of 4			55	55
Set of 4 Gutter Pairs			1·10	
Set of 4 Traffic Light Gutter Pairs			4·00	
First Day Cover				60
Presentation Pack (PO Pack No. 108)			70	
PHQ Cards (set of 4) (35)			80	1·20

Nos. 1083/6 show Hands placing National Flags in Ballot Boxes.

Special First Day of Issue Postmarks

Philatelic Bureau, Edinburgh	65
London SW	70

565 *Saddling 'Mahmoud' for the Derby, 1936* (Sir Alfred Munnings)

566 *The Liverpool Great National Steeple Chase, 1839* (aquatint by F. C. Turner)

567 *The First Spring Meeting, Newmarket, 1793* (J. N. Sartorius)

568 *Racing at Dorsett Ferry, Windsor, 1684* (Francis Barlow)

(Des S. Rose)

1979 (6 June). *Horseracing Paintings.* Bicentenary of the Derby (9p.). |MULTI COLOUR 'All-over' phosphor. Perf 15×14.

1087	**565**	9p. Saddling 'Mahmoud' for the Derby, 1936	10	10
1088	**566**	10½p. The Liverpool Great National Steeple Chase, 1839	15	15
1089	**567**	11p. The First Spring Meeting, Newmarket, 1793	15	15
1090	**568**	13p. Racing at Dorsett Ferry, Windsor, 1684	20	20
Set of 4			55	55
Set of 4 Gutter Pairs			1·10	
Set of 4 Traffic Light Gutter Pairs			4·50	
First Day Cover				60
Presentation Pack (PO Pack No. 109)			70	
PHQ Cards (set of 4) (36)			80	1·20

Special First Day of Issue Postmarks

Philatelic Bureau, Edinburgh	65
Epsom, Surrey	70

569 *The Tale of Peter Rabbit* (Beatrix Potter)

570 *The Wind in the Willows* (Kenneth Grahame)

571 *Winnie-the-Pooh* (A. A. Milne)

572 *Alice's Adventures in Wonderland* (Lewis Carroll)

(Des E. Hughes)

1979 (11 July). *International Year of the Child.* Children's Book Illustrations. |MULTI COLOUR 'All-over' phosphor. Perf 14×15.

1091	**569**	9p. The Tale of Peter Rabbit	15	15
1092	**570**	10½p. The Wind in the Willows	20	20
1093	**571**	11p. Winnie-the-Pooh	20	20
1094	**572**	13p. Alice's Adventures in Wonderland	25	25
Set of 4			75	75
Set of 4 Gutter Pairs			1·50	
Set of 4 Traffic Light Gutter Pairs			3·75	
First Day Cover				80
Presentation Pack (PO Pack No. 110)			1·00	
PHQ Cards (set of 4) (37)			80	1·40

Nos. 1091/4 depict original illustrations from four books.

Special First Day of Issue Postmark

Philatelic Bureau, Edinburgh 85

First Day of Issue handstamps were provided at Hartfield, East Sussex and Stourbridge, West Midlands for this issue.

573 Sir Rowland Hill

574 Postman, *circa* 1839

575 London Postman, *circa* 1839

576 Woman and Young Girl with Letters, 1840

(Des E. Stemp)

1979 (22 Aug–24 Oct). *Death Centenary of Sir Rowland Hill.* |MULTI COLOUR 'All-over' phosphor. Perf 14×15.

1095	**573**	10p. Sir Rowland Hill	15	15
		a. Imperf (horiz pair)	£8250	
1096	**574**	11½p. Postman, circa 1839	15	15
1097	**575**	13p. London Postman, circa 1839	20	20

1098	**576**	15p. Woman and Young Girl with Letters, 1840	25	25
Set of 4			70	70
Set of 4 Gutter Pairs			1·40	
Set of 4 Traffic Light Gutter Pairs			3·75	
First Day Cover				75
Presentation Pack (PO Pack No. 111)			80	
PHQ Cards (set of 4) (38)			50	1·20

MS1099 89×121 mm. Nos. 1095/8 (sold at 59½p.) (24 Oct) 70 75
- a. Imperforate £7250
- b. Brown-ochre (15p. background, etc.) omitted £8500
- c. Gold (Queen's head) omitted £750
- d. Brown-ochre, myrtle-green and gold omitted £20000
- e. Brt blue (13p. background, etc.) omitted £15000
- f. Myrtle-green (10p. (background), 15p.) omitted £8500
- g. Pale greenish yellow omitted £750
- h. Rosine omitted £2000
- i. Bistre-brown omitted £2000
- j. Grey-black and pale greenish yellow omitted .... —
- First Day Cover 80

The premium on No. **MS**1099 was used to support the London 1980 International Stamp Exhibition.

Examples of No. **MS**1099 showing face values on the stamps of 9p., 10½p., 11p. and 13p., with a sheet price of 53½p., were prepared, but not issued.

Special First Day of Issue Postmarks

Philatelic Bureau, Edinburgh (stamps) (22 Aug) 80
Philatelic Bureau, Edinburgh (miniature sheet) (24 Oct) 85
London EC (stamps) (22 Aug) 80
London EC (miniature sheet) (24 Oct) 85

First Day of Issue handstamps were provided at Kidderminster, Worcs on 22 August (pictorial) and 24 October (Type C) and at Sanquhar, Dumfriesshire on 22 August and 24 October (both Type C).

577 Policeman on the Beat

578 Policeman directing Traffic

579 Mounted Policewoman

580 River Patrol Boat

(Des B. Sanders)

1979 (26 Sept). *150th Anniversary of Metropolitan Police.* MULTI COLOUR Phosphorised paper. Perf 15×14.

1100	**577**	10p. Policeman on the Beat	15	15
1101	**578**	11½p. Policeman directing Traffic	15	15
1102	**579**	13p. Mounted Policewoman	20	20
1103	**580**	15p. River Patrol Boat	25	25
Set of 4			70	70
Set of 4 Gutter Pairs			1·40	
Set of 4 Traffic Light Gutter Pairs			3·75	
First Day Cover				75
Presentation Pack (PO Pack No. 112)			80	
PHQ Cards (set of 4) (39)			50	1·20

Special First Day of Issue Postmarks

Philatelic Bureau, Edinburgh 80
London SW 80

581 The Three Kings

582 Angel appearing to the Shepherds

583 The Nativity

584 Mary and Joseph travelling to Bethlehem

585 The Annunciation

(Des F. Wegner)

1979 (21 Nov). *Christmas, Nativity Scenes.* MULTI COLOUR One centre phosphor band (8p.) or phosphorised paper (others). Perf 15×14.

1104	**581**	8p. The Three Kings	10	10
		a. Imperf (pair)	£900	
1105	**582**	10p. Angel appearing to the Shepherds	15	15
		a. Imperf between (vert pair)	£2250	
		b. Imperf (pair)	£1200	
1106	**583**	11½p. The Nativity	15	15
1107	**584**	13p. Mary and Joseph travelling to Bethlehem	20	20
1108	**585**	15p. The Annunciation	20	20
Set of 5			75	75
Set of 5 Gutter Pairs			1·50	
Set of 5 Traffic Light Gutter Pairs			4·50	
First Day Cover				80
Presentation Pack (PO Pack No. 113)			80	
PHQ Cards (set of 5) (40)			50	1·20

Special First Day of Issue Postmarks

Philatelic Bureau, Edinburgh 85
Bethlehem, Llandeilo, Dyfed 85

Collectors Pack 1979
1979 (21 Nov). Comprises Nos. 1075/98 and 1100/8.
CP1108*a* Collectors Pack .... 4·50

586 Common Kingfisher

587 Dipper

588 Moorhen

589 Yellow Wagtails

(Des M. Warren)

1980 (16 Jan). *Centenary of Wild Bird Protection Act.* MULTI COLOUR Phosphorised paper. Perf 14×15.

1109	**586**	10p. Common Kingfisher	15	15
1110	**587**	11½p. Dipper	15	15
1111	**588**	13p. Moorhen	20	20
1112	**589**	15p. Yellow Wagtails	20	20
Set of 4			60	60
Set of 4 Gutter Pairs			1·20	
First Day Cover				65
Presentation Pack (PO Pack No. 115)			70	
PHQ Cards (set of 4) (41)			50	1·00

Special First Day of Issue Postmarks

Philatelic Bureau, Edinburgh 70
Sandy, Beds 75

590 *Rocket* approaching
Moorish Arch, Liverpool

591 First and Second Class
Carriages passing through Olive
Mount Cutting

592 Third Class Carriage and
Sheep Truck crossing Chat Moss

593 Horsebox and Carriage
Truck near Bridgewater Canal

594 Goods Truck and Mail-Coach
at Manchester

Grey step and dot above
(Cyl. 1A, R. 8/4)

(Des D. Gentleman)

1980 (12 Mar). *150th Anniversary of Liverpool and Manchester Railway.* Phosphorised paper. Perf 15×14.

1113	**590**	12p. *Rocket*...............................	15	10
		a. Strip of 5. Nos. 1113/17	75	60
		ab. Imperf (horiz strip of 5. Nos. 1113/17)	£7750	
		ac. Lemon omitted (horiz strip of 5. Nos. 1113/17)	£28000	
1114	**591**	12p. First and Second Class Carriages ...	15	10
1115	**592**	12p. Third Class Carriage and Sheep Truck...............	15	10
1116	**593**	12p. Horsebox and Carriage Truck	15	10
		a. Grey step............................	25·00	
1117	**594**	12p. Goods Truck and Mail-Coach...........	15	10
Set of 5.................................			75	60
Gutter Block of 10........................			1·50	
First Day Cover..........................				70
Presentation Pack (PO Pack No. 116)....			85	
PHQ Cards (set of 5) (42)................			50	1·20

Nos. 1113/7 were printed together, *se-tenant*, in horizontal strips of 5 throughout the sheet.

Special First Day of Issue Postmarks

Philatelic Bureau, Edinburgh 75
Liverpool 00
Manchester 80

INTERNATIONAL STAMP EXHIBITION
595 Montage of London Buildings

During the printing of No. 1118 the die was re-cut resulting in the following two types:

Type I (original). Top and bottom lines of shading in portrait oval broken. Hatched shading below left arm of Tower Bridge and hull of ship below right arm. Other points: Hatched shading on flag on Westminster Abbey, bottom right of Post Office Tower and archway of entrance to Westminster Abbey.

Type II (re-engraved). Lines in oval unbroken. Solid shading on bridge and ship. Also solid shading on flag, Post Office Tower and archway.

(Des J. Matthews. Eng G. Holt. Recess)

1980 (9 Apr–7 May). *London 1980 International Stamp Exhibition.* Phosphorised paper. Perf 14½×14.

1118	**595**	50p. Montage of London Buildings	75	70
		Ea. Type II.............................	75	70
Gutter Pair			1·50	
First Day Cover				75
Presentation Pack (PO Pack No. 117).....			85	
PHQ Card (43)			20	80
MS1119 90×123 mm. No. 1118Ea (sold at 75p.) (7 May)................			75	95
		a. Error. Imperf............................	£4500	
First Day Cover				95

Examples of No. 1118 are known in various shades of green.

Such shades result from problems with the drying of the printed sheets on the press, but are not listed as similar colours can be easily faked.

Philatelic Bureau, Edinburgh (stamp) (9 Apr.) 80
Philatelic Bureau, Edinburgh (miniature sheet) (7 May) ....1·00
London SW (stamp) (9 Apr.) ....1·00
London SW (miniature sheet) (7 May) ....1·00

10½p Buckingham Palace
596 Buckingham Palace

12p The Albert Memorial
597 The Albert Memorial

13½p Royal Opera House
598 Royal Opera House

15p Hampton Court
599 Hampton Court

17½p Kensington Palace
600 Kensington Palace

(Des Sir Hugh Casson)

1980 (7 May). *London Landmarks.* |MULTI COLOUR Phosphorised paper. Perf 14×15.

1120	**596**	10½p. Buckingham Palace	10	10
1121	**597**	12p. The Albert Memorial	15	15
		a. Imperf (vert pair)	£4000	
1122	**598**	13½p. Royal Opera House	20	15
		a. Imperf (pair)	£4000	
1123	**599**	15p. Hampton Court	20	20
1124	**600**	17½p. Kensington Palace	25	20
		a. Silver (Queen's head) omitted	£1100	
Set of 5			85	75
Set of 5 Gutter Pairs			4·25	
First Day Cover				80
Presentation Pack (PO Pack No. 118)			90	
PHQ Cards (set of 5) (43)			60	1·10

No. 1124a shows the Queen's head in pale greenish yellow, this colour being printed beneath the silver for technical reasons.

Philatelic Bureau, Edinburgh 85
Kingston-upon-Thames 85

601 Charlotte Brontë (*Jane Eyre*)

602 George Eliot (*The Mill on the Floss*)

603 Emily Brontë (*Wuthering Heights*)

604 Mrs Gaskell (*North and South*)

Normal

Missing jewel (R.3/3)

(Des Barbara Brown)

1980 (9 July). *Famous Authoresses.* |MULTI COLOUR Phosphorised paper. Perf 15×14.

1125	**601**	12p. Charlotte Brontë	15	15
		Ea. Missing 'p' in value (R. 4/6)	25·00	
		b. Missing jewel	25·00	
1126	**602**	13½p. George Eliot	15	15
		a. Pale blue omitted	£3250	
1127	**603**	15p. Emily Brontë	25	25
1128	**604**	17½p. Mrs Gaskell	30	30
		a. Imperf and slate-blue omitted (pair).	£850	
Set of 4			75	75
Set of 4 Gutter Pairs			1·50	
First Day Cover				80
Presentation Pack (PO Pack No. 119)			80	
PHQ Cards (set of 4) (44)			50	1·00

Nos. 1125/8 show authoresses and scenes from novels. Nos. 1125/6 also include the 'Europa' C.E.P.T. emblem.

Philatelic Bureau, Edinburgh 85
Haworth, Keighley, W. Yorks 90

605 Queen Elizabeth the Queen Mother

(Des J. Matthews from photograph by N. Parkinson)

1980 (4 Aug). *80th Birthday of Queen Elizabeth the Queen Mother.* |MULTI COLOUR Phosphorised paper. Perf 14×15.

1129	**605**	12p. Queen Elizabeth the Queen Mother..	25	25
		a. Imperf (horiz pair)	£2750	
Gutter Pair			50	
First Day Cover				50
PHQ Card (45)			20	40

Philatelic Bureau, Edinburgh 60
Glamis Castle, Forfar 65

606 Sir Henry Wood

607 Sir Thomas Beecham

608 Sir Malcolm Sargent

609 Sir John Barbirolli

(Des P. Gauld)

1980 (10 Sept). *British Conductors*. MULTI COLOUR Phosphorised paper. Perf 14×15.

1130	**606**	12p. Sir Henry Wood	15	15
1131	**607**	13½p. Sir Thomas Beecham	15	15
1132	**608**	15p. Sir Malcolm Sargent	25	25
1133	**609**	17½p. Sir John Barbirolli	30	30
Set of 4			75	75
Set of 4 Gutter Pairs			1·50	
First Day Cover				80
Presentation Pack (PO Pack No. 120)			80	
PHQ Cards (set of 4) (46)			60	1·00

Special First Day of Issues

Postmarks Philatelic Bureau, Edinburgh	85
London SW	90

610 Running

611 Rugby

612 Boxing

613 Cricket

(Des R. Goldsmith. Litho Questa)

1980 (10 Oct). *Sport Centenaries*. MULTI COLOUR Phosphorised paper. Perf 14×14½.

1134	**610**	12p. Running	15	15
		a. Gold (Queen's head) omitted	—	
1135	**611**	13½p. Rugby	15	15
1136	**612**	15p. Boxing	25	25
		a. Gold (Queen's head) omitted	£15000	
1137	**613**	17½p. Cricket	30	30
Set of 4			75	75
Set of 4 Gutter Pairs			1·50	
First Day Cover				80
Presentation Pack (PO Pack No. 121)			80	
PHQ Cards (set of 4) (47)			60	1·00

Centenaries: 12p. Amateur Athletics Association; 13½p. Welsh Rugby Union; 15p. Amateur Boxing Association; 17½p. First England-Australia Test Match.

Nos. 1134a and 1136a were caused by paper folds.

Special First Day of Issue Postmarks

Philatelic Bureau, Edinburgh	85
Cardiff	90

614 Christmas Tree   615 Candles

616 Apples and Mistletoe   617 Crown, Chains and Bell

618 Holly

(Des J. Matthews)

1980 (19 Nov). *Christmas.* |MULTI COLOUR| One centre phosphor band (10p.) or phosphorised paper (others). Perf 15×14.

1138	614	10p. Christmas Tree	10	10
		a. Imperf (horiz pair)	£2750	
1139	615	12p. Candles	15	15
1140	616	13½p. Apples and Mistletoe	15	15
		a. Imperf (pair)	£4000	
1141	617	15p. Crown, Chains and Bell	25	25
1142	618	17½p. Holly	25	25
Set of 5.......			80	80
Set of 5 Gutter Pairs.......			1·60	
First Day Cover.......				85
Presentation Pack (PO Pack No. 122).......			85	
PHQ Cards (set of 5) (48).......			75	1·00

Special First Day of Issue Postmarks

Philatelic Bureau, Edinburgh 90
Bethlehem, Llandeilo, Dyfed 95

Collectors Pack 1980
1980 (19 Nov). Comprises Nos. 1109/18 and 1120/42.
CP1142a Collectors Pack.. 5·50

619 St Valentine's Day   620 Morris Dancers

621 Lammastide   622 Medieval Mummers

T **619/20** also include the 'Europa' C.E.P.T. emblem.

(Des F. Wegner)

1981 (6 Feb). *Folklore.* |MULTI COLOUR| Phosphorised paper. Perf 15×14.

1143	619	14p. St Valentine's Day	20	20
1144	620	18p. Morris Dancers	20	20
1145	621	22p. Lammastide	30	35
1146	622	25p. Medieval Mummers	40	45
Set of 4.......			1·00	1·10
Set of 4 Gutter Pairs.......			2·00	
First Day Cover.......				1·10
Presentation Pack (PO Pack No. 124).......			1·10	
PHQ Cards (set of 4) (49).......			60	1·20

Nos. 1143/4 also include the 'Europa' C.E.P.T. emblem.

Special First Day of Issue Postmarks

Philatelic Bureau, Edinburgh ....1·20
London WC ....1·30

623 Blind Man with Guide Dog   **624** Hands spelling 'Deaf' in Sign Language

625 Disabled Man in Wheelchair   **626** Disabled Artist with Foot painting

(Des J. Gibbs)

1981 (25 Mar). *International Year of the Disabled.* |MULTI COLOUR| Phosphorised paper. Perf 15×14.

1147	623	14p. Blind Man with Guide Dog	20	20
		a. Imperf (pair)	£750	
1148	624	18p. Hands spelling 'Deaf'	20	20
1149	625	22p. Disabled Man in Wheelchair	35	35
1150	626	25p. Disabled Artist with Foot painting	45	45
Set of 4.......			1·10	1·10
Set of 4 Gutter Pairs.......			2·20	
First Day Cover.......				1·20
Presentation Pack (PO Pack No. 125).......			1·20	
PHQ Cards (set of 4) (50).......			60	1·20

All known examples of No. 1147a are creased.

Special First Day of Issue Postmarks

Philatelic Bureau, Edinburgh ....1·20
Windsor ....1·20

627 Small tortoiseshell   **628** Large Blue

629 Peacock   **630** Chequerd Skipper

(Des G. Beningfield)

1981 (13 May). *Butterflies.* |MULTI COLOUR| Phosphorised paper. Perf 14×15.

1151	627	14p. Small tortoiseshell	20	20
		a. Imperf (pair)	£9500	
1152	628	18p. Large Blue	20	20
1153	629	22p. Peacock	35	35
1154	630	25p. Chequerd Skipper	45	45
Set of 4.......			1·10	1·10
Set of 4 Gutter Pairs.......			2·20	
First Day Cover.......				1·20
Presentation Pack (PO Pack No. 126).......			1·20	
PHQ Cards (set of 4) (51).......			60	1·20

Special First Day of Issue Postmarks

Philatelic Bureau, Edinburgh ....1·20
London SW ....1·20

631 Glenfinnan, Scotland

632 Derwentwater, England

633 Stackpole Head, Wales

634 Giant's Causeway, Northern Ireland

635 St Kilda, Scotland

(Des M. Fairclough)

1981 (24 June). *50th Anniversary of National Trust for Scotland. British Landscapes.* |MULTI COLOUR| Phosphorised paper. Perf 15×14.

1155	**631**	14p. Glenfinnan, Scotland	20	20
1156	**632**	18p. Derwentwater, England	20	20
1157	**633**	20p. Stackpole Head, Wales	25	25
1158	**634**	22p. Giant's Causeway, Northern Ireland	35	35
1159	**635**	25p. St Kilda, Scotland	45	45
		Set of 5	1·30	1·30
		Set of 5 Gutter Pairs	2·60	
		First Day Cover		1·40
		Presentation Pack (PO Pack No. 127)	1·40	
		PHQ Cards (set of 5) (52)	75	1·40

Special First Day of Issue Postmarks
Philatelic Bureau, Edinburgh ....1·40
Glenfinnan ....1·40
Keswick ....1·40

636 Prince Charles and Lady Diana Spencer

(Des J. Matthews from photograph by Lord Snowdon)

1981 (22 July). *Royal Wedding.* |MULTI COLOUR| Phosphorised paper. Perf 14×15.

1160	**636**	14p. Prince Charles and Lady Diana Spencer	25	20
1161		25p. Prince Charles and Lady Diana Spencer	40	35
		Set of 2	60	50
		Set of 2 Gutter Pairs	1·20	
		First Day Cover		1·20
		Presentation Pack (PO Pack No. 127a)	1·10	
		Souvenir Book	1·20	
		PHQ Cards (set of 2) (53)	30	70

The souvenir book is a 12-page illustrated booklet with a set of mint stamps in a sachet attached to the front cover.

Special First Day of Issue Postmarks
Philatelic Bureau, Edinburgh ....1·20
Caernarfon, Gwynedd ....1·50
London EC ....1·30

637 'Expeditions'

638 'Skills'

639 'Service'

640 'Recreation'

(Des P. Sharland. Litho J.W.)

1981 (12 Aug). *25th Anniversary of Duke of Edinburgh's Award Scheme.* |MULTI COLOUR| Phosphorised paper. Perf 14.

1162	**637**	14p. 'Expeditions'	20	20
1163	**638**	18p. 'Skills'	20	20
1164	**639**	22p. 'Service'	35	35
1165	**640**	25p. 'Recreation'	45	45
		Set of 4	1·10	1·10
		Set of 4 Gutter Pairs	2·20	
		First Day Cover		1·20
		Presentation Pack (PO Pack No. 128)	1·20	
		PHQ Cards (set of 4) (54)	60	1·20

Special First Day of Issue Postmarks
Philatelic Bureau, Edinburgh ....1·30
London W2 ....1·50

641 Cockle-dredging from *Linsey II*

642 Hauling in Trawl Net

643 Lobster Potting

644 Hoisting Seine Net

(Des B. Sanders)

1981 (23 Sept). *Fishing Industry.* |MULTI COLOUR| Phosphorised paper. Perf 15×14.

1166	**641**	14p. Cockle-dredging from *Linsey II*	20	20
1167	**642**	18p. Hauling in Trawl Net	20	20
1168	**643**	22p. Lobster Potting	35	35
1169	**644**	25p. Hoisting Seine Net	45	45
		Set of 4	1·10	1·10
		Set of 4 Gutter Pairs	2·20	
		First Day Cover		1·20
		Presentation Pack (PO Pack No. 129)	1·20	
		PHQ Cards (set of 4) (55)	60	1·20

Nos. 1166/9 were issued on the occasion of the centenary of the Royal National Mission to Deep Sea Fishermen.

Special First Day of Issue Postmarks
Philatelic Bureau, Edinburgh ....1·30
Hull ....1·50

645 Father Christmas

646 Jesus Christ

647 Flying Angel

648 Joseph and Mary arriving at Bethlehem

649 Three Kings approaching Bethlehem

(Des Samantha Brown (11½p.), Tracy Jenkins (14p.), Lucinda Blackmore (18p.), Stephen Moore (22p.), Sophie Sharp (25p.))

1981 (18 Nov). *Christmas. Children's Pictures.* |MULTI COLOUR One phosphor band (11½p.) or phosphorised paper (others). Perf 15×14.

1170	**645**	11½p. Father Christmas	20	20
1171	**646**	14p. Jesus Christ	20	20
1172	**647**	18p. Flying Angel	20	20
1173	**648**	22p. Joseph and Mary arriving at Bethlehem	30	30
1174	**649**	25p. Three Kings approaching Bethlehem	40	40
Set of 5			1·20	1·20
Set of 5 Gutter Pairs			2·40	
First Day Cover				1·30
Presentation Pack (PO Pack No. 130)			1·30	
PHQ Cards (set of 5) (56)			75	1·30

Special First Day of Issue Postmarks

Philatelic Bureau, Edinburgh ....1·50
Bethlehem, Llandeilo, Dyfed ....1·50

Collectors Pack 1981

1981 (18 Nov). Comprises Nos. 1143/74.
CP11/4a Collectors Pack...7·25

650 Charles Darwin and Giant Tortoises

651 Darwin and Marine Iguanas

652 Darwin, Cactus Ground Finch and Large Ground Finch

653 Darwin and Prehistoric Skulls

(Des D. Gentleman)

1982 (10 Feb). *Death Centenary of Charles Darwin.* |MULTI COLOUR Phosphorised paper. Perf 15×14.

1175	**650**	15½p. Charles Darwin and Giant Tortoises	20	20
1176	**651**	19½p. Darwin and Marine Iguanas	25	25
1177	**652**	26p. Darwin, Cactus Ground Finch and Large Ground Finch	35	35
1178	**653**	29p. Darwin and Prehistoric Skulls	50	50
Set of 4			1·20	1·20
Set of 4 Gutter Pairs			2·40	
First Day Cover				1·30
Presentation Pack (PO Pack No. 132)			1·30	
PHQ Cards (set of 4) (57)			60	1·30

Special First Day of Issue Postmarks

Philatelic Bureau, Edinburgh ....1·50
Shrewsbury ....1·50

654 Boys' Brigade

655 Girls' Brigade

656 Boy Scout Movement

657 Girl Guide Movement

(Des B. Sanders)

1982 (24 Mar). *Youth Organizations.* |MULTI COLOUR Phosphorised paper. Perf 14×15.

1179	**654**	15½p. Boys' Brigade	20	20
1180	**655**	19½p. Girls' Brigade	25	25
1181	**656**	26p. Boy Scout Movement	35	35
1182	**657**	29p. Girl Guide Movement	50	50
Set of 4			1·20	1·20
Set of 4 Gutter Pairs			2·40	
First Day Cover				1·30
Presentation Pack (PO Pack No. 133)			1·30	
PHQ Cards (set of 4) (58)			60	1·30

Nos. 1179/82 were issued on the occasion of the 75th anniversary of the Boy Scout Movement; the 125th birth anniversary of Lord Baden-Powell and the centenary of the Boys' Brigade (1983).

Special First Day of Issue Postmarks

Edinburgh Philatelic Bureau ....1·50
Glasgow ....1·50
London SW ....1·50

658 Ballerina

659 Harlequin

26ᴾ

29ᴾ

660 Hamlet

661 Opera Singer

(Des A. George)

1982 (28 Apr). *Europa. British Theatre.* |MULTI COLOUR Phosphorised paper. Perf 14×15.

1183	**658**	15½p. Ballerina	20	20
1184	**659**	19½p. Harlequin	25	25
1185	**660**	26p. Hamlet	35	35
1186	**661**	29p. Opera Singer	50	50
Set of 4			1·20	1·20
Set of 4 Gutter Pairs			2·40	
First Day Cover				1·30
Presentation Pack (PO Pack No. 134)			1·30	
PHQ Cards (set of 4) (59)			60	1·30

Special First Day of Issue Postmarks

Philatelic Bureau, Edinburgh	1·50
Stratford-upon-Avon	1·50

15½ᴾ
HENRY VIII/MARY ROSE

19½ᴾ
ADMIRAL BLAKE/TRIUMPH

662 Henry VIII and *Mary Rose*

663 Admiral Blake and *Triumph*

24ᴾ
LORD NELSON/HMS VICTORY

26ᴾ
LORD FISHER/HMS DREADNOUGHT

664 Lord Nelson and HMS *Victory*

665 Lord Fisher and HMS *Dreadnought*

29ᴾ
VISCOUNT CUNNINGHAM/HMS WARSPITE

666 Viscount Cunningham and H.M.S. *Warspite*

(Des Marjorie Saynor. Eng Czesław Slania. Recess and photo)

1982 (16 June). *Maritime Heritage.* |MULTI COLOUR Phosphorised paper. Perf 15×14.

1187	**662**	15½p. Henry VIII and *Mary Rose*	20	20
		a. Imperf (pair)	£3500	
1188	**663**	19½p. Admiral Blake and *Triumph*	25	25
1189	**664**	24p. Lord Nelson and HMS *Victory*	35	35
1190	**665**	26p. Lord Fisher and HMS *Dreadnought*	40	40
		a. Imperf (pair)	£7500	
1191	**666**	29p. Viscount Cunningham and HMS. *Warspite*	50	50
Set of 5			1·60	1·60
Set of 5 Gutter Pairs			3·20	
First Day Cover				1·75
Presentation Pack (PO Pack No. 136)			1·75	
PHQ Cards (set of 5) (60)			75	1·80

Nos. 1187/91 were issued on the occasion of Maritime England Year, the Bicentenary of the Livery Grant by the City of London to the Worshipful Company of Shipwrights and the raising of the *Mary Rose* from Portsmouth Harbour.

Several used examples of the 15½p. have been seen with the black recess (ship and waves) omitted.................................£1250

Special First Day of Issue Postmarks

Philatelic Bureau, Edinburgh	1·75
Portsmouth	1·75

15½ᴾ
British Textiles
William Morris: Strawberry Thief

19½ᴾ
British Textiles
Steiner & Co. Untitled

667 'Strawberry Thief' (William Morris)

668 Untitled (Steiner and Co)

26ᴾ

British Textiles
Paul Nash: Cherry Orchard

29ᴾ
British Textiles
Andrew Foster: Chevron

669 'Cherry Orchard' (Paul Nash)

670 'Chevron' (Andrew Foster)

(Des Peter Hatch Partnership)

1982 (23 July). *British Textiles.* |MULTI COLOUR Phosphorised paper. Perf 14×15.

1192	**667**	15½p. 'Strawberry Thief' (William Morris)	20	20
		a. Imperf (horiz pair)	£3250	
1193	**668**	19½p. Untitled (Steiner and Co)	25	25
		a. Imperf (vert pair)	£6500	
1194	**669**	26p. 'Cherry Orchard' (Paul Nash)	35	35
1195	**670**	29p. 'Chevron' (Andrew Foster)	50	50
Set of 4			1·20	1·20
Set of 4 Gutter Pairs			2·40	
First Day Cover				1·30
Presentation Pack (PO Pack No. 137)			1·30	
PHQ Cards (set of 4) (61)			60	1·30

Nos. 1192/5 were issued on the occasion of the 250th birth anniversary of Sir Richard Arkwright (inventor of spinning machine).

Special First Day of Issue Postmarks

Philatelic Bureau, Edinburgh	1·30
Rochdale	1·30

15½ᴾ
INFORMATION TECHNOLOGY

671 Development of Communications

26ᴾ
INFORMATION TECHNOLOGY

672 Technological Aids

(Des Delaney and Ireland)

1982 (8 Sept). *Information Technology.* |MULTI COLOUR Phosphorised paper. Perf 14×15.

1196	**671**	15½p. Development of Communications.	25	25
		a. Imperf (pair)	£550	
1197	**672**	26p. Technological Aids	35	35
		a. Imperf (pair)	£3750	
Set of 2			55	55
Set of 2 Gutter Pairs			1·10	
First Day Cover				60
Presentation Pack (PO Pack No. 138)			60	
PHQ Cards (set of 2) (62)			30	60

Special First Day of Issue Postmarks

Philatelic Bureau, Edinburgh	60
London WC	60

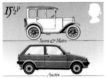
673 Austin 'Seven' and 'Metro'

674 Ford 'Model T' and 'Escort'

675 Jaguar 'SS 1' and 'XJ6'

676 Rolls-Royce 'Silver Ghost' and 'Silver Spirit'

(Des S. Paine. Litho Questa)

1982 (13 Oct). *British Motor Cars.* MULTI/COLOUR Phosphorised paper. Perf 14½×14.

1198	**673**	15½p. Austin 'Seven' and 'Metro'	20	20
1199	**674**	19½p. Ford 'Model T' and 'Escort'	25	25
		Ea. Rose-red, grey and black ptgs double	£1400	
		Eb. Black printed double	£4750	
1200	**675**	26p. Jaguar 'SS 1' and 'XJ6'	35	35
1201	**676**	29p. Rolls-Royce 'Silver Ghost' and 'Silver Spirit'	50	50
		Ea. Black ptg quadruple	£1100	
		Eb. Brt orange, carmine-red, grey and black ptgs double	£1800	
		Ec. Black ptg quadruple grey ptg triple and purple and carmine ptgs double	£1800	
Set of 4			1·20	1·20
Set of 4 Gutter Pairs			2·40	
First Day Cover				1·30
Presentation Pack (PO Pack No. 139)			1·30	
PHQ Cards (set of 4) (63)			60	1·30

The price for Nos. 1199Eb is for a complete doubling of both cars, examples showing doubling of only one car or parts of two cars are worth less.

Special First Day of Issue Postmarks

Philatelic Bureau, Edinburgh	1·30
Birmingham	1·50
Crewe	1·50

677 'While Shepherds Watched'

678 'The Holly and the Ivy'

679 'I Saw Three Ships'

680 'We Three Kings'

681 'Good King Wenceslas'

(Des Barbara Brown)

1982 (17 Nov). *Christmas. Carols.* MULTI/COLOUR One phosphor band (12½p.) or phosphorised paper (others). Perf 15×14.

1202	**677**	12½p. 'While Shepherds Watched'	20	20
1203	**678**	15½p. 'The Holly and the Ivy'	20	20
		a. Imperf (pair)	£5000	
1204	**679**	19½p. 'I Saw Three Ships'	25	25
		a. Imperf (pair)	£5500	
1205	**680**	26p. 'We Three Kings'	35	30

1206	**681**	29p. 'Good King Wenceslas'	50	50
Set of 5			1·35	1·35
Set of 5 Gutter Pairs			2·70	
First Day Cover				1·40
Presentation Pack (PO Pack No. 140)			1·40	
PHQ Cards (set of 5) (64)			75	1·40

Special Day of Issue Postmarks

Philatelic Bureau, Edinburgh	1·40
Bethlehem, Llandeilo, Dyfed	1·40

Collectors Pack 1982
1982 (Nov 17). Comprises Nos. 1175/1206.
CP1206a Collectors Pack ... 12·00

682 Atlantic Salmon

683 Northern Pike

684 Brown Trout

685 Eurasian Perch

(Des A. Jardine)

1983 (26 Jan). *British River Fish.* MULTI/COLOUR Phosphorised paper. Perf 15×14.

1207	**682**	15½p. Atlantic Salmon	20	20
		a. Imperf (pair)	£3000	
1208	**683**	19½p. Northern Pike	25	25
1209	**684**	26p. Brown Trout	35	35
		a. Imperf (pair)	£3250	
1210	**685**	29p. Eurasian Perch	50	50
Set of 4			1·20	1·20
Set of 4 Gutter Pairs			2·40	
First Day Cover				1·30
Presentation Pack (PO Pack No. 142)			1·30	
PHQ Cards (set of 4) (65)			60	1·30

All known examples of No. 1209a are creased.

Special First Day of Issue Postmarks

Philatelic Bureau, Edinburgh	1·50
Peterborough	1·30

686 Tropical Island

687 Desert

688 Temperate Farmland

689 Mountain Range

(Des D. Fraser)

1983 (9 Mar). *Commonwealth Day. Geographical Regions.* |MULTI COLOUR|
Phosphorised paper. Perf 14×15.

1211	**686**	15½p. Tropical Island	20	20
1212	**687**	19½p. Desert	25	25
1213	**688**	26p. Temperate Farmland	35	35
1214	**689**	29p. Mountain Range	50	50
Set of 4			1·20	1·20
Set of 4 Gutter Pairs			2·40	
First Day Cover				1·30
Presentation Pack (PO Pack No. 143)			1·30	
PHQ Cards (set of 4) (66)			60	1·30

Special First Day of Issue Postmarks

Philatelic Bureau, Edinburgh ....1·30
London SW ....1·30

690 Humber Bridge   **691** Thames Flood Barrier

692 *Iolair* (oilfield emergency
support vessel)

(Des M. Taylor)

1983 (25 May). *Europa. Engineering Achievements.* |MULTI COLOUR| Phosphorised
paper. Perf 15×14.

1215	**690**	16p. Humber Bridge	20	20
1216	**691**	20½p. Thames Flood Barrier	30	30
1217	**692**	28p. *Iolair*	50	50
Set of 3			90	90
Set of 3 Gutter Pairs			1·80	
First Day Cover				1·00
Presentation Pack (PO Pack No. 144)			1·00	
PHQ Cards (set of 3) (67)			40	1·00

Special First Day of Issue Postmarks

Philatelic Bureau, Edinburgh ....1·00
Hull ....1·10

693 Musketeer and
Pikeman, The Royal Scots
(1633)

694 Fusilier and Ensign,
The Royal Welch Fusiliers
(mid-18th-century)

695 Riflemen, 95th Rifles
(The Royal Green Jackets)
(1805)

696 Sergeant (khaki
service) and Guardsman
(full dress), The Irish
Guards (1900)

697 Paratroopers, The
Parachute Regiment (1983)

(Des E. Stemp)

1983 (6 July). *British Army Uniforms.* |MULTI COLOUR| Phosphorised paper.
Perf 14×15.

1218	**693**	16p. The Royal Scots	20	20
1219	**694**	20½p. The Royal Welch Fusiliers	25	25
1220	**695**	26p. The Royal Green Jackets	35	35
		a. Imperf (pair)	£6500	
1221	**696**	28p. The Irish Guards	40	40
		a. Imperf (pair)	£4500	
1222	**697**	31p. The Parachute Regiment	50	50
Set of 5			1·60	1·60
Set of 5 Gutter Pairs			3·20	
First Day Cover				1·75
Presentation Pack (PO Pack No. 145)			1·75	
PHQ Cards (set of 5) (68)			75	1·75

Nos. 1218/22 were issued on the occasion of the 350th anniversary
of the Royal Scots, the senior line regiment of the British Army.

Special First Day of Issue Postmarks

Philatelic Bureau, Edinburgh ....1·75
Aldershot ....1·75

698 20th-century
Garden, Sissinghurst

699 19th-century
Garden, Biddulph
Grange

700 18th-century
Garden, Blenheim

701 17th-century
Garden, Pitmedden

(Des Liz Butler. Litho J.W.)

1983 (24 Aug). *British Gardens.* |MULTI COLOUR| Phosphorised paper. Perf 14.

1223	**698**	16p. Sissinghurst	20	20
1224	**699**	20½p. Biddulph Grange	25	25
1225	**700**	28p. Blenheim	35	35
1226	**701**	31p. Pitmedden	50	50
Set of 4			1·20	1·20
Set of 4 Gutter Pairs			2·40	
First Day Cover				1·30
Presentation Pack (PO Pack No. 146)			1·30	
PHQ Cards (set of 4) (69)			60	1·30

Nos. 1223/6 were issued on the occasion of the death bicentenary
of 'Capability' Brown (landscape gardener).

Special First Day of Issue Postmarks

Philatelic Bureau, Edinburgh ....1·30
Oxford ....1·50

702 Merry-go-round

703 Big Wheel, Helter-skelter and Performing Animals

704 Side Shows

705 Early Produce Fair

(Des A. Restall)

1983 (5 Oct). *British Fairs*. |MULTI COLOUR Phosphorised paper. Perf 15×14.

1227	**702**	16p. Merry-go-round	20	20
1228	**703**	20½p. Big Wheel, Helter-skelter and Performing Animals	25	25
1229	**704**	28p. Side Shows	35	35
1230	**705**	31p. Early Produce Fair	50	50
Set of 4			1·20	1·20
Set of 4 Gutter Pairs			2·40	
First Day Cover				1·30
Presentation Pack (PO Pack No. 147)			1·30	
PHQ Cards (set of 4) (70)			60	1·30

Nos. 1227/30 were issued to mark the 850th anniversary of St Bartholomew's Fair, Smithfield, London.

Special First Day of Issue Postmarks

Philatelic Bureau, Edinburgh	1·30
Nottingham	1·30

706 'Christmas Post' (pillar-box)

707 'The Three Kings' (chimney-pots)

708 'World at Peace' (Dove and Blackbird)

709 'Light of Christmas' (street lamp)

710 'Christmas Dove' (hedge sculpture)

(Des T. Meeuwissen)

1983 (16 Nov). *Christmas*. |MULTI COLOUR One phosphor band (12½p.) or phosphorised paper (others). Perf 15×14.

1231	**706**	12½p. 'Christmas Post' (pillar-box)	20	20
		a. Imperf (horiz pair)	£3500	
1232	**707**	16p. 'The Three Kings' (chimney-pots)	20	20
		a. Imperf (pair)	£2600	
1233	**708**	20½p. 'World at Peace' (Dove and Blackbird)	25	25
1234	**709**	28p. 'Light of Christmas' (street lamp)	35	35
1235	**710**	31p. Christmas Dove' (hedge sculpture)	50	50
Set of 5			1·35	1·35
Set of 5 Gutter Pairs			2·70	

First Day Cover		1·50
Presentation Pack (PO Pack No. 148)	1·50	
PHQ Cards (set of 5) (71)	75	1·50

Special First Day of Issue Postmarks

Philatelic Bureau, Edinburgh	1·50
Bethlehem, Llandeilo, Dyfed	1·50

Collectors Pack 1983
1983 (Nov 16). Comprises Nos. 1207/35.
CP1235a Collectors Pack .... 13·25

711 Arms of the College of Arms

712 Arms of King Richard III (founder)

713 Arms of the Earl Marshal of England

714 Arms of the City of London

(Des J. Matthews)

1984 (17 Jan). *500th Anniversary of College of Arms*. |MULTI COLOUR Phosphorised paper. Perf 14½.

1236	**711**	16p. Arms of the College of Arms	25	25
1237	**712**	20½p. Arms of King Richard III (founder)	30	30
1238	**713**	28p. Arms of the Earl Marshal of England	40	40
1239	**714**	31p. Arms of the City of London	50	50
		a. Imperf (horiz pair)	£12000	
Set of 4			1·35	1·35
Set of 4 Gutter Pairs			2·70	
First Day Cover				1·50
Presentation Pack (PO Pack No. 150)			1·50	
PHQ Cards (set of 4) (72)			60	1·50

Special First Day of Issue Postmarks

Philatelic Bureau, Edinburgh	1·50
London EC	1·50

715 Highland Cow

716 Chillingham Wild Bull

717 Hereford Bull

718 Welsh Black Bull

719 Irish Moiled Cow

(Des B. Driscoll)

1984 (6 Mar). *British Cattle.* Phosphorised paper. Perf 15×14.

1240	**715**	16p. Highland Cow	25	25
		a. Imperf (vert pair)	£12500	
1241	**716**	20½p. Chillingham Wild Bull	30	30
1242	**717**	26p. Hereford Bull	35	35
1243	**718**	28p. Welsh Black Bull	40	40
1244	**719**	31p. Irish Moiled Cow	50	50
		a. Imperf (pair)	—	
Set of 5			1·60	1·60
Set of 5 Gutter Pairs			3·20	
First Day Cover				1·75
Presentation Pack (PO Pack No. 151)			1·75	
PHQ Cards (set of 5) (73)			75	1·75

Nos. 1240/4 were issued on the occasion of the centenary of the Highland Cattle Society and the bicentenary of the Royal Highland and Agricultural Society of Scotland.

Special First Day of Issue Postmarks

Philatelic Bureau, Edinburgh ....1·75
Oban, Argyll ....1·90

720 Garden Festival Hall, Liverpool

721 Milburngate Centre, Durham

722 Bush House, Bristol

723 Commercial Street Development, Perth

(Des R. Maddox and Trickett and Webb Ltd)

1984 (10 Apr). *Urban Renewal.* Phosphorised paper. Perf 15×14.

1245	**720**	16p. Garden Festival Hall, Liverpool	25	25
1246	**721**	20½p. Milburngate Centre, Durham	30	30
		a. Imperf (horiz pair)	£9500	
1247	**722**	28p. Bush House, Bristol	40	40
1248	**723**	31p. Commercial Street Development, Perth	50	50
		a. Imperf (pair)	£7000	
Set of 4			1·35	1·35
Set of 4 Gutter Pairs			2·70	
First Day Cover				1·50
Presentation Pack (PO Pack No. 152)			1·50	
PHQ Cards (set of 4) (74)			60	1·50

Nos. 1245/8 were issued on the occasion of 150th anniversaries of the Royal Institute of British Architects and the Chartered Institute of Building, and to commemorate the first International Gardens Festival, Liverpool.

Special First Day of Issue Postmarks

Philatelic Bureau, Edinburgh ....1·50
Liverpool ....1·50

724 C.E.P.T. 25th Anniversary Logo

725 Abduction of Europa

(Des J. Larrivière (T **724**), F. Wegner (T **725**))

1984 (15 May). *25th Anniversary of C.E.P.T. (Europa)* (T **724**) and *Second Elections to European Parliament* (T **725**). Phosphorised paper. Perf 15×14.

1249	**724**	16p. C.E.P.T. 25th Anniversary Logo	30	30
		a. Horiz pair. Nos. 1249/50	60	60
		ab. Imperf (horiz pair)	£6250	
1250	**725**	16p. Abduction of Europa	30	30
1251	**724**	20½p. C.E.P.T. 25th Anniversary Logo	35	35
		a. Horiz pair. Nos. 1251/2	70	70
		ab. Imperf (horiz pair)	£7000	
1252	**725**	20½p. Abduction of Europa	35	35

Set of 4	1·20	1·20
Set of 2 Gutter Blocks of 4	2·40	
First Day Cover		1·30
Presentation Pack (PO Pack No. 153)	1·30	
PHQ Cards (set of 4) (75)	60	1·30

Nos. 1249/50 and 1251/2 were each printed together, *se-tenant*, in horizontal pairs throughout the sheets.

Special First Day of Issue Postmarks

Philatelic Bureau, Edinburgh ....1·30
London SW ....1·50

726 Lancaster House

(Des P. Hogarth)

1984 (5 June). *London Economic Summit Conference.* Phosphorised paper. Perf 14×15.

1253	**726**	31p. Lancaster House	50	50
Gutter Pair			1·00	
First Day Cover				60
PHQ Card (76)			20	60

Special First Day of Issue Postmarks

Philatelic Bureau, Edinburgh 60
London SW 60

727 View of Earth from 'Apollo 11'

728 Navigational Chart of English Channel

729 Greenwich Observatory

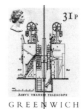

730 Sir George Airy's Transit Telescope

(Des H. Waller. Litho Questa)

1984 (26 June). *Centenary of the Greenwich Meridian.* Phosphorised paper. Perf 14×14½.

1254	**727**	16p. View of Earth from 'Apollo 11'	25	25
		Ea. Black ptg double	†	£1500
1255	**728**	20½p. Navigational Chart of English Channel	30	30
1256	**729**	28p. Greenwich Observatory	40	40
1257	**730**	31p. Sir George Airy's Transit Telescope	50	50
Set of 4			1·35	1·35
Set of 4 Gutter Pairs			2·70	
First Day Cover				1·50
Presentation Pack (PO Pack No. 154)			1·50	
PHQ Cards (set of 4) (77)			60	1·50

On Nos. 1254/7 the Meridian is represented by a scarlet line.

Special First Day of Issue Postmarks

Philatelic Bureau, Edinburgh ....3·50
London SE10 ....3·50

731 Bath Mail Coach, 1784

732 Attack on Exeter Mail, 1816

733 Norwich Mail in Thunderstorm, 1827

734 Holyhead and Liverpool Mails leaving London, 1828

735 Edinburgh Mail Snowbound, 1831

(Des K. Bassford and S. Paine. Eng C. Slania. Recess and photo)

1984 (31 July). *Bicentenary of First Mail Coach Run, Bath and Bristol to London.* Phosphorised paper. Perf 15×14.

1258	**731**	16p. Bath Mail Coach, 1784	25	25
		a. Horiz strip of 5. Nos. 1258/62	1·20	1·20
		ab. Imperf (horiz pair. Nos. 1261/2)	£7000	
1259	**732**	16p. Attack on Exeter Mail, 1816	25	25
1260	**733**	16p. Norwich Mail in Thunderstorm, 1827	25	25
1261	**734**	16p. Holyhead and Liverpool Mails leaving London, 1828	25	25
1262	**735**	16p. Edinburgh Mail Snowbound, 1831	25	25
Set of 5			1·20	1·20
Gutter Block of 10			2·40	
First Day Cover				1·30
Presentation Pack (PO Pack No. 155)			1·30	
Souvenir Book			3·25	
PHQ Cards (set of 5) (78)			75	1·30

Nos. 1258/62 were printed together, *se-tenant*, in horizontal strips of five throughout the sheet.

No. 1258ab also includes No. 1260 perforated at left only.

The souvenir book is a 24-page illustrated booklet with a set of mint stamps in a sachet attached to the front cover.

Special First Day of Issue Postmarks

Philatelic Bureau, Edinburgh ....1·30
Bristol ....1·40

736 Nigerian Clinic

737 Violinist and Acropolis, Athens

738 Building Project, Sri Lanka

739 British Council Library, Middle East

(Des F. Newell and J. Sorrell)

1984 (25 Sept). *50th Anniversary of the British Council.* Phosphorised paper. Perf 15×14.

1263	**736**	17p. Nigerian Clinic	25	25
1264	**737**	22p. Violinist and Acropolis, Athens	30	30
1265	**738**	31p. Building Project, Sri Lanka	40	40
1266	**739**	34p. British Council Library, Middle East.	50	50
Set of 4			1·35	1·35
Set of 4 Gutter Pairs			2·70	
First Day Cover				1·50
Presentation Pack (PO Pack No. 156)			1·50	
PHQ Cards (set of 4) (79)			60	1·50

Special First Day of Issue Postmarks

London SW ....1·50
Philatelic Bureau, Edinburgh ....1·50

740 The Holy Family

741 Arrival in Bethlehem

742 Shepherd and Lamb

743 Virgin and Child

744 Offering of Frankincense

(Des Yvonne Gilbert)

1984 (20 Nov). *Christmas.* One phosphor band (13p.) or phosphorised paper (others). Perf 15×14.

1267	**740**	13p. The Holy Family	25	25
		Eu. Underprint Type **4**	60	
1268	**741**	17p. Arrival in Bethlehem	25	25
		a. Imperf (pair)	£4750	
1269	**742**	22p. Shepherd and Lamb	30	30
1270	**743**	31p. Virgin and Child	40	40
1271	**744**	34p. Offering of Frankincense	50	50
Set of 5			1·60	1·60
Set of 5 Gutter Pairs			3·20	
First Day Cover				1·75
Presentation Pack (PO Pack No. 157)			1·75	
PHQ Cards (set of 5) (80)			75	1·75

Examples of No. 1267Eu from the 1984 Christmas booklet (No. FX7) show a random pattern of blue double-lined stars printed on the reverse over the gum.

Special First Day of Issue Postmarks

Philatelic Bureau, Edinburgh ....1·75
Bethlehem, Llandeilo, Dyfed ....1·75

Collectors Pack 1984

1984 (Nov 20). Comprises Nos. 1236/71.
CP1271*a* Collectors Pack... 15·50

Post Office Yearbook

1984. Comprises Nos. 1236/71 in 24-page hardbound book with slip case, illustrated in colour .... 42·00

745 'Flying Scotsman'

746 'Golden Arrow'

747 'Cheltenham Flyer'   **748** 'Royal Scot'

749 'Cornish Riviera'

(Des Terrance Cuneo)

1985 (22 Jan). *Famous Trains.* |MULTI COLOUR Phosphorised paper. Perf 15×14.

1272	**745**	17p. 'Flying Scotsman'	25	25
		a. Imperf (pair)	£4000	
1273	**746**	22p. 'Golden Arrow'	30	30
1274	**747**	29p. 'Cheltenham Flyer'	40	40
1275	**748**	31p. 'Royal Scot'	40	40
1276	**749**	34p. 'Cornish Riviera'	50	50
Set of 5			1·70	1·70
Set of 5 Gutter Pairs			3·40	
First Day Cover				1·85
Presentation Pack (PO Pack No. 159)			1·85	
PHQ Cards (set of 5) (81)			75	1·85

Nos. 1272/6 were issued on the occasion of the 150th anniversary of the Great Western Railway Company.

Special First Day of Issue Postmarks

Philatelic Bureau, Edinburgh ....2·00
Bristol ....2·20

750 Buff tailed bumble bee   **751** Seven spotted Ladybird

752 Wart-biter bush-cricket   **753** Stag Beetle

754 Emperor dragonfly

(Des G. Beningfield)

1985 (12 Mar). *Insects.* |MULTI COLOUR Phosphorised paper. Perf 14×15.

1277	**750**	17p. Buff tailed bumble bee	25	25
1278	**751**	22p. Seven spotted Ladybird	30	30
1279	**752**	29p. Wart-biter bush-cricket	40	40
1280	**753**	31p. Stag beetle	40	40
1281	**754**	34p. Emperor dragonfly	50	50

a. Imperf (vert pair)	—	
Set of 5	1·70	1·70
Set of 5 Gutter Pairs	3·40	
First Day Cover		1·85
Presentation Pack (PO Pack No. 160)	1·85	
PHQ Cards (set of 5) (82)	75	1·85

Nos. 1277/81 were issued on the occasion of the centenaries of the Royal Entomological Society of London's Royal Charter, and of the Selborne Society.

Special First Day of Issue Postmarks

Philatelic Bureau, Edinburgh ....1·85
London SW ....2·00

755 'Water Music' (George Frederick Handel)   **756** 'The Planets Suite' (Gustav Holst)

757 'The First Cuckoo' (Frederick Delius)   **758** 'Sea Pictures' (Edward Elgar)

(Des W. McLean)

1985 (14 May). *Europa. European Music Year. British Composers.* |MULTI COLOUR Phosphorised paper. Perf 14×14½.

1282	**755**	17p. 'Water Music' (George Frederick Handel)	25	25
		a. Imperf (vert pair)	£6500	
1283	**756**	22p. 'The Planets Suite' (Gustav Holst)	30	30
		a. Imperf (pair)	£6500	
1284	**757**	31p. 'The First Cuckoo' (Frederick Delius)	45	45
1285	**758**	34p. 'Sea Pictures' (Edward Elgar)	55	55
Set of 4			1·40	1·40
Set of 4 Gutter Pairs			2·80	
First Day Cover				1·50
Presentation Pack (PO Pack No. 161)			1·50	
PHQ Cards (set of 4) (83)			60	1·50

Nos. 1282/5 were issued on the occasion of the 300th birth anniversary of Handel.

Special First Day of Issue Postmarks

Philatelic Bureau, Edinburgh ....1·50
Worcester ....1·75

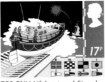

759 RNLI Lifeboat and Signal Flags   **760** Beachy Head Lighthouse and Chart

761 'Marecs A' Communications Satellite and Dish Aerials   **762** Buoys

(Des F. Newell and J. Sorrell. Litho J.W.)

1985 (18 June). *Safety at Sea.* |MULTI COLOUR Phosphorised paper. Perf 14.

1286	**759**	17p. RNLI Lifeboat and Signal Flags	25	25
1287	**760**	22p. Beachy Head Lighthouse and Chart	30	30
1288	**761**	31p. 'Marecs A' Communications Satellite and Dish Aerials	45	45

1289	**762**	34p. Buoys	55	55
Set of 4			1·40	1·40
Set of 4 Gutter Pairs			2·80	
First Day Cover				1·50
Presentation Pack (PO Pack No. 162)			1·50	
PHQ Cards (set of 4) (84)			60	1·50

Nos. 1286/9 were issued on the occasion of the bicentenary of the unimmersible lifeboat and the 50th anniversary of Radar.

Special First Day of Issue Postmarks

Philatelic Bureau, Edinburgh ....1·50
Eastbourne ....1·50

763 Datapost Motorcyclist, City of London

764 Rural Postbus

765 Parcel Delivery in Winter

766 Town Letter Delivery

(Des P. Hogarth)

1985 (30 July). *350 Years of Royal Mail Public Postal Service.* MULTI COLOUR Phosphorised paper. Perf 14×15.

1290	**763**	17p. Datapost Motorcyclist	25	25
		a. Imperf on 3 sides (vert pair)	£2800	
		Eu. Underprint Type **5**	50	
1291	**764**	22p. Rural Postbus	30	30
		a. Imperf (vert pair)	—	
1292	**765**	31p. Parcel Delivery in Winter	45	45
		a. Imperf	£3500	
1293	**766**	34p. Town Letter Delivery	55	55
		a. Imperf between (vert pair)	£1700	
		b. Imperf (vert pair)	—	
Set of 4			1·40	1·40
Set of 4 Gutter Pairs			2·80	
First Day Cover				1·50
Presentation Pack (PO Pack No. 163)			1·50	
PHQ Cards (set of 4) (85)			60	1·50

No. 1290a shows perforation indentations at right, but is imperforate at top, bottom and on the left-hand side.

Examples of No. 1290Eu from the 1985 £1·70 booklet (sold at £1·53) (No. FT4) show a blue double-lined D in a random pattern, on the reverse over the gum.

Special First Day of Issue Postmarks

Philatelic Bureau, Edinburgh ....1·50
Bagshot, Surrey ....1·50

767 King Arthur and Merlin

768 Lady of the Lake

769 Queen Guinevere and Sir Lancelot

770 Sir Galahad

(Des Yvonne Gilbert)

1985 (3 Sept). *Arthurian Legends.* MULTI COLOUR Phosphorised paper. Perf 15×14.

1294	**767**	17p. King Arthur and Merlin	25	25
		a. Imperf (pair)	£6500	
1295	**768**	22p. Lady of the Lake	30	30
1296	**769**	31p. Queen Guinevere and Sir Lancelot	45	45
1297	**770**	34p. Sir Galahad	55	55
Set of 4			1·40	1·40
Set of 4 Gutter Pairs			2·80	
First Day Cover				1·50
Presentation Pack (PO Pack No. 164)			1·50	
PHQ Cards (set of 4) (86)			60	1·50

Nos. 1294/7 were issued on the occasion of the 500th anniversary of the printing of Sir Thomas Malory's *Morte d'Arthur*.

Trials are known with face value and inscription in a different type face.

Special First Day of Issue Postmarks

Philatelic Bureau, Edinburgh ....1·50
Tintagel, Cornwall ....1·50

771 Peter Sellers (from photo by Bill Brandt)

772 David Niven (from photo by Cornell Lucas)

773 Charlie Chaplin (from photo by Lord Snowdon)

774 Vivien Leigh (from photo by Angus McBean)

775 Alfred Hitchcock (from photo by Howard Coster)

(Des K. Bassford)

1985 (8 Oct). *British Film Year.* MULTI COLOUR Phosphorised paper. Perf 14½.

1298	**771**	17p. Peter Sellers	25	25
1299	**772**	22p. David Niven	30	30
1300	**773**	29p. Charlie Chaplin	45	45
1301	**774**	31p. Vivien Leigh	50	50
1302	**775**	34p. Alfred Hitchcock	55	55
Set of 5			1·95	1·95
Set of 5 Gutter Pairs			3·90	
First Day Cover				2·10
Presentation Pack (PO Pack No. 165)			2·10	
Souvenir Book			4·75	
PHQ Cards (set of 5) (87)			75	2·10

The souvenir book is a 24-page illustrated booklet with a set of mint stamps in a sachet attached to the front cover.

Special First Day of Issue Postmarks

Philatelic Bureau, Edinburgh ....2·10
London WC ....2·10

776 Principal Boy   **777** Genie

778 Dame

779 Good Fairy

780 Pantomime Cat

(Des A. George)

1985 (19 Nov). *Christmas. Pantomime Characters.* |MULTI COLOUR| One phosphor band (12p.) or phosphorised paper (others). Perf 15×14.

1303	**776**	12p. Principal Boy	20	20
		a. Imperf (pair)	£3000	
		Eu. Underprint Type **4**	50	
1304	**777**	17p. Genie	25	25
		a. Imperf (pair)	£6500	
1305	**778**	22p. Dame	30	30
1306	**779**	31p. Good Fairy	40	40
1307	**780**	34p. Pantomime Cat	50	50
Set of 5			1·45	1·45
Set of 5 Gutter Pairs			2·90	
First Day Cover				1·60
Presentation Pack (PO Pack No. 166)			1·60	
PHQ Cards (set of 5) (88)			75	1·60
Christmas Folder (contains No. 1303×50)			25·00	

Examples of No. 1303Eu from the 1985 Christmas booklet (No. FX8) show a random pattern of blue double-lined stars printed on the reverse over the gum.

Special First Day of Issue Postmarks

Philatelic Bureau, Edinburgh ....1·60
Bethlehem, Llandeilo, Dyfed ....1·75

Collectors Pack 1985

1985 Nov 19 Comprises Nos. 1272/1307.
CP1307*a* Collectors Pack... 15·50

Post Office Yearbook

1985. Comprises Nos. 1272/1307 in 32-page hardbound book with slip case, illustrated in colour...................... 30·00

17 PENCE · INDUSTRY YEAR 1986
781 Light Bulb and North Sea Oil Drilling Rig (Energy)

22 PENCE · INDUSTRY YEAR 1986
782 Thermometer and Pharmaceutical Laboratory (Health)

31 PENCE · INDUSTRY YEAR 1986
783 Garden Hoe Steelworks (Steel)

34 PENCE · INDUSTRY YEAR 1986
784 Loaf of Bread and Cornfield (Agriculture)

(Des K. Bassford. Litho Questa)

1986 (14 Jan). *Industry Year.* |MULTI COLOUR| Phosphorised paper. Perf 14½×14.

1308	**781**	17p. Light Bulb and North Sea Oil Drilling Rig (Energy)	25	25
1309	**782**	22p. Thermometer and Pharmaceutical Laboratory (Health)	30	30
1310	**783**	31p. Garden Hoe Steelworks (Steel)	45	45
1311	**784**	34p. Loaf of Bread and Cornfield (Agriculture)	55	55
Set of 4			1·45	1·45
Set of 4 Gutter Pairs			2·90	
First Day Cover				1·60
Presentation Pack (PO Pack No. 168)			1·60	
PHQ Cards (set of 4) (89)			60	1·60

Special First Day of Issue Postmarks

Philatelic Bureau, Edinburgh ....1·60
Birmingham ....1·60

785 Dr Edmond Halley as Comet

786 *Giotto* Spacecraft approaching Comet

787 'Maybe Twice in a Lifetime'

788 Comet orbiting Sun and Planets

(Des R. Steadman)

1986 (18 Feb). *Appearance of Halley's Comet.* |MULTI COLOUR| Phosphorised paper. Perf 15×14.

1312	**785**	17p. Dr Edmond Halley as Comet	25	25
		a. Imperf (pair)	—	
1313	**786**	22p. *Giotto* Spacecraft approaching Comet	30	30
1314	**787**	31p. 'Maybe Twice in a Lifetime'	45	45
		a. Imperf (pair)	—	
1315	**788**	34p. Comet orbiting Sun and Planets	55	55
Set of 4			1·45	1·45
Set of 4 Gutter Pairs			2·90	
First Day Cover				1·60
Presentation Pack (PO Pack No. 168*)			1·60	
PHQ Cards (set of 4) (90)			60	1·60

*The presentation pack was incorrectly numbered '169'.

Special First Day of Issue Postmarks

Philaelic Bureau, Edinburgh ....1·60
London SE10 ....1·75

789 Queen Elizabeth in 1928, 1942 and 1952

790 Queen Elizabeth in 1958, 1973 and 1982

(Des J. Matthews)

1986 (21 Apr). *60th Birthday of Queen Elizabeth II.* |MULTI COLOUR| Phosphorised paper. Perf 15×14.

1316	**789**	17p. Queen Elizabeth in 1928, 1942 and 1952. Grey-black, turquoise-green, brt green, green and dull blue	30	40
		a. Pair. Nos. 1316/17	80	1·00
1317	**790**	17p. Queen Elizabeth in 1958, 1973 and 1982. Grey-black, dull blue, greenish blue and indigo	30	40
1318	**789**	34p. Queen Elizabeth in 1928, 1942 and 1952. Grey-black, dp dull purple, yellow-orange and red	60	75
		a. Pair. Nos. 1318/19	1·40	1·80

1319 **790** 34p. Queen Elizabeth in 1958, 1973
and 1982. Grey-black, olive-
brown, yellow-brown, olive-grey
and red.. 60 75
Set of 4.. 1·95 2·40
Set of 2 Gutter Blocks of 4............................... 3·90
First Day Cover .... 2·40
Presentation Pack (PO Pack No. 170)............ 2·10
Souvenir Book .... 3·75
PHQ Cards (set of 4) (91)................................... 60 2·40
Nos. 1316/17 and 1318/19 were each printed together, *se-tenant*, in horizontal pairs throughout the sheet.
The souvenir book is a special booklet, fully illustrated and containing a mint set of stamps.

Special First Day of Issue Postmarks
Philatelic Bureau, Edinburgh ....2·40
Windsor...2·40

NATURE CONSERVATION
17P

NATURE CONSERVATION
22P

SPECIES AT RISK
BARN OWL
(TYTO ALBA)
791 Barn Owl

SPECIES AT RISK
PINE MARTEN
(MARTES MARTES)
792 Pine Marten

NATURE CONSERVATION
31P

NATURE CONSERVATION
34P

SPECIES AT RISK
WILD CAT
(FELIS SILVESTRIS)
793 Wild Cat

SPECIES AT RISK
NATTERJACK TOAD
(BUFO CALAMITA)
794 Natterjack Toad

(Des K. Lilly)

1986 (20 May). *Europa. Nature Conservation–Endangered Species.* MULTI COLOUR Phosphorised paper. Perf 14½×14.
1320 **791** 17p. Barn Owl................................. 25 25
1321 **792** 22p. Pine Marten......................... 30 30
1322 **793** 31p. Wild Cat............................... 45 45
1323 **794** 34p. Natterjack Toad.................. 55 55
Set of 4.. 1·45 1·45
Set of 4 Gutter Pairs .... 2·90
First Day Cover .... 1·60
Presentation Pack (PO Pack No. 171)............ 1·60
PHQ Cards (set of 4) (92)................................... 60 1·60

Special First Day of Issue Postmarks
Philatelic Bureau, Edinburgh ....1·60
Lincoln...1·75

DOMESDAY BOOK 1086
17P

DOMESDAY BOOK 1086
22P

795 Peasants working in Fields
796 Freemen working at Town Trades

DOMESDAY BOOK 1086
31P

DOMESDAY BOOK 1086
34P

797 Knight and Retainers
798 Lord at Banquet

(Des Tayburn Design Consultancy)

1986 (17 Jun). *900th Anniversary of Domesday Book.* MULTI COLOUR Phosphorised paper. Perf 15×14.
1324 **795** 17p. Peasants working in Fields 25 25
1325 **796** 22p. Freemen working at Town Trades.. 30 30
1326 **797** 31p. Knight and Retainers....................... 45 45
1327 **798** 34p. Lord at Banquet 55 55
Set of 4.. 1·45 1·45
Set of 4 Gutter Pairs .... 2·90
First Day Cover .... 1·60

Presentation Pack (PO Pack No. 172).....................................1·60
PHQ Cards (set of 4) (93) .... 60 1·60

Special First Day of Issue Postmarks
Philatelic Bureau, Edinburgh ....1·60
Gloucester..1·60

17P
COMMONWEALTH GAMES EDINBURGH 1986

22P
COMMONWEALTH GAMES EDINBURGH 1986

799 Athletics
800 Rowing

29P
COMMONWEALTH GAMES EDINBURGH 1986

31P
COMMONWEALTH GAMES EDINBURGH 1986

801 Weightlifting
802 Rifle Shooting

34P
WORLD HOCKEY CUP LONDON 1986

803 Hockey

(Des N. Cudworth)

1986 (15 July). *Thirteenth Commonwealth Games, Edinburgh and World Hockey Cup for Men, London* (34p.). MULTI COLOUR Phosphorised paper. Perf 15×14.
1328 **799** 17p. Athletics.............................. 25 25
1329 **800** 22p. Rowing............................... 30 30
a. Imperf (pair)....................... —
1330 **801** 29p. Weightlifting..................... 45 45
1331 **802** 31p. Rifle Shooting................... 45 45
1332 **803** 34p. Hockey............................... 55 55
a. Imperf (pair)....................... £5500
Set of 5.. 1·80 1·80
Set of 5 Gutter Pairs .... 3·60
First Day Cover .... 1·90
Presentation Pack (PO Pack No. 173)............ 1·90
PHQ Cards (set of 5) (94).................................... 75 1·90
No. 1332 also marked the centenary of the Hockey Association.

Special First Day of Issue Postmarks
Philatelic Bureau, Edinburgh ....1·90
Head Post Office, Edinburgh..1·90

12P

17P

804 Prince Andrew and Miss Sarah Ferguson (from photo by Gene Nocon)
805 Prince Andrew and Miss Sarah Ferguson (from photo by Gene Nocon)

(Des J. Matthews)

1986 (22 July). *Royal Wedding.* MULTI COLOUR One phosphor band (12p.) or phosphorised paper (17p.). Perf 14×15.
1333 **804** 12p. Prince Andrew and Miss Sarah
Ferguson....................................... 25 25
1334 **805** 17p. Prince Andrew and Miss Sarah
Ferguson....................................... 40 40
a. Imperf (pair)........................ £1200
Set of 2.. 60 60
Set of 2 Gutter Pairs .... 1·20
First Day Cover 70
Presentation Pack (PO Pack No. 174)............ 75
PHQ Cards (set of 2) (95).................................... 30 75

Philatelic Bureau, Edinburgh 70
London, SW1 75

806 Stylized Cross on
Ballot Paper

(Des J. Gibbs. Litho Questa)

1986 (19 Aug). *32nd Commonwealth Parliamentary Association Conference.* |MULTI COLOUR| Phosphorised paper. Perf 14×14½.

1335	**806**	34p. Stylized Cross on Ballot Paper.........	50	50
		a. Imperf between (vert pair)	—	
Gutter Pair			1·00	
First Day Cover				55
PHQ Card (96)			15	55

Philatelic Bureau, Edinburgh 55
London, SW1 55

807 Lord Dowding and
Hawker Hurricane Mk I

808 Lord Tedder and
Hawker Typhoon IB

809 Lord Trenchard and de
Havilland DH.9A

810 Sir Arthur Harris and
Avro Type 683 Lancaster

811 Lord Portal and de
Havilland DH.98 Mosquito

(Des B. Sanders)

1986 (16 Sept). *History of the Royal Air Force.* |MULTI COLOUR| Phosphorised paper. Perf 14½.

1336	**807**	17p. Lord Dowding and Hawker Hurricane Mk I	25	25
		a. Imperf (pair)...........................	£4250	
1337	**808**	22p. Lord Tedder and Hawker Typhoon IB................	35	35
		a. Face value omitted*...........................	£950	
		b. Queen's head omitted*.....................	£950	
1338	**809**	29p. Lord Trenchard and de Havilland DH.9A........................	45	45
1339	**810**	31p. Sir Arthur Harris and Avro Type 683 Lancaster	50	50
1340	**811**	34p. Lord Portal and de Havilland DH.98 Mosquito.	55	55
Set of 5...			1·95	1·95
Set of 5 Gutter Pairs			3·90	
First Day Cover				2·10
Presentation Pack (PO Pack No. 175)..............			2·10	
PHQ Cards (set of 5) (97)			75	2·10

Nos. 1336/40 were issued to celebrate the 50th anniversary of the first R.A.F. Commands.

* Nos. 1337a/b come from three consecutive sheets on which the stamps in the first vertical row are without the face value and those in the second vertical row the Queen's head.

Philatelic Bureau, Edinburgh ....2·10
Farnborough ....2·10

812 The Glastonbury Thorn

813 The Tanad Valley Plygain

814 The Hebrides Tribute

815 The Dewsbury Church Knell

816 The Hereford Boy Bishop

(Des Lynda Gray)

1986 (18 Nov–2 Dec). *Christmas. Folk Customs.* |MULTI COLOUR| One phosphor band (12p., 13p.) or phosphorised paper (others). Perf 15×14.

1341	**812**	12p. The Glastonbury Thorn	25	25
		a. Imperf (pair)...........................	£4000	
1342		13p. The Glastonburg Thorn	25	25
		Eu. Underprint Type **4** (2.12)	50	
1343	**813**	18p. The Tanad Valley Plygain	30	30
1344	**814**	22p. The Hebrides Tribute........................	40	40
1345	**815**	31p. The Dewsbury Church Knell	45	45
1346	**816**	34p. The Hereford Boy Bishop	50	50
Set of 6...			1·90	1·90
Set of 6 Gutter Pairs			3·80	
First Day Covers (2)...				2·40
Presentation Pack (Nos. 1342/6) (PO Pack No. 176)			2·00	
PHQ Cards (Nos. 1342/6) (*set of 5*) (98)...........			75	1·75
Christmas Folder (contains No. 1342Eu×36)			18·00	

No. 1341 represented a discount of 1p., available between 2 and 24 December 1986, on the current second class postage rate.

Philatelic Bureau, Edinburgh (Nos. 1342/6) (18 Nov) ....1·90
Bethlehem, Llandeilo, Dyfed (Nos. 1342/6) (18 Nov) ....2·00
Philatelic Bureau, Edinburgh (No. 1341) (2 Dec) 50

Collectors Pack 1986

1986 Nov 18 Comprises Nos. 1308/40 and 1342/6.
CP1346a Collectors Pack.. 15·50

Post Office Yearbook

1986 Nov 18 Comprises Nos. 1308/46 in 32-page hardbound book with slip case, illustrated in colour.. 23·00

817 North American
Blanket Flower

818 Globe Thistle

819 Echeveria   **820** Autumn Crocus

(Adapted J. Matthews)

1987 (20 Jan). *Flower Photographs by Alfred Lammer.* |MULTI COLOUR Phosphorised paper. Perf 14½×14.

1347	**817**	18p. North American Blanket Flower	25	25
1348	**818**	22p. Globe Thistle...................................	30	30
1349	**819**	31p. Echeveria......................................	45	45
		a. Imperf (pair)................................	£8000	
1350	**820**	34p. Autumn Crocus...........................	55	55
Set of 4..			1·45	1·45
Set of 4 Gutter Pairs			2·90	
First Day Cover				1·60
Presentation Pack (PO Pack No. 178)...............			1·60	
PHQ Cards (set of 4) (99)			60	1·60

Special First Day of Issue Postmarks

Philatelic Bureau, Edinburgh ....1·60
Richmond, Surrey ....1·75

821 The Principia Mathematica

822 Motion of Bodies in Ellipses

823 Optick Treatise

824 The System of the World

(Des Sarah Godwin)

1987 (24 Mar). *300th Anniversary of The Principia Mathematica by Sir Isaac Newton.* |MULTI COLOUR Phosphorised paper. Perf 14×15.

1351	**821**	18p. The Principia Mathematica................	25	25
		a. Imperf (pair)................................	£7500	
1352	**822**	22p. Motion of Bodies in Ellipses	30	30
1353	**823**	31p. Optick Treatise..............................	45	45
1354	**824**	34p. The System of the World.................	55	55
Set of 4..			1·45	1·45
Set of 4 Gutter Pairs			2·90	
First Day Cover				1·60
Presentation Pack (PO Pack No. 179)...............			1·60	
PHQ Cards (set of 4) (100)			60	1·60

Special First Day of Issue Postmarks

Philatelic Bureau, Edinburgh .... 1·60
Woolsthorpe, Lincs .... 1·75

825 Willis Faber and Dumas Building, Ipswich

826 Pompidou Centre, Paris

827 Staatsgalerie, Stuttgart

828 European Investment Bank, Luxembourg

(Des B. Tattersfield)

1987 (12 May). *Europa. British Architects in Europe.* |MULTI COLOUR Phosphorised paper. Perf 15×14.

1355	**825**	18p. Willis Faber and Dumas Building, Ipswich	25	25
1356	**826**	22p. Pompidou Centre, Paris...................	30	30
1357	**827**	31p. Staatsgalerie, Stuttgart..................	45	45
		a. Imperf (horiz pair)	£7500	
1358	**828**	34p. European Investment Bank, Luxembourg......................................	55	55
Set of 4..			1·45	1·45
Set of 4 Gutter Pairs			2·90	
First Day Cover				1·60
Presentation Pack (PO Pack No. 180)...............			1·60	
PHQ Cards (set of 4) (101).............................			50	1·60

Special First Day of Issue Postmarks

Philatelic Bureau, Edinburgh .... 1·60
Ipswich .... 1·60

829 Brigade Members with Ashford Litter, 1887

830 Bandaging Blitz Victim, 1940

831 Volunteer with fainting Girl, 1965

832 Transport of Transplant Organ by Air Wing, 1987

(Des Debbie Cook. Litho Questa)

1987 (16 June). *Centenary of St John Ambulance Brigade.* |MULTI COLOUR Phosphorised paper. Perf 14×14½.

1359	**829**	18p. Brigade Members with Ashford Litter, 1887	25	25
		Ea. Black ptg double............................	†	£950
		Eb. Black ptg triple..............................	†	£1300
1360	**830**	22p. Bandaging Blitz Victim, 1940...........	30	30
1361	**831**	31p. Volunteer with fainting Girl, 1965..	45	45
1362	**832**	34p. Transport of Transplant Organ by Air Wing, 1987	55	55
Set of 4..			1·45	1·45
Set of 4 Gutter Pairs			2·90	
First Day Cover				1·60
Presentation Pack (PO Pack No. 181)...............			1·60	
PHQ Cards (set of 4) (102)			60	1·60

Special First Day of Issue Postmarks

Philatelic Bureau, Edinburgh .... 1·60
London, EC1 .... 1·60

833 Arms of the Lord Lyon King of Arms

834 Scottish Heraldic Banner of Prince Charles

835 Arms of Royal Scottish Academy of Painting, Sculpture and Architecture

836 Arms of Royal Society of Edinburgh

(Des J. Matthews)

1987 (21 July). *300th Anniversary of Revival of Order of the Thistle.* MULTI COLOUR Phosphorised paper. Perf 14½.

1363	**833**	18p. Arms of the Lord Lyon King of Arms	25	25
1364	**834**	22p. Scottish Heraldic Banner of Prince Charles	30	30
1365	**835**	31p. Arms of Royal Scottish Academy of Painting, Sculpture and Architecture	45	45
1366	**836**	34p. Arms of Royal Society of Edinburgh	55	55
Set of 4			1·45	1·45
Set of 4 Gutter Pairs			2·90	
First Day Cover				1·60
Presentation Pack (PO Pack No. 182)			1·60	
PHQ Cards (set of 4) (103)			60	1·60

Special First Day of Issue Postmarks

Philatelic Bureau, Edinburgh .... 1·60
Rothesay, Isle of Bute .... 1·75

837 Crystal Palace, 'Monarch of the Glen' (Landseer) and Grace Darling

838 Great Eastern, Beeton's Book of Household Management and Prince Albert

839 Albert Memorial, Ballot Box and Disraeli

840 Diamond Jubilee Emblem, Newspaper Placard for Relief of Mafeking and Morse Key

(Des M. Dempsey. Eng C. Slania. Recess and photo)

1987 (8 Sept). *150th Anniversary of Queen Victoria's Accession.* MULTI COLOUR Phosphorised paper. Perf 15×14.

1367	**837**	18p. Crystal Palace, 'Monarch of the Glen' (Landseer) and Grace Darling	25	25
1368	**838**	22p. Great Eastern, Beeton's Book of Household Management and Prince Albert	30	30
1369	**839**	31p. Albert Memorial, Ballot Box and Disraeli	45	45
1370	**840**	34p. Diamond Jubilee Emblem, Newspaper Placard for Relief of Mafeking and Morse Key	55	55
Set of 4			1·45	1·45
Set of 4 Gutter Pairs			1·90	
First Day Cover				1·60

Presentation Pack (PO Pack No. 183) .... 1·60
PHQ Cards (set of 4) (104) 60   1·600

Special First Day of Issue Postmarks

Philatelic Bureau, Edinburgh .... 1·60
Newport, Isle of Wight .... 1·60

841 Pot by Bernard Leach

842 Pot by Elizabeth Fritsch

843 Pot by Lucie Rie

844 Pot by Hans Coper

(Des T. Evans)

1987 (13 Oct). *Studio Pottery.* MULTI COLOUR Phosphorised paper. Perf 14½×14.

1371	**841**	18p. Pot by Bernard Leach	25	25
1372	**842**	26p. Pot by Elizabeth Fritsch	35	35
1373	**843**	31p. Pot by Lucie Rie	45	45
1374	**844**	34p. Pot by Hans Coper	55	55
		a. Imperf (vert pair)	£6000	
Set of 4			1·45	1·45
Set of 4 Gutter Pairs			2·90	
First Day Cover				1·60
Presentation Pack (PO Pack No. 184)			1·60	
PHQ Cards (set of 4) (105)			60	1·60

Special First Day of Issue Postmarks

Philatelic Bureau, Edinburgh .... 1·60
St Ives, Cornwall .... 1·60

845 Decorating the Christmas Tree

846 Waiting for Father Christmas

847 Sleeping Child and Father Christmas in Sleigh

848 Child reading

849 Child playing Recorder and Snowman

(Des M. Foreman)

1987 (17 Nov). *Christmas.* MULTI COLOUR One phosphor band (13p.) or phosphorised paper (others). Perf 15×14.

1375	**845**	13p. Decorating the Christmas Tree	20	20
		Eu. Underprint Type **4**	50	
1376	**846**	18p. Waiting for Father Christmas	25	25

1377	**847**	26p. Sleeping Child and Father		
		Christmas in Sleigh	30	30
1378	**848**	31p. Child reading	40	40
1379	**849**	34p. Child playing Recorder and		
		Snowman	50	50

Set of 5 .... 1·50   1·50
Set of 5 Gutter Pairs .... 3·00
First Day Cover .... 1·60
Presentation Pack (PO Pack No. 185) .... 1·60
PHQ Cards (set of 5) (106) 75   1·60
Christmas Folder (contains No. 1375Eu×36) .... 18·00

Examples of the 13p. value from special folders, containing 36 stamps and sold for £4·60, show a blue underprint of doublelined stars printed on the reverse over the gum.

Special First Day of Issue Postmarks

Philatelic Bureau, Edinburgh ....1·60
Bethlehem, Llandeilo, Dyfed ....1·70

Collectors Pack 1987

1987 Nov 17 Comprises Nos. 1347/79.
CP1379a Collectors Pack .... 15·50

Post Office Yearbook

1987 Nov 17 Comprises Nos. 1347/79 in 32-page hardbound book with slip case, illustrated in colour........................ 13·00

850 Short-spined Sea scorpion
('Bull-rout') (Jonathan Couch)

851 Yellow Waterlily
(Major Joshua Swatkin)

852 Whistling ('Bewick's') Swan
(Edward Lear)

853 *Morchella esculenta*
(James Sowerby)

(Des. E. Hughes)

1988 (19 Jan). *Bicentenary of Linnean Society. Archive Illustrations.* |MULTI COLOUR| Phosphorised paper. Perf 15×14.

1380	**850**	18p. Short-spined Sea scorpion		
		('Bull-rout')	25	25
1381	**851**	26p. Yellow Waterlily........................	35	35
1382	**852**	31p. Whistling ('Bewick's') Swan.......	45	45
		a. Imperf (horiz pair)........................	£5000	
1383	**853**	34p. *Morchella esculenta*...........	60	60

Set of 4.. 1·50   1·50
Set of 4 Gutter Pairs.. 3·00
First Day Cover .... 1·65
Presentation Pack (PO Pack No. 187) .... 1·65
PHQ Cards (set of 4) (107)........................ 60   1·65

Special First Day of Issue Postmarks

Philatelic Bureau, Edinburgh ....1·65
London, W1 ....1·75

854 Revd William Morgan
(Bible translator, 1588)

855 William Salesbury (New
Testament translator, 1567)

856 Bishop Richard Davies
(New Testament translator,
1567)

857 Bishop Richard Parry
(editor of Revised Welsh
Bible, 1620)

(Des K. Bowen)

1988 (1 Mar). *400th Anniversary of Welsh Bible.* |MULTI COLOUR| Phosphorised paper. Perf 14½×14.

1384	**854**	18p. Revd William Morgan........................	25	25
		a. Imperf (vert pair)	£5500	
1385	**855**	26p. William Salesbury........................	35	35
1386	**856**	31p. Bishop Richard Davies	45	45
1387	**857**	34p. Bishop Richard Parry	60	60

Set of 4.. 1·50   1·50
Set of 4 Gutter Pairs .... 3·00
First Day Cover .... 1·65
Presentation Pack (PO Pack No. 188)........................ 1·65
PHQ Cards (set of 4) (108)........................ 60   1·65

Special First Day of Issue Postmarks

Philatelic Bureau, Edinburgh ....1·65
Ty Mawr, Wybrnant, Gwynedd ....1·75

858 Gymnastics (Centenary
of British Amateur
Gymnastics Association)

859 Downhill Skiing
(Ski Club of Great Britain)

860 Tennis (Centenary of
Lawn Tennis Association)

861 Football (Centenary of
Football League)

(Des J. Sutton)

1988 (22 Mar). *Sports Organizations.* |MULTI COLOUR| Phosphorised paper. Perf 14½.

1388	**858**	18p. Gymnastics	25	25
		a. Imperf (pair)........................	25	25
1389	**859**	26p. Downhill Skiing........................	35	35
1390	**860**	31p. Tennis........................	45	45
1391	**861**	34p. Football........................	60	60

Set of 4.. 1·50   1·50
Set of 4 Gutter Pairs .... 3·00
First Day Cover .... 1·65
Presentation Pack (PO Pack No. 189)........................ 1·65
PHQ Cards (set of 4) (109)........................ 50   1·65

Special First Day of Issue Postmarks

Philatelic Bureau, Edinburgh ....1·65
Wembley ....1·80

862 *Mallard* and Mailbags on
Pick-up Arms

863 Loading Transatlantic Mail
on Liner *Queen Elizabeth*

864 Glasgow Tram No. 1173 and Pillar Box

865 Imperial Airways Handley Page H.P.45 *Horatius* and Airmail Van

(Des M. Dempsey)

1988 (10 May). *Europa. Transport and Mail Services in 1930s.* |MULTI COLOUR Phosphorised paper. Perf 15×14.

1392	**862**	18p. *Mallard* and Mailbags on Pick-up Arms	25	25
1393	**863**	26p. Loading Transatlantic Mail on Liner *Queen Elizabeth*	35	35
1394	**864**	31p. Glasgow Tram No. 1173 and Pillar Box	45	45
1395	**865**	34p. Imperial Airways Handley Page H.P.45 *Horatius* and Airmail Van	60	60
Set of 4			1·50	1·50
Set of 4 Gutter Pairs			3·00	
First Day Cover				1·65
Presentation Pack (PO Pack No. 190)			1·65	
PHQ Cards (set of 4) (110)			60	1·65

Trials exist with alternative face values; 19p, 27p, 32p and 35p.

Special First Day of Issue Postmarks

Philatelic Bureau, Edinburgh	1·65
Glasgow	1·75

866 Early Settler and Sailing Clipper

867 Queen Elizabeth II with British and Australian Parliament Buildings

868 W. G. Grace (cricketer) and Tennis Racquet

869 Shakespeare, John Lennon (entertainer) and Sydney Opera House

(Des G. Emery. Litho Questa)

1988 (21 June). *Bicentenary of Australian Settlement.* |MULTI COLOUR Phosphorised paper. Perf 14½.

1396	**866**	18p. Early Settler and Sailing Clipper	25	25
		a. Horiz pair. Nos. 1396/7	55	55
1397	**867**	18p. Queen Elizabeth II with British and Australian Parliament Buildings	25	25
1398	**868**	34p. W. G. Grace and Tennis Racquet	50	50
		a. Horiz pair. Nos. 1398/9	1·10	1·10
1399	**869**	34p. Shakespeare, John Lennon and Sydney Opera House	50	50
Set of 4			1·50	1·50
Set of 2 Gutter Blocks of 4			3·00	
First Day Cover				1·65
Presentation Pack (PO Pack No. 191)			1·65	
Souvenir Book			6·00	
PHQ Cards (set of 4) (111)			60	1·65

Nos. 1396/7 and 1398/9 were each printed together, *se-tenant*, in horizontal pairs throughout the sheets, each pair showing a background design of the Australian flag.

The 40 page souvenir book contains the British and Australian sets which were issued on the same day in similar designs.

Special First Day of Issue Postmarks

Philatelic Bureau, Edinburgh	1·65
Portsmouth	1·75

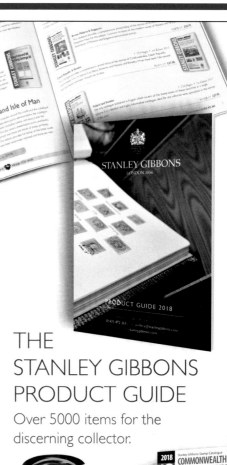

ARMADA · LIZARD · 19 JULY 1588

870 Spanish Galeasse off The Lizard

ARMADA · PLYMOUTH · 21 JULY 1588

871 English Fleet leaving Plymouth

ARMADA · ISLE of WIGHT · 25 JULY 1588

872 Engagement off Isle of Wight

ARMADA · CALAIS · 28-29 JULY 1588

873 Attack of English Fire-ships, Calais

ARMADA · NORTH SEA · 30 JULY · 2 AUG 1588

874 Armada in Storm, North Sea

(Des G. Evernden)

1988 (19 July). *400th Anniversary of Spanish Armada.* Phosphorised paper. Perf 15×14.

1400	**870**	18p. Spanish Galeasse off The Lizard	25	25
		a. Horiz strip of 5. Nos. 1400/4	1·30	1·30
1401	**871**	18p. English Fleet leaving Plymouth	25	25
1402	**872**	18p. Engagement off Isle of Wight	25	25
1403	**873**	18p. Attack of English Fire-ships, Calais	25	25
		a. '88' for '1988' in imprint (strip of 5)	30·00	
1404	**874**	18p. Armada in Storm, North Sea	25	25
		a. '988' for '1988' in imprint (strip of 5)	30·00	
Set of 5			1·30	1·30
Gutter Block of 10			2·60	
First Day Cover				1·40
Presentation Pack (PO Pack No. 192)			1·40	
PHQ Cards (set of 5) (112)			75	1·40

Nos. 1400/4 were printed together, *se-tenant*, in horizontal strips of five throughout the sheet, forming a composite design.

On R. 3/10 the imprint reads '88', with traces of the '9' visible, on R. 4/4 it reads '988', both on the Dot pane. Both were quickly retouched to show '1988'.

Special First Day of Issue Postmarks

Philatelic Bureau, Edinburgh	1·40
Plymouth	1·75

The Owl and the Pussy-cat went to sea
In a beautiful pea-green boat,
EDWARD LEAR · 1812-1888

875 'The Owl and the Pussy-cat'

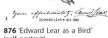

EDWARD LEAR · 1812-1888

876 'Edward Lear as a Bird' (self-portrait)

EDWARD LEAR · 1812-1888

877 'Cat' (from alphabet book)

There was a Young Lady whose bonnet,
Came untied when the birds sate upon it;
EDWARD LEAR · 1812-1888

878 'There was a Young Lady whose Bonnet...' (limerick)

(Des M. Swatridge and S. Dew)

1988 (6–27 Sept). *Death Centenary of Edward Lear (artist and author).* Phosphorised paper. Perf 15×14.

1405	**875**	19p. 'The Owl and the Pussy-cat'	25	25
1406	**876**	27p. 'Edward Lear as a Bird' (self-portrait)	35	35
1407	**877**	32p. 'Cat' (from alphabet book)	45	45
1408	**878**	35p. 'There was a Young Lady whose Bonnet...' (limerick)	60	60
Set of 4			1·50	1·50
Set of 4 Gutter Pairs			3·00	
First Day Cover				1·65
Presentation Pack (PO Pack No. 193)			1·65	
PHQ Cards (set of 4) (113)			60	1·65
MS1409 122×90 mm. Nos. 1405/8 (sold at £1·35) (27 Sept)			3·25	3·50
First Day Cover				3·75

The premium on No. **MS**1409 was used to support the 'Stamp World London 90' International Stamp Exhibition.

Special First Day of Issue Postmarks

Philatelic Bureau, Edinburgh (stamps) (6 Sept)	1·65
Philatelic Bureau, Edinburgh (miniature sheet) (27 Sept)	3·75
London N7 (stamps) (6 Sept)	1·75
London N22 (miniature sheet) (27 Sept)	3·85

CARRICKFERGUS CASTLE

879 Carrickfergus Castle

CAERNARFON CASTLE

880 Caernarfon Castle

EDINBURGH CASTLE

881 Edinburgh Castle

WINDSOR CASTLE

882 Windsor Castle

(Des from photos by Prince Andrew, Duke of York. Eng C. Matthews. Recess Harrison)

1988 (18 Oct). Ordinary paper. Perf 15×14.

1410	**879**	£1 Carrickfergus Castle	3·50	25
1411	**880**	£1·50 Caernarfon Castle	3·75	50
1412	**881**	£2 Edinburgh Castle	6·50	75
1413	**882**	£5 Windsor Castle	17·00	1·50
Set of 4			28·00	2·75
Set of 4 Gutter Pairs (vert or horiz)			60·00	
First Day Cover				16·00
Presentation Pack (PO Pack No. 18)			30·00	

For similar designs, but with silhouette of Queen's head see Nos. 1611/14 and 1993/6.

Special First Day of Issue Postmarks

(For illustrations see Introduction)

Philatelic Bureau Edinburgh (Type H)	16·00
Windsor, Berkshire (Type 1)	20·00

883 Journey to Bethlehem

884 Shepherds and Star

885 Three Wise Men

886 Nativity

887 The Annunciation

(Des L. Trickett)

1988 (15 Nov). *Christmas. Christmas Cards.* ▨ One phosphor band (14p.) or phosphorised paper (others). Perf 15×14.

1414	**883**	14p. Journey to Bethlehem	25	25
		a. Error. '13p' instead of '14p'	£9750	
		b. Imperf (pair)	£2500	
1415	**884**	19p. Shepherds and Star	25	25
		a. Imperf (pair)	£1700	
1416	**885**	27p. Three Wise Men	35	35
1417	**886**	32p. Nativity	40	40
1418	**887**	35p. The Annunciation	55	55
Set of 5			1·60	1·60
Set of 5 Gutter Pairs			3·20	
First Day Cover				1·75
Presentation Pack (PO Pack No. 194)			1·75	
PHQ Cards (set of 5) (114)			75	1·75

Examples of No. 1414a were found in some 1988 Post Office Yearbooks.

Special First Day of Issue Postmarks

Philatelic Bureau, Edinburgh	1·75
Bethlehem, Llandeilo, Dyfed	1·90

Collectors Pack 1988

1988 Nov 15 Comprises Nos. 1380/1408, 1414/18.

CP1418*a* Collectors Pack	15·50

Post Office Yearbook

1988 Nov 15 Comprises Nos. 1380/1404, MS1409, 1414/18 in 32-page hardbound book with slip case, illustrated in colour .... 13·00

888 Atlantic Puffin   889 Avocet

890 Oystercatcher   891 Northern Gannet

(Des D. Cordery)

1989 (17 Jan). *Centenary of Royal Society for the Protection of Birds.* ▨ Phosphorised paper. Perf 14×15.

1419	**888**	19p. Atlantic Puffin	25	25
1420	**889**	27p. Avocet	35	35
1421	**890**	32p. Oystercatcher	45	45
1422	**891**	35p. Northern Gannet	60	60
Set of 4			1·50	1·50
Set of 4 Gutter Pairs			3·00	
First Day Cover				1·65
Presentation Pack (PO Pack No. 196)			1·65	
PHQ Cards (set of 4) (115)			60	1·65

Special First Day of Issue Postmarks

Philatelic Bureau, Edinburgh	1·65
Sandy, Bedfordshire	1·80

892 Rose   893 Cupid

894 Yachts   895 Fruit

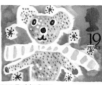

896 Teddy Bear

(Des P. Sutton)

1989 (31 Jan). *Greetings Stamps.* ▨ Phosphorised paper. Perf 15×14.

1423	**892**	19p. Rose	50	60
		a. Booklet pane. Nos. 1423/7×2 plus 12 half stamp-size labels	24·00	
		b. Horiz strip of 5. Nos. 1423/7	10·00	12·00
1424	**893**	19p. Cupid	50	60
1425	**894**	19p. Yachts	50	60
1426	**895**	19p. Fruit	50	60
1427	**896**	19p. Teddy Bear	50	60
Set of 5			10·00	12·00
First Day Cover				12·00

Nos. 1423/7 were printed together, *se-tenant*, in horizontal strips of five, two such strips forming the booklet pane with twelve half stamp-size labels.

Nos. 1423/7 were only issued in £1·90 booklets No. FY1.

Special First Day of Issue Postmarks

Philatelic Bureau, Edinburgh	12·00
Lover, Salisbury, Wilts	12·00

897 Fruit and Vegetables   898 Meat Products

899 Dairy Products   900 Cereal Products

(Des Sedley Place Ltd)

1989 (7 Mar). *Food and Farming Year.* ▨ Phosphorised paper. Perf 14×14½.

1428	**897**	19p. Fruit and Vegetables	25	25
1429	**898**	27p. Meat Products	35	35
1430	**899**	32p. Dairy Products	45	45
1431	**900**	35p. Cereal Products	60	60
Set of 4			1·50	1·50
Set of 4 Gutter Pairs			8·50	
First Day Cover				1·60
Presentation Pack (PO Pack No. 197)			1·60	
PHQ Cards (set of 4) (116)			60	1·60

Special First Day of Issue Postmarks

Philatelic Bureau, Edinburgh ....1·60
Stoneleigh, Kenilworth, Warwicks ....1·75

901 Mortar Board (150th Anniversary of Public Education in England)

902 Cross on Ballot Paper (3rd Direct Elections to European Parliament)

903 Posthorn (26th Postal, Telegraph and Telephone International Congress, Brighton)

904 Globe (Inter-Parliamentary Union Centenary Conference, London)

(Des Lewis Moberly from firework set-pieces. Litho Questa)

1989 (11 Apr). *Anniversaries.* Multi Colour Phosphorised paper. Perf 14×14½.

1432	**901**	19p. Mortar Board	25	25
		a. Horiz pair. Nos. 1432/3	60	60
1433	**902**	19p. Cross on Ballot Paper	25	25
1434	**903**	35p. Posthorn	50	50
		a. Horiz pair. Nos. 1434/5	1·10	1·10
1435	**904**	35p. Globe	50	50
Set of 4			1·50	1·50
Set of 2 Gutter Strips of 4			3·00	
First Day Cover				1·60
Presentation Pack (PO Pack No. 198)			1·60	
PHQ Cards (set of 4) (117)			60	1·60

Nos. 1432/3 and 1434/5 were each printed together, *se-tenant*, in horizontal pairs throughout the sheets. Stamps as No. 1435, but inscribed 'ONE HUNDREDTH CONFERENCE' were prepared, but not issued.

Special First Day of Issue Postmarks

Philatelic Bureau, Edinburgh ....1·60
London SW ....1·75

905 Toy Train and Aeroplanes

906 Building Bricks

907 Dice and Board Games

908 Toy Robot, Boat and Doll's House

(Des D. Fern)

1989 (16 May). *Europa. Games and Toys.* Multi Colour Phosphorised paper. Perf 14×15.

1436	**905**	19p. Toy Train and Aeroplanes	25	25
1437	**906**	27p. Building Bricks	35	35
1438	**907**	32p. Dice and Board Games	45	45
1439	**908**	35p. Toy Robot, Boat and Doll's House.	60	60
Set of 4			1·50	1·50
Set of 4 Gutter Strips			3·00	
First Day Cover				1·65
Presentation Pack (PO Pack No. 199)			1·65	
PHQ Cards (set of 4) (118)			60	1·65

Special First Day of Issue Postmarks

Philatelic Bureau, Edinburgh ....1·65
Leeds...1·75

909 Ironbridge, Shropshire

910 Tin Mine, St Agnes Head, Cornwall

911 Cotton Mills, New Lanark, Strathclyde

912 Pontcysyllte Aqueduct, Clwyd

912a Horizontal versions of T 909/12

(Des R. Maddox)

1989 (4–25 July). *Industrial Archaeology.* Multi Colour Phosphorised paper. Perf 14×15.

1440	**909**	19p. Ironbridge, Shropshire	25	25
1441	**910**	27p. Tin Mine, St Agnes Head, Cornwall	35	35
1442	**911**	32p. Cotton Mills, New Lanark, Strathclyde	45	45
1443	**912**	35p. Pontcysyllte Aqueduct, Clwyd	60	60
Set of 4			1·50	1·50
Set of 4 Gutter Pairs			3·00	
First Day Cover				1·65
Presentation Pack (PO Pack No. 200)			1·65	
PHQ Cards (set of 4) (119)			50	1·65
MS1444	**912a**	122×90 mm. Horizontal versions of T 909/12 (sold at £1.40) (25 July)	3·00	3·00
First Day Cover				3·00

The premium on No. **MS**1444 was used to support the 'Stamp World London 90' International Stamp Exhibition.

Special First Day of Issue Postmarks

Philatelic Bureau, Edinburgh (stamps) (4 July) ....1·65
Philatelic Bureau, Edinburgh (miniature sheet) (25 July) ....3·00
Telford (stamps) (4 July) ....1·75
New Lanark (miniature sheet) (25 July) ....3·20

For Nos. 1445/52 see Decimal Machin Definitives section.

915 Snowflake (×10)

916 *Calliphora erythrocephala* (×5) (fly)

917 Blood Cells (×500)

918 Microchip (×600)

(Des K. Bassford. Litho Questa)

1989 (5 Sept). *150th Anniversary of Royal Microscopical Society.* |MULTI COLOUR| Phosphorised paper. Perf 14½×14.

1453	**915**	19p. Snowflake	25	25
1454	**916**	27p. *Calliphora erythrocephala*	35	35
1455	**917**	32p. Blood Cells	45	45
1456	**918**	35p. Microchip	60	60
Set of 4			1·50	1·50
Set of 4 Gutter Pairs			3·00	
First Day Cover				1·65
Presentation Pack (PO Pack No. 201)			1·65	
PHQ Cards (set of 4) (120)			60	1·65

Special First Day of Issue Postmarks

Philatelic Bureau, Edinburgh .... 1·65
Oxford .... 1·75

919 Royal Mail Coach

920 Escort of Blues and Royals

921 Lord Mayor's Coach

922 Passing St Paul's

923 Blues and Royals Drum Horse

(Des P. Cox)

1989 (17 Oct). *Lord Mayor's Show, London.* |MULTI COLOUR| Phosphorised paper. Perf 14×15.

1457	**919**	20p. Royal Mail Coach	25	25
		a. Horiz strip of 5. Nos. 1457/61	1·35	1·35
		ab. Imperf (horiz strip of 5. Nos. 1457/61)	£12000	
		ac. Imperf (horiz strip of 4. Nos. 1457/60)	£10000	
		ad. Imperf (horiz strip of 3. Nos. 1457/9)	£8000	
1458	**920**	20p. Escort of Blues and Royals	25	25
1459	**921**	20p. Lord Mayor's Coach	25	25
1460	**922**	20p. Passing St Paul's	25	25
1461	**923**	20p. Blues and Royals Drum Horse	25	25
Set of 5			1·35	1·35
Gutter Strip of 10			2·70	
First Day Cover				1·40
Presentation Pack (PO Pack No. 202)			1·50	
PHQ Cards (set of 5) (121)			75	1·35

Nos. 1457/61 were printed together, *se-tenant*, in horizontal strips of five throughout the sheet. This issue commemorates the 800th anniversary of the installation of the first Lord Mayor of London.

Nos. 1457ab/ad come from a sheet partly imperf at left. Stamps of Types **919/23**, but each with face value of 19p., were prepared but not issued. One mint *se-tenant* strip has been recorded.

See also No. 2957.

Special First Day of Issue Postmarks

Philatelic Bureau, Edinburgh .... 1·40
London, EC4 .... 1·50

924 14th-century Peasants from Stained-glass Window

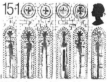

925 Arches and Roundels, West Front

926 Octagon Tower

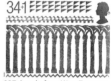

927 Arcade from West Transept

928 Triple Arch from West Front

(Des D. Gentleman)

1989 (14 Nov). *Christmas. 800th Anniversary of Ely Cathedral.* |MULTI COLOUR| One phosphor band (15p., 15p.+1p.) or phosphorised paper (others). Perf 15×14.

1462	**924**	15p. 14th-century Peasants from Stained-glass Window	25	25
1463	**925**	15p. +1p. Arches and Roundels, West Front	25	25
		a. Imperf (pair)	£3500	
1464	**926**	20p. +1p. Octagon Tower	35	35
		a. Imperf (pair)	£3500	
1465	**927**	34p. +1p. Arcade from West Transept	45	45
1466	**928**	37p. +1p. Triple Arch from West Front	60	60
Set of 5			1·70	1·70
Set of 5 Gutter Pairs			3·40	
First Day Cover				1·80
Presentation Pack (PO Pack No. 203)			1·80	
PHQ Cards (set of 5) (122)			75	1·70

Trials are known showing different values and including an additional design.

Special First Day of Issue Postmarks

Philatelic Bureau, Edinburgh .... 1·80
Bethlehem, Llandeilo, Dyfed .... 1·80
Ely .... 1·80

Collectors Pack 1989

1989 Nov 14 Comprises Nos. 1419/22, 1428/43 and 1453/66.
CP1466a Collectors Pack .... 15·50

Post Office Yearbook

1989 (14 Nov). Comprises Nos. 1419/22, 1428/44 and
1453/66 in hardbound book with slip case,
illustrated in colour .... 14·00

929 Queen
Victoria and
Queen Elizabeth II

(Des J. Matthews (after Wyon and Machin))

1990 (10 Jan–12 June). *150th Anniversary of the Penny Black.*

(a) Photo Harrison. P 15×14.

1467	**929**	15p. Queen Victoria and Queen Elizabeth II	30	30
		a. Imperf (pair)	£2750	
		l. Booklet pane. No. 1467×10 with horizontal edges of pane imperf (30.1.90)	4·75	
1468		15p. brt blue (1 side band at left) (30.1.90)	3·75	3·75
		Ea. Band at right (20.3.90)	1·75	1·75
		l. Booklet pane. No. 1468×2 and 1470 plus label	9·75	
1469		20p. brownish black and cream (phosphorised paper)	40	40
		a. Imperf (pair)	£2250	
		l. Booklet pane. No. 1469×5 plus label with vertical edges of pane imperf (30.1.90)	5·00	
		m. Booklet pane. No. 1469×10 with horizontal edges of pane imperf (30.1.90)	5·25	
		n. Booklet pane. No. 1469×6 with margins all round (20.3.90)	1·50	
		r. Booklet pane. No. 1469×4 with three edges of pane imperf (17.4.90)	3·75	
1470		20p. brownish black and cream (2 bands) (30.1.90)	80	80
1471		29p. dp mauve (phosphorised paper) ...	55	55
1472		29p. dp mauve (2 bands) (20.3.90)	3·75	3·75
1473		34p. dp bluish grey (phosphorised paper)	70	70
1474		37p. rosine (phosphorised paper)	75	75

(b) Litho Walsall. P 14 (from booklets).

1475	**929**	15p. Queen Victoria and Queen Elizabeth II (30.1.90)	50	50
		l. Booklet pane. No. 1475×4 with three edges of pane imperf	3·00	
		m. Booklet pane. No. 1475×10 with three edges of pane imperf (12.6.90)	5·50	
1476		20p. brownish black and cream (phosphorised paper) (30.1.90)	50	50
		l. Booklet pane. No. 1476×5 plus label with three edges of pane imperf	8·00	
		m. Booklet pane. No. 1476×4 with three edges of pane imperf	4·00	
		n. Booklet pane. No. 1476×10 with three edges of pane imperf (12.6.90).	8·00	

(c) Litho Questa. P 15×14 (from booklets).

1477	**929**	15p. Queen Victoria and Queen Elizabeth II (17.4.90)	85	85
1478		20p. brownish black (phosphorised paper) (17.4.90)	85	85
Set of 5 (Nos. 1467, 1469, 1471, 1473/4)			2·50	2·50
First Day Cover (Nos. 1467, 1469, 1471, 1473/4)				2·60
Presentation Pack (Nos. 1467, 1469, 1471, 1473/4)				
(PO Pack No. 21)			2·90	

Nos. 1475/6 do not exist perforated on all four sides, but come
with either one or two adjacent sides imperforate.

Nos. 1468, 1468Ea, 1470, 1472 and 1475/8 were only issued in
stamp booklets, Nos. JA1 to JD3. Nos. 1468Ea, 1470 and 1472 occur in
the *se-tenant* pane from the 1990 London Life £5 booklet. This pane is
listed as No. X906m.

For illustrations showing the difference between photogravure and
lithography see beneath Type **367**.

For No. 1469 in miniature sheet see No. **MS**1501.

For No. 1476 with one elliptical hole on each vertical side see Nos.
2133 and 2955.

For Type **929** redrawn with '1st' face value see No. 2133*a*.

Colour trials are known denominated 19p. in several colours.

Special First Day of Issue Postmark

Philatelic Bureau, Edinburgh (in red) ....2·60
Windsor, Berks (Type G, see Introduction) (in red) ....2·75

1 8 4 0 · R S P C A · 1 9 9 0
930 Kitten

1 8 4 0 · R S P C A · 1 9 9 0
931 Rabbit

1 8 4 0 · R S P C A · 1 9 9 0
932 Duckling

1 8 4 0 · R S P C A · 1 9 9 0
933 Puppy

(Des T. Evans. Litho Questa)

1990 (23 Jan). *150th Anniversary of Royal Society for Prevention of Cruelty
to Animals.* MULTI COLOUR Phosphorised paper. Perf 14×14½.

1479	**930**	20p. Kitten	30	30
		a. Silver (Queen's head and face value) omitted	£675	
1480	**931**	29p. Rabbit	45	45
		a. Imperf (horiz pair)	£5500	
1481	**932**	34p. Duckling	55	55
		a. Silver (Queen's head and face value) omitted	£1250	
1482	**933**	37p. Puppy	65	65
Set of 4			1·80	1·80
Set of 4 Gutter Pairs			3·60	
First Day Cover				1·95
Presentation Pack (PO Pack No. 205)			1·95	
PHQ Cards (set of 4) (123)			80	1·95

Special First Day of Issue Postmarks

Philatelic Bureau, Edinburgh ....1·95
Horsham ....2·20

934 Teddy Bear

935 Dennis the Menace

936 Punch

937 Cheshire Cat

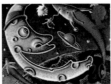

938 The Man in the Moon

939 The Laughing Policeman

940 Clown

941 Mona Lisa

942 Queen of Hearts

943 Stan Laurel (comedian)

(Des Michael Peters and Partners Ltd)

1990 (6 Feb). *Greetings Stamps. Smiles.* |MULTI COLOUR| Two phosphor bands. Perf 15×14.

1483	**934**	20p. Teddy Bear	60	70
		a. Booklet pane. Nos. 1483/92 with margins all round	11·50	12·50
1484	**935**	20p. Dennis the Menace	60	70
1485	**936**	20p. Punch	60	70
1486	**937**	20p. Cheshire Cat	60	70
1487	**938**	20p. The Man in the Moon	60	70
1488	**939**	20p. The Laughing Policeman	60	70
1489	**940**	20p. Clown	60	70
1490	**941**	20p. Mona Lisa	60	70
1491	**942**	20p. Queen of Hearts	60	70
1492	**943**	20p. Stan Laurel	60	70
Set of 10			11·50	12·50
First Day Cover				12·50

Nos. 1483/92 were only issued in £2 booklets No. KX1. The design of Nos. 1483, 1485/7, 1489 and 1492 extend onto the pane margin.

For Types **934/43** inscribed (1st), see Nos. 1550/59.

SET PRICES. Please note that set prices for booklet greetings stamps are for complete panes. Sets of single stamps are worth considerably less.

Special First Day of Issue Postmarks

| Philatelic Bureau, Edinburgh | 12·50 |
| Giggleswick, North Yorkshire | 12·50 |

944 Alexandra Palace ('Stamp World London 90' Exhibition)

945 Glasgow School of Art

946 British Philatelic Bureau, Edinburgh

947 Templeton Carpet Factory, Glasgow

(Des P. Hogarth)

1990 (6–20 Mar). *Europa* (Nos. 1493 and 1495) and *Glasgow 1990 European City of Culture* (Nos. 1494 and 1496). |MULTI COLOUR| Phosphorised paper. Perf 14×15.

1493	**944**	20p. Alexandra Palace ('Stamp World London 90' Exhibition)	25	25
		a. Booklet pane. No. 1493×4 with margins all round (20 Mar)	1·40	
1494	**945**	20p. Glasgow School of Art	35	35

1495	**946**	29p. British Philatelic Bureau, Edinburgh	45	45
1496	**947**	37p. Templeton Carpet Factory, Glasgow	60	60
Set of 4			1·50	1·50
Set of 4 Gutter Pairs			3·00	
First Day Cover				1·65
Presentation Pack (PO Pack No. 206)			1·65	
PHQ Cards (set of 4) (124)			80	1·65

Booklet pane No. 1493a comes from the £5 'London Life' booklet No. DX11.

Special First Day of Issue Postmarks

| Philatelic Bureau, Edinburgh | 1·65 |
| Glasgow | 1·80 |

948 Export Achievement Award

949 Technological Achievement Award

(Des S. Broom. Litho Questa)

1990 (10 Apr). *25th Anniversary of Queen's Awards for Export and Technology.* |MULTI COLOUR| Phosphorised paper. Perf 14×14½.

1497	**948**	20p. Export Achievement Award	25	25
		a. Horiz pair. Nos. 1497/8	60	60
1498	**949**	20p. Technological Achievement Award	25	25
1499	**948**	37p. Export Achievement Award	50	50
		a. Horiz pair. Nos. 1499/500	1·10	1·10
1500	**949**	37p. Technological Achievement Award	50	50
Set of 4			1·50	1·50
Set of 2 Gutter Strips of 4			3·00	
First Day Cover				1·65
Presentation Pack (PO Pack No. 207)			1·65	
PHQ Cards (set of 4) (125)			80	1·65

Nos. 1497/8 and 1499/1500 were each printed together, *se-tenant*, in horizontal pairs throughout the sheets.

Special First Day of Issue Postmarks

| Philatelic Bureau, Edinburgh | 1·65 |
| London, SW | 1·80 |

949a

(Des Sedley Place Design Ltd. Eng C. Matthews. Recess and photo Harrison)

1990 (3 May). *Stamp World London '90 International Stamp Exhibition.* Sheet 122×89 mm containing No. 1469. Phosphorised paper. Perf 15×14.

MS1501	**949a**	20p. brownish black and cream (sold at £1)	2·30	2·30
		a. Error. Imperf	—	
		b. Black (recess-printing) omitted	—	
		c. Black (recess-printing) inverted	—	
First Day Cover				2·40
Souvenir Book (Nos. 1467, 1469, 1471, 1473/4 and MS1501)			8·50	

The premium on No. **MS**1501 was used to support the 'Stamp World London '90' International Stamp Exhibition. In No. **MS**1501 only the example of the 20p. is perforated.

No. **MS**1501b shows an albino impression on the reverse. The 1d. black and Seahorse background are omitted due to one sheet becoming attached to the underside of another prior to recess printing. No. **MS**1501c shows the recess part of the design inverted in relation to the photogravure of Type **929**.

For the single 20p stamp, see No. 1469. For the same stamp redrawn with '1st' face value or with one elliptical hole on each vertical side see Nos. 2133 and 2955/6.

Special First Day of Issue Postmarks
Philatelic Bureau, Edinburgh (in red) ....2·40
City of London (in red)..2·40

A First Day of Issue handstamp as Type B was provided at Alexandra Palace, London N22 for this issue.

KEW GARDENS 1840-1990
950 Cycad and Sir Joseph Banks Building

KEW GARDENS 1840-1990
951 Stone Pine and Princess of Wales Conservatory

KEW GARDENS 1840-1990
952 Willow Tree and Palm House

KEW GARDENS 1840-1990
953 Cedar Tree and Pagoda

(Des P. Leith)

1990 (5 June). *150th Anniversary of Kew Gardens.* |MULTI COLOUR| Phosphorised paper. Perf 14×15.

1502	**950**	20p. Cycad and Sir Joseph Banks Building.......................	25	25
1503	**951**	29p. Stone Pine and Princess of Wales Conservatory..........................	35	35
1504	**952**	34p. Willow Tree and Palm House..........	45	45
1505	**953**	37p. Cedar Tree and Pagoda.....................	60	60
Set of 4..			1·50	1·50
Set of 4 Gutter Pairs			3·00	
First Day Cover				1·65
Presentation Pack (PO Pack No. 208)................			1·65	
PHQ Cards (set of 4) (126)....................................			80	1·65

Special First Day of Issue Postmarks
Philatelic Bureau, Edinburgh .... 1·65
Kew, Richmond .... 1·80

954 Thomas Hardy and Clyffe Clump, Dorset

(Des J. Gibbs)

1990 (10 July). *150th Birth Anniversary of Thomas Hardy (author).* |MULTI COLOUR| Phosphorised paper. Perf 14×15.

1506	**954**	20p. Thomas Hardy	30	30
		a. Imperf (pair)...............................	£8500	
Gutter Pair			60	
First Day Cover				60
Presentation Pack (PO Pack No. 209)................			55	
PHQ Card (127)..			20	30

Special First Day of Issue Postmarks
Philatelic Bureau, Edinburgh 60
Dorchester 65

955 Queen Elizabeth the Queen Mother

956 Queen Elizabeth

957 Elizabeth, Duchess of York

958 Lady Elizabeth Bowes-Lyon

(Des J. Gorham from photographs by N. Parkinson (20p.), Dorothy Wilding (29p.), B. Park (34p.), Rita Martin (37p.))

1990 (2 Aug). *90th Birthday of Queen Elizabeth the Queen Mother.* |MULTI COLOUR| Phosphorised paper. Perf 14×15.

1507	**955**	20p. Queen Elizabeth the Queen Mother..	40	40
1508	**956**	29p. Queen Elizabeth...........................	60	60
1509	**957**	34p. Elizabeth, Duchess of York..............	90	90
1510	**958**	37p. Lady Elizabeth Bowes-Lyon..............	1·10	1·10
Set of 4..			2·75	2·75
Set of 4 Gutter Pairs			5·50	
First Day Cover				2·85
Presentation Pack (PO Pack No. 210)................			2·85	
PHQ Cards (set of 4) (128)....................................			80	2·85

For these designs with Queen's head and frame in black see Nos. 2280/3.

Special First Day of Issue Postmarks
Philatelic Bureau, Edinburgh .... 2·85
Westminster, SW1 .... 2·85

For Nos. 1511/16 see Decimal Machin Definitives section.

959 Victoria Cross

960 George Cross

961 Distinguished Service Cross and Distinguished Service Medal

962 Military Cross and Military Medal

963 Distinguished Flying Cross
and Distinguished Flying Medal

(Des J. Gibbs and J. Harwood)

1990 (11 Sept). *Gallantry Award.* |MULTI COLOUR| Phosphorised paper. Perf 14×15 (vert) or 15×14 (horiz).

1517	**959**	20p. Victoria Cross	35	35
1518	**960**	20p. George Cross	35	35
1519	**961**	20p. Distinguished Service Cross and Distinguished Service Medal	35	35
		a. Imperf (pair)	£3000	
1520	**962**	20p. Military Cross and Military Medal	35	35
1521	**963**	20p. Distinguished Flying Cross and Distinguished Flying Medal	35	35
Set of 5			1·50	1·50
Set of 5 Gutter Pairs			3·00	
First Day Cover				1·65
Presentation Pack (PO Pack No. 211)			1·65	
PHQ Cards (set of 5) (129)			1·00	1·65

For Type **959** with 'all-over' phosphor and Perf 14×14½ see No. 2666.

Special First Day of Issue Postmarks

Philatelic Bureau, Edinburgh .... 1·65
Westminster, SW1 .... 1·80

964 Armagh Observatory, Jodrell Bank Radio Telescope and La Palma Telescope

965 Newton's Moon and Tides Diagram and Early Telescopes

966 Greenwich Old Observatory and Early Astronomical Equipment

967 Stonehenge, Gyroscope and Navigation by Stars

(Des J. Fisher. Litho Questa)

1990 (16 Oct). *Astronomy.* |MULTI COLOUR| Phosphorised paper. Perf 14×14½.

1522	**964**	22p. Armagh Observatory, Jodrell Bank Radio Telescope and La Palma Telescope	25	25
		a. Gold (Queen's head) omitted	£900	
1523	**965**	26p. Newton's Moon and Tides Diagram and Early Telescopes	35	35
1524	**966**	31p. Greenwich Old Observatory and Early Astronomical Equipment	45	45
1525	**967**	37p. Stonehenge, Gyroscope and Navigation by Stars	60	60
Set of 4			1·50	1·50
Set of 4 Gutter Pairs			3·00	
First Day Cover				1·65
Presentation Pack (PO Pack No. 212)			1·65	
PHQ Cards (set of 4) (130)			80	1·65

Nos. 1522/5 marked the centenary of the British Astronomical Association and the bicentenary of the Armagh Observatory.

Special First Day of Issue Postmarks

Philatelic Bureau, Edinburgh .... 1·65
Armagh .... 1·80

968 Building a Snowman

969 Fetching the Christmas Tree

970 Carol Singing

971 Tobogganing

972 Ice-skating

(Des J. Gorham and A. Davidson)

1990 (13 Nov). *Christmas.* |MULTI COLOUR| One phosphor band (17p.) or phosphorised paper (others). Perf 15×14.

1526	**968**	17p. Building a Snowman	25	25
		a. Imperf (pair)	£3000	
		b. Booklet pane of 20	5·00	
1527	**969**	22p. Fetching the Christmas Tree	25	25
		a. Imperf (horiz pair)	£3000	
1528	**970**	26p. Carol Singing	35	35
1529	**971**	31p. Tobogganing	45	40
1530	**972**	37p. Ice-skating	60	60
Set of 5			1·50	1·50
Set of 5 Gutter Pairs			3·00	
First Day Cover				1·60
Presentation Pack (PO Pack No. 213)			1·65	
PHQ Cards (set of 5) (131)			1·00	1·65

Booklet pane No. 1526b has the horizontal edges of the pane imperforate.

Special First Day of Issue Postmarks

Philatelic Bureau, Edinburgh .... 1·60
Bethlehem, Llandeilo, Dyfed .... 1·60

Collectors Pack 1990
1990 (13 Nov). Comprises Nos. 1479/82, 1493/1510 and 1517/30.
CP1530a Collectors Pack .... 17·50

Post Office Yearbook
1990 (13 Nov). Comprises Nos. 1479/82, 1493/1500, 1502/10, 1517/30 in hardbound book with slip case, illustrated in colour YB1530a Yearbook .... 17·50

973 *King Charles Spaniel*

974 *A Pointer*

975 *Two Hounds in a Landscape*

976 *A Rough Dog*

977 *Fino and Tiny*

(Des Carroll, Dempsey and Thirkell Ltd)

1991 (8 Jan). *Dogs. Paintings by George Stubbs.* ⎸MULTI COLOUR Phosphorised paper.
P 14×14½.

1531	**973**	22p. King Charles Spaniel	25	25
		a. Imperf (pair)	£2800	
1532	**974**	26p. A Pointer	30	30
1533	**975**	31p. Two Hounds in a Landscape	40	40
		a. Imperf (pair)	£3750	
1534	**976**	33p. A Rough Dog	45	45
1535	**977**	37p. Fino and Tiny	60	60
Set of 5			1·80	1·80
Set of 5 Gutter Pairs			3·60	
First Day Cover				2·00
Presentation Pack (PO Pack No. 215)			2·00	
PHQ Cards (set of 5) (132)			60	1·80

Special First Day of Issue Postmarks

Philatelic Bureau, Edinburgh ....2·00
Birmingham ....2·00

978 Thrush's Nest

979 Shooting Star and Rainbow

980 Magpies and Charm
Bracelet

981 Black Cat

982 Common Kingfisher with
Key

983 Mallard and Frog

984 Four-leaf Clover in Boot
and Match Box

985 Pot of Gold at End of
Rainbow

986 Heart-shaped Butterflies

987 Wishing Well and Sixpence

(Des T. Meeuwissen)

1991 (5 Feb). *Greetings Stamps. Good Luck.* ⎸MULTI COLOUR Two phosphor bands.
Perf 15×14.

1536	**978**	(1st) Thrush's Nest	80	80
		a. Booklet pane. Nos. 1536/45 plus 12 half stamp-size labels with margins on 3 sides	9·00	9·00
1537	**979**	(1st) Shooting Star and Rainbow	80	80
1538	**980**	(1st) Magpies and Charm Bracelet	80	80
1539	**981**	(1st) Black Cat	80	80
1540	**982**	(1st) Common Kingfisher with Key	80	80
1541	**983**	(1st) Mallard and Frog	80	80
1542	**984**	(1st) Four-leaf clover in Boot and Match Box	80	80
1543	**985**	(1st) Pot of Gold at End of Rainbow	80	80
1544	**986**	(1st) Heart-shaped Butterflies	80	80
1545	**987**	(1st) Wishing Well and Sixpence	80	80
Set of 10			9·00	9·00
First Day Cover				9·25

Nos. 1536/45 were only issued in £2·20 booklets, No. KX2 (*sold at £2·40 from 16 September 1991*)
The backgrounds of the stamps form a composite design.

Special First Day of Issue Postmarks

Philatelic Bureau, Edinburgh ....9·20
Greetwell, Lincs ....9·20

988 Michael Faraday
(inventor of electric
motor) (Birth
Bicentenary)

989 Charles Babbage
(computer science
pioneer) (Birth
Bicentenary)

990 Radar Sweep of East
Anglia (50th Anniversary
of Operational Radar
Network)

991 Gloster Whittle
E28/39 over East Anglia
(50th Anniversary of First
Flight of Sir Frank
Whittle's Jet Engine)

(Des P. Till (Nos. 1546/7), J. Harwood (Nos. 1548/9))

1991 (5 Mar). *Scientific Achievements.* ⎸MULTI COLOUR Phosphorised paper.
Perf 14×15.

1546	**988**	22p. Michael Faraday	35	35
		a. Imperf (pair)	£650	
1547	**989**	22p. Charles Babbage	35	35
1548	**990**	31p. Radar Sweep of East Anglia	55	55
1549	**991**	37p. Gloster Whittle E28/39 over East Anglia	65	65
Set of 4			1·70	1·70
Set of 4 Gutter Pairs			3·40	
First Day Cover				1·85
Presentation Pack (PO Pack No. 216)			1·85	
PHQ Cards (set of 4) (133)			50	1·85

Special First Day of Issue Postmarks

Philatelic Bureau, Edinburgh ....1·85
South Kensington, London, SW7 ....2·00

992 Teddy Bear

(Des Michael Peters and Partners Ltd)

1991 (26 Mar). *Greeting Stamps. Smiles.* As Nos. 1483/92, but inscribed '1st' as T **992**. |MULTI COLOUR Two phosphor bands. Perf 15×14.

1550	**992**	(1st) Teddy Bear	1·00	50
		a. Booklet pane. Nos. 1550/9 plus 12 half stamp-size labels with margins on 3 sides	9·00	9·25
1551	**935**	(1st) Dennis the Menace	1·00	50
1552	**936**	(1st) Punch	1·00	50
1553	**937**	(1st) Cheshire Cat	1·00	50
1554	**938**	(1st) The Man in the Moon	1·00	50
1555	**939**	(1st) The Laughing Policeman	1·00	50
1556	**940**	(1st) Clown	1·00	50
1557	**941**	(1st) Mona Lisa	1·00	50
1558	**942**	(1st) Queen of Hearts	1·00	50
1559	**943**	(1st) Stan Laurel	1·00	50
Set of 10			9·00	9·25
First Day Cover				9·50

Nos. 1550/9 were originally issued in £2·20 booklets, No. KX3 (*sold at £2·40 from 16 September 1991 and at £2·50 from 1 November 1993*). The designs of Nos. 1550, 1552/4, 1556 and 1559 extend onto the pane margin.

The stamps were re-issued in sheets of 10, printed in photogravure by Questa, each with *se-tenant* label on 22 May 2000 in connection with 'customised' stamps available at 'Stamp Show 2000'. The labels show either a pattern of ribbons at £2·95 (LS1), or a personal photograph for £5·95.

A similar sheet, but printed in lithography by Questa instead of in photogravure, appeared on 3 July 2001 (LS5). Stamps from this sheet were perforated 14½×14 instead of the previous 15×14. Sheets showing greetings on the labels were available from the Bureau or Postshops at £2·95 each or with personal photographs at £12·95 for two. Similar sheets each containing ten examples of Nos. 1550/1 and 1555/7 were only available with personal photograph. From 29 October 2001 sheets with personal photographs could also be purchased, on an experimental basis, from photo-booths situated at six post offices.

On 1 October 2002 three further sheets appeared printed in lithography by Questa. One contained Nos. 1550/1 each×10 with greetings labels and cost £5·95 (LS9). Both designs were also available in sheets of 20 with personal photographs at £14·95 a sheet.

SET PRICES. Please note that set prices for booklet greetings stamps are for complete panes. Sets of single stamps are worth considerably less.

Special First Day of Issue Postmarks

Philatelic Bureau, Edinburgh ...... 9·50
Laugherton, Lincs ...... 9·50

993 Man Looking at Space

994 Man Looking at Space

995 Space Looking at Man

996 Space Looking at Man

(Des J. M. Folon)

1991 (23 Apr). *Europa. Europe in space.* |MULTI COLOUR Phosphorised paper. Perf 14½×14.

1560	**993**	22p. Man Looking at Space	35	35
		a. Horiz pair. Nos 1560/1	75	75
1561	**994**	22p. Man Looking at Space	35	35
1562	**995**	37p. Space Looking at Man	65	65
		a. Horiz pair. Nos 1562/3	1·40	1·40
1563	**996**	37p. Space Looking at Man	65	65
Set of 4			1·90	1·95

Set of 2 Gutter Pairs of 4	3·80	
First Day Cover		2·10
Presentation Pack (PO Pack No. 217)	2·10	
PHQ Cards (set of 4) (134)	80	2·10

Nos. 1560/1 and 1562/3 were each printed together, *se-tenant*, in horizontal pairs throughout the sheets, each pair forming a composite design.

Special First Day of Issue Postmarks

Philatelic Bureau, Edinburgh ...... 2·10
Cambridge ...... 2·25

997 Fencing

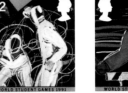

998 Hurdling

999 Diving

1000 Rugby

(Des Huntley Muir Partners)

1991 (11 June). *World Student Games, Sheffield* (Nos.1564/6) and *World Cup Rugby Championship, London* (No. 1567). |MULTI COLOUR Phosphorised paper. P 14½×14.

1564	**997**	22p. Fencing	35	35
1565	**998**	26p. Hurdling	45	45
1566	**999**	31p. Diving	55	55
1567	**1000**	37p. Rugby	75	75
Set of 4			1·90	1·90
Set of 4 Gutter Pairs			3·80	
First Day Cover				2·10
Presentation Pack (PO Pack No. 218)			2·10	
PHQ Cards (set of 4) (135)			80	2·10

Special First Day of Issue Postmarks

Philatelic Bureau, Edinburgh ...... 2·10
Sheffield ...... 2·25

Rosa Silver Jubilee
1001 'Silver Jubilee'

Rosa Mme Alfred Carrière
1002 'Mme Alfred Carrière'

Rosa moyesii
1003 *Rosa moyesii*

Rosa Harvest Fayre
1004 'Harvest Fayre'

Rosa Mutabilis
1005 'Mutabilis'

(Des Yvonne Skargon. Litho Questa)

1991 (16 July). *Ninth World Congress of Roses, Belfast.* MULTI COLOUR *Phosphorised paper. Perf 14½×14.*

1568	**1001**	22p. 'Silver Jubilee'	30	30
		a. Silver (Queen's head) omitted	£3000	
		Eb. Black printing double	£4750	£3500
1569	**1002**	26p. 'Mme Alfred Carrière'	35	35
1570	**1003**	31p. *Rosa moyesii*	40	40
1571	**1004**	33p. 'Harvest Fayre'	55	55
1572	**1005**	37p. 'Mutabilis'	65	65
Set of 5			2·00	2·00
Set of 5 Gutter Pairs			4·00	
First Day Cover				2·20
Presentation Pack (PO Pack No. 219)			2·20	
PHQ Cards (set of 5) (136)			60	2·20

Special First Day of Issue Postmarks

Philatelic Bureau, Edinburgh	2·20
Belfast	2·40

1006 Iguanodon

1007 Stegosaurus

1008 Tyrannosaurus

1009 Protoceratops

1010 Triceratops

(Des B. Kneale)

1991 (20 Aug). *150th Anniversary of Dinosaurs' Identification by Owen.* MULTI COLOUR *Phosphorised paper. Perf 14½×14.*

1573	**1006**	22p. Iguanodon	35	35
		a. Imperf (pair)	£3750	
1574	**1007**	26p. Stegosaurus	40	40
1575	**1008**	31p. Tyrannosaurus	45	45
1576	**1009**	33p. Protoceratops	60	60
1577	**1010**	37p. Triceratops	75	75
Set of 5			2·25	2·25
Set of 5 Gutter Pairs			4·50	
First Day Cover				2·75
Presentation Pack (PO Pack No. 220)			3·00	
PHQ Cards (set of 5) (137)			1·00	2·50

Special First Day of Issue Postmarks

Philatelic Bureau, Edinburgh	2·75
Plymouth	3·00

1011 Map of 1816

1012 Map of 1906

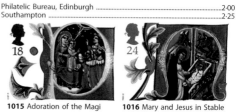

1013 Map of 1959

1014 Map of 1991

(Des H. Brown. Recess and litho Harrison (24p.), litho Harrison (28p.), Questa (33p., 39p.))

1991 (17 Sept). *Bicentenary of Ordnance Survey. Maps of Hamstreet, Kent.* MULTI COLOUR *Phosphorised paper. Perf 14½×14.*

1578	**1011**	24p. Map of 1816	35	35
		Ea. Black (litho) printing treble and magenta printing double	£1250	
		Eb. Black (litho) and magenta printing double	£1800	
		Ec. Black (litho) printing double	£1800	
1579	**1012**	28p. Map of 1906	45	45
1580	**1013**	33p. Map of 1959	55	55
1581	**1014**	39p. Map of 1991	75	75
Set of 4			1·90	1·90
Set of 4 Gutter Pairs			8·50	
First Day Cover				2·00
Presentation Pack (PO Pack No. 221)			2·20	
PHQ Cards (set of 4) (138)			80	2·00

Mint examples of Type **1012** exist with a face value of 26p. (*Price* £5000).

Special First Day of Issue Postmarks

Philatelic Bureau, Edinburgh	2·00
Southampton	2·25

1015 Adoration of the Magi

1016 Mary and Jesus in Stable

1017 Holy Family and Angel

1018 The Annunciation

1019 The Flight into Egypt

(Des D. Driver)

1991 (12 Nov). *Christmas. Illuminated Letters from 'Acts of Mary and Jesus' Manuscript in Bodleian Library, Oxford. One phosphor band* MULTI COLOUR *(18p.) or phosphorised paper (others). Perf 15×14.*

1582	**1015**	18p. Adoration of the Magi	25	25
		a. Imperf (pair)	—	
		b. Booklet pane of 20	5·00	
1583	**1016**	24p. Mary and Jesus in Stable	30	30
1584	**1017**	28p. Holy Family and Angel	40	40
1585	**1018**	33p. The Annunciation	55	55
		a. Imperf (pair)	—	
1586	**1019**	39p. The Flight into Egypt	70	70
Set of 5			1·90	1·90
Set of 5 Gutter Pairs			3·80	
First Day Cover				2·00
Presentation Pack (PO Pack No. 222)			2·10	
PHQ Cards (set of 5) (139)			60	2·00

Booklet pane No. 1582b has margins at left, top and bottom.

Special First Day of Issue Postmarks

Philatelic Bureau, Edinburgh	2·00
Bethlehem, Landeilo, Dyfed	2·00

Collectors Pack 1991

1991 (12 Nov). Comprises Nos. 1531/5, 1546/9 and 1560/86.
CP1586a Collectors Pack..................................... 18·00

Post Office Yearbook

1991 (13 Nov). Comprises Nos. 1531/5, 1546/9 and 1560/86 in hardbound book with slip case, illustrated in colour..................................... 15·50

1020 Fallow Deer in Scottish Forest

1021 Hare on North Yorkshire Moors

1022 Fox in the Fens

1023 Redwing and Home Counties Village

1024 Welsh Mountain Sheep in Snowdonia

(Des J. Gorham and K. Bowen)

1992 (14 Jan–25 Feb). *The Four Seasons. Wintertime.* |MULTI COLOUR| One phosphor band (18p.) or phosphorised paper (others). Perf 15×14.

1587	**1020**	18p. Fallow Deer in Scottish Forest........	25	25
1588	**1021**	24p. Hare on North Yorkshire Moors......	30	30
		a. Imperf (pair)......................................	£850	
1589	**1022**	28p. Fox in the Fens..................................	45	45
1590	**1023**	33p. Redwing and Home Counties Village...	55	55
1591	**1024**	39p. Welsh Mountain Sheep in Snowdonia...	70	70
		a. Booklet pane. No. 1591×4 with margins all round (25 Feb).............	2·80	

Set of 5... 2·00 2·00
Set of 5 Gutter Pairs...................................... 4·00
First Day Cover... 2·10
Presentation Pack (PO Pack No. 224)........... 2·25
PHQ Cards (set of 5) (140)........................... 1·00 2·10

Booklet pane No. 1591a comes from the £6 'Cymru-Wales' booklet No. DX13.

Special First Day of Issue Postmarks

Philatelic Bureau, Edinburgh..2·10
Brecon...2·10

1025 Flower Spray

1026 Double Locket

1027 Key

1028 Model Car and Cigarette Cards

1029 Compass and Map

1030 Pocket Watch

1031 1854 1d. Red Stamp and Pen

1032 Pearl Necklace and Pen

1033 Marbles

1034 Bucket, Spade and Starfish

(Des Trickett and Webb Ltd)

1992 (28 Jan). *Greetings Stamps. Memories.* |MULTI COLOUR| Two phosphor bands. Perf 15×14.

1592	**1025**	(1st) Flower Spray............................	1·00	50
		a. Booklet pane. Nos. 1592/1601 plus 12 half stamp-size labels with margins on 3 sides..................	9·00	9·25
1593	**1026**	(1st) Double Locket..........................	1·00	50
1594	**1027**	(1st) Key..	1·00	50
1595	**1028**	(1st) Model Car and Cigarette Cards........	1·00	50
1596	**1029**	(1st) Compass and Map...................	1·00	50
1597	**1030**	(1st) Pocket Watch..........................	1·00	50
1598	**1031**	(1st) 1854 1d. Red Stamp and Pen.........	1·00	50
1599	**1032**	(1st) Pearl Necklace and Pen.........	1·00	50
1600	**1033**	(1st) Marbles....................................	1·00	50
1601	**1034**	(1st) Bucket, Spade and Starfish...............	1·00	50

Set of 10.. 9·00 9·25
First Day Cover... 9·50
Presentation Pack (PO Pack No. G1)............. 10·00

Nos. 1592/1601 were only issued in £2·40 booklets, No. KX4 (*sold at £2·50 from 1 November 1993 and at £2·60 from 8 July 1996*)
The backgrounds of the stamps form a composite design.

Special First Day of Issue Postmarks

Philatelic Bureau, Edinburgh...9·50
Whimsey, Gloucestershire ....9·50

1035 Queen Elizabeth in Coronation Robes and Parliamentary Emblem

1036 Queen Elizabeth in Garter Robes and Archiepiscopal Arms

1037 Queen Elizabeth with Baby Prince Andrew and Royal Arms

1038 Queen Elizabeth at Trooping the Colour and Service Emblems

1039 Queen Elizabeth and Commonwealth Emblem

(Des Why Not Associates. Litho Questa)

1992 (6 Feb). *40th Anniversary of Accession.* |MULTI COLOUR| Two phosphor bands. Perf 14½×14.

1602	**1035**	24p. Queen Elizabeth in Coronation Robes and Parliamentary Emblem	40	50
		a. Horiz strip of 5. Nos. 1602/6	2·75	3·20
1603	**1036**	24p. Queen Elizabeth in Garter Robes and Archiepiscopal Arms	40	50
1604	**1037**	24p. Queen Elizabeth with Baby Prince Andrew and Royal Arms	40	50
1605	**1038**	24p. Queen Elizabeth at Trooping the Colour and Service Emblems	40	50
1606	**1039**	24p. Queen Elizabeth and Commonwealth Emblem	40	50
Set of 5			2·75	3·20
Gutter Block of 10			5·50	
First Day Cover				3·25
Presentation Pack (PO Pack No. 225)			3·25	
PHQ Cards (set of 5) (141)			1·00	3·20

Nos. 1602/6 were printed together, *se-tenant*, in horizontal strips of five throughout the sheet.

Special First Day of Issue Postmarks

Philatelic Bureau, Edinburgh .... 3·25
Buckingham Palace, London SW1 .... 3·50

1040 Tennyson in 1888 and *The Beguiling of Merlin* (Sir Edward Burne-Jones)

1041 Tennyson in 1856 and *April Love* (Arthur Hughes)

1042 Tennyson in 1864 and *I am Sick of the Shadows* (John Waterhouse)

1043 Tennyson as a Young Man and *Mariana* (Dante Gabriel Rossetti)

(Des Irene von Treskow)

1992 (10 Mar). *Death Centenary of Alfred, Lord Tennyson (poet).* |MULTI COLOUR| Phosphorised paper. Perf 14½×14.

1607	**1040**	24p. Tennyson in 1888 and *The Beguiling of Merlin*	35	35
1608	**1041**	28p. Tennyson in 1856 and *April Love*	50	50
1609	**1042**	33p. Tennyson in 1864 and *I am Sick of the Shadows*	60	60
1610	**1043**	39p. Tennyson as a Young Man and *Mariana*	75	75
Set of 4			2·00	2·00
Set of 4 Gutter Pairs			4·00	
First Day Cover				2·20
Presentation Pack (PO Pack No. 226)			2·25	
PHQ Cards (Set of 4) (142)			80	2·20

Special First Day of Issue Postmarks

Philatelic Bureau, Edinburgh .... 2·20
Isle of Wight .... 2·20

£1.50 CAERNARFON CASTLE

1044 Caernarfon Castle

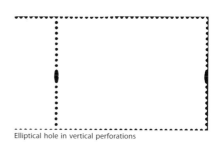

Elliptical hole in vertical perforations

CASTLE

Harrison Plates (Nos. 1611/14)

CASTLE

Enschedé Plates (Nos. 1993/6)

(Des from photos by Prince Andrew, Duke of York. Eng C. Matthews. Recess Harrison)

1992 (24 Mar)–**95**. Designs as Nos. 1410/13, but showing Queen's head in silhouette as T **1044**. |MULTI COLOUR| Perf 15×14 (with one elliptical hole in each vertical side).

1611	**879**	£1 Carrickfergus Castle. Bottle green and gold†	5·50	50
1612	**1044**	£1·50 Caernarfon Castle†	6·00	75
1613	**881**	£2 Edinburgh Castle. Indigo and gold†	8·00	1·00
1613*a*	**879**	£3 Carrickfergus Castle. Reddish violet and gold† (22.8.95)	19·00	1·75
1614	**882**	£5 Windsor Castle. Deep brown and gold†	18·00	2·00
		a. Gold† (Queen's head) omitted	£575	
Set of 5			50·00	5·50
Set of 5 Gutter Pairs (vert or horiz)			£100	
First Day Cover (Nos. 1611/13, 1614)				20·00
First Day Cover (No. 1613a)				6·00
Presentation Pack (PO Pack No. 27) (Nos. 1611/13, 1614)			38·00	
Presentation Pack (PO Pack No. 33) (No. 1613a)			20·00	
PHQ Cards†† (Nos. 1611/13, 1614) (D2–5)			50	4·50
PHQ Card (No. 1613a) (D8)			80	2·00

† The Queen's head on these stamps is printed in optically variable ink which changes colour from gold to green when viewed from different angles.

In 1994 the £1, £1·50, £2 and £5 were issued with the Queen's head re-etched, showing a pattern of diagonal lines, as opposed to the horizontal and diagonal lines of the original versions.

†† The PHQ Cards for this issue did not appear until 16 February 1993. The Bureau FDI cancellation is 3 March 1993 (the date of issue of the £10).

The £1·50 (5 March 1996), £2 (2 May 1996), £3 (February 1997) and £5 (17 September 1996) subsequently appeared on PVA (white gum) instead of the tinted PVAD previously used.

See also Nos. 1410/3 and 1993/6.

Special First Day of Issue Postmarks

(for illustrations see Introduction)

Philatelic Bureau, Edinburgh (Type H) (£1, £1·50, £2, £5) .... 20·00
Windsor, Berkshire (Type I) (£1, £1·50, £2, £5) .... 20·00
Philatelic Bureau, Edinburgh (Type H) (£3) .... 6·00
Carrickfergus, Antrim (as Type I) (£3) .... 7·00

1045 British Olympic Association Logo (Olympic Games, Barcelona)

1046 British Paralympic Association Symbol (Paralympics '92, Barcelona)

1047 *Santa Maria* (500th Anniversary of Discovery of America by Columbus)

1048 *Kaisei* (Japanese cadet brigantine) (Grand Regatta Columbus, 1992)

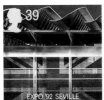

1049 British Pavilion, 'EXPO '92', Seville

(Des K. Bassford (Nos. 1615/16, 1619), K. Bassford and S. Paine. Eng C. Matthews (Nos. 1617/18). Litho Questa (Nos. 1615/16, 1619) or recess and litho Harrison (Nos. 1617/18))

1992 (7 Apr). *Europa. International Events.* |MULTI COLOUR Phosphorised paper. Perf 14×14½.

1615	**1045**	24p. British Olympic Association Logo..	30	30
		a. Horiz pair. Nos. 1615/16....................	80	80
1616	**1046**	24p. British Paralympic Association Symbol..................................	30	30
1617	**1047**	24p. *Santa Maria*	40	40
		a. Cream omitted.......................................		
1618	**1048**	39p. *Kaisei*	65	65
1619	**1049**	39p. British Pavilion, 'EXPO '92', Seville...	65	65
Set of 5..			2·20	2·20
Set of 3 Gutter Pairs and a Gutter Strip of 4			4·40	
First Day Cover				2·40
Presentation Pack (PO Pack No. 227).....................................			2·40	
PHQ Cards (set of 5) (143)			1·00	2·40

Nos. 1615/16 were printed together, *se-tenant*, in horizontal pairs throughout the sheet.

Special First Day of Issue Postmarks

Philatelic Bureau, Edinburgh	2·40
Liverpool	.2·50

1050 Pikeman

1051 Drummer

1052 Musketeer

1053 Standard Bearer

(Des J. Sancha)

1992 (16 June). *350th Anniversary of the Civil War.* |MULTI COLOUR Phosphorised paper. Perf 14½×14.

1620	**1050**	24p. Pikeman	35	35
		a. Imperf (pair).............................	£550	
1621	**1051**	28p. Drummer	45	45
1622	**1052**	33p. Musketeer	55	55
1623	**1053**	39p. Standard Bearer.......................	70	70
Set of 4..			1·85	1·85
Set of 4 Gutter Pairs			3·70	
First Day Cover				2·00
Presentation Pack (PO Pack No. 228).....................................			2·00	
PHQ Cards (set of 4) (144)			80	2·00

Special First Day of Issue Postmarks

Philatelic Bureau, Edinburgh	2·00
Banbury, Oxfordshire	2·00

1054 *The Yeomen of the Guard*

1055 *The Gondoliers*

1056 *The Mikado*

1057 *The Pirates of Penzance*

1058 *Iolanthe*

(Des Lynda Gray)

1992 (21 July). *150th Birth Anniversary of Sir Arthur Sullivan (composer). Gilbert and Sullivan Operas.* |MULTI COLOUR One phosphor band (18p.) or phosphorised paper (others). Perf 14½×14.

1624	**1054**	18p. *The Yeomen of the Guard*	25	25
1625	**1055**	24p. *The Gondoliers*	30	30
		a. Imperf (pair)..............................	£700	
1626	**1056**	28p. *The Mikado*	40	40
1627	**1057**	33p. *The Pirates of Penzance*	55	55
1628	**1058**	39p. *Iolanthe*	70	70
Set of 5..			4·50	4·75
Set of 5 Gutter Pairs			2·00	
First Day Cover				4·00
Presentation Pack (PO Pack No. 229).....................................			2·20	
PHQ Cards (set of 5) (145)			1·00	2·20

Special First Day of Issue Postmarks

Philatelic Bureau, Edinburgh	2·20
Birmingham	2·20

1059 'Acid Rain Kills'

1060 'Ozone Layer'

1061 'Greenhouse Effect'

1062 'Bird of Hope'

Large full stop
after '4'
(Dot cyl. R. 10/6)

(Des Christopher Hall (24p.), Lewis Fowler (28p.), Sarah Warren (33p.), Alice Newton-Mold (39p.). Adapted Trickett and Webb Ltd)

1992 (15 Sept). *Protection of the Environment. Children's Paintings.* MULTI COLOUR Phosphorised paper. Perf 14×14½.

1629	**1059**	24p. 'Acid Rain Kills'	35	35
		a. Large full stop after '4'	20·00	
1630	**1060**	28p. 'Ozone Layer'	40	40
1631	**1061**	33p. 'Greenhouse Effect'	55	55
1632	**1062**	39p. 'Bird of Hope'	70	70
Set of 4			1·80	1·80
Set of 4 Gutter Pairs			3·60	
First Day Cover				1·95
Presentation Pack (PO Pack No. 230)			2·00	
PHQ Cards (set of 4) (146)			80	1·95

Special First Day of Issue Postmarks

Philatelic Bureau, Edinburgh (in green)	1·95
Torridon (in green)	2·10

1063 European Star

(Des D. Hockney)

1992 (13 Oct). *Single European Market.* MULTI COLOUR Phosphorised paper. Perf 15×14.

1633	**1063**	24p. European Star	40	40
Gutter Pair			80	
First Day Cover				75
Presentation Pack (PO Pack No. 231)			80	
PHQ Card (147)			20	50

Special First Day of Issue Postmarks

Philatelic Bureau, Edinburgh	75
Westminster	1·00

1064 'Angel Gabriel', St James's, Pangbourne

1065 'Madonna and Child', St Mary's, Bibury

1066 'King with Gold', Our Lady and St Peter, Leatherhead

1067 'Shepherds', All Saints, Porthcawl

1068 'Kings with Frankincense and Myrrh', Our Lady and St Peter, Leatherhead

(Des Carroll, Dempsey and Thirkell Ltd from windows by Karl Parsons (18, 24, 33p.) and Paul Woodroffe (28p. 39p.))

1992 (10 Nov). *Christmas. Stained Glass Windows.* MULTI COLOUR One centre band (18p.) or phosphorised paper (others). Perf 15×14.

1634	**1064**	18p. 'Angel Gabriel'	25	25
		a. Booklet pane of 20	5·00	
		b. Imperf (pair)	£200	
1635	**1065**	24p. 'Madonna and Child'	30	30
1636	**1066**	28p. 'King with Gold'	40	40
1637	**1067**	33p. 'Shepherds'	55	55
1638	**1068**	39p. 'Kings with Frankincense and Myrrh'	70	70
Set of 5			2·00	2·00
Set of 5 Gutter Pairs			4·00	
First Day Cover				2·10
Presentation Pack (PO Pack No. 232)			2·20	
PHQ Cards (set of 5) (148)			1·00	2·10

Booklet pane No. 1634a comes from a special £3 Christmas booklet and has margins at left, top and bottom.

Special First Day of Issue Postmarks

Philatelic Bureau, Edinburgh	2·10
Bethlehem, Llandeilo, Dyfed	2·10
Pangbourne	2·20

Collectors Pack 1992

1992 (10 Nov). Comprises Nos. 1587/91, 1602/10 and 1615/38.
CP1638a Collectors Pack .... 19·00

Post Office Yearbook

1992 (11 Nov). Comprises Nos. 1587/91, 1602/10 and 1615/38 in hardbound book with slip case, illustrated in colour .... 19·00

1069 Mute Swan Cob and St Catherine's Chapel, Abbotsbury

1070 Cygnet and Decoy

1071 Swans and Cygnet

1072 Eggs in Nest and Tithe Barn, Abbotsbury

1073 Young Swan and
the Fleet

(Des D. Gentleman)

1993 (19 Jan). *600th Anniversary of Abbotsbury Swannery.* |MULTI COLOUR| One
phosphor band (18p.) or phosphorised paper (others). Perf 14×15.

1639	**1069**	18p. Mute Swan Cob	30	30
1640	**1070**	24p. Cygnet	50	50
1641	**1071**	28p. Swans and Cygnet	80	80
1642	**1072**	33p. Eggs in Nest	1·00	1·00
1643	**1073**	39p. Young Swan	1·40	1·40
Set of 5			3·75	3·75
Set of 5 Gutter Pairs			7·50	
First Day Cover				3·85
Presentation Pack (PO Pack No. 234)			4·00	
PHQ Cards (set of 5) (149)			1·00	3·85

Special First Day of Issue Postmarks

Philatelic Bureau, Edinburgh	3·85
Abbotsbury, Dorset	3·85

1074 Long John Silver and
Parrot (*Treasure Island*)

1075 Tweedledum and
Tweedledee (*Alice Through
the Looking-Glass*)

1076 William (*William books*)

1077 Mole and Toad (*The Wind
in the Willows*)

1078 Teacher and Wilfrid
('*The Bash Street Kids*')

1079 Peter Rabbit and Mrs.
Rabbit (*The Tale of Peter Rabbit*)

1080 Snowman (*The Snowman*)
and Father Christmas (*Father
Christmas*)

1081 The Big Friendly Giant
and Sophie (*The BFG*)

1082 Bill Badger and Rupert Bear

1083 Aladdin and the Genie

(Des Newell and Sorell)

1993 (2 Feb–10 Aug). *Greetings Stamps. Gift Giving.* |MULTI COLOUR| Two phosphor
bands. Perf 15×14 (with one elliptical hole in each horizontal side).

1644	**1074**	(1st) Long John Silver and Parrot	1·00	70
		a. Booklet pane. Nos. 1644/53	9·00	9·25
1645	**1075**	(1st) Tweedledum and Tweedledee	1·00	70
1646	**1076**	(1st) William	1·00	70
1647	**1077**	(1st) Mole and Toad	1·00	70
1648	**1078**	(1st) Teacher and Wilfrid	1·00	70
1649	**1079**	(1st) Peter Rabbit and Mrs. Rabbit (Mrs. Rabbit in blue dress)	1·00	70
		a. Peter Rabbit and Mrs. Rabbit (Mrs. Rabbit in lilac dress) (10 Aug)	1·25	1·40
		b. Booklet pane. No. 1649a×4 with margins all round (10 Aug)	5·00	
1650	**1080**	(1st) Snowman and Father Christmas	1·00	70
1651	**1081**	(1st) The Big Friendly Giant and Sophie	1·00	70
1652	**1082**	(1st) Bill Badger and Rupert Bear	1·00	70
1653	**1083**	(1st) Aladdin and the Genie	1·00	70
Set of 10			9·00	9·25
First Day Cover				9·50
Presentation Pack (PO Pack No. G2)			11·00	
PHQ Cards (set of 10) (GS1)			2·00	9·50

Nos. 1644/53 were issued in £2·40 booklets, No. KX5 (*sold at £2·50
from 1 November 1993*), together with a pane of 20 half stamp-sized
labels. The stamps and labels were affixed to the booklet cover by a
common gutter margin

No. 1649a and booklet pane 1649b come from the £6 (£5·64)
'Beatrix Potter' booklet No. DX15.

> **SET PRICES.** Please note that set prices for booklet greetings
> stamps are for complete panes. Sets of single stamps are worth
> considerably less.

Special First Day of Issue Postmarks

Philatelic Bureau, Edinburgh (No. 1644a) (2 Feb)	9·50
Greetland (No. 1644a) (2 Feb)	9·50
Philatelic Bureau, Edinburgh (No. 1649b) (10 Aug)	5·50
Keswick (No. 1649b) (10 Aug)	5·50

1084 Decorated Enamel Dial

1085 Escapement,
Remontoire and Fusée

1086 Balance, Spring and
Temperature Compensator

1087 Back of Movement

(Des H. Brown and D. Penny. Litho Questa)

1993 (16 Feb). *300th Birth Anniversary of John Harrison (inventor of the
marine chronometer). Details of 'H4' Clock.* |MULTI COLOUR| Phosphorised
paper. Perf 14½×14.

1654	**1084**	24p. Decorated Enamel Dial	30	30
1655	**1085**	28p. Escapement, Remontoire and Fusée	45	45
1656	**1086**	33p. Balance, Spring and Temperature Compensator	55	55
1657	**1087**	39p. Back of Movement	70	70
Set of 4			1·80	1·80
Set of 4 Gutter Pairs			3·60	
First Day Cover				2·00
Presentation Pack (PO Pack No. 235)			2·00	
PHQ Cards (set of 4) (150)			80	2·00

Special First Day of Issue Postmarks

Philatelic Bureau, Edinburgh	2·00
Greenwich	2·25

147

1088 Britannia

(Des B. Craddock, adapted Roundel Design Group. Litho (silver die-stamped, Braille symbol for 'TEN' embossed) Questa)

1993 (2 Mar). *Granite paper.* |MULTI COLOUR| Perf 14×14½ (with two elliptical holes in each horizontal side).

1658	**1088**	£10 Britannia	40·00	12·00
		a. Silver omitted	£5000	
		b. Braille symbol for 'TEN' omitted	£3000	
First Day Cover				25·00
Presentation Pack (PO Pack No. 28)			45·00	
PHQ Card (D1)			50	12·00

The paper used for No. 1658 contains fluorescent coloured fibres which, together with the ink used on the shield, react under U.V. light.

Examples from Plate 2A also show 'Ten Pounds' at the bottom right-hand corner under U.V light.

Special First Day of Issue Postmarks

Philatelic Bureau, Edinburgh	18·00
Windsor	20·00

1089 *Dendrobium hellwigianum*   **1090** *Paphiopedilum Maudiae 'Magnificum'*

1091 *Cymbidium lowianum*   **1092** *Vanda Rothschildiana*

1093 *Dendrobium vexillarius var albiviride*

(Des Pandora Sellars)

1993 (16 Mar). *14th World Orchid Conference, Glasgow.* |MULTI COLOUR| One phosphor band (18p.) or phosphorised paper (others). Perf 15×14.

1659	**1089**	18p. Dendrobium hellwigianum	30	30
		a. Imperf (pair)	£6000	
1660	**1090**	24p. Paphiopedilum Maudiae 'Magnificum'	35	35
1661	**1091**	28p. Cymbidium lowianum	45	45
1662	**1092**	33p. Vanda Rothschildiana	50	50
		a. Copyright logo and '1993' omitted (R. 10/6, dot pane)	15·00	15·00
1663	**1093**	39p. Dendrobium vexillarius var albiviride	60	60
Set of 5			2·00	2·00
Set of 5 Gutter Pairs			4·00	
First Day Cover				2·20
Presentation Pack (PO Pack No. 236)			2·20	
PHQ Cards (set of 5) (151)			1·00	2·20

Special First Day of Issue Postmarks

Philatelic Bureau, Edinburgh	2·20
Glasgow	2·35

For Nos. 1664/72 and Y1667/1803 see Decimal Machin Definitives section.

1094 *Family Group* (bronze sculpture) (Henry Moore)   **1095** *Kew Gardens* (lithograph) (Edward Bawden)

1096 *St Francis and the Birds* (Stanley Spencer)   **1097** *Still Life: Odyssey I* (Ben Nicholson)

(Des. A. Dastor)

1993 (11 May). *Europa. Contemporary Art.* |MULTI COLOUR| Phosphorised paper. Perf 14×14½.

1767	**1094**	24p. Family Group (bronze sculpture) (Henry Moore)	35	35
1768	**1095**	28p. Kew Gardens (lithograph) (Edward Bawden)	50	50
1769	**1096**	33p. St Francis and the Birds (Stanley Spencer)	60	60
1770	**1097**	39p. Still Life: Odyssey I (Ben Nicholson)..	70	70
Set of 4			2·00	2·00
Set of 4 Gutter Pairs			4·00	
First Day Cover				2·20
Presentation Pack (PO Pack No. 237)			2·20	
PHQ Cards (set of 4) (152)			80	2·20

Special First Day of Issue Postmarks

British Philatelic Bureau, Edinburgh	2·20
London SW	2·35

1098 Emperor Claudius (from gold coin)   **1099** Emperor Hadrian (bronze head)

1100 Goddess Roma (from gemstone)   **1101** Christ (Hinton St Mary mosaic)

(Des J. Gibbs)

1993 (15 June). *Roman Britain.* |MULTI COLOUR| Phosphorised paper with two phosphor bands. Perf 14×14½.

1771	**1098**	24p. Emperor Claudius	35	35
1772	**1099**	28p. Emperor Hadrian	50	50
1773	**1100**	33p. Goddess Roma	60	60
1774	**1101**	39p. Christ	70	70
Set of 4			2·00	2·00
Set of 4 Gutter Pairs			4·00	
First Day Cover				2·15
Presentation Pack (PO Pack No. 238)			2·20	
PHQ Cards (set of 4) (153)			80	2·15

Special First Day of Issue Postmarks

British Philatelic Bureau, Edinburgh.. 2·15
Caerllion .... 2·15

1102 *Midland Maid* and other Narrow Boats, Grand Junction Canal

1103 *Yorkshire Lass* and other Humber Keels, Stainforth and Keadby Canal

1104 *Valley Princess* and other Horse-drawn Barges, Brecknock and Abergavenny Canal

1105 Steam Barges, including *Pride of Scotland*, and Fishing Boats, Crinan Canal

(Des T. Lewery. Litho Questa)

1993 (20 July). *Inland Waterways.* |MULTI COLOUR Two phosphor bands. Perf 14½×14.

1775	**1102**	24p. Narrow Boats, Grand Junction Canal...........................	35	35
1776	**1103**	28p. Humber Keels, Stainforth and Keadby Canal.................	50	50
1777	**1104**	33p. Horse-drawn Barges, Brecknock and Abergavenny Canal..................	60	60
1778	**1105**	39p. Steam Barges and Fishing Boats, Crinan Canal................	70	70

Set of 4... 2·00   2·00
Set of 4 Gutter Pairs .... 4·00
First Day Cover ....   2·15
Presentation Pack (PO Pack No. 239)................. 2·20
PHQ Cards (set of 4) (154)..................................... 50   2·15

Nos. 1775/8 commemorate the bicentenary of the Acts of Parliament authorising the canals depicted.

Special First Day of Issue Postmarks

British Philatelic Bureau, Edinburgh .... 2·15
Gloucester .... 2·25

1106 Horse Chestnut   **1107** Blackberry

1108 Hazel   **1109** Rowan

1110 Pear

(Des Charlotte Knox)

1993 (14 Sept). *The Four Seasons. Autumn. Fruits and Leaves.* |MULTI COLOUR One phosphor band (18p.) or phosphorised paper (others). Perf 15×14.

1779	**1106**	18p. Horse Chestnut........................	30	30
1780	**1107**	24p. Blackberry................................	35	35
1781	**1108**	28p. Hazel..	45	45
1782	**1109**	33p. Rowan..	50	50
1783	**1110**	39p. Pear..	60	60

Set of 5... 2·00   2·00
Set of 5 Gutter Pairs .... 4·00

First Day Cover ....   2·20
Presentation Pack (PO Pack No. 240)..................... 2·20
PHQ Cards (set of 5) (155)... 1·00   2·20

Special First Day of Issue Postmarks

British Philatelic Bureau, Edinburgh.. 2·20
Taunton .... 2·50

1111 The Reigate Squire

1112 The Hound of the Baskervilles

1113 The Six Napoleons

1114 The Greek Interpreter

1115 The Final Problem

(Des A. Davidson. Litho Questa)

1993 (12 Oct). *Sherlock Holmes. Centenary of the Publication of 'The Final Problem'.* |MULTI COLOUR Phosphorised paper. Perf 14×14½.

1784	**1111**	24p. The Reigate Squire.................................	30	30
		a. Horiz strip of 5. Nos. 1784/8..............	1·90	2·35
1785	**1112**	24p. The Hound of the Baskervilles...........	30	30
1786	**1113**	24p. The Six Napoleons..................................	30	30
1787	**1114**	24p. The Greek Interpreter...........................	30	30
1788	**1115**	24p. The Final Problem..................................	30	30

Set of 5... 1·90   2·35
Gutter strip of 10.. 3·80
First Day Cover ....   2·50
Presentation Pack (PO Pack No. 241)................................... 2·75
PHQ Cards (set of 5) (156).. 1·00   2·50

Nos. 1784/8 were printed together, *se-tenant*, in horizontal strips of five throughout the sheet.

Special First Day of Issue Postmarks

British Philatelic Bureau, Edinburgh .... 2·50
London NW1 .... 2·75

A First Day of Issue handstamp was provided at Autumn Stampex, London SW1, for this issue.

For No. 1789 see Decimal Machin Definitives section.

1117 Bob Cratchit and Tiny Tim   1118 Mr. and Mrs. Fezziwig

1119 Scrooge   1120 The Prize Turkey

1121 Mr. Scrooge's Nephew

(Des Q. Blake)

1993 (9 Nov). *Christmas. 150th Anniversary of Publication of 'A Christmas Carol' by Charles Dickens.* |MULTI COLOUR One phosphor band (19p.) or phosphorised paper (others). Perf 15×14.

1790	1117	19p. Bob Cratchit and Tiny Tim	30	30
		a. Imperf (pair)	£7000	
1791	1118	25p. Mr. and Mrs. Fezziwig	40	40
1792	1119	30p. Scrooge	50	50
1793	1120	35p. The Prize Turkey	55	55
1794	1121	41p. Mr. Scrooge's Nephew	65	65
Set of 5			2·10	2·10
Set of 5 Gutter Pairs			4·20	
First Day Cover				2·50
Presentation Pack (PO Pack No. 242)			2·75	
PHQ Cards (set of 5) (157)			1·00	2·20

Special First Day of Issue Postmarks

British Philatelic Bureau, Edinburgh .... 2·50
Bethlehem, Llandeilo .... 2·50

A First Day of Issue handstamp (pictorial) was provided at the City of London for this issue.

Collectors Pack 1993
1993 (9 Nov). Comprises Nos. 1639/43, 1654/7, 1659/63, 1767/88 and 1790/4.
CP1794a Collectors Pack .... 22·00

Post Office Yearbook
1993 (9 Nov). Comprises Nos. 1639/43, 1654/7, 1659/63, 1767/88 *and* 1790/4 in hardbound book with slip case, illustrated in colour .... 20·00

1122 Class 5 No. 44957 and   1123 Class A1 No. 60149
Class B1 No. 61342 on West   *Amadis* at Kings Cross
Highland Line

1124 Class 4 No. 43000 on   1125 Class 4 No. 42455
Turntable at Blyth North   near Wigan Central

1126 Class 'Castle' No. 7002
Devizes Castle on Bridge
crossing Worcester and
Birmingham Canal

(Des B. Delaney)

1994 (18 Jan). *The Age of Steam. Railway Photographs by Colin Gifford.* |MULTI COLOUR One phosphor band (19p.) or phosphorised paper with two bands (others). Perf 14½.

1795	1122	19p. Class 5 No. 44957 and Class B1 No. 61342	30	30
1796	1123	25p. Class A1 No. 60149 *Amadis*	40	40
1797	1124	30p. Class 4 No. 43000 on Turntable	50	50
1798	1125	35p. Class 4 No. 42455	60	60
1799	1126	41p. Class 'Castle' No. 7002 *Devizes Castle* on Bridge	70	70
Set of 5			2·25	2·25
Set of 5 Gutter Pairs			4·50	
First Day Cover				2·50
Presentation Pack (PO Pack No. 244)			3·00	
PHQ Cards (set of 5) (158)			1·00	2·50

Nos. 1796/9 are on phosphorised paper and also show two phosphor bands.

Special First Day of Issue Postmarks

Philatelic Bureau, Edinburgh .... 2·50
York .... 2·50

A First Day of Issue handstamp (pictorial) was provided at Bridge of Orchy for this issue.

1127 Dan Dare and the Mekon   1128 The Three Bears

1129 Rupert Bear   1130 Alice (*Alice in Wonderland*)

1131 Noggin and the Ice   1132 Peter Rabbit posting
Dragon   Letter

1133 Red Riding Hood and   1134 Orlando Marmalade Cat
the Wolf

1135 Biggles

1136 Paddington Bear on Station

(Des Newell and Sorrell)

1994 (1 Feb). *Greetings Stamps. 'Messages'.* [MULTI COLOUR] Two phosphor bands. Perf 15×14 (with one elliptical hole in each vertical side).

1800	**1127**	(1st) Dan Dare and the Mekon	1·00	50
		a. Booklet pane. Nos. 1800/9	9·00	9·00
1801	**1128**	(1st) The Three Bears	1·00	50
1802	**1129**	(1st) Rupert Bear	1·00	50
1803	**1130**	(1st) Alice (*Alice in Wonderland*)	1·00	50
1804	**1131**	(1st) Noggin and the Ice Dragon	1·00	50
1805	**1132**	(1st) Peter Rabbit posting Letter	1·00	50
1806	**1133**	(1st) Red Riding Hood and the Wolf	1·00	50
1807	**1134**	(1st) Orlando Marmalade Cat	1·00	50
1808	**1135**	(1st) Biggles	1·00	50
1809	**1136**	(1st) Paddington Bear on Station	1·00	50
Set of 10			9·00	9·00
First Day Cover				9·25
Presentation Pack (PO Pack No. G3)			11·00	
PHQ Cards (set of 10) (GS2)			2·00	9·25

Nos. 1800/9 were issued in £2·50 stamp booklets, No. KX6 (*sold at £2·60 from 8 July 1996*), together with a pane of 20 half stampsized labels

The stamps and labels were attached *to* the booklet cover by a common gutter margin.

Special First Day of Issue Postmarks

British Philatelic Bureau, Edinburgh	9·25
Penn, Wolverhampton	9·25

1137 Castell Y Waun (Chirk Castle), Clwyd, Wales

1138 Ben Arkle, Sutherland, Scotland

1139 Mourne Mountains, County Down, Northern Ireland

1140 Dersingham, Norfolk, England

1141 Dolwyddelan, Gwynedd, Wales

1994 (1 Mar – 26 July). *25th Anniversary of Investiture of the Prince of Wales. Paintings by Prince Charles.* [MULTI COLOUR] One phosphor band (19p.) or phosphorised paper (others). Perf 15×14.

1810	**1137**	19p. Castell Y Waun (Chirk Castle), Clwyd, Wales	30	30
1811	**1138**	25p. Ben Arkle, Sutherland, Scotland	35	35
1812	**1139**	30p. Mourne Mountains, County Down, Northern Ireland	45	45
		a. Booklet pane. No. 1812×4 with margins all round (26 July)	1·80	1·80
1813	**1140**	35p. Dersingham, Norfolk, England	60	60
1814	**1141**	41p. Dolwyddelan, Gwynedd, Wales	70	70
Set of 5			2·10	2·10
Set of 5 Gutter Pairs			4·20	
First Day Cover				2·40
Presentation Pack (PO Pack No. 245)			2·45	
PHQ Cards (set of 5) (159)			1·00	2·35

Booklet pane No. 1812a comes from the £6·04 'Northern Ireland' booklet No. DX16.

Special First Day of Issue Postmarks

British Philatelic Bureau, Edinburgh	2·40
Caernarfon	2·40

1142 Bather at Blackpool

1143 'Where's my Little Lad?'

1144 'Wish You were Here!'

1145 Punch and Judy Show

1146 'The Tower Crane' Machine

(Des M. Dempsey and B. Dare. Litho Questa)

1994 (12 Apr). *Centenary of Picture Postcards.* [MULTI COLOUR] One side band (19p.) or two phosphor bands (others). Perf 14×14½.

1815	**1142**	19p. Bather at Blackpool	30	30
1816	**1143**	25p. 'Where's my Little Lad?'	35	35
1817	**1144**	30p. 'Wish you were Here!'	45	45
1818	**1145**	35p. Punch and Judy Show	60	60
1819	**1146**	41p. 'The Tower Crane' Machine	70	70
Set of 5			2·10	2·10
Set of 5 Gutter Pairs			4·20	
First Day Cover				2·40
Presentation Pack (PO Pack No. 246)			2·45	
PHQ Cards (set of 5) (160)			1·00	2·40

Special First Day of Issue Postmarks

British Philatelic Bureau, Edinburgh	2·40
Blackpool	2·40

1147 British Lion and French Cockerel over Tunnel

1148 Symbolic Hands over Train

(Des G. Hardie (T **1147**), J.-P. Cousin (T **1148**))

1994 (3 May). *Opening of Channel Tunnel.* |MULTI COLOUR Phosphorised paper. Perf 14×14½

1820	**1147**	25p. British Lion and French Cockerel ...	30	35
		a. Horiz pair. Nos. 1820/1	1·00	1·10
1821	**1148**	25p. Symbolic Hands over Train	30	35
1822	**1147**	41p. British Lion and French Cockerel ...	50	60
		a. Horiz pair. Nos. 1822/3	1·50	1·70
		ab. Imperf (horiz pair)	£4750	
1823	**1148**	41p. Symbolic Hands over Train	50	60
Set of 4			2·25	2·50
First Day Cover				2·60
First Day Covers (2) (UK and French stamps)				6·00
Presentation Pack (PO Pack No. 247)			2·60	
Presentation Pack (UK and French Stamps)			15·00	
Souvenir Book			32·00	
PHQ Cards (set of 4) (161)			60	2·50

Nos. 1820/1 and 1822/3 were printed together, *se-tenant*, in horizontal pairs throughout the sheets.

Stamps in similar designs were also issued by France. These are included in the joint presentation pack and souvenir book.

Special First Day of Issue Postmarks

British Philatelic Bureau, Edinburgh......................................2·60
Folkestone ....3·00

1149 Groundcrew replacing Smoke Canisters on Douglas Boston of 88 Sqn

1150 H.M.S. *Warspite* (battleship) shelling Enemy Positions

1151 Commandos landing on Gold Beach

1152 Infantry regrouping on Sword Beach

1153 Tank and Infantry advancing, Ouistreham

(Des K. Bassford from contemporary photographs. Litho Questa)

1994 (6 June). *50th Anniversary of D-Day.* |MULTI COLOUR Two phosphor bands. Perf 14½×14.

1824	**1149**	25p. Groundcrew replacing Smoke Canisters on Douglas Boston...........	35	30
		a. Horiz strip of 5. Nos. 1824/8	2·10	1·75
1825	**1150**	25p. H.M.S. *Warspite* shelling Enemy Positions..	35	30
1826	**1151**	25p. Commandos landing on Gold Beach	35	30
1827	**1152**	25p. Infantry regrouping on Sword Beach	35	30
1828	**1153**	25p. Tank and Infantry advancing, Ouistreham......................................	35	30
Set of 5..			2·10	1·75
Gutter block of 10..			4·20	
First Day Cover				1·85
Presentation Pack (PO Pack No. 248)..................			2·40	
PHQ Cards (set of 5) (162).................................			1·00	1·85

Nos. 1824/8 were printed together, *se-tenant*, in horizontal strips of five throughout the sheet.

Special First Day of Issue Postmarks

British Philatelic Bureau, Edinburgh...1·85
Portsmouth ....1·85

1154 The Old Course, St Andrews

1155 The 18th Hole, Muirfield

1156 The 15th Hole ('Luckyslap'), Carnoustie

1157 The 8th Hole ('The Postage Stamp'), Royal Troon

1158 The 9th Hole, Turnberry

(Des P. Hogarth)

1994 (5 July). *Scottish Golf Courses.* |MULTI COLOUR One phosphor band (19p.) or phosphorised paper (others). Perf 14½×14.

1829	**1154**	19p. The Old Course, St Andrews...........	30	30
1830	**1155**	25p. The 18th Hole, Muirfield..................	35	35
1831	**1156**	30p. The 15th Hole ('Luckyslap'), Carnoustie.....................................	45	45
1832	**1157**	35p. The 8th Hole ('The Postage Stamp'), Royal Troon...........................	60	60
1833	**1158**	41p. The 9th Hole, Turnberry....................	70	70
Set of 5..			2·10	2·10
Set of 5 Gutter Pairs			4·20	
First Day Cover				2·25
Presentation Pack (PO Pack No. 249)..................			2·45	
PHQ Cards (set of 5) (163).................................			1·00	2·25

Nos. 1829/33 commemorate the 250th anniversary of golf's first set of rules produced by the Honourable Company of Edinburgh Golfers.

Special First Day of Issue Postmarks

British Philatelic Bureau, Edinburgh ....2·25
Turnberry ....2·50

AMSER HAF/SUMMERTIME Llanelwedd
1159 Royal Welsh Show, Llanelwedd

SUMMERTIME Wimbledon
1160 All England Tennis Championships, Wimbledon

SUMMERTIME Cowes
1161 Cowes Week

SUMMERTIME Lord's
1162 Test Match, Lord's

SUMMERTIME Braemar
1163 Braemar Gathering

(Des M. Cook)

1994 (2 Aug). *The Four Seasons. Summertime.* [MULTI COLOUR] One phosphor band (19p.) or phosphorised paper (others). Perf 15×14.

1834	**1159**	19p. Royal Welsh Show, Llanelwedd......	30	30
1835	**1160**	25p. All England Tennis Championships, Wimbledon	35	35
1836	**1161**	30p. Cowes Week....................	45	45
1837	**1162**	35p. Test Match, Lord's..............	60	60
1838	**1163**	41p. Braemar Gathering............	70	70
Set of 5........................			2·10	2·10
Set of 5 Gutter Pairs............			4·20	
First Day Cover..................				2·25
Presentation Pack (PO Pack No. 250).............			2·45	
PHQ Cards (set of 5) (164)...........			1·00	2·25

Special First Day of Issue Postmarks

British Philatelic Bureau, Edinburgh..............................2·25
Wimbledon ....2·25

1164 Ultrasonic Imaging

1165 Scanning Electron Microscopy

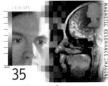

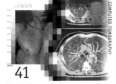

1166 Magnetic Resonance Imaging

1167 Computed Tomography

(Des P. Vermier and J.-P. Tibbles. Gravure Enschedé)

1994 (27 Sept). *Europa. Medical Discoveries.* [MULTI COLOUR] Phosphorised paper. P 14×14½.

1839	**1164**	25p. Ultrasonic Imaging..............	40	40
		a. Imperf (vert pair)	£7000	
1840	**1165**	30p. Scanning Electron Microscopy.......	50	50
1841	**1166**	35p. Magnetic Resonance Imaging........	60	60
1842	**1167**	41p. Computed Tomography....................	70	70
Set of 4........................			2·00	2·00
Set of 4 Gutter Pairs............			4·00	
First Day Cover..................				2·25
Presentation Pack (PO Pack No. 251).............			2·45	
PHQ Cards (set of 4) (165)...........			80	2·25

Special First Day of Issue Postmarks

British Philatelic Bureau, Edinburgh ....2·25
Cambridge ....2·25

1168 Mary and Joseph

1169 Three Wise Men

1170 Mary with Doll

1171 Shepherds

1172 Angels

(Des Yvonne Gilbert)

1994 (1 Nov). *Christmas. Children's Nativity Plays.* [MULTI COLOUR] One phosphor band (19p.) or phosphorised paper (others). Perf 15×14.

1843	**1168**	19p. Mary and Joseph	30	30
		a. Imperf (pair)................	£175	
1844	**1169**	25p. Three Wise Men..................	35	35
1845	**1170**	30p. Mary with Doll..................	45	45
		a. Imperf (pair)................	—	
1846	**1171**	35p. Shepherds..................	55	60
1847	**1172**	41p. Angels..................	65	70
Set of 5........................			2·00	2·10
Set of 5 Gutter Pairs............			4·00	
First Day Cover..................				2·25
Presentation Pack (PO Pack No. 252).............			2·25	
PHQ Cards (set of 5) (166)...........			60	2·25

Special First Day of Issue Postmarks

British Philatelic Bureau, Edinburgh ....2·25
Bethlehem, Llandeilo ....2·25

Collectors Pack 1994
1994 (14 Nov). Comprises Nos. 1795/1847.
CP1847*a* Collectors Pack.................................. 27·00

Post Office Yearbook
1994 (14 Nov). Comprises Nos. 1795/9 *and* 1810/47 *in* hardbound book with slip case, illustrated in colour.................................. 20·00

1173 'Sophie' (black cat)

1174 'Puskas' (Siamese) and 'Tigger' (tabby)

1175 'Chloe' (ginger cat)

1176 'Kikko' (tortoiseshell) and 'Rosie' (Abyssinian)

1177 'Fred' (black and white cat)

(Des Elizabeth Blackadder. Litho Questa)

1995 (17 Jan). *Cats.* |MULTI COLOUR| One phosphor band (19p.) or two phosphor bands (others). Perf 14½×14.

1848	**1173**	19p. 'Sophie'	30	30
1849	**1174**	25p. 'Puskas' and 'Tigger'	40	40
1850	**1175**	30p. 'Chloe'	50	50
1851	**1176**	35p. 'Kikko' and 'Rosie'	60	60
1852	**1177**	41p. 'Fred'	70	70
	Set of 5		2·20	2·20
	Set of 5 Gutter Pairs		4·40	
	First Day Cover			2·40
	Presentation Pack (PO Pack No. 254)		2·50	
	PHQ Cards (set of 5) (167)		1·00	2·40

Special First Day of Issue Postmarks

British Philatelic Bureau, Edinburgh	2·40
Kitts Green	2·40

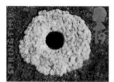

1178 Dandelions

1179 Chestnut Leaves

1180 Garlic Leaves

1181 Hazel Leaves

1182 Spring Grass

1995 (14 Mar). *The Four Seasons. Springtime.* Plant Sculptures by Andy Goldsworthy. |MULTI COLOUR| One phosphor band (19p.) or two phosphor bands (others). Perf 15×14.

1853	**1178**	19p. Dandelions	30	30
1854	**1179**	25p. Chestnut Leaves	35	35
1855	**1180**	30p. Garlic Leaves	45	45
1856	**1181**	35p. Hazel Leaves	55	55
1857	**1182**	41p. Spring Grass	65	65
	Set of 5		2·00	2·00
	Set of 5 Gutter Pairs		4·00	
	First Day Cover			2·20
	Presentation Pack (PO Pack No. 255)		2·45	
	PHQ Cards (set of 5) (168)		1·00	2·20

Special First Day of Issue Postmarks

British Philatelic Bureau, Edinburgh	2·20
Springfield	2·20

1183 *La Danse à la Campagne* (Renoir)

1184 *Troilus and Criseyde* (Peter Brookes)

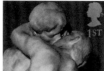

1185 *The Kiss* (Rodin)

1186 *Girls on the Town* (Beryl Cook)

1187 *Jazz* (Andrew Mockett)

1188 *Girls performing a Kathak Dance* (Aurangzeb period)

1189 *Alice Keppel with her Daughter* (Alice Hughes)

1190 *Children Playing* (L. S. Lowry)

1191 *Circus Clowns* (Emily Firmin and Justin Mitchell)

1192 Decoration from *All the Love Poems of Shakespeare* (Eric Gill)

(Des Newell and Sorrell. Litho Walsall)

1995 (21 Mar). *Greetings Stamps. 'Greetings in Art'.* |MULTI COLOUR| Two phosphor bands. Perf 14½×14 (with one elliptical hole in each vertical side).

1858	**1183**	(1st) *La Danse à la Campagne*	1·00	50
		a. Booklet pane. Nos. 1858/67	9·00	9·00
		ab. Silver (Queen's head and '1ST') and phosphor omitted	£11500	
1859	**1184**	(1st) *Troilus and Criseyde*	1·00	50
1860	**1185**	(1st) *The Kiss*	1·00	50
1861	**1186**	(1st) *Girls on the Town*	1·00	50
1862	**1187**	(1st) *Jazz*	1·00	50
1863	**1188**	(1st) *Girls performing a Kathak Dance*	1·00	50
1864	**1189**	(1st) *Alice Keppel with her Daughter*	1·00	50
1865	**1190**	(1st) *Children Playing*	1·00	50
1866	**1191**	(1st) *Circus Clowns*	1·00	50
1867	**1192**	(1st) Decoration from *All the Love Poems of Shakespeare*	1·00	50
	Set of 10		9·00	9·00
	First Day Cover			9·25
	Presentation Pack (PO Pack No. G4)		10·00	
	PHQ Cards (set of 10) (GS3)		2·00	9·20

Nos. 1858/67 were issued in £2·50 stamp booklets, No. KX7 (*sold at £2·60 from 8 July 1996*), together with a pane of 20 half stampsized labels

The stamps and labels were attached to the booklet cover by a common gutter margin.

No. 1858ab exists on first day covers bearing the Philatelic Bureau Edinburgh First Day of Issue postmark.

Special First Day of Issue Postmarks

British Philatelic Bureau, Edinburgh	9·25
Lover	9·25

The National Trust *Celebrating 100 Years* **19**

1193 Fireplace Decoration, Attingham Park, Shropshire

The National Trust *Protecting Land* **25**

1194 Oak Seedling

The National Trust
Conserving Art 30

1195 Carved Table Leg, Attingham Park

The National Trust
Saving Coast 35

1196 St David's Head, Dyfed, Wales

The National Trust
Repairing Buildings 41

1197 Elizabethan Window, Little Moreton Hall, Cheshire

(Des T. Evans)

1995 (11–25 Apr). *Centenary of The National Trust.* |MULTI COLOUR| One phosphor band (19p.), two phosphor bands (25p., 35p.) or phosphorised paper (30p., 41p.). Perf 14×15.

1868	**1193**	19p. Fireplace Decoration	30	30
1869	**1194**	25p. Oak Seedling	35	35
		a. Booklet pane. No. 1869×6 with margins all round (25 Apr)	2·00	
1870	**1195**	30p. Carved Table Leg	45	45
1871	**1196**	35p. St David's Head	55	55
1872	**1197**	41p. Elizabethan Window	65	65
Set of 5			2·00	2·00
Set of 5 Gutter Pairs			4·00	
First Day Cover				2·20
Presentation Pack (PO Pack No. 256)			2·45	
PHQ Cards (set of 5) (169)			1·00	2·20

Booklet pane No. 1869a comes from the £6 'National Trust' booklet No. DX17.

Special First Day of Issue Postmarks

British Philatelic Bureau, Edinburgh .... 2·20
Alfriston .... 2·20

1198 British Troops and French Civilians celebrating

1199 Symbolic Hands and Red Cross

1200 St Paul's Cathedral and Searchlights

1201 Symbolic Hand releasing Peace Dove

1202 Symbolic Hands

(Des J. Gorham (Nos. 1873, 1875), J-M. Folon (others))

1995 (2 May). *Europa. Peace and Freedom.* |MULTI COLOUR| One phosphor band (Nos. 1873/4) or two phosphor bands (others). Perf 14½×14.

1873	**1198**	19p. British Troops and French Civilians celebrating	35	35
1874	**1199**	19p. Symbolic Hands and Red Cross	35	35
1875	**1200**	25p. St Paul's Cathedral and Searchlights	45	45
1876	**1201**	25p. Symbolic Hand releasing Peace Dove	45	45
		a. Imperf (vert pair)	—	
1877	**1202**	30p. Symbolic Hands	60	60
Set of 5			2·00	2·00
Set of 5 Gutter Pairs			4·00	
First Day Cover				2·20
Presentation Pack (PO Pack No. 257)			2·45	
PHQ Cards (set of 5) (170)			60	2·20

Nos. 1873 and 1875 commemorate the 50th anniversary of the end of the Second World War, No. 1874 the 125th anniversary of the British Red Cross Society and Nos. 1876/7 the 50th anniversary of the United Nations.

Nos. 1876/7 include the 'EUROPA' emblem.

For No. 1875 with the face value expressed as '1st' see No. **MS**2547.

Special First Day of Issue Postmarks

British Philatelic Bureau, Edinburgh .... 2·20
London SW .... 2·40

A First Day of Issue handstamp (pictorial) was provided at London EC4 for this issue.

1203 The Time Machine

1204 The First Men in the Moon

1205 The War of the Worlds

1206 The Shape of Things to Come

(Des Siobhan Keaney. Litho Questa)

1995 (6 June). *Science Fiction. Novels by H. G. Wells.* |MULTI COLOUR| Two phosphor bands. Perf 14½×14.

1878	**1203**	25p. The Time Machine	40	40
1879	**1204**	30p. The First Men in the Moon	50	50
1880	**1205**	35p. The War of the Worlds	60	60
1881	**1206**	41p. The Shape of Things to Come	70	70
Set of 4			2·00	2·00
Set of 4 Gutter Pairs			4·00	
First Day Cover				2·20
Presentation Pack (PO Pack No. 258)			2·45	
PHQ Cards (set of 4) (171)			50	2·20

Nos. 1878/81 commemorate the centenary of publication of Wells's *The Time Machine.*

Special First Day of Issue Postmarks

British Philatelic Bureau, Edinburgh .... 2·20
Wells .... 2·40

1207 The Swan, 1595

1208 The Rose, 1592

1209 The Globe, 1599

1210 The Hope, 1613

1211 The Globe, 1614

(Des C. Hodges. Litho Walsall)

1995 (8 Aug). *Reconstruction of Shakespeare's Globe Theatre.* |MULTI COLOUR| Two phosphor bands. Perf 14½.

1882	**1207**	25p. The Swan, 1595	40	30
		a. Horiz strip of 5. Nos. 1882/6	2·00	2·20
1883	**1208**	25p. The Rose, 1592	40	30
1884	**1209**	25p. The Globe, 1599	40	30
1885	**1210**	25p. The Hope, 1613	40	30
1886	**1211**	25p. The Globe, 1614	40	30
Set of 5			2·00	2·20
Gutter Strip of 10			4·00	
First Day Cover				2·25
Presentation Pack (PO Pack No. 259)			2·45	
PHQ Cards (set of 5) (172)			1·00	2·25

Nos. 1882/6 were issued together, *se-tenant*, in horizontal strips of five throughout the sheet with the backgrounds forming a composite design.

Special First Day of Issue Postmarks

British Philatelic Bureau, Edinburgh .... 2·25
Stratford-upon-Avon .... 2·25

1212 Sir Rowland Hill and Uniform Penny Postage Petition

1213 Hill and Penny Black

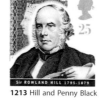

1214 Guglielmo Marconi and Early Wireless

1215 Marconi and Sinking of *Titanic* (liner)

(Des The Four Hundred, Eng C. Slania. Recess and litho Harrison)

1995 (5 Sept). *Pioneers of Communications.* |MULTI COLOUR| One phosphor band (19p.) or phosphorised paper (others). Perf 14½×14.

1887	**1212**	19p. Sir Rowland Hill and Uniform Penny Postage Petition	40	40
1888	**1213**	25p. Hill and Penny Black	50	50
		a. Silver (Queen's head and face value) omitted	£950	
1889	**1214**	41p. Guglielmo Marconi and Early Wireless	65	65
1890	**1215**	60p. Marconi and Sinking of *Titanic* (liner)	75	75
Set of 4			2·10	2·10
Set of 4 Gutter Pairs			4·20	
First Day Cover				2·25
Presentation Pack (PO Pack No. 260)			2·50	
PHQ Cards (set of 4) (173)			80	2·25

Nos. 1887/8 mark the birth bicentenary of Sir Rowland Hill and Nos. 1889/90 the centenary of the first radio transmissions.

Special First Day of Issue Postmarks

British Philatelic Bureau, Edinburgh .... 2·25
London EC .... 2·25

1216 Harold Wagstaff

1217 Gus Risman

1218 Jim Sullivan

1219 Billy Batten

1220 Brian Bevan

(Des C. Birmingham)

1995 (3 Oct). *Centenary of Rugby League.* |MULTI COLOUR| One phosphor band (19p.) or two phosphor bands (others). Perf 14½×14.

1891	**1216**	19p. Harold Wagstaff	30	30
1892	**1217**	25p. Gus Risman	35	35
1893	**1218**	30p. Jim Sullivan	45	45
1894	**1219**	35p. Billy Batten	55	55
1895	**1220**	41p. Brian Bevan	65	65
Set of 5			2·10	2·10
Set of 5 Gutter Pairs			4·20	
First Day Cover				2·25
Presentation Pack (PO Pack No. 261)			2·45	
PHQ Cards (set of 5) (174)			1·00	2·25

Special First Day of Issue Postmarks

British Philatelic Bureau, Edinburgh .... 2·25
Huddersfield .... 2·25

A First Day of Issue handstamp (pictorial) was provided at Headingly, Leeds for this issue.

1221 European Robin in Mouth of Pillar Box

1222 European Robin on Railings and Holly

1223 European Robin on Snow-covered Milk Bottles

1224 European Robin on Road Sign

1225 European Robin on Door Knob and Christmas Wreath

(Des K. Lilly)

1995 (30 Oct). *Christmas. Christmas Robins.* MULTI COLOUR One phosphor band (19p.) or two phosphor bands (others). Perf 15×14.

1896	**1221**	19p. Robin in Mouth of Pillar Box	30	30
1897	**1222**	25p. Robin on Railings	35	40
1898	**1223**	30p. Robin on Milk Bottles	50	55
1899	**1224**	41p. Robin on Road Sign	60	65
1900	**1225**	60p. Robin on Door Knob	75	80
Set of 5			2·25	2·50
Set of 5 Gutter Pairs			4·50	
First Day Cover				2·70
Presentation Pack (PO Pack No. 262)			2·50	
PHQ Cards (*set of 5*) (175)			1·00	2·70

The 19p. value was re-issued on 3 October 2000 in sheets of 20, each with a *se-tenant* label showing Christmas greetings (*sold for* £3·99) (LS2) or a personal photograph (*sold for* £7·99). These sheets were printed in photogravure by Questa and were sold by the Philatelic Bureau and selected philatelic outlets. Similar sheets were available from 9 October 2001 when the price for a personalised version was increased to £8·75. These could also be purchased, on an experimental basis, from photo-booths at six post offices.

Special First Day of Issue Postmarks

British Philatelic Bureau, Edinburgh ..... 2·70
Bethlehem, Llandeilo ..... 2·70

Year Pack 1995

1995 (30 Oct). Comprises Nos. 1848/1900.
CP1900*a* Year Pack ..... 25·00

Post Office Yearbook

1995 (30 Oct). Comprises Nos. 1848/57 and 1868/1900 in hardback book with slip case, illustrated in colour ..... 20·00

1226 Opening Lines of *To a Mouse* and Fieldmouse

1227 *O my Luve's like a red, red rose* and Wild Rose

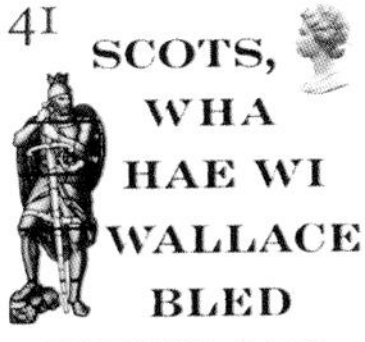

1228 *Scots, wha hae wi Wallace bled* and Sir William Wallace

1229 *Auld Lang Syne* and Highland Dancers

(Des Tayburn Design Consultancy. Litho Questa)

1996 (25 Jan). *Death Bicentenary of Robert Burns (Scottish poet).* MULTI COLOUR One phosphor band (19p.) or two phosphor bands (others). Perf 14½.

1901	**1226**	19p. Opening Lines of *To a Mouse* and Fieldmouse	40	40
1902	**1227**	25p. *O my Luve's like a red, red rose* and Wild Rose	50	50
1903	**1228**	41p. *Scots, wha hae wi Wallace bled* and Sir William Wallace	65	70
1904	**1229**	60p. *Auld Lang Syne* and Highland Dancers	75	80
Set of 4			2·00	2·20
Set of 4 Gutter Pairs			4·20	
First Day Cover				2·40
Presentation Pack (PO Pack No. 264)			2·45	
PHQ Cards (*set of 4*) (176)			80	2·40

Special First Day of Issue Postmarks

British Philatelic Bureau, Edinburgh ..... 2·40
Dumfries ..... 2·40

1230 'MORE! LOVE' (Mel Calman)

1231 'Sincerely' (Charles Barsotti)

1232 'Do you have something for the HUMAN CONDITION?' (Leo Cullum)

1233 'MENTAL FLOSS' (Mel Calman)

1234 '4.55 P.M.' (Charles Barsotti)

1235 'Dear lottery prize winner' (Larry)

1236 'I'm writing to you because....' (Mel Calman)

1237 'FETCH THIS, FETCH THAT' (Charles Barsotti)

1238 'My day starts before I'm ready for it' (Mel Calman)

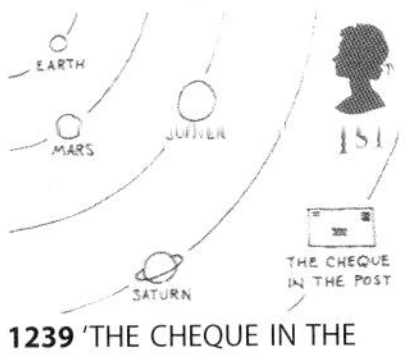

1239 'THE CHEQUE IN THE POST' (Jack Ziegler)

(Des M. Wolff. Litho Walsall)

1996 (26 Feb–11 Nov). *Greetings Stamps. Cartoons.* MULTI COLOUR 'All over' phosphor. Perf 14½×14 (with one elliptical hole in each vertical side).

1905	**1230**	(1st) 'MORE! LOVE'	1·00	50
		a. Booklet pane. Nos. 1905/14	9·00	9·00
		p. Two phosphor bands (11 Nov)	1·00	1·00
		pa. Booklet pane. Nos. 1905p/14p	24·00	25·00
1906	**1231**	(1st) 'Sincerely'	1·00	50
		p. Two phosphor bands (11 Nov)	1·00	1·00
1907	**1232**	(1st) 'Do you have something for the HUMAN CONDITION?'	1·00	50
		p. Two phosphor bands (11 Nov)	1·00	1·00
1908	**1233**	(1st) 'MENTAL FLOSS'	1·00	50
		p. Two phosphor bands (11 Nov)	1·00	1·00
1909	**1234**	(1st) '4.55 P.M.'	1·00	50

1910	**1235**	(1st) 'Dear lottery prize winner'..............	1·00	1·00
		p. Two phosphor bands (11 Nov).......	1·00	50
1911	**1236**	(1st) 'I'm writing to you because....'.	1·00	1·00
		p. Two phosphor bands (11 Nov).......	1·00	50
1912	**1237**	(1st) 'FETCH THIS, FETCH THAT'................	1·00	1·00
		p. Two phosphor bands (11 Nov).......	1·00	50
1913	**1238**	(1st) 'My day starts before I'm ready for it' (Mel Calman)...................	1·00	1·00
		p. Two phosphor bands (11 Nov).......	1·00	50
1914	**1239**	(1st) 'THE CHEQUE IN THE POST' (Jack Ziegler)...................	1·00	1·00
		p. Two phosphor bands (11 Nov).......	1·00	50
Set of 10 (Nos. 1905/14)			9·00	1·00
Set of 10 (Nos. 1905p/14p)			24·00	9·00
First Day Cover (1905/14)				25·00
Presentation Pack (1905/14) (PO Pack No. G5).......			10·00	9·50
PHQ Cards (set of 10) (GS4)			2·00	9·00

Nos. 1905/14 were issued in £2·50 stamp booklets, Nos. KX8/a (*sold at £2·60 from 8 July 1996*), together with a pane of twenty half stamp-sized labels. The stamps and labels were attached to the booklet cover by a common gutter margin.

These designs were re-issued on 18 December 2001 in sheets of 10, each with a *se-tenant* label showing cartoon comments (*sold for £2·95*) (LS6). They were re-issued again on 29 July 2003 in sheets of 20 (*sold for £6·15*) containing two of each design, each stamp accompanied by a half stamp-size label showing a crossword grid (clues printed on the bottom sheet margin) (LS13). Sheets of 20 with personal photographs on the labels and a crossword puzzle in the bottom sheet margin were also available, at £14·95 a sheet from Royal Mail, Edinburgh and Post Office philatelic outlets, or £15 a sheet from photo booths.

All these sheets were printed in lithography by Questa with two phosphor bands and perforated 14½×14 (without elliptical holes), and were available from the bureau and other selected philatelic outlets.

Special First Day of Issue Postmarks

British Philatelic Bureau, Edinburgh...9·50
Titterhill, Haytons Bent, Ludlow..9·50

1240 'Muscovy Duck'

1241 'Lapwing'

1242 'White-fronted Goose'

1243 'Bittern'

1244 'Whooper Swan'

(Des Moseley Webb)

1996 (12 Mar). *50th Anniversary of the Wildfowl and Wetlands Trust. Bird Paintings by C. F. Tunnicliffe.* |MULTI COLOUR| One phosphor band (19p.) or phosphorised paper (others). Perf 14×14½.

1915	**1240**	19p. 'Muscovy Duck'....................	30	30
1916	**1241**	25p. 'Lapwing'........................	35	35
1917	**1242**	30p. 'White-fronted Goose'............	45	45
1918	**1243**	35p. 'Bittern'........................	55	55
1919	**1244**	41p. 'Whooper Swan'...................	65	65
Set of 5...................................			2·10	2·10
Set of 5 Gutter Pairs			4·20	
First Day Cover				2·45
Presentation Pack (PO Pack No. 265)........			2·50	
PHQ Cards (set of 5) (177).................			1·00	2·40

Special First Day of Issue Postmarks

British Philatelic Bureau, Edinburgh ....2·45
Slimbridge, Gloucester ....2·75

1245 The Odeon, Harrogate

1246 Laurence Olivier and Vivien Leigh in *Lady Hamilton* (film)

1247 Old Cinema Ticket

1248 Pathé News Still

1249 Cinema Sign, The Odeon, Manchester

(Des The Chase, Gravure Harrison)

1996 (16 Apr). *Centenary of Cinema.* |MULTI COLOUR| One phosphor band (19p.) or two phosphor bands (others). Perf 14×14½.

1920	**1245**	19p. The Odeon, Harrogate......................	30	30
1921	**1246**	25p. Laurence Olivier and Vivien Leigh in *Lady Hamilton*	35	35
1922	**1247**	30p. Old Cinema Ticket	45	45
1923	**1248**	35p. Pathé News Still.....................	60	60
1924	**1249**	41p. Cinema Sign, The Odeon, Manchester...................	70	70
Set of 5...			2·20	2·20
Set of 5 Gutter Pairs			4·40	
First Day Cover				2·45
Presentation Pack (PO Pack No. 266)....................			2·50	
PHQ Cards (set of 5) (178).............................			1·00	2·45

Special First Day of Issue Postmarks

British Philatelic Bureau, Edinburgh...2·45
London, WC2..2·45

1250 Dixie Dean

1251 Bobby Moore

1252 Duncan Edwards

1253 Billy Wright

1254 Danny Blanchflower

(Des H. Brown. Litho Questa)

1996 (14 May). *European Football Championship.* |MULTI COLOUR| One phosphor band (19p.) or two phosphor bands (others). Perf 14½×14.

1925	**1250**	19p. Dixie Dean	30	30
		a. Booklet pane. No. 1925×4 with margins all round	1·50	
1926	**1251**	25p. Bobby Moore	40	40
		a. Booklet pane. No. 1926×4 with margins all round	2·00	
1927	**1252**	35p. Duncan Edwards	50	50
		a. Booklet pane. Nos. 1927/9, each ×2, with margins all round	3·50	
1928	**1253**	41p. Billy Wright	60	60
1929	**1254**	60p. Danny Blanchflower	90	90
Set of 5			2·50	2·50
Set of 5 Gutter Pairs			5·00	
First Day Cover				2·75
Presentation Pack (PO Pack No. 267)			2·75	
PHQ Cards (set of 5) (179)			1·00	2·75

Booklet panes Nos. 1925a, 1926a and 1927a come from the £6·48 'European Football Championship' booklet, No. DX18.

Special First Day of Issue Postmarks

British Philatelic Bureau, Edinburgh	2·75
Wembley	2·75

1255 Athlete on Starting Blocks   **1256** Throwing the Javelin

1257 Basketball   **1258** Swimming

1259 Athlete celebrating and Olympic Rings

(Des N. Knight. Litho Questa)

1996 (9 July). *Olympic and Paralympic Games, Atlanta.* |MULTI COLOUR| Two phosphor bands. Perf 14½×14.

1930	**1255**	26p. Athlete on Starting Blocks	30	30
		a. Horiz strip of 5. Nos. 1930/4	2·00	2·10
1931	**1256**	26p. Throwing the Javelin	30	30
1932	**1257**	26p. Basketball	30	30
1933	**1258**	26p. Swimming	30	30
1934	**1259**	26p. Athlete celebrating and Olympic Rings	30	30
Set of 5			2·00	2·10
Gutter Strip of 10			4·00	
First Day Cover				2·50
Presentation Pack (PO Pack No. 268)			2·40	
PHQ Cards (set of 5) (180)			1·00	2·50

Nos. 1930/4 were printed together, *se-tenant*, in horizontal strips of five throughout the sheet.

For these designs with face value expressed as '1st' see **MS**2554.

Special First Day of Issue Postmarks

British Philatelic Bureau, Edinburgh	2·50
Much Wenlock	2·75

1260 Prof. Dorothy Hodgkin (scientist)   **1261** Dame Margot Fonteyn (ballerina)

1262 Dame Elisabeth Frink (sculptress)   **1263** Dame Daphne du Maurier (novelist)

1264 Dame Marea Hartman (sports administrator)

(Des Stephanie Nash Gravure Harrison)

1996 (6 Aug). *Europa. Famous Women.* |MULTI COLOUR| One phosphor band (20p.) or two phosphor bands (others). Perf 14½.

1935	**1260**	20p. Prof. Dorothy Hodgkin	30	30
1936	**1261**	26p. Dame Margot Fonteyn	35	35
		a. Imperf (horiz pair)	£700	
1937	**1262**	31p. Dame Elisabeth Frink	50	50
1938	**1263**	37p. Dame Daphne du Maurier	60	60
1939	**1264**	43p. Dame Marea Hartman	70	70
Set of 5			2·25	2·25
Set of 5 Gutter Pairs			4·50	
First Day Cover				2·50
Presentation Pack (PO Pack No. 269)			2·75	
PHQ Cards (set of 5) (181)			1·00	2·50

Nos. 1936/7 include the 'EUROPA' emblem.

Special First Day of Issue Postmarks

British Philatelic Bureau, Edinburgh	2·50
Fowey	2·75

1265 *Muffin the Mule*   **1266** *Sooty*

1267 *Stingray*   **1268** *The Clangers*

1269 *Dangermouse*

(Des Tutssels. Gravure Harrison (No. 1940a) or Enschedé (others))

1996 (3 Sept)–**97.** *50th Anniversary of Children's Television.* |MULTI COLOUR| One phosphor band (20p.) or two phosphor bands (others). Perf 14½×14.

1940	**1265**	20p. *Muffin the Mule*	30	30
		a. Perf 15×14 (23.9.97)	65	65
		ab. Booklet pane. No. 1940a×4 with margins all round	2·75	
1941	**1266**	26p. *Sooty*	35	35
1942	**1267**	31p. *Stingray*	50	50
1943	**1268**	37p. *The Clangers*	60	60
1944	**1269**	43p. *Dangermouse*	70	70
		Set of 5	2·25	2·25
		Set of 5 Gutter Pairs	4·50	
		First Day Cover		2·75
		Presentation Pack (PO Pack No. 270)	3·00	
		PHQ Cards (set of 5) (182)	1·00	2·75

Booklet pane No. 1940a comes from the 1997 £6·15 'B.B.C.' stamp booklet, No. DX19.

Special First Day of Issue Postmarks

British Philatelic Bureau, Edinburgh .... 2·75
Alexandra Palace, London .... 2·75

1270 Triumph TR3

1271 MG TD

1272 Austin-Healey 100

1273 Jaguar XK120

1274 Morgan Plus 4

(Des S. Clay. Gravure Harrison)

1996 (1 Oct). *Classic Sports Cars.* |MULTI COLOUR| One phosphor band (20p.) or two phosphor bands (others). Perf 14½.

1945	**1270**	20p. Triumph TR3	30	30
1946	**1271**	26p. MG TD	50	50
		a. Imperf (pair)	£5000	
1947	**1272**	37p. Austin-Healey 100	60	65
		a. Imperf (pair)	£2000	
1948	**1273**	43p. Jaguar XK120	70	75
		a. Imperf (horiz pair)	£3750	
1949	**1274**	63p. Morgan Plus 4	90	95
		Set of 5	2·75	2·85
		Set of 5 Gutter Pairs	5·50	
		First Day Cover		3·00
		Presentation Pack (PO Pack No. 271)	3·00	
		PHQ Cards (set of 5) (183)	1·00	3·00

On Nos. 1946/9 the right-hand phosphor band on each stamp is three times the width of that on the left.

Special First Day of Issue Postmarks

British Philatelic Bureau, Edinburgh............ 3·00
Beaulieu, Brockenhurst .... 3·00

A pictorial First Day of Issue handstamp was provided at London E1 for this issue.

1275 The Three Kings

1276 The Annunciation

1277 The Journey to Bethlehem

1278 The Nativity

1279 The Shepherds

(Des Laura Stoddart, Gravure Harrison)

1996 (28 Oct). *Christmas.* |MULTI COLOUR| One phosphor band (2nd) or two phosphor bands (others). Perf 15×14.

1950	**1275**	(2nd) The Three Kings	60	35
1951	**1276**	(1st) The Annunciation	70	55
1952	**1277**	31p. The Journey to Bethlehem	50	65
1953	**1278**	43p. The Nativity	50	75
1954	**1279**	63p. The Shepherds	70	95
		Set of 5	2·75	3·00
		Set of 5 Gutter Pairs	5·50	
		First Day Cover		3·00
		Presentation Pack (PO Pack No. 272)	3·00	
		PHQ Cards (set of 5) (184)	1·00	3·00

Special First Day of Issue Postmarks

British Philatelic Bureau, Edinburgh .... 3·00
Bethlehem, Llandeilo .... 3·00

Year Pack 1996

1996 (28 Oct). Comprises Nos. 1901/54.
CP1954a Year Pack............ 27·50

Post Office Yearbook

1996 (28 Oct). Comprises Nos. 1901/4 and 1915/54 in hardback book with slip case, illustrated in colour............ 21·00

1280 *Gentiana acaulis* (Georg Ehret)

1281 *Magnolia grandiflora* (Ehret)

1282 *Camellia japonica* (Alfred Chandler)

1283 *Tulipa* (Ehret)

1284 *Fuchsia 'Princess of Wales'* (Augusta Withers)

1285 *Tulipa gesneriana* (Ehret)

1286 *Gazania splendens* (Charlotte Sowerby)

1287 *Iris latifolia* (Ehret)

1288 *Hippeastrum rutilum* (Pierre-Joseph Redoute)

1289 *Passiflora coerulea* (Ehret)

(Des Tutssels. Litho Walsall)

1997 (6 Jan). *Greeting Stamps. 19th-century Flower Paintings.* |MULTI COLOUR| Two phosphor bands. Perf 14½×14 (with one elliptical hole in each vertical side).

1955	**1280**	(1st) *Gentiana acaulis*	1·00	50
		a. Booklet pane. Nos. 1955/64	9·00	9·00
		ab. Gold, blue-green and phosphor omitted	—	
1956	**1281**	(1st) *Magnolia grandiflora*	1·00	50
1957	**1282**	(1st) *Camellia japonica*	1·00	50
1958	**1283**	(1st) *Tulipa*	1·00	50
1959	**1284**	(1st) *Fuchsia 'Princess of Wales'*	1·00	50
1960	**1285**	(1st) *Tulipa gesneriana*	1·00	50
1961	**1286**	(1st) *Gazania splendens*	1·00	50
1962	**1287**	(1st) *Iris latifolia*	1·00	50
1963	**1288**	(1st) *Hippeastrum rutilum*	1·00	50
1964	**1289**	(1st) *Passiflora coerulea*	1·00	50
Set of 10			9·00	9·00
First Day Cover				9·50
Presentation Pack (PO Pack No. G6)			10·00	
PHQ Cards (set of 10) (GS5)			2·00	9·50

Nos. 1955/64 were issued in £2·60 stamp booklets Nos KX9/12 together with a pane of twenty half-sized labels. The stamps and labels were attached to the booklet cover by a common gutter margin.

Nos. 1955/64 were re-issued on 21 January 2003 in *se-tenant* sheets of 20, each accompanied by a label showing further flowers (*sold at* £5·95) (LS11) or personal photographs (*sold at* £14·95). These stamps were printed in lithography by Questa and are without elliptical holes in the perforations.

For booklet stamps in designs as Nos. 1955, 1958 and 1962 and perforated 15×14, printed by Enschedé see Nos. 2463/5.

See also Nos. 2942/3.

Special First Day of Issue Postmarks
British Philatelic Bureau, Edinburgh.....................................9·50
Kew, Richmond, Surrey..9·50

1290 *'King Henry VIII'*

1291 *'Catherine of Aragon'*

1292 *'Anne Boleyn'*   **1293** *'Jane Seymour'*   **1294** *'Anne of Cleves'*

1295 *'Catherine Howard'*   **1296** *'Catherine Parr'*

(Des Kate Stephens from contemporary paintings. Gravure Harrison)

1997 (21 Jan). *450th Death Anniversary of King Henry VIII.* |MULTI COLOUR| Two phosphor bands. Perf 15 (No. 1965) or 14×15 (others).

1965	**1290**	26p. *'King Henry VIII'*	50	50
		a. Imperf (vert pair)	£7250	
1966	**1291**	26p. *'Catherine of Aragon'*	50	50
		a. Horiz strip of 6. Nos. 1966/71	2·80	3·00
1967	**1292**	26p. *'Anne Boleyn'*	50	50
1968	**1293**	26p. *'Jane Seymour'*	50	50
1969	**1294**	26p. *'Anne of Cleves'*	50	50
1970	**1295**	26p. *'Catherine Howard'*	50	50
1971	**1296**	26p. *'Catherine Parr'*	50	50
Set of 7			3·20	3·50
Set of 1 Gutter Pair and a Gutter Strip of 12			6·40	
First Day Cover				3·75
Presentation Pack (PO Pack No. 274)			4·75	
PHQ Cards (set of 7) (185)			1·40	3·75

Nos. 1966/71 were printed together, *se-tenant*, in horizontal strips of six throughout the sheet.

Special First Day of Issue Postmarks
British Philatelic Bureau, Edinburgh..3·75
Hampton Court, East Molesey...4·00

1297 St Columba in Boat

1298 St Columba on Iona

1299 St Augustine with King Ethelbert

1300 St Augustine with Model of Cathedral

(Des Claire Melinsky. Gravure Enschedé)

1997 (11 Mar). *Religious Anniversaries.* |MULTI COLOUR| Two phosphor bands. Perf 14½.

1972	**1297**	26p. St Columba in Boat	40	40
		a. Imperf (pair)	£1800	
1973	**1298**	37p. St Columba on Iona	60	60
1974	**1299**	43p. St Augustine with King Ethelbert	80	85
1975	**1300**	63p. St Augustine with Model of Cathedral	90	95
Set of 4			2·50	2·60
Set of 4 Gutter Pairs			5·00	
First Day Cover				3·00
Presentation Pack (PO Pack No. 275)			3·25	

PHQ Cards (set of 4) (186).. 80   3·00
Nos. 1972/3 commemorate the 1400th death anniversary of St Columba and Nos. 1974/5 the 1400th anniversary of the arrival of St Augustine of Canterbury in Kent.

Special First Day of Issue Postmarks

British Philatelic Bureau, Edinburgh ....3·00
Isle of Iona ....3·00

For Nos. 1976/7 see Decimal Machin Definitives section. Nos. 1978/9 are no longer used.

1303 Dracula

1304 Frankenstein

1305 Dr. Jekyll and Mr. Hyde

1306 The Hound of the Baskervilles

(Des I. Pollock. Gravure Walsall)

1997 (13 May). Europa. Tales and Legends. Horror Stories. |MULTI COLOUR Two phosphor bands. Perf 14×15.

1980	**1303**	26p. Dracula	40	40
1981	**1304**	31p. Frankenstein	55	60
1982	**1305**	37p. Dr. Jekyll and Mr. Hyde................	70	75
1983	**1306**	43p. The Hound of the Baskervilles...........	80	85
Set of 4			2·25	2·40
Set of 4 Gutter Pairs			4·50	
First Day Cover				2·75
Presentation Pack (PO Pack No. 276).................			3·00	
PHQ Cards (set of 4) (187)...............................			80	2·75

Nos. 1980/3 commemorate the birth bicentenary of Mary Shelley (creator of Frankenstein) with the 26p. and 31p. values incorporating the 'EUROPA' emblem. Each value has features printed in fluorescent ink which are visible under ultra-violet light.

Special First Day of Issue Postmarks

British Philatelic Bureau, Edinburgh.. 2·75
Whitby.. 2·75

1307 Reginald Mitchell and Supermarine Spitfire MkIIA

1308 Roy Chadwick and Avro Lancaster MkI

1309 Ronald Bishop and de Havilland Mosquito B MkXVI

1310 George Carter and Gloster Meteor T Mk7

1311 Sir Sydney Camm and Hawker Hunter FGA Mk9

(Des Turner Duckworth, Gravure Harrison)

1997 (10 June). British Aircraft Designers. |MULTI COLOUR One phosphor band (20p.) or two phosphor bands (others). Perf 15×14.

1984	**1307**	20p. Reginald Mitchell and Supermarine Spitfire MkIIA..............	40	40
1985	**1308**	26p. Roy Chadwick and Avro Lancaster MkI..............................	50	50
1986	**1309**	37p. sRonald Bishop and de Havilland Mosquito B MkXVI..............	60	60
1987	**1310**	43p. George Carter and Gloster Meteor T Mk7	80	80
1988	**1311**	63p. Sir Sydney Camm and Hawker Hunter FGA Mk9	90	90
Set of 5			3·00	3·00
Set of 5 Gutter Pairs			6·00	
First Day Cover				3·20
Presentation Pack (PO Pack No. 277).................			3·50	
PHQ Cards (set of 5) (188)...............................			1·00	3·20

See also No. 2868.

Special First Day of Issue Postmarks

British Philatelic Bureau, Edinburgh.. 3·20
Duxford, Cambridge .... 3·20

1312 Carriage Horse and Coachman

1313 Lifeguards Horse and Trooper

1314 Blues and Royals Drum Horse and Drummer

1315 Duke of Edinburgh's Horse and Groom

(Des J.-L. Benard. Litho Walsall)

1997 (8 July). 'All the Queen's Horses'. 50th Anniversary of the British Horse Society. |MULTI COLOUR One phosphor band (20p.) or two phosphor bands (others). Perf 14½.

1989	**1312**	20p. Carriage Horse and Coachman.......	40	40
1990	**1313**	26p. Lifeguards Horse and Trooper........	55	60
1991	**1314**	43p. Blues and Royals Drum Horse and Drummer	70	75
1992	**1315**	63p. Duke of Edinburgh's Horse and Groom......................................	85	85
Set of 4			2·30	2·40
Set of 4 Gutter Pairs			4·60	
First Day Cover				2·75
Presentation Pack (PO Pack No. 278).................			3·00	
PHQ Cards (set of 4) (189)			50	2·75

Special First Day of Issue Postmarks

British Philatelic Bureau, Edinburgh.. 2·75
Windsor, Berks .... 2·75

1315a Caernarfon Castle

CASTLE

Harrison plates (Nos. 1611/14)

CASTLE

Enschedé plates (Nos. 1993/6)

Differences between Harrison and Enschedé:

Harrison- 'C' has top serif and tail of letter points to right.
'A' has flat top. 'S' has top and bottom serifs.

Enschedé- 'C' has no top serif and tail of letter points upwards.
'A' has pointed top. 'S' has no serifs.

Harrison plates (Nos. 1611/14) Enschedé plates (Nos. 1993/6)

(Des from photos by Prince Andrew, Duke of York. Eng Inge Madle Recess (Queen's head by silk screen process) Enschedé)

1997 (29 July). Designs as Nos. 1611/14 with Queen's head in silhouette as *T* **1044**, but re-engraved with differences in inscription as shown above. Perf 15×14 (with one elliptical hole in each vertical side).

1993	**1315a**	£1·50 Caernarfon Castle	12·00	6·00
		a. Gold (Queen's head) omitted	—	£1400
1994	**881**	£2 Edinburgh Castle. Indigo and gold†	14·00	2·25
		a. Gold (Queen's head) omitted	£700	
1995	**879**	£3 Carrickfergus Castle. Violet and gold†	30·00	3·50
		a. Gold (Queen's head) omitted	£3500	
1996	**882**	£5 Windsor Castle. Deep brown and gold†	35·00	10·00
		a. Gold (Queen's head) omitted	£5000	
Set of 4			80·00	18·00
Set of 4 Gutter Pairs (vert or horiz)			£175	
Presentation Pack (PO Pack No. 40)			£150	

† The Queen's head on these stamps is printed in optically variable ink which changes colour from gold to green when viewed from different angles. No. 1996a occurs on R. 5/8 and 6/8 from some sheets.
See also Nos. 1410/3.

1316 Haroldswick, Shetland

1317 Painswick, Gloucestershire

1318 Beddgelert, Gwynedd

1319 Ballyroney, County Down

(Des T. Millington. Gravure Enschedé)

1997 (12 Aug). *Sub-Post Offices.* |MULTI COLOUR One phosphor band (20p.) or two phosphor bands (others). Perf 14½.

1997	**1316**	20p. Haroldswick, Shetland	40	40
1998	**1317**	26p. Painswick, Gloucestershire	55	60
1999	**1318**	43p. Beddgelert, Gwynedd	70	75
2000	**1319**	63p. Ballyroney, County Down	85	85
Set of 4			2·30	2·40
Set of 4 Gutter Pairs			4·60	
First Day Cover				2·75
Presentation Pack (PO Pack No. 279)			3·00	
PHQ Cards (set of 4) (190)			80	2·75

Nos. 1997/2000 were issued on the occasion of the Centenary of the National Federation of Sub-Postmasters.

Special First Day of Issue Postmarks

British Philatelic Bureau, Edinburgh .... 2·75
Wakefield .... 2·75

PRINTERS. Harrison and Sons Ltd became De La Rue Security Print on 8 September 1997. This was not reflected in the sheet imprints until mid-1998.

Enid Blyton's *Noddy*
1320 Noddy

Enid Blyton's *Famous Five*
1321 Famous Five

Enid Blyton's *Secret Seven*
1322 Secret Seven

Enid Blyton's *Faraway Tree*
1323 Faraway Tree

Enid Blyton's *Malory Towers*
1324 Malory Towers

(Des C. Birmingham. Gravure Enschedé)

1997 (9 Sept). *Birth Centenary of Enid Blyton (children's author).* |MULTI COLOUR One phosphor band (20p.) or two phosphor bands (others). Perf 14×14½.

2001	**1320**	20p. Noddy	30	30
2002	**1321**	26p. Famous Five	50	50
2003	**1322**	37p. Secret Seven	55	60
2004	**1323**	43p. Faraway Tree	65	70
2005	**1324**	63p. Malory Towers	75	80
Set of 5			2·50	2·65
Set of 5 Gutter Pairs			5·00	
First Day Cover				2·75
Presentation Pack (PO Pack No. 280)			3·00	
PHQ Cards (set of 5) (191)			1·00	2·75

Special First Day of Issue Postmarks

British Philatelic Bureau, Edinburgh .... 2·75
Beaconsfield .... 2·75

1325 Children and Father Christmas pulling Cracker

1326 Father Christmas with Traditional Cracker

1327 Father Christmas riding Cracker

1328 Father Christmas on Snowball

1329 Father Christmas and Chimney

(Des J. Gorham and M. Thomas (1st), J. Gorham (others)
Gravure Harrison)

1997 (27 Oct). *Christmas. 150th Anniversary of the Christmas Cracker.* |MULTI COLOUR| One phosphor band (2nd) or two phosphor bands (others). Perf 15×14.

2006	**1325**	(2nd) Children and Father Christmas pulling Cracker	90	35
		a. Imperf (pair)	£1500	
2007	**1326**	(1st) Father Christmas with Traditional Cracker	1·00	55
2008	**1327**	31p. Father Christmas riding Cracker	50	60
		a. Imperf (pair)	£2750	
2009	**1328**	43p. Father Christmas on Snowball	50	70
2010	**1329**	63p. Father Christmas and Chimney	70	80
Set of 5			3·25	2·75
Set of 5 Gutter Pairs			6·50	
First Day Cover				3·00
Presentation Pack (PO Pack No. 282)			4·00	
PHQ Cards (set of 5) (192)			1·00	3·00

The 1st value was re-issued on 3 October 2000 in sheets of 10, each with a *se-tenant* label showing Christmas greetings (*sold for* £2·95) (LS3) or a personal photograph (*sold for* £5·95). These sheets were printed in photogravure by Questa and were sold by the Philatelic Bureau and selected philatelic outlets. Similar sheets were available from 9 October 2001 when the price for the personalised version was increased to £12·95 for two sheets. These could also be purchased, on an experimental basis, from photo-booths situated at six post offices. From 1 October 2002 the size of the sheet was increased to 20 either with greetings labels (*sold at* £5·95) (LS10) or personal photographs (*sold at* £14·95). These stamps were printed by Questa in lithography and perforated 14½×14.

Special First Day of Issue Postmarks

British Philatelic Bureau, Edinburgh .... 3·00
Bethlehem, Llandeilo .... 3·00

1330 Wedding Photograph, 1947

1331 Queen Elizabeth II and Prince Philip, 1997

(Des D. Driver (20p., 43p.), Lord Snowdon (26p., 63p.)
Gravure Harrison)

1997 (13 Nov). *Royal Golden Wedding.* One phosphor band (20p.) or two phosphor bands (others). Perf 15.

2011	**1330**	20p. Wedding Photograph, 1947. Gold, yellow-brown and grey-black	40	40
		a. Imperf (pair)	—	
		b. Face value omitted	—	
2012	**1331**	26p. Queen Elizabeth II and Prince Philip, 1997. Multicoloured	60	60
		a. Imperf (vert pair)	£6500	
2013	**1330**	43p. Wedding Photograph, 1947. Gold, bluish green and grey-black	1·10	1·10
2014	**1331**	63p. Queen Elizabeth II and Prince Philip, 1997. Multicoloured	1·50	1·50
Set of 4			3·25	3·25
Set of 4 Gutter Pairs			6·50	
First Day Cover				3·50
Presentation Pack (PO Pack No. 281)			3·75	

Souvenir Book (contains Nos. 1668, 1989/92 and 2011/14)		22·00	
PHQ Cards (set of 4) (192)		80	3·50

For 26p. and (1st) Machin printed in gold, see Nos. 1672, Y1692, 2295, U2942, U2948/52, U2958, U2964/8, U3002 and U3015.

Special First Day of Issue Postmarks

British Philatelic Bureau, Edinburgh .... 3·50
London, SW1 .... 3·75

Year Pack 1997
1997 (13 Nov). Comprises Nos. 1965/75, 1980/92 and 1997/ 2014.
CP2014a Year Pack .... 32·00

Post Office Yearbook
1997 (13 Nov). Comprises Nos. 1965/75, 1980/92 and 1997/ 2014 in hardback book with slip case .... 26·00

1332 Common Dormouse

1333 Lady's Slipper Orchid

1334 Song Thrush

1335 Shining Ram's-horn Snail

1336 Mole Cricket

1337 Devil's Bolete

(Des R. Maude. Litho Questa)

1998 (20 Jan). *Endangered Species.* |MULTI COLOUR| One side phosphor band (20p.) or two phosphor bands (others). Perf 14×14½.

2015	**1332**	20p. Common Dormouse	40	40
2016	**1333**	26p. Lady's Slipper Orchid	50	50
2017	**1334**	31p. Song Thrush	60	60
2018	**1335**	37p. Shining Ram's-horn Snail	70	70
2019	**1336**	43p. Mole Cricket	85	85
2020	**1337**	63p. Devil's Bolete	1·00	1·00
Set of 6			3·75	3·75
Set of 6 Gutter Pairs			7·50	
First Day Cover				3·95
Presentation Pack (PO Pack No. 284)			4·25	
PHQ Cards (set of 6) (194)			1·20	3·95

Special First Day of Issue Postmarks

British Philatelic Bureau, Edinburgh .... 3·95
Selborne, Alton .... 3·95

1338 Diana, Princess of Wales (photo by Lord Snowdon)

1339 At British Lung Foundation Function, April 1997 (photo by John Stillwell)

1340 Wearing Tiara, 1991 (photo by Lord Snowdon)

1341 On Visit to Birmingham, October 1995 (photo by Tim Graham)

1342 In Evening Dress, 1987 (photo by Terence Donavan)

(Des B. Robinson. Gravure Harrison)

1998 (3 Feb). *Diana, Princess of Wales Commemoration.* |MULTI COLOUR Two phosphor bands. Perf 14×15.

2021	1338	26p. Diana, Princess of Wales	50	30
		a. Horiz strip of 5. Nos. 2021/5	1·95	1·95
		ab. Imperf (horiz strip of 5. Nos. 2021/5)	—	
		ac. Imperf (horiz strip of 4. Nos. 2021/4)	£12500	
		ad. Imperf (horiz strip of 3. Nos. 2021/3)	£8500	
2022	1339	26p. At British Lung Foundation Function, April 1997	50	30
2023	1340	26p. Wearing Tiara, 1991	50	30
2024	1341	26p. On Visit to Birmingham, October 1995	50	30
2025	1342	26p. In Evening Dress, 1987	50	30
Set of 5			2·25	1·95
Gutter Strip of 10			4·50	
First Day Cover				3·00
Presentation Pack (unnumbered)			8·00	
Presentation Pack (Welsh)			60·00	

Nos. 2021/5 were printed together, *se-tenant*, in horizontal strips of five throughout the sheet.

No. 2021ac shows No. 2025 perforated at right only. In addition to the generally issued Presentation Pack a further pack with all text printed in English and Welsh was available.

Special First Day of Issue Postmarks

British Philatelic Bureau, Edinburgh	3·00
Kensington, London	3·00

1343 Lion of England and Griffin of Edward III

1344 Falcon of Plantagenet and Bull of Clarence

1345 Lion of Mortimer and Yale of Beaufort

1346 Greyhound of Richmond and Dragon of Wales

1347 Unicorn of Scotland and Horse of Hanover

(Des J. Matthews. Recess and litho Harrison)

1998 (24 Feb). *650th Anniversary of the Order of the Garter. The Queen's Beasts.* |MULTI COLOUR Two phosphor bands. Perf 15×14.

2026	1343	26p. Lion of England and Griffin of Edward III	50	30
		a. Horiz strip of 5. Nos. 2026/30	2·25	2·15
		ab. Missing green (on Nos. 2026, 2028/9) (horiz strip of 5)	—	
		Eay. Horiz strip of 5. Phosphor omitted	25·00	
2027	1344	26p. Falcon of Plantagenet and Bull of Clarence	50	30
2028	1345	26p. Lion of Mortimer and Yale of Beaufort	50	30
2029	1346	26p. Greyhound of Richmond and Dragon of Wales	50	30
2030	1347	26p. Unicorn of Scotland and Horse of Hanover	50	30
Set of 5			2·25	2·15
Gutter Block of 10			4·50	
First Day Cover				2·75
Presentation Pack (PO Pack No. 285)			2·50	
PHQ Cards (set of 5) (195)			1·00	2·25

Nos. 2026/30 were printed together, *se-tenant*, in horizontal strips of five throughout the sheet. The phosphor bands on Nos. 2026/30 are only half the height of the stamps and do not cover the silver parts of the designs.

Special First Day of Issue Postmarks

British Philatelic Bureau, Edinburgh	2·75
London SW1	2·75

1348

(Des G. Knipe, adapted Dew Gibbons Design Group. Gravure Walsall)

1998 (10 Mar). As *T* **157** (Wilding Definitive of 1952–54) but with face values in decimal currency as *T* **1348**. One side phosphor band (20p.) or two phosphor bands (others). Perf 14 (with one elliptical hole in each vertical side).

2031	1348	20p. light green (1 band at right)	40	40
		Ea. Band at left	40	40
		b. Booklet pane. Nos. 2031/Ea each×3 with margins all round	2·50	
		c. Booklet pane. Nos. 2031/Ea and 2032/3, all×2, and central label with margins all round	4·50	
2032		26p. red-brown	50	50
		a. Booklet pane. No. 2032×9 with margins all round	3·20	
		b. Booklet pane. Nos. 2032/3, each×3 with margins all round	4·20	
2033		37p. light purple	1·10	1·10
Set of 3 (cheapest)			2·00	2·00
First Day Cover (No. 2031c)				4·75

Nos. 2031/3 were only issued in the 1998 £7·49 Wilding Definitives stamp booklet No. DX20.

For further Wilding designs with decimal face values and on paper watermarked W **1565** see Nos. 2258/9, **MS**2326, **MS**2367 and 2378/9.

Special First Day of Issue Postmarks

British Philatelic Bureau, Edinburgh	4·75
London SW1	4·75

1349 St John's Point Lighthouse, County Down

1350 Smalls Lighthouse, Pembrokeshire

1351 Needles Rock Lighthouse, Isle of Wight, c 1900

1352 Bell Rock Lighthouse, Arbroath, mid-19th-century

1353 Original Eddystone Lighthouse, Plymouth, 1698

(Des D. Davis and J. Boon. Litho Questa)

1998 (24 Mar). *Lighthouses*. |MULTI COLOUR| One side phosphor band (20p.) or two phosphor bands (others). Perf 14½×14.

2034	**1349**	20p. St John's Point Lighthouse	40	40
2035	**1350**	26p. Smalls Lighthouse	50	50
2036	**1351**	37p. Needles Rock Lighthouse	60	60
2037	**1352**	43p. Bell Rock Lighthouse	80	80
2038	**1353**	63p. Original Eddystone Lighthouse	90	90
Set of 5			3·00	3·00
Set of 5 Gutter Pairs			6·00	
First Day Cover			†	3·20
Presentation Pack (PO Pack No. 286)			3·50	
PHQ Cards (set of 5) (196)			1·00	3·20

Nos. 2034/8 commemorate the 300th anniversary of the first Eddystone Lighthouse and the final year of manned lighthouses.

Special First Day of Issue Postmarks

British Philatelic Bureau, Edinburgh	3·20
Plymouth	3·20

For Nos. 2039/40 see Decimal Machin Definitives section.

1354 Tommy Cooper

1355 Eric Morecambe

1356 Joyce Grenfell

1357 Les Dawson

1358 Peter Cook

(Des G. Scarfe. Litho Walsall)

1998 (23 Apr). *Comedians*. |MULTI COLOUR| One side phosphor band (20p.) or two phosphor bands (others). Perf 14½×14.

2041	**1354**	20p. Tommy Cooper	40	40
		Ea. Vermilion printed double		£1100
		Eb. Vermilion and black both printed quadruple with rose-pink and new blue both printed double	†	£1800
		Ec. Vermilion and black both printed double	†	£1500
2042	**1355**	26p. Eric Morecambe	50	50
		Ea. Vermilion printed double	£600	
		Eb. Vermilion printed triple	£900	
		Ec. Black printed double, vermilion printed triple	£2000	
		Ed. Black and vermilion printed triple.	£2000	
		Ee. Vermilion and black both printed quadruple		
2043	**1356**	37p. Joyce Grenfell	60	60
2044	**1357**	43p. Les Dawson	80	80
2045	**1358**	63p. Peter Cook	90	90
		Ea Vermilion printed triple	†	—
Set of 5			3·00	3·00
Set of 5 Gutter Pairs			6·00	
First Day Cover				3·20
Presentation Pack (PO Pack No. 287)			3·50	
PHQ Cards (set of 5) (197)			60	3·20

Stamps as Type **1356**, but with a face value of 30p., were prepared but not issued. Mint examples and a first day cover have been reported (*Price* £2800).

On No. 2045Ea the red can appear double and the black also shows slight doubling. It is only known on the first day cover.

Special First Day of Issue Postmarks

British Philatelic Bureau, Edinburgh	3·20
Morecambe	3·20

1359 Hands forming Heart

1360 Adult and Child holding Hands

1361 Hands forming Cradle

1362 Hand taking Pulse

(Des V. Frost from photos by A. Wilson. Litho Questa)

1998 (23 June). *50th Anniversary of the National Health Service.* |MULTI COLOUR
One side phosphor band (20p.) or two phosphor bands (others).
Perf 14×14½.

2046	**1359**	20p. Hands forming Heart	40	40
2047	**1360**	26p. Adult and Child holding Hands	50	50
2048	**1361**	43p. Hands forming Cradle	80	80
2049	**1362**	63p. Hand taking Pulse	90	90
Set of 4			2·25	2·25
Set of 4 Gutter Pairs			4·50	
First Day Cover				2·75
Presentation Pack (PO Pack No. 288)			2·65	
PHQ Cards (set of 4) (198)			50	2·50

Special First Day of Issue Postmarks

British Philatelic Bureau, Edinburgh .... 2·75
Tredegar, Wales .... 2·75

1363 *The Hobbit* (J. R. R. Tolkien)

1364 *The Lion, The Witch and the Wardrobe* (C. S. Lewis)

1365 *The Phoenix and the Carpet* (E. Nesbit)

1366 *The Borrowers* (Mary Norton)

1367 *Through the Looking Glass* (Lewis Carroll)

(Des P. Malone. Gravure D.L.R.)

1998 (21 July). *Famous Children's Fantasy Novels.* |MULTI COLOUR One centre
phosphor band (20p.) or two phosphor bands (others). Perf 15×14.

2050	**1363**	20p. The Hobbit	35	35
2051	**1364**	26p. The Lion, The Witch and the Wardrobe	45	45
		a. Imperf (pair)	£3000	
2052	**1365**	37p. The Phoenix and the Carpet	60	60
2053	**1366**	43p. The Borrowers	80	80
2054	**1367**	63p. Through the Looking Glass	90	90
Set of 5			2·95	2·95
Set of 5 Gutter Pairs			5·70	
First Day Cover				3·00
Presentation Pack (PO Pack No. 289)			3·25	
PHQ Cards (set of 5) (199)			1·00	3·00

Nos. 2050/4 commemorate the birth centenary of C. S. Lewis and
the death centenary of Lewis Carroll.

The PHQ card showing the Type **1363** design is known incorrectly
inscribed 'Tolkein'.

Special First Day of Issue Postmarks

British Philatelic Bureau, Edinburgh .... 3·00
Oxford .... 3·00

1368 Woman in Yellow Feathered Costume

1369 Woman in Blue Costume and Headdress

1370 Group of Children in White and Gold Robes

1371 Child in 'Tree' Costume

(Des T. Hazael. Gravure Walsall)

1998 (25 Aug). *Europa. Festivals. Notting Hill Carnival.* |MULTI COLOUR One
centre phosphor band (20p.) or two phosphor bands (others).
Perf 14×14½.

2055	**1368**	20p. Woman in Yellow Feathered Costume	40	40
		a. Imperf (pair)	£950	
2056	**1369**	26p. Woman in Blue Costume and Headdress	60	60
2057	**1370**	43p. Group of Children in White and Gold Robes	75	75
2058	**1371**	63p. Child in 'Tree' Costume	1·00	1·00
Set of 4			2·50	2·50
Set of 4 Gutter Pairs			5·00	
First Day Cover				3·00
Presentation Pack (PO Pack No. 290)			2·75	
PHQ Cards (set of 4) (200)			80	3·00

The 20p. and 26p. incorporate the 'EUROPA' emblem.

Special First Day of Issue Postmarks

British Philatelic Bureau, Edinburgh .... 3·00
London W11 .... 3·00

1372 Sir Malcolm Campbell's *Bluebird*, 1925

1373 Sir Henry Segrave's *Sunbeam*, 1926

1374 John G. Parry Thomas's *Babs*, 1926

1375 John R. Cobb's *Railton Mobil Special*, 1947

1376 Donald Campbell's *Bluebird CN7*, 1964

(Des Roundel Design Group. Gravure De La Rue)

1998 (29 Sept–13 Oct). *British Land Speed Record Holders.* |MULTI COLOUR One
phosphor band (20p.) or two phosphor bands (others). Perf 15×14.

2059	**1372**	20p. Sir Malcolm Campbell's Bluebird	30	30
		a. Perf 14½×13½ (1 side band at right) (13.10.98)	75	75
		aEb. Band at left	75	75
		ac. Booklet pane. Nos. 2059a and 2059aEb, each×2, with margins all round	3·25	
2060	**1373**	26p. Sir Henry Segrave's Sunbeam	40	40
		a. Rosine (face value) omitted	£4000	
		Eb. '2' from face value omitted	£3000	
		Ec. '6' from face value omitted	£3000	
2061	**1374**	30p. John G. Parry Thomas's Babs	60	60
2062	**1375**	43p. John R. Cobb's Railton Mobil Special	80	80
2063	**1376**	63p. Donald Campbell's Bluebird CN7	90	90
Set of 5			2·75	2·75
Set of 5 Gutter Pairs			5·50	

First Day Cover .... 3·00
Presentation Pack (PO Pack No. 291)...................................... 3·35
PHQ Cards *(set of 5)* (201).. 1·00   3·00

Nos. 2059/63 commemorate the 50th death anniversary of Sir Malcolm Campbell.

Nos. 2060a/Ec occur on the fourth vertical row of several sheets. Other examples show one or other of the figures partially omitted. Nos. 2059a/aEb come from the £6·16 British Land Speed Record Holders stamp booklet, No. DX21, and were printed by Walsall. There are minor differences of design between No. 2059 (sheet stamp printed by De La Rue) and Nos. 2059a/aEb (booklet stamps printed by Walsall), which omit the date and copyright symbol.

Special First Day of Issue Postmarks

British Philatelic Bureau, Edinburgh ....3·00
Pendine ....3·00

The mis-spelling 'PHILΛLETIC' in the Bureau datestamp was later corrected; same price, either spelling.

1377 Angel with Hands raised in Blessing

1378 Angel praying

1379 Angel playing Flute

1380 Angel playing Lute

1381 Angel praying

(Des Irene von Treskow. Gravure De La Rue)

1998 (2 Nov). *Christmas. Angels.* |MULTI COLOUR One centre phosphor band (20p.) or two phosphor bands (others). Perf 15×14.

2064	**1377**	20p. Angel with Hands raised in Blessing	35	35
		a. Imperf (pair)	£850	
2065	**1378**	26p. Angel praying	45	45
		a. Imperf (pair)	£3250	
2066	**1379**	30p. Angel playing Flute	60	60
		a. Imperf (pair)	£850	
2067	**1380**	43p. Angel playing Lute	80	80
		a. Imperf (pair)	£5000	
2068	**1381**	63p. Angel praying	90	90

Set of 5.. 2·80   2·80
Set of 5 Gutter Pairs .... 3·70
First Day Cover .... 3·00
Presentation Pack (PO Pack No. 292).................. 3·35
PHQ Cards *(set of 5)* (202)................................ 60   3·00

Special First Day of Issue Postmarks

British Philatelic Bureau, Edinburgh...3·00
Bethlehem ....3·00

Year Pack 1998
1998 (2 Nov). Comprises Nos. 2015/30, 2034/8 and 2041/68.
CP2068*a* Year Pack.. 40·00

Post Office Yearbook
1998 (2 Nov). Comprises Nos. 2015/30, 2034/8 and 2041/68 in hardback book with slip case................. 35·00

1382 Greenwich Meridian and Clock (John Harrison's chronometer)

1383 Industrial Worker and Blast Furnace (James Watt's discovery of steam power)

1384 Early Photos of Leaves (Henry Fox-Talbot's photographic experiments)

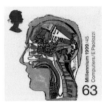

1385 Computer inside Human Head (Alan Turing's work on computers)

(Des D. Gentleman (20p.), P. Howson (26p.), Z. and Barbara Baran (43p.), E. Paolozzi (63p.), gravure, Questa (63p. No. 2072a), Enschedé (20p.) or De La Rue (others))

1999 (12 Jan – 21 Sept). *Millennium Series. The Inventors' Tale.* |MULTI COLOUR One centre phosphor band (20p.) or two phosphor bands (others). P 14×14½.

2069	**1382**	20p. Greenwich Meridian and Clock	40	40
		a. Imperf (horiz pair)	£3750	
2070	**1383**	26p. Industrial Worker and Blast Furnace	60	60
2071	**1384**	43p. Early Photos of Leaves	80	80
2072	**1385**	63p. Computer inside Human Head	1·00	1·00
		a. Perf 13½×14 (21 Sept)	1·75	1·75
		ab. Booklet pane. No. 2072a×4 with margins all round	7·50	

Set of 4.. 2·50   2·50
Set of 4 Gutter Pairs .... 5·00
First Day Cover (Philatelic Bureau) (Type J, see Introduction).. 4·20
First Day Cover (Greenwich, London SE)............ 4·20
Presentation Pack (PO Pack No. 294).................. 3·20
PHQ Cards *(set of 4)* (203)................................ 80   2·80

No. 2072a comes from the £6·99 World Changers booklet, No. DX23.

1386 Airliner hugging Globe (International air travel)

1387 Woman on Bicycle (Development of the bicycle)

1388 Victorian Railway Station (Growth of public transport)

1389 Captain Cook and Maori (Captain James Cook's voyages)

(Des G. Hardie (20p.), Sara Fanelli (26p.), J. Lawrence (43p.),
A. Klimowski (63p.). Gravure Enschedé (20p., 63p.) or De La Rue (26p.).
Litho Enschedé (43p.))

1999 (2 Feb). *Millennium Series. The Travellers' Tale.* |MULTI COLOUR One centre
phosphor band (20p.) or two phosphor bands (others). Perf 14×14½.

2073	**1386**	20p. Airliner hugging Globe............................	40	40
2074	**1387**	26p. Woman on Bicycle...................................	60	60
2075	**1388**	43p. Victorian Railway Station.....................	80	80
2076	**1389**	63p. Captain Cook and Maori....................	1·00	1·00
Set of 4..			2·50	2·50
Set of 4 Gutter Pairs...			5·00	

First Day Cover (Philatelic Bureau)
(Type J, see Introduction).. 3·40
First Day Cover (Coventry).. 3·40
Presentation Pack (PO Pack No. 295)................. 3·20
PHQ Cards (set of 4) (204)................................. 80 3·00

> For Nos. 2077/9 see Decimal Machins Definitive section

1391 Vaccinating Child
(pattern in cow markings)
(Jenner's development of
smallpox vaccine)

1392 Patient on Trolley
(nursing care)

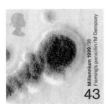

1393 Penicillin Mould
(Fleming's discovery of
penicillin)

1394 Sculpture of Test-tube
Baby (development of in-vitro
fertilization)

(Des P. Brookes (20p.), Susan Macfarlane (26p.), M. Dempsey (43p.), A.
Gormley (63p.). Gravure Questa)

1999 (2 Mar – 21 Sept). *Millennium Series. The Patients' Tale.* |MULTI COLOUR One
centre phosphor band (20p.) or two phosphor bands (others).
Perf 13½×14.

2080	**1391**	20p. Vaccinating Child..................................	40	40
		a. Booklet pane. No. 2080×4 with margins all round (21 Sept)............	1·60	
2081	**1392**	26p. Patient on Trolley..................................	60	60
		a. Imperf (pair)...	£6000	
2082	**1393**	43p. Penicillin Mould....................................	80	80
2083	**1394**	63p. Sculpture of Test-tube Baby...........	1·00	1·00
Set of 4..			2·50	2·50
Set of 4 Gutter Pairs...			5·00	

First Day Cover (Philatelic Bureau) (Type J, see
Introduction)... 3·40
First Day Cover (Oldham).. 3·40
Presentation Pack (PO Pack No. 296)................. 3·20
PHQ Cards (set of 4) (205)................................. 80 3·00
No. 2080a comes from the £6·99 World Changers booklet, No. DX23.

1395 Dove and Norman
Settler (medieval migration to
Scotland)

1396 Pilgrim Fathers and
Native American (17th-
century migration to America)

1397 Sailing Ship and
Aspects of Settlement (19th-
century migration
to Australia)

1398 Hummingbird and
Superimposed Stylized Face
(20th-century migration to
Great Britain)

(Des J. Byrne (20p.), W. McLean (26p.), J. Fisher (43p.), G. Powell (63p.).
Litho (20p.) or gravure (others) Walsall)

1999 (6 Apr – 12 May). *Millennium Series. The Settlers' Tale.* |MULTI COLOUR One
centre phosphor band (20p.) or two phosphor bands (others).
Perf 14×14½.

2084	**1395**	20p. Dove and Norman Settler................	40	40
2085	**1396**	26p. Pilgrim Fathers and Native Amercian......................................	60	60
		a. Booklet pane. Nos. 2085 and 2089 with margins all round (12 May)....	3·00	
2086	**1397**	43p. Sailing Ship and Aspects of Settlement...................................	80	80
2087	**1398**	63p. Hummingbird and Superimposed Stylized Face...............................	1·00	1·00
Set of 4..			2·50	2·50
Set of 4 Gutter Pairs...			5·00	

First Day Cover (Philatelic Bureau) (Type J, see
Introduction) .... 3·40
First Day Cover (Plymouth)................................... 3·40
Presentation Pack (PO Pack No. 297)................. 3·20
PHQ Cards (set of 4) (206)................................. 80 3·00
No. 2085a comes from the £2·60 booklet, No. HBA1.
Imperf pairs of Nos. 2085 and 2089 are known and believed to be
of proof status (*Price £750*).
Imperf pairs of No. 2085 with silver and phosphor omitted are
known and believed to be of proof status (*Price £350*).
Imperf pairs of No. 2086 are known with gold, chocolate and
phosphor omitted and believed to be of proof status (*Price £350*).

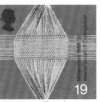

1399 Woven Threads
(woollen industry)

1400 *Salts Mill, Saltaire*
(worsted cloth industry)

1401 Hull on Slipway
(shipbuilding)

1402 Lloyd's Building (City of
London finance centre)

(Des P. Collingwood (19p.), D. Hockney (26p.), B. Sanderson (44p.),
B. Neiland (64p.). Litho (19p.) or gravure (others) De La Rue)

1999 (4 May). *Millennium Series. The Workers' Tale.* |MULTI COLOUR One centre phosphor band (19p.) or two phosphor bands (others). Perf 14×14½.

2088	**1399**	19p. Woven Threads	40	40
		a. Bronze (Queen's head) omitted	£675	
		aEy. Bronze and phosphor omitted	£675	
2089	**1400**	26p. Salts Mill, Saltaire	60	60
2090	**1401**	44p. Hull on Slipway	80	80
2091	**1402**	64p. Lloyd's Building	1·00	1·00
	Set of 4		2·50	2·50
	Set of 4 Gutter Pairs		5·00	
	First Day Cover (Philatelic Bureau) (Type J, see Introduction)		3·40	
	First Day Cover (Belfast)		3·40	
	Presentation Pack (PO Pack No. 298)		3·20	
	PHQ Cards (set of 4) (207)		80	3·00

For No. 2089, printed by Walsall in photogravure, see booklet pane No. 2085a.

1403 Freddie Mercury (lead singer of Queen) ('Popular Music')

1404 Bobby Moore with World Cup, 1966 ('Sport')

1405 Dalek from *Dr. Who* (science-fiction series) ('Television')

1406 Charlie Chaplin (film star) ('Cinema')

(Des P. Blake (19p.), M. White (26p.), Lord Snowdon (44p.),
R. Steadman (64p.). Gravure Enschedé)

1999 (1 June). *Millennium Series. The Entertainers' Tale.* |MULTI COLOUR One centre phosphor band (19p.) or two phosphor bands (others). Perf 14×14½.

2092	**1403**	19p. Freddie Mercury	40	40
2093	**1404**	26p. Bobby Moore with World Cup	60	60
2094	**1405**	44p. Dalek from *Dr. Who*	80	80
2095	**1406**	64p. Charlie Chaplin	1·00	1·00
	Set of 4		2·50	2·50
	Set of 4 Gutter Pairs		5·00	
	First Day Cover (Philatelic Bureau) (Type J, see Introduction)		3·40	
	First Day Cover (Wembley)		3·40	
	Presentation Pack (PO Pack No. 299)		3·20	
	PHQ Cards (set of 4) (208)		80	3·00

1407 Prince Edward and Miss Sophie Rhys-Jones (from photos by John Swannell)

1408

(Adapted J. Gibbs. Gravure De La Rue)

1999 (15 June). *Royal Wedding.* |MULTI COLOUR Two phosphor bands. Perf 15×14.

2096	**1407**	26p. Prince Edward and Miss Sophie Rhys-Jones (from photos by John Swannell)	40	40
		a. Imperf (pair)	£1800	
2097	**1408**	64p. Prince Edward and Miss Sophie Rhys-Jones	1·00	1·00
	Set of 2		1·30	1·30
	Set of 2 Gutter Pairs		2·60	
	First Day Cover (Philatelic Bureau)		2·00	
	First Day Cover (Windsor)		2·00	
	Presentation Pack (PO Pack No. M01)		2·00	
	PHQ Cards (set of 2) (PSM1)		80	1·80

1409 Suffragette behind Prison Window (Equal Rights for Women)

1410 Water Tap (Right to Health)

1411 Generations of School Children (Right to Education)

1412 'MAGNA CARTA' (Human Rights)

(Des Natasha Kerr (19p.), M. Craig-Martin (26p.), A. Drummond (44p.),
A. Kitching (64p.). Gravure De La Rue)

1999 (6 July). *Millennium Series. The Citizens' Tale.* |MULTI COLOUR One centre phosphor band (19p.) or two phosphor bands (others). Perf 14×14½.

2098	**1409**	19p. Suffragette behind Prison Window	40	40
2099	**1410**	26p. Water Tap	60	60
2100	**1411**	44p. Generations of School Children	80	80
2101	**1412**	64p. 'MAGNA CARTA'	1·00	1·00
	Set of 4		2·50	2·50
	Set of 4 Gutter Pairs		5·00	
	First Day Cover (Philatelic Bureau) (Type J, see Introduction)		3·40	
	First Day Cover (Newtown, Powis)		3·40	
	Presentation Pack (PO Pack No. 300)		3·20	
	PHQ Cards (set of 4) (209)		80	3·00

1413 Molecular Structures (DNA Decoding)

1414 Galapagos Finch and Fossilized Skeleton (Darwin's Theory of Evolution)

1415 Rotation of Polarized Light by Magnetism (Faraday's work on Electricity)

1416 Saturn (development of astronomical telescopes)

(Des M. Curtis (19p.), R. Harris Ching (26p.), C. Gray (44p.), from Hubble Space Telescope photograph (64p.). Gravure (19p., 64p.) or litho (26p., 44p.) Questa)

1999 (3 Aug – 21 Sept). *Millennium Series. The Scientists' Tale.* MULTI COLOUR One centre phosphor band (19p.) or two phosphor bands (others). P 13½×14 (19p., 64p.) or 14×14½ (26p., 44p.).

2102	**1413**	19p. Molecular Structures	40	40
2103	**1414**	26p. Galapagos Finch and Fossilized Skeleton	60	60
		a. Imperf (pair)	£1200	
		b. Perf 14½×14 (21 Sept)	1·50	1·50
		ba. Booklet pane. No. 2103b×4 with margins all round	6·50	
2104	**1415**	44p. Rotation of Polarized Light by Magnetism	80	80
		a. Perf 14½×14 (21 Sept)	1·50	1·50
		ab. Booklet pane. No. 2104a×4 with margins all round	6·50	
2105	**1416**	64p. Saturn	1·00	1·00
Set of 4			2·50	2·50
Set of 4 Gutter Pairs			5·00	
First Day Cover (Philatelic Bureau) (Type J, see Introduction)				3·40
First Day Cover (Cambridge)				3·40
Presentation Pack (PO Pack No. 301)			3·20	
PHQ Cards (set of 4) (210)			80	3·00

Nos. 2103b and 2104a come from the £6·99 World Changers booklet, No. DX23.

1999 (11 Aug). *Solar Eclipse.* Sheet 89×121 mm. MULTI COLOUR Two phosphor bands. Perf 14×14½.

MS2106 T **1416**a×4 (sold at 64p)	11·00	11·00
a. Imperf	—	
First Day Cover (Philatelic Bureau)		11·50
First Day Cover (Falmouth)		11·50

1417 Upland Landscape (Strip Farming)

1418 Horse-drawn Rotary Seed Drill (Mechanical Farming)

1419 Man peeling Potato (Food Imports)

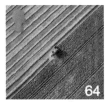

1420 Aerial View of Combine Harvester (Satellite Agriculture)

(Des D. Tress (19p.), C. Wormell (26p.), Tessa Traeger (44p.), R. Cooke (64p.). Gravure Walsall (No. 2108a) or De La Rue (others))

1999 (7 – 21 Sept). *Millennium Series. The Farmers' Tale.* MULTI COLOUR One centre phosphor band (19p.) or two phosphor bands (others). Perf 14×14½.

2107	**1417**	19p. Upland Landscape	40	40
2108	**1418**	26p. Horse-drawn Rotary Seed Drill	60	60
		a. Booklet pane. No. 2108×2 with margins all round (21 Sept)	3·00	
2109	**1419**	44p. Man peeling Potato	80	80
2110	**1420**	64p. Aerial View of Combine Harvester	1·00	1·00
Set of 4			2·50	2·50
Set of 4 Gutter Pairs			5·00	
First Day Cover (Philatelic Bureau) (Type J, see Introduction)				3·40
First Day Cover (Laxton, Newark)				3·40
Presentation Pack (PO Pack No. 302)			3·20	
PHQ Cards (set of 4) (211)			80	3·00

The 19p. includes the 'EUROPA' emblem. No. 2108a comes from the £2·60 booklet, No. HBA2.

1421 Robert the Bruce (Battle of Bannockburn, 1314)

1422 Cavalier and Horse (English Civil War)

1423 War Graves Cemetery, The Somme (World Wars)

1424 Soldiers with Boy (Peace-keeping)

(Des A. Davidson (19p.), R. Kelly (26p.), D. McCullin (44p.), C. Corr (64p.). Litho (19p.) or gravure (others) Walsall)

1999 (5 Oct). *Millennium Series. The Soldiers' Tale.* MULTI COLOUR One centre phosphor band (19p.) or two phosphor bands (others). Perf 14×14½.

2111	**1421**	19p. Robert the Bruce	40	40
2112	**1422**	26p. Cavalier and Horse	60	60
2113	**1423**	44p. War Graves Cemetery, The Somme	80	80
2114	**1424**	64p. Soldiers with Boy	1·00	1·00
Set of 4			2·50	2·50
Set of 4 Gutter Pairs			5·00	
First Day Cover (Philatelic Bureau) (Type J, see Introduction)				3·40
First Day Cover (London SW)				3·40
Presentation Pack (PO Pack No. 303*)			3·20	
PHQ Cards (set of 4) (212)			80	3·00

*The presentation pack was numbered 302 in error.

1425 'Hark the herald angels sing' and Hymn book (John Wesley)

1426 King James I and Bible (Authorised Version of Bible)

1427 St Andrews Cathedral, Fife ('Pilgrimage')

1428 Nativity ('First Christmas')

(Des B. Neuenschwander (19p.), Clare Melinsky (26p.), Catherine Yass (44p.), C. Aitchison (64p.). Gravure De La Rue)

1999 (2 Nov). *Millennium Series. The Christians' Tale.* MULTI COLOUR One centre phosphor band (19p.) or two phosphor bands (others). Perf 14×14½.

2115	**1425**	19p. 'Hark the herald angels sing' and Hymn book	40	40
		a. Imperf (pair)	£700	
2116	**1426**	26p. King James I and Bible	60	60
2117	**1427**	44p. St Andrews Cathedral, Fife	80	80
2118	**1428**	64p. Nativity	1·00	1·00
Set of 4			2·50	2·50
Set of 4 Gutter Pairs			5·00	
First Day Cover (Philatelic Bureau) (Type J, see Introduction)				3·40
First Day Cover (St Andrews, Fife)				3·40

Presentation Pack (PO Pack No. 304).. 3·20
PHQ Cards (set of 4) (213).. 80 3·00

1429 'World of the Stage'
(Allen Jones)

1430 'World of Music'
(Bridget Riley)

1431 'World of Literature'
(Lisa Milroy)

1432 'New Worlds'
(Sir Howard Hodgkin)

(Gravure Walsall)

1999 (7 Dec). *Millennium Series. The Artists' Tale.* |MULTI COLOUR| One centre phosphor band (19p.) or two phosphor bands (others). Perf 14×14½.

2119	**1429**	19p. 'World of the Stage'..........................	40	40
2120	**1430**	26p. 'World of Music'..........................	60	60
2121	**1431**	44p. 'World of Literature'..........................	80	80
2122	**1432**	64p. 'New Worlds'..........................	1·00	1·00

Set of 4 .... 2·50 2·50
Set of 4 Gutter Pairs .... 5·00
First Day Cover (Philatelic Bureau) (Type J, see
Introduction) .... 3·40
First Day Cover (Stratford-upon-Avon) .... 3·40
Presentation Pack (PO Pack No. 305) .... 3·20
PHQ Cards (set of 4) (214) .... 80 3·00

Year Pack 1999

1999 (7 Dec). Comprises Nos. 2069/76, 2080/105 and 2107/22.
CP2122a Year Pack.. 65·00

Post Office Yearbook

1999 (7 Dec). Comprises Nos. 2069/76, 2080/105 and
2107/22 in hardback book with slip case .... 50·00

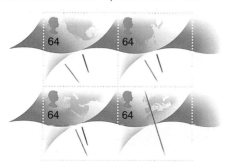

1433a (Illustration reduced. Actual Size 121×90 mm)

(Des D. Gentleman. Gravure De La Rue)

1999 (14 Dec). *Millennium Series. 'Millennium Timekeeper'.* Sheet 120×89 mm. |MULTI COLOUR| Two phosphor bands. Perf 14×14½.
MS2123 **1433a** 64p. Clock face and map of North
America; 64p. Clock face and map of Asia; 64p.
Clock face and map of Middle East; 64p. Clock face
and map of Europe.. 11·00 11·00
First Day Cover (Philatelic Bureau) .... 11·00
First Day Cover (Greenwich SE) .... 11·00
Presentation Pack (PO Pack No. M02) .... 12·00
PHQ Cards (set of 5) (PSM02) .... 1·00 11·00
No. **MS**2123 also exists overprinted 'EARLS COURT, LONDON 22-28 MAY 2000 THE STAMP SHOW 2000' from Exhibition Premium Passes, costing £10, available from 1 March 2000 (Price £17).
The five PHQ cards show the four individual stamps and the complete miniature sheet.

For No. 2124 see Decimal Machin Definitives section.

1438 Barn Owl (World Owl Trust, Muncaster)

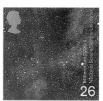

1439 Night Sky (National Space Science Centre, Leicester)

1440 River Goyt and Textile Mills (Torrs Walkway, New Mills)

1441 Gannets (Seabird Centre, North Berwick)

(Litho (44p.), gravure (others) Walsall (No. 2126a/ab) or Questa (others))

2000 (18 Jan)–02. *Millennium Projects (1st series). 'Above and Beyond'.* |MULTI COLOUR| One centre phosphor band (19p.) or two phosphor bands (others). Perf 14×14½ (1st, 44p.) or 13½×14 (others).

2125	**1438**	19p. Barn Owl (World Owl Trust, Muncaster)..............................	40	40
		a. Imperf (pair)...............................	£1000	
2126	**1439**	26p. Night Sky (National Space Science Centre, Leicester)..........	70	70
		aa. Imperf (pair).............................	£1000	
2126a		(1st) greenish yellow, magenta, pale new blue, black and silver (26.5.00)	2·20	2·20
		ab. Booklet pane. Nos. 2126a and 2139 with margins all round	3·00	
		ac. Booklet pane. No. 2126a×4 with margins all round (24.9.02).......	9·00	
2127	**1440**	44p. River Goyt and Textile Mills (Torrs Walkway, New Mills)..........	1·00	1·00
2128	**1441**	64p. Gannets (Seabird Centre, North Berwick)........................	1·20	1·20

Set of 4 (ex No. 2126a) .... 3·10 3·10
Set of 4 Gutter Pairs .... 6·20
First Day Cover (Nos. 2125/8) (Philatelic Bureau) (Type J, see Introduction) .... 4·00 4·00
First Day Cover (Nos. 2125/8) (Muncaster, Ravenglass).. 4·00 4·00
First Day Cover (No. 2126ab) (Philatelic Bureau) .... 4·00 4·00
First Day Cover (No. 2126ab) (Leicester)................. 4·00 4·00
Presentation Pack (PO Pack No. 307)................. 3·70
PHQ Cards (set of 4) (215).................... 80 3·50
No. 2126ab comes from the £2·70 Millennium booklet, No. HBA3. No. 2162ac comes from the 'Across the Universe' sponsored booklet, No. DX29.
Imperforate pairs of No. 2125 with Queen's head in gold, Nos. 2126 and 2139 with inscriptions in an alternative typeface and No. 2128 with inscriptions in silver are all of proof status (Prices from £200).

1442 Millennium Beacon (Beacons across The Land)

1443 Garratt Steam Locomotive No. 143 pulling Train (Rheilffordd Eryri, Welsh Highland Railway)

1444 Lightning (Dynamic Earth Centre, Edinburgh)

1445 Multicoloured Lights (Lighting Croydon's Skyline)

(Gravure De La Rue)

2000 (1 Feb). *Millennium Projects* (2nd series). *'Fire and Light'.* |MULTI COLOUR| One centre phosphor band (19p.) or two phosphor bands (others). Perf 14×14½.

2129	**1442**	19p. Millennium Beacon (Beacons across The Land)	40	40
2130	**1443**	26p. Garratt Steam Locomotive No. 143 pulling Train (Rheilffordd Eryri, Welsh Highland Railway).......	70	70
2131	**1444**	44p. Lightning (Dynamic Earth Centre, Edinburgh).......	1·00	1·00
2132	**1445**	64p. Multicoloured Lights (Lighting Croydon's Skyline).....................	1·20	1·20
Set of 4..........			3·10	3·10
Set of 4 Gutter Pairs..........			6·20	
First Day Cover (Philatelic Bureau)				
(Type J, see Introduction)..........			4·00	
First Day Cover (Edinburgh 3°10'W)..........			4·00	
Presentation Pack (PO Pack No. 308)..........			3·70	
PHQ Cards (set of 4) (216)..........			50	3·50

1446 Queen Victoria and Queen Elizabeth II

(Des J. Matthews. Gravure Walsall)

2000 (15 Feb)-**2017**. T **929** redrawn as T **1446** (No.2133a). Two phosphor bands. Perf 14 (No. 2133a) or perf 14½×14 (both with one elliptical hole in each vertical side).

2133	**929**	20p brownish black and cream (5.6.17)..........	1·10	1·10
2133a	**1446**	(1st) brownish black and cream..........	1·10	1·10
		l. Booklet pane. No. 2133×6 with margins all round..........	5·50	
First Day Cover (No. 2133l) (Philatelic Bureau)..........			5·50	
First Day Cover (No. 2133l) (London SW5)..........			5·50	

No. 2133 comes from the £15·14 50th Anniversary of the Machin booklet, DY21.

No. 2133a was only issued in the £7·50 'Special by Design' booklet, No. DX24. For Nos. 2133/a but printed Litho see Nos. 2955/6.

Also see Nos. 1478 and **MS**1501.

1447 Beach Pebbles (Turning the Tide, Durham Coast)

1448 Frog's Legs and Water Lilies (National Pondlife Centre, Merseyside)

1449 Cliff Boardwalk (Parc Arfordirol, Llanelli Coast)

1450 Reflections in Water (Portsmouth Harbour Development)

(Litho (44p.), gravure (others) Walsall)

2000 (7 Mar). *Millennium Projects* (3rd series). *'Water and Coast'.* |MULTI COLOUR| One centre phosphor band (19p.) or two phosphor bands (others). Perf 14×14½.

2134	**1447**	19p. Beach Pebbles (Turning the Tide, Durham Coast)..........	40	40
2135	**1448**	26p. Frog's Legs and Water Lilies (National Pondlife Centre, Merseyside)..........	70	70
2136	**1449**	44p. Cliff Boardwalk (Parc Arfordirol, Llanelli Coast)..........	1·00	1·00
2137	**1450**	64p. Reflections in Water (Portsmouth Harbour Development)..........	1·20	1·20
		a. Phosphor omitted..........	£175	
Set of 4..........			3·10	3·10
Set of 4 Gutter Pairs..........			6·20	
First Day Cover (Philatelic Bureau)				
(Type J, see Introduction)..........			4·00	
First Day Cover (Llanelli)..........			4·00	
Presentation Pack (PO Pack No. 309)..........			3·70	
PHQ Cards (set of 4) (217)..........			1·20	4·50

1451 Reed Beds, River Braid (ECOS, Ballymena)

1452 South American Leaf-cutter Ants ('Web of Life' Exhibition, London Zoo)

1453 Solar Sensors (Earth Centre, Doncaster)

1454 Hydroponic Leaves (Project SUZY, Teesside)

(Gravure De La Rue)

2000 (4 Apr). *Millennium Projects* (4th series). *'Life and Earth'.* |MULTI COLOUR| One centre phosphor band (2nd) or two phosphor bands (others). P 14×14½.

2138	**1451**	(2nd) Reed Beds, River Braid..........	90	90
2139	**1452**	(1st) South American Leaf-cutter Ants..........	1·00	1·00
		a. Imperf (pair)..........		
2140	**1453**	44p. Solar Sensors..........	1·00	1·00
2141	**1454**	64p. Hydroponic Leaves..........	1·20	1·20
Set of 4..........			3·75	3·75
Set of 4 Gutter Pairs..........			7·50	
First Day Cover (Philatelic Bureau)				
(Type J, see Introduction)..........			4·00	
First Day Cover (Doncaster)..........			4·00	
Presentation Pack (PO Pack No. 310)..........			4·25	
PHQ Cards (set of 4) (218)..........			1·20	4·50

For No. 2139 printed by Walsall in photogravure, see booklet pane No. 2126ab.

Types **1453/4** with face values of 45p. and 65p. were prepared, but not issued.

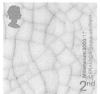

1455 Pottery Glaze (Ceramica Museum, Stoke-on-Trent)   1456 Bankside Galleries (Tate Modern, London)

1457 Road Marking (Cycle Network Artworks)   1458 People of Salford (Lowry Centre, Salford)

(Gravure Enschedé)

2000 (2 May). *Millennium Projects* (5th series). *'Art and Craft'.* |MULTI COLOUR One centre phosphor band (2nd) or two phosphor bands (others). P 14×14½.

2142	**1455**	(2nd) Pottery Glaze	90	90
2143	**1456**	(1st) Bankside Galleries	1·00	1·00
2144	**1457**	45p. Road Marking	1·00	1·00
2145	**1458**	65p. *People of Salford*	1·20	1·20

Set of 4	3·75	3.75
Set of 4 Gutter Pairs	7·50	
First Day Cover (Philatelic Bureau)		
(Type J, see Introduction)		4.00
First Day Cover (Salford)		4.00
Presentation Pack (PO Pack No. 311)	4·25	
PHQ Cards (set of 4) (219)	1·20	4·50

For Nos. **MS**2146/7 see Decimal Machin Definitives section.

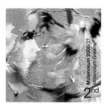

1460 Children playing (Millennium Greens Project)   1461 Millennium Bridge, Gateshead

1462 Daisies (Mile End Park, London)   1463 African Hut and Thatched Cottage ('On the Meridian Line' Project)

(Gravure (2nd, 45p.) or litho (1st, 65p.) Walsall)

2000 (6 June). *Millennium Projects* (6th series). *'People and Places'.* |MULTI COLOUR One centre phosphor band (2nd) or two phosphor bands (others). P 14×14½.

2148	**1460**	(2nd) Children playing	90	90
2149	**1461**	(1st) Millennium Bridge, Gateshead	1·00	1·00
2150	**1462**	45p. Daisies	1·00	1·00
2151	**1463**	65p. African Hut and Thatched Cottage	1·20	1·20

Set of 4	3·75	3.75
Set of 4 Gutter Pairs	7·50	
First Day Cover (Philatelic Bureau)		
(Type J, see Introduction)		4.00
First Day Cover (Gateshead)		4.00
Presentation Pack (PO Pack No. 312)	4·25	
PHQ Cards (set of 4) (220)	1·20	4·50

1464 Raising the Stone (Strangford Stone, Killyleagh)   1465 Horse's Hooves (Trans Pennine Trail, Derbyshire)

1466 Cyclist (Kingdom of Fife Cycle Ways, Scotland)   1467 Bluebell Wood (Groundwork's 'Changing Places' Project)

(Gravure Walsall (Nos. 2153a, 2155a) or Enschedé (others))

2000 (4 July–18 Sept). *Millennium Projects* (7th series). *'Stone and Soil'.* |MULTI COLOUR One centre phosphor band (2nd) or two phosphor bands (others). Perf 14×14½

2152	**1464**	(2nd) Raising the Stone	90	90
2153	**1465**	(1st) Horse's Hooves	1·00	1·00
		a. Booklet pane. Nos. 2153 and 2157 with margins all round (18 Sept)	2·40	
2154	**1466**	45p. Cyclist	90	90
2155	**1467**	65p. Bluebell Wood	1·10	1·10
		a. Booklet pane. No. 2155×2 with margins all round (18 Sept)	2·25	

Set of 4	3·50	3·50
Set of 4 Gutter Pairs	7·00	
First Day Cover (Philatelic Bureau)		
(Type J, see Introduction)		4·00
First Day Cover (Killyleagh)		4·00
Presentation Pack (PO Pack No. 313)	4·00	
PHQ Cards (set of 4) (221)	1·20	4·25

No. 2153a comes from the £2·70 'Millenium' booklet, No. HBA4. No. 2155a comes from the £7 'Treasury of Trees' booklet, No. DX26.

1468 Tree Roots ('Yews for the Millennium' Project)   1469 Sunflower ('Eden' Project, St Austell)

1470 Sycamore Seeds (Millennium Seed Bank, Wakehurst Place, West Sussex)   1471 Forest, Doire Dach ('Forest for Scotland')

(Gravure Walsall (Nos. 2156a, 2158a, 2159a) or De La Rue (others))

2000 (1 Aug–18 Sept). *Millennium Projects* (8th series). *'Tree and Leaf'.* |MULTI COLOUR One centre phosphor band (2nd) or two phosphor bands (others). Perf 14×14½.

2156	**1468**	(2nd) Tree Roots	90	90
		a. Booklet pane. No. 2156×4 with margins all round (18 Sept)	4·00	
2157	**1469**	(1st) Sunflower	1·00	1·00
2158	**1470**	45p. Sycamore Seeds	90	90
		a. Booklet pane. No. 2158×4 with margins all round (18 Sept)	3·75	
2159	**1471**	65p. Forest, Doire Dach	1·10	1·10
		a. Booklet pane. No. 2159×2 with margins all round (18 Sept)	2·40	

Set of 4	3·50	3·50
Set of 4 Gutter Pairs	7·00	
First Day Cover (Philatelic Bureau)		
(Type J, see Introduction)		4·00
First Day Cover (St Austell)		4·00
Presentation Pack (PO Pack No. 314)	4·00	
PHQ Cards (set of 4) (222)	1·20	4·25

Nos. 2156a, 2158a and 2159a come from the £7 Treasury of Trees booklet, No. DX26. For No. 2157 printed by Walsall in photogravure, see booklet pane No. 2153a.

1472 Queen Elizabeth the Queen Mother

1472a Royal Family on Queen Mother's 100th Birthday

(Des J. Gibbs from photo by J. Swannell. Gravure Questa (Nos. 2160, **MS**2161a) or De La Rue (No. **MS**2161))

2000 (4 Aug). *Queen Elizabeth the Queen Mother's 100th Birthday.* |MULTI COLOUR| Phosphorised paper plus two phosphor bands. Perf 14½.

2160	**1472**	27p. Queen Elizabeth the Queen Mother	1·20	1·20
		a. Booklet pane. No. 2160×4 with margins all round	5·00	
MS2161	121×89mm. **1472a** 27p.×4, Royal Family on Queen Mother's 100th Birthday		5·00	5·00
		a. Booklet pane. As No. **MS**2161, but larger, 150×95 mm, and with additional silver frame	5·00	5·00
First Day Cover (No. 2160a) (Philatelic Bureau)			5·00	5·00
First Day Cover (No. 2160a) (London SW1)			5·00	5·00
First Day Cover (**MS**2161) (Philatelic Bureau)			5·00	5·00
First Day Cover (**MS**2161) (London SW1)			5·00	5·00
Presentation Pack (**MS**2161) (PO Pack No. M04)			11·00	
PHQ Cards (set of 5) (PSM04)			1·50	5·50

No. 2160 was only issued in the £7·08 'The Life of the Century' booklet, No. DX25 and as part of Nos. **MS**2161/a.

The complete miniature sheet is shown on one of the PHQ cards with the others depicting individual stamps.

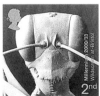

1473 *Head of Gigantiops destructor* (Ant) (Wildscreen at Bristol)

1474 Gathering Water Lilies on Broads (Norfolk and Norwich Project)

1475 X-ray of Hand holding Computer Mouse (Millennium Point, Birmingham)

1476 Tartan Wool Holder (Scottish Cultural Resources Access Network)

(Litho Walsall)

2000 (5 Sept). *Millennium Projects* (9th series). *'Mind and Matter'.* |MULTI COLOUR| One centre phosphor band (2nd) or two phosphor bands (others). P 14×14½.

2162	**1473**	(2nd) Head of *Gigantiops destructor* (Ant)	90	90
2163	**1474**	(1st) Gathering Water Lilies on Broads ..	1·00	1·00
2164	**1475**	45p. X-ray of Hand holding Computer Mouse	90	90
2165	**1476**	65p. Tartan Wool Holder	1·10	1·10
Set of 4			3·50	3·50
Set of 4 Gutter Pairs			7·00	
First Day Cover (Philatelic Bureau)				
(Type J, see Introduction)				4·00
First Day Cover (Norwich)				4·00
Presentation Pack (PO Pack No. 315)			4·00	
PHQ Cards (set of 4) (223)			1·20	4·25

1477 Acrobatic Performers (Millennium Dome)

1478 Football Players (Hampden Park, Glasgow)

1479 Bather (Bath Spa Project)

1480 Hen's Egg under Magnification (Centre for Life, Newcastle)

(Litho (2nd) or gravure (others) Questa)

2000 (3 Oct). *Millennium Projects* (10th series). *'Body and Bone'.* |MULTI COLOUR| One centre phosphor band (2nd) or two phosphor bands (others). P 14×14½ (2nd) or 13½×14 (others).

2166	**1477**	(2nd) Acrobatic Performers	90	90
2167	**1478**	(1st) Football Players	1·00	1·00
2168	**1479**	45p. Bather	90	90
2169	**1480**	65p. Hen's Egg under Magnification	1·10	1·10
Set of 4			3·50	3·50
Set of 4 Gutter Pairs			7·00	
First Day Cover (Philatelic Bureau)				
(Type J, see Introduction)				4·00
First Day Cover (Glasgow)				4·50
Presentation Pack (PO Pack No. 316)			4·00	
PHQ Cards (set of 4) (224)			1·20	4·25

1481 Virgin and Child Stained Glass Window, St Edmundsbury Cathedral (Suffolk Cathedral Millennium Project)

1482 Floodlit Church of St Peter and St Paul, Overstowey (Church Floodlighting Trust)

1483 12th-cent Latin Gradual (St Patrick Centre, Downpatrick)

1484 Chapter House Ceiling, York Minster (York Millennium Mystery Plays)

(Gravure De La Rue)

2000 (7 Nov). *Millennium Projects* (11th series). *'Spirit and Faith'.* |MULTI COLOUR One centre phosphor band (2nd) or two phosphor bands (others). Perf 14×14½.

2170	**1481**	(2nd) Virgin and Child Stained Glass Window, St Edmundsbury Cathedral	90	90
		a. Imperf pair	£700	
2171	**1482**	(1st) Floodlit Church of St Peter and St Paul, Overstowey	1·00	1·00
		a. Imperf (pair)	£850	
2172	**1483**	45p. 12th-cent Latin Gradual	90	90
2173	**1484**	65p. Chapter House Ceiling, York Minster	1·10	1·10
		Set of 4	3·50	3·50
		Set of 4 Gutter Pairs	7·00	

First Day Cover (Philatelic Bureau) (Type J, see Introduction) ... 4·00
First Day Cover (Downpatrick) ... 4·00
Presentation Pack (PO Pack No. 317) ... 4·00
PHQ Cards (set of 4) (225) ... 1·20 4·25

No. 2173 has been reported with the gold omitted, leaving the Queen's head in yellow. It is only known used.

Post Office Yearbook
2000 (Nov 7). Comprises Nos. 2125/6, 2127/32, 2134/45, 2148/59 and **MS**2161/77 in hardback book with slip case ... 48·00

The last two issues in the Millennium Projects Series were supplied for insertion into the above at a later date.

1485 Church Bells (Ringing in the Millennium)

1486 Eye (Year of the Artist)

1487 Top of Harp (Canolfan Mileniwm, Cardiff)

1488 Silhouetted Figure within Latticework (TS2K Creative Enterprise Centres, London)

(Gravure De La Rue)

2000 (5 Dec). *Millennium Projects* (12th series). *'Sound and Vision'.* |MULTI COLOUR One centre phosphor band (2nd) or two phosphor bands (others). Perf 14×14½.

2174	**1485**	(2nd) Church Bells	90	90
2175	**1486**	(1st) Eye	1·00	1·00
2176	**1487**	45p. Top of Harp	90	90
2177	**1488**	65p. Silhouetted Figure within Latticework	1·10	1·10
		Set of 4	3·50	3·50
		Set of 4 Gutter Pairs	7·00	

First Day Cover (Philatelic Bureau) (Type J, see Introduction) ... 4·00
First Day Cover (Cardiff) ... 4·00
Presentation Pack (PO Pack No. 318) ... 4·00
PHQ Cards (set of 4) (226) ... 1·20 4·25

Collectors Pack 2000
2000 (Dec 5) Comprises Nos. 2125/6, 2127/32, 2134/45, 2148/59 and **MS**2161/77.
CP2177a Collectors Pack ... 65·00

1489 'Flower' ('Nurture Children')

1490 'Tiger' ('Listen to Children')

1491 'Owl' ('Teach Children')

1492 'Butterfly' ('Ensure Children's Freedom')

(Des Why Not Associates. Gravure De La Rue)

2001 (16 Jan). *New Millennium. Rights of the Child. Face Paintings.* |MULTI COLOUR One centre phosphor band (2nd) or two phosphor bands (others). Perf 14×14½.

2178	**1489**	(2nd) 'Flower' ('Nurture Children')	90	90
2179	**1490**	(1st) 'Tiger' ('Listen to Children')	1·00	1·00
2180	**1491**	45p. 'Owl' ('Teach Children')	1·00	1·00
2181	**1492**	65p. 'Butterfly' ('Ensure Children's Freedom')	1·20	1·20
		Set of 4	3·75	3·75
		Set of 4 Gutter Pairs	7·50	

First Day Cover (Philatelic Bureau) ... 4·00
First Day Cover (Hope, Hope Valley) ... 4·00
Presentation Pack (PO Pack No. 319) ... 4·25
PHQ Cards (set of 4) (227) ... 1·20 4·25

1493 'Love'

1494 'THANKS'

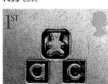

1495 'abc' (New Baby)

1496 'WELCOME'

1497 'Cheers'

(Des Springpoint Design. Gravure Enschedé)

2001 (6 Feb). *Greetings Stamps. 'Occasions'.* |MULTI COLOUR Two phosphor bands. P 14×14½.

2182	**1493**	(1st) 'Love'	1·00	1·00
2183	**1494**	(1st) 'THANKS'	1·00	1·00
2184	**1495**	(1st) 'abc' (New Baby)	1·00	1·00
2185	**1496**	(1st) 'WELCOME'	1·00	1·00
2186	**1497**	(1st) 'Cheers'	1·00	1·00
		Set of 5	4·50	4·50
		Set of 5 Gutter Pairs	9·00	

First Day Cover (Philatelic Bureau) ... 4·75
First Day Cover (Merry Hill, Wolverhampton) ... 4·75
Presentation Pack (13 Feb) (PO Pack No. M05) ... 7·25
PHQ Cards (set of 5) (PSM05) ... 1·50 5·00

The silver-grey backgrounds are printed in Iriodin ink which gives a shiny effect.

Further packs of Nos. 2182/6 were sold from 3 July 2001. These comprised the listed stamps in blocks of ten (from sheets) with an insert describing the occasion (*Price £10 per pack*).

Nos. 2182/6 were re-issued on 1 May 2001 in sheets of 20 printed by Questa in lithography instead of photogravure, in connection with the 'customised' stamps scheme. Such sheets contained twenty examples of either Nos. 2182, 2184 or 2185, or ten each of Nos. 2183 and 2186. Sheets with personal photographs printed on the labels were available from Royal Mail in Edinburgh at £12 each. From 5 June 2001 a similar sheet (LS4) containing four of each design in horizontal strips, with postal symbols on the labels, was sold at £5·95.

1498 Dog and Owner on Bench

1499 Dog in Bath

1500 Boxer at Dog Show

1501 Cat in Handbag

1502 Cat on Gate

1503 Dog in Car

1504 Cat at Window

1505 Dog Behind Fence

1506 Cat watching Bird

1507 Cat in Washbasin

(Des johnson banks. Gravure Walsall)

2001 (13 Feb). *Cats and Dogs.* |MULTI COLOUR| Self-adhesive. Two phosphor bands. P 15×14 die-cut.

2187	**1498**	(1st) Dog and Owner on Bench	1·00	1·00
		a. Sheetlet. Nos. 2187/96	9·00	9·00
		aa. Imperf (sheetlet)	—	
		b. Booklet pane. Nos. 2187/96 plus No. 2040×2	22·00	
		ba. Imperf (pane)	—	
2188	**1499**	(1st) Dog in Bath	1·00	1·00
2189	**1500**	(1st) Boxer at Dog Show	1·00	1·00
2190	**1501**	(1st) Cat in Handbag	1·00	1·00
2191	**1502**	(1st) Cat on Gate	1·00	1·00
2192	**1503**	(1st) Dog in Car	1·00	1·00
2193	**1504**	(1st) Cat at Window	1·00	1·00
2194	**1505**	(1st) Dog Behind Fence	1·00	1·00
2195	**1506**	(1st) Cat watching Bird	1·00	1·00
2196	**1507**	(1st) Cat in Washbasin	1·00	1·00
2187/96		*Set of 10*	9·00	9·00
		First Day Cover (Philatelic Bureau)		9·75
		First Day Cover (Petts Wood, Orpington)		9·75
		Presentation Pack (PO Pack No. 320)	9·75	
		PHQ Cards (set of 10) (228)	3·00	12·00

Nos. 2187/96 were printed together in sheetlets of ten (5×2), with the surplus self-adhesive paper around each stamp retained. The pane has vertical roulettes between rows 2/3 and 4/5 with the design on the reverse of the backing paper similar to Booklet No. PM1.

1508 'RAIN'

1509 'FAIR'

1510 'STORMY'

1511 'VERY DRY'

(Des H. Brown and T. Meeuwissen. Gravure De La Rue)

2001 (13 Mar). *The Weather.* |MULTI COLOUR| One side phosphor band (19p.) or two phosphor bands (others). Perf 14½.

2197	**1508**	19p. 'RAIN'	70	70
2198	**1509**	27p. 'FAIR'	80	80
2199	**1510**	45p. 'STORMY'	95	95
2200	**1511**	65p. 'VERY DRY'	1·10	1·10
		Set of 4	3·25	3·25
		Set of 4 Gutter Pairs	6·50	
		First Day Cover (Philatelic Bureau)		3·50
		First Day Cover (Fraserburgh)		3·50
		Presentation Pack (PO Pack No. 321)	9·00	
MS2201		105×105 mm. Nos. 2197/200	9·25	9·25
		First Day Cover (Philatelic Bureau)		10·00
		First Day Cover (Fraserburgh)		10·00
		PHQ Cards (set of 5) (229)	1·50	14·00

Nos. 2197/200 show the four quadrants of a barometer dial which are combined on the miniature sheet. The reddish violet on both the 27p. and the miniature sheet is printed in thermochromic ink which changes from reddish violet to light blue when exposed to heat. The PHQ cards depict the four values and the miniature sheet.

1512 Vanguard Class Submarine, 1992

1513 Swiftsure Class Submarine, 1973

1514 Unity Class Submarine, 1939

1515 'Holland' Type Submarine, 1901

1516 White Ensign

1517 Union Jack

1518 'Jolly Roger' flown by HMS *Proteus* (submarine)

1519 Flag of Chief of Defence Staff

1520 Leyland X2 Open-top, London General B Type, Leyland Titan TD1 and AEC Regent 1

1521 AEC Regent 1, Daimler COG5, Utility Guy Arab Mk II and AEC Regent III RT Type

(Des D. Davis. Gravure Questa)

2001 (10 Apr–22 Oct). *Centenary of Royal Navy Submarine Service.* MULTICOLOUR One centre phosphor band (2nd) or two phosphor bands (others). Perf 15×14.

(a) Submarines. Ordinary gum.

2202	**1512**	(2nd) Vanguard Class Submarine, 1992...	90	90
		a. Perf 15½×15 (22 Oct)	1·95	1·95
		ab. Booklet pane. Nos. 2202a and 2204a, each×2, with margins all round	7·00	
2203	**1513**	(1st) Swiftsure Class Submarine, 1973 ...	1·00	1·00
		a. Perf 15½×15 (22 Oct)	1·95	1·95
		b. Imperf (pair)	£1400	
		ab. Booklet pane. Nos. 2203a and 2205a, each×2, with margins all round	8·00	
2204	**1514**	45p. Unity Class Submarine, 1939	90	90
		a. Perf 15½×15 (22 Oct)	1·95	1·95
2205	**1515**	65p. 'Holland' Type Submarine, 1901	1·10	1·10
		a. Perf 15½×15 (22 Oct)	1·95	1·95
Set of 4			3·50	3·50
Set of 4 Gutter Pairs			7·00	
First Day Cover (Philatelic Bureau)				3·75
First Day Cover (Portsmouth)				3·75
Presentation Pack (PO Pack No. 322)			16·00	
PHQ Cards (set of 4) (230)			1·20	4·00

1522 AEC Regent III RT Type, Bristol KSW5G Open-top, AEC Routemaster and Bristol Lodekka FSF6G

1523 Bristol Lodekka FSF6G, Leyland Titan PD3/4, Leyland Atlantean PDR1/1 and Daimler Fleetline CRG6LX-33

1524 Daimler Fleetline CRG6LX-33, MCW Metrobus DR102/43, Leyland Olympian ONLXB/1R and Dennis Trident

(b) Flags. Ordinary gum. Perf 14½.

MS2206 92×97 mm. **1516** (1st) White Ensign; **1517** (1st) Union Jack; **1518** (1st) 'Jolly Roger' flown by HMS *Proteus* (submarine); **1519** (1st) Flag of Chief of Defence Staff (22 Oct) .... 5·25 5·25

a. Booklet pane. As No. **MS**2206 but larger, 152×96 mm.	5·25	
First Day Cover (Tallents House)		4·75
First Day Cover (Rosyth, Dunfermline)		5·25
Presentation Pack (PO Pack No. M06)	15·00	
PHQ Cards (set of 5) (PSM07)	1·50	6·00

(c) Self-adhesive. Die-cut P 15½×14 (No. 2207) or 14½ (others).

2207	**1513**	(1st) Swiftsure Class Submarine, 1973 (17 Apr)	30·00	30·00
		a. Booklet pane. No. 2207×2 plus No. 2040×4	70·00	
		ab. Booklet pane. Imperf	£3750	
2208	**1516**	(1st) White Ensign (22 Oct)	7·00	7·00
		a. Booklet pane. Nos. 2208/9 plus No. 2040×4	15·00	
		ab. Booklet pane. Imperf		
2209	**1518**	(1st) Jolly Roger flown by HMS *Proteus* (submarine) (22 Oct)	7·00	7·00

The five PHQ cards depict the four designs and the complete miniature sheet, **MS**2206.

Nos. 2202a/5a were only issued in the £6·76 'Unseen and Unheard' booklet, No. DX27, and Nos. 2207/9 only come from two different £1·62 self-adhesive booklets, Nos. PM2 and PM4.

Type **1516** was re-issued on 21 June 2005 in sheets of 20, printed in lithography by Cartor and sold at £6·55, containing four vertical rows of five stamps alternated with half stamp-size printed labels showing signal flags (LS25). These sheets with personalised photographs were available at £14·95 from the Royal Mail.

It was subsequently issued, printed in lithography, perf 14½, in booklets DX35 and DX41 (see No. 2581).

Type **1517** was re-issued on 27 July 2004 in sheets of 20, printed in lithography by Walsall and sold at £6·15, containing vertical strips of five stamps alternated with half stamp-size printed labels (LS20). These sheets with personalised photographs were available at £14·95 from the Royal Mail in Edinburgh.

It was subsequently issued, printed in lithography, perf 14½, in booklet DX41 (see No. 2805).

Type **1518** was subsequently issued, printed in lithography, perf 14½, in booklet DX47 (see No. 2970).

(Des M. English. Litho Questa)

2001 (15 May). *150th Anniversary of First Double-decker Bus.* MULTICOLOUR 'All-over' phosphor. Perf 14½×14.

2210	**1520**	(1st) Leyland X2 Open-top, London General B Type, Leyland Titan TD1 and AEC Regent 1	1·00	1·00
		a. Horiz strip of 5. Nos. 2210/14..........	4·50	4·50
		ab. Imperf (horiz strip of 5)	£4800	
		b. Grey omitted..	—	
2211	**1521**	(1st) AEC Regent 1, Daimler COG5, Utility Guy Arab Mk II and AEC Regent III RT Type........................	1·00	1·00
2212	**1522**	(1st) AEC Regent III RT Type, Bristol KSW5G Open-top, AEC Routemaster and Bristol Lodekka FSF6G	1·00	1·00
		a. Grey omitted..	—	
2213	**1523**	(1st) Bristol Lodekka FSF6G, Leyland Titan PD3/4, Leyland Atlantean PDR1/1 and Daimler Fleetline CRG6LX-33	1·00	1·00
		a. Grey omitted..	—	
2214	**1524**	(1st) Daimler Fleetline CRG6LX-33, MCW Metrobus DR102/43, Leyland Olympian ONLXB/1R and Dennis Trident	1·00	1·00
		a. Grey omitted..	—	
Set of 5			4·50	4·50
Gutter Strip of 10			8·50	
First Day Cover (Philatelic Bureau)				4·75
First Day Cover (Covent Garden, London WC2)				4·75
Presentation Pack (PO Pack No. 323)			9·00	
PHQ Cards (set of 6) (231)			1·80	5·50
MS2215 120×105 mm. Nos. 2210/14			6·00	6·00
First Day Cover (Philatelic Bureau)				7·50
First Day Cover (Covent Garden, London WC2)				7·50

Nos. 2210/14 were printed together, *se-tenant*, in horizontal strips of five throughout the sheet. The illustrations of the first bus on No. 2210 and the last bus on No. 2214 continue onto the sheet margins.

In No. **MS**2215 the illustrations of the AEC Regent III RT Type and the Daimler Fleetline CRG6LX-33 appear twice.

The six PHQ cards show the six stamps and **MS**2215.

1525 Toque Hat by Pip Hackett

1526 Butterfly Hat by Dai Rees

1527 Top Hat by Stephen Jones

1528 Spiral Hat by Philip Treacy

(Des Rose Design from photos by N. Knight. Litho Enschedé)

2001 (19 June). *Fashion Hats.* |MULTI COLOUR| 'All-over' phosphor. Perf 14½.

2216	**1525**	(1st) Toque Hat by Pip Hackett	1·00	1·00
2217	**1526**	(E) Butterfly Hat by Dai Rees	1·50	1·50
2218	**1527**	45p. Top Hat by Stephen Jones	90	90
2219	**1528**	65p. Spiral Hat by Philip Treacy	1·10	1·10
	Set of 4		4·00	4·00
	Set of 4 Gutter Pairs		8·00	
	First Day Cover (Tallents House)			4·25
	First Day Cover (Ascot)			4·25
	Presentation Pack (PO Pack No. 324)		4·50	
	PHQ Cards (*set of 4*) (232)		1·50	4·50

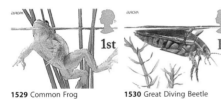

1529 Common Frog   **1530** Great Diving Beetle

1531 Three-Spined Stickleback

1532 Southern Hawker Dragonfly

(Des J. Gibbs. Gravure De La Rue)

2001 (10 July). *Europa. Pond Life.* |MULTI COLOUR| Two phosphor bands. Perf 15×14.

2220	**1529**	(1st) Common Frog	1·00	1·00
2221	**1530**	(E) Great Diving Beetle	1·50	1·50
2222	**1531**	45p. Three-Spined Stickleback	90	1·00
2223	**1532**	65p. Southern Hawker Dragonfly	1·10	1·20
	Set of 4		4·00	4·00
	Set of 4 Gutter Pairs		8·00	
	First Day Cover (Tallents House)			4·75
	First Day Cover (Oundle, Peterborough)			5·00
	Presentation Pack (PO Pack No. 325)		5·00	
	PHQ Cards (*set of 4*) (233)		1·50	4·50

The 1st and E values incorporate the 'EUROPA' emblem. The bluish silver on all four values is in Iriodin ink and was used as a background for those parts of the design below the water line.

1533 Policeman

1534 Clown

1535 Mr Punch

1536 Judy

1537 Beadle

1538 Crocodile

(Des K. Bernstein from puppets by Bryan Clarkez)

2001 (4 Sept). *Punch and Judy Show Puppets.* |MULTI COLOUR| Two phosphor bands. Perf 14×15.

(a) Gravure Walsall. Ordinary gum.

2224	**1533**	(1st) Policeman	1·00	1·00
		a. Horiz strip of 6. Nos. 2224/9	5·50	5·50
2225	**1534**	(1st) Clown	1·00	1·00
2226	**1535**	(1st) Mr Punch	1·00	1·00
2227	**1536**	(1st) Judy	1·00	1·00
2228	**1537**	(1st) Beadle	1·00	1·00
2229	**1538**	(1st) Crocodile	1·00	1·00
	Set of 6		5·50	5·50
	Gutter Block of 12		11·00	
	First Day Cover (Tallents House)			6·25
	First Day Cover (Blackpool)			6·50
	Presentation Pack (PO Pack No. 326)		6·00	
	PHQ Cards (*set of 6*) (234)		1·80	6·30

(b) Gravure Questa. Self-adhesive. Die-cut Perf 14×15½.

2230	**1535**	(1st) Mr Punch (4 Sept)	7·00	7·00
		a. Booklet pane. Nos. 2230/1 plus No. 2040×4	15·00	
2231	**1536**	(1st) Judy (4 Sept)	7·00	7·00

Nos. 2224/9 were printed together, *se-tenant*, as horizontal strips of 6 in sheets of 60 (6×10).

Nos. 2230/1 were only issued in £1·62 stamp booklets, No. PM3.

Imperforate strips of 6 with alternative background colours to 2224, 2228 and 2229 are of proof status (*Price* £3000).

CHEMISTRY
Nobel Prize 100th Anniversary
1539 Carbon 60 Molecule (Chemistry)

ECONOMIC SCIENCES
Nobel Prize 100th Anniversary
1540 Globe (Economic Sciences)

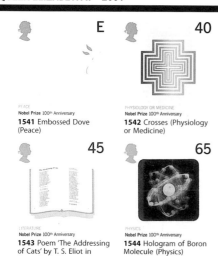

PEACE
Nobel Prize 100th Anniversary
1541 Embossed Dove
(Peace)

PHYSIOLOGY OR MEDICINE
Nobel Prize 100th Anniversary
1542 Crosses (Physiology
or Medicine)

LITERATURE
Nobel Prize 100th Anniversary
1543 Poem 'The Addressing
of Cats' by T. S. Eliot in
Open Book (Literature)

PHYSICS
Nobel Prize 100th Anniversary
1544 Hologram of Boron
Molecule (Physics)

(Des P. Vermier. Eng Ing Madle (1st). Litho and silk-screen ptg (2nd), litho and recess (1st), litho and embossed (E), litho (45p.), litho and hologram (65p.) Enschedé)

2001 (2 Oct). *Centenary of Nobel Prizes.* |MULTI COLOUR| One side phosphor band (2nd) or phosphor frame (others). Perf 14½.

2232	**1539**	(2nd) Carbon 60 Molecule (Chemistry) ...	90	90
2233	**1540**	(1st) Globe (Economic Sciences)...............	1·00	1·00
2234	**1541**	(E) Embossed Dove (Peace)................	1·50	1·50
2235	**1542**	40p. Crosses (Physiology or Medicine)	1·50	1·50
2236	**1543**	45p. Poem 'The Addressing of Cats' by T. S. Eliot in Open Book (Literature)	2·00	2·00
2237	**1544**	65p. Hologram of Boron Molecule (Physics)	2·50	2·50
Set of 6		....	8·50	8·50
Set of 6 Gutter Pairs		....	17·00	
First Day Cover (Tallents House)		....		9·00
First Day Cover (Cambridge)		....		9·00
Presentation Pack (PO Pack No. 327)		......	15·00	
PHQ Cards (set of 6) (235)		....	1·80	9·75

The grey-black on No. 2232 is printed in thermochromic ink which temporarily changes to pale grey when exposed to heat. The centre of No. 2235 is coated with a eucalyptus scent.

Trials, differing slightly from the issued stamps, are known for all values.

No. 2237 has been reported completely imperforate, its status is unknown

1545 Robins with Snowman

1546 Robins on Bird Table

1547 Robins skating on Bird Bath

1548 Robins with Christmas Pudding

1549 Robins in Paper Chain Nest

(Des A. Robins and H. Brown. Gravure De La Rue)

2001 (6 Nov). *Christmas. Robins.* Self-adhesive. |MULTI COLOUR| One centre phosphor band (2nd) or two phosphor bands (others). Die-cut perf 14½.

2238	**1545**	(2nd) Robins with Snowman.............	90	90
		a. Booklet pane. No. 2238×24	16·00	
		b. Imperf (pair)............................	£600	
2239	**1546**	(1st) Robins on Bird Table	1·00	1·00
		a. Booklet pane. No. 2239×12	11·00	
2240	**1547**	(E) Robins skating on Bird Bath	1·50	1·50
2241	**1548**	45p. Robins with Christmas Pudding.....	1·00	1·10
2242	**1549**	65p. Robins in Paper Chain Nest..............	1·10	1·20
		a. Imperf (pair) (die-cut perforations and roulettes omitted)	£1100	
		ab. Imperf (pair) (die-cut perforations only omitted)..............................	£500	
		b. Imperf backing paper (pair) (roulettes omitted)	£225	
Set of 5		....	5·00	5·00
First Day Cover (Tallents House)		....		5·50
First Day Cover (Bethlehem, Llandeilo)		....		5·50
Presentation Pack (PO Pack No. 328)		....	6·00	
PHQ Cards (set of 5) (236)		....	1·50	5·50

Nos. 2238/40 were each printed in sheets of 50 with the surplus backing paper around each stamp retained and separated by gauge 9 roulettes.

The 1st value was re-issued on 30 September 2003 in sheets of 20 (sold at £6·15) printed in lithography instead of photogravure, each stamp accompanied by a stamp-size label showing a snowman (LS14). Sheets with personal photographs printed on the labels were available from Royal Mail, Edinburgh for £14·95 or photobooths at selected post offices and Safeway stores for £15.

The 2nd and 1st values were re-issued together on 1 November 2005 in sheets of 20, printed in lithography by Cartor (sold at £5·60), containing ten 2nd class and ten 1st class, each stamp accompanied by a label showing a snowman (LS27). Separate sheets of 20 2nd class and 20 1st class were available with personalised photographs at £9·95 (2nd) or £14·95 (1st) from Royal Mail.

No. 2238b shows both the die-cut perforations and the roulettes omitted. Stamps from booklet panes Nos. 2238a and 2239a differ from those in sheets by omitting the roulettes in the backing paper between each stamp. Instead there are roulettes after the first and then every alternate horizontal row to assist with the folding of the booklets.

Trials of (2nd) and (1st) stamps in alternative designs are known.

Year Pack 2001
2001 (6 Nov). Comprises Nos. 2178/2200, 2202/6, 2210/14, 2216/29 and 2232/42.
CP2242a Year Pack.. 70·00

Post Office Yearbook
2001 (6 Nov). Comprises Nos. 2178/96, **MS**2201/6, 2210/14, 2216/29 and 2232/42 in hardback book with slip case .... 48·00

1550 'How the Whale got his Throat'

1551 'How the Camel got his Hump'

1552 'How the Rhinoceros got his Skin'

1553 'How the Leopard got his Spots'

1554 'The Elephant's Child'

1555 'The Sing-Song of Old Man Kangaroo'

1556 'The Beginning of the Armadillos'

1557 'The Crab that played with the Sea'

1558 'The Cat that walked by Himself'

1559 'The Butterfly that stamped'

(Des I. Cohen. Gravure Walsall)

2002 (15 Jan). *Centenary of Publication of Rudyard Kipling's Just So Stories.* Self-adhesive. Two phosphor bands. Die-cut Perf 15×14.

2243	**1550**	(1st) 'How the Whale got his Throat'......	1·00	1·00
		a. Sheetlet. Nos. 2243/52........................	9·00	9·00
2244	**1551**	(1st) 'How the Camel got his Hump'......	1·00	1·00
2245	**1552**	(1st) 'How the Rhinoceros got his Skin'..	1·00	1·00
2246	**1553**	(1st) 'How the Leopard got his Spots'....	1·00	1·00
2247	**1554**	(1st) 'The Elephant's Child'.....................	1·00	1·00
2248	**1555**	(1st) 'The Sing-Song of Old Man Kangaroo'....................................	1·00	1·00
2249	**1556**	(1st) 'The Beginning of the Armadillos'...................................	1·00	1·00
2250	**1557**	(1st) 'The Crab that played with the Sea'..	1·00	1·00
2251	**1558**	(1st) 'The Cat that walked by Himself'...	1·00	1·00
2252	**1559**	(1st) 'The Butterfly that stamped'...........	1·00	1·00
Set of 10...			9·00	9·00
First Day Cover (Tallents House)..				9·25
First Day Cover (Burwash, Etchingham)...............................				9·25
Presentation Pack (PO Pack No. 330)....................................			10·00	
PHQ Cards (set of 10) (237)..			3·00	11·00

Nos. 2243/52 were printed together in sheetlets of ten (5×2), with the surplus self-adhesive paper around each stamp retained.

No. 2243a was in the form of an unfolded booklet with vertical roulettes between columns 2/3 and 4/5 and the backing design beining an illustrated booklet cover. However, since it was sold unfolded, we treat it as asheetlet rather than a booklet.

1560 Queen Elizabeth II, 1952 (Dorothy Wilding)

1561 Queen Elizabeth II, 1968 (Cecil Beaton)

1562 Queen Elizabeth II, 1978 (Lord Snowdon)

1563 Queen Elizabeth II, 1984 (Yousef Karsh)

1564 Queen Elizabeth II, 1996 (Tim Graham)

1565

(Des Kate Stephens. Gravure De La Rue)

2002 (6 Feb). *Golden Jubilee.* Studio portraits of Queen Elizabeth II by photographers named. One centre phosphor band (2nd) or two phosphor bands (others). W **1565** (sideways). Perf 14½×14.

2253	**1560**	(2nd) Queen Elizabeth II, 1952 (Dorothy Wilding).....................	90	90
		a. Watermark upright........................	3·00	3·00
		b. Booklet pane. Nos. 2253a/6a with margins all round..............................	7·50	
2254	**1561**	(1st) Queen Elizabeth II, 1968 (Cecil Beaton)............................	1·00	1·00
		a. Watermark upright........................	1·35	1·35
		b. Booklet pane. Nos. 2254a/7a with margins all round..............................	8·00	
2255	**1562**	(E) Queen Elizabeth II, 1978 (Lord Snowdon).......................	1·50	1·50
		a. Watermark upright........................	1·75	1·35
2256	**1563**	45p. Queen Elizabeth II, 1984 (Yousef Karsh).........................	1·00	1·10
		a. Watermark upright........................	1·35	1·35
2257	**1564**	65p. Queen Elizabeth II, 1996 (Tim Graham)..........................	1·10	1·10
		a. Watermark upright........................	3·00	3·00
Set of 5..			5·00	5·00
Set of 5 Gutter Pairs...			10·00	
First Day Cover (Tallents House)...				5·25
First Day Cover (Windsor)...				5·50
Presentation Pack (PO Pack No. 331)...................................			7·00	
PHQ Cards (set of 5) (238)...			1·50	5·75

The turquoise-green is used as an underlay for the black colour on all five values.

Nos. 2253a/7a were only issued in the £7·29 'A Glorious Accesion' booklet, No DX28.

Trials, including dates and with values in a different typeface, are known for all values.

1566

(Des M. Farrar-Bell (2nd), Enid Marx (1st). Gravure Enschedé)

2002 (6 Feb). As T **154/5** (Wilding definitive of 1952-54), but with service indicator as T **1566**. One centre phosphor band (2nd) or two phosphor bands (1st). W **1565**. Uncoated paper. Perf 15×14 (with one elliptical hole in each vertical side).

2258	**1566**	(2nd) carmine-red....................................	1·10	1·10
		Ea. Watermark diagonal...........................	1·95	1·95
		b. Booklet pane. Nos. 2258×4, 2258Ea and 2259×4 with centre blank label and margins all round..........	7·50	
2259	–	(1st) green..	1·20	1·20
Set of 2..			2·10	2·10
First Day Cover (No. 2258b) (Tallents House)....................				7·50
First Day Cover (No. 2258b) (Windsor)...............................				7·50

Nos. 2258/9 were only issued in the £7·29 'A Gracious Accession' booklet, No. DX28.

No. 2258b contains a block of 8, four of each value, with a blank central label, plus an additional 2nd value shown to the left at such an angle so as to produce a diagonal watermark. First day cover postmarks were as Nos. 2253/7.

1567 Rabbits ('a new baby')

1568 'LOVE'

1569 Aircraft Sky-writing 'hello'

1570 Bear pulling Potted Topiary Tree (Moving Home)

1571 Flowers ('best wishes')

(Des I. Bilbey (Nos. 2260, 2264), A. Kitching (No. 2261), Hoop Associates (No. 2262) and G. Percy (No. 2263))

2002 (5 Mar)–**03**. *Greetings Stamps. 'Occasions'.* |MULTI COLOUR| Two phosphor bands.

(a) *Litho Questa. Ordinary gum. Perf* 15×14.

2260	**1567**	(1st) Rabbits ('a new baby')	1·10	1·10
2261	**1568**	(1st) 'LOVE'	1·10	1·10
2262	**1569**	(1st) Aircraft Sky-writing 'hello'	1·10	1·10
2263	**1570**	(1st) Bear pulling Potted Topiary Tree (Moving Home)	1·10	1·10
2264	**1571**	(1st) ('best wishes')	1·10	1·10
Set of 5			5·00	5·00
Set of 5 Gutter Pairs			10·00	
First Day Cover (Tallents House)				5·25
First Day Cover (Merry Hill, Wolverhampton)				5·50
Presentation Pack (PO Pack No. M07)			5·25	
PHQ Cards (set of 5) (PSM08)			1·50	6·00

(b) *Gravure Questa. Self-adhesive. Die-cut Perf* 15×14.

2264a	**1569**	(1st) Aircraft Sky-writing 'hello' (4.3.03)..	3·00	3·00
		ab. Booklet pane. No. 2264a×2 plus No. 2295×4		7·50

Nos. 2260/4 were re-issued on 23 April 2002 in sheets of 20 with half stamp-size labels, with either the five designs *se-tenant* with greetings on the labels (LS7, *sold at* £5·95) or in sheets of one design with personal photographs on the labels (*sold at* £12·95). These stamps, printed by Questa in lithography, were perforated 14 instead of 15×14.

Type **1569** was re-issued in sheets of 20 with half stamp-size *se-tenant* labels all printed in lithography as follows: on 30 January 2004 for Hong Kong Stamp Expo (LS17, Walsall), on 21 April 2005 for Pacific Explorer 2005 World Stamp Expo (LS24, Walsall, P 14), on 25 May 2006 for Washington 2006 International Stamp Exhibition (LS30, Cartor, P 14), on 14 November 2006 for Belgica 2006 International Stamp Exhibition (LS36, Cartor, P 14), on 5 August 2008 for Beijing 2008 Olympic Expo (LS48, Cartor, P 14), on 3 August 2009 for Thaipex 09 Stamp Exhibition (LS64, Cartor, P 14), on 21 October 2009 for Italia 2009 International Stamp Exhibition (LS66, Cartor, P 14) and on 4 December 2009 for MonacoPhil International Stamp Exhibition (LS69, Cartor, P 14).

No. 2264a was only issued in £1·62 stamp booklets, No. PM8, in which the surplus self-adhesive paper around each stamp was removed.

1576 Broadstairs, Kent

1577 St Abb's Head, Scottish Borders

1578 Dunster Beach, Somerset

1579 Newquay Beach, Cornwall

1580 Portrush, County Antrim

1581 Sand-spit, Conwy

(Des R. Cooke. Litho Walsall)

2002 (19 Mar). *British Coastlines.* |MULTI COLOUR| Two phosphor bands. Perf 14½.

2265	**1572**	27p. Studland Bay, Dorset	50	50
		a. Block of 10. Nos. 2265/74	4·50	4·50
		b. Silver omitted (block of 10)	£9500	
2266	**1573**	27p. Luskentyre, South Harris	50	50
2267	**1574**	27p. Cliffs, Dover, Kent	50	50
2268	**1575**	27p. Padstow Harbour, Cornwall	50	50
2269	**1576**	27p. Broadstairs, Kent	50	50
2270	**1577**	27p. St Abb's Head, Scottish Borders	50	50
2271	**1578**	27p. Dunster Beach, Somerset	50	50
2272	**1579**	27p. Newquay Beach, Cornwall	50	50
2273	**1580**	27p. Portrush, County Antrim	50	50
2274	**1581**	27p. Sand-spit, Conwy	50	50
Set of 10			4·50	4·50
Gutter Block of 20			9·00	
First Day Cover (Tallents House)				4·75
First Day Cover (Poolewe, Achnasheen)				5·00
Presentation Pack (PO Pack No. 332)			5·00	
PHQ Cards (set of 10) (239)			3·00	6·00

Nos. 2265/74 were printed together, *se-tenant*, in blocks of ten (5×2) throughout the sheet.

1572 Studland Bay, Dorset

1573 Luskentyre, South Harris

1574 Cliffs, Dover, Kent

1575 Padstow Harbour, Cornwall

1582 Slack Wire Act

1583 Lion Tamer

1584 Trick Tri-cyclists

1585 Krazy Kar

1586 Equestrienne

(Des R. Fuller. Gravure Questa)

2002 (10 Apr*). *Europa. Circus.* One centre phosphor band (2nd) or two phosphor bands (others). Perf 14½.

2275	**1582**	(2nd) Slack Wire Act	90	90
2276	**1583**	(1st) Lion Tamer	1·00	1·00
		a. Imperf (vert pair)	£2500	
2277	**1584**	(E) Trick Tri-cyclists	1·50	1·50
		a. Imperf (pair)	£3000	
2278	**1585**	45p. Krazy Kar	1·00	1·10
2279	**1586**	65p. Equestrienne	1·10	1·20
Set of 5			5·00	5·00
Set of 5 Gutter Pairs			10·00	
First Day Cover (Tallents House)				5·25
First Day Cover (Clowne, Chesterfield)				5·50
Presentation Pack (PO Pack No. 333)			5·75	
PHQ Cards (set of 5) (240)			1·50	5·75

The 1st and E values incorporate the 'EUROPA' emblem.

* Due to the funeral of the Queen Mother, the issue of Nos. 2275/9 was delayed from 9 April, the date which appears on first day covers.

1587 Queen Elizabeth the Queen Mother

(Des J. Gorham from photographs by N. Parkinson (1st), Dorothy Wilding (E), B. Park (45p.), Rita Martin (65p.). Gravure De La Rue)

2002 (25 Apr). *Queen Elizabeth the Queen Mother Commemoration.* Vert designs as T **955/8** with changed face values and showing both the Queen's head and frame in black as in T **1587.** Two phosphor bands. Perf 14×15.

2280	**1587**	(1st) Queen Elizabeth the Queen Mother	1·00	1·00
2281	**956**	(E) Queen Elizabeth	1·50	1·50
2282	**957**	45p. Elizabeth, Duchess of York	1·00	1·10
2283	**958**	65p. Lady Elizabeth Bowes-Lyon	1·10	1·20
Set of 4			4·25	4·25
Set of 4 Gutter Pairs			8·50	
First Day Cover (Tallents House)				4·50
First Day Cover (London SW1)				4·75
Presentation Pack (PO Pack No. M08)			4·75	

1588 Airbus A340-600 (2002)

1589 Concorde (1976)

1590 Trident (1964)

1591 VC10 (1964)

1592 Comet (1952)

(Des Roundel)

2002 (2 May). *50th Anniversary of Passenger Jet Aviation. Airliners.* One centre phosphor band (2nd) or two phosphor bands (others). Perf 14½.

(a) Gravure De La Rue. Ordinary gum.

2284	**1588**	(2nd) Airbus A340-600 (2002)	90	90
2285	**1589**	(1st) Concorde (1976)	1·00	1·00
2286	**1590**	(E) Trident (1964)	1·50	1·50
2287	**1591**	45p. VC10 (1964)	1·50	1·50
2288	**1592**	65p. Comet (1952)	1·80	1·80
Set of 5			6·00	6·00
Set of 5 Gutter Pairs			12·00	
First Day Cover (Tallents House)				6·50
First Day Cover (Heathrow Airport, London)				7·00
Presentation Pack (PO Pack No. 334)			7·00	
MS2289 120×105 mm. Nos. 2284/8			7·00	7·00
First Day Cover (Tallents House)				7·50
First Day Cover (Heathrow Airport, London)				7·50
PHQ Cards (set of 6) (241)			1·80	12·00

(b) Gravure Questa. Self-adhesive. Die-cut Perf 14½.

2290	**1589**	(1st) Concorde (1976)	3·00	3·00
		a. Booklet pane. No. 2040×4 and No. 2290×2	6·25	6·25

No. 2290 was only issued in £1·62 stamp booklets, No. PM5. See also No. 2897.

1593 Crowned Lion with Shield of St George

1594 Top Left Quarter of English Flag, and Football

1595 Top Right Quarter of English Flag, and Football

1596 Bottom Left Quarter of English Flag, and Football

1597 Bottom Right Quarter of English Flag, and Football

(Des Sedley Place (No. 2291), H. Brown (No. **MS**2292). Gravure Walsall)

2002 (21 May). *World Cup Football Championship, Japan and Korea.* Two phosphor bands. Perf 14½×**14.**

(a) Ordinary gum.

2291	**1593**	(1st) Crowned Lion with Shield of St George	1·25	1·25
		Gutter Pair	2·50	

MS2292 145×74 mm. No. 2291; **1594** (1st) Top Left Quarter of English Flag, and Football; **1595** (1st) Top Right Quarter of English Flag, and Football; **1596** (1st) Bottom Left Quarter of English Flag, and Football; **1597** (1st) Bottom Right Quarter of English Flag, and Football. Perf 14½ (square) or

15×14 (horiz)...	5·00	5·00
First Day Cover (**MS**2292) (Tallents House)		5·50
First Day Cover (**MS**2292) (Wembley)........................		5·50
Presentation Pack (**MS**2292) (P. O. Pack No. 335)	5·75	
PHQ Cards (set of 6) (242)................................	1·80	7·50

(b) Self-adhesive. Die-cut Perf 15×14.

2293	**1594**	(1st) Top Left Quarter of English Flag, and Football.............................	2·50	2·50
		a. Booklet pane. Nos. 2293/4 plus No. 2040×4	6·25	6·25
2294	**1595**	(1st) Top Right Quarter of English Flag, and Football.............................	2·50	2·50

The complete miniature sheet is shown on one of the PHQ cards with the others depicting individual stamps from No. **MS**2292 and No. 2291.

Nos. 2293/4 were only issued in £1·62 stamp booklets, No. PM6.

Stamps as Type **1597** also exist in sheets of 20 with *se-tenant* labels, printed in lithography by Questa (LS8). Such sheets, with the labels showing match scenes or supporters, were available at £5·95 from philatelic outlets, or with personal photographs at £12·95 from Royal Mail in Edinburgh.

Stamps as Type **1593** but with 'WORLD CUP 2002' inscription omitted were issued on 17 May 2007 in sheets of 20 with *se-tenant* labels showing scenes from Wembley Stadium, printed in lithography by Cartor (LS39).

For Nos. 2295/8 see Decimal Machin Definitives section.

1598 Swimming

1599 Running

1600 Cycling

1601 Long Jumping

1602 Wheelchair Racing

(Des Madeleine Bennett. Gravure Enschedé)

2002 (16 July). *17th Commonwealth Games, Manchester.* |MULTI COLOUR| One side phosphor band (2nd) or two phosphor bands (others). Perf 14½.

2299	**1598**	(2nd) Swimming...............................	90	90
2300	**1599**	(1st) Running	1·00	1·00
2301	**1600**	(E) Cycling......................................	1·50	1·50
2302	**1601**	47p. Long Jumping	1·20	1·30
2303	**1602**	68p. Wheelchair Racing................	1·40	1·50
Set of 5...			5·50	5·50
Set of 5 Gutter Pairs			11·00	
First Day Cover (Tallents House)				6·00
First Day Cover (Manchester)				6·00
Presentation Pack (PO Pack No. 336)..................			6·00	
PHQ Cards (set of 5) (243)...............................			1·50	6·75

On Nos. 2300/3 the phosphor bands appear at the right and the centre of each stamp.

1603 Tinkerbell

1604 Wendy, John and Michael Darling in front of Big Ben

1605 Crocodile and Alarm Clock **1606** Captain Hook

1607 Peter Pan

(Des Tutssels. Gravure De La Rue)

2002 (20 Aug). *150th Anniversary of Great Ormond Street Children's Hospital. Peter Pan by Sir James Barrie.* |MULTI COLOUR| One centre phosphor band (2nd) or two phosphor bands (others). Perf 15×14.

2304	**1603**	(2nd) Tinkerbell..............................	90	90
2305	**1604**	(1st) Wendy, John and Michael Darling in front of Big Ben...........	1·00	1·00
2306	**1605**	(E) Crocodile and Alarm Clock..............	1·50	1·50
2307	**1606**	47p. Captain Hook.........................	1·20	1·30
2308	**1607**	68p. Peter Pan...............................	1·40	1·50
Set of 5			5·50	5·50
Set of 5 Gutter Pairs			11·00	
First Day Cover (Tallents House)........................				6·00
First Day Cover (Hook)				6·00
Presentation Pack (PO Pack No. 337)..................			6·00	
PHQ Cards (set of 5) (244)................................			1·50	6·75

1608 Millennium Bridge, 2001 **1609** Tower Bridge, 1894

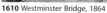

1610 Westminster Bridge, 1864 **1611** *Blackfriars Bridge, c1800* (William Marlow)

1612 *London Bridge, c1670* (Wenceslaus Hollar)

(Des Sarah Davies and R. Maude)

2002 (10 Sept). *Bridges of London.* |MULTI COLOUR| One centre phosphor band (2nd) or two phosphor bands (others).

(a) Litho Questa. Ordinary gum. Perf 15×14.

2309	**1608**	(2nd) Millennium Bridge, 2001...................	90	90
2310	**1609**	(1st) Tower Bridge, 1894	1·00	1·00

2311	**1610**	(E) Westminster Bridge, 1864	1·50	1·50
2312	**1611**	47p. Blackfriars Bridge, c1800	1·60	1·60
2313	**1612**	68p. London Bridge, c1670	1·80	1·80

Set of 5	6·00	6·00
Set of 5 Gutter Pairs	12·00	
First Day Cover (Tallents House)		6·25
First Day Cover (London SE1)		6·25
Presentation Pack (PO Pack No. 338)	30·00	
PHQ Cards (set of 5) (245)	1·50	7·00

(b) Gravure Questa. Self-adhesive. Die-cut Perf 15×14.

2314	**1609**	(1st) Tower Bridge, 1894	3·00
		a. Booklet pane. No. 2314×2, and	
		No. 2295×4	7·00

No. 2314 was only issued in £1·62 stamp booklets in which the surplus self-adhesive paper around each stamp was removed, No. PM7.

1613a Galaxies and Nebulae (*Illustration reduced. Actual size* 120×89 mm)

(Des Rose Design. Gravure Questa)

2002 (24 Sept). *Astronomy.* Sheet 120×89 mm. |MULTI COLOUR| Two phosphor bands. Perf 14½×14.

MS2315 **1613a** Galaxies and Nebulae (1st) Planetary nebula in Aquila; (1st) Seyfert 2 galaxy in Pegasus; (1st) Planetary nebula in Norma; (1st) Seyfert 2 galaxy in Circinus .... 4·00 4·00

a. Booklet pane. As No. **MS**2315, but larger, 150×95 mm	5·75
First Day Cover (Tallents House)	4·75
First Day Cover (Star, Glenrothes)	4·75
Presentation Pack (PO Pack No. 339)	11·00
PHQ Cards (set of 5) (246)	1·50 5·00

Booklet pane No. **MS**2315a comes from the £6·83 'Across the Universe' booklet No. DX29. The five PHQ cards depict the four designs and the complete miniature sheet.

1614 Green Pillar Box, 1857

1615 Horizontal Aperture Box, 1874

1616 Air Mail Box, 1934

1617 Double Aperture Box, 1939

1618 Modern Style Box, 1980

(Des Silk Pearce. Eng C. Slania. Recess and litho Enschedé)

2002 (8 Oct). *150th Anniversary of the First Pillar Box.* |MULTI COLOUR| One centre phosphor band (2nd) or two phosphor bands (others). Perf 14×14½.

2316	**1614**	(2nd) Green Pillar Box, 1857	90	90
2317	**1615**	(1st) Horizontal Aperture Box, 1874	80	80
2318	**1616**	(E) Air Mail Box, 1934	1·50	1·50
2319	**1617**	47p. Double Aperture Box, 1939	1·00	1·10
2320	**1618**	68p. Modern Style Box, 1980	1·20	1·30

Set of 5	5·00	5·00
Set of 5 Gutter Pairs	10·00	
First Day Cover (Tallents House)		5·25
First Day Cover (Bishops Caundle, Sherborne)		5·25
Presentation Pack (PO Pack No. 340)	5·25	
PHQ Cards (set of 5) (247)	1·50	5·50

1619 Blue Spruce Star

1620 Holly

1621 Ivy

1622 Mistletoe

1623 Pine Cone

(Des Rose Design. Gravure De La Rue)

2002 (5 Nov). *Christmas. Self-adhesive.* |MULTI COLOUR| One centre phosphor band (2nd) or two phosphor bands (others). Die-cut Perf 14½×14.

2321	**1619**	(2nd) Blue Spruce Star	90	90
		a. Booklet pane. No. 2321×24	16·00	
		b. Imperf (pair)	80·00	
2322	**1620**	(1st) Holly	1·00	1·00
		a. Booklet pane. No. 2322×12	11·00	
		b. Imperf (pair)	£250	
2323	**1621**	(E) Ivy	1·50	1·50
2324	**1622**	47p. Mistletoe	1·20	1·20
2325	**1623**	68p. Pine Cone	1·40	1·40

Set of 5	5·00	5·00
First Day Cover (Tallents House)		5·25
First Day Cover (Bethlehem, Llandeilo)		5·25
Presentation Pack (PO Pack No. 341)	5·25	
PHQ Cards (set of 5) (248)	1·50	5·75

Nos. 2321/5 were each printed in sheets of 50, with the surplus backing paper around each stamp retained, separated by gauge 9 roulettes. Nos. 2321b and 2322b show both the die-cut perforations and the roulettes omitted.

Year Pack 2002

2002 (5 Nov). Comprises Nos. 2243/57, 2260/4, 2265/88, **MS**2292, 2299/313 and **MS**2315/25.

CP2325a Year Pack	65·00

Post Office Yearbook

2002 (5 Nov). Comprises Nos. 2243/57, 2260/4, 2265/88, 2291/2, 2299/313 and **MS**2315/25 in hardback book with slip case .... 48·00

The Wilding definitives collection I ~ 1952 - 1953

1623a

(Des Rose Design. Gravure De La Rue)

2002 (5 Dec). *50th Anniv of Wilding Definitives* (1st issue). Sheet 124×70 mm, printed on pale cream. One centre phosphor band (2nd) or two phosphor bands (others). W **1565**. Perf 15×14 (with one elliptical hole in each vertical side).

MS2326 **1623a** 1p. orange-red; 2p. ultramarine; 5p. red-brown; (2nd) carmine-red; (1st) green; 33p. brown; 37p. magenta; 47p. bistre-brown; 50p. green and label showing national emblems .... 5·00 5·00
a. Imperf £8000
First Day Cover (Tallents House) .... 5·00
First Day Cover (Windsor) .... 5·00
Presentation Pack (PO Pack No. 59) .... 25·00
PHQ Cards (set of 5) (D21) .... 70 5·00
The five PHQ cards depict the 1st, 2nd, 33p., 37p. and 47p. stamps.

1624 Barn Owl landing

1625 Barn Owl with folded Wings and Legs down

1626 Barn Owl with extended Wings and Legs down

1627 Barn Owl in Flight with Wings lowered

1628 Barn Owl in Flight with Wings raised

1629 Kestrel with Wings folded

1630 Kestrel with Wings fully extended upwards

1631 Kestrel with Wings horizontal

1632 Kestrel with wings partly extended downwards

1633 Kestrel with wings fully extended downwards

(Des J. Gibbs from photographs by S. Dalton. Litho Walsall)

2003 (14 Jan). *Birds of Prey.* MULTICOLOUR Phosphor background. Perf 14½.

2327	**1624**	(1st) Barn Owl landing.................................	1·00	1·00
		a. Block of 10. Nos. 2327/36	9·00	9·00
		ab. Brownish grey and phosphor omitted	£2250	
2328	**1625**	(1st) Barn Owl with folded Wings and Legs down	1·00	1·00
2329	**1626**	(1st) Barn Owl with extended Wings and Legs down	1·00	1·00
2330	**1627**	(1st) Barn Owl in Flight with Wings lowered	1·00	1·00
2331	**1628**	(1st) Barn Owl in Flight with Wings raised	1·00	1·00
2332	**1629**	(1st) Kestrel with Wings folded	1·00	1·00
2333	**1630**	(1st) Kestrel with Wings fully extended upwards	1·00	1·00
2334	**1631**	(1st) Kestrel with Wings horizontal.........	1·00	1·00
2335	**1632**	(1st) Kestrel with wings partly extended downwards	1·00	1·00
2336	**1633**	(1st) Kestrel with wings fully extended downwards	1·00	1·00
Set of 10			9·00	9·00
Gutter Block of 20			18·00	
First Day Cover (Tallents House)				9·25
First Day Cover (Hawkshead Ambleside).....................				9·25
Presentation Pack (PO Pack No. 343).........................			9·50	
PHQ Cards (set of 10) (249)			3·00	11·00

Nos. 2327/36 were printed together, *se-tenant*, in blocks of ten (5×2) throughout the sheet.

No. 2327ab shows the owl white on Nos. 2327/31, and the face value with Queen's head omitted on Nos. 2332/6.

1634 'Gold star, See me, Playtime'

1635 'I♥U, XXXX, S.W.A.L.K.'

1636 'Angel, Poppet, Little terror'

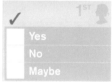

1637 'Yes, No, Maybe'

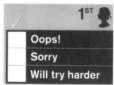

1638 'Oops!, Sorry, Will try harder'

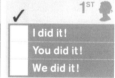

1639 'I did it!, You did it!, We did it!'

(Des UNA, Sara Wiegand and M. Exon. Litho Questa)

2003 (4 Feb). *Greetings Stamps. Occasions.* MULTICOLOUR Two phosphor bands. Perf 14½×14.

2337	**1634**	(1st) 'Gold star, See me, Playtime'............	1·00	1·00
		a. Block of 6. Nos. 2337/42..................	5·50	5·50
		b. Imperf (block of 6)	£3750	
2338	**1635**	(1st) 'I♥U, XXXX, S.W.A.L.K.'.................	1·00	1·00
2339	**1636**	(1st) 'Angel, Poppet, Little terror'.............	1·00	1·00
2340	**1637**	(1st) 'Yes, No, Maybe'.............................	1·00	1·00

2341	**1638**	(1st) 'Oops!, Sorry, Will try harder'	1·00	1·00
2342	**1639**	(1st) 'I did it!, You did it!, We did it!'	1·00	1·00

Set of 6 .... 5·50 5·50
Gutter Block of 12 .... 11·00
First Day Cover (Tallents House) .... 5·75
First Day Cover (Merry Hill, Wolverhampton) .... 5·75
Presentation Pack (PO Pack No. M09) .... 6·00
PHQ Cards (*set of 6*) (PSM09) .... 1·80 6·25

Nos. 2337/42 were printed together, *se-tenant,* in blocks of six (3×2) throughout the sheet.

Nos. 2337/42 were also issued in sheets of 20 (containing four of Nos. 2338 and 2340 and three each of the others) with *se-tenant* labels (LS12). Such sheets with the labels showing printed faces were available at £5·95 from philatelic outlets, or with personalised photographs at £14·95 from Royal Mail in Edinburgh.

1640 Completing the Genome Jigsaw

1641 Ape with Moustache and Scientist

1642 DNA Snakes and Ladders

1643 'Animal Scientists'

1644 Genome Crystal Ball

(Des Williams Murray Hamm and P. Brookes. Litho Enschedé)

2003 (25 Feb). *50th Anniversary of Discovery of DNA.* |MULTI COLOUR| One centre phosphor band (2nd) or two phosphor bands (others). Perf 14½.

2343	**1640**	(2nd) Completing the Genome Jigsaw	90	90
		a. Booklet pane. Nos. 2343/4, each×2, with margins all round	3·50	
2344	**1641**	(1st) Ape with Moustache and Scientist	1·00	1·00
2345	**1642**	(E) DNA Snakes and Ladders	1·50	1·50
		a. Booklet pane. No. 2345×4 with margins all round	5·25	
2346	**1643**	47p. Animal Scientists'	1·30	1·40
2347	**1644**	68p. Genome Crystal Ball	1·50	1·60

Set of 5 .... 5·75 5·75
Set of 5 Gutter Pairs .... 11·50
First Day Cover (Tallents House) .... 6·25
First Day Cover (Cambridge) .... 6·50
Presentation Pack (PO Pack No. 344) .... 6·00
PHQ Cards (*set of 5*) (250) .... 1·50 6·25

Booklet panes Nos. 2343a and 2345a come from the £6·99 'Microcosmos' booklet, No. DX30

1645 Strawberry

1646 Potato

1647 Apple

1648 Red Pepper

1649 Pear

1650 Orange

1651 Tomato

1652 Lemon

1653 Brussels Sprout

1654 Aubergine

(Des johnson banks. Gravure Walsall)

2003 (25 Mar). *Fruit and Vegetables.* Self-adhesive. |MULTI COLOUR| Two phosphor bands. Perf 14½×14 die-cut (without teeth around protruding tops or bottoms of the designs).

2348	**1645**	(1st) Strawberry	1·00	1·00
		a. Sheetlet. Nos. 2348/57 and pane of decorative labels	9·00	
		ab. Imperf (block of 10)	£3500	
2349	**1646**	(1st) Potato	1·00	1·00
2350	**1647**	(1st) Apple	1·00	1·00
2351	**1648**	(1st) Red Pepper	1·00	1·00
2352	**1649**	(1st) Pear	1·00	1·00
2353	**1650**	(1st) Orange	1·00	1·00
2354	**1651**	(1st) Tomato	1·00	1·00
2355	**1652**	(1st) Lemon	1·00	1·00
2356	**1653**	(1st) Brussels Sprout	1·00	1·00
2357	**1654**	(1st) Aubergine	1·00	1·00

Set of 10 .... 9·00 9·00
First Day Cover (Tallents House) .... 9·25
First Day Cover (Pear Tree, Derby) .... 9·25
Presentation Pack (PO Pack No. 345) .... 12·00
PHQ Cards (*set of 10*) (251) .... 3·00 10·50

Nos. 2348/57 were printed together in sheets of ten with the surplus self-adhesive paper around each stamp retained. The stamp pane is accompanied by a similar-sized pane of self-adhesive labels showing ears, eyes, mouths, hats, etc which are intended for the adornment of fruit and vegetables depicted. This pane is separated from the stamps by a line of roulettes.

Nos. 2348/57 were re-issued on 7th March 2006 in sheets of 20, containing two of each of the ten designs accompanied by *se-tenant* labels with speech bubbles and stickers showing eyes, hats, etc. in the sheet margin (LS29). These sheets were printed in lithography by Cartor and *sold for* £6·55.

No. 2355 was also available in sheets of 20 with personal photographs on the labels at £14·95 per sheet from Royal Mail, Edinburgh.

For Nos. 2357a/59 (Overseas Booklet Stamps) see Decimal Machin Definitives sections

1656 Amy Johnson (pilot) and Bi-plane

1657 Members of 1953 Everest Team

1658 Freya Stark (traveller and writer) and Desert

1659 Ernest Shackleton (Antarctic explorer) and Wreck of *Endurance*

1660 Francis Chichester (yachtsman) and *Gipsy Moth IV*

1661 Robert Falcon Scott (Antarctic explorer) and Norwegian Expedition at the Pole

(Des H. Brown)

2003 (29 Apr). *Extreme Endeavours* (*British Explorers*). |MULTI COLOUR| One centre phosphor band (2nd) or two phosphor bands (others). Perf 15×14½.

(a) Gravure Questa. Ordinary gum.

2360	**1656**	(2nd) Amy Johnson	90	90
2361	**1657**	(1st) Members of 1953 Everest Team	1·00	1·00
2362	**1658**	(E) Freya Stark	1·50	1·50
2363	**1659**	42p. Ernest Shackleton	1·00	1·00
2364	**1660**	47p. Francis Chichester	1·10	1·20
2365	**1661**	68p. Robert Falcon Scott	1·30	1·40
Set of 6			6·25	6·25
Set of 6 Gutter Pairs			12·50	
First Day Cover (Tallents House)				7·00
First Day Cover (Plymouth)				7·00
Presentation Pack (PO Pack No. 346)			7·25	
PHQ Cards (set of 6) (252)			1·80	6·50

(b) Gravure De La Rue. Self-adhesive. Die-cut Perf 14½.

2366	**1657**	(1st) Members of 1953 Everest Team	3·00	3·00
		a. Booklet pane. No. 2366×2 plus		
		No. 2295×4	7·50	

The phosphor bands on Nos. 2361/5 are at the centre and right of each stamp.

No. 2366 was only issued in £1·62 stamp booklets, No. PM9, in which the surplus self-adhesive paper around each stamp was removed.

Gummed perforated trials with alternative face values and/or designs are known.

The Wilding definitives collection II ~ 1953 - 1959

1661a

Des Rose Design. Gravure De La Rue)

2003 (20 May). *50th Anniversary of Wilding Definitives* (2nd issue). Sheet 124×70 mm, , printed on pale cream. One centre phosphor band (20p.) or two phosphor bands (others). W **1565**. Perf 15×14 (with one elliptical hole in each vertical side).

MS2367 **1661a** 4p. deep lilac; 8p. ultramarine; 10p. reddish purple; 20p. bright green; 28p. bronze-green; 34p. brown-purple; (E) chestnut; 42p. Prussian blue; 68p. grey-blue and label showing national emblems .... 4·50   4·75

a. Imperf		
First Day Cover (Tallents House)		5·50
First Day Cover (Windsor)		5·50
Presentation Pack (PO Pack No. 61)	9·00	

1662 Guardsmen in Coronation Procession

1663 East End Children reading Coronation Party Poster

1664 Queen Elizabeth II in Coronation Chair with Bishops of Durham and Bath and Wells

1665 Children in Plymouth working on Royal Montage

1666 Queen Elizabeth II in Coronation Robes (photograph by Cecil Beaton)

1667 Children's Race at East End Street Party

1668 Coronation Coach passing through Marble Arch

1669 Children in Fancy Dress

1670 Coronation Coach outside Buckingham Palace

1671 Children eating at London Street Party

1674 Prince William in September 2001 (Camera Press)

1675 Prince William in September 2001 (Tim Graham)

(Des Kate Stephens. Gravure De La Rue (sheets) or Walsall (booklets))

2003 (2 June). *50th Anniversary of Coronation.* W **1565**. |MULTI COLOUR| Two phosphor bands. Perf 14½×14.

2368	**1662**	(1st) Guardsmen in Coronation Procession	1·00	1·00
		a. Block of 10. Nos. 2368/77	9·00	9·00
		b. Booklet pane. Nos. 2368, 2370, 2373 and 2375 with margins all round	3·75	
2369	**1663**	(1st) East End Children	1·00	1·00
		b. Booklet pane. Nos. 2369, 2372, 2374 and 2377 with margins all round	3·75	
2370	**1664**	(1st) Queen Elizabeth II in Coronation Chair	1·00	1·00
2371	**1665**	(1st) Children in Plymouth	1·00	1·00
2372	**1666**	(1st) Queen Elizabeth II in Coronation Robes	1·00	1·00
2373	**1667**	(1st) Children's Race	1·00	1·00
2374	**1668**	(1st) Coronation Coach passing through Marble Arch	1·00	1·00
2375	**1669**	(1st) Children in Fancy Dress	1·00	1·00
2376	**1670**	(1st) Coronation Coach outside Buckingham Palace	1·00	1·00
2377	**1671**	(1st) Children eating at London Street Party	1·00	1·00
Set of 10			9·00	9·00
Gutter Block of 20			18·00	
First Day Cover (Tallents House)				9·50
First Day Cover (London SW1)				9·50
Presentation Pack (PO Pack No. 347)			10·00	
PHQ Cards (set of 10) (253)			3·00	10·00

Nos. 2368/77 were printed together, *se-tenant*, as blocks of ten (5×2) in sheets of 60 (2 panes of 30). No. 2372 does not show a silhouette of the Queen's head in gold as do the other nine designs.

Booklet pane Nos. 2368b/9b come from the £7·46 'A perfect Coronation' booklet, No. DX31.

(Gravure Walsall)

2003 (2 June). *50th Anniversary of Coronation.* Booklet stamps. Designs as T **160** (Wilding definitive of 1952) and **163** (Coronation commemorative of 1953), but with values in decimal currency as T **1348**. W **1565**. Two phosphor bands. Perf 15×14 (with one elliptical hole in each vertical side for Nos. 2378/9).

2378	**160**	47p. bistre-brown	2·00	2·00
		a. Booklet pane. Nos. 2378/9, each×2, and 2380 with margins all round	33·00	
2379		68p. grey-blue	2·50	2·50
2380	**163**	£1 deep yellow-green	26·00	26·00
Set of 3			30·00	30·00

Nos. 2378/80 were only issued in the £7·46 'A Perfect Coronation' booklet, No. DX31. Stamps as Nos. 2378/9, but on pale cream, were also included in the Wilding miniature sheets, Nos. **MS**2326 or **MS**2367. A £1 design as No. 2380, but on phosphorised paper, was previously included in the 'Stamp Show 2000' miniature sheet, No. **MS**2147.

1672 Prince William in September 2001 (Brendan Beirne)

1673 Prince William in September 2000 (Tim Graham)

(Des Madeleine Bennett. Gravure Walsall)

2003 (17 June). *21st Birthday of Prince William of Wales.* |MULTI COLOUR| Phosphor backgrounds. Perf 14½.

2381	**1672**	28p. Prince William in September 2001	95	95
2382	**1673**	(E) Prince William in September 2000	1·50	1·50
2383	**1674**	47p. Prince William in September 2001	1·90	1·90
2384	**1675**	68p. Prince William in September 2001	2·30	2·30
Set of 4			6·00	6·00
Set of 4 Gutter Pairs			12·00	
First Day Cover (Tallents House)				6·25
First Day Cover (Cardiff)				6·25
Presentation Pack (PO Pack No. 348)			8·00	
PHQ Cards (set of 4) (254)			1·20	6·75

1676 Loch Assynt, Sutherland

1677 Ben More, Isle of Mull

1678 Rothiemurchus, Cairngorms

1679 Dalveen Pass, Lowther Hills

1680 Glenfinnan Viaduct, Lochaber

1681 Papa Little, Shetland Islands

(Des Phelan Barker. Gravure De La Rue)

2003 (15 July). *A British Journey: Scotland.* |MULTI COLOUR| One centre phosphor band (2nd) or two phosphor bands (others). Perf 14½.

(a) Ordinary gum.

2385	**1676**	(2nd) Loch Assynt, Sutherland	90	90
2386	**1677**	(1st) Ben More, Isle of Mull	1·00	1·00
2387	**1678**	(E) Rothiemurchus, Cairngorms	1·50	1·50

2388	**1679**	42p. Dalveen Pass, Lowther Hills..............	1·00	1·00
2389	**1680**	47p. Glenfinnan Viaduct, Lochaber.........	1·10	1·20
2390	**1681**	68p. Papa Little, Shetland Islands	1·25	1·35

Set of 6... 6·25 6·25
Set of 6 Gutter Pairs .... 12·50
First Day Cover (Tallents House)...................... 6·75
First Day Cover (Baltasound, Unst, Shetland)...................... 6·75
Presentation Pack (PO Pack No. 349).............. 7·00
PHQ Cards (set of 6) (255)................................ 1·80 6·75

(b) Self-adhesive. Die-cut Perf 14½.

2391	**1677**	(1st) Ben More, Isle of Mull........................	3·00	3·00
		a. Booklet pane. No. 2391×2, and		
		No. 2295×4	8·00	

Perforated trials of this set with alternative face values or designs are known.

No. 2391 was only issued in £1·68 stamp booklets, No. PM10, in which the surplus self-adhesive paper around each stamp was removed.

1682 'The Station'
(Andrew Davidson)

1683 'Black Swan'
(Stanley Chew)

1684 'The Cross Keys'
(George Mackenney)

1685 'The Mayflower'
(Ralph Ellis)

1686 'The Barley Sheaf' (Joy Cooper)

(Des Elmwood. Gravure De La Rue)

2003 (12 Aug). *Europa. British Pub Signs.* |MULTI COLOUR| Two phosphor bands. Perf 14×14½.

2392	**1682**	(1st) 'The Station'...	1·00	1·00
		a. Booklet pane. No. 2392×4 with		
		margins all round (16.3.04)........	3·00	
2393	**1683**	(E) 'Black Swan'..	1·50	1 50
2394	**1684**	42p. 'The Cross Keys'....................................	1·00	1·00
2395	**1685**	47p. 'The Mayflower'....................................	1·20	1·20
2396	**1686**	68p. 'The Barley Sheaf'.................................	1·40	1·40

Set of 5... 5·50 5·50
Set of 5 Gutter Pairs .... 11·00
First Day Cover (Tallents House)...................... 5·75
First Day Cover (Cross Keys, Hereford) .... 5·75
Presentation Pack (PO Pack No. 350).............. 5·75
PHQ Cards (set of 5) (256)................................ 1·50 6·00

The 1st and E values include the 'EUROPA' emblem. No. 2392a comes from the £7·44 'Letters by Night' booklet, No. DX32.

MECCANO
Constructor Biplane c1931

1687 Meccano Constructor Biplane, *c.*1931

WELLS-BRIMTOY
Clockwork Double-decker Omnibus c1938

1688 Wells-Brimtoy Clockwork Double-decker Omnibus, *c.*1938

HORNBY
M1 Clockwork Locomotive and Tender c1948

DINKY TOYS
Ford Zephyr c1956

1689 Hornby M1 Clockwork Locomotive and Tender, *c.*1948

1690 Dinky Toys Ford Zephyr, *c.*1956

METTOY
Friction Drive
Space Ship Eagle c1960

1691 Mettoy Friction Drive Space Ship *Eagle, c.*1960

(Des Trickett and Webb)

2003 (18 Sept). *Classic Transport Toys.* |MULTI COLOUR| Two phosphor bands.

(a) Gravure Enschedé. Ordinary gum. P 14½×14.

2397	**1687**	(1st) Meccano Constructor Biplane	1·00	1·00
2398	**1688**	(E) Wells-Brimtoy Clockwork Double-		
		decker Omnibus.....................................	1·50	1·50
2399	**1689**	42p. Hornby M1 Clockwork Locomotive		
		and Tender..	95	1·00
2400	**1690**	47p. Dinky Toys Ford Zephyr	1·20	1·30
2401	**1691**	68p. Mettoy Friction Drive Space Ship		
		Eagle...	1·40	1·50

Set of 5... 5·50 5·50
Set of 5 Gutter Pairs .... 11·00
First Day Cover (Tallents House)...................... 5·75
First Day Cover (Toye, Downpatrick)............... 5·75
Presentation Pack (PO Pack No. 351).............. 6·00
PHQ Cards (set of 6) (257)................................ 1·80 6·00
MS2402 115×105mm.Nos. 2397/401 .... 5·50 5·50
First Day Cover.. 6·75

(b) Gravure De La Rue. Self-adhesive. Die-cut Perf 14½×14.

2403	**1687**	(1st) Meccano Constructor Biplane	3·00	3·00
		a. Booklet pane. No. 2403×2 and No.		
		2295×4	6·75	

The complete miniature sheet is shown on one of the PHQ cards with the others depicting individual stamps.

No. 2403 was only issued in £1·68 stamp booklets, No. PM11, in which the surplus self-adhesive paper around each stamp was removed.

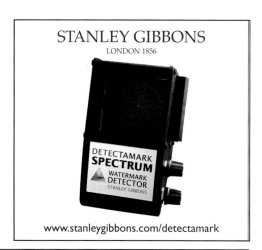

1692 Coffin of Denytenamun, Egyptian, c.900BC

1693 Alexander the Great, Greek, c.200BC

1694 Sutton Hoo Helmet, Anglo-Saxon, c.AD600

1695 Sculpture of Parvati, South Indian, c.AD1550

1696 Mask of Xiuhtecuhtli, Mixtec-Aztec, c.AD1500

1697 Hoa Hakananai'a, Easter Island, c.AD1000

(Des Rose Design. Gravure Walsall)

2003 (7 Oct). *250th Anniversary of the British Museum.* |MULTI COLOUR| One side phosphor band (2nd), two phosphor bands ((1st), (E), 47p.) or phosphor background at left and band at right (42p., 68p.). Perf 14×14½.

2404	**1692**	(2nd) Coffin of Denytenamun	90	90
2405	**1693**	(1st) Alexander the Great	1·00	1·00
2406	**1694**	(E) Sutton Hoo Helmet	1·50	1·50
2407	**1695**	42p. Sculpture of Parvati	90	1·00
2408	**1696**	47p. Mask of Xiuhtecuhtli	1·00	1·00
2409	**1697**	68p. Hoa Hakananai'a	1·10	1·20
Set of 6			6·00	6·00
Set of 6 Gutter Pairs			12·00	
First Day Cover (Tallents House)				6·50
First Day Cover (London WC1)				6·50
Presentation Pack (PO Pack No. 352)			7·00	
PHQ Cards (set of 6) (258)			1·80	6·00

1698 Ice Spiral

1699 Icicle Star

1700 Wall of Ice Blocks

1701 Ice Ball

1702 Ice Hole

1703 Snow Pyramids

(Des D. Davis. Gravure De La Rue)

2003 (4 Nov). *Christmas. Ice Sculptures by Andy Goldsworthy.* Self-adhesive. |MULTI COLOUR| One side phosphor band (2nd), 'all-over' phosphor (1st) or two bands (others). Die-cut Perf 14½×14.

2410	**1698**	(2nd) Ice Spiral	90	90
		a. Booklet pane. No. 2410×24	16·00	
2411	**1699**	(1st) Icicle Star	1·00	1·00
		a. Booklet pane. No. 2411×12	11·00	
2412	**1700**	(E) Wall of Ice Blocks	1·50	1·50
2413	**1701**	53p. Ice Ball	1·20	1·20
2414	**1702**	68p. Ice Hole	1·40	1·50
2415	**1703**	£1.12 Snow Pyramids	1·50	1·60
Set of 6			6·75	6·75
First Day Cover (Tallents House)				7·50
First Day Cover (Bethlehem, Llandeilo)				7·50
Presentation Pack (PO Pack No. 353)			7·25	
PHQ Cards (set of 6) (259)			1·80	7·00

Nos. 2410/15 were each printed in sheets of 50 with the surplus backing paper around each stamp removed.

The 2nd and 1st class were also issued in separate sheets of 20 printed in lithography instead of photogravure, each stamp accompanied by a half stamp-size *se-tenant* label showing either ice sculptures (2nd) or animals (1st) (LS15/16). Both sheets have the backing paper around each stamp retained. The 2nd class was sold for £4·20 and the 1st class for £6·15. These sheets were also available with personal photographs instead of labels at £9·95 (2nd) or £14·95 (1st) from Royal Mail, Edinburgh or £15 from photo-booths at selected post offices and Safeway stores.

Year Pack 2003

2003 (4 Nov). Comprises Nos. 2327/57, 2360/5, 2368/77, 2381/90, 2392/401 and 2404/15

CP2415a Year Pack .... 72·00

Post Office Yearbook

2003 (4 Nov). Comprises Nos. 2327/57, 2360/5, 2368/77, 2381/90, 2392/401 and 2404/15 in hardback book with slipcase .... 54·00

WORLD CHAMPIONS 22 NOVEMBER 2003 TELSTRA STADIUM SYDNEY

1704 (*Illustration reduced. Actual size 115×88 mm*)

(Des Why Not Associates. Litho Walsall)

2003 (19 Dec). *England's Victory in Rugby World Cup Championship, Australia.* Sheet 115×85 mm. |MULTI COLOUR| Two phosphor bands. Perf 14.

MS2416	**1704**	(1st) England flags and fans; (1st) England team standing in circle before match; 68p. World Cup trophy; 68p. Victorious England players after match	9·00	9·00
First Day Cover (Tallents House)				9·25
First Day Cover (Twickenham)				9·25
Presentation Pack (PO Pack No. M9B)			20·00	

1705 Dolgoch, Rheilffordd Talyllyn Railway, Gwynedd

1706 CR Class 439, Bo'ness and Kinneil Railway, West Lothian

1707 GCR Class 8K, Leicestershire

1708 GWR Manor Class *Bradley Manor*, Severn Valley Railway, Worcestershire

1709 SR West Country Class *Blackmoor Vale*, Bluebell Railway, East Sussex

1710 BR Standard Class, Keighley and Worth Valley Railway, Yorkshire

(Des Roundel. Litho De La Rue)

2004 (13 Jan–16 Mar). *Classic Locomotives.* |MULTI COLOUR| One side phosphor band (20p.) or two phosphor bands (others). Perf 14½.

2417	**1705**	20p. *Dolgoch*, Rheilffordd Talyllyn Railway	65	65
2418	**1706**	28p. CR Class 439, Bo'ness and Kinneil Railway	75	75
		a. Booklet pane. Nos. 2418/20 with margins all round (16 Mar)	2·25	
2419	**1707**	(E) GCR Class 8K	1·50	1·50
2420	**1708**	42p. GWR Manor Class *Bradley Manor*, Severn Valley Railway	1·00	1·10
2421	**1709**	47p. SR West Country Class *Blackmoor Vale*, Bluebell Railway	1·10	1·20
		a. Imperf (pair)	£3000	
2422	**1710**	68p. BR Standard Class, Keighley and Worth Valley Railway	1·20	1·30
Set of 6			5·50	5·50
Set of 6 Gutter Pairs			11·00	
First Day Cover (Tallents House)				6·00
First Day Cover (York)				6·00
Presentation Pack (PO Pack No. 355)			10·00	
PHQ Cards (set of 7) (260)			2·00	6·25
MS2423 190×67 mm. Nos. 2417/22			14·50	14·50
First Day Cover (Tallents House)				15·00
First Day Cover (York)				15·00

No. 2418a comes from the £7·44 'Letters by Night' booklet, No. DX32.

The seven PHQ cards depict the six individual stamps and the miniature sheet.

1711 Postman

1712 Face

1713 Duck

1714 Baby

1715 Aircraft

(Des S. Kambayashi. Litho De La Rue)

2004 (3 Feb). *Occasions.* |MULTI COLOUR| Two phosphor bands. Perf 14½×14.

2424	**1711**	(1st) Postman	1·00	1·00
		a. Horiz strip of 5. Nos. 2424/8	4·50	4·50
		ab. Imperf strip of 5		
2425	**1712**	(1st) Face	1·00	1·00
2426	**1713**	(1st) Duck	1·00	1·00
2427	**1714**	(1st) Baby	1·00	1·00
2428	**1715**	(1st) Aircraft	1·00	1·00
Set of 5			4·50	4·50
Gutter Block of 10			9·00	
First Day Cover (Tallents House)				6·25
First Day Cover (Merry Hill, Wolverhampton)				6·25
Presentation Pack (PO Pack No. M10)			5·75	
PHQ Cards (set of 5) (PSM10)			1·50	6·00

Nos. 2424/8 were printed together, *se-tenant*, as horizontal strips of five in sheets of 25 (5×5). Nos. 2424/8 were also issued in sheets of 20 containing vertical strips of the five designs alternated with half stamp-size labels (LS18). These sheets with printed labels were available at £6·15 from philatelic outlets, or with personalised photographs at £14·95 from Royal Mail in Edinburgh.

1716 Map showing Middle Earth

1717 Forest of Lothlórien in Spring

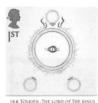

1718 Dust-jacket for *The Fellowship of the Ring*

1719 Rivendell

1720 The Hall at Bag End

1721 Orthanc

JRR TOLKIEN · THE LORD OF THE RINGS
1722 Doors of Durin

JRR TOLKIEN · THE LORD OF THE RINGS
1723 Barad-dûr

JRR TOLKIEN · THE LORD OF THE RINGS
1724 Minas Tirith

JRR TOLKIEN · THE LORD OF THE RINGS
1725 Fangorn Forest

(Des HGV Design. Litho Walsall)

2004 (26 Feb). *50th Anniversary of Publication of The Fellowship of the Ring and The Two Towers by J. R. R. Tolkien.* |MULTI COLOUR Two phosphor bands. Perf 14½.

2429	**1716**	(1st) Map showing Middle Earth	1·00	1·00
		a. Block of 10. Nos. 2429/38	9·00	9·00
2430	**1717**	(1st) Forest of Lothlórien in Spring	1·00	1·00
2431	**1718**	(1st) Dust-jacket for *The Fellowship of the Ring*	1·00	1·00
2432	**1719**	(1st) Rivendell	1·00	1·00
2433	**1720**	(1st) The Hall at Bag End	1·00	1·00
2434	**1721**	(1st) Orthanc	1·00	1·00
2435	**1722**	(1st) Doors of Durin	1·00	1·00
2436	**1723**	(1st) Barad-dûr	1·00	1·00
2437	**1724**	(1st) Minas Tirith	1·00	1·00
2438	**1725**	(1st) Fangorn Forest	1·00	1·00
Set of 10			9·00	9·00
Gutter Block of 20			18·00	
First Day Cover (Tallents House)				9·25
First Day Cover (Oxford)				9·25
Presentation Pack (PO Pack No. 356)			10·50	
PHQ Cards (set of 10) (261)			3·00	10·50

Nos. 2429/38 were printed together, *se-tenant*, in blocks of ten (5×2) throughout the sheet.

1726 Ely Island, Lower Lough Erne

1727 Giant's Causeway, Antrim Coast

1728 Slemish, Antrim Mountains

1729 Banns Road, Mourne Mountains

1730 Glenelly Valley, Sperrins

1731 Islandmore, Strangford Lough

(Des Phelan Barker. Gravure Enschedé (sheets) or De La Rue (booklet))

2004 (16 Mar). *A British Journey: Northern Ireland.* |MULTI COLOUR One side phosphor band (2nd) or two phosphor bands (others). Perf 14½.

(a) Ordinary gum.

2439	**1726**	(2nd) Ely Island, Lower Lough Erne	90	90
2440	**1727**	(1st) Giant's Causeway, Antrim Coast	1·00	1·00
2441	**1728**	(E) Slemish, Antrim Mountains	1·50	1·50
2442	**1729**	42p. Banns Road, Mourne Mountains	70	85
2443	**1730**	47p. Glenelly Valley, Sperrins	85	95
2444	**1731**	68p. Islandmore, Strangford Lough	95	1·10
Set of 6			5·50	5·50
Set of 6 Gutter Pairs			11·00	
First Day Cover (Tallents House)				5·75
First Day Cover (Garrison, Enniskillen)				5·75
Presentation Pack (PO Pack No. 357)			6·00	
PHQ Cards (set of 6) (262)			1·80	5·75

(b) Self-adhesive. Die-cut Perf 14½.

2445	**1727**	(1st) Giant's Causeway, Antrim Coast	3·25	3·25
		a. Booklet pane. No. 2445×2 and No. 2295×4	6·75	
		ab. Imperf (pane)	—	

No. 2445 was only issued in £1·68 stamp booklets No. PM12 in which the surplus self-adhesive paper around each stamp was removed.

28 *Lace 1 (trial proof) 1968* (Sir Terry Frost)

57 **1733** *Coccinelle* (Sonia Delaunay)

(Des Rose Design. Gravure Walsall)

2004 (6 Apr). *Contemporary Paintings. Centenary of the Entente Cordiale.* |MULTI COLOUR Two phosphor bands. Perf 14×14½.

2446	**1732**	28p. *Lace 1 (trial proof) 1968*	80	80
2447	**1733**	57p. *Coccinelle*	1·20	1·20
Set of 2			1·75	1·75
Set of 2 Gutter Pairs			3·50	
Set of 2 Traffic Light Gutter Blocks of 4			10·00	
First Day Cover (Tallents House)				1·90
First Day Cover (London SW1)				1·90
First Day Cover (UK and French stamps)				5·00
Presentation Pack (PO Pack No. 358)			8·00	
Presentation Pack (UK and French stamps)			8·00	
PHQ Cards (set of 2) (263)			60	2·00

Stamps in similar designs were issued by France and these are included in the joint Presentation Pack.

1734 *RMS Queen Mary 2*, 2004 (Edward D. Walker)

1735 *SS Canberra*, 1961 (David Cobb)

1736 *RMS Queen Mary*, 1936 (Charles Pears)

1737 *RMS Mauretania*, 1907 (Thomas Henry)

1738 *SS City of New York*, 1888 (Raphael Monleon y Torres)

1739 *PS Great Western*, 1838 (Joseph Walter)

(Des J. Gibbs. Gravure De La Rue)

2004 (13 Apr). *Ocean Liners.* |MULTI COLOUR| Two phosphor bands. Perf 14½×14.

(a) Ordinary gum.

2448	**1734**	(1st) RMS Queen Mary 2, 2004	1·00	1·00
2449	**1735**	(E) SS Canberra, 1961	1·50	1·50
		a. Imperf (pair)	£600	
2450	**1736**	42p. RMS Queen Mary, 1936	70	80
2451	**1737**	47p. RMS Mauretania, 1907	75	85
2452	**1738**	57p. SS City of New York, 1888	80	90
2453	**1739**	68p. PS Great Western, 1838	85	95

Set of 6 .... 5·00 5·00
Set of 6 Gutter Pairs .... 10·00
First Day Cover (Tallents House) .... 5·50
First Day Cover (Southampton) .... 5·50
Presentation Pack (PO Pack No. 359) .... 5·50
PHQ Cards (set of 7) (264) .... 2·00 5·25
MS2454 114×104mm. Nos. 2448/53 .... 7·25 7·25
First Day Cover (Tallents House) .... 7·50
First Day Cover (Southampton) .... 7·50

(b) Self-adhesive. Die-cut Perf 14½×14.

2455	**1734**	(1st) RMS Queen Mary 2, 2004	3·25	3·25
		a. Booklet pane. No. 2455×2 and No. 2295×4	6·75	

Nos. 2448/55 commemorate the introduction to service of the *Queen Mary 2*.

The complete miniature sheet is shown on one of the PHQ cards with the others depicting individual stamps. No. 2455 was only issued in £1·68 stamp booklets No. PM13 in which the surplus self-adhesive paper around each stamp was removed.

No. **MS**2454 is known to exist with a face value of '53' on No. 2452. It is known perforated and imperforate. See also No. 2614.

1740 *Dianthus Allwoodii* Group

1741 Dahlia 'Garden Princess'

1742 Clematis 'Arabella'

1743 Miltonia 'French Lake'

1744 Lilium 'Lemon Pixie'

1745 Delphinium 'Clifford Sky'

(Des Rose Design. Gravure Enschedé)

2004 (25 May). *Bicentenary of the Royal Horticultural Society* (1st issue). |MULTI COLOUR| One side phosphor band (2nd) or 'all-over' phosphor (others). Perf 14½.

2456	**1740**	(2nd) Dianthus Allwoodii Group	90	90
		a. Booklet pane. Nos. 2456, 2458/9 and 2461 with margins all round ..	5·50	
2457	**1741**	(1st) Dahlia 'Garden Princess'	1·00	1·00
		a. Booklet pane. Nos. 2457 and 2460, each×2, with margins all round	4·75	
2458	**1742**	(E) Clematis 'Arabella'	1·50	1·50
2459	**1743**	42p. Miltonia 'French Lake'	80	85
2460	**1744**	47p. Lilium 'Lemon Pixie'	85	90
2461	**1745**	68p. Delphinium 'Clifford Sky'	90	1·00

Set of 6 .... 5·50 5·50
Set of 6 Gutter Pairs .... 11·00
First Day Cover (Tallents House) .... 5·75
First Day Cover (Wisley, Woking) .... 5·75
Presentation Pack (PO Pack No. 360) .... 5·75
PHQ Cards (set of 7) (265) .... 2·00 6·50
MS2462 115×105 mm. Nos. 2456/61 .... 6·50 6·50

First Day Cover (Tallents House) .... 7·25
First Day Cover (Wisley, Woking) .... 7·25

Booklet panes Nos. 2456a/7a come from the £7·23 'Glory of the Garden' booklet, No. DX33. The complete miniature sheet is shown on one of the PHQ cards with the others depicting individual stamps.

The 1st class stamp was also issued in sheets of 20, printed in lithography by Walsall and *sold at* £6·15, containing vertical strips of five stamps alternated with printed labels giving information about dahlias (LS19). These sheets with personalised photographs were available at £14·95 from the Royal Mail in Edinburgh.

(Litho Enschedé)

2004 (25 May). *Bicentenary of the Royal Horticultural Society* (2nd issue). Booklet stamps. Designs as Nos. 1955, 1958 and 1962 (1997 Greeting Stamps 19th-century Flower Paintings). |MULTI COLOUR| Two phosphor bands. Perf 15×14 (with one elliptical hole in each vert side.)

2463	**1280**	(1st) Gentiana acaulis (Georg Ehret)	2·80	2·80
		a. Booklet pane. Nos. 2463, 2464×2 and 2465 with margins all round ..	7·00	
2464	**1283**	(1st) Tulipa (Ehret)	1·40	1·40
2465	**1287**	(1st) Iris latifolia (Ehret)	2·80	2·80

Set of 3 .... 6·50 6·50

On Nos. 2463/5 the phosphor bands appear at the left and the centre of each stamp. Nos. 2463/5 were only issued in the £7·23 Glory of the Garden booklet, No. DX33.

1746 Barmouth Bridge

1747 Hyddgen, Plynlimon

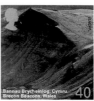
1748 Brecon Beacons

1749 Pen-pych, Rhondda Valley

1750 Rhewl, Dee Valley

1751 Marloes Sands

(Des Phelan Barker. Gravure De La Rue)

2004 (15 June). *A British Journey: Wales.* |MULTI COLOUR| One centre phosphor band (2nd), 'all-over' phosphor (1st) or two phosphor bands (others). Perf 14½.

(a) Ordinary gum.

2466	**1746**	(2nd) Barmouth Bridge	90	90
		a. Imperf (pair)	£700	
2467	**1747**	(1st) Hyddgen, Plynlimon	1·00	1·00
		a. Imperf (pair)	£700	
2468	**1748**	40p. Brecon Beacons	70	70
2469	**1749**	43p. Pen-pych, Rhondda Valley	75	75
2470	**1750**	47p. Rhewl, Dee Valley	80	85
		a. Imperf (pair)	£500	
2471	**1751**	68p. Marloes Sands	90	95
		a. Imperf (pair)	£700	

Set of 6 .... 4·50 4·50
Set of 6 Gutter Pairs .... 9·00
First Day Cover (Tallents House) .... 4·75
First Day Cover (Llanfair) .... 4·75
Presentation Pack (PO Pack No. 361) .... 4·75
PHQ Cards (set of 6) (266) .... 1·80 5·25

(b) Self-adhesive. Die-cut Perf 14½.

2472	**1747**	(1st) Hyddgen, Plynlimon	3·25	3·25
		a. Booklet pane. No. 2472×2 and No. 2295×4	6·75	

The 1st and 40p. values include the 'EUROPA' emblem.

Imperf pairs of Type **1748** and Type **1749** with alternative face values are of proof status. (*Price £1000 per pair*).

No. 2472 was only issued in £1·68 stamp booklets, No. PM14, in which the surplus self-adhesive paper around each stamp was removed.

1752 Sir Rowland Hill Award

1753 William Shipley (Founder of Royal Society of Arts)

1754 'RSA' as Typewriter Keys and Shorthand

1755 Chimney Sweep

1756 'Gill Typeface'

1757 'Zero Waste'

(Des D. Birdsall. Litho Walsall)

2004 (10 Aug). *250th Anniversary of the Royal Society of Arts.* |MULTI| |COLOUR| Two phosphor bands. Perf 14.

2473	**1752**	(1st) Sir Rowland Hill Award	1·00	1·00
2474	**1753**	40p. William Shipley	75	75
2475	**1754**	43p. 'RSA' as Typewriter Keys and Shorthand	80	80
2476	**1755**	47p. Chimney Sweep	1·00	1·00
2477	**1756**	57p. 'Gill Typeface'	1·25	1·25
2478	**1757**	68p. 'Zero Waste'	1·50	1·50
		Set of 6	5·50	5·50
		Set of 6 Gutter Pairs	11·00	
		First Day Cover (Tallents House)		5·75
		First Day Cover (London WC2)		5·75
		Presentation Pack (PO Pack No. 362)	6·00	
		PHQ Cards (set of 6) (267)	1·80	6·50

1758 Pine Marten

1759 Roe Deer

1760 Badger

1761 Yellow-necked Mouse

1762 Wild Cat

1763 Red Squirrel

1764 Stoat

1765 Natterer's Bat

1766 Mole

1767 Fox

(Des Kate Stephens. Gravure Enschedé)

2004 (16 Sept). *Woodland Animals.* |MULTI| |COLOUR| Two phosphor bands. Perf 14½.

2479	**1758**	(1st) Pine Marten	1·00	1·00
		a. Block of 10. Nos. 2479/88	9·00	9·00
2480	**1759**	(1st) Roe Deer	1·00	1·00
2481	**1760**	(1st) Badger	1·00	1·00
2482	**1761**	(1st) Yellow-necked Mouse	1·00	1·00
2483	**1762**	(1st) Wild Cat	1·00	1·00
2484	**1763**	(1st) Red Squirrel	1·00	1·00
2485	**1764**	(1st) Stoat	1·00	1·00
2486	**1765**	(1st) Natterer's Bat	1·00	1·00
2487	**1766**	(1st) Mole	1·00	1·00
2488	**1767**	(1st) Fox	1·00	1·00
		Set of 10	9·00	9·00
		Gutter Block of 20	18·00	
		Traffic Light Gutter Block of 20	40·00	
		First Day Cover (Tallents House)		9·25
		First Day Cover (Woodland, Bishop Auckland)		9·25
		Presentation Pack (PO Pack No. 363)	10·00	
		PHQ Cards (set of 10) (268)	3·00	10·00

Nos. 2479/88 were printed together, *se-tenant*, in blocks of ten (5×2) throughout sheets of 30.

1768 Pte. McNamara, 5th Dragoon Guards, Heavy Brigade charge, Battle of Balaklava

1769 Piper Muir, 42nd Regt of Foot, amphibious assault on Kerch

1770 Sgt. Maj. Edwards, Scots Fusilier Guards, gallant action, Battle of Inkerman

1771 Sgt. Powell, 1st Regt of Foot Guards, Battles of Alma and Inkerman

1772 Sgt. Maj. Poole, Royal Sappers and Miners, defensive line, Battle of Inkerman

1773 Sgt. Glasgow, Royal Artillery, gun battery besieged Sevastopol

(Des Atelier Works. Litho Walsall)

2004 (12 Oct). *150th Anniversary of the Crimean War.* One centre phosphor band (2nd) or two phosphor bands (others). Perf 14.

2489	**1768**	(2nd) Pte. McNamara	90	90
		a. Greyish silver and phosphor omitted	£1200	
2490	**1769**	(1st) Piper Muir	1·00	1·00
2491	**1770**	40p. Sgt. Maj. Edwards	1·00	1·00
2492	**1771**	57p. Sgt. Powell	1·10	1·10
		a. Imperf	£700	
2493	**1772**	68p. Sgt. Maj. Poole	1·25	1·25
		a. Imperf	£2000	
2494	**1773**	£1·12 Sgt. Glasgow	1·60	1·60
Set of 6			6·00	6·00
Set of 6 Gutter Pairs			12·00	
Set of 6 Traffic Light Gutter Pairs			38·00	
First Day Cover (Tallents House)				6·25
First Day Cover (London SW3)				6·50
Presentation Pack (PO Pack No. 364)			6·25	
PHQ Cards (set of 6) (269)			1·80	7·00

Nos. 2489/94 show 'Crimean Heroes' photographs taken in 1856.

1774 Father Christmas on Snowy Roof

1775 Celebrating the Sunrise

1776 On Roof in Gale

1777 With Umbrella in Rain

1778 On Edge of Roof with Torch

1779 Sheltering behind Chimney

(Des R. Briggs. Gravure De La Rue)

2004 (2 Nov). *Christmas.* One centre phosphor band (2nd) or two phosphor bands (others). Perf 14½×14.

(a) Self-adhesive.

2495	**1774**	(2nd) Father Christmas on Snowy Roof	90	90
		a. Booklet pane. No. 2495×24	16·00	
2496	**1775**	(1st) Celebrating the Sunrise	1·00	1·00
		a. Booklet pane. No. 2496×12	12·00	
2497	**1776**	40p. On Roof in Gale	80	80
2498	**1777**	57p. With Umbrella in Rain	1·00	1·00
2499	**1778**	68p. On Edge of Roof with Torch	1·10	1·10
2500	**1779**	£1·12 Sheltering behind Chimney	1·20	1·20
Set of 6			5·50	5·50
First Day Cover (Tallents House)				5·75
First Day Cover (Bethlehem, Llandeilo)				6·00
Presentation Pack (PO Pack No. 365)			5.75	
PHQ Cards (set of 7) (270)			2·00	6·25

(b) Ordinary gum.

MS2501	115×105 mm. As Nos. 2495/500		6·00	6·00
First Day Cover (Tallents House)				6·25
First Day Cover (Bethlehem, Llandeilo)				6·50

Nos. 2495/500 were each printed in sheets of 50 with the surplus backing paper around each stamp removed.

The seven PHQ cards depict the six individual stamps and the miniature sheet.

The 2nd and 1st class were also issued together in sheets of 20, *sold at* £5·40, containing ten 2nd class and ten 1st class, each value arranged in vertical rows of five alternated with rows of half stamp-size labels showing Father Christmas (LS21). Separate sheets of 20 2nd class and 20 1st class were available with personalised photographs at £9·95 (2nd class) or £14·95 (1st class) from Royal Mail, Edinburgh. These sheets were printed in lithography instead of photogravure and had the backing paper around the stamps retained.

Trials are known showing alternative face values.

Year Pack 2004
2004 (2 Nov). Comprises Nos. 2417/22, 2424/44, 2446/53, 2456/61, 2466/71 and 2473/500.

CP2500a Year Pack		65·00

Post Office Yearbook
2004 (2 Nov). Comprises Nos. 2417/22, 2424/44, 2446/53, 2456/61, 2466/71 and 2473/500 in hardback book with slipcase ... 60·00

1780 British Saddleback Pigs

1781 Khaki Campbell Ducks

1782 Clydesdale Mare and Foal

1783 Dairy Shorthorn Cattle

1784 Border Collie Dog

1785 Light Sussex Chicks

1786 Suffolk Sheep

1787 Bagot Goat

1788 Norfolk Black Turkeys   **1789** Embden Geese

(Des C. Wormell. Gravure Enschedé)

2005 (11 Jan). *Farm Animals.* [MULTI COLOUR] Two phosphor bands. Perf 14½.

2502	**1780**	(1st) British Saddleback Pigs	1·00	1·00
		a. Block of 10. Nos. 2502/11	9·00	9·00
2503	**1781**	(1st) Khaki Campbell Ducks	1·00	1·00
2504	**1782**	(1st) Clydesdale Mare and Foal	1·00	1·00
2505	**1783**	(1st) Dairy Shorthorn Cattle	1·00	1·00
2506	**1784**	(1st) Border Collie Dog	1·00	1·00
2507	**1785**	(1st) Light Sussex Chicks	1·00	1·00
2508	**1786**	(1st) Suffolk Sheep	1·00	1·00
2509	**1787**	(1st) Bagot Goat	1·00	1·00
2510	**1788**	(1st) Norfolk Black Turkeys	1·00	1·00
2511	**1789**	(1st) Embden Geese	1·00	1·00
Set of 10			9·00	9·00
Gutter Block of 20			18·00	
Traffic Light Gutter Block of 20			65·00	
First Day Cover (Tallents House)				9·25
First Day Cover (Paddock, Huddersfield)				9·50
Presentation Pack (PO Pack No. 367)			9·25	
PHQ Cards (set of 10) (271)			3·00	10·50

Nos. 2502/11 were printed together, *se-tenant*, in blocks of ten (5×2) throughout sheets of 30. Nos. 2502/11 were also issued in sheets of 20, containing two of each of the ten designs, arranged in vertical strips of five alternated with printed labels showing black/white illustrations of farm scenes (LS 22). These sheets were printed in lithography by Walsall and sold for £6·15.

They were also available with personal photographs on the labels at £14·95 per sheet from Royal Mail, Edinburgh.

1790 Old Harry Rocks, Studland Bay   **1791** Wheal Coates, St Agnes

1792 Start Point, Start Bay   **1793** Horton Down, Wiltshire

1794 Chiselcombe, Exmoor   **1795** St James's Stone, Lundy

(Des J. Phelan and Lissa Barker. Gravure De La Rue)

2005 (8 Feb). *A British Journey: South West England.* [MULTI COLOUR] One centre phosphor band (2nd) or two phosphor bands (others). Perf 14½.

2512	**1790**	(2nd) Old Harry Rocks, Studland Bay	90	90
2513	**1791**	(1st) Wheal Coates, St Agnes	1·00	1·00
2514	**1792**	40p. Start Point, Start Bay	75	75
2515	**1793**	43p. Horton Down, Wiltshire	85	85
2516	**1794**	57p. Chiselcombe, Exmoor	1·00	1·00
2517	**1795**	68p. St James's Stone, Lundy	1·20	1·20
Set of 6			5·25	5·25
Set of 6 Gutter Pairs			10·50	
First Day Cover (Tallents House)				5·50

First Day Cover (The Lizard, Helston) .... 5·75
Presentation Pack (PO Pack No. 368) .... 5·50
PHQ Cards (set of 6) (262) .... 1·80   5·75

Perforated examples of Type **1794** are known with face value of 47p are known (*price* £3000).

1796 'Mr Rochester'   **1797** 'Come to Me'

1798 'In the Comfort of her Bonnet'   **1799** 'La Ligne des Rats'

1800 'Refectory'   **1801** 'Inspection'

(Des P. Willberg. Litho Walsall)

2005 (24 Feb). *150th Death Anniversary of Charlotte Brontë.* Illustrations of scenes from *Jane Eyre* by Paula Rego. [MULTI COLOUR] One centre phosphor band (2nd), or two phosphor bands (others). Perf 14×14½.

2518	**1796**	(2nd) 'Mr Rochester'	90	90
		a. Booklet pane. Nos. 2518/19, both×2, with margins all round	3·50	
2519	**1797**	(1st) 'Come to Me'	1·00	1·00
2520	**1798**	40p. 'In the Comfort of her Bonnet'	1·00	1·00
		a. Booklet pane. Nos. 2520/3 with margins all round	4·50	
2521	**1799**	57p. 'La Ligne des Rats'	1·20	1·20
2522	**1800**	68p. 'Refectory'	1·40	1·40
2523	**1801**	£1.12 'Inspection'	1·60	1·60
Set of 6			6·50	6·50
Set of 6 Gutter Pairs			13·00	
Set of 6 Traffic Light Gutter Blocks of 4			48·00	
First Day Cover (Tallents House)				6·75
First Day Cover (Haworth, Keighley)				7·00
Presentation Pack (PO Pack No. 369)			6·75	
PHQ Cards (set of 7) (273)			2·00	7·00
MS2524 114×105 mm. Nos. 2518/23			6·50	6·50
First Day Cover (Tallents House)				6·75
First Day Cover (Haworth, Keighley)				7·00

Booklet panes Nos. 2518a and 2520a come from the £7·43 'The Brontë Sisters' booklet, No. DX34. The complete miniature sheet is shown on one of the PHQ cards with the others depicting individual stamps.

1802 Spinning Coin   **1803** Rabbit out of Hat Trick

1804 Knotted Scarf Trick

1805 Card Trick

1806 Pyramid under Fez Trick

(Des G. Hardie and Tatham Design. Gravure Walsall)

2005 (15 Mar). *Centenary of the Magic Circle.* |MULTI COLOUR Two phosphor bands. Perf 14½×14.

2525	**1802**	(1st) Spinning Coin	1·00	1·00
2526	**1803**	40p. Rabbit out of Hat Trick	1·00	1·00
2527	**1804**	47p. Knotted Scarf Trick	1·20	1·20
2528	**1805**	68p. Card Trick	1·35	1·35
2529	**1806**	£1.12 Pyramid under Fez Trick	1·50	1·50
Set of 5			5·50	5·50
Set of 5 Gutter Pairs			11·00	
First Day Cover (Tallents House)				5·75
First Day Cover (London NW1)				6·00
Presentation Pack (PO Pack No. 370)			8·00	
PHQ Cards (set of 5) (274)			1·50	6·00

Nos. 2525/9 are each printed with instructions for the illusion or trick on the stamp. No. 2525 can be rubbed with a coin to reveal the 'head' or 'tail' of a coin. The two versions, which appear identical before rubbing, are printed in alternate rows of the sheet, indicated by the letters H and T in the side margins of the sheet. Nos. 2526 and 2528 each show optical illusions. The bright mauve on No. 2527 and the bright mauve, new blue, and lilac on No. 2529 are printed in thermochromic inks which fade temporarily when exposed to heat, making the pyramid under the centre fez visible.

The 1st class stamp was also issued in sheets of 20, printed in lithography instead of photogravure and sold at £6·15, containing vertical rows of five stamps alternated with half stamp-size printed labels illustrating magic tricks (LS23). These sheets were also available with personal photographs on the labels at £14·95 per sheet from Royal Mail, Edinburgh.

1806a First Castles Definitives (*Illustration reduced. Actual size 127×73 mm*)

(Des Sedley Place. Recess and litho Enschedé)

2005 (22 Mar). *50th Anniversary of First Castles Definitives.* Printed on pale cream paper. 'All-over' phosphor. Perf 11×11½.

MS2530 127×73 mm. **1806a** First Castles Definitives 50p. brownish-black; 50p. black; £1 dull vermilion;

£1 royal blue	4·50	4·50
First Day Cover (Tallents House)		5·75
First Day Cover (Windsor)		5·75
Presentation Pack (PO Pack No. 69)	5·75	
PHQ Cards (set of 5) (D28)	1·50	5·75

The five PHQ cards depict the whole miniature sheet and the four stamps it contains.

1807 Royal Wedding (*Illustration reduced. Actual size 85×115 mm*)

(Des Rose Design. Litho Enschedé)

2005 (9 Apr). *Royal Wedding.* Sheet 85×115 mm. |MULTI COLOUR 'All-over' phosphor. Perf 13½×14.

MS2531 **1807** Royal Wedding 30p.×2 Prince Charles and Mrs Camilla Parker Bowles laughing; 68p.×2 Prince Charles and Mrs Camilla Parker Bowles

smiling into camera	4·50	4·50
First Day Cover (Tallents House)		5·00
First Day Cover (Windsor)		5·00
Presentation Pack (PO Pack No. M10)	8·00	

No. **MS**2531 was officially issued on 9th April. It was originally intended for issue on 8th April, and many post offices put it on sale on that day. Royal Mail first day covers were dated 8th April, but could be ordered with a 9th April Windsor handstamp. Our prices cover either date.

1808 Hadrian's Wall, England

1809 Uluru-Kata Tjuta National Park, Australia

1810 Stonehenge, England

1811 Wet Tropics of Queensland, Australia

1812 Blenheim Palace, England

1813 Greater Blue Mountains Area, Australia

1814 Heart of Neolithic Orkney, Scotland

1815 Purnululu National Park, Australia

(Des J. Godfrey. Litho Enschedé)

2005 (21 Apr). *World Heritage Sites.* |MULTI COLOUR| One side phosphor band (2nd) or two phosphor bands (others). Perf 14½.

2532	**1808**	2nd Hadrian's Wall, England	90	90
		a. Horiz pair. Nos. 2532/3	1·80	1·80
2533	**1809**	2nd Uluru-Kata Tjuta National Park, Australia	90	90
2534	**1810**	1st Stonehenge, England	1·00	1·00
		a. Horiz pair. Nos. 2534/5	2·00	2·00
2535	**1811**	1st Wet Tropics of Queensland, Australia	1·00	1·00
2536	**1812**	47p. Blenheim Palace, England	80	80
		a. Horiz pair. Nos. 2536/7	1·60	1·60
2537	**1813**	47p. Greater Blue Mountains Area, Australia	80	80
2538	**1814**	68p. Heart of Neolithic Orkney, Scotland	1·00	1·00
		a. Horiz pair. Nos. 2538/9	2·00	2·00
2539	**1815**	68p. Purnululu National Park, Australia	1·00	1·00
Set of 8			6·50	6·50
Set of 4 Gutter Strips of 4			13·00	
Set of 4 Traffic Light Gutter Blocks of 8			32·00	
First Day Cover (Tallents House)				7·75
First Day Cover (Blenheim Palace, Woodstock)				7·75
First Day Covers (2) (UK and Australian stamps)				12·50
Presentation Pack (PO Pack No. 371)			7·50	
Presentation Pack (UK and Australian stamps)			11·00	
PHQ Cards (set of 8) (275)			2·50	7·50

The two designs of each value were printed together, *se-tenant*, in horizontal pairs in sheets of 30 (6×5).

Stamps in these designs were also issued by Australia and these are included in the joint Presentation Pack.

1816 Ensign of the Scots Guards, 2002

1817 Queen taking the salute as Colonel-in-Chief of the Grenadier Guards, 1983

1818 Trumpeter of the Household Cavalry, 2004

1819 Welsh Guardsman, 1990s

1820 Queen riding side-saddle, 1972

1821 Queen and Duke of Edinburgh in carriage, 2004

(Des A. Altmann. Litho Walsall)

2005 (7 June). *Trooping the Colour.* |MULTI COLOUR| One phosphor band (2nd), two phosphor bands (others). Perf 14½.

2540	**1816**	(2nd) Ensign of the Scots Guards, 2002	90	90
2541	**1817**	(1st) Queen taking the salute as Colonel-in-Chief of the Grenadier Guards, 1983	1·00	1·00
2542	**1818**	42p. Trumpeter of the Household Cavalry, 2004	85	85
2543	**1819**	60p. Welsh Guardsman, 1990s	1·00	1·00
2544	**1820**	68p. Queen riding side-saddle, 1972	1·10	1·10
2545	**1821**	£1·12 Queen and Duke of Edinburgh in carriage, 2004	1·30	1·30
Set of 6			5·50	5·50
Set of 6 Gutter Pairs			11·00	
First Day Cover (Tallents House)				6·00
First Day Cover (London SW1)				6·00
Presentation Pack (PO Pack No. 372)			5·75	
PHQ Cards (set of 7) (276)			2·00	11·00
MS2546 115×105 mm. Nos. 2540/5			5·50	5·50
First Day Cover (Tallents House)				5·75
First Day Cover (London SW1)				5·75

The seven PHQ cards show the six stamps and **MS**2546.

1822 End of the War (*Illustration reduced. Actual size 115×105 mm*)

(Des J. Matthews. Gravure Enschedé)

2005 (5 July). *60th Anniversary of End of the Second World War.* Sheet 115×105 mm containing design as T **1200** (1995 Peace and Freedom) but with service indicator and No. 1668×5. |MULTI COLOUR| Two phosphor bands. Perf 15×14 (with one elliptical hole in each vert side) (1668) or 14½×14 (other).

MS2547	**1822**	End of the War (1st) gold×5; (1st) silver, blue and grey-black	5·00	5·25
First Day Cover (Tallents House)				5·50
First Day Cover (Peacehaven, Newhaven)				5·50

1823 Norton F.1, Road Version of Race Winner (1991)

1824 BSA Rocket 3, Early Three Cylinder 'Superbike' (1969)

1825 Vincent Black Shadow, Fastest Standard Motorcycle (1949)

1826 Triumph Speed Twin, Two Cylinder Innovation (1938)

1827 Brough Superior, Bespoke Luxury Motorcycle (1930)

1828 Royal Enfield, Small Engined Motor Bicycle (1914)

(Des I. Chilvers and M. English. Litho Walsall)

2005 (19 July). *Motorcycles.* Two phosphor bands. Perf 14×14½.

2548	**1823**	(1st) Norton F.1	90	90
2549	**1824**	40p. BSA Rocket 3	60	60
2550	**1825**	42p. Vincent Black Shadow	65	65
2551	**1826**	47p. Triumph Speed Twin	80	80
2552	**1827**	60p. Brough Superior	1.00	1.00
2553	**1828**	68p. Royal Enfield	1.20	1.20
Set of 6			4.50	4.50
Set of 6 Gutter Pairs			9.00	
First Day Cover (Tallents House)				5.75
First Day Cover (Solihull)				5.75
Presentation Pack (PO Pack No. 373)			5.25	
PHQ Cards (set of 6) (277)			1.80	5.75

1829 London 2012 Host City (*Illustration reduced. Actual size* 115×105 mm)

(Des CDT Design. Litho Walsall)

2005 (5 Aug). *London's Successful Bid for Olympic Games,* 2012. Sheet 115×105 mm containing designs as T **1255/9,** but with service indicator. Two phosphor bands. Perf 14½.

MS2554 **1829** London 2012 Host City (1st) Athlete celebrating×2; (1st) Throwing the javelin; (1st) Swimming; (1st) Athlete on starting blocks; (1st) Basketball	5.00	5.00
First Day Cover (Tallents House)		5.75
First Day Cover (London E15)		5.75
Presentation Pack (PO Pack No. M11)	5.25	

Stamps from **MS2554** are all inscribed 'London 2012 – Host City' and have imprint date '2005'. The design as Type **1259** omits the Olympic rings.

1830 African Woman eating Rice

1831 Indian Woman drinking Tea

1832 Boy eating Sushi

1833 Woman eating Pasta

1834 Woman eating Chips

1835 Teenage Boy eating Apple

(Des Catell Ronca and Rose Design. Gravure Enschedé)

2005 (23 Aug). *Europa. Gastronomy.* Changing Tastes in Britain. One side phosphor band (2nd) or two phosphor bands (others). Perf 14½.

2555	**1830**	(2nd) African Woman eating Rice	90	90
2556	**1831**	(1st) Indian Woman drinking Tea	1.00	1.00
2557	**1832**	42p. Boy eating Sushi	60	60
2558	**1833**	47p. Woman eating Pasta	75	75
2559	**1834**	60p. Woman eating Chips	90	1.00
2560	**1835**	68p. Teenage Boy eating Apple	1.10	1.20
Set of 6			4.75	4.75
Set of 6 Gutter Pairs			9.50	
First Day Cover (Tallents House)				5.00
First Day Cover (Cookstown)				5.00
Presentation Pack (PO Pack No. 374)			5.00	
PHQ Cards (set of 6) (278)			1.80	5.75

The 1st snd 42p values include the 'EUROPA' emblem.

1836 Inspector Morse

1837 Emmerdale

1838 Rising Damp

1839 The Avengers

1840 The South Bank Show

1841 Who Wants to be a Millionaire

(Des Kate Stephens. Litho D.L.R.)

2005 (15 Sept). *50th Anniversary of Independent Television. Classic ITV Programmes.* |MULTI COLOUR| One side phosphor band (2nd) or two phosphor bands (others). Perf 14½×14.

2561	**1836**	(2nd) *Inspector Morse*............................	90	90
2562	**1837**	(1st) *Emmerdale*	1·00	1·00
2563	**1838**	42p. *Rising Damp*	60	60
2564	**1839**	47p. *The Avengers*	75	75
2565	**1840**	60p. *The South Bank Show*..............	90	90
2566	**1841**	68p. *Who Wants to be a Millionaire*.........	1·10	1·10
Set of 6...			4·75	4·75
Set of 6 Gutter Pairs.....................................			9·50	
First Day Cover (Tallents House)......................				5·25
First Day Cover (London SE19)........................				5·25
Presentation Pack (PO Pack No. 375).............			5·00	
PHQ Cards (set of 6) (279).............................			1·80	5·75

The 1st class stamps were also issued in sheets of 20 sold at £6·55, printed in lithography by Walsall, containing four vertical rows of five stamps alternated with half stamp-size labels (LS26). These sheets with personalised photographs were available at £14·95 from the Royal Mail.

1842 *Gazania splendens* (Charlotte Sowerby) **1842a** Aircraft Sky-writing 'hello' **1842b** 'LOVE'

1842c Union Jack **1842d** Teddy Bear **1842c** European Robin in Mouth of Pillar Box

(Gravure Walsall)

2005 (4 Oct). *Smilers Booklet stamps* (1st series). Designs as Types **992, 1221, 1286, 1517** and **1569** but smaller, 20×23 mm and inscribed '1st' as T **1842/a**. Self-adhesive. |MULTI COLOUR| Two phosphor bands. Die-cut Perf 15×14.

2567	**1842**	(1st) *Gazania splendens*.....................	1·10	1·20
		a. Booklet pane. Nos. 2567/72	9·00	
2568	**1842a**	(1st) Aircraft Sky-writing 'hello'.................	1·10	1·20
2569	**1842b**	(1st) 'LOVE'.....................................	1·10	1·20
2570	**1842c**	(1st) Union Jack...............................	1·10	1·20
2571	**1842d**	(1st) Teddy Bear...............................	1·10	1·20
2572	**1842e**	(1st) European Robin in Mouth of Pillar Box ...	1·10	1·20
Set of 6...			9·00	9·00
First Day Cover (Tallents House) (Type K, see Introduction)				9·00
First Day Cover (Windsor) (Type K).................				9·00

Nos. 2567/72 were only issued in stamp booklets, Nos. QA1 and QA2, in which the surplus backing paper around each stamp was removed.

Stamps in these designs in separate sheets printed in lithography by Cartor were available with personal photographs on the labels at £14·95 *per sheet* from Royal Mail, Edinburgh.

Nos. 2567/72 were issued on 4 July 2006 in sheets of 20 with *se-tenant* greetings labels, No. LS32, printed by Cartor in lithography instead of photogravure and sold at £6·95 *per sheet*.

Nos. 2568/70 were re-issued on 15 January 2008 in sheets of 20 with circular labels printed in lithography by Cartor and sold at £7·35 (LS45). These sheets were perforated with one elliptical hole on each vert side.

These three designs were available in separate sheets of 10 (*sold at £8·95*) or 20 (*sold at £14·95*) with personal photographs on the labels from Royal Mail, Edinburgh.

No. 2572 was issued on 8 May 2010 with other greetings stamps in sheets of 20 with *se-tenant* greetings labels, printed in lithography by Cartor, No. LS73, and sold for £10 *per sheet*. These sheets were printed with one elliptical hole in each vertical side.

For stamp as No. 2569 with one elliptical hole in each vertical side see No. 2693.

For stamps as Nos. 2567/8 and 2570 with one elliptical hole in each vertical side see Nos. 2819/21.

THE ASHES ENGLAND WINNERS 2005

1843 Cricket Scenes (*Illustration reduced. Actual size* 115×90 *mm*)

(Des Why Not Associates. Litho Cartor)

2005 (6 Oct). *England's Ashes Victory.* Sheet 115×90 mm. |MULTI COLOUR| Two phosphor bands. Perf 14½×14.

MS2573	**1843**	Cricket Scenes (1st) England team with Ashes trophy; (1st) Kevin Pietersen, Michael Vaughan and Andrew Flintoff on opening day of First Test, Lords; 68p. Michael Vaughan, Third Test, Old Trafford; 68p. Second Test cricket, Edgbaston	4·00	4·00
First Day Cover (Tallents House)....................				5·00
First Day Cover (London SE11).......................				5·00
Presentation Pack (PO Pack No. M12)			4·25	

1844 *Entrepreante* with dismasted British *Belle Isle*

1845 Nelson wounded on Deck of HMS *Victory*

1846 British Cutter *Entrepreante* attempting to rescue Crew of burning French *Achille*

1847 Cutter and HMS *Pickle* (schooner)

1848 British Fleet attacking in Two Columns

1849 Franco/Spanish Fleet putting to Sea from Cadiz

(Des D. Davis. Litho Cartor)

2005 (18 Oct). *Bicentenary of the Battle of Trafalgar* (1st issue). *Scenes from 'Panorama of the Battle of Trafalgar' by William Heath.* |MULTI COLOUR| Two phosphor bands. Perf 15×14½.

2574	**1844**	(1st) *Entrepreante* with dismasted British *Belle Isle*...................	75	80
		a. Horiz pair. Nos. 2574/5	1·60	1·70
		b. Booklet pane. Nos. 2574, 2576 and 2578	2·80	

2575	**1845**	(1st) Nelson wounded on Deck of HMS *Victory*	1·00	1·00
		b. Booklet pane. Nos. 2575, 2577 and 2579	2·80	
2576	**1846**	42p. British Cutter *Entrepreante* attempting to rescue Crew of burning French *Achille*	70	80
		a. Horiz pair. Nos. 2576/7	1·40	1·40
2577	**1847**	42p. Cutter and HMS *Pickle* (schooner)	70	80
2578	**1848**	68p. British Fleet attacking in Two Columns	1·00	1·10
		a. Horiz pair. Nos. 2578/9	2·00	2·00
2579	**1849**	68p. Franco/Spanish Fleet putting to Sea from Cadiz	1·00	1·10
Set of 6			5·00	5·00
Set of 3 Gutter Strips of 4			10·00	
First Day Cover (Tallents House)				5·50
First Day Cover (Portsmouth)				5·50
Presentation Pack (PO Pack No. 376)			5·75	
PHQ Cards (set of 7) (280)			2·00	11·50
MS2580 190×68 mm. Nos. 2574/9			5·25	5·50
First Day Cover (Tallents House)				5·75
First Day Cover (Portsmouth)				5·75

Nos. 2574/5, 2576/7 and 2578/9 were each printed together, *se-tenant*, in horizontal pairs throughout the sheets, each pair forming a composite design.

The phosphor bands are at just left of centre and at right of each stamp.

Booklet panes Nos. 2574b/5b come from the £7·26 Battle of Trafalgar booklet, No. DX35. The seven PHQ cards depict the six individual stamps and the miniature sheet.

(Litho Cartor or De La Rue)

2005 (18 Oct). *Bicentenary of the Battle of Trafalgar* (2nd issue). Booklet stamp. Design as Type **1516** (2001 White Ensign from Submarine Centenary). ^{MULTI COLOUR} Two phosphor bands. Perf 14½.

2581	**1516**	(1st) White Ensign. Multicoloured	1·50	1·50
		a. Booklet pane. No. 2581×3 with margins all round	7·00	

No. 2581 was issued in the £7·26 Trafalgar Bicentenary booklet, No. DX35, printed by Cartor, the £7·40 James Bond booklet, No. DX41, which was printed by De La Rue (see booklet pane No. 2805a) and the £7·93 Royal Navy Uniforms booklet, No. DX47.

1850 Black Madonna and Child from Haiti

1851 'Madonna and Child' (Marianne Stokes)

1852 'The Virgin Mary with the Infant Christ'

1853 Choctaw Virgin Mother and Child (Fr. John Giuliani)

1854 'Madonna and the Infant Jesus' (from India)

1855 'Come let us adore Him' (Dianne Tchumut)

(Des Irene Von Treskow. Gravure De La Rue)

2005 (1 Nov). *Christmas. Madonna and Child Paintings.* ^{MULTI COLOUR} One side phosphor band (2nd) or two phosphor bands (others). Perf 14½×14.

(a) Self-adhesive

2582	**1850**	(2nd) Black Madonna and Child from Haiti	90	90
		a. Booklet pane. No. 2582×24	19·50	
2583	**1851**	(1st) 'Madonna and Child'	1·00	1·00
		a. Booklet pane. No. 2583×12	10·50	

2584	**1852**	42p. 'The Virgin Mary with the Infant Christ'	90	90
2585	**1853**	60p. Choctaw Virgin Mother and Child	1·00	1·00
2586	**1854**	68p. 'Madonna and the Infant Jesus'	1·20	1·20
2587	**1855**	£1·12 'Come let us adore Him'	1·40	1·40
Set of 6			5·75	5·75
First Day Cover (Tallents House)				6·00
First Day Cover (Bethlehem, Llandeilo)				6·00
Presentation Pack (PO Pack No. 377)			6·00	
PHQ Cards (set of 7) (281)			2·00	12·00

The seven PHQ cards depict the six individual stamps and the miniature sheet.

(b) Ordinary gum

MS2588 115×102 mm. As Nos. 2582/7		5·75	5·75
First Day Cover (Tallents House)			6·00
First Day Cover (Bethlehem, Llandeilo)			6·00

Year Pack

2005 (1 Nov). Comprises Nos. 2502/23, 2525/9. **MS**2531/45, 2548/53, 2555/66, 2574/9 and 2582/7.

CP2587a Year Pack		65·00

Post Office Yearbook

2005 (1 Nov). Comprises Nos. 2502/23, 2525/9, **MS**2531/45, 2548/53, 2555/66, 2574/9 and 2582/7.

YB2587a Yearbook		60·00

Miniature Sheet Collection

2005 (1 Nov). Comprises Nos. **MS**2524, **MS**2530/1, **MS**2546/7, **MS**2554, **MS**2573, **MS**2580 and **MS**2588.

MS2588a Miniature Sheet Collection		45·00

1856 *The Tale of Mr. Jeremy Fisher* (Beatrix Potter)

1857 *Kipper* (Mick Inkpen)

1858 *The Enormous Crocodile* (Roald Dahl)

1859 *More About Paddington* (Michael Bond)

1860 *Comic Adventures of Boots* (Satoshi Kitamura)

1861 *Alice's Adventures in Wonderland* (Lewis Carroll)

1862 *The Very Hungry Caterpillar* (Eric Carle)

1863 *Maisy's ABC* (Lucy Cousins)

(Des Rose Design. Litho D.L.R.)

2006 (10 Jan). *Animal Tales.* |MULTI COLOUR| One side phosphor band (2nd) or two phosphor bands (others). Perf 14½.

2589	**1856**	(2nd) The Tale of Mr. Jeremy Fisher (Beatrix Potter)		90	90
		a. Horiz pair. Nos. 2589/90		1·80	1·80
2590	**1857**	(2nd) Kipper (Mick Inkpen)		90	90
2591	**1858**	(1st) The Enormous Crocodile (Roald Dahl)		1·00	1·00
		a. Horiz pair. Nos. 2591/2		2·00	2.00
2592	**1859**	(1st) More About Paddington (Michael Bond)		1·00	1·00
2593	**1860**	42p. Comic Adventures of Boots (Satoshi Kitamura)		80	80
		a. Horiz pair. Nos. 2593/4		1·60	1·60
2594	**1861**	42p. Alice's Adventures in Wonderland (Lewis Carroll)		80	80
2595	**1862**	68p. The Very Hungry Caterpillar (Eric Carle)		1·00	1·00
		a. Horiz pair. Nos. 2595/6		2·00	2·00
2596	**1863**	68p. Maisy's ABC (Lucy Cousins)		1·00	1·00

Set of 8 ... 6·75 6·75
Set of 4 Gutter Blocks of 4 ... 13·50
Set of 4 Traffic Light Gutter Blocks of 8 ... 50·00
First Day Cover (Tallents House) ... 7·75
First Day Cover (Mousehole, Penzance, Cornwall) ... 7·75
First Day Cover (Nos. 2595/6 UK and US stamps) ... 4·00
Presentation Pack (PO Pack No. 379) ... 8·75
PHQ Cards (set of 8) (282) ... 2·50 7·75

Nos. 2589/90, 2591/2, 2593/4 and 2595/6 were printed together, *se-tenant*, in horizontal pairs of 60 (2 panes 6×5).

A design as No. 2592 but self-adhesive was issued in sheets of 20, printed in lithography by Cartor *sold at* £6·55, containing four vertical rows of five stamps alternated with printed labels (LS28). This sheet was also available with personal photographs on the labels at £14·95 from Royal Mail.

No. 2595 contains two die-cut holes.

1864 Carding Mill Valley, Shropshire

1865 Beachy Head, Sussex

1866 St Paul's Cathedral, London

1867 Brancaster, Norfolk

1868 Derwent Edge, Peak District

1869 Robin Hood's Bay, Yorkshire

1870 Buttermere, Lake District

1871 Chipping Campden, Cotswolds

1872 St Boniface Down, Isle of Wight

1873 Chamberlain Square, Birmingham

(Des Phelan Barker Design Consultants. Gravure D.L.R.)

2006 (7 Feb). *A British Journey: England.* |MULTI COLOUR| Two phosphor bands. Perf 14½.

2597	**1864**	(1st) Carding Mill Valley, Shropshire	1·00	1·00
		a. Block of 10. Nos. 2597/2606	9·00	9·00
2598	**1865**	(1st) Beachy Head, Sussex	1·00	1·00
2599	**1866**	(1st) St Paul's Cathedral, London	1·00	1·00
2600	**1867**	(1st) Brancaster, Norfolk	1·00	1·00
2601	**1868**	(1st) Derwent Edge, Peak District	1·00	1·00
2602	**1869**	(1st) Robin Hood's Bay, Yorkshire	1·00	1·00
2603	**1870**	(1st) Buttermere, Lake District	1·00	1·00
2604	**1871**	(1st) Chipping Campden, Cotswolds	1·00	1·00
2605	**1872**	(1st) St Boniface Down, Isle of Wight	1·00	1·00
2606	**1873**	(1st) Chamberlain Square, Birmingham	1·00	1·00

Set of 10 ... 9·00 9·00
Gutter Block of 20 ... 18·00
First Day Cover (Tallents House) ... 9·50
First Day Cover (Tea Green, Luton) ... 9·75
Presentation Pack (PO Pack No. 380) ... 10·00
PHQ Cards (set of 10) (283) ... 3·00 9·75

Nos. 2597/606 were printed together, *se-tenant*, as blocks of ten (5×2) in sheets of 60 (2 panes of 30).

1874 Royal Albert Bridge

1875 Box Tunnel

1876 Paddington Station

1877 PSS *Great Eastern* (paddle steamer)

1878 Clifton Suspension Bridge Design

1879 Maidenhead Bridge

(Des Hat-trick Design. Litho Enschedé)

2006 (23 Feb). *Birth Bicentenary of Isambard Kingdom Brunel* (*engineer*) (1st issue). |MULTI COLOUR| Phosphor-coated paper (42p.) or two phosphor bands (others). Perf 14×13½.

2607	**1874**	(1st) Royal Albert Bridge	1·00	1·00
		a. Booklet pane. Nos. 2607, 2609 and 2612	2·50	
2608	**1875**	40p. Box Tunnel	60	60
		a. Booklet pane. Nos. 2608 and 2610/11	2·50	
2609	**1876**	42p. Paddington Station	65	65
2610	**1877**	47p. PSS *Great Eastern*	80	80
		a. Booklet pane. No. 2610 and No. 2614×2	7·00	
2611	**1878**	60p. Clifton Suspension Bridge	1·00	1·00
2612	**1879**	68p. Maidenhead Bridge	1·20	1·20
Set of 6			4·75	4·75
Set of 6 Gutter Pairs			9·50	
First Day Cover (Tallents House)				5·25
First Day Cover (Bristol)				5·25
Presentation Pack (PO Pack No. 381)			5·75	
PHQ Cards (set of 7) (284)			2·00	11·00
MS2613 190×65 mm. Nos. 2607/12			5·00	5·00
		a. Imperforate	—	
First Day Cover (Tallents House)				5·50
First Day Cover (Bristol)				5·50

The phosphor bands on Nos. 2607/8 and 2610/12 are at just left of centre and at right of each stamp.

Booklet panes Nos. 2607a/8a and 2610a come from the £7·40 Isambard Kingdom Brunel booklet, No. DX36. The complete miniature sheet is shown on one of the PHQ Cards with the others depicting individual stamps.

(Litho Enschedé)

2006 (23 Feb). *Birth Bicentenary of Isambard Kingdom Brunel* (2nd issue). Booklet stamp. Design as Type **1739** ('PSS *Great Western*' from 2004 Ocean Liners). |MULTI COLOUR| Two phosphor bands. Perf 14½×14.

2614	**1739**	68p. 'PPS *Great Western*, 1838' (Joseph Walter). Multicoloured	2·50	2·50

No. 2614 was only issued in the £7·40 Isambard Kingdom Brunel booklet, No. DX36.

1880 Sabre-tooth Cat

1881 Giant Deer

1882 Woolly Rhino

1883 Woolly Mammoth

1884 Cave Bear

(Des A. Davidson and H. Brown. Litho Enschedé)

2006 (21 Mar). *Ice Age Animals*. Black and silver. Two phosphor bands. Perf 14½.

2615	**1880**	(1st) Sabre-tooth Cat	1·00	1·00
2616	**1881**	42p. Giant Deer	90	90
2617	**1882**	47p. Woolly Rhino	1·00	1·00
2618	**1883**	68p. Woolly Mammoth	1·10	1·10
2619	**1884**	£1·12 Cave Bear	1·50	1·50
Set of 5			5·00	5·00
Set of 5 Gutter Pairs			10·00	
First Day Cover (Tallents House)				5·50

First Day Cover (Freezywater, Enfield)		5·50
Presentation Pack (PO Pack No. 382)	5·50	
PHQ Cards (set of 5) (285)	1·50	5·75

1885 On *Britannia*, 1972

1886 At Royal Windsor Horse Show, 1985

1887 At Heathrow Airport, 2001

1888 As Young Princess Elizabeth with Duchess of York, 1931

1889 At State Banquet, Ottawa, 1951

1890 Queen in 1960

1891 As Princess Elizabeth, 1940

1892 With Duke of Edinburgh, 1951

(Des Sedley Place. Gravure Enschedé)

2006 (18 Apr). *80th Birthday of Queen Elizabeth II*. Black, turquoise-green and grey. One side phosphor band (No. 2620), one centre phosphor band (No. 2621) or two phosphor bands (others). Perf 14½.

2620	**1885**	(2nd) On *Britannia*, 1972	90	90
		a. Horiz pair. Nos. 2620/1	1·80	1·80
2621	**1886**	(2nd) At Royal Windsor Horse Show, 1985	90	90
2622	**1887**	(1st) At Heathrow Airport, 2001	1·00	1·00
		a. Horiz pair. Nos. 2622/3	2·00	2·00
2623	**1888**	(1st) As Young Princess Elizabeth with Duchess of York, 1931	1·00	1·00
2624	**1889**	44p. At State Banquet, Ottawa, 1951	75	75
		a. Horiz pair. Nos. 2624/5	1·50	1·50
2625	**1890**	44p. Queen in 1960	75	75
2626	**1891**	72p. As Princess Elizabeth, 1940	1·00	1·00
		a. Horiz pair. Nos. 2626/7	2·00	2·00
2627	**1892**	72p. With Duke of Edinburgh, 1951	1·00	1·00
Set of 8			6·50	6·50
Set of 4 Gutter Strips of 4			13·00	
First Day Cover (Tallents House)				6·75
First Day Cover (Windsor)				6·75
Presentation Pack (PO Pack No. 383)			7·00	
PHQ Cards (set of 8) (286)			2·50	7·50

Nos. 2620/1, 2622/3, 2624/5 and 2626/7 were each printed together, *se-tenant*, as horizontal pairs in sheets of 60 (2 panes 6×5).

1893 England (1966)

1894 Italy (1934, 1938, 1982)

World Cup Winners

44

1895 Argentina (1978, 1986)

World Cup Winners

50

1896 Germany (1954, 1974, 1990)

World Cup Winners

64

1897 France (1998)

World Cup Winners

72

1898 Brazil (1958, 1962, 1970, 1994, 2002)

(Des Madeleine Bennett. Litho Walsall)

2006 (6 June). *World Cup Football Championship, Germany. World Cup Winners.* MULTI COLOUR Two phosphor bands. Perf 14½.

2628	**1893**	(1st) England	1·00	1·00
2629	**1894**	42p. Italy	80	80
2630	**1895**	44p. Argentina	85	85
2631	**1896**	50p. Germany	1·00	1·00
2632	**1897**	64p. France	1·20	1·20
2633	**1898**	72p. Brazil	1·40	1·40
Set of 6			5·50	5·50
Set of 6 Gutter Pairs			11·00	
First Day Cover (Tallents House)				5·75
First Day Cover (Balls Park, Hertford)				5·75
Presentation Pack (PO Pack No. 384)			6·00	
PHQ Cards (set of 6) (287)			1·80	6·50

The 1st class stamp was also issued in sheets of 20, sold for £6·95, printed in lithography by Cartor, containing four vertical rows of five stamps alternated with labels showing scenes from the 1966 World Cup final (LS31).

1899 30 St Mary Axe, London

1900 Maggie's Centre, Dundee

1901 Selfridges, Birmingham

1902 Downland Gridshell, Chichester

1903 An Turas, Isle of Tiree

1904 The Deep, Hull

(Des Roundel. Gravure Walsall)

2006 (20 June). *Modern Architecture.* MULTI COLOUR Two phosphor bands. Perf 14½.

2634	**1899**	(1st) 30 St Mary Axe, London	1·00	1·00
2635	**1900**	42p. Maggie's Centre, Dundee	65	65

2636	**1901**	44p. Selfridges, Birmingham	70	70
2637	**1902**	50p. Downland Gridshell, Chichester	85	85
2638	**1903**	64p. An Turas, Isle of Tiree	1·00	1·00
2639	**1904**	72p. The Deep, Hull	1·30	1·30
Set of 6			5·00	5·00
Set of 6 Gutter Pairs			10·00	
First Day Cover (Tallents House)				5·50
First Day Cover (London EC3)				5·50
Presentation Pack (PO Pack No. 385)			5·50	
PHQ Cards (set of 6) (288)			1·80	5·75

1905 *Sir Winston Churchill* (Walter Sickert)

1906 *Sir Joshua Reynolds* (self-portrait)

1907 *T. S. Eliot* (Patrick Heron)

1908 *Emmeline Pankhurst* (Georgina Agnes Brackenbury)

1909 *Virginia Woolf* (photo by George Charles Beresford)

1910 *Bust of Sir Walter Scott* (Sir Francis Leggatt Chantry)

1911 *Mary Seacole* (Albert Charles Challen)

1912 *William Shakespeare* (attrib to John Taylor)

1913 *Dame Cicely Saunders* (Catherine Goodman)

1914 *Charles Darwin* (John Collier)

(Des P. Willberg. Gravure De La Rue)

2006 (18 July). *150th Anniversary of National Portrait Gallery, London.* MULTI COLOUR Two phosphor bands. Perf 14½.

2640	**1905**	(1st) Sir Winston Churchill	1·00	1·00
		a. Block of 10. Nos. 2640/9	9·00	9·00
2641	**1906**	(1st) Sir Joshua Reynolds	1·00	1·00
2642	**1907**	(1st) T. S. Eliot	1·00	1·00
2643	**1908**	(1st) Emmeline Pankhurst	1·00	1·00

2644	**1909**	(1st) *Virginia Woolf*.......................................	1·00	1·00
2645	**1910**	(1st) *Bust of Sir Walter Scott*......................	1·00	1·00
2646	**1911**	(1st) *Mary Seacole*.......................................	1·00	1·00
2647	**1912**	(1st) *William Shakespeare*...........................	1·00	1·00
2648	**1913**	(1st) *Dame Cicely Saunders*........................	1·00	1·00
2649	**1914**	(1st) *Charles Darwin*....................................	1·00	1·00
Set of 10		....	9·00	9·00
Gutter Block of 20		....	18·00	
Traffic Light Gutter Block of 20		....	40·00	
First Day Cover (Tallents House)		....		9·25
First Day Cover (London WC2)		....		9·50
Presentation Pack (PO Pack No. 386)		....	11·00	
PHQ Cards (set of 10) (289)		....	3·00	10·00

Nos. 2640/9 were printed together, *se-tenant*, as blocks of ten (5×2) in sheets of 60 (2 panes of 30).

For Nos. 2650/7 and **MS**2658 see Decimal Machin Definitives section.

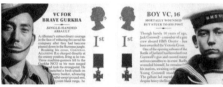

1918 Corporal Agansing Rai   **1919** Boy Seaman Jack Cornwell

1920 Midshipman Charles Lucas   **1921** Captain Noel Chavasse

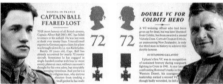

1922 Captain Albert Ball   **1923** Captain Charles Upham

(Des Atelier Works. Litho Enschedé)

2006 (21 Sept). *150th Anniversary of the Victoria Cross* (1st issue). |MULTI COLOUR| One side phosphor band. Perf 14½×14.

2659	**1918**	(1st) Corporal Agansing Rai.......................	1·00	1·00
		a. Horiz pair. Nos. 2659/60.......................	2·00	2·00
		b. Booklet pane. Nos. 2659, 2661		
		and 2663	3·50	
		ba. Booklet pane. Bronze and		
		phosphor omitted	£12500	
2660	**1919**	(1st) Boy Seaman Jack Cornwell...............	1·00	1·00
		b. Booklet pane. Nos. 2660, 2662		
		and 2664	3·50	
		ba. Booklet pane. Bronze and		
		phosphor omitted	£12500	
2661	**1920**	64p. Midshipman Charles Lucas............	90	90
		a. Horiz pair. Nos. 2661/2.......................	1·80	1·80
2662	**1921**	64p. Captain Noel Chavasse...................	90	90
2663	**1922**	72p. Captain Albert Ball........................	1·20	1·20
		a. Horiz pair. Nos. 2663/4.......................	2·40	2·40
2664	**1923**	72p. Captain Charles Upham.................	1·20	1·20
Set of 6		....	6·00	6·00
Set of 3 Gutter Strips of 4		....	12·00	
First Day Cover (Tallents House)		....		6·25
First Day Cover (Cuffley, Potters Bar, Herts)		....		6·25
Presentation Pack (PO Pack No. 387)		....	6·25	
MS2665		190×67 mm. Nos. 2659/64 and 2666..............	6·50	6·50
		a. Imperforate..	—	
First Day Cover (Tallents House)		....		6·50
First Day Cover (Cuffley, Potters Bar, Herts)		....		6·50
PHQ Cards (set of 7) (290)		....	2·00	13·50

Nos. 2659/60, 2661/2 and 2663/4 were each printed together, *se-tenant*, as horizontal pairs in sheets of 60 (2 panes 6×5).

Booklet panes Nos. 2659b/60b come from the £7·44 Victoria Cross booklet No. DX37.

The seven PHQ Cards depict the six individual stamps and the miniature sheet.

(Litho Enschedé)

2006 (21 Sept). *150th Anniversary of the Victoria Cross* (2nd issue). Booklet stamp. Design as No. 1517 (1990 Gallantry Awards). |MULTI COLOUR| 'All-over' phosphor. Perf 14×14½.

| 2666 | **959** | 20p. Victoria Cross..................................... | 1·50 | 1·50 |
| | | a. Booklet pane. Nos. 2666×4 .... | 6·50 | 6·50 |

No. 2666 was only issued in No. **MS**2665 and in the £7·44 Victoria Cross booklet, No. DX37.

1924 Sitar Player and Dancer   **1925** Reggae Bass Guitarist and African Drummer

1926 Fiddler and Harpist   **1927** Sax Player and Blues Guitarist

1928 Maraca Player and Salsa Dancers

(Des CDT Design. Litho Cartor)

2006 (3 Oct). *Europa. Integration. Sounds of Britain.* |MULTI COLOUR| 'All-over' phosphor. Perf 14½.

2667	**1924**	(1st) Sitar Player and Dancer..................	1·00	1·00
2668	**1925**	42p. Reggae Bass Guitarist and		
		African Drummer.....................................	1·00	1·00
2669	**1926**	50p. Fiddler and Harpist.........................	1·10	1·10
2670	**1927**	72p. Sax Player and Blues Guitarist......	1·20	1·20
2671	**1928**	£1·19 Maraca Player and Salsa Dancers	1·70	1·70
Set of 5		....	5·50	5·50
Set of 5 Gutter Pairs		....	11·00	
Set of 5 Traffic Light Gutter Blocks of 4		....	26·00	
First Day Cover (Tallents House)		....		6·00
First Day Cover (Rock, Kidderminster, Worcs)		....		6·00
Presentation Pack (PO Pack No. 388)		....	6·00	
PHQ Cards (set of 5) (291)		....	1·50	6·25

The 1st class and 50p. values include the 'EUROPA' emblem.

1929 'New Baby' (Alison Carmichael)   **1930** 'Best Wishes' (Alan Kitching)   **1931** 'THANK YOU' (Alan Kitching)

1932 Balloons (Ivan Chermayeff)   **1933** Firework (Kam Tang)   **1934** Champagne, Flowers and Butterflies (Olaf Hajek)

(Des NB Studio. Gravure Walsall)

2006 (17 Oct). *Smilers Booklet stamps* (2nd series). *Occasions.* Self-adhesive. |MULTI COLOUR| Two phosphor bands. Die-cut Perf 15×14.

2672	**1929**	(1st) 'New Baby'	1·00	1·00
		a. Booklet pane. Nos. 2672/7	6·00	6·00
2673	**1930**	(1st) 'Best Wishes'	1·00	1·00
2674	**1931**	(1st) 'THANK YOU'	1·00	1·00
2675	**1932**	(1st) Balloons	1·00	1·00
2676	**1933**	(1st) Firework	1·00	1·00
2677	**1934**	(1st) Champagne, Flowers and		
		Butterflies	1·00	1·00
Set of 6			6·00	6·00
First Day Cover (Tallents House)				6·25
First Day Cover (Grinshill, Shrewsbury)				6·25
Presentation Pack (PO Pack No. M13)			10·00	
PHQ Cards (set of 6) (D29)			1·80	7·00

Nos. 2672/7 were issued in £1·92 stamp booklets, No. QA3, in which the surplus backing paper around each stamp was removed.

Nos. 2672/7 were also issued in sheets of 20, No. LS33, containing four of Nos. 2672 and 2677 and three of each of the other designs, each stamp accompanied by a *se-tenant* greetings label. These sheets were printed by Cartor in lithography instead of photogravure and sold at £6·95 each.

These designs were available in separate sheets with personal photographs printed on the labels from Royal Mail in Edinburgh at £14·95 each.

Stamps as No. 2672 but perforated with one elliptical hole on each vertical side were issued on 28 October 2008 in sheets of 20 with circular *se-tenant* Peter Rabbit labels, No. LS50. These sheets were printed by Cartor in lithography instead of photogravure and sold for £7·95 each.

Similar sheets of ten stamps and ten *se-tenant* labels were sold in £7·95 packs.

No. 2674 was issued on 8 May 2010 with other greetings stamps in sheets of 20 with *se-tenant* greetings labels printed in lithography by Cartor, No. LS73, sold for £10 pre sheet. These sheets were printed with one elliptical hole in each vertical side.

1935 Snowman   **1936** Father   **1937** Snowman
                    Christmas

1938 Father Christmas   **1939** Reindeer   **1940** Christmas
                                                  Tree

(Des T. Kiuchi, Rose Design and CDT Design. Gravure De La Rue)

2006 (7 Nov). *Christmas.* |MULTI COLOUR| One centre phosphor band (No. 2678) or two phosphor bands (others). Perf 15×14.

(a) Self-adhesive.

2678	**1935**	(2nd) Snowman	90	90
		a. Booklet pane. No. 2678×12	9·75	
2679	**1936**	(1st) Father Christmas	1·00	1·00
		a. Booklet pane. No. 2679×12	11·00	
2680	**1937**	(2nd Large) Snowman	1·00	1·00
2681	**1938**	(1st Large) Father Christmas	1·20	1·20
2682	**1939**	72p. Reindeer	1·10	1·10
2683	**1940**	£1·19 Christmas Tree	1·50	1·50
Set of 6			6·00	6·00
First Day Cover (Tallents House)				7·00
First Day Cover (Bethlehem, Llandeilo)				7·00
Presentation Pack (PO Pack No. 389)			7·25	
PHQ Cards (set of 7) (292)			2·00	13·50

(b) Ordinary gum.

MS2684 115×102 mm. As Nos. 2678/83			6·50	6·75
First Day Cover (Tallents House)				7·00
First Day Cover (Bethlehem, Llandeilo)				7·00

The seven PHQ Cards depict the six individual stamps and the miniature sheet.

The 2nd and 1st class stamps were also issued together in sheets of 20 sold at £6, printed in lithography by Cartor, containing ten 1st class and ten 2nd class stamps, each value arranged in vertical rows of five alternating with rows of printed labels (LS34). The phosphor bands have the date ('2006') reversed out at the bottom (2nd) or bottom left (others). Separate sheets of 20 1st or 20 2nd class were available with personalised photographs at £9·95 (2nd class) or £14·95 (1st class) and in 2010 the same designs with one elliptical hole on each vertical side were available from Royal Mail, Edinburgh. All these sheets had the backing paper around the stamps retained.

1941 Lest We Forget (*Illustration reduced. Actual size* 124×71 *mm*)

(Des Hat-trick Design. Gravure De La Rue)

2006 (9 Nov). *Lest We Forget* (1st issue). *90th Anniversary of the Battle of the Somme.* Sheet 124×71 mm containing new stamp as No. 2883 and designs as Nos. EN17 (Type I), NI102, S120 and W109. |MULTI COLOUR| Two phosphor bands. Perf 14½ (1st) or 15×14 (with one elliptical hole in each vertical side) (72p).

MS2685 **1941** Lest We Forget (1st) Poppies on barbed			
wire stems; 72p.×4 As Nos. EN17 (Type I), NI102, S120			
and W109		5·50	5·50
First Day Cover (Tallents House)			6·00
First Day Cover (London SW1)			6·00
Presentation Pack (PO Pack No. 390)		7·25	

No. **MS**2685 (including the Northern Ireland stamp) is printed in gravure.

The 1st class stamp was also issued in sheets of 20 with *se-tenant* labels showing war memorials, printed in lithography by Cartor (LS35).

See also Nos. **MS**2796 and **MS**2886.

Year Pack

2006 (9 Nov). Comprises Nos. 2589/612, 2615/49, 2659/64, 2667/71, 2678/83 and **MS**2685.

| CP2685a Year Pack | 65·00 |

Post Office Yearbook

2006 (9 Nov). Comprises Nos. 2589/612, 2615/49, 2659/64, 2667/71, 2678/83 and **MS**2685.

| YB2685a Yearbook | 75·00 |

Miniature Sheet Collection

2006 (30 Nov). Comprises Nos. **MS**2613, **MS**2658, **MS**2665, **MS**2684/5, **MS**S153 and **MS**W143.

| **MS**2685a Miniature Sheet Collection | 38·00 |

1942 *with the beatles*   **1943** *Sgt Pepper's
                                  Lonely Hearts Club Band*

1944 *Help!*   **1945** *Abbey Road*

1946 *Revolver*   **1947** *Let It Be*

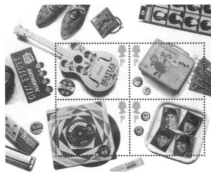

1948 Beatles Memorabilia (*Illustration reduced. Actual size 115×89 mm*)

(Des johnson banks)

2007 (9 Jan). *The Beatles. Album Covers.* [MULTI COLOUR] Two phosphor bands.

(a) Self-adhesive. Gravure Walsall. Die-cut irregular Perf 13½-14½.

2686	**1942**	(1st) *with the beatles*	1·00	1·00
		a. Horiz pair. Nos. 2686/7	2·00	
2687	**1943**	(1st) *Sgt Pepper's Lonely Hearts Club Band*	1·00	1·00
2688	**1944**	64p. *Help!*	90	90
		a. Horiz pair. Nos. 2688/9	1·80	
2689	**1945**	64p. *Abbey Road*	90	90
2690	**1946**	72p. *Revolver*	1·25	1·25
		a. Horiz pair. Nos. 2690/1	2·50	
2691	**1947**	72p. *Let It Be*	1·25	1·25
Set of 6			6·00	6·00
First Day Cover (Tallents House)				6·25
First Day Cover (Liverpool)				6·50
Presentation Pack (Nos. 2686/**MS**2692)				
(PO Pack No. 392)			10·00	
PHQ Cards (set of 11) (293)			3·25	15·50

(b) Ordinary gum. Litho Walsall. P 14.

MS2692 115×89 mm. **1948** Beatles Memorabilia (1st) Guitar; (1st) Yellow Submarine lunch-box and key-rings; (1st) Record 'Love Me Do'; (1st) Beatles tea tray and badges .... 3·75 3·75

First Day Cover (Tallents House)		6·25
First Day Cover (Liverpool)		6·50

Nos. 2686/91 are all die-cut in the shape of a pile of records.

Nos. 2686/7, 2688/9 and 2690/1 were each printed together in sheets of 60 (2 panes of 30), with the two designs alternating horizontally and the surplus backing paper around each stamp removed.

Nos. 2686/92 commemorate the 50th anniversary of the first meeting of Paul McCartney and John Lennon.

The complete miniature sheet is on one of the eleven PHQ cards, with the others depicting individual stamps, including those from **MS**2692.

(Gravure Walsall)

2007 (16 Jan)-**08**. *Smilers Booklet stamp* (3rd series). *'LOVE' design as No. 2569.* Self-adhesive. [MULTI COLOUR] Two phosphor bands. Die-cut Perf 15×14 (with one elliptical hole in each vertical side).

2693	**1842a**	(1st) multicoloured	5·50	5·50
		a. Booklet pane. No. 2655×5 and No. 2693	17·50	
		b. Booklet pane. No. 2693×2 with two attached labels and No. 2295×4 (15.1.08)	16·00	

No. 2693 was issued in stamp booklets, Nos. SA1 and SA2, in which the surplus backing paper around each stamp was removed.

No. 2693 was reissued on 8 May 2010 with other greetings stamps in sheets of 20 with *se-tenant* greetings labels printed in lithography by Cartor, No. LS73, sold for £10 per sheet.

Nos. 2694/8 are left vacant.

1949 Moon Jellyfish

1950 Common Starfish

1951 Beadlet Anemone

1952 Bass

1953 Thornback Ray

1954 Lesser Octopus

1955 Common Mussels

1956 Grey Seal

1957 Shore Crab

1958 Common Sun Star

(Des A. Ross. Litho Walsall)

2007 (1 Feb). *Sea Life.* [MULTI COLOUR] Two phosphor bands. Perf 14½.

2699	**1949**	(1st) Moon Jellyfish	1·00	1·00
		a. Block of 10. Nos. 2699/708	9·00	9·00
2700	**1950**	(1st) Common Starfish	1·00	1·00
2701	**1951**	(1st) Beadlet Anemone	1·00	1·00
2702	**1952**	(1st) Bass	1·00	1·00
2703	**1953**	(1st) Thornback Ray	1·00	1·00
2704	**1954**	(1st) Lesser Octopus	1·00	1·00
2705	**1955**	(1st) Common Mussels	1·00	1·00
2706	**1956**	(1st) Grey Seal	1·00	1·00
2707	**1957**	(1st) Shore Crab	1·00	1·00
2708	**1958**	(1st) Common Sun Star	1·00	1·00
Set of 10			9·00	9·00
Gutter Block of 20			18·00	
First Day Cover (Tallents House)				9·25
First Day Cover (Seal Sands, Middlesbrough, Cleveland)				9·50
Presentation Pack (PO Pack No. 393)			9·50	
PHQ Cards (set of 10) (294)			3·00	10·50

Nos. 2699/708 were printed together, *se-tenant*, as blocks of ten (5×2) in sheets of 60 (2 panes of 30).

1959 Saturn Nebula C55

1960 Eskimo Nebula C39

1961 Cat's Eye Nebula C6

1962 Helix Nebula C63

1963 Flaming Star Nebula C31   **1964** The Spindle C53

(Des D. Davis. Gravure Walsall)

2007 (13 Feb). *50th Anniversary of 'The Sky at Night'* (*TV programme*). *Nebulae*. Self-adhesive. Two phosphor bands. Die-cut Perf 14½×14.

2709	**1959**	(1st) Saturn Nebula C55	1·00	1·00
		a. Horiz pair. Nos. 2709/10	1·80	
2710	**1960**	(1st) Eskimo Nebula C39	2·00	2·00
2711	**1961**	50p. Cat's Eye Nebula C6	1·00	1·00
		a. Horiz pair. Nos. 2711/12	1·80	
2712	**1962**	50p. Helix Nebula C63	90	90
2713	**1963**	72p. Flaming Star Nebula C31	1·20	1·20
		a. Horiz pair. Nos. 2713/14	2·40	
2714	**1964**	72p. The Spindle C53	1·20	1·20
Set of 6			5·75	5·75
First Day Cover (Tallents House)				6·25
First Day Cover (Star, Glenrothes, Fife)				6·25
Presentation Pack (PO Pack No. 394)			7·00	
PHQ Cards (set of 6) (295)			1·80	7·00

Nos. 2709/10, 2711/12 and 2713/14 were each printed together in sheets of 60 (2 panes of 30), with the two designs alternating horizontally and the surplus backing paper around each stamp removed.

1965 Iron Bridge (Thomas Telford)   **1966** Steam Locomotive and Railway Tracks

1967 Map of British Isles and Australia (telephone)   **1968** Camera and Television (John Logie Baird)

1969 Globe as Web (email and internet)   **1970** Couple with Suitcases on Moon (space travel)

(Des P. Willberg. Gravure De La Rue)

2007 (1 Mar). *World of Invention* (1st issue). Self-adhesive. Two phosphor bands. Die-cut Perf 14½×14.

2715	**1965**	(1st) Iron Bridge	1·00	1·00
		a. Horiz pair. Nos. 2715/16	2·00	
2716	**1966**	(1st) Steam Locomotive and Railway Tracks	1·00	1·00
2717	**1967**	64p. Map of British Isles and Australia	90	90
		a. Horiz pair. Nos. 2717/18	1·80	
2718	**1968**	64p. Camera and Television	90	90
2719	**1969**	72p. Globe as Web	1·25	1·25
		a. Horiz pair. Nos. 2719/20	2·50	
2720	**1970**	72p. Couple with Suitcases on Moon	1·25	1·25
Set of 6			6·00	6·00
First Day Cover (Tallents House)				6·25
First Day Cover (Pont Menai, Menai Bridge, Gwynedd)				6·25
Presentation Pack (PO Pack No. 395)			6·25	
PHQ Cards (set of 7) (296)			2·00	7·25

Nos. 2715/16, 2717/18 and 2719/20 were each printed together in sheets of 60 (2 panes of 30), with the two designs alternating horizontally and the surplus backing paper around each stamp removed.

The seven PHQ Cards depict the six individual stamps and **MS**2727.

(Gravure De La Rue)

2007 (1 Mar). *World of Invention* (2nd issue). Two phosphor bands. Perf 14½×14.

2721	**1965**	(1st) Iron Bridge	1·00	1·00
		a. Booklet pane. Nos. 2721/4	7·00	
		b. Booklet pane. Nos. 2721/2 and 2725/6	7·00	
2722	**1966**	(1st) Steam Locomotive and Railway Tracks	1·00	1·00
2723	**1967**	64p. Map of British Isles and Australia	2·50	2·50
2724	**1968**	64p. Camera and Television	2·50	2·50
2725	**1969**	72p. Globe as Web	2·50	2·50
2726	**1970**	72p. Couple with Suitcases on Moon	2·50	2·50
Set of 6			11·00	11·00
MS2727 115×104 mm. Nos. 2721/6			12·00	12·00
First Day Cover (Tallents House)				12·00
First Day Cover (Pont Menai, Menai Bridge, Gwynedd)				12·00

Nos. 2721/6 were only issued in the £7·49 World of Invention booklet, No. DX38 and in No. **MS**2727.

1971 William Wilberforce and Anti-slavery Poster   **1972** Olaudah Equiano and Map of Slave Trade Routes

1973 Granville Sharp and Slave Ship   **1974** Thomas Clarkson and Diagram of Slave Ship

1975 Hannah More and Title Page of *The Sorrows of Yamba*   **1976** Ignatius Sancho and Trade/Business Card

(Des Howard Brown. Litho Cartor)

2007 (22 Mar). *Bicentenary of the Abolition of the Slave Trade*. Two phosphor bands. Perf 14½.

2728	**1971**	(1st) William Wilberforce	1·00	1·00
		a. Horiz pair. Nos. 2728/9	2·00	
		ab. Gold and phosphor omitted	£3500	
2729	**1972**	(1st) Olaudah Equiano	1·00	1·00
2730	**1973**	50p. Granville Sharp	80	80
		a. Horiz pair. Nos. 2730/1	1·60	
2731	**1974**	50p. Thomas Clarkson	80	80
2732	**1975**	72p. Hannah More	90	90
		a. Horiz pair. Nos. 2732/3	1·80	
2733	**1976**	72p. Ignatius Sancho	90	90
Set of 6			5·00	5·00
Set of 3 Gutter Strips of 4			10·00	
Set of 3 Traffic Light Gutter Strips of 4			42·00	
First Day Cover (Tallents House)				5·75
First Day Cover (Hull)				5·75
Presentation Pack (PO Pack No. 396)			6·00	
PHQ Cards (set of 6) (297)			1·80	6·00

Nos. 2728/9, 2730/1 and 2732/3 were each printed together, *se-tenant*, in horizontal pairs throughout the sheets.

1977 Ice Cream Cone

1978 Sandcastle

1979 Carousel Horse

1980 Beach Huts

1981 Deckchairs

1982 Beach Donkeys

(Des Phelan Barker. Gravure De La Rue)

2007 (15 May). *Beside the Seaside.* |MULTI COLOUR| Two phosphor bands. *Perf 14½.*

2734	**1977**	1st Ice Cream Cone	1·00	1·00
2735	**1978**	46p. Sandcastle	80	80
2736	**1979**	48p. Carousel Horse	90	90
2737	**1980**	54p. Beach Huts	1·00	1·00
2738	**1981**	69p. Deckchairs	1·10	1·10
2739	**1982**	78p. Beach Donkeys	1·20	1·20
Set of 6			5·50	5·50
Set of 6 Gutter Pairs			11·00	
First Day Cover (Tallents House)				5·75
First Day Cover (Blackpool)				5·75
Presentation Pack (PO Pack No. 397)			6·00	
PHQ Cards (set of 6) (298)			1·80	6·25

See also No. 2848.

1983 Wembley Stadium (*Illustration reduced. Actual size 113×103 mm*)

(Des Roundel. Gravure De La Rue)

2007 (17 May). New Wembley Stadium, London. Sheet 113×103 mm containing design as Type 1593 but with 'WORLD CUP 2002' inscription omitted, and Nos. EN6a and EN18, each×2. |MULTI COLOUR| One centre phosphor band (2nd) or two phosphor bands (others). Perf 14½×14 (1st) or 15×14 (with one elliptical hole in each vertical side) (2nd, 78p.).

MS2740 **1983** Wembley Stadium (1st) As Type 1593; (2nd) No. EN6a×2; 78p. No. EN18×2 and one central stamp-size label			4·75	4·75
First Day Cover (Tallents House)			4·75	4·75

First Day Cover (Wembley).. 4·75   4·75
The design as Type 1593 omits the 'WORLD CUP 2002' inscription at the left of the stamp.

1984 Arnold Machin

1985 1967 4d. Machin

1986 The Machin Definitives (*Illustration reduced. Actual size 127×73 mm*)

(Des Jeffery Matthews and Together Design. Gravure and embossed De La Rue)

2007 (5 June). *40th Anniversary of the First Machin Definitives.* 'All-over' phosphor (1st) or two phosphor bands (others). Perf 14½ (1st) or 15×14 (with one elliptical hole in each vertical side) (£1).

2741	**1984**	(1st) Arnold Machin	1·80	1·80
		a. Booklet pane. Nos. 2741/2, each×2, with margins all round	7·50	
2742	**1985**	(1st) 1967 4d. Machin	1·80	1·80
MS2743		127×73mm **1986** The Machin Definitives Nos. 2741/2, Y1743 and Y1744	4·75	4·75
		a. Imperf	£8500	
First Day Cover (**MS**2743) (Tallents House)				5·00
First Day Cover (**MS**2743) (Windsor)				5·00
First Day Cover (**MS**2743) (Stoke-on-Trent)				5·00
Presentation Pack (**MS**2743) (PO Pack No. 398)			5·50	
PHQ Cards (set of 3) (Nos. 2741/**MS**2743) (299)			1·00	7·50

Nos. 2741/2 were only issued in the £7·66 The Machin - The Making of a Masterpiece booklet, No. DX39 and in No. **MS**2743. Stamps as Type **1984** but with phosphor frames were issued in sheets of 20 with *se-tenant* labels showing the 1967–9 Machin definitives (LS40). These sheets were sold for £7·35.

1987 Stirling Moss in Vanwall 2.5L, 1957

1988 Graham Hill in BRM P57, 1962

1989 Jim Clark in Lotus 25 Climax, 1963

1990 Jackie Stewart in Tyrrell 006/2, 1973

1991 James Hunt in McLaren M23, 1976

1992 Nigel Mansell in Williams FW11, 1986

(Des True North. Litho Cartor)

2007 (3 July). *Grand Prix. Racing Cars.* [MULTI COLOUR] Two phosphor bands. Perf 14½.

2744	**1987**	(1st) Stirling Moss in Vanwall 2.5L.......	1·00	1·00
2745	**1988**	(1st) Graham Hill in BRM P57	1·00	1·00
2746	**1989**	54p. Jim Clark in Lotus 25 Climax	90	90
2747	**1990**	54p. Jackie Stewart in Tyrrell 006/2	90	90
2748	**1991**	78p. James Hunt in McLaren M23........	1·20	1·20
2749	**1992**	78p. Nigel Mansell in Williams FW11 ...	1·20	1·20

Set of 6..	5·50	5·50
Set of 6 Gutter Pairs.........................	11·00	
First Day Cover (Tallents House)		6·00
First Day Cover (Silverstone, Towcester, Northants)		6·00
Presentation Pack (PO Pack No. 399)..................	6·00	
PHQ Cards (set of 6) (300)...............................	1·80	6·25

Nos. 2744/9 commemorate the 50th anniversary of Stirling Moss' Victory in the British Grand Prix and the centenary of the opening of Brooklands race track.

1993 *Harry Potter and the Philosopher's Stone*

1994 *Harry Potter and the Chamber of Secrets*

1995 *Harry Potter and the Prisoner of Azkaban*

1996 *Harry Potter and the Goblet of Fire*

1997 *Harry Potter and the Order of the Phoenix*

1998 *Harry Potter and the Half-Blood Prince*

1999 *Harry Potter and the Deathly Hallows*

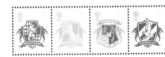

2000 Crests of Hogwarts School and its Four Houses (*illustration reduced. Actual size 123×70 mm*)

(True North. Litho Walsall)

2007 (17 July). *Publication of Final Book in the Harry Potter Series.* [MULTI COLOUR]

(a) Book Covers. 'All-over' phosphor. P 14½.

2750	**1993**	(1st) *Harry Potter and the Philosopher's Stone*........................	1·00	1·00
		a. Horiz strip of 7. Nos. 2750/6	6·25	6·25
2751	**1994**	(1st) *Harry Potter and the Chamber of Secrets*	1·00	1·00
2752	**1995**	(1st) *Harry Potter and the Prisoner of Azkaban*	1·00	1·00
2753	**1996**	(1st) *Harry Potter and the Goblet of Fire*................................	1·00	1·00

2754	**1997**	(1st) *Harry Potter and the Order of the Phoenix*...........................	1·00	1·00
2755	**1998**	(1st) *Harry Potter and the Half-Blood Prince*................................	1·00	1·00
2756	**1999**	(1st) *Harry Potter and the Deathly Hallows*...............................	1·00	1·00

Set of 7..	6·25	6·25
Gutter Block of 14.............................	12·50	
Traffic Light Gutter Block of 14........	32·00	
First Day Cover (Tallents House)		6·50
First Day Cover (Broom, Alcester, Warwickshire)........		6·50
Presentation Pack (Nos. 2750/7) (PO Pack No. M16).......	12·00	
PHQ Cards (set of 13) (HP)	4·00	19·50

(b) Crests of Hogwarts School and its Four Houses. [MULTI COLOUR] Two phosphor bands. P 15×14.

MS2757 123×70 mm. **2000** Crests of Hogwarts School and its Four Houses (1st) Gryffindor; (1st) Hufflepuff; (1st) Hogwarts; (1st) Ravenclaw; (1st) Slytherin	4·50	4·50
First Day Cover (Tallents House).................		5·75
First Day Cover (Broom, Alcester, Warwickshire)............		5·75

Nos. 2750/6 were printed together, *se-tenant*, as horizontal strips of seven stamps in sheets of 56 (2 panes 7×4).

The complete miniature sheet is shown on one of the thirteen PHQ cards with the others depicting individual stamps including those from **MS**2757.

Stamps as those within **MS**2757 but self-adhesive were issued in sheets of 20 containing the five designs *se-tenant* with labels depicting either magic spells (LS41, *sold for £7·35*) or personal photographs (*sold for £14·95*). The magic spells labels are printed in thermochromic ink which fades temporarily when exposed to heat, revealing the meaning of the spells.

2001 Scout and Camp Fire

2002 Scouts Rock climbing

2003 Scout planting Tree

2004 Adult Volunteer teaching Scout Archery

2005 Scouts learning gliding

2006 Scouts from Many Nations

(Des Gez Fry and The Work Room. Litho Enschedé)

2007 (26 July). *Europa. Centenary of Scouting and 21st World Scout Jamboree, Chelmsford, Essex.* [MULTI COLOUR] Two phosphor bands. Perf 14½×14.

2758	**2001**	(1st) Scout and Camp Fire......................	1·00	1·00
2759	**2002**	46p. Scouts Rock climbing......................	80	80
2760	**2003**	48p. Scout planting Tree.........................	85	85
2761	**2004**	54p. Adult Volunteer teaching Scout Archery..	95	95
2762	**2005**	69p. Scouts learning gliding..................	1·10	1·10
2763	**2006**	78p. Scouts from Many Nations	1·30	1·30

Set of 6..	5·50	5·50
Set of 6 Gutter Pairs.........................	11·00	
First Day Cover (Tallents House)		6·00
First Day Cover (Brownsea Island, Poole, Dorset)............		6·00
Presentation Pack (PO Pack No. 400).................	6·00	
PHQ Cards (set of 6) (301)................................	1·80	6·25

The 1st class and 48p. values include the 'EUROPA' emblem.

2007 White-tailed Eagle   **2008** Bearded Tit

2009 Red Kite   **2010** Cirl Bunting

2011 Marsh Harrier   **2012** Avocet

2013 Bittern   **2014** Dartford Warbler

2015 Corncrake   **2016** Peregrine Falcon

(Des Kate Stephens. Litho Da La Rue)

2007 (4 Sept). *Action for Species* (1st series). Birds. Two phosphor bands. Perf 14½.

2764	**2007**	(1st) White-tailed Eagle	1·00	1·00
		a. Block of 10. Nos. 2764/73	9·00	9·00
2765	**2008**	(1st) Bearded Tit	1·00	1·00
2766	**2009**	(1st) Red Kite	1·00	1·00
2767	**2010**	(1st) Cirl Bunting	1·00	1·00
2768	**2011**	(1st) Marsh Harrier	1·00	1·00
2769	**2012**	(1st) Avocet	1·00	1·00
2770	**2013**	(1st) Bittern	1·00	1·00
2771	**2014**	(1st) Dartford Warbler	1·00	1·00
2772	**2015**	(1st) Corncrake	1·00	1·00
2773	**2016**	(1st) Peregrine Falcon	1·00	1·00
Set of 10			9·00	9·00
Gutter Block of 20			18·00	
First Day Cover (Tallents House)				9·50
First Day Cover (Dartford)				9·50
Presentation Pack (PO Pack No. 401)			10·00	
PHQ Cards (set of 10) (302)			3·00	9·75

Nos. 2764/73 were printed together, *se-tenant*, as blocks of ten (5×2) in sheets of 60 (2 panes of 30).

2017 NCO, Royal Military Police, 1999   **2018** Tank Commander, 5th Royal Tank Regiment, 1944

2019 Observer, Royal Field Artillery, 1917   **2020** Rifleman, 95th Rifles, 1813

2021 Grenadier, Royal Regiment of Foot of Ireland, 1704   **2022** Trooper, Earl of Oxford's Horse, 1661

(Des Graham Turner and Atelier Works. Litho Enschedé)

2007 (20 Sept)-**15**. *Military Uniforms* (1st series). *British Army Uniforms.* Two phosphor bands. Perf 14½.

2774	**2017**	(1st) NCO, Royal Military Police	1·00	1·00
		a. Horiz strip of 3. Nos. 2774/6	3·00	3·00
		b. Booklet pane. Nos. 2774/6 with margins all round (14.5.15)	3·00	
2775	**2018**	(1st) Tank Commander, 5th Royal Tank Regiment	1·00	1·00
2776	**2019**	(1st) Observer, Royal Field Artillery	1·00	1·00
		b. Booklet pane No. 2776×4 with margins all round	3·95	
2777	**2020**	78p. Rifleman, 95th Rifles	1·20	1·20
		a. Horiz strip of 3. Nos. 2777/9	3·75	3·75
		b. Booklet pane. Nos. 2777/9 with margins all round	3·75	3·75
2778	**2021**	78p. Grenadier, Royal Regiment of Foot of Ireland	1·20	1·20
2779	**2022**	78p. Trooper, Earl of Oxford's Horse	1·20	1·20
Set of 6			6·50	6·50
Set of 2 Gutter blocks of 6			13·00	
Set of 2 Traffic Light Gutter blocks of 6			30·00	
First Day Cover (Tallents House)				7·00
First Day Cover (Boot, Holmrook, Cumbria)				7·00
Presentation Pack (PO Pack No. 402)			7·00	
PHQ Cards (set of 6) (303)			1·80	7·00

Nos. 2774/6 and 2777/9 were each printed together, *se-tenant*, in horizontal strips of three stamps in sheets of 60 (2 panes 6×5).

Booklet panes Nos. 2774b and 2777b come from the £7·66 British Army Uniforms booklet, No., DX40. 2776b comes from the £13·96 Centenary of First World War (2nd issue) booklet, No DY13.

2023 Leaving St Paul's Cathedral after Thanksgiving Service, 2006   **2024** Inspecting King's Troop Royal Horse Artillery, Regents Park, 1997

2025 At Garter Ceremony, Windsor, 1980

2026 At Royal Ascot, 1969

2027 At Premiere of *The Guns of Navarone*, 1961

2028 At Clydebank, 1947

2029 Photographs of the Royal Family (*illustration reduced. Actual size 115×89 mm*)

(Des Studio David Hillman)

2007 (16 Oct). *Diamond Wedding of Queen Elizabeth II and Duke of Edinburgh.* Blackish brown and black.

(a) Ordinary gum. Litho Cartor. 'All-over' phosphor. P 14½×14.

2780	**2023**	(1st) Leaving St Paul's Cathedral.............	1·00	1·00
		a. Horiz pair. Nos. 2780/1	2·00	2·00
2781	**2024**	(1st) Inspecting King's Troop Royal Horse Artillery	1·00	1·00
2782	**2025**	54p. At Garter Ceremony	85	85
		a. Horiz pair. Nos. 2782/3	1·70	1·70
2783	**2026**	54p. At Royal Ascot..................................	85	85
2784	**2027**	78p. At Premiere of The Guns of Navarone	1·20	1·30
		a. Horiz pair. Nos. 2784/5	2·40	2·60
2785	**2028**	78p. At Clydebank	1·20	1·30

Set of 6.. 5·50 5·75
Set of 3 Gutter blocks of 4 .... 11·00
First Day Cover (Tallents House)..................... 7·25
First Day Cover (Windsor, Berks).................... 7·25
Presentation Pack (Nos. 2780/**MS**2786)
(PO Pack No. 403).. 11·00
PHQ Cards (set of 11) (304)............................ 3·25 15·50

(b) Self-adhesive. Gravure Walsall. Two phosphor bands. P 14½.

MS2786 115×89 *mm.* **2029** Photographs of the Royal Family (1st) Royal family, Balmoral, 1972; (1st) Queen and Prince Philip, Buckingham Palace, 2007; 69p. Royal family, Windsor Castle, 1965; 78p. Princess Elizabeth, Prince Philip, Prince Charles and Princess Anne, Clarence House, 1951 .... 4·00 4·25
First Day Cover (Tallents House)..................... 5·75
First Day Cover (Windsor, Berks).................... 5·75

Nos. 2780/1, 2782/3 and 2784/5 were each printed together, *se-tenant*, in horizontal pairs throughout the sheets.

The complete miniature sheet is shown on one of the eleven PHQ cards with the others depicting individual stamps including those from **MS**2786.

2030 *Madonna and Child* (William Dyce), *c* 1827

2031 *The Madonna of Humility* (Lippo di Dalmasio), *c* 1390–1400)

(Des Peter Willberg. Gravure De La Rue)

2007 (6 Nov). *Christmas* (1st issue). *Paintings of the Madonna and Child.* Self-adhesive. One centre phosphor band (2nd) or two phosphor bands (1st). Die-cut Perf 15×14 (with one elliptical hole in each vertical side).

2787	**2030**	(2nd) Madonna and Child	90	90
2788	**2031**	(1st) The Madonna of Humility	1·10	1·10

First Day Cover (Tallents House).................................... 2·75
First Day Cover (Bethlehem, Llandeilo)........................ 2·75

2032 Angel playing Trumpet ('PEACE')

2033 Angel playing Lute ('GOODWILL')

2034 Angel playing Trumpet ('PEACE')

2035 Angel playing Lute ('GOODWILL')

2036 Angel playing Flute ('JOY')

2037 Angel playing Tambourine ('GLORY')

(Des Marco Ventura and Rose Design. Gravure De La Rue)

2007 (6 Nov). *Christmas* (2nd issue). *Angels.* One centre phosphor band (2789) or two phosphor bands (others). Perf 15×14.

(a) Self-adhesive.

2789	**2032**	(2nd) Angel playing Trumpet......................	90	90
		a. Booklet pane. No. 2789×12.............	9·75	
2790	**2033**	(1st) Angel playing Lute............................	1·00	1·00
		a. Booklet pane. No. 2790×12.............	11·00	
2791	**2034**	(2nd Large) Angel playing Trumpet	1·20	1·20
2792	**2035**	(1st Large) Angel playing Lute	1·50	1·50
2793	**2036**	78p. Angel playing Flute..........................	1·50	1·50
2794	**2037**	£1·24 Angel playing Tambourine..............	2·25	2·25

Set of 6.. 7·50 7·50
First Day Cover (Tallents House)..................... 7·75
First Day Cover (Bethlehem, Llandeilo) .... 8·00
Presentation Pack (Nos. 2787/94) (PO Pack No. 404)...... 9·75
PHQ Cards (set of 9) (305)............................. 2·75 17·50

(b) Ordinary gum.

MS2795 115×102 mm. As Nos. 2789/94........ 7·50 7·50
First Day Cover (Tallents House)..................... 7·75
First Day Cover (Bethlehem, Llandeilo) .... 8·00

The phosphor bands on Nos. 2791/2 are at the centre and right of each stamp.

The PHQ cards depict Nos. 2787/94 and **MS**2795.

The 2nd class, 1st class and 78p. stamps were also issued together in sheets of 20 sold at £8·30 containing eight 1st class, eight 2nd class and four 78p. stamps, arranged in vertical strips of five stamps alternated with printed labels (LS42). Separate sheets of 20 1st, 20 2nd or ten 78p. were available with personalised photographs from Royal Mail, Edinburgh. These were sold at £9·95 for 20 2nd or £14·95 for 20 1st or 10 78p. All these sheets were printed in lithography by Cartor and had the backing paper around the stamps retained.

2038 Lest We Forget (*Illustration reduced. Actual size 124×70 mm*)

(Des Hat-trick design. Litho De La Rue)

2007 (8 Nov). *Lest We Forget (2nd issue). 90th Anniversary of the Battle of Passchendaele.* Sheet 124×70 mm containing new stamp as No. 2884 and designs as Nos. EN18, NI128, S121 and W110. [MULTI COLOUR] Two phosphor bands. Perf 14½ (1st) or 15×14 (with one elliptical hole in each vertical side) (78p.).

MS2796 **2038** Lest We Forget (1st) Soldiers in
poppy flower; 78p.×4 As Nos. EN18, NI128, S121
and W110 .... 6·00   6·00
First Day Cover (Tallents House) .... 6·25
First Day Cover (London SW1) .... 6·25
Presentation Pack (PO Pack No. 405) .... 6·50

No. MS2796 (including the England, Northern Ireland, Scotland and Wales stamps) is printed in lithography.

A single example of the 'Soldiers in Poppy' stamp from MS2796 is known without the silver (Queen's head and value) omitted.

The 1st class stamp was also issued in sheets of 20 with *se-tenant* labels showing soldiers and their letters home, printed in lithography by Cartor and sold at £7·35 (LS43).

Year Pack

2007 (8 Nov). Comprises Nos. 2686/92, 2699/720, 2728/39, MS2743/94 and MS2796.
CP2796a Year Pack .... 120·00

Post Office Yearbook

2007 (8 Nov). Comprises Nos. 2686/92, 2699/720, 2728/39, MS2743/94 and MS2796.
YB2796a Yearbook .... 80·00

Miniature Sheet Collection

2007 (8 Nov). Comprises Nos. MS2692, MS2727, MS2740, MS2743, MS2757, MS2786 and MS2795/6.
MS2796a Miniature Sheet Collection .... 47·00

2039 *Casino Royale*

2040 *Dr. No*

2041 *Goldfinger*

2042 *Diamonds are Forever*

2043 *For Your Eyes Only*

2044 *From Russia with Love*

(Des A2. Litho De La Rue)

2008 (8 Jan). *Birth Centenary of Ian Fleming* (author of James Bond books). *Book Covers.* [MULTI COLOUR] Two phosphor bands. Perf 14½×14.

2797	**2039**	(1st) *Casino Royale*	1·00	1·00
		a. Booklet pane. Nos. 2797, 2799		
		and 2801 with margins all round	3·00	
2798	**2040**	(1st) *Dr. No*	1·00	1·00
		a. Booklet pane. Nos. 2798, 2800		
		and 2802 with margins all round	3·00	
		aa. Phosphor omitted	£1000	
2799	**2041**	54p. *Goldfinger*	90	90
2800	**2042**	54p. *Diamonds are Forever*	90	90
2801	**2043**	78p. *For Your Eyes Only*	1·20	1·20
2802	**2044**	78p. *From Russia with Love*	1·20	1·20
Set of 6			5·50	5·50
Set of 6 Gutter Pairs			11·00	
First Day Cover (Tallents House)				6·75
First Day Cover (London SE1)				6·75
Presentation Pack (PO Pack No. 407)			6·50	
PHQ Cards (set of 7) (306)			2·00	15·50
MS2803 189×68 mm. Nos. 2797/2802			9·25	9·25
First Day Cover (Tallents House)				9·25
First Day Cover (London SE1)				9·25

Booklet panes Nos. 2797a/8a come from the £7·40 Ian Fleming's James Bond booklet, No. DX41.

No. 2804 is vacant.

(Litho De La Rue)

2008 (8 Jan). *Ian Fleming's James Bond.* Booklet stamp. Design as Type **1517** (2001 Union Jack from Submarine Centenary). |MULTI COLOUR| Two phosphor bands. Perf 14½.

2805	**1517**	(1st) multicoloured	2·00	2·00
		a. Booklet pane.		
		Nos. 2581 and 2805, each×2,		
		with margins all round	7·00	

No. 2805 was issued in the £7·40 Ian Fleming's James Bond booklet, No. DX41. It had previously been issued in Post Office Label sheet LS20.

For White Ensign stamp from booklet No. DX41 see No. 2581.

2045 Assistance Dog carrying Letter (Retriever 'Rowan')

2046 Mountain Rescue Dog (Cross-bred 'Merrick')

2047 Police Dog (German Shepherd 'Max')

2048 Customs Dog (Springer Spaniel 'Max')

2049 Sheepdog (Border Collie 'Bob')

2050 Guide Dog (Labrador 'Warwick')

(Des Redpath Design. Litho Cartor)

2008 (5 Feb). *Working Dogs.* |MULTI COLOUR| Two phosphor bands. Perf 14½.

2806	**2045**	(1st) Assistance Dog carrying Letter	1·00	1·00
2807	**2046**	46p. Mountain Rescue Dog	80	80
2808	**2047**	48p. Police Dog	80	80
2809	**2048**	54p. Customs Dog	1·00	1·00
2810	**2049**	69p. Sheepdog	1·10	1·10
2811	**2050**	78p. Guide Dog	1·20	1·20
Set of 6			5·25	5·25
Set of 6 Gutter Pairs			10·50	
First Day Cover (Tallents House)				6·75
First Day Cover (Hound Green, Basingstoke, Hants)				6·75
Presentation Pack (PO Pack No. 408)			6·50	
PHQ Cards (set of 6) (307)			1·80	6·25

The 1st class value includes the 'EUROPA' emblem.

2051 Henry IV (1399–1413)

2052 Henry V (1413–1422)

2053 Henry VI (1422–1461 & 1470–1)

2054 Edward IV (1461–1470 & 1471–1483)

2055 Edward V (1483)

2056 Richard III (1483–1485)

2057 The Age of Lancaster and York (*Illustration reduced. Actual size* 123×70 mm)

(Des Atelier Works. Litho Cartor)

2008 (28 Feb). *Kings and Queens* (1st issue). Houses of Lancaster and York. |MULTI COLOUR| Two phosphor bands. Perf 14½.

2812	**2051**	(1st) Henry IV	1·00	1·00
2813	**2052**	(1st) Henry V	1·00	1·00
2814	**2053**	54p. Henry VI	1·00	1·00
2815	**2054**	54p. Edward IV	1·00	1·00
2816	**2055**	69p. Edward V	1·10	1·10
2817	**2056**	69p. Richard III	1·10	1·10
Set of 6			5·25	5·25
Set of 6 Gutter Pairs			10·50	
Set of 6 Traffic Light Gutter Blocks of 4			35·00	
First Day Cover (Tallents House)				6·75
First Day Cover (Tewkesbury)				6·75
Presentation Pack (PO Pack No. 409) (2812/**MS**2818)			11·00	
PHQ Cards (set of 11) (308)			3·25	15·00

MS2818 123×70 mm. **2057** The Age of Lancaster and York (1st) Owain Glyn Dwr ('Parliament'), 1404; (1st) Henry V's triumph at Battle of Agincourt, 1415; 78p. Yorkist victory at Battle of Tewkesbury, 1471; 78p. William Caxton, first English printer, 1477 .... 4·00 4·25

First Day Cover (Tallents House) .... 5·00
First Day Cover (Tewkesbury) .... 5·00

The complete miniature sheet is shown on one of the eleven PHQ cards with the others depicting individual stamps including those from **MS**2818.

(Gravure Walsall)

2008 (28 Feb). *Smilers* Booklet stamps (4th series). As Nos. 2567/8, 2570 and 2675/7. Self-adhesive. |MULTI COLOUR| Two phosphor bands. Die-cut Perf 15×14 (with one elliptical hole in each vertical side).

2819	**1842a**	(1st) Aircraft Sky-writing 'hello'	5·50	5·50
		a. Booklet pane. Nos. 2819/24	30·00	
2820	**1842**	(1st) Gazania splendens	5·50	5·50
2821	**1842c**	(1st) Union Jack	5·50	5·50
2822	**1932**	(1st) Balloons	5·50	5·50
2823	**1933**	(1st) Firework	5·50	5·50
2824	**1934**	(1st) Champagne, Flowers and Butterflies	5·50	5·50
Set of 6			30·00	30·00

Nos. 2819/24 were issued in £2·04 booklets, No. QA4, in which the surplus backing paper around each stamp was removed.

Similar sheets of ten stamps and ten *se-tenant* labels were only sold in packs for £7·95 each.

No. 2819 was re-issued again on 8 May 2010 for London 2010 Festival of Stamps in sheets of 20 *se-tenant* (No. LS72) printed in lithography by Cartor and originally sold for £8·50 per sheet.

Nos. 2820 and 2822 were each issued on 28 October 2008 in separate sheets of 20, Nos. LS51/3, with circular *se-tenant* labels showing the Almond Blossom fairy (2820), Mr. Men or Noddy (2822). These sheets were printed in lithography by Cartor and originally sold for £9·95 per sheet.

No. 2819 is also present on label sheets LS92 and LS100 and No. 2823 on label sheet LS91.

Nos. 2819, 2820 and 2822 were issued again on 30 April 2009 in separate sheets of 20, Nos. LS60/3, with circular *se-tenant* labels showing Jeremy Fisher (2819), Wild Cherry fairy (2820), Little Miss Sunshine or Big Ears (2822), sold for £8·50 per sheet.

Similar sheets of ten stamps and ten *se-tenant* labels were sold in £7·95 packs.

Nos. 2821/3 were issued on 8 May 2010 with other greetings stamps in sheets of 20 with *se-tenant* greetings labels, No. LS73 sold for £10 per sheet.

No. 2821 was issued on 12 February 2011 in sheets of 20 with *se-tenant* labels for Indipex International Stamp Exhibition, No. LS76, sold at £8·50 per sheet.

No. 2819 was issued in sheets of 20 with *se-tenant* labels on 28 July 2011 for Philanippon '11 World Stamp Exhibition, Yokohama (LS77), on 18 June 2012 for Indonesia 2012 International Stamp Exhibition, Jakarta (LS81), on 10 May 2013 for Australia 2013 World Stamp Exhibition, Melbourne (LS86) on 2 August 2013 for Bangkok 2013 World Stamp Exhibition, Thailand (LS87), on 13 May 2015 for Europhilex London 2015 Exhibition (LS95) and on 28 May 2016 for New York World Stamp Show (LS100), on 1 December 2015 for Kuala Lumpar 2015 (LS92).

No. 2823 was issued in sheets of 20 with *se-tenant* labels on 20 January 2012 for Lunar New Year, Year of the Dragon (LS80), on 7 February 2013 for Year of the Snake (LS84), 10 December 2013 for Year of the Horse (LS89), on 19 November 2014 for Year of the Sheep, on 9 November 2015 for Year of the Monkey (LS98) and on 15 November 2016 for Year of the Rooster (LS104).

All the above sheets were printed by Cartor (known from late 2013 onwards as International Security Printers) in lithography instead of photogravure.

2058 Lifeboat, Barra

2059 Lifeboat approaching Dinghy, Appledore

2060 Helicopter Winchman, Portland

2061 Inshore lifeboat, St Ives

2062 Rescue Helicopter, Lee-on-Solent

2063 Launch of Lifeboat, Dinbych-y-Pysgod, Tenby

(Des Hat-trick Design. Litho Walsall)

2008 (13 Mar). *Rescue at Sea.* |MULTI COLOUR 'All-over' phosphor. Perf 14½×14*.

2825	**2058**	(1st) Lifeboat, Barra	1·00	1·00
2826	**2059**	46p. Lifeboat approaching Dinghy, Appledore	80	80
2827	**2060**	48p. Helicopter Winchman, Portland	90	90
2828	**2061**	54p. Inshore lifeboat, St Ives	1·00	1·00
2829	**2062**	69p. Rescue Helicopter, Lee-on-Solent	1·10	1·10
2830	**2063**	78p. Launch of Lifeboat, Dinbych-y-Pysgod, Tenby	1·20	1·20
Set of 6			5·25	5·25
Set of 6 Gutter Pairs			10·50	
First Day Cover (Tallents House)				6·50
First Day Cover (Poole, Dorset)				6·50
Presentation Pack (PO Pack No. 411)			6·00	
PHQ Cards (set of 6) (309)			1·50	6·25

* Nos. 2825/30 have interrupted perforations along the top and bottom edges of the stamps, the gaps in the perforations forming the three dots and three dashes that spell out 'SOS' in morse code.

2064 *Lysandra bellargus* (Adonis blue)

2065 *Coenagrion mercuriale* (southern damselfly)

2066 *Formica rufibarbis* (red-barbed ant)

2067 *Pareulype berberata* (barberry carpet moth)

2068 *Lucanus cervus* (stag beetle)

2069 *Cryptocephalus coryli* (hazel pot beetle)

2070 *Gryllus campestris* (field cricket)

2071 *Hesperia comma* (silver-spotted skipper)

2072 *Pseudepipona herrichii* (Purbeck mason wasp)

2073 *Gnorimus nobilis* (noble chafer)

(Des Andrew Ross. Litho De La Rue)

2008 (15 Apr). *Action for Species* (2nd series). Insects. |MULTI COLOUR Phosphor background. Perf 14½.

2831	**2064**	(1st) *Lysandra bellargus* (Adonis blue)	1·00	1·00
		a. Block of 10. Nos. 2831/40	9·00	9·00
2832	**2065**	(1st) *Coenagrion mercuriale* (southern damselfly)	1·00	1·00
2833	**2066**	(1st) *Formica rufibarbis* (red-barbed ant)	1·00	1·00
2834	**2067**	(1st) *Pareulype berberata* (barberry carpet moth)	1·00	1·00
2835	**2068**	(1st) *Lucanus cervus* (stag beetle)	1·00	1·00
2836	**2069**	(1st) *Cryptocephalus coryli* (hazel pot beetle)	1·00	1·00
2837	**2070**	(1st) *Gryllus campestris* (field cricket)	1·00	1·00
2838	**2071**	(1st) *Hesperia comma* (silver-spotted skipper)	1·00	1·00
2839	**2072**	(1st) *Pseudepipona herrichii* (Purbeck mason wasp)	1·00	1·00
2840	**2073**	(1st) *Gnorimus nobilis* (noble chafer)	1·00	1·00
Set of 10			9·00	9·00
Gutter Block of 20			18·00	
First Day Cover (Tallents House)				9·25
First Day Cover (Crawley, W. Sussex)				9·50
Presentation Pack (PO Pack No. 412)			10·00	

PHQ Cards (set of 10) (310) .... 3·00   9·75
Nos. 2831/40 were printed together, *se-tenant*, as blocks of ten (5×2) in sheets of 60 (2 panes of 30).

2074 Lichfield
Cathedral

2075 Belfast Cathedral

2076 Gloucester
Cathedral

2077 St David's
Cathedral

2078 Westminster
Cathedral

2079 St Magnus
Cathedral, Kirkwall,
Orkney

2080 St Paul's Cathedral (*Illustration reduced. Actual size 115×89 mm*)

(Des Howard Brown. Litho Enschedé)

2008 (13 May). *Cathedrals.* |MULTI COLOUR| 'All-over' phosphor. Perf 14½.

2841	**2074**	(1st) Lichfield Cathedral	1·00	1·00
2842	**2075**	48p. Belfast Cathedral	85	85
2843	**2076**	50p. Gloucester Cathedral	1·00	1·00
2844	**2077**	56p. St David's Cathedral	1·10	1·10
2845	**2078**	72p. Westminster Cathedral	1·25	1·25
2846	**2079**	81p. St Magnus Cathedral, Kirkwall,		
		Orkney	1·40	1·40

Set of 6 .... 6·00   6·00
Set of 6 Gutter Pairs .... 12·00
Set of 6 Traffic Light Gutter Pairs .... 32·00
First Day Cover (Tallents House) ....   6·75
First Day Cover (London EC4) ....   6·75
Presentation Pack (PO Pack No. 413) (2841/**MS**2847) .... 11·00
PHQ Cards (set of 11) (311) .... 3·25   16·00
MS2847 115×89 mm. **2080** St Paul's Cathedral (1st)
    multicoloured; (1st) multicoloured; 81p. multi-
    coloured; 81p. multicoloured. Perf 14½×14 .... 4·00   4·00
First Day Cover (Tallents House) .... 4·50
First Day Cover (London EC4) .... 4·50

No. **MS**2847 commemorates the 300th anniversary of St Paul's Cathedral.
The complete miniature sheet is shown on one of the eleven PHQ cards with the others depicting individual stamps including those from **MS**2847.

(Gravure Walsall)

2008 (13 May). *Beside the Seaside* (2nd series). As Type 1977 but self-adhesive. |MULTI COLOUR| Two phosphor bands. Die-cut Perf 14½.
2848   **1977**   (1st) Ice Cream Cone. Multicoloured ...   2·00   2·00
    a. Booklet pane. No. 2848×2 and
        No. 2295×4 ....   6·75
No. 2848 was only issued in £2·16 booklets, No. PM15, in which the surplus self-adhesive paper was removed from around the 1st class gold stamps (No. 2295), but retained from around No. 2848.

2081 *Carry on Sergeant*

2082 *Dracula*

2083 *Carry on Cleo*

2084 *The Curse of Frankenstein*

2085 *Carry on Screaming*

2086 *The Mummy*

(Des Elmwood. Litho Walsall)

2008 (10 June). *Posters for Carry On and Hammer Horror Films.* |MULTI COLOUR| Two phosphor bands. Perf 14.

2849	**2081**	(1st) *Carry on Sergeant*	1·00	1·00
2850	**2082**	48p. *Dracula*	80	80
2851	**2083**	50p. *Carry on Cleo*	90	90
2852	**2084**	56p. *The Curse of Frankenstein*	1·00	1·00
2853	**2085**	72p. *Carry on Screaming*	1·10	1·10
2854	**2086**	81p. *The Mummy*	1·20	1·20

Set of 6 .... 5·50   5·50
Set of 6 Gutter Pairs .... 11·00
First Day Cover (Tallents House) ....   6·25
First Day Cover (Bray, Maidenhead, Berks) ....   6·25
Presentation Pack (PO Pack No. 414) .... 6·25
PHQ Cards (set of 6) (312) .... 1·50   7·00
PHQ Cards ('brick wall' background) and Stamps Set ...... 7·00
Nos. 2849/54 commemorate the 50th anniversary of *Dracula* and the first *Carry On* film (*Carry on Sergeant*).

2087 Red Arrows, Dartmouth
Regatta Airshow, 2006

2088 RAF Falcons Parachute
Team, Biggin Hill, 2006

2089 Spectator watching Red
Arrows, Farnborough, 2006

2090 Prototype Avro Vulcan
Bombers and Avro 707s,
Farnborough, 1953

2091 Parachutist Robert Wyndham on Wing of Avro 504, 1933

2092 Air Race rounding the Beacon, Hendon, *c.* 1912

(Des Roundel. Gravure De La Rue)

2008 (17 July). *Air Displays.* Two phosphor bands. Perf 14½×14.

2855	**2087**	(1st) Red Arrows	1·00	1·00
2856	**2088**	48p. RAF Falcons Parachute Team	80	80
2857	**2089**	50p. Spectator watching Red Arrows	90	90
2858	**2090**	56p. Prototype Avro Vulcan Bombers and Avro 707s	1·00	1·00
2859	**2091**	72p. Parachutist Robert Wyndham on Wing of Avro 504	1·10	1·10
2860	**2092**	81p. Air Race rounding the Beacon	1·20	1·20
Set of 6			5·50	5·50
Set of 6 Gutter Pairs			11·00	
First Day Cover (Tallents House)				6·25
First Day Cover (Farnborough, Hants)				6·25
Presentation Pack (PO Pack No. 415)			6·25	
PHQ Cards (set of 6) (313)			1·75	6·25

The 1st class stamp was also issued in sheets of 20 with *se-tenant* labels, printed in lithography by Cartor, and sold for £7·75 per sheet (LS47).

2093 Landmarks of Beijing and London (*Illustration reduced. Actual size 115×76 mm*)

(Des Why Not Associates. Litho Walsall)

2008 (22 Aug). *Handover of Olympic Flag from Beijing to London.* Sheet 115×76 mm. Phosphorised paper. Perf 14½.

MS2861 **2093**	Landmarks of Beijing and London (1st) National Stadium, Beijing; (1st) London Eye; (1st) Tower of London; (1st) Corner Tower of the Forbidden City, Beijing	5·00	5·00
	a. UV varnish (Olympic Rings) omitted	£8750	
First Day Cover (Tallents House)			5·25
First Day Cover (London E15)			5·25
Presentation Pack (PO Pack No. M17)		30·00	
PHQ Cards (set of 5) (OGH)		60	5·00

The Olympic rings overprinted on **MS**2861 are in silk-screen varnish.

The five PHQ cards show the four individual stamps and the complete miniature sheet.

Stamps in these designs were also issued by China.

2094 Drum Major, RAF Central Band, 2007

2095 Helicopter Rescue Winchman, 1984

2096 Hawker Hunter Pilot, 1951

2097 Lancaster Air Gunner, 1944

2098 WAAF Plotter, 1940

2099 Pilot, 1918

(Des Graham Turner and Atelier Works. Litho Walsall)

2008 (18 Sept). *Military Uniforms* (2nd series). RAF Uniforms. Two phosphor bands. Perf 14.

2862	**2094**	(1st) Drum Major, RAF Central Band	1·00	1·00
		a. Horiz strip of 3. Nos. 2862/4	3·00	3·00
		b. Booklet pane. Nos. 2862/4 with margins all round	3·00	
2863	**2095**	(1st) Helicopter Rescue Winchman	1·00	1·00
2864	**2096**	(1st) Hawker Hunter Pilot	1·00	1·00
2865	**2097**	81p. Lancaster Air Gunner	1·40	1·40
		a. Horiz strip of 3. Nos. 2865/7	4·25	4·25
		b. Booklet pane. Nos. 2865/7 with margins all round	4·25	
2866	**2098**	81p. WAAF Plotter	1·40	1·40
2867	**2099**	81p. Pilot	1·40	1·40
Set of 6			6·75	6·75
Set of 2 Gutter Strips of 6			13·50	
Set of 2 Traffic Light Gutter Blocks of 12			28·00	
First Day Cover (Tallents House)				7·00
First Day Cover (Hendon, London NW9)				7·00
Presentation Pack (PO Pack No. 416)			7·00	
PHQ Cards (set of 6) (314)			1·75	7·75

Nos. 2862/4 and 2865/7 were each printed together, *se-tenant*, as horizontal strips of three stamps of 60 (2 panes 6×5).

Booklet panes Nos. 2862b and 2865b come from the £7·15 Pilot to Plane, RAF Uniforms booklet No. DX42.

(Litho Walsall)

2008 (18 Sept). *'Pilot to Plane'. RAF Uniforms.* Booklet stamps. Designs as Types 1307 (Spitfire from 1997 British Aircraft Designers) and 2087 (Red Arrows from 2008 Air Displays). Two phosphor bands. Perf 14.

2868	**1307**	20p. Reginald Mitchell and Supermarine Spitfire MkIIA	1·25	1·25
		a. Booklet pane. Nos. 2868/9, each×2, with margins all round	6·00	
2869	**2087**	(1st) Red Arrows	1·25	1·25

Nos. 2868/9 were only issued in the £7·15 Pilot to Plane, RAF Uniforms booklet, No. DX42.

2100 Millicent Garrett Fawcett (suffragist)

2101 Elizabeth Garrett Anderson (physician – women's health)

2102 Marie Stopes (family planning pioneer)

2103 Eleanor Rathbone (family allowance campaigner)

2104 Claudia Jones (civil rights activist)

2105 Barbara Castle (politician – Equal Pay Act)

(Des Together Design. Gravure Walsall)

2008 (14 Oct). *Women of Distinction.* 'All-over' phosphor. Perf 14×14½.

2870	**2100**	(1st) Millicent Garrett Fawcett	1·00	1·00
2871	**2101**	48p. Elizabeth Garrett Anderson	80	80
2872	**2102**	50p. Marie Stopes	90	90
2873	**2103**	56p. Eleanor Rathbone	1·00	1·00
2874	**2104**	72p. Claudia Jones	1·10	1·10
2875	**2105**	81p. Barbara Castle	1·20	1·20
Set of 6			5·25	5·25
Set of 6 Gutter Pairs			10·50	
First Day Cover (Tallents House)				6·25
First Day Cover (Aldeburgh, Suffolk)				6·25
Presentation Pack (PO Pack No. 417)			6·00	
PHQ Cards (set of 6) (315)			1·75	6·25

SELF-ADHESIVE STAMPS: Collectors are reminded that from November 2008, self-adhesive stamps no longer incorporated a layer of water-soluble gum and will not 'soak-off'. It is advised that, from this point, all used self-adhesive stamps are collected with a neat margin of backing paper.

2106 Ugly Sisters from *Cinderella*

2107 Genie from *Aladdin*

2108 Ugly Sisters from *Cinderella*

2109 Captain Hook from *Peter Pan*

2110 Genie from *Aladdin*

2111 Wicked Queen from *Snow White*

(Des Steve Haskins. Gravure De La Rue)

2008 (4 Nov). *Christmas.* One centre band (2876) or two phosphor bands (others). Perf 15×14.

(a) Self-adhesive

2876	**2106**	(2nd) Ugly Sisters	90	90
		a. Booklet pane. No. 2876×12	9·75	
2877	**2107**	(1st) Genie	1·00	1·00
		a. Booklet pane. No. 2877×12	11·00	
2878	**2108**	(2nd Large) Ugly Sisters	1·20	1·20
2879	**2109**	50p. Captain Hook	1·00	1·00
2880	**2110**	(1st Large) Genie	1·50	1·50
2881	**2111**	81p. Wicked Queen	1·75	1·75
Set of 6			6·25	6·25
First Day Cover (Tallents House)				6·50
First Day Cover (Bethlehem, Llandeilo)				6·50
Presentation Pack (PO Pack No. 418)			6·75	
PHQ Cards (set of 7) (316)			2·00	12·00

(b) Ordinary gum

MS2882 114×102 mm. As Nos. 2876/81	6·50	6·50
First Day Cover (Tallents House)		6·75
First Day Cover (Bethlehem, Llandeilo)		7·00

The phosphor bands on Nos. 2878/9 are at the centre and right of each stamp.

The seven PHQ cards depict the six stamps and **MS**2882.

The 2nd class, 1st class and 81p. stamps were also issued together in sheets of 20, sold for £8·85, containing eight 1st class, eight 2nd class and four 81p. stamps, arranged in vertical strips of five stamps alternated with printed labels (LS54). Separate sheets of ten 1st, 20 1st, 20 2nd or ten 81p. stamps were available with personalised photographs from Royal Mail, Edinburgh. These were sold at £7·50 for ten 1st, £8·50 for 20 2nd or £13·50 for 20 1st or ten 81p. All these sheets were printed in lithography by Cartor and had the backing paper around the stamps retained.

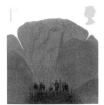

2112 Seven Poppies on Barbed Wire Stems

2113 Soldiers in Poppy Flower

2114 Soldier's Face in Poppy Flower

2115 Lest We Forget (*Illustration reduced. Actual size 124×70 mm*)

(Des Hat–trick design. Litho De La Rue)

2008 (6 Nov). *'Lest We Forget'* (3rd issue). 90th Anniversary of the Armistice. Two phosphor bands. Perf 14½ (1st) or 15×14 (with one elliptical hole in each vertical side) (81p.).

2883	**2112**	(1st) Seven Poppies on Barbed Wire Stems	1·00	1·00
		a. Horiz strip of 3. Nos. 2883/5	2·75	2·75
2884	**2113**	(1st) Soldiers in Poppy Flower	1·00	1·00
2885	**2114**	(1st) Soldier's Face in Poppy Flower	1·00	1·00
Set of 3			2·75	2·75
Gutter Strip of 6			5·50	
Traffic Light Gutter Block of 12			16·00	
MS2886 124×70 mm. **2115** Lest We Forget No. 2885 and as Nos. EN19, NI129, S122 and W111			5·75	5·75
First Day Cover (Tallents House)				6·75
First Day Cover (London SW1)				6·75
Presentation Pack (PO Pack No. 419)			6·50	
PHQ Cards (set of 6) (317)			1·80	9·50

Nos. 2883/5 were printed together, *se-tenant*, in horizontal strips of three stamps in sheets of 30.

No. **MS**2886 (including the Northern Ireland, Scotland and Wales stamps) is printed in lithography.

The six PHQ cards depict Nos. **MS**2685, **MS**2796 and 2883/**MS**2886.

The 1st class stamp, Type **2114**, was also issued in sheets of 20 with *se-tenant* labels showing artifacts from the trenches, printed in lithography by Cartor and sold at £7·75 (LS55).

No. 2885 has the two phosphor bands shaped around each side of the poppy.

A Miniature Sheet Collection containing Nos. **MS**2685, **MS**2796, **MS**2886 and a replica embroidered postcard in a folder was sold for £26·95.

Year Pack

2008 (6 Nov). Comprises Nos. 2797/802, 2806/**MS**2818, 2825/**MS**2847, 2849/67, 2870/81, **MS**2886 and **MS**NI152

CP2886a Year Pack	85·00

Post Office Yearbook

2008 (6 Nov). Comprises Nos. 2797/802, 2806/**MS**2818, 2825/**MS**2847, 2849/67, 2870/81, **MS**2886 and **MS**NI152/3

YB2886a Yearbook	85·00

Miniature Sheet Collection

2008 (6 Nov). Comprises Nos. **MS**2803, **MS**2818, **MS**2847, **MS**2861, **MS**2882, **MS**2886 and **MS**NI152/3

MS2886a Miniature Sheet Collection	45·00

2116 Supermarine Spitfire
(R. J. Mitchell)

2117 Mini Skirt (Mary Quant)

2118 Mini (Sir Alec Issigonis)

2119 Anglepoise Lamp
(George Carwardine)

2120 Concorde
(Aérospatiale-BAC)

2121 K2 Telephone Kiosk
(Sir Giles Gilbert Scott)

2122 Polypropylene Chair
(Robin Day)

2123 Penguin Books
(Edward Young)

2124 London Underground
Map (based on original
design by Harry Beck)

2125 Routemaster Bus
(design team led by
AAM Durrant)

(Des HGV Design. Litho Cartor)

2009 (13 Jan). *British Design Classics* (1st series). MULTI COLOUR Phosphor background. Perf 14½.

2887	2116	(1st) Supermarine Spitfire	1·00	1·00
		a. Block of 10. Nos. 2887/96	9·00	9·00
		ab. Black printed treble	—	
		b. Booklet pane. Nos. 2887, 2889 and 2896×2	3·75	
2888	2117	(1st) Mini Skirt	1·00	1·00
		a. Booklet pane. Nos. 2888, 2890, 2892 and 2893/5	5·25	
2889	2118	(1st) Mini	1·00	1·00
2890	2119	(1st) Anglepoise Lamp	1·00	1·00
2891	2120	(1st) Concorde	1·00	1·00
		a. Booklet pane. Nos. 2891 and 2897, each×2	11·50	
2892	2121	(1st) K2 Telephone Kiosk	1·00	1·00
2893	2122	(1st) Polypropylene Chair	1·00	1·00
2894	2123	(1st) Penguin Books	1·00	1·00
2895	2124	(1st) London Underground Map	1·00	1·00
2896	2125	(1st) Routemaster Bus	1·00	1·00
Set of 10			9·00	9·00
Gutter Block of 20			18·00	

First Day Cover (Tallents House)		9·00
First Day Cover (Longbridge, Birmingham)		9·00
Presentation Pack (PO Pack No. 421)	10·50	
PHQ Cards (set of 10) (318)	3·00	9·75

Nos. 2887/96 were printed together, *se-tenant*, in blocks of ten (2×5) throughout sheets of 30 stamps.

Booklet panes Nos. 2887b/8a and 2891a come from the £7·68 British Design Classics booklet, No. DX44.

No. 2889 was also issued in sheets of 20 with *se-tenant* labels, perforated 14×14½, on 13 January 2009. No. LS56, sold at £7·75 per sheet.

No. 2891 was also issued on 2 March 2009 in sheets of 20 with *se-tenant* labels, No. LS57, and sold at £7·75 per sheet.

No. 2887 was also issued on 15 September 2010 in sheets of 20 with *se-tenant* labels, No. LS74, sold at £8·50 per sheet.

The above sheets were all printed in lithography by Cartor and perforated 14×14½.

For self-adhesive versions of these stamps see Nos. 2911/5b.

(Litho Cartor)

2009 (13 Jan). *British Design Classics* (2nd series). Booklet stamp. Design as No. 2285 (Concorde from 2002 Passenger Jet Aviation). MULTI COLOUR Two phosphor bands. Perf 14½.

2897	1589	(1st) Concorde (1976). Multicoloured..	4·50	4·50

No. 2897 was only issued in the £7·68 British Design Classics booklet, No. DX44.

2126 Charles Darwin

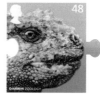

2127 Marine Iguana

2128 Finches

2129 Atoll

2130 Bee Orchid

2131 Orang-utan

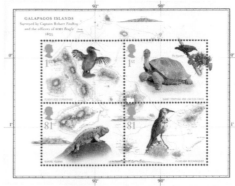

2132 Fauna and Map of the Galapagos Islands (*Illustration reduced. Actual size 115×89 mm*)

(Des Hat-trick design (Nos. 2898/903) or Howard Brown (**MS**2904))

2009 (12 Feb). *Birth Bicentenary of Charles Darwin* (*naturalist and evolutionary theorist*) (1st issue). MULTI COLOUR

(*a*) Self-adhesive. Gravure De La Rue. 'All-over' phosphor. Perf 14.

2898	2126	(1st) Charles Darwin	1·00	1·00
2899	2127	48p. Marine Iguana	1·10	1·10
2900	2128	50p. Finches	1·20	1·20

2901	**2129**	56p. Atoll	1·40	1·40
2902	**2130**	72p. Bee Orchid	1·80	1·80
2903	**2131**	81p. Orang-utan	2·00	2·00

Set of 6.. 7·50 7·50
First Day Cover (Tallents House) .... 8·25
First Day Cover (Shrewsbury) .... 8·25
Presentation Pack (PO Pack No. 423) (2898/**MS**2904).... 10·50
PHQ Cards (set of 11) (320)............................... 3·25 16·50

(b) Ordinary gum. Litho De La Rue. Two phosphor bands. Perf 14.

MS2904 115×89 mm. **2132** Fauna and Map of
the Galapagos Islands (1st) Flightless cormorant;
(1st) Giant tortoise and cactus finch; 81p. Marine
iguana; 81p. Floreana mockingbird............................... 4·00 4·25
        a. Booklet pane. No. **MS**2904
        150×96 mm.............................. 4·00

First Day Cover (Tallents House) .... 5·25
First Day Cover (Shrewsbury) .... 5·25

Nos. 2898/903 have 'jigsaw' perforations on the two vertical sides.

Booklet pane No. 2904a comes from the £7·75 Charles Darwin booklet No. DX45.

The complete miniature sheet is shown on one of the eleven PHQ cards with the others depicting individual stamps, including those from the miniature sheet.

(Gravure De La Rue)

2009 (12 Feb). *Birth Bicentenary of Charles Darwin (naturalist and evolutionary theorist)* (2nd issue). MULTI COLOUR Phosphorised paper. Perf 14.

2905	**2126**	(1st) Charles Darwin...............................	6·00	6·00
		a. Booklet pane. Nos. 2905 and 2909/10	16·00	
2906	**2127**	48p. Marine Iguana...............................	6·00	6·00
		a. Booklet pane. Nos. 2906/8	16·00	
2907	**2128**	50p. Finches	6·00	6·00
2908	**2129**	56p. Atoll	6·00	6·00
2909	**2130**	72p. Bee Orchid	6·00	6·00
2910	**2131**	81p. Orang-utan	6·00	6·00

Set of 6.. 32·00 32·00

Nos. 2905/10 were only issued in the £7·75 Charles Darwin booklet, No. DX45. They also have 'Jigsaw' perforations on both vertical sides.

For Nos. U2911/54, U2975/3037, U3045/52 U3055/9 and U3060/85 see Decimal Machin Definitives section.

(Gravure Walsall)

2009 (10 Mar)–**2010**. *British Design Classics* (3rd series). Booklet stamps. Designs as Nos. 2887/9, 2891/2 and 2896. Self-adhesive. MULTI COLOUR Phosphor background. Die-cut perf 14½.

2911	**2121**	(1st) K2 Telephone Kiosk........................	1·50	1·50
		a. Booklet pane. Nos. 2911/12 and U2983×4	5·75	
2912	**2125**	(1st) Routemaster Bus...........................	1·50	1·50
2913	**2118**	(1st) Mini (21.4.09)..............................	1·50	1·50
		a. Booklet pane. No. 2913×2 and U2983×4	5·75	
2914	**2120**	(1st) Concorde (18.8.09)........................	1·50	1·50
		a. Booklet pane. No. 2914×2 and U2983×4	5·75	
2915	**2117**	(1st) Mini Skirt (17.9.09)........................	1·50	1·50
		a. Booklet pane. No. 2915×2 and U983×4	5·75	
2915b	**2116**	(1st) Supermarine Spitfire (15.9.10)......	1·50	1·50
		ba. Booklet pane. No. 2915b×2 and U2983×4	5·75	

Set of 6.. 9·00 9·00

Nos. 2911/15b were only issued in booklets, Nos. PM16/17, PM19/20 and PM25, initially sold for £2·16 (PM16) or £2·34 (PM17, PM19/20) or £2·46 (PM25).

2135 Richard Arkwright and Spinning Machine (textiles)

2136 Josiah Wedgwood and Black Basalt Teapot and Vase (ceramics)

2137 George Stephenson and *Locomotion* (railways)

2138 Henry Maudslay and Table Engine (machine making)

2139 James Brindley and Bridgewater Canal Aqueduct (canal engineering)

2140 John McAdam (road building)

(Des Webb and Webb. Litho Enschedé)

2009 (10 Mar). *Pioneers of the Industrial Revolution.* MULTI COLOUR 'All-over' phosphor. Perf 14×14½.

2916	**2133**	(1st) Matthew Boulton...........................	1·00	1·00
		a. Horiz pair. Nos. 2916/17...............	2·00	2·00
2917	**2134**	(1st) James Watt...................................	1·00	1·00
2918	**2135**	50p. Richard Arkwright..........................	70	70
		a. Horiz pair. Nos. 2918/19...............	1·40	1·40
2919	**2136**	50p. Josiah Wedgwood	70	70
2920	**2137**	56p. George Stephenson	85	85
		a. Horiz pair. Nos. 2920/1.................	1·70	1·70
2921	**2138**	56p. Henry Maudslay............................	85	85
2922	**2139**	72p. James Brindley.............................	1·00	1·00
		a. Horiz pair. Nos. 2922/3.................	2·00	2·00
2923	**2140**	72p. John McAdam...............................	1·00	1·00

Set of 8.. 6·50 6·50
Set of 4 *Gutter Strips of 4* .... 13·00
First Day Cover (Tallents House) .... 7·50
First Day Cover (Steam Mills, Cinderford) .... 7·50
Presentation Pack (PO Pack No. 425).......................... 7·25
PHQ Cards (set of 8) (321).. 2·40 8·00

Nos. 2916/17, 2918/19, 2920/1 and 2922/3 were each printed together, *se-tenant*, as horizontal pairs in sheets of 60 (2 panes 6×5).

2133 Matthew Boulton and Factory (manufacturing)

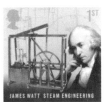

2134 James Watt and Boulton & Watt Condensing Engine (steam engineering)

2141 Henry VII (1485–1509)

2142 Henry VIII (1509–47)

2143 Edward VI (1547–53)

2144 Lady Jane Grey (1553)

2145 Mary I (1553–8)

2146 Elizabeth I (1558–1603)

2147 The Age of the Tudors (*Illustration reduced. Actual size 123×70 mm*)
(Des Atelier Works. Litho Cartor)

2009 (21 Apr). *Kings and Queens* (2nd issue). House of Tudor. |MULTI COLOUR| Two phosphor bands. Perf 14.

2924	**2141**	(1st) Henry VII	1·00	1·00
2925	**2142**	(1st) Henry VIII	1·00	1·00
2926	**2143**	62p. Edward VI	90	90
2927	**2144**	62p. Lady Jane Grey	90	90
		a. Imperf (pair)	£4250	
2928	**2145**	81p. Mary I	1·20	1·20
2929	**2146**	81p. Elizabeth I	1·20	1·20
	Set of 6		5·50	5·50
	Set of 6 Gutter Pairs		11·00	
	Set of 6 Traffic Light Gutter Blocks of 4		30·00	
	First Day Cover (Tallents House)			7·50
	First Day Cover (London SE10)			7·50
	Presentation Pack (PO Pack No. 426) (2924/**MS**2930)		7·25	
	PHQ Cards (set of 11) (322)		3·25	16·00

MS2930 123×70 mm. **2147** The Age of the Tudors (1st) *Mary Rose* (galleon), 1510; (1st) Field of Cloth of Gold Royal Conference, 1520; 90p. Royal Exchange (centre of commerce), 1565; 90p. Francis Drake (circumnavigation), 1580 .... 4·25 4·25
First Day Cover (Tallents House) .... 5·00
First Day Cover (London SE10) .... 5·00

The complete miniature sheet is shown on one of the eleven PHQ cards with the others depicting individual stamps including those from **MS**2930.

The PHQ Card for the Royal Exchange design has the inscription for Sir Francis Drake and *vice versa*.

2148 *Allium sphaerocephalon* (Round-headed Leek)

2149 *Luronium natans* (Floating Water-plantain)

2150 *Cypripedium calceolus* (Lady's Slipper Orchid)

2151 *Polygala amarella* (Dwarf Milkwort)

2152 *Saxifraga hirculus* (Marsh Saxifrage)

2153 *Stachys germanica* (Downy Woundwort)

2154 *Euphorbia serrulata* (Upright Spurge)

2155 *Pyrus cordata* (Plymouth Pear)

2156 *Polygonum maritimum* (Sea Knotgrass)

2157 *Dianthus armeria* (Deptford Pink)

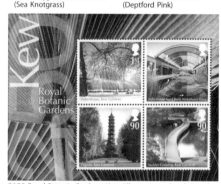
2158 Royal Botanic Gardens, Kew (*Illustration reduced. Actual size 115×89 mm*)

(Des Studio Dempsey. Litho Cartor)

2009 (19 May). *Action for Species* (3rd series). Plants. |MULTI COLOUR|

(a) Phosphor background. Perf 14½

2931	**2148**	(1st) *Allium sphaerocephalon* (Round-headed Leek)	1·00	1·00
		a. Block of 10. Nos. 2931/40	8·50	8·50
2932	**2149**	(1st) *Luronium natans* (Floating Water-plantain)	1·00	1·00
2933	**2150**	(1st) *Cypripedium calceolus* (Lady's Slipper Orchid)	1·00	1·00
2934	**2151**	(1st) *Polygala amarella* (Dwarf Milkwort)	1·00	1·00
2935	**2152**	(1st) *Saxifraga hirculus* (Marsh Saxifrage)	1·00	1·00

2936 **2153** (1st) *Stachys germanica* (Downy
Woundwort) .... 1·00 1·00
2937 **2154** (1st) *Euphorbia serrulata* (Upright
Spurge)................................ 1·00 1·00
2938 **2155** (1st) *Pyrus cordata* (Plymouth Pear) 1·00 1·00
2939 **2156** (1st) *Polygonum maritimum* (Sea
Knotgrass) .... 1·00 1·00
2940 **2157** (1st) *Dianthus armeria* (Deptford
Pink)................................... 1·00 1·00
Set of 10.. 9·00 9·00
Gutter Block of 10................................... 18·00
First Day Cover (Tallents House) .... 11·00
First Day Cover (Kew, Richmond) .... 11·00
Presentation Pack (PO Pack No. 427) (2931/**MS2941**) .... 15·00
PHQ Cards (set of 15) (323)........................... 13·50

(b) *250th Anniversary of Royal Botanic Gardens, Kew.*
|MULTI COLOUR| *Two phosphor bands. Perf 14×14½.*
MS2941 115×89 mm. **2158** Royal Botanic Gardens,
Kew (1st) Palm House, Kew Gardens; (1st)
Millennium Seed Bank, Wakehurst Place; 90p.
Pagoda, Kew Gardens; 90p. Sackler Crossing, Kew
Gardens .... 4·25 4·25
First Day Cover (Tallents House) .... 5·00
First Day Cover (Kew, Richmond) .... 5·00

Nos. 2931/40 were printed together, *se-tenant*, as blocks of ten
(5×2) in sheets of 60 (2 panes of 30).
The complete miniature sheet is shown on one of the 15 PHQ
cards with the others depicting individual stamps including those from
MS2941.

(Gravure Walsall)

2009 (21 May). *50th Anniversary of NAFAS* (*National Association of
Flower Arrangement Societies*). Booklet stamps. Designs as Nos. 1958
and 1962 (1997 Greeting Stamps, 19th-century Flower Paintings).
Self-adhesive. |MULTI COLOUR| Two phosphor bands. Die-cut Perf 14 (with one
elliptical hole in each vert side).
2942 **1287** (1st) *Iris latifolia*............................. 4·25 4·25
a. Booklet pane. Nos. 2942/3 and
U2983×4............................... 8·75
2943 **1283** (1st) *Tulipa*.................................... 4·25 4·25
Nos. 2942/3 were only issued in stamp booklets, No. PM18.

2159 Dragon   **2160** Unicorn

2161 Giant   **2162** Pixie

2163 Mermaid   **2164** Fairy

(Des Dave McKean and Morgan Radcliffe. Gravure De La Rue)

2009 (16 June). *Mythical Creatures.* |MULTI COLOUR| 'All-over' phosphor. Perf 14½.
2944 **2159** (1st) Dragon .... 1·00 1·00
2945 **2160** (1st) Unicorn .... 1·00 1·00
2946 **2161** 62p. Giant .... 1·00 1·00
2947 **2162** 62p. Pixie .... 1·00 1·00
2948 **2163** 90p. Mermaid .... 1·50 1·50
2949 **2164** 90p. Fairy .... 1·50 1·50
Set of 6 .... 6·25 6·25
Set of 6 Gutter Pairs .... 12·50
First Day Cover (Tallents House) .... 8·00
First Day Cover (Dragonby, Scunthorpe)............... 8·00
Presentation Pack (PO Pack No. 428)................... 7·00

PHQ Cards (set of 6) (324) .... 1·75 8·00

2165 George V   **2166** Edward VII
Type B Wall Letter Box,   Ludlow Letter Box,
1933–6   1901–10

2167 Victorian Lamp   **2168** Elizabeth II
Letter Box, 1896   Type A Wall Letter
          Box, 1962–3

2169 Post Boxes (*Illustration reduced. Actual size 145×74 mm*)

(Des Elmwood. Litho Cartor)

2009 (18 Aug). *Post Boxes.* |MULTI COLOUR| 'All-over' phosphor. Perf 14.
2950 **2165** (1st) George V Type B Wall Letter
Box .... 1·00 1·00
a. Booklet pane. Nos. 2950/3 with
margins all round .... 4·00
2951 **2166** 56p. Edward VII Ludlow Letter Box ...... 1·10 1·10
2952 **2167** 81p. Victorian Lamp Letter Box .... 1·20 1·20
2953 **2168** 90p. Elizabeth II Type A Wall Letter
Box .... 1·30 1·30
Set of 4.. 4·00 4·00
MS2954 145×74 mm. **2169** Post Boxes Nos. 2950/3 .. 4·25 4·25
First Day Cover (Tallents House) .... 5·00
First Day Cover (Wakefield, W. Yorkshire)................ 5·00
Presentation Pack (PO Pack No. 430)................... 4·75
PHQ Cards (set of 5) (325)........................... 1·50 9·25
Nos. 2950/3 were only issued in the £8·18 Treasures of the Archive
booklet, No. DX46 and in No. **MS2954**.
The five PHQ cards show the four individual stamps and the
miniature sheet.
Type **2165** was also issued in sheets of 20 with *se-tenant* labels
showing post boxes, No. LS65, sold for £8·35 per sheet.

(Litho Cartor)

2009 (18 Aug). *Treasures of the Archive* (1st series). Booklet stamps.
Designs as Types **929** (1990 150th anniversary of the Penny Black)
and **1446** (with redrawn 1st face value). Printed in lithography.
Two phosphor bands. Perf 14½×14 (with one elliptical hole in
each vert side).
2955 **929** 20p. brownish-black and grey-brown 80 80
1446 a. Booklet pane. Nos. 2955/6,
each×4 with central label and
margins all round .... 7·00
2956 (1st) brownish-black and grey-brown .... 1·20 1·20
Nos. 2955/6 were only issued in the £8·18 Treasures of the Archive
booklet, No. DX46.
For Nos. 2955/6 printed gravure see Nos. 2133/a.
Also see Nos. 1478 and **MS**1501.

(Litho Cartor)

2009 (18 Aug). *Treasures of the Archive* (2nd series). Booklet stamps. Design as Type 919 (1989 Lord Mayor's Show). |MULTI COLOUR| 'All-over' phosphor. Perf 14.

| 2957 | **919** | 20p. Royal Mail Coach. Multicoloured.... | 1·50 | 1·50 |
| | | a. Booklet pane. No. 2957×4 with margins all round .... | 6·00 | |

No. 2957 was only issued in the £8·18 Treasures of the Archive booklet, No. DX46.

2170 Firefighting

2171 Chemical Fire

2172 Emergency Rescue

2173 Flood Rescue

2174 Search and Rescue

2175 Fire Safety

(Des Rose Design. Gravure De La Rue)

2009 (1 Sept). *Fire and Rescue Service.* |MULTI COLOUR| 'All-over' phosphor. Perf 14×14½.

2958	**2170**	(1st) Firefighting	1·00	1·00
2959	**2171**	54p. Chemical Fire	90	90
2960	**2172**	56p. Emergency Rescue	1·10	1·10
2961	**2173**	62p. Flood Rescue	1·20	1·20
2962	**2174**	81p. Search and Rescue	1·30	1·40
2963	**2175**	90p. Fire Safety	1·40	1·40
Set of 6			6·00	6·00
Set of 6 Gutter Pairs			12·00	
First Day Cover (Tallents House)				7·50
First Day Cover (Hose, Melton Mowbray)				7·50
Presentation Pack (PO Pack No. 429)......................			6·75	
PHQ Cards (set of 6) (326)			1·80	7·50

2176 Flight Deck Officer, 2009

2177 Captain, 1941

2178 Second Officer WRNS, 1918

2179 Able Seaman, 1880

2180 Royal Marine, 1805

2181 Admiral, 1795

(Des Graham Turner and Atelier Works. Litho Cartor)

2009 (17 Sept). *Military Uniforms* (3rd series). Royal Navy Uniforms. |MULTI COLOUR| Phosphor background. Perf 14.

2964	**2176**	(1st) Flight Deck Officer	1·00	1·00
		a. Horiz strip of 3. Nos. 2964/6.........	3·00	3·00
		b. Booklet pane. Nos. 2964/6 with margins all round	3·00	
2965	**2177**	(1st) Captain...	1·00	1·00
2966	**2178**	(1st) Second Officer WRNS.....................	1·00	1·00
2967	**2179**	90p. Able Seaman....................................	1·40	1·40
		a. Horiz strip of 3. Nos. 2967/9.........	4·00	4·00
		b. Booklet pane. Nos. 2967/9 with margins all round	4·00	
2968	**2180**	90p. Royal Marine...................................	1·40	1·40
2969	**2181**	90p. Admiral..	1·40	1·40
Set of 6..			6·75	6·75
Set of 2 Gutter Strips of 6..			13·50	
Set of 2 Traffic Light Gutter Blocks of 12			30·00	
First Day Cover (Tallents House).................................				8·25
First Day Cover (Portsmouth).......................................				8·25
Presentation Pack (PO Pack No. 431).......................			7·50	
PHQ Cards (set of 6) (327)..			1·80	7·75

Nos. 2964/6 and 2967/9 were each printed together, *se-tenant*, as horizontal strips of three in sheets of 60 (2 panes 6×5).

Booklet panes Nos. 2964b and 2967b were from the £7·93 Royal Navy Uniforms booklet, No. DX47.

(Litho Cartor)

2009 (17 Sept). *Royal Navy Uniforms.* Booklet stamp. Design as Type 1518 (Jolly Roger flag from 2001 Submarine Centenary). |MULTI COLOUR| Two phosphor bands. Perf 14½.

| 2970 | **1518** | (1st) 'Jolly Roger' flown by HMS *Proteus* (submarine) .... | 5·00 | 5·00 |
| | | a. Booklet pane. Nos. 2970 and 2581, each×2 with margins all round .... | 12·00 | |

No. 2970 was only issued in the £7·93 Royal Navy Uniforms booklet, No. DX47.

2182 Fred Perry 1909–95 (lawn tennis champion)

2183 Henry Purcell 1659–95 (composer and musician)

2184 Sir Matt Busby 1909–94 (footballer and football manager)

2185 William Gladstone 1809–98 (statesman and Prime Minister)

2186 Mary Wollstonecraft 1759–97 (pioneering feminist)

2187 Sir Arthur Conan Doyle 1859–1930 (writer and creator of Sherlock Holmes)

2188 Donald Campbell 1921–67 (water speed record broken 1959)

2189 Judy Fryd 1909–2000 (campaigner and founder of MENCAP)

2190 Samuel Johnson 1709–84 (lexicographer, critic and poet)

2191 Sir Martin Ryle 1918–84 (radio survey of the Universe 1959)

(Des Together Design. Litho Cartor)

2009 (8 Oct). *Eminent Britons.* Multi Colour Phosphor background. Perf 14½.

2971	**2182**	(1st) Fred Perry	1·00	1·00
		a. Horiz strip of 5. Nos. 2971/5	4·50	4·50
2972	**2183**	(1st) Henry Purcell	1·00	1·00
2973	**2184**	(1st) Sir Matt Busby	1·00	1·00
2974	**2185**	(1st) William Gladstone	1·00	1·00
2975	**2186**	(1st) Mary Wollstonecraft	1·00	1·00
2976	**2187**	(1st) Sir Arthur Conan Doyle	1·00	1·00
		a. Horiz strip of 5. Nos. 2976/80	4·50	4·50
2977	**2188**	(1st) Donald Campbell	1·00	1·00
2978	**2189**	(1st) Judy Fryd	1·00	1·00
2979	**2190**	(1st) Samuel Johnson	1·00	1·00
2980	**2191**	(1st) Sir Martin Ryle	1·00	1·00
Set of 10			9·00	9·00
Set of 2 Gutter Strips of 10			18·00	
First Day Cover (Tallents House)				9·25
First Day Cover (Britannia, Bacup, Lancashire)				9·25
Presentation Pack (PO Pack No. 432)			10·50	
PHQ Cards (set of 10) (328)			3·00	9·75

Nos. 2971/5 and 2976/80 were each printed together, *se-tenant*, as horizontal strips of five stamps in sheets of 50 (2 panes 5×5).

No. 2980 includes the 'EUROPA' emblem.

2192 Canoe Slalom

2193 Paralympic Games Archery

2194 Athletics: Track

2195 Diving

2196 Paralympic Games Boccia

2197 Judo

2198 Paralympic Games Dressage

2199 Badminton

2200 Weightlifting

2201 Basketball

(Des John Royle (2981), George Hardie (2982), Nathalie Guinamard (2983), Julian Opie (2984), David Doyle (2985), Paul Slater (2986), Andrew Davidson (2987), David Holmes (2988), Guy Billout (2989), Huntley Muir (2990) and Studio David Hillman (all). Litho Cartor)

2009 (22 Oct)–**2012**. *Olympic and Paralympic Games, London (2012)* (1st issue). Multi Colour 'All-over' phosphor. Perf 14½.

2981	**2192**	(1st) Canoe Slalom	1·00	1·00
		a. Horiz strip of 5. Nos. 2981/5	4·50	4·50
2982	**2193**	(1st) Paralympic Games Archery	1·00	1·00
		b. Booklet pane. Nos. 2982 and 2987 with margins all round (27.7.12)	3·75	
2983	**2194**	(1st) Athletics: Track	1·00	1·00
		b. Booklet pane. Nos. 2983 and 3104 with margins all round (27.7.12)	3·75	
2984	**2195**	(1st) Diving	1·00	1·00
		b. Booklet pane. Nos. 2984 and 3196 with margins all round (27.7.12)	3·75	
2985	**2196**	(1st) Paralympic Games Boccia	1·00	1·00
2986	**2197**	(1st) Judo	1·00	1·00
		a. Horiz strip of 5. Nos. 2986/90	4·50	4·50
2987	**2198**	(1st) Paralympic Games Dressage	1·00	1·00
2988	**2199**	(1st) Badminton	1·00	1·00
2989	**2200**	(1st) Weightlifting	1·00	1·00
2990	**2201**	(1st) Basketball	1·00	1·00
Set of 10			9·00	9·00
Set of 2 Gutter Strips of 10			18·00	
First Day Cover (Tallents House)				9·25
First Day Cover (Badminton, Glos)				9·25
Presentation Pack (PO Pack No. M18)			10·50	
PHQ Cards (set of 10) (OXPG1)			3·00	10·00

Nos. 2981/5 and 2986/90 were each printed together, *se-tenant*, as horizontal strips of five stamps in sheets of 50 (2 panes 5×5).

2202 Angel playing Lute (William Morris), Church of St. James, Staveley, Kendal, Cumbria

2203 Madonna and Child (Henry Holiday), Church of Ormesby St Michael, Great Yarmouth, Norfolk

2204 Angel playing Lute (William Morris), Church of St James, Staveley, Kendal, Cumbria

2205 Joseph (Henry Holiday), Parish Church of St Michael, Minehead, Somerset

2206 Madonna and Child (Henry Holiday), Church of Ormesby St Michael, Ormesby, Great Yarmouth, Norfolk

2207 Wise Man (Sir Edward Burne-Jones), Church of St Mary the Virgin, Rye, East Sussex

2208 Shepherd (Henry Holiday), St Mary's Church, Upavon, Wiltshire

(Des Andrew Ross. Gravure De La Rue)

2009 (3 Nov). *Christmas. Stained Glass Windows.* |MULTI COLOUR| One centre band (**2202**) or two phosphor bands (others). Perf 14½×14 (with one elliptical hole in each vert side).

(a) Self-adhesive.

2991	**2202**	(2nd) Angel playing Lute............................	90	90
		a. Booklet pane. No. 2991×12..........	9·75	
2992	**2203**	(1st) Madonna and Child.......................	1·00	1·00
		a. Booklet pane. No. 2992×12..........	10·50	
2993	**2204**	(2nd Large) Angel playing Lute.............	1·10	1·10
2994	**2205**	56p. Joseph	1·10	1·10
2995	**2206**	(1st Large) Madonna and Child.............	1·40	1·40
2996	**2207**	90p. Wise Man....................................	1·80	1·80
2997	**2208**	£1·35 Shepherd..................................	2·40	2·40
Set of 7..			8·75	8·75
First Day Cover (Tallents House)............................				9·00
First Day Cover (Bethlehem, Llandeilo)...................				9·00
Presentation Pack (PO Pack No. 433)......................			9·25	
PHQ Cards (set of 8) (328).....................................			2·40	17·50

(b) Ordinary gum.

MS2998 115×102 mm. As Nos. 2991/7................		8·25	8·25
First Day Cover (Tallents House)............................			9·00
First Day Cover (Bethlehem, Llandeilo)...................			9·00

The eight PHQ cards show the seven stamps and **MS**2998.

The 2nd class, 1st class, 56p and 90p stamps were also issued together in sheets of 20 (No. LS67), sold for £9, containing eight 2nd class, eight 1st class, two 56p and two 90p stamps, each stamp accompanied by a *se-tenant* label.

Separate sheets of 20 2nd, 20 1st, ten 1st, ten 56p and ten 90p were available with personal photographs from Royal Mail, Edinburgh. These were sold at £7·50 for ten 1st, £9·50 for 20 2nd or ten 56p or £13·50 for 20 1st or ten 90p.

All these sheets were printed in lithography by Cartor and had the backing paper around the stamps retained.

For the 2nd class stamp with ordinary gum see No. 3186*a*.

For Nos. U3045/52 see Decimal Machin Definitives section.

Year Pack

2009 (3 Nov). Comprises Nos. 2887/96, 2898/**MS**2904, 2916/**MS**2941, 2944/9, **MS**2954, 2958/69, 2971/97, **MS**S157 and **MS**W147.
CP2998*a* Year Pack.. 95·00

Post Office Yearbook

2009 (3 Nov). Comprises Nos. 2887/96, 2898/**MS**2904, 2916/**MS**2941, 2944/9, **MS**2954, 2958/69 and 2971/97, **MS**S157 and **MS**W147.
YB2998*a* Yearbook.. 95·00

Miniature Sheet Collection

2009 (3 Nov). Comprises Nos. **MS**2904, **MS**2930, **MS**2941, **MS**2954, **MS**2998, **MS**S157 and **MS**W147.
MS2998*a* Miniature Sheet Collection....................................... 32·00

2209 *The Division Bell* (Pink Floyd)

2210 *A Rush of Blood to the Head* (Coldplay)

2211 *Parklife* (Blur)

2212 *Power Corruption and Lies* (New Order)

2213 *Let It Bleed* (Rolling Stones)

2214 *London Calling* (The Clash)

2215 *Tubular Bells* (Mike Oldfield)

2216 *IV* (Led Zeppelin)

2217 *Screamadelica* (Primal Scream)

2218 *The Rise and Fall of Ziggy Stardust and the Spiders from Mars* (David Bowie)

(Des Studio Dempsey)

2010 (7 Jan). *Classic Album Covers (1st issue).* |MULTI COLOUR| 'All-over' phosphor.

(a) Self-adhesive. Gravure De La Rue. Die-cut Perf 14½ (interrupted)

2999	**2209**	(1st) The Division Bell (Pink Floyd)........	1·00	1·00
		a. Horiz strip of 5. Nos. 2999/3003..	4·50	—
3000	**2210**	(1st) A Rush of Blood to the Head (Coldplay).....................................	1·00	1·00
3001	**2211**	(1st) Parklife (Blur).............................	1·00	1·00
3002	**2212**	(1st) Power Corruption and Lies (New Order)...	1·00	1·00
3003	**2213**	(1st) Let It Bleed (Rolling Stones).........	1·00	1·00
3004	**2214**	(1st) London Calling (The Clash)...........	1·00	1·00
		a. Horiz strip of 5. Nos. 3004/8........	4·50	—
3005	**2215**	(1st) Tubular Bells (Mike Oldfield)........	1·00	1·00
3006	**2216**	(1st) IV (Led Zeppelin)........................	1·00	1·00
3007	**2217**	(1st) Screamadelica (Primal Scream).....	1·00	1·00
3008	**2218**	(1st) The Rise and Fall of Ziggy Stardust and the Spiders from Mars (David Bowie)................................	1·00	1·00
Set of 10..			9·00	9·00
First Day Cover (Tallents House)............................				9·25
First Day Cover (Oldfield, Keighley)........................				9·25
Presentation Pack (PO Pack No. 435)......................			11·00	
PHQ Cards (set of 10) (330)..................................			4·00	12·00

Nos. 2999/3003 and 3004/8 were each printed together, as horizontal strips of five stamps in sheets of 50 (2 panes of 25).

The right-hand edges of Nos. 2999/3008 are all cut around to show the vinyl disc protruding from the open edge of the album cover.

2010 (7 Jan). *Classic Album Covers (2nd issue).* |MULTI COLOUR| 'All-over' phosphor. Litho Cartor. Perf 14½ (interrupted).

3009	**2213**	(1st) Let It Bleed (Rolling Stones)...........	1·25	1·25
		a. Booklet pane. Nos. 3009/14	7·80	
3010	**2216**	(1st) IV (Led Zeppelin)...........................	1·25	1·25

3011	**2218**	(1st) *The Rise and Fall of Ziggy Stardust and the Spiders from Mars* (David Bowie)	1·25	1·25
3012	**2212**	(1st) *Power Corruption and Lies* (New Order)	1·25	1·25
3013	**2217**	(1st) *Screamadelica* (Primal Scream)	1·25	1·25
3014	**2209**	(1st) *The Division Bell* (Pink Floyd)	1·25	1·25
3015	**2215**	(1st) *Tubular Bells* (Mike Oldfield)	1·25	1·25
		a. Booklet pane. Nos. 3015/18	5·20	
3016	**2214**	(1st) *London Calling* (The Clash)	1·25	1·25
3017	**2211**	(1st) *Parklife* (Blur)	1·25	1·25
3018	**2210**	(1st) *A Rush of Blood to the Head* (Coldplay)	1·25	1·25
3009/18 Set of 10			13·00	13·00
MS3019 223×189 mm. Nos. 3009/18			25·00	25·00
First Day Cover (Tallents House)				15·00
First Day Cover (Oldfield, Keighley)				15·00

Nos. 3009/18 were only issued in the £8·06 Classic Album Covers booklet, No. DX48 and in No. **MS**3019.

The right-hand edges of Nos. 3009/18 and the miniature sheet **MS**3019 are all cut around in an imperforate section to show the vinyl disc protruding from the open edge of the album cover.

A miniature sheet containing No. 3014×10 *The Division Bell* (Pink Floyd) was issued on 6 March 2010 and sold for £4·75 per sheet.

(Gravure Walsall)

2010 (7 Jan–25 Feb). *Olympic and Paralympic Games, London* (2012) (2nd issue). Booklet stamps. Designs as Nos. 2982/3, 2986 and 2990. Self-adhesive. |MULTI COLOUR 'All-over' phosphor. Die-cut Perf 14½.

3020	**2197**	(1st) Judo	1·50	1·50
		a. Booklet pane. Nos. 3020/1 and U2983×4	1·50	1·50
3021	**2193**	(1st) Paralympic Games Archery	1·50	1·50
3022	**2194**	(1st) Athletics: Track (25 Feb)	1·50	1·50
		a. Booklet pane. Nos. 3022/3 and U3016×4	5·75	
3023	**2201**	(1st) Basketball (25 Feb)	1·50	1·50
Set of 4			5·75	5·75

Nos. 3020/1 and 3022/3 were only issued in separate booklets, Nos. PM21/2, each sold for £2·34.

2219 Smilers (*Illustration reduced. Actual size 124×71 mm*)

(Des Hat-trick Design. Litho Cartor)

2010 (26 Jan). *Business and Consumer Smilers*. Sheet 124×71 mm. |MULTI COLOUR Two phosphor bands. Perf 14½×14 (with one elliptical hole in each vertical side).

MS3024 **2219**	Smilers (1st) Propellor driven aircraft (Andrew Davidson); (1st) Vintage sports roadster (Andrew Davidson); (1st) Recreation of crown seal (Neil Oliver); (1st) Birthday cake (Annabel Wright); (1st) Steam locomotive (Andrew Davidson); (1st) Ocean liner (Andrew Davidson); (1st) Six poppies on barbed wire stems; (1st) Birthday present (Annabel Wright); (Europe up to 20 grams) Bird carrying envelope (Lucy Davey); (Worldwide up to 20 grams) 'Hello' in plane vapour trail (Lucy Davey)	9·50	9·50
First Day Cover (Tallents House)			9·75
First Day Cover (Happy Valley, Malvern)			9·75
Presentation Pack (PO Pack No. M19)		10·50	
PHQ Cards (set of 11) (D31)		4·25	20·00

MS3024 was sold for £4·58.

The eleven PHQ cards show the ten individual stamps and the complete miniature sheet.

Stamps in designs as within **MS**3024 but self-adhesive were available printed together, *se-tenant*, in sheets of 20 containing two of each design with greetings labels (No. LS70), sold for £9·70 per sheet.

The (1st) birthday cake, (1st) birthday present, Europe and Worldwide designs were also available in separate sheets with personal photographs.

A stamp as the crown seal design in **MS**3024 but self-adhesive was issued on 15 September 2011 in sheets of 20 with postmark labels for the 350th Anniversary of the Postmark, No. LS78 sold for £9·50.

The other 1st class designs were for the business customised service.

Stamps as the (1st) birthday cake (×4), (1st) birthday present (×4), Europe bird carrying envelope (×2) and Worldwide 'Hello' in plane vapour trail (×2) designs but self-adhesive were issued together with Nos. 2572, 2674, 2693 and 2821/3 on 8 May 2010 in sheets of 20 stamps with *se-tenant* greetings labels printed in lithography by Cartor, No. LS73, and sold for £10 per sheet.

Girlguiding UK

2220 Girlguiding UK (*Illustration reduced. Actual size 190×67 mm*)

(Des Together Design. Litho Cartor)

2010 (2 Feb). *Centenary of Girlguiding*. Sheet 190×67 mm. |MULTI COLOUR Phosphor background. Perf 14×14½.

MS3025 **2220**	Girlguiding UK (1st) Rainbows; 56p. Brownies; 81p. Guides; 90p. Senior Section members	4·25	4·50
First Day Cover (Tallents House)			5·25
First Day Cover (Guide, Blackburn)			5·25
Presentation Pack (PO Pack No. 436)		5·50	
PHQ Cards (set of 5) (331)		2·00	9·00

The five PHQ cards show the four individual stamps and the complete miniature sheet.

2221 Sir Robert Boyle (chemistry)

2222 Sir Isaac Newton (optics)

2223 Benjamin Franklin (electricity)

2224 Edward Jenner (pioneer of smallpox vaccination)

2225 Charles Babbage (computing)

2226 Alfred Russel Wallace (theory of evolution)

2227 Joseph Lister (antiseptic surgery)

2228 Ernest Rutherford (atomic structure)

2229 Dorothy Hodgkin (crystallography)

2230 Sir Nicholas Shackleton (earth sciences)

(Des Hat-trick Design. Litho Cartor)

2010 (25 Feb). *350th Anniversary of the Royal Society.* |MULTI COLOUR 'All-over' phosphor. Perf 14½.

3026	**2221**	(1st) Sir Robert Boyle..................................	1·00	1·00
		a. Block of 10. Nos. 3026/35	9·00	9·00
		b. Booklet pane. Nos. 3026, 3030/1 and 3035 with margins all round	3·50	
3027	**2222**	(1st) Sir Isaac Newton	1·00	1·00
		a. Booklet pane. Nos. 3027/8 and 3033×2 with margins all round...	5·00	
3028	**2223**	(1st) Benjamin Franklin............................	1·00	1·00
3029	**2224**	(1st) Edward Jenner..................................	1·00	1·00
		a. Booklet pane. Nos. 3029×2, 3032 and 3034 with margins all round	3·50	
3030	**2225**	(1st) Charles Babbage...............................	1·00	1·00
3031	**2226**	(1st) Alfred Russel Wallace	1·00	1·00
3032	**2227**	(1st) Joseph Lister.....................................	1·00	1·00
3033	**2228**	(1st) Ernest Rutherford............................	1·00	1·00
3034	**2229**	(1st) Dorothy Hodgkin..............................	1·00	1·00
3035	**2230**	(1st) Sir Nicholas Shackleton...................	1·00	1·00
Set of 10			9·00	9·00
Gutter Block of 20			18·00	
First Day Cover (Tallents House)...........				10·00
First Day Cover (London SW1)...............				10·00
Presentation Pack (PO Pack No. 437).....			11·00	
PHQ Cards (set of 10) (332)...................			4·00	11·50

Nos. 3026/35 were printed together, *se-tenant*, as blocks of ten (5×2) in sheets of 60 (2 panes of 30).

Booklet panes Nos. 3026b/7a and 3029a come from the £7·72 The Royal Society booklet, No. DX49.

2231 'Pixie' (mastiff cross)

2232 'Button'

2233 'Herbie' (mongrel)

2234 'Mr. Tumnus'

2235 'Tafka' (border collie)

2236 'Boris' (bulldog cross)

2237 'Casey' (lurcher)

2238 'Tigger'

2239 'Leonard' (Jack Russell cross)

2240 'Tia' (terrier cross)

(Des CDT Design. Litho Cartor)

2010 (11 Mar). *150th Anniversary of Battersea Dogs and Cats Home.* |MULTI COLOUR Phosphor background. Perf 14½.

3036	**2231**	(1st) 'Pixie' (mastiff cross).........................	1·00	1·00
		a. Block of 10. Nos. 3036/45	9·00	9·00
3037	**2232**	(1st) 'Button'..	1·00	1·00
3038	**2233**	(1st) 'Herbie' (mongrel).............................	1·00	1·00
3039	**2234**	(1st) 'Mr. Tumnus'......................................	1·00	1·00
3040	**2235**	(1st) 'Tafka' (border collie)	1·00	1·00
3041	**2236**	(1st) 'Boris' (bulldog cross)	1·00	1·00
3042	**2237**	(1st) 'Casey' (lurcher).................................	1·00	1·00
3043	**2238**	(1st) 'Tigger'...	1·00	1·00
3044	**2239**	(1st) 'Leonard' (Jack Russell cross)	1·00	1·00
3045	**2240**	(1st) 'Tia' (terrier cross).............................	1·00	1·00
Set of 10			9·00	9·00
Gutter Block of 20			18·00	
First Day Cover (Tallents House)..........				9·50
First Day Cover (London SW8)..............				9·50
Presentation Pack (PO Pack No. 438)....			11·00	
PHQ Cards (set of 10) (333)..................			4·00	11·50

Nos. 3036/45 were printed together, *se-tenant*, as blocks of ten (5×2) in sheets of 60 (2 panes of 30).

2241 James I (1406–37)

2242 James II (1437–60)

2243 James III (1460–88)

2244 James IV (1488–1513)

2245 James V (1513–42)

2246 Mary (1542–67)

2247 James VI (1567–1625)

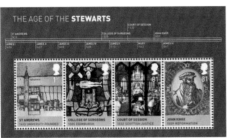
2248 The Age of the Stewarts (*Illustration reduced. Actual size* 123×70 *mm*)

(Des Atelier Works. Litho Cartor)

2010 (23 Mar). *Kings and Queens* (3rd issue). House of Stewart. |MULTI|COLOUR| Two phosphor bands. Perf 14.

3046	**2241**	(1st) James I	1·00	1·00
3047	**2242**	(1st) James II	1·00	1·00
3048	**2243**	(1st) James III	1·00	1·00
3049	**2244**	62p. James IV	1·00	1·00
3050	**2245**	62p. James V	1·00	1·00
3051	**2246**	81p. Mary	1·25	1·25
3052	**2247**	81p. James VI	1·25	1·25
Set of 7			6·75	6·75
Set of 7 Gutter Pairs			13·50	
Set of 7 Traffic Light Gutter Blocks of 4			30·00	
First Day Cover (Tallents House)				8·00
First Day Cover (Linlithgow, West Lothian)				8·00
Presentation Pack (PO Pack No. 439) (3046/**MS**3053)			10·00	
PHQ Cards (set of 12) (334)			4·75	11·50

MS3053 123×70 mm. **2248** The Age of the Stewarts (1st) Foundation of the University of St Andrews, 1413; (1st) Foundation of the College of Surgeons, Edinburgh, 1505; 81p. Foundation of Court of Session, 1532; 81p. John Knox (Reformation, 1559) . . . 4·25 4·25

First Day Cover (Tallents House)		4·75
First Day Cover (Linlithgow, West Lothian)		4·75

The complete miniature sheet is shown on one of the twelve PHQ cards with the others depicting individual stamps including those from **MS**3053.

2249 Humpback Whale (*Megaptera novaeangliae*)

2250 Wildcat (*Felis silvestris*)

2251 Brown Long-eared Bat (*Plecotus auritus*)

2252 Polecat (*Mustela putorius*)

2253 Sperm Whale (*Physeter macrocephalus*)

2254 Water Vole (*Arvicola terrestris*)

2255 Greater Horseshoe Bat (*Rhinolophus ferrumequinum*)

2256 Otter (*Lutra lutra*)

2257 Dormouse (*Muscardinus avellanarius*)

2258 Hedgehog (*Erinaceus europaeus*)

(Des Jason Godfrey. Litho Cartor)

2010 (13 Apr). *Action for Species* (4th series). Mammals. |MULTI|COLOUR| 'All-over' phosphor. Perf 14½.

3054	**2249**	(1st) Humpback Whale	1·00	1·00
		a. Block of 10. Nos. 3054/63	9·00	9·00
3055	**2250**	(1st) Wildcat	1·00	1·00
3056	**2251**	(1st) Brown Long-eared Bat	1·00	1·00
3057	**2252**	(1st) Polecat	1·00	1·00
3058	**2253**	(1st) Sperm Whale	1·00	1·00
3059	**2254**	(1st) Water Vole	1·00	1·00
3060	**2255**	(1st) Greater Horseshoe Bat	1·00	1·00
3061	**2256**	(1st) Otter	1·00	1·00
3062	**2257**	(1st) Dormouse	1·00	1·00
3063	**2258**	(1st) Hedgehog	1·00	1·00
Set of 10			9·00	9·00
Gutter Block of 20			18·00	
First Day Cover (Tallents House)				9·50
First Day Cover (Batts Corner, Farnham)				9·50
Presentation Pack (PO Pack No. 440)			11·00	
PHQ Cards (set of 10) (335)			4·00	11·00

Nos. 3054/63 were printed together, *se-tenant*, as blocks of ten (5×2) in sheets of 60 (2 panes of 30).

No. 3064, T **2259** is vacant.

2260 King George V and Queen Elizabeth II (1st); Two portraits of King George V (£1) (*Illustration reduced. Actual size 141×74 mm*)

(Des Sedley Place. Litho Cartor)

2010 (6 May). *London 2010 Festival of Stamps and Centenary of Accession of King George V* (1st issue). 'All-over' phosphor. Perf 14½×14.

MS3065	141×74 mm	**2260**	(1st) rosine; £1 blackish		
	brown, grey-brown and silver			3·75	4·00
First Day Cover (Tallents House)					12·00
First Day Cover (Sandringham, Norfolk)					12·00

A miniature sheet as No. **MS**3065 but inscr 'BUSINESS DESIGN CENTRE, LONDON 8–15 MAY 2010' along the top right margin was only available at London 2010 Festival of Stamps (*Price 9.75*).

The eight PHQ cards depict the individual stamps from **MS**3065 and **MS**3072 and the complete miniature sheets.

2261 King George V and Queen Elizabeth II

2262 1924 British Empire Exhibition 1½d. Brown Stamp

2263 1924 British Empire Exhibition 1d. Scarlet Stamp

2264 Two Portraits of King George V

2265 1913 £1 Green 'Sea Horses' Design Stamp

2266 1913 10s. Blue 'Sea Horses' Design Stamp

LONDON 2010 FESTIVAL OF STAMPS

2267 (*Illustration reduced. Actual size 115×90 mm*)

(Des Sedley Place. Litho Cartor (Nos. 3066 and 3069) or recess and litho Enschedé (others))

2010 (6–8 May). *London 2010 Festival of Stamps and Centenary of Accession of King George V* (2nd issue). (ex Nos. 3066, 3069) 'All-over' phosphor. Perf 14½×14.

3066	**2261**	(1st) rosine (6 May)	1·25	1·25
		a. Booklet pane. Nos. 3066 and 3069, each×3 with margins all round (8 May)	11·50	
3067	**2262**	(1st) 1924 British Empire Exhibition 1½d. Brown Stamp (8 May)	1·50	1·50
		a. Booklet pane. Nos. 3067/8, each×2	6·00	
3068	**2263**	(1st) 1924 British Empire Exhibition 1d. Scarlet Stamp (8 May)	1·50	1·50
3069	**2264**	£1 blackish brown, grey-brown and silver (8 May)	2·50	2·50
3070	**2265**	£1 1913 £1 Green 'Sea Horses' Design Stamp (8 May)	2·25	2·25
		a. Booklet pane. Nos. 3070/1 with margins all round	4·50	
3071	**2266**	£1 1913 10s. Blue 'Sea Horses' Design Stamp (8 May)	2·25	2·25
3066/71 *Set of 6*			11·00	11·00
Gutter Pair (No. 3066)			3·50	
MS3072 115×90 mm **2267** Nos. 3067/8 and 3070/1 (8 May)			4·50	4·75
First Day Cover (**MS**3072) (Tallents House)				12·00
First Day Cover (**MS**3072) (London N1)				12·00
Presentation Pack (**MS**3065 and **MS**3072) (PO Pack No. 441)			8·50	
PHQ Cards (set of 8) (336)			3·25	13·00

No. 3066 was also issued as a sheet stamp on 6 May 2010.

Nos. 3066/71 come from the £11·15 'King George V' booklet, No. DX50.

Nos. 3066 and 3069 also come from **MS**3065, issued on 6 May 2010.

Nos. 3067/8 and 3070/1 also come from **MS**3072, issued on 8 May 2010.

For presentation pack and PHQ cards for No. **MS**3072 see under **MS**3065.

For No. **MS**3073 see Decimal Machin Definitives section

2269 Winston Churchill

2270 Land Girl

2271 Home Guard

2272 Evacuees

2273 Air Raid Wardens

2274 Woman working in Factory

2275 Royal Broadcast by Princess Elizabeth and Princess Margaret

2276 Fire Service

(Des Why Not Associates. Litho Cartor)

2010 (13 May). *Britain Alone* (1st issue). Pale stone, pale bistre and black. 'All-over' phosphor. Perf 14½.

3074	**2269**	(1st) Winston Churchill	1·00	1·00
		a. Booklet pane. Nos. 3074/5 and 3079/80 with margins all round..	4·50	
3075	**2270**	(1st) Land Girl	1·00	1·00
3076	**2271**	60p. Home Guard	90	90
		a. Booklet pane. Nos. 3076/8 and 3081	4·50	
3077	**2272**	60p. Evacuees	90	90
3078	**2273**	67p. Air Raid Wardens	1·00	1·00
3079	**2274**	67p. Woman working in Factory	1·00	1·00
3080	**2275**	97p. Royal Broadcast by Princess Elizabeth and Princess Margaret	1·35	1·35
3081	**2276**	97p. Fire Service	1·35	1·35
Set of 8			7·50	7·50
Set of 8 Gutter Pairs			15·00	
First Day Cover (Tallents House)				8·50
First Day Cover (Dover, Kent)				8·50
Presentation Pack (PO Pack No. 442)				
(3074/81 and **MS**3086)			13·00	
PHQ Cards (set of 13) (337)			5·25	11·00

The thirteen PHQ cards depict Nos. 3074/85 and the complete miniature sheet **MS**3086.

Booklet panes Nos. 3074a and 3076a come from the £9·76 'Britain Alone' booklet, No. DX51.

2277 Evacuation of British Soldiers from Dunkirk

2278 Vessels from Upper Thames Patrol in 'Operation Little Ships'

2279 Rescued Soldiers on Board Royal Navy Destroyer, Dover

2280 Steamship and Other Boat loaded with Troops

2281 Evacuation of British Troops from Dunkirk, 1940 (*Illustration reduced. Actual size* 115×89 *mm*)

(Des Why Not Associates. Litho Cartor)

2010 (13 May). *Britain Alone* (2nd issue). Pale stone, pale bistre and black. 'All-over' phosphor. Perf 14½.

3082	**2277**	(1st) Evacuation of British Soldiers	1·35	1·35
		a. Booklet pane. Nos. 3082/5 with margins all round	5·00	
3083	**2278**	60p. Vessels from Upper Thames Patrol	1·35	1·35
3084	**2279**	88p. Rescued Soldiers	1·35	1·35
3085	**2280**	97p. Steamship and Other Boat loaded with Troops	1·35	1·35
3082/5 *Set of 4*			5·00	5·00
MS3086 115×89 mm. **2281** Evacuation of British Troops from Dunkirk, 1940 Nos. 3082/5			5·00	5·00
First Day Cover (**MS**3086) (Tallents House)				5·50
First Day Cover (**MS**3086) (Dover, Kent)				5·50

Nos. 3082/5 were only issued in the £9·76 'Britain Alone' booklet, No. DX51, and in No. **MS**3086.

2282 James I (1603–25)

2283 Charles I (1625–49)

2284 Charles II (1660–85)

2285 James II (1685–8)

2286 William III (1689–1702)

2287 Mary II (1689–94)

2288 Anne (1702–14)

2289 The Age of the Stuarts (*Illustration reduced. Actual size 123×70 mm*)

(Des Atelier Works. Litho Cartor)

2010 (15 June). *Kings and Queens* (4th issue). House of Stuart. |MULTI COLOUR| Two phosphor bands. Perf 14.

3087	**2282**	(1st) James I	1·00	1·00
3088	**2283**	(1st) Charles I	1·00	1·00
3089	**2284**	60p. Charles II	90	90
3090	**2285**	90p. James II	90	90
3091	**2286**	67p. William III	1·10	1·10
3092	**2287**	67p. Mary II	1·10	1·10
3093	**2288**	88p. Anne	1·40	1·40
Set of 7			6·50	6·50
Set of 7 Gutter Pairs			13·00	
Set of 7 Traffic Light Gutter Blocks of 4			30·00	
First Day Cover (Tallents House)				8·50
First Day Cover (Royal Oak, Filey)				8·50
Presentation Pack (PO Pack No. 443)				
(3087/93 and **MS**3094)			10·00	
PHQ Cards (set of 12) (338)			4·75	15·50

MS3094 123×70 mm. **2289** The Age of the Stuarts (1st) William Harvey (discovery of blood circulation, 1628); 60p. Civil War Battle of Naseby, 1645; 88p. John Milton (*Paradise Lost*, 1667); 97p. Castle Howard (John Vanbrugh, 1712) .... 4·75 4·75
First Day Cover (Tallents House) .... 5·00
First Day Cover (Royal Oak, Filey) .... 5·00
The complete miniature sheet is shown on one of the twelve PHQ cards with the others depicting individual stamps including those from **MS**3094.

(Gravure Walsall)

2010 (15 June). *Mammals.* Booklet stamps. Designs as Nos. 3061 and 3063. Self-adhesive. |MULTI COLOUR| Die-cut Perf 14½.

3095	**2256**	(1st) Otter	2·75	2·75
		a. Booklet pane. Nos. 3095/6 and No. U3016×4	10·75	
3096	**2258**	(1st) Hedgehog	2·75	2·75

Nos. 3095/6 were only issued in booklets, No. PM23.

2290 Paralympic Games: Rowing

2291 Shooting

2292 Modern Pentathlon

2293 Taekwondo

2294 Cycling

2295 Paralympic Games: Table Tennis

2296 Hockey

2297 Football

2298 Paralympic Games: Goalball

2299 Boxing

(Des Marion Hill (3097), David Hillman (3098), Katherine Baxter (3099), James Fryer (3100), Matthew Dennis (3101), Michael Craig Martin (3102), Darren Hopes (3103), Alex Williamson (3104), Tobatron (3105), Stephen Ledwidge (3106), Studio David Hillman (all). Litho Cartor)

2010 (27 July). *Olympic and Paralympic Games, London (2012)* (3rd issue). |MULTI COLOUR| 'All-over' phosphor. Perf 14½.

3097	**2290**	(1st) Paralympic Games: Rowing	1·00	1·00
		a. Horiz strip of 5. Nos. 3097/101	4·50	4·50
3098	**2291**	(1st) Shooting	1·00	1·00
3099	**2292**	(1st) Modern Pentathlon	1·00	1·00
3100	**2293**	(1st) Taekwondo	1·00	1·00
3101	**2294**	(1st) Cycling	1·00	1·00
3102	**2295**	(1st) Paralympic Games: Table Tennis	1·00	1·00
		a. Horiz strip of 5. Nos. 3102/6	4·50	4·50
3103	**2296**	(1st) Hockey	1·00	1·00
3104	**2297**	(1st) Football	1·00	1·00
3105	**2298**	(1st) Paralympic Games: Goalball	1·00	1·00
3106	**2299**	(1st) Boxing	1·00	1·00
Set of 10			9·00	9·00
Set of 2 Gutter Strips of 10			18·00	
First Day Cover (Tallents House)				9·25
First Day Cover (Rowington, Warwick)				9·25
Presentation Pack (PO Pack No. 444)			11·00	
PHQ Cards (set of 10) (339)			4·00	11·00

Nos. 3097/101 and 3102/6 were each printed together, *se-tenant*, in horizontal strips of five stamps in sheets of 50 (2 panes 5×5).

(Gravure Walsall)

2010 (27 July - 12 Oct). *Olympic and Paralympic Games, London (2012)* (4th issue). Booklet stamps. Designs as Nos. 3097, 3101/2 and 3104. Self-adhesive. |MULTI COLOUR| 'All-over' phosphor. Die-cut perf 14½.

3107	**2290**	(1st) Paralympic Games: Rowing	1·50	1·50
		a. Booklet pane. Nos. 3107/8 and Nos. U3016×4	5·75	
3108	**2295**	(1st) Paralympic Games: Table Tennis	1·50	1·50
3108a	**2297**	(1st) Football (12 Oct)	1·50	1·50
		ab. Booklet pane. Nos. 3108a/b and U3016×4	5·75	
3108b	**2294**	(1st) Cycling (12 Oct)	1·50	1·50
Set of 4			6·00	6·00

Nos. 3107/8 and 3108a/b were only issued in two separate stamp booklets, Nos. PM24 and PM26, each originally sold for £2·46.

2300 LMS Coronation Class Locomotive, Euston Station, 1938

2301 BR Class 9F Locomotive *Evening Star*, Midsomer Norton, 1962

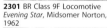

2302 GWR King Class Locomotive *King William IV*, near Teignmouth, 1935

2303 LNER Class A1 Locomotive *Royal Lancer*, 1929

2304 SR King Arthur Class Locomotive *Sir Mador de la Porte*, Bournmouth Central Station, 1935–9

2305 LMS NCC Class WT No. 2, Larne Harbour, *c.* 1947

(Des Delaney Design Consultants. Gravure De La Rue)

2010 (19 Aug). *Great British Railways.* Gold, bluish grey and black. 'All-over' phosphor. Perf 14.

3109	**2300**	(1st) LMS Coronation Class Locomotive	1·00	1·00
3110	**2301**	(1st) BR Class 9F Locomotive *Evening Star*	1·00	1·00
3111	**2302**	67p. GWR King Class Locomotive *King William IV*	90	90
3112	**2303**	67p. LNER Class A1 Locomotive *Royal Lancer*	90	90
3113	**2304**	97p. SR King Arthur Class Locomotive *Sir Mador de la Porte*	1·25	1·25
3114	**2305**	97p. LMS NCC Class WT No. 2	1·25	1·25
Set of 6			6·00	6·00
Set of 6 Gutter Pairs			12·00	
First Day Cover (Tallents House)				7·00
First Day Cover (Swindon)				7·00
Presentation Pack (PO Pack No. 445)			7·00	
PHQ Cards (set of 6) (340)			2·40	7·50

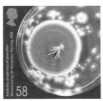

2306 Heart-regulating Beta Blockers (Sir James Black, 1962)

2307 Antibiotic Properties of Penicillin (Sir Alexander Fleming, 1928)

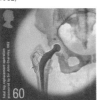
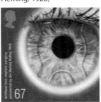

2308 Total Hip Replacement Operation (Sir John Charnley, 1962)

2309 Artificial Lens Implant Surgery (Sir Harold Ridley, 1949)

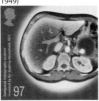

2310 Malaria Parasite transmitted by Mosquitoes (proved by Sir Ronald Ross, 1897)

2311 Computed Tomography Scanner (Sir Godfrey Hounsfield, 1971)

(Des Howard Brown. Litho Cartor)

2010 (16 Sept). *Medical Breakthroughs.* MULTICOLOUR 'All-over' phosphor. Perf 14×14½.

3115	**2306**	(1st) Heart-regulating Beta Blockers	1·00	1·00
3116	**2307**	58p. Antibiotic Properties of Penicillin	90	90
3117	**2308**	60p. Total Hip Replacement Operation	1·00	1·00
3118	**2309**	67p. Artificial Lens Implant Surgery	1·10	1·10
3119	**2310**	88p. Malaria Parasite transmitted by Mosquitoes	1·25	1·25
3120	**2311**	97p. Computed Tomography Scanner	1·45	1·45
Set of 6			6·00	6·00

Set of 6 Gutter Pairs	12·00	
First Day Cover (Tallents House)		8·00
First Day Cover (Paddington, London W2)		8·00
Presentation Pack (PO Pack No. 446)	7·25	
PHQ Cards (set of 6) (341)	2·40	7·50

2312 Winnie the Pooh and Christopher Robin (*Now we are Six*)

2313 Winnie the Pooh and Piglet (*The House at Pooh Corner*)

2314 Winnie the Pooh and Rabbit (*Winnie the Pooh*)

2315 Winnie the Pooh and Eeyore (*Winnie the Pooh*)

2316 Winnie the Pooh and Friends (*Winnie the Pooh*)

2317 Winnie the Pooh and Tigger (*The House at Pooh Corner*)

2318 Winnie the Pooh

(Des Magpie Studio. Litho Cartor)

2010 (12 Oct). *Europa. Children's Books. Winnie the Pooh* by A. A. Milne. Book Illustrations by E. H. Shepard. Yellow-brown, pale stone and black. 'All-over' phosphor. Perf 14×14½.

3121	**2312**	(1st) Winnie the Pooh and Christopher Robin	1·00	1·00
3122	**2313**	58p. Winnie the Pooh and Piglet	90	90
3123	**2314**	60p. Winnie the Pooh and Rabbit	1·00	1·00
3124	**2315**	67p. Winnie the Pooh and Eeyore	1·10	1·10
3125	**2316**	88p. Winnie the Pooh and Friends	1·25	1·25
3126	**2317**	97p. Winnie the Pooh and Tigger	1·45	1·45
Set of 6			6·00	6·00
Set of 6 Gutter Pairs			12·00	
First Day Cover (Tallents House)				8·00
First Day Cover (Hartfield, East Sussex)				8·00
Presentation Pack (PO Pack No. 447) (Nos. 3121/6 and **MS**3127)			11·50	
PHQ Cards (set of 11) (342)			4·25	15·00

MS3127 115×89 mm. **2318** Winnie the Pooh (1st) Winnie the Pooh and Christopher Robin (from *Now we are Six*); 60p. Christopher Robin reads to Winnie the Pooh (from *Winnie the Pooh*); 88p. Winnie the Pooh and Christopher Robin sailing in umbrella (from *Winnie the Pooh*); 97p. Christopher Robin (putting on wellingtons) and Pooh (from *Winnie the Pooh*). Perf 14½...................................... 4·75   4·75
First Day Cover (Tallents House)...................................... 6·25
First Day Cover (Hartfield, East Sussex)...................... 6·25

Stamps from **MS**3127 show lines from poem 'We Too' by A. A. Milne: 'Wherever I am, there's always Pooh' (1st); 'There's always Pooh and Me. Whatever I do, he wants to do' (60p.); 'Where are you going to-day?' says Pooh: 'Well that's very odd 'cos I was too' (88p.); 'Let's go together,' says Pooh, says he. 'Let's go together,' says Pooh (97p.).

The 1st class value includes the 'EUROPA' emblem.

The eleven PHQ cards show the six stamps, the four individual stamps within **MS**3127 and the complete miniature sheet.

> **SELF-ADHESIVE STAMPS:** Collectors are reminded that used self-adhesive stamps will no longer 'soak-off'. They should be collected with a neat margin of backing paper.

2319 Wallace and Gromit Carol singing

2320 Gromit posting Christmas Cards

2321 Wallace and Gromit Carol singing

2322 Wallace and Gromit decorating Christmas Tree

2323 Gromit posting Christmas Cards

2324 Gromit carrying Christmas Pudding

2325 Gromit wearing Oversized Sweater

(Gravure De La Rue)

2010 (2 Nov). *Christmas with Wallace and Gromit.* One centre band (3128) or two bands (others). Perf 14½×14 (with one elliptical hole in each vert side).

(a) Self-adhesive

3128	**2319**	(2nd) Wallace and Gromit Carol singing......................	90	90
		a. Booklet pane. No. 3128×12..........	9·75	
3129	**2320**	(1st) Gromit posting Christmas Cards .	1·00	1·00
		a. Booklet pane. No. 3129×12..........	10·75	
3130	**2321**	(2nd) Wallace and Gromit Carol (Large) singing......................	1·10	1·00
3131	**2322**	60p. Wallace and Gromit decorating Christmas Tree..................................	1·10	1·10
3132	**2323**	(1st) Gromit posting Christmas (Large) Cards	1·40	1·40
3133	**2324**	97p. Gromit carrying Christmas Pudding	1·40	1·40
3134	**2325**	£1·46 Gromit wearing Oversized Sweater	2·00	2·00
Set of 7........................			8·00	8·00
First Day Cover (Tallents House).........................				9·50
First Day Cover (Bethlehem, Llandeilo).............				9·50
Presentation Pack (PO Pack No. 448).....................................			10·00	
PHQ Cards (set of 8) (343)...............................			3·25	16·50

(b) Ordinary gum

MS3135 115×102 mm. Nos. 3128/34...................		8·00	8·00
First Day Cover (Tallents House).............			9·50
First Day Cover (Bethlehem, Llandeilo)..........			9·50

The eight PHQ cards show the seven individual stamps and the miniature sheet.

The 2nd class, 1st class, 60p and 97p stamps were also issued together in sheets of 20 (No. LS75) sold for £9·30, containing eight 2nd class, eight 1st class, two 60p and two 97p stamps, each stamp accompanied by a *se-tenant* label.

Separate sheets of 20 2nd, 20 1st, ten 1st, ten 60p and ten 97p were available with personal photographs on the labels from Royal Mail, Edinburgh. These were sold at £7·80 for ten 1st, £9·95 for 20 2nd or ten 60p, £13·95 for 20 1st and £14·50 for ten 97p.

All these sheets were printed in lithography by Cartor and had the backing paper around the stamps retained.

Year Pack

2010 (2 Nov). Comprises Nos. 2999/3008, **MS**3025/63, **MS**3065, **MS**3072, 3074/81, **MS**3086/94, 3097/106 and 3109/34.
CP3135a Year Pack .... 125·00

Post Office Yearbook

2010 (2 Nov). Comprises Nos. 2999/3008, **MS**3025/63, **MS**3065, **MS**3072, 3074/81, **MS**3086/94, 3097/106 and 3109/34.
YB3135a Yearbook.. 110·00

Miniature Sheet Collection

2010 (2 Nov). Comprises Nos. **MS**3024, **MS**3025, **MS**3053, **MS**3065, **MS**3072, **MS**3086, **MS**3094, **MS**3127 and **MS**3135.
MS3135a Miniature Sheet Collection.................................. 50·00

2326 *Joe 90*

2327 *Captain Scarlet*

2328 Thunderbird 2 (*Thunderbirds*)

2329 *Stingray*

2330 *Fireball XL5*

2331 *Supercar*

2332 Thunderbird 4; Thunderbird 3; Thunderbird 2; Thunderbird 1 (*Illustration reduced. Actual size 116×89 mm*)

(Des GBH)

2011 (11 Jan). *F.A.B. The Genius of Gerry Anderson* (producer of TV programmes). 'All-over' phosphor.

(a) Ordinary gum. Litho Cartor. Perf 14

3136	**2326**	(1st) *Joe 90*.................................	1·00	1·00
		a. Horiz strip of 3. Nos. 3136/8..........	3·00	3·00
3137	**2327**	(1st) *Captain Scarlet*....................	1·00	1·00
3138	**2328**	(1st) Thunderbird 2 (*Thunderbirds*)	1·00	1·00
3139	**2329**	97p. *Stingray*	1·50	1·50
		a. Horiz strip of 3. Nos. 3139/41.......	4·50	4·50
3140	**2330**	97p. *Fireball XL5*............................	1·50	1·50
3141	**2331**	97p. *Supercar*.................................	1·50	1·50
Set of 6....................			6·75	6·75

Set of 2 Gutter Strips of 6		13·50	
First Day Cover (Tallents House)			7·75
First Day Cover (Slough)			7·75
Presentation Pack (PO Pack No. 450)			
(Nos. 3136/41 and **MS**3142)		12·50	
PHQ Cards (set of 11) (344)		4·25	17·00

(b) Microlenticular Cartor and Outer Aspect Ltd, New Zealand. Perf 14

MS3142 116×89 mm. **2332** 41p. Thunderbird 4; 60p. Thunderbird 3; 88p. Thunderbird 2; 97p. Thunderbird 1 .... 5·25 5·50

MS3142*a* Error imperforate................................ —

First Day Cover (Tallents House) .... 6·00

First Day Cover (Slough) .... 6·00

(c) Self-adhesive. Gravure Walsall. Die-cut Perf 14

3143 **2328** (1st) Thunderbird 2 (*Thunderbirds*) .... 1·50 1·50
　　　a. Booklet pane. No. 3143×2 and
　　　U3016×4 .... 5·75

Nos. 3136/8 and 3139/41 were each printed together, *se-tenant*, as horizontal strips of three stamps in sheets of 60 (2 panes 6×5).

The stamps within **MS**3142 use microlenticular technology to show each vehicle's launch sequences when the miniature sheet is tilted. One example of **MS**3142*a* is known on a first day cover.

The complete miniature sheet is shown on one of the eleven PHQ cards with the others depicting individual stamps including those from **MS**3142.

No. 3143 was only issued in booklets, No. PM27, sold for £2·46.

2333 Classic Locomotives of England

(Des Delaney Design Consultants. Litho Cartor)

2011 (1 Feb). *Classic Locomotives* (1st series). England. Sheet 180×74 mm. |MULTI COLOUR| 'All-over' phosphor. Perf 14.

MS3144 **2333** Classic Locomotives of England (1st) BR Dean Goods No. 2532; 60p. Peckett R2 *Thor*; 88p. Lancashire and Yorkshire Railway 1093 No. 1100; 97p. BR WD No. 90662.................. 4·25 4·50

First Day Cover (Tallents House) .... 5·00

First Day Cover (Liverpool) .... 5·00

Presentation Pack (PO Pack No. 451).................. 5·25

PHQ Cards (set of 5) (345)............................... 2·00 9·00

The five PHQ cards show the four individual stamps and the complete miniature sheet.

2338 Rocky Horror Show

2339 Me and My Girl

2340 Return to the Forbidden Planet

2341 Billy Elliot

(Des Webb and Webb. Litho Cartor)

2011 (24 Feb). *Musicals.* |MULTI COLOUR| 'All-over' phosphor. Perf 14.

3145	**2334**	(1st) *Oliver*	1·00	1·00
3146	**2335**	(1st) *Blood Brothers*.........................	1·00	1·00
3147	**2336**	(1st) *We Will Rock You*.....................	1·00	1·00
3148	**2337**	(1st) *Spamalot*.................................	1·00	1·00
3149	**2338**	97p. *Rocky Horror Show*	1·30	1·30
3150	**2339**	97p. *Me and My Girl*.........................	1·30	1·30
3151	**2340**	97p. *Return to the Forbidden Planet*......	1·30	1·30
3152	**2341**	97p. *Billy Elliot*.................................	1·30	1·30
Set of 8...			8·25	8·25
Set of 8 Gutter Pairs			16·50	
Set of 8 Traffic Light Gutter Pairs			25·00	
First Day Cover (Tallents House)				9·25
First Day Cover (Dancers End, Tring).................				9·25
Presentation Pack (PO Pack No. 452).................			9·75	
PHQ Cards (set of 8) (346)			3·25	11·00

(Gravure Walsall)

2011 (24 Feb). *50th Anniversary of the British Heart Foundation.* Booklet stamp. Design as No. 3115. Self-adhesive. |MULTI COLOUR| 'All-over' phosphor. Die-cut Perf 14×14½.

3153 **2306** (1st) Heart-regulating Beta Blockers .... 1·50 1·50
　　　a. Booklet pane. No. 3153×2 and
　　　U3016×4 .... 5·75

No. 3153 was only issued in booklets, No. PM28, sold for £2·46.

2334 Oliver

2335 Blood Brothers

2342 Rincewind (Terry Pratchett's *Discworld*)

2343 Nanny Ogg (Terry Pratchett's *Discworld*)

2336 We Will Rock You

2337 Spamalot

2344 Michael Gambon as Dumbledore (J. K. Rowling's *Harry Potter*)

2345 Ralph Fiennes as Lord Voldemort (J. K. Rowling's *Harry Potter*)

2346 Merlin (Arthurian Legend)

2347 Morgan Le Fay (Arthurian Legend)

2348 Aslan (C. S. Lewis's Narnia)

2349 Tilda Swinton as The White Witch (C. S. Lewis's Narnia)

(Des So Design Consultants. Gravure De La Rue)

2011 (8 Mar). *Magical Realms.* |MULTI COLOUR| 'All-over' phosphor. Perf 14½.

3154	**2342**	(1st) Rincewind	1·00	1·00
		a. Vert pair. Nos. 3154/5	2·00	2·00
3155	**2343**	(1st) Nanny Ogg	1·00	1·00
3156	**2344**	(1st) Michael Gambon as Dumbledore	1·00	1·00
		a. Vert pair. Nos. 3156/7	2·00	2·00
3157	**2345**	(1st) Ralph Fiennes as Lord Voldemort	1·00	1·00
3158	**2346**	60p. Merlin	95	95
		a. Vert pair. Nos. 3158/9	1·90	1·90
3159	**2347**	60p. Morgan Le Fay	95	95
3160	**2348**	97p. Aslan	1·20	1·20
		a. Vert pair. Nos. 3160/1	2·40	2·40
3161	**2349**	97p. Tilda Swinton as The White Witch	1·20	1·20
Set of 8			7·50	7·50
Set of 4 Gutter Strips of 4			15·00	
First Day Cover (Tallents House)				7·75
First Day Cover (Merlins Bridge, Haverfordwest)				7·75
Presentation Pack (PO Pack No. 453)			8·50	
Presentation Pack ('Heroes and Villains' containing Nos. 3156/7, each×5) (2 Dec)			11.75	
PHQ Cards (set of 8) (347)			3·25	9·25

Nos. 3154/5, 3156/7, 3158/9 and 3160/1 were each printed together, *se-tenant*, as vertical pairs in sheets of 60 (2 panes 5×6).

For Nos. U3055/9 see Decimal Machin Definitives section

2350 African Elephant

2351 Mountain Gorilla

2352 Siberian Tiger

2353 Polar Bear

2354 Amur Leopard

2355 Iberian Lynx

2356 Red Panda

2357 Black Rhinoceros

2358 African Wild Dog

2359 Golden Lion Tamarin

2360 Wildlife of the Amazon Rainforest (*Illustration reduced. Actual size 115×89 mm*)

(Des Janice Nicholson and Rose Design (**MS**3172) or Rose Design Consultants (others). Litho Cartor)

2011 (22 Mar). *50th Anniversary of the WWF.* |MULTI COLOUR| 'All-over' phosphor. Perf 14 (**MS**3172/a) or 14½ (others).

3162	**2350**	(1st) African Elephant	1·00	1·00
		a. Horiz strip of 5. Nos. 3162/6	4·50	4·50
		b. Booklet pane. Nos. 3162/3 and 3170/1 with margins all round	3·75	
3163	**2351**	(1st) Mountain Gorilla	1·00	1·00
3164	**2352**	(1st) Siberian Tiger	1·00	1·00
		b. Booklet pane. Nos. 3164/9 with margins all round	5·50	
3165	**2353**	(1st) Polar Bear	1·00	1·00
3166	**2354**	(1st) Amur Leopard	1·00	1·00
3167	**2355**	(1st) Iberian Lynx	1·00	1·00
		a. Horiz strip of 5. Nos. 3167/71	4·50	4·50
3168	**2356**	(1st) Red Panda	1·00	1·00
3169	**2357**	(1st) Black Rhinoceros	1·00	1·00
3170	**2358**	(1st) African Wild Dog	1·00	1·00
3171	**2359**	(1st) Golden Lion Tamarin	1·00	1·00
Set of 10			9·00	9·00
Set of 2 Gutter Strips of 10			18·00	
First Day Cover (Tallents House)				9·50
First Day Cover (Godalming, Surrey)				9·50
Presentation Pack (PO Pack No. 454) (Nos. 3162/71 and **MS**3172)			15·00	
PHQ Cards (set of 15) (348)			6·00	21·00

MS3172 115×89 mm. **2360** Wildlife of the Amazon Rainforest (1st) Spider monkey; 60p. Hyacinth macaw; 88p. Poison dart frog; 97p. Jaguar ... 4·25 4·50

a. Booklet pane. No. **MS**3172 but
125×96 mm with line of roulettes
at left .... 4·50

First Day Cover (Tallents House).. 5·25
First Day Cover (Godalming, Surrey).................................... 5·25

Nos. 3162/6 and 3167/71 were each printed together, *se-tenant*, as horizontal strips of five stamps in sheets of 50 (2 panes 5×5).

Booklet panes Nos. 3162b, 3164b and **MS**3172a come from the £9·05 'WWF' booklet, No. DX52.

The complete miniature sheet is shown on one of the fifteen PHQ cards with the others depicting individual stamps including those from **MS**3172.

The 1st class value from **MS**3172 includes the 'EUROPA' emblem.

2361 David Tennant as *Hamlet*, 2008

2362 Antony Sher as Prospero, *The Tempest*, 2009

2363 Chuk Iwuji as *Henry VI*, 2006

2364 Paul Schofield as *King Lear*, 1962

2365 Sara Kestelman as Titania, *A Midsummer Night's Dream*, 1970

2366 Ian McKellen and Francesca Annis as *Romeo and Juliet*, 1976

2367 The Four Theatres of the Royal Shakespeare Company, Stratford-upon-Avon (*Illustration reduced. Actual size 115×89 mm*)

(Des Hat-trick. Gravure (Nos. 3173/8) or litho (**MS**3179) Walsall (Nos. 3173/8) or Cartor (**MS**3179))

2011 (21 Apr). 50th Anniversary of the Royal Shakespeare Company. Black, brownish black and bright scarlet. 'All-over' phosphor. Perf 14½ (Nos. 3173/8) or 14 (**MS**3179).

3173	**2361**	(1st) David Tennant as *Hamlet*................	1·00	1·00
3174	**2362**	66p. Antony Sher as Prospero, *The Tempest*	1·00	1·00
3175	**2363**	68p. Chuk Iwuji as *Henry VI*.....................	1·10	1·10
3176	**2364**	76p. Paul Schofield as *King Lear*	1·25	1·25

3177	**2365**	£1 Sara Kestelman as Titania, *A Midsummer Night's Dream*.............	1·50	1·50
3178	**2366**	£1·10 Ian McKellen and Francesca Annis as *Romeo and Juliet*.............	1·75	1·75
Set of 6			6·75	6·75
Set of 6 Gutter Pairs			13·50	
First Day Cover (Tallents House)..........................				8·00
First Day Cover (Stratford-upon-Avon)...............				8·00
Presentation Pack (PO Pack No. 455)				
(Nos. 3173/8 and **MS**3179).................................			13·00	
PHQ Cards (set of 11) (349).................................			4·50	18·00

MS3179 115×89 mm. **2367** The Four Theatres of the Royal Shakespeare Company, Stratford-upon-Avon (1st) Janet Suzman as Ophelia, *Hamlet*, 1965, Royal Shakespeare Theatre; 68p. Patrick Stewart in *Antony and Cleopatra*, 2006, Swan Theatre; 76p. Geoffrey Streatfield in *Henry V*, 2007, The Courtyard Theatre; £1 Judy Dench as Lady Macbeth, 1976, The Other Place .... 4·25 4·25

First Day Cover (Tallents House).. 5·00
First Day Cover (Stratford-upon-Avon).......................... 5·00

The 11 PHQ cards show the six stamps, the four individual stamps within **MS**3179 and the complete miniature sheet.

2368 Prince William and Miss Catherine Middleton (*Illustration reduced. Actual size 115×89 mm*)

(Litho Walsall)

2011 (21 Apr). *Royal Wedding*. Official Engagement Portraits by Mario Testino. Sheet 115×89 mm. MULTI COLOUR 'All-over' phosphor. Perf 14½×14.

MS3180 **2368** Prince William and Miss Catherine Middleton (1st)×2 Prince William and Miss Catherine Middleton embracing; £1·10×2 Formal portrait of Prince William and Miss Catherine Middleton in Council Chamber, St James's Palace .... 5·50 5·50

First Day Cover (Tallents House).. 7·00
First Day Cover (London SW1).. 7·00
Presentation Pack (PO Pack No. M20) .... 13·00
Commemorative Document .... 15·00

2369 'Cray' (fabric print by William Morris), 1884

2370 'Cherries' (detail from panel by Philip Webb), 1867

2371 'Seaweed' (wallpaper pattern by John Henry Dearle), 1901

2372 'Peony' (ceramic tile design by Kate Faulkner), 1877

2373 'Acanthus' (tile by William Morris and William De Morgan), 1876

2374 'The Merchant's Daughter' (detail of stained glass window by Edward Burne-Jones), 1864

(Des Kate Stephens. Litho Cartor or Walsall (booklet stamps))

2011 (5 May). *150th Anniversary of Morris and Company (designers and manufacturers of textiles, wallpaper and furniture)* (1st issue). MULTI COLOUR 'All-over' phosphor. Perf 14×14½

3181	**2369**	(1st) 'Cray'	1·00	1·00
		a. Booklet pane. Nos. 3181 and 3183/5 with margins all round	5·25	
3182	**2370**	(1st) 'Cherries'	1·00	1·00
		a. Booklet pane. Nos. 3182 and 3186, each×2, with margins all round	5·25	
3183	**2371**	76p. 'Seaweed'	1·25	1·25
3184	**2372**	76p. 'Peony'	1·25	1·25
3185	**2373**	£1·10 'Acanthus'	1·70	1·70
3186	**2374**	£1·10 'The Merchant's Daughter'	1·70	1·70
Set of 6			7·00	7·00
Set of 6 Gutter Pairs			14·00	
First Day Cover (Tallents House)				8·00
First Day Cover (Walthamstow)				8·00
Presentation Pack (PO Pack No. 456)			7·75	
PHQ Cards (set of 6) (350)			2·40	8·25

Nos. 3181/6 were also issued in premium booklets, No. DY1, sold for £9·99.

2011 (5 May). *150th Anniversary of Morris and Company* (2nd issue). Design as Type 2202 (2009 Christmas. Stained-glass Windows). MULTI COLOUR One centre band. Perf 14½×14 (with one elliptical hole in each vert side).

3186a	**2202**	(2nd) Angel playing Lute (William Morris), Church of St James, Staveley, Kendal, Cumbria	1·50	1·50
		ab. Booklet pane. No. 3186a×4 with central label and margins all round	6·00	

No. 3186a was only issued in premium booklets, No. DY1, sold for £9·99.

2375 Thomas the Tank Engine

2376 James the Red Engine

2377 Percy the Small Engine

2378 Daisy (diesel railcar)

2379 Toby the Tram Engine

2380 Gordon the Big Engine

2381 Book Illustrations by John T. Kenny (76p.) or C. Reginald Dalby (others) (*Illustration reduced. Actual size* 115×89 *mm*)

2382 'Goodbye, Bertie', called Thomas (from *Tank Engine Thomas Again*)

(Des Elmwood. Litho Cartor)

2011 (14 June). *Thomas the Tank Engine.* (**MS**3193) MULTI COLOUR 'All-over' phosphor.

*(a) Ordinary gum. Perf 14 (**MS**3193) or 14½×14 (others)*

3187	**2375**	(1st) Thomas the Tank Engine	1·00	1·00
3188	**2376**	66p. James the Red Engine	1·00	1·00
3189	**2377**	68p. Percy the Small Engine	1·10	1·10
3190	**2378**	76p. Daisy (diesel railcar)	1·25	1·25
3191	**2379**	£1 Toby the Tram Engine	1·50	1·50
3192	**2380**	£1·10 Gordon the Big Engine	1·75	1·75
Set of 6			6·75	6·75
Set of 6 Gutter Pairs			13·50	
First Day Cover (Tallents House)				8·00
First Day Cover (Box, Corsham, Wiltshire)				8·00
Presentation Pack (PO Pack No. 457) (Nos. 3187/92 and **MS**3193)			13·00	
PHQ Cards (set of 11) (351)			4·50	18·00

MS3193 115×89 mm. **2381** (1st) 'Goodbye, Bertie', called Thomas (from *Tank Engine Thomas Again*); 68p. James was more dirty than hurt (from *Toby the Tram Engine*); 76p. 'Yes, Sir', Percy shivered miserably (from *The Eight Famous*); £1. They told Henry, 'We shall leave you there for always' (from *The Three Railway Engines*) ... 4·25 | 4·25

First Day Cover (Tallents House)	5·00
First Day Cover (Box, Corsham, Wiltshire)	5·00

(b) Self-adhesive. Die-cut perf 14 (Gravure Walsall)

3194	**2382**	(1st) 'Goodbye, Bertie', called Thomas (from *Tank Engine Thomas Again*)	1·50	1·50
		a. Booklet pane. Nos. 3194×2 and U3016×4	5·75	

Nos. 3187/92 show scenes from TV series *Thomas and Friends*, and Nos. **MS**3193/4 book illustrations from *The Railway Series*.

No. 3194 was only issued in stamp booklets, No. PM29, originally sold for £2·76.

The 11 PHQ cards show the six stamps, the four individual stamps within **MS**3193 and the complete miniature sheet.

2383 Paralympic Games: Sailing

2384 Athletics: Field

2385 Volleyball

2386 Wheelchair Rugby

2387 Wrestling

2388 Wheelchair Tennis

2389 Fencing

2390 Gymnastics

2391 Triathlon

2392 Handball

(Des Lara Harwood and Heart (3195), Anthony Pike and The Art Market (3196), Ben Dalling (3197), Matthew Hollings and Illustration Ltd (3198), Daniel Stolle and Anna Goodson Management (3199), David McConochie and The Art Market (3200), Lyndon Hayes and Dutch Uncle Agency (3201), Kathy Wyatt (3202), Adam Simpson and Heart (3203), David Cutter and Folio (3204). Litho Cartor)

2011 (27 July). *Olympic and Paralympic Games, London (2012)* (5th issue). |MULTI COLOUR| 'All-over' phosphor. Perf 14½.

3195	**2383**	(1st) Paralympic Games: Sailing	1·00	1·00
		a. Horiz strip of 5. Nos. 3195/9	4·50	4·50
3196	**2384**	(1st) Athletics: Field	1·00	1·00
3197	**2385**	(1st) Volleyball	1·00	1·00
3198	**2386**	(1st) Wheelchair Rugby	1·00	1·00
3199	**2387**	(1st) Wrestling	1·00	1·00
3200	**2388**	(1st) Wheelchair Tennis	1·00	1·00
		a. Horiz strip of 5. Nos. 3200/4	4·50	4·50
3201	**2389**	(1st) Fencing	1·00	1·00
3202	**2390**	(1st) Gymnastics	1·00	1·00
3203	**2391**	(1st) Triathlon	1·00	1·00
3204	**2392**	(1st) Handball	1·00	1·00
Set of 10			9·00	9·00
Set of 2 Gutter Strips of 10			18·00	
First Day Cover (Tallents House)				9·00
First Day Cover (Rugby, Warks)				9·00
Presentation Pack (PO Pack No. 458)			10·00	
PHQ Cards (set of 10) (352)			4·00	12·00
MS3204a 210×300 mm. Nos. 2981/90, 3097/3106 and 3195/3204			35·00	35·00

Nos. 3195/9 and 3200/4 were each printed together, *se-tenant*, in horizontal strips of five stamps in sheets of 50 (2 panes 5×5).

(Gravure Walsall)

2011 (27 July–15 Sept). *Olympic and Paralympic Games (2012)* (6th issue). Booklet stamps. Designs as Nos. 3195, 3198 and 3201/2 . Self-adhesive. |MULTI COLOUR| 'All-over' phosphor. Die-cut Perf 14½×14.

3205	**2386**	(1st) Wheelchair Rugby	1·50	1·50
		a. Booklet pane. Nos. 3205/6 and U3016×4	5·50	
3206	**2383**	(1st) Paralympic Games: Sailing	1·50	1·50
3206a	**2390**	(1st) Gymnastics (15.9)	1·50	1·50
		ab. Booklet pane. Nos. 3206a/b and U3016×4	5·50	5·50
3206b	**2389**	(1st) Fencing (15.9)	1·50	1·50

Nos. 3205/6 and 3206a/b were only issued in two separate stamp booklets, Nos. PM30 and PM32, each originally sold for £2·76.

2393 The Sovereign's Sceptre with Cross

2394 St Edward's Crown

2395 Rod and Sceptre with Doves

2396 Queen Mary's Crown

2397 The Sovereign's Orb

2398 Jewelled Sword of Offering

2399 Imperial State Crown

2400 Coronation Spoon

(Des Purpose. Litho Cartor)

2011 (23 Aug). *Crown Jewels.* |MULTI COLOUR| Phosphor background. Perf 14×14½.

3207	**2393**	(1st) The Sovereign's Sceptre with Cross	1·00	1·00
3208	**2394**	(1st) St Edward's Crown	1·00	1·00
3209	**2395**	68p. Rod and Sceptre with Doves	1·10	1·10
3210	**2396**	68p. Queen Mary's Crown	1·10	1·10
3211	**2397**	76p. The Sovereign's Orb	1·20	1·20
3212	**2398**	76p. Jewelled Sword of Offering	1·20	1·20
3213	**2399**	£1·10 Imperial State Crown	1·60	1·60
3214	**2400**	£1·10 Coronation Spoon	1·60	1·60
Set of 8			8·75	8·75
Set of 8 Gutter Pairs			17·50	
First Day Cover (Tallents House)				10·00
First Day Cover (London EC3)				10·00
Presentation Pack (PO Pack No. 459)			10·00	
PHQ Cards (set of 8) (353)			3·25	11·00

2401 BR Dean Goods No. 2532

(Gravure Walsall)

2011 (23 Aug). *Classic Locomotives.* Black and gold. Booklet stamp. Design as 1st class stamp within MS**3144**. Self-adhesive. Die-cut Perf 14.

3215	**2401**	(1st) BR Dean Goods No. 2532	1·50	1·50
		a. Booklet pane. No. 3215×2 and U3016×4	5·75	

No. 3215 was only issued in booklets, No. PM31, originally sold for £2·76.

2402 Pilot Gustav Hamel receiving Mailbag

2403 Gustav Hamel in Cockpit

2404 Pilot Clement Greswell and Blériot Monoplane

2405 Delivery of First Airmail to Postmaster General at Windsor

2406 First United Kingdom Aerial Post, 9 September 1911 (*Illustration reduced. Actual size* 146×74 *mm*)

(Des Robert Maude and Sarah Davies. Litho Cartor)

2011 (9 Sept). *Centenary of First United Kingdom Aerial Post* (1st issue). MULTICOLOUR 'All-over' phosphor. Perf 14.

3216	**2402**	(1st) Pilot Gustav Hamel receiving Mailbag	1·75	1·75
		a. Booklet pane. Nos. 3216×2 and 3219, with margins all round	8·50	
3217	**2403**	68p. Pilot Gustav Hamel receiving Mailbag	1·75	1·75
		a. Booklet pane. Nos. 3217×2 and 3218	8·50	
3218	**2404**	£1 Pilot Clement Greswell and Blériot Monoplane	5·00	5·00
3219	**2405**	£1·10 Delivery of First Airmail to Postmaster General at Windsor	5·00	5·00
Set of 4			13·50	13·50
MS3220	146×74 mm. **2406** First United Kingdom Aerial Post, 9 September 1911 Nos. 3216/19		4·50	4·75
First Day Cover (Tallents House)				5·75
First Day Cover (Hendon, London NW4)				5·75
Presentation Pack (PO Pack No. 460)			5·50	
PHQ Cards (set of 5) (354)			2·00	19·50

Nos. 3216/19 were only issued in £9·99 stamp booklets, No. DY2, and in MS3220.

The five PHQ cards show the four individual stamps and the complete miniature sheet.

2407 Windsor Castle

(Recess and litho Cartor)

2011 (9 Sept). *Centenary of First United Kingdom Aerial Post* (2nd issue). Black and cream. Perf 11×11½.

3221	**2407**	50p. Windsor Castle	2·00	2·00
		a. Booklet pane. No. 3221×4, with margins all round	8·25	

No. 3221 was only issued in £9·97 stamp booklets, No. DY2.

For No. **MS**3222 see Decimal Machin Definitives section

2409 George I (1714-27)

2410 George II (1727-60)

2411 George III (1760-1820)

2412 George IV (1820-30)

2413 William IV (1830-7)

2414 Victoria (1837-1901)

2415 The Age of the Hanoverians (*Illustration reduced. Actual size* 123×70 *mm*)

(Des Atelier Works. Litho Cartor)

2011 (15 Sept). *Kings and Queens* (5th issue). House of Hanover. MULTICOLOUR Two phosphor bands. Perf 14.

3223	**2409**	(1st) George I	1·00	1·00
3224	**2410**	(1st) George II	1·00	1·00
3225	**2411**	76p. George III	1·25	1·25
3226	**2412**	76p. George IV	1·25	1·25
3227	**2413**	£1·10 William IV	1·70	1·70
3228	**2414**	£1·10 Victoria	1·70	1·70
Set of 6			7·00	7·00
Set of 6 Gutter Pairs			14·00	
Set of 6 Traffic Light Gutter Blocks of 4			50·00	
First Day Cover (Tallents House)				8·00
First Day Cover (London SW1)				8·00
Presentation Pack (PO Pack No. 461) (Nos. 3223/8 and **MS**3229)			12·75	
PHQ Cards (set of 11) (355)			4·50	18·00

MS3229 123×70 mm. **2415** The Age of the Hanoverians (1st) Robert Walpole (first Prime Minister), 1721; 68p. Ceiling by Robert Adam, Kedleston Hall, 1763; 76p. Penny Black (uniform postage), 1840; £1 Queen Victoria (Diamond Jubilee), 1897.

	4·25	4·25
First Day Cover (Tallents House)		5·00
First Day Cover (London SW1)		5·00

The complete miniature sheet is shown on one of the 11 PHQ cards with the others depicting individual stamps including those from **MS**3229.

2416 Angel of the North

2417 Blackpool Tower

2418 Carrick-a-Rede, Co. Antrim

2419 Downing Street

2420 Edinburgh Castle

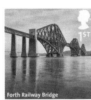

2421 Forth Railway Bridge

2422 Glastonbury Tor

2423 Harlech Castle

2424 Ironbridge

2425 Jodrell Bank

2426 Kursaal, Southend, Essex

2427 Lindisfarne Priory

(Des Robert Maude and Sarah Davies. Litho Cartor)

2011 (13 Oct). *UK A–Z* (1st series). |MULTI COLOUR| 'All-over' phosphor. Perf 14½.

3230	2416	(1st) Angel of the North	1·00	1·00
		a. Horiz strip of 6. Nos. 3230/5	4·50	4·50
3231	2417	(1st) Blackpool Tower	1·00	1·00
3232	2418	(1st) Carrick-a-Rede, Co. Antrim	1·00	1·00
3233	2419	(1st) Downing Street	1·00	1·00
3234	2420	(1st) Edinburgh Castle	1·00	1·00
3235	2421	(1st) Forth Railway Bridge	1·00	1·00
3236	2422	(1st) Glastonbury Tor	1·00	1·00
		a. Horiz strip of 6. Nos. 3236/41	4·50	4·50
3237	2423	(1st) Harlech Castle	1·00	1·00
3238	2424	(1st) Ironbridge	1·00	1·00

3239	2425	(1st) Jodrell Bank	1·00	1·00
3240	2426	(1st) Kursaal, Southend, Essex	1·00	1·00
3241	2427	(1st) Lindisfarne Priory	1·00	1·00
	Set of 12		9·00	9·00
	Set of 2 Gutter Strips of 12		18·00	
	Set of 2 Traffic Light Gutter Strips of 24		48·00	
	First Day Covers (2) (Tallents House)			11·00
	First Day Covers (2) (Blackpool)			11·00
	Presentation Pack (PO Pack No. 462)		12·00	
	PHQ Cards (set of 12) (356)		4·75	13·00

Nos. 3230/5 and 3236/41 were each printed together, *se-tenant*, as horizontal strips of six stamps in sheets of 60 (2 panes of 30).

2428 Joseph visited by the Angel (Matthew 1:21)

2429 Madonna and Child (Matthew 1:23)

2430 Joseph visited by the Angel (Matthew 1:21)

2431 Madonna and Child (Matthew 1:23)

2432 Baby Jesus in the Manger (Luke 2:7)

2433 Shepherds visited by the Angel (Luke 2:10)

2434 Wise Men and Star (Matthew 2:10)

(Des Peter Malone/The Artworks and Together Design. Gravure De La Rue)

2011 (8 Nov). *Christmas. 400th Anniversary of the King James Bible.* |MULTI COLOUR| One centre band (3242) or two phosphor bands (others). Perf 14½×14 (with one elliptical hole in each vert side).

(a) Self-adhesive

3242	2428	(2nd) Joseph visited by the Angel	90	90
		a. Booklet pane. No. 3242×12	9·75	
3243	2429	(1st) Madonna and Child	1·00	1·00
		a. Booklet pane. No. 3243×12	10·75	
3244	2430	(2nd Joseph visited by the Large) Angel	1·10	1·10
3245	2431	(1st Madonna and Large) Child	1·40	1·40
3246	2432	68p. Baby Jesus in the Manger	1·20	1·20
3247	2433	£1·10 Shepherds visited by the Angel	1·85	1·85
3248	2434	£1·65 Wise Men and Star	2·50	2·50
	Set of 7		9·00	9·00
	First Day Cover (Tallents House)			11·00
	First Day Cover (Bethlehem, Llandeilo)			11·00
	Presentation Pack (PO Pack No. 463)		10·00	
	PHQ Cards (set of 8) (357)		3·25	19·50

(b) Ordinary gum

MS3249	116×102 mm. As Nos. 3242/8		9·00	9·00
	First Day Cover (Tallents House)			10·00
	First Day Cover (Bethlehem, Llandeilo)			10·00

The eight PHQ cards show the seven individual stamps and the miniature sheet.

The 2nd class, 1st class, 68p., and £1·10 stamps were also issued in sheets of 20 (No. LS79) printed in lithography and sold for £10·45, containing eight 2nd class, eight 1st class, two 68p. and two £1·10 stamps, each stamp accompanied by a *se-tenant* label with a verse from the King James Bible.

Separate sheets of 20 2nd, ten 1st, ten 68p. and ten £1·10 were available with personal photographs on the labels from Royal Mail, Edinburgh. These were sold at £8·30 for ten 1st, £10·95 for 20 2nd, £10·75 for ten 68p. or £15·80 for ten £1·10.

Year Pack

2011 (8 Nov). Comprises Nos. 3136/42, **MS**3144/52, 3154/93, 3195/3204, 3207/14, **MS**3220 and 3223/48.

CP3244a	Year Pack	130·00

Post Office Yearbook

2011 (8 Nov). Comprises Nos. 3136/42, **MS**3144/52, 3154/93, 3195/3204, 3207/14, **MS**3220 and 3223/48.

YB3244a	Yearbook	130·00

Miniature Sheet Collection

2011 (8 Nov). Comprises Nos. **MS**3142, **MS**3144, **MS**3172, **MS**3179/80, **MS**3193, **MS**3220, **MS**3229 and **MS**3249.

MS3244a Miniature Sheet Collection.................................. 45·00

2435 Paralympic
Games Emblem

2436 Olympic
Games Emblem

(Gravure Walsall (booklets) or De La Rue (others))

2012 (5 Jan). *Olympic and Paralympic Games* (7th issue). Self-adhesive. Two phosphor bands. Die-cut Perf 14½×14 (with one elliptical hole on each vert side).

3250	**2435**	(1st) Paralympic Games Emblem. Black and orange-red..............	1·25	1·25
		a. Booklet pane. Nos. 3250/1, each×3.........................	7·00	
3251	**2436**	(1st) Olympic Games Emblem. Black and orange-red...........	1·25	1·25
3252	**2435**	(Worldwide up to 20g) Paralympic Games Emblem. Black, bright scarlet and greenish blue.........................	2·25	2·25
3253	**2436**	(Worldwide up to 20g) Olympic Games Emblem. Black, bright scarlet and greenish blue...	2·25	2·25

Set of 4.. 7·00 7·00
First Day Cover (Tallents House)...................................... 8·00
First Day Cover (Sennen, Penzance, Cornwall).................. 8·00
Presentation Pack (PO Pack No. D92)................ 9·00
PHQ Cards (set of 4) (D32)........................ 1·50 8·00

Nos. 3250/1 were printed together in sheets of 50 (2 panes 5×5), with the two designs alternating horizontally and vertically. The upper pane had No. 3250 at top left and contained 13 of No. 3250 and 12 of No. 3251. The lower pane had No. 3251 at top left and contained 13 of No. 3251 and 12 of No. 3250.

Nos. 3252/3 were also issued in stamp booklets, No. MB9/10, originally sold for £2·76.

Booklet pane 3250a exists in two versions which differ in the order of the stamps within the block of six.

Nos. 3252/3 were printed together in sheets of 25 (5×5) with the two designs alternating horizontally and vertically. There were two versions of the sheets of 25, one having No. 3252 at top left and containing 13 of No. 3252 and 12 of No. 3253, and the other having No. 3253 at top left and containing 13 of No. 3253 and 12 of No. 3252.

Nos. 3250/3 were also issued on 27 June 2012 in sheets of 20 containing Nos. 3250/1, each×8, and 3252/3, each×2, all with *se-tenant* labels showing Games venues (No. LS82). These sheets are printed in lithography by Cartor.

2437 *Charlie and the Chocolate Factory*

2438 *Fantastic Mr. Fox*

2439 *James and the Giant Peach*

2440 *Matilda*

2441 *The Twits*

2442 *The Witches*

(Des Magpie Studio. Litho Cartor)

2012 (10 Jan). *Roald Dahl's Children's Stories* (1st issue). Book Illustrations by Quentin Blake. 'All-over' phosphor. Perf 14.

3254	**2437**	(1st) Charlie and the Chocolate Factory....................................	1·00	1·00
		a. Booklet pane. Nos. 3254 and 3256/7 with margins all round....	3·50	
3255	**2438**	66p. Fantastic Mr. Fox	1·00	1·00
		a. Booklet pane. Nos. 3255 and 3258/9 with margins all round....	4·50	

3256	**2439**	68p. James and the Giant Peach.............	1·10	1·10
3257	**2440**	76p. Matilda....................................	1·25	1·25
3258	**2441**	£1 The Twits....................................	1·50	1·50
3259	**2442**	£1·10 The Witches..........................	1·75	1·75

Set of 6.. 6·75 6·75
Set of 6 Gutter Pairs... 13·50
Set of 6 Traffic Light Gutter Blocks of 4............................ 30·00
First Day Cover (Tallents House)...................................... 9·00
First Day Cover (Great Missenden, Bucks) .... 9·00
Presentation Pack (PO Pack No. 465)
(Nos. 3254/9 and **MS**3264)........................ 16·00
PHQ Cards (set of 11) (358)........................ 4·25 25·00

2443 The BFG carrying Sophie in his Hand

2444 The BFG wakes up the Giants

2445 Sophie sitting on Buckingham Palace Window-sill

2446 The BFG and Sophie at Writing Desk

2447 Roald Dahl's *The BFG* (*Illustration reduced. Actual size* 114×89 *mm*)

(Des Magpie Studio. Litho Cartor)

2012 (10 Jan). *Roald Dahl's Children's Stories* (2nd issue). Book Illustrations by Quentin Blake. 'All-over' phosphor. Perf 14×14½.

3260	**2443**	(1st) The BFG carrying Sophie in his Hand....................................	2·25	2·25
		a. Booklet pane. Nos. 3260/3.............	9·00	9·00
3261	**2444**	68p. The BFG wakes up the Giants......	2·25	2·25
3262	**2445**	76p. Sophie sitting on Buckingham Palace Window-sill.............................	2·25	2·25
3263	**2446**	£1 The BFG and Sophie at Writing Desk....................................	2·25	2·25

Set of 4.. 9·00 9·00
MS3264 115×89 mm. **2447** Roald Dahl's *The BFG*
Nos. 3260/3........................ 9·00 9·00
First Day Cover (Tallents House)...................................... 9·50
First Day Cover (Great Missenden, Bucks) .... 9·50

Nos. 3260/3 were only issued in £11·47 premium booklets, No. DY3, and in **MS**3264.

The complete miniature sheet is shown on one of the eleven PHQ cards with the others showing individual stamps including those from **MS**3264.

No. **MS**3264 commemorates the 30th anniversary of the publication of *The BFG*.

2448 Edward VII
(1901-10)

2449 George V
(1910-36)

2450 Edward VIII
(1936)

2451 George VI
(1936-52)

2452 Elizabeth II (1952-)

2453 The Age of the Windsors (*Illustration reduced. Actual size 123×70 mm*)

(Des Atelier Works. Litho Cartor)

2012 (2 Feb). *Kings and Queens* (6th issue). House of Windsor. |MULTI COLOUR| Two phosphor bands. Perf 14.

3265	**2448**	(1st) Edward VII	1·00	1·00
3266	**2449**	68p. George V	1·00	1·00
3267	**2450**	76p. Edward VIII	1·40	1·40
3268	**2451**	£1 George VI	1·85	1·85
3269	**2452**	£1·10 Elizabeth II	2·25	2·25
Set of 5			6·75	6·75
Set of 5 Gutter Pairs			13·50	
Set of 5 Traffic Light Gutter Blocks of 4			25·00	
First Day Cover (Tallents House)				5·50
First Day Cover (Windsor, Berkshire)				5·50
Presentation Pack (PO Pack No. 466)				
(Nos. 3265/9 and **MS**3270)			11·50	
PHQ Cards (set of 10) (359)			4·00	16·50

MS3270 123×70 mm. **2453** The Age of the Windsors (1st) Scott Expedition to South Pole, 1912; 68p. Queen Elizabeth the Queen Mother and King George VI in bomb damaged street, *c.* 1940; 76p. England's winning World Cup football team, 1966; £1 Channel Tunnel, 1996.

	4·25	4·25
First Day Cover (Tallents House)		5·50
First Day Cover (Windsor, Berkshire)		5·50

The complete miniature sheet is shown on one of the ten PHQ cards with the others depicting individual stamps including those from **MS**3270.

No. 3271 is vacant.

For Nos. U3271/8 see Decimal Machin Definitives section

HER MAJESTY QUEEN ELIZABETH II
DIAMOND JUBILEE

2454 Diamond Jubilee (*Illustration reduced. Actual size 146×74 mm*)

(Des Sedley Place. Gravure Walsall)

2012 (6 Feb). *Diamond Jubilee*. (2nd issue). |MULTI COLOUR| Two phosphor bands. Perf 14½×14 (with one elliptical hole in each vertical side).

MS3272 146×74 mm. **2454** Diamond Jubilee (1st)×6 Portrait from photograph by Dorothy Wilding; 1960 £1 Banknote portrait by Robert Austin; 1971 £5 Banknote portrait by Harry Eccleston; 1953 Coinage portrait by Mary Gillick; 1971 decimal coin portrait by Arnold Machin; As No. U3271

	5·50	5·50
First Day Cover (Tallents House)		6·00
First Day Cover (London SW1)		6·00
Presentation Pack (PO Pack No. 93)	6·75	
PHQ Cards (set of 7) (D33)	2·75	11·00
Commemorative Document	10·00	

The 1st class slate-blue Machin stamp from **MS**3272 has an iridescent overprint reading 'DIAMOND JUBILEE' and the source code 'MMND'.

The seven PHQ cards show the six individual stamps and the complete miniature sheet.

2455 Coventry Cathedral, 1962 (Sir Basil Spence, architect)

2456 Frederick Delius (1862-1934, composer)

2457 'Orange Tree' Embroidery (Mary 'May' Morris 1862-1938, designer and textile artist)

2458 Odette Hallowes (1912-95, SOE agent in occupied France)

2459 Steam Engine, 1712 (Thomas Newcomen, inventor of atmospheric steam engine)

2460 Kathleen Ferrier (1912-53, contralto)

2461 Interior of Palace of Westminster (Augustus Pugin 1812-52, Gothic revival architect and designer)

2462 Montagu Rhodes James (1862-1936 scholar and author)

2463 Bombe Code Breaking Machine (Alan Turing 1912-54, mathematician and World War II code breaker)

2464 Joan Mary Fry (1862-1955 relief worker and social reformer)

2466 *The Dandy* and Desperate Dan

2467 *The Beano* and Dennis the Menace

2468 *Eagle* and Dan Dare

2469 *The Topper* and Beryl the Peril

(Des Purpose. Litho Cartor)

2012 (23 Feb). *Britons of Distinction.* |MULTI COLOUR| 'All-over' phosphor. Perf 14½.

3273	2455	(1st) Coventry Cathedral	1·00	1·00
		a. Horiz strip of 5. Nos. 3273/7	4·50	4·50
3274	2456	(1st) Frederick Delius	1·00	1·00
3275	2457	(1st) 'Orange Tree' Embroidery	1·00	1·00
3276	2458	(1st) Odette Hallowes	1·00	1·00
3277	2459	(1st) Steam Engine, 1712	1·00	1·00
3278	2460	(1st) Kathleen Ferrier	1·00	1·00
		a. Horiz strip of 5. Nos. 3278/82	4·50	4·50
3279	2461	(1st) Interior of Palace of Westminster	1·00	1·00
3280	2462	(1st) Montagu Rhodes James	1·00	1·00
3281	2463	(1st) Bombe Code Breaking Machine	1·00	1·00
3282	2464	(1st) Joan Mary Fry	1·00	1·00
Set of 10			9·00	9·00
Set of 2 Gutter Strips of 10			18·00	
First Day Cover (Tallents House)				9·25
First Day Cover (Coventry)				9·25
Presentation Pack (PO Pack No. 467)			9·50	
PHQ Cards (set of 10) (360)			4·00	11·50

Nos. 3273/7 and 3278/82 were each printed together, *se-tenant*, as horizontal strips of five stamps in sheets of 50 (2 panes 5×5).

No. 3281 also comes from booklet pane No. 3679b in £14·60 Inventive Britain booklet, No. DY12.

2465 Classic Locomotives of Scotland (*Illustration reduced. Actual size* 180×74 *mm*)

2470 *Tiger* and Roy of the Rovers

2471 *Bunty* and the Four Marys

(Des Delaney Design Consultants. Litho Cartor)

2012 (8 Mar). *Classic Locomotives* (2nd series). Scotland. Sheet 180×74 mm. |MULTI COLOUR| 'All-over' phosphor. Perf 14.

MS3283 **2465** Classic Locomotives of Scotland (1st) BR Class D34 Nos. 62471 *Glen Falloch* and 62496 *Glen Loy* at Ardlui, 9 May 1959; 68p. BR Class D40 No. 62276 *Andrew Bain* at Macduff, July 1950; £1 Andrew Barclay No. 807 *Bon Accord* propelling wagons along Miller Street, Aberdeen, June 1962; £1·10 BR Class 4P No. 54767 *Clan Mackinnon* pulling fish train, Kyle of Lochalsh,

October 1948	4·75	4·75
First Day Cover (Tallents House)		6·00
First Day Cover (Glasgow)		6·00
Presentation Pack (PO Pack No. 468)	5·50	
PHQ Cards (set of 5) (361)	2·00	9·00

The five PHQ cards show the four individual stamps and the complete miniature sheet.

2472 *Buster* and Cartoon Character Buster

2473 *Valiant* and the Steel Claw

2474 *Twinkle* and Nurse Nancy

2475 *2000 AD* and Judge Dredd

(Des The Chase. Litho Cartor)

2012 (20 Mar). *Comics.* |MULTI COLOUR| 'All-over' phosphor. Perf 14½.

3284	2466	(1st) *The Dandy* and Desperate Dan	1·00	1·00
		a. Horiz strip of 5. Nos. 3284/8	4·50	4·50
3285	2467	(1st) *The Beano* and Dennis the Menace	1·00	1·00

3286	2468	(1st) *Eagle* and Dan Dare..........................	1·00	1·00
3287	2469	(1st) *The Topper* and Beryl the Peril	1·00	1·00
3288	2470	(1st) *Tiger* and Roy of the Rovers.........	1·00	1·00
3289	2471	(1st) *Bunty* and the Four Marys	1·00	1·00
		a. Horiz strip of 5. Nos. 3289/93.......	4·50	4·50
3290	2472	(1st) *Buster* and Cartoon Character		
		Buster..	1·00	1·00
3291	2473	(1st) *Valiant* and the Steel Claw............	1·00	1·00
3292	2474	(1st) *Twinkle* and Nurse Nancy	1·00	1·00
3293	2475	(1st) *2000 AD* and Judge Dredd.............	1·00	1·00
Set of 10			9·00	9·00
Set of 2 Gutter Strips of 5			18·00	
First Day Cover (Tallents House)				15·00
First Day Cover (Dundee)				15·00
Presentation Pack (PO Pack No. 469)			10·00	
PHQ Cards (set of 10)			4·00	11·50

2476 Manchester Town Hall

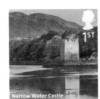

2477 Narrow Water Castle, Co. Down

2478 Old Bailey, London

2479 Portmeirion, Wales

2480 The Queen's College, Oxford

2481 Roman Baths, Bath

2482 Stirling Castle, Scotland

2483 Tyne Bridge, Newcastle

2484 Urquhart Castle, Scotland

2485 Victoria and Albert Museum, London

2486 White Cliffs of Dover

2487 Station X, Bletchley Park, Buckinghamshire

2488 York Minster

2489 London Zoo

(Des Robert Maude and Sarah Davies. Litho Cartor)

2012 (10 Apr). *UK A-Z* (2nd series). MULTI COLOUR 'All-over' phosphor. Perf 14½.

3294	2476	(1st) Manchester Town Hall	1·00	1·00
		a. Horiz strip of 6. Nos. 3294/9	5·50	5·50
3295	2477	(1st) Narrow Water Castle, Co.		
		Down	1·00	1·00
3296	2478	(1st) Old Bailey, London	1·00	1·00
3297	2479	(1st) Portmeirion, Wales	1·00	1·00
3298	2480	(1st) The Queen's College,		
		Oxford....................................	1·00	1·00
3299	2481	(1st) Roman Baths, Bath	1·00	1·00
3300	2482	(1st) Stirling Castle, Scotland	1·00	1·00
		a. Horiz strip of 6. Nos. 3300/5	5·50	5·50
3301	2483	(1st) Tyne Bridge, Newcastle	1·00	1·00
3302	2484	(1st) Urquhart Castle, Scotland	1·00	1·00
3303	2485	(1st) Victoria and Albert		
		Museum, London	1·00	1·00
3304	2486	(1st) White Cliffs of Dover..............	1·00	1·00
3305	2487	(1st) Station X, Bletchley Park,		
		Buckinghamshire....................	1·00	1·00
3306	2488	(1st) York Minster...........................	1·00	1·00
		a. Horiz pair. Nos. 3306/7..........	2·00	2·00
3307	2489	(1st) London Zoo	1·00	1·00
Set of 14			12·50	12·50
Set of 2 Gutter Strips of 12 and 1 Gutter Strip of 4			25·00	
Set of 2 Traffic Light Gutter Strips of 24 and 1 Gutter				
Block of 8			50·00	
First Day Covers (2) (Tallents House)..........................				15·00
First Day Covers (2) (Dover, Kent)..............................				15·00
Presentation Pack (PO Pack No. 470)			14·00	
PHQ Cards (set of 14) (363)....................................			5·50	15·00
MS3308 297×210 mm. Nos. 3230/41 and 3294/307			£100	£110

Nos. 3294/9 and 3300/5 were each printed together, *se-tenant*, as horizontal strips of six stamps in sheets of 60 (2 panes 6×5).

Nos. 3306/7 were printed together, *se-tenant*, as horizontal pairs in sheets of 60 (2 panes 6×5).

No. 3303 includes the 'EUROPA' emblem.

No. 3305 also comes from booklet pane No. 3679b in £14·60 Inventive Britain booklet No DY12.

2490 Skirt Suit by Hardy Amies, late 1940s

2491 Outfit by Norman Hartnell, 1950s

2492 Jacket designed by John Pearce for Granny Takes a Trip Boutique, 1960s

2493 Print by Celia Birtwell for Outfit by Ossie Clark, late 1960s

2494 Suit designed for Ringo Starr by Tommy Nutter

2495 Outfit by Jean Muir, late 1970s/early 1980s

2496 'Royal' Dress by Zandra Rhodes, 1981

2497 Harlequin dress by Vivienne Westwood, 1993

2498 Suit by Paul Smith, 2003

2499 'Black Raven' by Alexander McQueen, 2009

(Des Johnson Banks. Litho Cartor)

2012 (15 May). *Great British Fashion*. [MULTI COLOUR] Phosphor background. Perf 14½×14.

3309	**2490**	(1st) Skirt Suit by Hardy Amies	1·00	1·00
		a. Horiz strip of 5. Nos. 3309/13	4·50	4·50
3310	**2491**	(1st) Outfit by Norman Hartnell	1·00	1·00
3311	**2492**	(1st) Jacket designed by John Pearce	1·00	1·00
3312	**2493**	(1st) Print by Celia Birtwell for Outfit by Ossie Clark	1·00	1·00
3313	**2494**	(1st) Suit designed	1·00	1·00
3314	**2495**	(1st) Outfit by Jean Muir	1·00	1·00
		a. Horiz strip of 5. Nos. 3314/18	4·50	4·50
3315	**2496**	(1st) 'Royal' Dress by Zandra Rhodes	1·00	1·00
3316	**2497**	(1st) Harlequin dress by Vivienne Westwood	1·00	1·00
3317	**2498**	(1st) Suit by Paul Smith	1·00	1·00

3318	**2499**	(1st) 'Black Raven' by Alexander McQueen	1·00	1·00
Set of 10			9·00	9·00
Set of 2 Gutter Strips of 10			18·00	
Set of 2 Traffic Light Gutter Strips of 20			40·00	
First Day Cover (Tallents House)				11·00
First Day Cover (London W1)				11·00
Presentation Pack (PO Pack No. 471)			10·00	
PHQ Cards (set of 10) (364)			4·00	12·00

Nos. 3309/13 and 3314/18 were each printed together, *se-tenant*, as horizontal strips of five stamps in sheets of 50 (2 panes 5×5).

2500 Queen Elizabeth II at Golden Jubilee Service, St Paul's Cathedral, London, 2002

2501 Queen Elizabeth II Trooping the Colour, 1967

2502 Queen Elizabeth II inspecting 2nd Battalion Royal Welsh, Tidworth, 1 March 2007

2503 First Christmas Television Broadcast, 1957

2504 Silver Jubilee Walkabout, 1977

2505 Queen Elizabeth II in Garter Ceremony Procession, 1997

2506 Queen Elizabeth II addressing the UN General Assembly, 1957

2507 Queen Elizabeth II at Commonwealth Games, Brisbane, Australia, 1982

(Des Kate Stephens. Gravure De La Rue (A3319/20, A3323/6) or Enschedé (A3321/2), Litho Walsall (B3319/26) or gravure Walsall (3327))

2012 (31 May). *Diamond Jubilee* (3rd issue). [MULTI COLOUR] 'All-over' phosphor.

(a) Sheet stamps. Ordinary gum. gravure. Perf 14×14½.

A3319	**2500**	(1st) Queen Elizabeth II at Golden Jubilee Service, St Paul's Cathedral, London, 2002	1·00	1·00
		a. Horiz pair. Nos. A3319/20	2·00	2·00
A3320	**2501**	(1st) Queen Elizabeth II Trooping the Colour, 1967	1·00	1·00
A3321	**2502**	77p. Queen Elizabeth II inspecting 2nd Battalion Royal Welsh, Tidworth, 1 March 2007	1·00	1·00
		a. Horiz pair. Nos. A3321/2	2·00	2·00
A3322	**2503**	77p. First Christmas Television Broadcast, 1957	1·00	1·00
A3323	**2504**	87p. Silver Jubilee Walkabout, 1977	1·25	1·25
		a. Horiz pair. Nos. A3323/4	2·50	2·50

A3324	**2505**	87p. Queen Elizabeth II in Garter Ceremony Procession, 1997	1·25	1·25
A3325	**2506**	£1·28 Queen Elizabeth II addressing the UN General Assembly, 1957...	1·80	1·80
		a. Horiz pair. Nos. A3325/6................	3·50	3·50
A3326	**2507**	£1·28 Queen Elizabeth II at Commonwealth Games, Brisbane, Australia, 1982........	1·80	1·80

Set of 8.. 9·00 9·00
Set of 4 Gutter Strips of 4 .... 18·00
First Day Cover (Tallents House)............................... 11·00
First Day Cover (Windsor, Berkshire)........................... 11·00
Presentation Pack (PO Pack No. 472)........................ 17·00
PHQ Cards (Set of 8) (365)....................... 3·25 12·00

(b) Booklet stamps. Ordinary gum. Litho. Perf 14×14½.

B3319	**2500**	(1st) Queen Elizabeth II at Golden Jubilee Service, St Paul's Cathedral, London, 2002................	1·40	1·40
		b. Booklet pane. Nos. B3319 and B3323/5 with margins all round..	6·00	
B3320	**2501**	(1st) Queen Elizabeth II Trooping the Colour, 1967................................	1·40	1·40
		b. Booklet pane. Nos. B3320/1 with margins all round	3·00	
B3321	**2502**	77p. Queen Elizabeth II inspecting 2nd Battalion Royal Welsh, Tidworth, 1 March 2007................	1·40	1·40
B3322	**2503**	77p. First Christmas Television Broadcast, 1957................................	1·40	1·40
		b. Booklet pane. Nos. B3322 and B3326 with margins all round......	3·00	
B3323	**2504**	87p. Silver Jubilee Walkabout, 1977....	1·40	1·40
B3324	**2505**	87p. Queen Elizabeth II in Garter Ceremony Procession, 1997....	1·40	1·40
B3325	**2506**	£1·28 Queen Elizabeth II addressing the UN General Assembly, 1957..	1·40	1·40
B3326	**2507**	£1·28 Queen Elizabeth II at Commonwealth Games, Brisbane, Australia, 1982........	1·40	1·40

Set of 8.. 11·00 11·00

(c) Self-adhesive booklet stamp. gravure. Die-cut perf 14.

| 3327 | **2500** | (1st) Queen Elizabeth II at Golden Jubilee Service, St Paul's Cathedral, London, 2002................ | 1·50 | 1·50 |
| | | a. Booklet pane. No. 3327×2 and No. U3274×4............................ | 6·00 | |

Nos. A3319/20, A3321/2, A3323/4 and A3325/6 were printed together, *se-tenant*, as horizontal pairs in sheets of 60 (2 panes 6×5).
Nos. B3319/26 come from £12·77 booklets, No. DY4.
No. 3327 was only issued in stamp booklets, No. PM33, originally sold for £3·60.

(Des Sedley Place. Gravure Walsall)

2012 (31 May). *Diamond Jubilee* (4th issue). As Type **159** but redrawn with 1st value indicator. [MULTI COLOUR] Two phosphor bands. Perf 14½×14 (with one elliptical hole in each vert side).
3329   (1st) light brown... 1·20 1·20
First Day Cover (No. 3328a), (Tallents House or Windsor) ... 7·50
A similar stamp was included in **MS**3272.
The stamp and pane, formerly listed as Nos. 3328/a have been renumbered as U3279/a and will be found in the Machins section of this catalogue.

2508 Mr Bumble
(*Oliver Twist*)

2509 Mr Pickwick
(*The Pickwick Papers*)

2510 The Marchioness
(*The Old Curiosity Shop*)

2511 Mrs Gamp
(*Martin Chuzzlewit*)

2512 Captain Cuttle
(*Dombey and Son*)

2513 Mr Micawber
(*David Copperfield*)

Charles Dickens 1812–1870

"No one who can read, ever looks at a book, even unopened on a shelf, like one who cannot."

2514 Scenes from *Nicholas Nickleby, Bleak House, Little Dorrit* and *A Tale of Two Cities* (*Illustration reduced. Actual size 190×67 mm*)

(Des Howard Brown. Litho Cartor)

2012 (19 June). *Birth Bicentenary of Charles Dickens.* Illustrations from Character Sketches from Charles Dickens, c. 1890 by Joseph Clayton Clarke ('Kyd') (3330/5) or Book Illustrations by Hablot Knight Browne ('Phiz') (**MS**3336). [MULTI COLOUR] One centre band (2nd) or 'all-over' phosphor (others). Perf 14 (3330/5) or 14×14½ (**MS**3336).

3330	**2508**	(2nd) Mr Bumble (*Oliver Twist*)	90	90
3331	**2509**	(1st) Mr Pickwick (*The Pickwick Papers*).........................	1·00	1·00
3332	**2510**	77p. The Marchioness (*The Old Curiosity Shop*)	1·00	1·00
3333	**2511**	87p. Mrs Gamp (*Martin Chuzzlewit*)......	1·40	1·40
3334	**2512**	£1·28 Captain Cuttle (*Dombey and Son*)...........................	2·00	2·00
3335	**2513**	£1·90 Mr Micawber (*David Copperfield*).	3·00	3·00

Set of 6.. 8·50 8·50
Set of 6 Gutter Pairs .... 17·00
Set of 6 Traffic Light Gutter Blocks of 4 ...... 38·00
First Day Cover (Tallents House)............................... 11·00
First Day Cover (Portsmouth) .... 11·00
Presentation Pack (PO Pack No. 473)
(Nos. 3330/5 and **MS**3336)...................... 14·00
PHQ Cards (set of 11) (366)....................... 4·50 17·00
MS3336   190×67 mm. **2514** Scenes from *Nicholas Nickleby, Bleak House, Little Dorrit* and *A Tale of Two Cities* (1st)×4 Nicholas Nickleby caning headmaster Wackford Squeers (*Nicholas Nickleby*); Mrs. Bagnet is charmed with Mr. Bucket (*Bleak House*); Amy Dorrit introduces Maggy to Arthur Clennam (*Little Dorrit*); Charles Darnay arrested by French revolutionaries (*A Tale of Two Cities*).................... 3·75 3·75
First Day Cover (Tallents House)............................... 4·50
First Day Cover (Portsmouth) .... 4·50
The complete miniature sheet is shown on one of the eleven PHQ cards with the others depicting individual stamps including those from **MS**3336.

(Litho Cartor)

2012 (27 July). *Olympic and Paralympic Games* (8th issue). Designs as Nos. 3250/3. [MULTI COLOUR] Two phosphor bands. Perf 14½×14 (with one elliptical hole in each vert side).

3337	**2436**	(1st) Olympic Games Eblem. Black and orange-red	4·00	4·00
		a. Booklet pane. Nos. 3337/8, each×3, and 3339/40 with central label and margins all round.........	38·00	
3338	**2435**	(1st) Paralympic Games Emblem. Black and orange-red.....................	4·00	4·00
3339	**2436**	(Worldwide up to 20g) Olympic Games Eblem. Black, bright scarlet and greenish blue	10·00	10·00
3340	**2435**	(Worldwide up to 20g) Paralympic Games Emblem. Black, bright scarlet and greenish blue	10·00	10·00

Set of 4 .... 18·00 18·00
First Day Cover (No. 3337a) (Tallents House)......................... 20·00
First Day Cover (No. 3337a) (London E20) .... 20·00
Nos. 3339/40 were for use on Worldwide Mail up to 20g.
Nos. 3337/40 were only issued in £10·71 stamp booklets, No. DY5.

2515 Sports and London Landmarks (*Illustration reduced. Actual size* 192×75 *mm*)

(Des Hat-trick design. Litho Cartor)

2012 (27 July). *Welcome to London, Olympic Games.* Sheet 192×75 mm. |MULTI|COLOUR| 'All-over' phosphor. Perf 14½.

MS3341 2515 Sports and London Landmarks (1st) Fencer and Tower Bridge; (1st) Athletes in race and Olympic Stadium; £1·28 Diver and Tate Modern; £1·28 Cyclist and London Eye.. 5·50   5·50
First Day Cover (Tallents House)... 10·00
First Day Cover (London E20) .... 10·00
Presentation Pack (PO Pack No. 474) .... 20·00
PHQ Cards (set of 5) (367) .... 2·00   9·00
The five PHQ Cards show the four individual stamps and the complete miniature sheet.

2516 Helen Glover and Heather Stanning (rowing: women's pairs)

2517 Bradley Wiggins (cycling: road, men's time trial)

2518 Tim Baillie and Etienne Stott (canoe slalom: men's canoe double (C2))

2519 Peter Wilson (shooting: shotgun men's double trap)

2520 Philip Hindes, Chris Hoy and Jason Kenny (cycling: track men's team sprint)

2521 Katherine Grainger and Anna Watkins (rowing: women's double sculls)

2522 Steven Burke, Ed Clancy, Peter Kennaugh and Geraint Thomas (cycling: track men's team pursuit)

2523 Victoria Pendleton (cycling: track women's keirin)

2524 Alex Gregory, Tom James, Pete Reed and Andrew Triggs Hodge (rowing: men's fours)

2525 Katherine Copeland and Sophie Hosking (rowing: lightweight women's double sculls)

2526 Dani King, Joanna Rowsell and Laura Trott (cycling: track women's team pursuit)

2527 Jessica Ennis (athletics: combined women's heptathlon)

2528 Greg Rutherford (athletics: field men's long jump)

2529 Mo Farah (athletics: track men's 10,000m)

2530 Ben Ainslie (sailing: Finn men's heavyweight dinghy)

2531 Andy Murray (tennis: men's singles)

2532 Scott Brash, Peter Charles, Ben Maher and Nick Skelton (equestrian: jumping team)

2533 Jason Kenny (cycling: track men's sprint)

2534 Alistair Brownlee (men's triathlon)

2535 Carl Hester, Laura Bechtolsheimer and Charlotte Dujardin (equestrian: dressage team)

2536 Laura Trott (cycling: track women's omnium)

2537 Chris Hoy (cycling: track men's keirin)

2538 Charlotte Dujardin (equestrian: dressage individual)

2539 Nicola Adams (boxing: women's fly weight)

2540 Jade Jones (taekwondo: women's under 57kg)

2541 Ed McKeever (canoe sprint: men's kayak single (K1) 200m)

2542 Mo Farah (athletics: track men's 5000m)

2543 Luke Campbell (boxing: men's bantam weight)

2544 Anthony Joshua (boxing: men's super heavy weight)

(Des True North and Royal Mail. Litho with digital overprint Walsall and six regional printers)

2012 (2–13 Aug). *British Gold Medal Winners at London Olympic Games.* Self-adhesive. Two phosphor panels. Die-cut perf 15×14½.

3342	2516	(1st) Helen Glover and Heather Stanning		1·30	1·30
		a. Sheetlet. No. 3342×6		6·75	6·75
3343	2517	(1st) Bradley Wiggins (1 Sept)		1·30	1·30
		a. Sheetlet. No. 3343×6		6·75	6·75
3344	2518	(1st) Tim Baillie and Etienne Stott (3 Aug)		1·30	1·30
		a. Sheetlet. No. 3344×6		6·75	6·75
3345	2519	(1st) Peter Wilson (3 Aug)		1·30	1·30
		a. Sheetlet. No. 3345×6		6·75	6·75
3346	2520	(1st) Philip Hindes, Chris Hoy and Jason Kenny (3 Aug)		1·30	1·30
		a. Sheetlet. No. 3346×6		6·75	6·75
3347	2521	(1st) Katherine Grainger and Anna Watkins (4 Aug)		1·30	1·30
		a. Sheetlet. No. 3347×6		6·75	6·75
3348	2522	(1st) Steven Burke, Ed Clancy, Peter Kennaugh and Geraint Thomas (4 Aug)		1·30	1·30
		a. Sheetlet. No. 3348×6		6·75	6·75
		b. Phosphor omitted		35·00	
3349	2523	(1st) Victoria Pendleton (4 Aug)		1·30	1·30
		a. Sheetlet. No. 3349×6		6·75	6·75
		b. Phosphor omitted		35·00	
3350	2524	(1st) Alex Gregory, Tom James, Pete Reed and Andrew Triggs Hodge (5 Aug)		1·30	1·30
		a. Sheetlet. No. 3350×6		6·75	6·75
		b. Phosphor omitted		35·00	
3351	2525	(1st) Katherine Copeland and Sophie Hosking (5 Aug)		1·30	1·30
		a. Sheetlet. No. 3351×6		6·75	6·75
		ab. Black ptg double			
		b. Phosphor omitted		35·00	
3352	2526	(1st) Dani King, Joanna Rowsell and Laura Trott (5 Aug)		1·30	1·30
		a. Sheetlet. No. 3352×6		6·75	6·75
		b. Phosphor omitted		35·00	
3353	2527	(1st) Jessica Ennis (5 Aug)		1·30	1·30
		a. Sheetlet. No. 3353×6		6·75	6·75
		b. Phosphor omitted		35·00	
3354	2528	(1st) Greg Rutherford (5 Aug)		1·30	1·30
		a. Sheetlet. No. 3354×6		6·75	6·75
3355	2529	(1st) Mo Farah (5 Aug)		1·30	1·30
		a. Sheetlet. No. 3355×6		6·75	6·75
3356	2530	(1st) Ben Ainslie (6 Aug)		1·30	1·30
		a. Sheetlet. No. 3356×6		6·75	6·75
3357	2531	(1st) Andy Murray (6 Aug)		1·30	1·30
		a. Sheetlet. No. 3357×6		6·75	6·75
3358	2532	(1st) Scott Brash, Peter Charles, Ben Maher and Nick Skelton (7 Aug)		1·30	1·30
		a. Sheetlet. No. 3358×6		6·75	6·75
3359	2533	(1st) Jason Kenny (7 Aug)		1·30	1·30
		a. Sheetlet. No. 3359×6		6·75	6·75
3360	2534	(1st) Alistair Brownlee (8 Aug)		1·30	1·30
		a. Sheetlet. No. 3360×6		6·75	6·75
3361	2535	(1st) Carl Hester, Laura Bechtolsheimer and Charlotte Dujardin (8 Aug)		1·30	1·30
		a. Sheetlet. No. 3361×6		6·75	6·75
3362	2536	(1st) Laura Trott (8 Aug)		1·30	1·30
		a. Sheetlet. No. 3362×6		6·75	6·75
3363	2537	(1st) Chris Hoy (8 Aug)		1·30	1·30
		a. Sheetlet. No. 3363×6		6·75	6·75
3364	2538	(1st) Charlotte Dujardin (10 Aug)		1·30	1·30
		a. Sheetlet. No. 3364×6		6·75	6·75
3365	2539	(1st) Nicola Adams (10 Aug)		1·30	1·30
		a. Sheetlet. No. 3365×6		6·75	6·75
3366	2540	(1st) Jade Jones (10 Aug)		1·30	1·30
		a. Sheetlet. No. 3366×6		6·75	6·75
3367	2541	(1st) Ed McKeever (12 Aug)		1·30	1·30

		a. Sheetlet. No. 3367×6.......................	6·75	6·75
		ab. Black printed double........................		
		ac. Types 2541 and 2542 printed together on the same stamps......		
3368	**2542**	(1st) Mo Farah (12 Aug).................	1·30	1·30
		a. Sheetlet. No. 3368×6.......................	6·75	6·75
		ab. Black printed double........................		
3369	**2543**	(1st) Luke Campbell (12 Aug).................	1·30	1·30
		a. Sheetlet. No. 3369×6.......................	6·75	6·75
3370	**2544**	(1st) Anthony Joshua (13 Aug)..............	1·30	1·30
		a. Sheetlet. No. 3370×6.......................	6·75	6·75

Set of 29 Single Stamps...................................	35·00	35·00
3342a/70a *Set of* 29 sheetlets.........................	175·00	175·00
First Day Covers (Sheetlets, Nos. 3342a/70a) (29) (Tallents House) or (London E20))		250·00
First Day Cover (any single gold medal stamp (Tallents House))		4·25
First Day Cover (any single gold medal stamp) (London E20)........		4·25

The self-adhesive base sheetlets for Nos. 3342/70 were produced by Walsall with the image, name and event of the winning athletes digitally printed by regional printers in six different locations: Attleborough, Edinburgh, London, Preston, Solihull and Swindon. Nos. 3368/70 were not produced by the Preston printer due to machinery breakdown. Post office sheets comprised four sheetlets of six stamps (3×2), the sheetlets being separated by roulettes. The four sheetlets had one of the following inscriptions on the left margin: emblem 'TEAM GB' and Olympic rings; 'The XXX Olympiad'; barcode; Sheet number, Issue date and Printer location. Individual stamps had to be cut from the sheetlets using scissors.

Stamps for Royal Mail first day covers came from special coil printings on non-phosphor paper, so all stamps exist, phosphor omitted, used, from this source. Nos. 3348b/53b were subsequently released to the trade in unused coils.

2545 Paralympic Sports and London Landmarks (*Illustration reduced. Actual size* 193×75 *mm*)

(Des Pearce Marchbank. Litho Cartor)

2012 (29 Aug). Welcome to London, Paralympic Games. Sheet 193×75 mm. MULTI COLOUR 'All-over' phosphor. Perf 14½.

MS3371 **2545** Paralympic Sports and London Landmarks (1st) Athlete wearing running blades and Olympic Stadium; (1st) Wheelchair basketball player and Palace of Westminster; £1·28 Powerlifter, Millennium Bridge and St Paul's Cathedral; £1·28 Cyclist and London Eye.............. 5·50   5·50

First Day Cover (Tallents House).............................		10·00
First Day Cover (London E20)		10·00
Presentation Pack (PO Pack No. 475).................	9·00	
PHQ Cards (set of 5) (368).................................	2·00	9·00

The five PHQ Cards show the four individual stamps and the complete miniature sheet.

2546 Sarah Storey (cycling: track women's C5 pursuit)

2547 Jonathan Fox (swimming: men's 100m backstroke, S7)

2548 Mark Colbourne (cycling: track men's C1 pursuit)

2549 Hannah Cockroft (athletics: track women's 100m, T34)

2550 Neil Fachie and Barney Storey (cycling: men's B 1km time trial)

2551 Richard Whitehead (athletics: track men's 200m, T42)

2552 Natasha Baker (equestrian: individual championship test, grade II)

2553 Sarah Storey (cycling: track – women's C4-5 500m time trial)

2554 Ellie Simmonds (swimming: women's 400m freestyle, S6)

2555 Pamela Relph, Naomi Riches, James Roe, David Smith and Lily van den Broecke (rowing: mixed coxed four, LTAmix4+)

2556 Aled Davies (athletics: field men's discus, F42)

2557 Anthony Kappes and Craig MacLean (cycling: track men's B sprint)

2558 Jessica-Jane Applegate (swimming: women's 200m freestyle, S14)

2559 Sophie Christiansen (equestrian: individual championship test, grade 1a)

2560 David Weir (athletics: track men's 5000m, T54)

2561 Natasha Baker (equestrian: individual freestyle test, grade II)

2562 Ellie Simmonds (swimming: women's 200m individual medley, SM6)

2563 Mickey Bushell (athletics: track men's 100m, T53)

2564 Danielle Brown (archery: women's individual compound, open)

2565 Heather Frederiksen (swimming: women's 100m backstroke, S8)

2566 Sophie Christiansen (equestrian: individual freestyle test, grade 1a)

2567 David Weir (athletics: track men's 1500m, T54)

2568 Sarah Storey (cycling: road women's C5 time trial)

2569 Ollie Hynd (swimming: men's 200m individual medley, SM8)

2570 Sophie Christiansen, Deb Criddle, Lee Pearson and Sophie Wells (equestrian team, open)

2571 Helena Lucas (sailing: single-person keelboat, 2·4mR)

2572 Sarah Storey (cycling: road women's C4-5 road race)

2573 Josef Craig (swimming: men's 400m freestyle, S7)

2574 Hannah Cockroft (athletics: track women's 200m, T34)

2575 David Weir (athletics: track men's 800m, T54)

2576 Jonnie Peacock (athletics: track men's 100m, T44)

2577 Josie Pearson (athletics: field women's discus, F51/52/53)

2578 David Stone (cycling: road mixed T1-2 road race)

2579 David Weir (athletics: road men's marathon, T54)

(Des True North and Royal Mail. Litho with digital overprint Walsall and six regional printers)

2012 (31 Aug–10 Sept). *British Gold Medal Winners at London Paralympic Games.* Self-adhesive. |MULTI COLOUR| Two phosphor panels. Die-cut Perf 15×14½.

3372	**2546**	(1st) Sarah Storey	1·30	1·30
		a. Sheetlet. No. 3372×2	2·50	2·50
3373	**2547**	(1st) Jonathan Fox (1 Sept)	1·30	1·30
		a. Sheetlet. No. 3373×2	2·50	2·50
3374	**2548**	(1st) Mark Colbourne (3 Sept)	1·30	1·30
		a. Sheetlet. No. 3374×2	2·50	2·50
3375	**2549**	(1st) Hannah Cockroft (3 Sept)	1·30	1·30
		a. Sheetlet. No. 3375×2	2·50	2·50
3376	**2550**	(1st) Neil Fachie and Barney Storey (3 Sept)	1·30	1·30
		a. Sheetlet. No. 3376×2	2·50	2·50
3377	**2551**	(1st) Richard Whitehead (3 Sept)	1·30	1·30
		a. Sheetlet. No. 3377×2	2·50	2·50
3378	**2552**	(1st) Natasha Baker (3 Sept)	1·30	1·30
		a. Sheetlet. No. 3378×2	2·50	2·50
3379	**2553**	(1st) Sarah Storey (3 Sept)	1·30	1·30
		a. Sheetlet. No. 3379×2	2·50	2·50
3380	**2554**	(1st) Ellie Simmonds (3 Sept)	1·30	1·30
		a. Sheetlet. No. 3380×2	2·50	2·50
3381	**2555**	(1st) Pamela Relph, Naomi Riches, James Roe, David Smith and Lily van den Broecke (4 Sept)	1·30	1·30
		a. Sheetlet. No. 3381×2	2·50	2·50
3382	**2556**	(1st) Aled Davies (4 Sept)	1·30	1·30
		a. Sheetlet. No. 3382×2	2·50	2·50
3383	**2557**	(1st) Anthony Kappes and Craig MacLean (4 Sept)	1·30	1·30
		a. Sheetlet. No. 3383×2	2·50	2·50
3384	**2558**	(1st) Jessica-Jane Applegate (4 Sept)	1·30	1·30
		a. Sheetlet. No. 3384×2	2·50	2·50
3385	**2559**	(1st) Sophie Christiansen (4 Sept)	1·30	1·30
		a. Sheetlet. No. 3385×2	2·50	2·50
3386	**2560**	(1st) David Weir (4 Sept)	1·30	1·30
		a. Sheetlet. No. 3386×2	2·50	2·50
3387	**2561**	(1st) Natasha Baker (4 Sept)	1·30	1·30
		a. Sheetlet. No. 3387×2	2·50	2·50
3388	**2562**	(1st) Ellie Simmonds (4 Sept)	1·30	1·30
		a. Sheetlet. No. 3388×2	2·50	2·50
3389	**2563**	(1st) Mickey Bushell (5 Sept)	1·30	1·30
		a. Sheetlet. No. 3389×2	2·50	2·50
3390	**2564**	(1st) Danielle Brown (5 Sept)	1·30	1·30
		a. Sheetlet. No. 3390×2	2·50	2·50
3391	**2565**	(1st) Heather Frederiksen (5 Sept)	1·30	1·30
		a. Sheetlet. No. 3391×2	2·50	2·50
3392	**2566**	(1st) Sophie Christiansen (5 Sept)	1·30	1·30
		a. Sheetlet. No. 3392×2	2 50	2 50
3393	**2567**	(1st) David Weir (7 Sept)	1·30	1·30
		a. Sheetlet. No. 3393×2	2·50	2·50
3394	**2568**	(1st) Sarah Storey (7 Sept)	1·30	1·30
		a. Sheetlet. No. 3394×2	2·50	2·50
3395	**2569**	(1st) Ollie Hynd (7 Sept)	1·30	1·30
		a. Sheetlet. No. 3395×2	2·50	2·50
3396	**2570**	(1st) Sophie Christiansen, Deb Criddle, Lee Pearson and Sophie Wells (7 Sept)	1·30	1·30
		a. Sheetlet. No. 3396×2	2·50	2·50
3397	**2571**	(1st) Helena Lucas (8 Sept)	1·30	1·30
		a. Sheetlet. No. 3397×2	2·50	2·50
3398	**2572**	(1st) Sarah Storey (8 Sept)	1·30	1·30
		a. Sheetlet. No. 3398×2	2·50	2·50
3399	**2573**	(1st) Josef Craig (8 Sept)	1·30	1·30
		a. Sheetlet. No. 3399×2	2·50	2·50
3400	**2574**	(1st) Hannah Cockroft (8 Sept)	1·30	1·30
		a. Sheetlet. No. 3400×2	2·50	2·50
3401	**2575**	(1st) David Weir (10 Sept)	1·30	1·30
		a. Sheetlet. No. 3401×2	2·50	2·50
3402	**2576**	(1st) Jonnie Peacock (10 Sept)	1·30	1·30
		a. Sheetlet. No. 3402×2	2·50	2·50
3403	**2577**	(1st) Josie Pearson (10 Sept)	1·30	1·30
		a. Sheetlet. No. 3403×2	2·50	2·50
3404	**2578**	(1st) David Stone (10 Sept)	1·30	1·30
		a. Sheetlet. No. 3404×2	2·50	2·50
3405	**2579**	(1st) David Weir (10 Sept)	1·30	1·30

a. Sheetlet. No. 3405×2	2·50	2·50
Set of 34	£40	£40
3372a/3405a *Set of 34 sheetlets.*	£78	£78
First Day Covers (Sheetlets Nos. 3372a/3405a) (34) (Tallents House)		125·00
First Day Covers (Sheetlets Nos. 3372a/3405a) (34) (London E20)		125·00
First Day Cover (any single gold medal stamp) (Tallents House)		4·25
First Day Cover (any single gold medal stamp) (London E20)		4·25

The self-adhesive base sheetlets for Nos. 3372/405 were produced by Walsall with the image, name and event of the winning athletes digitally printed by regional printers in six different locations: Attleborough, Edinburgh, London, Preston, Solihull and Swindon. These sheetlets of 16 stamps were divided by roulettes into eight panes of two stamps (1×2). The left margins are inscribed as follows (reading downwards): emblem and 'ParalympicsGB'; 'London 2012 Paralympic Games'; barcode; Sheet number, Issue date and Printer location.

Nos. 3372, 3373 and 3405 were each printed in separate sheetlets of 16 stamps. Nos. 3374/7, 3381/4, 3385/8, 3389/92, 3393/6, 3397/400 and 3401/4 were printed in sheetlets of 16 containing four stamps of each design. The sheetlets of 16 containing Nos. 3378/80 contained four each of Nos. 3378/9 and eight of No. 3380.

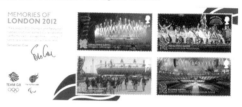

2580 Scenes from Olympic and Paralympic Games (*Illustration reduced. Actual size* 192×75 *mm*)

Des The Chase. Litho Walsall)

2012 (27 Sept). *Memories of London 2012 Olympic and Paralympic Games.* Sheet 192×75 mm. |MULTI COLOUR| 'All-over' phosphor. Perf 14½.

MS3406 **2580** Scenes from Olympic and Paralympic Games (1st) Procession of athletes, Paralympic Games; (1st) Games makers and Olympic Stadium; £1·28 Opening ceremony of Paralympic Games; £1·28 Olympic Games closing ceremony and handover to Rio ... 9·00 9·00

First Day Cover (Tallents House)		13·00
First Day Cover (London E20)		13·00
Presentation Pack (PO Pack No. 476)	17·50	
PHQ Cards (set of 5) (369)	2·00	16·50

The five PHQ Cards show the four individual stamps and the complete miniature sheet.

2581 BR Class D34 Nos. 62471 *Glen Falloch* and 62496 *Glen Loy* at Ardlui, 9 May 1959

(Gravure Walsall)

2012 (27 Sept). *Classic Locomotives of Scotland.* Booklet stamp. Design as 1st class stamp within **MS**3283. Self-adhesive. |MULTI COLOUR| 'All-over' phosphor. Die-cut perf 14.

3407	**2581**	(1st) BR Class D34 Nos. 62471 *Glen Falloch* and 62496 *Glen Loy*	1·25	1·25
		a. Booklet pane. No. 3407×2 and U3274×4	5·75	

No. 3407 was only issued in booklets, No. PM34, originally sold for £3·60.

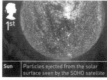

2582 Sun and Particles ejected from Solar Surface seen from SOHO Observatory

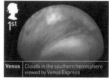

2583 Venus with Clouds in Southern Hemisphere seen from *Venus Express*

2584 Ice in Martian Impact Crater seen from *Mars Express*

2585 Surface of Asteroid Lutetia seen from *Rosetta Probe*

2586 Saturn and its Rings seen from *Cassini Satellite*

2587 Titan (Saturn's largest moon) seen from *Huygens Probe*

(Des Osborne Ross Design. Litho Cartor)

2012 (16 Oct). *Space Science.* MULTI COLOUR 'All-over' phosphor. Perf 14.

3408	**2582**	(1st) Sun	1·00	1·00
3409	**2583**	(1st) Venus	1·00	1·00
3410	**2584**	77p. Ice in Martian Impact Crater	1·20	1·20
3411	**2585**	77p. Surface of Asteroid Lutetia	1·20	1·20
3412	**2586**	£1·28 Saturn and its Rings	2·00	2·00
3413	**2587**	£1·28 Titan (Saturn's largest moon)	2·00	2·00
Set of 6			7·50	7·50
Set of 6 Gutter Pairs			15·00	
First Day Cover (Tallents House)				9·75
First Day Cover (Star, Gaerwen Gwynnedd)				9·75
Presentation Pack (PO Pack No. 477)			8·75	
PHQ Cards (set of 6) (370)			2·40	9·00

2588 Six Poppies on Barbed Wire Stems

(Des Hat-trick Design. Gravure Walsall)

2012 (23 Oct). *Lest We Forget* (4th issue). Self-adhesive. MULTI COLOUR Two phosphor bands. Perf 14½×14 (with one elliptical hole in each vert side).

3414	**2588**	(1st) Six Poppies on Barbed Wire Stems	1·25	1·25

For Type **2588** with ordinary gum, see No. 3717.

> **SELF-ADHESIVE STAMPS:** Collectors are reminded that used self-adhesive stamps will no longer 'soak-off'. They should be collected with a neat margin of backing paper.

2589 Reindeer with Decorated Antlers

2590 Santa with Robin

2591 Reindeer with Decorated Antlers

2592 Snowman and Penguin

2593 Santa with Robin

2594 Robin with Star Decoration in Beak

2595 Cat and Mouse decorating Christmas Tree

(Des Axel Scheffler and Webb and Webb Design. Gravure Walsall (3415a, 3416a) or De La Rue (others))

2012 (6 Nov). *Christmas.* Illustrations by Axel Scheffler. MULTI COLOUR One centre band (3415) or two phosphor bands (others). Perf 14½×14 (with one elliptical hole in each vert side).

(a) Self-adhesive.

3415	**2589**	(2nd) Reindeer with Decorated Antlers	90	90
		a. Booklet pane. No. 3415×12	9·75	
3416	**2590**	(1st) Santa with Robin	1·00	1·00
		a. Booklet pane. No. 3416×12	10·50	
3417	**2591**	(2nd Large) Reindeer with Decorated Antlers	1·10	1·10
3418	**2592**	87p. Snowman and Penguin	1·35	1·35
3419	**2593**	(1st Large) Santa with Robin	1·40	1·40
3420	**2594**	£1·28 Robin with Star Decoration in Beak	2·00	2·00
3421	**2595**	£1·90 Cat and Mouse decorating Christmas Tree	3·00	3·00
Set of 7			9·75	9·75
First Day Cover (Tallents House)				12·50
First Day Cover (Bethlehem, Llandeilo)				12·50
Presentation Pack (PO Pack No. 478)			11·50	
PHQ Cards (set of 8) (371)			3·25	21·00

(b) Ordinary gum.

MS3422	115×102 mm. As Nos. 3415/21	9·75	9·75
First Day Cover (Tallents House)			10·00
First Day Cover (Bethlehem, Llandeilo)			10·00

The eight PHQ cards depict the seven individual stamps and the miniature sheet.

The 2nd class, 1st class, 87p. and £1·28 stamps were also issued in sheets of 20 (LS83) containing eight 2nd class, eight 1st class, two 87p. and two £1·28 stamps, each with a *se-tenant* label. These sheets were printed in lithography and sold for £13·10 each.

Separate sheets of 20 2nd, 20 1st, ten 1st, ten 87p. and ten £1·28 were available with personal photographs on the labels from Royal Mail, Edinburgh. These were sold at £13·99 for 20 2nd, £18·25 for 20 1st, £9·99 for ten 1st, £13·55 for ten 87p. and £18·50 for ten £1·28.

The 1st class stamp printed in lithography, from either Post Office label sheets or 'Personalised Smilers' sheets is known with the black printing double.

Year Pack
2012 (6 Nov). Comprises Nos. 3254/9, **MS**3264/70, **MS**3272/307, 3309/18, A3319/26, 3330/6, **MS**3341, **MS**3371, **MS**3406, 3408/13 and 3415/21
CP3422*a* Year Pack .... 175·00

Post Office Yearbook
2012 (6 Nov). Comprises Nos. 3254/9, **MS**3264/70, **MS**3272/307, 3309/18, A3319/26, 3330/6, **MS**3341, **MS**3371, **MS**3406, 3408/13 and 3415/21
YB3422*a* Yearbook .... 300·00

Miniature Sheet Collection
2012 (6 Nov). Comprises Nos. **MS**3264, **MS**3270, **MS**3272, **MS**3283, **MS**3336, **MS**3341, **MS**3371, **MS**3406 and **MS**3422
MS3422*a* Miniature Sheet Collection .... 55·00

2596 Steam Locomotive on Metropolitan Railway, 1863

2597 Navvies excavating 'Deep Cut' Tube Tunnel, 1898

2598 Commuters in Carriage, 1911

2599 Boston Manor Art Deco Station, 1934

2600 Train on 'Deep Cut' Line, 1938

2601 Canary Wharf Station, 1999

2602 Classic London Underground Posters

(Des NB Studios (**MS**3429) or Hat-trick Design (others). Litho Cartor (3423/9) or gravure Walsall (3430))

2013 (9 Jan). *150th Anniv. of the London Underground.* |MULTI/COLOUR| One centre band (2nd) or 'all-over' phosphor (others).

(a) Ordinary gum. Perf 14½.

3423	**2596**	(2nd) Steam Locomotive on Metropolitan Railway	90	90
3424	**2597**	(2nd) Navvies excavating 'Deep Cut' Tube Tunnel	90	90
3425	**2598**	(1st) Commuters in Carriage	1·00	1·00
3426	**2599**	(1st) Boston Manor Art Deco Station	1·00	1·00
3427	**2600**	£1·28 Train on 'Deep Cut' Line	2·00	2·00
3428	**2601**	£1·28 Canary Wharf Station	2·00	2·00
Set of 6			7·00	7·00
Set of 6 Gutter Pairs			14·00	
First Day Cover (Tallents House)				8·75
First Day Cover (London W2)				8·75
Presentation Pack (PO Pack No. 480)				
(Nos. 3423/8 and **MS**3429)			15·00	
PHQ Cards (set of 11) (372)			4·50	18·00

MS3429 184×74 mm. **2602** Classic London Underground Posters (1st) Golders Green, 1908, By Underground to fresh air (Maxwell Armfield), 1915 and Summer Sales (Mary Koop), 1925; 77p. For the Zoo (Charles Paine), 1921, Power (Edward McKnight-Kauffer), 1931 and The Seen (James Fitton), 1948; 87p. A train every 90 seconds (Abram Games), 1937, Thanks to the Underground (Zero (Hans Schleger)), 1935 and Cut travelling time, Victoria Line (Tom Eckersley), 1969; £1·28 The London Transport Collection (Tom Eckersley), 1975, London Zoo (Abram Games), 1976 and The Tate Gallery by Tube (David Booth), 1987

	5·00	5·25
First Day Cover (Tallents House)		6·50
First Day Cover (London W2)		6·50

(b) Self-adhesive. Die-cut perf 14½.

3430	**2599**	(1st) Boston Manor Art Deco Station	1·35	1·35
		a. Booklet pane. Nos. 3430×2 and U3022×4	5·75	

2603 Elinor and Marianne Dashwood *(Sense and Sensibility)*

2604 Elizabeth Bennet and Portrait of Mr Darcy *(Pride and Prejudice)*

2605 Fanny Price

(Mansfield Park)

2606 Emma Woodhouse and Mr Knightley *(Emma)*

2607 Catherine Morland *(Northanger Abbey)*

2608 Anne Elliot and Captain Wentworth *(Persuasion)*

(Des Angela Barrett and Webb and Webb. Litho Cartor)

2013 (21 Feb). *Bicentenary of the Publication of Jane Austen's Pride and Prejudice.* |MULTI/COLOUR| 'All-over' phosphor. Perf 14.

3431	**2603**	(1st) Elinor and Marianne Dashwood	1·00	1·00
3432	**2604**	(1st) Elizabeth Bennet and Portrait of Mr Darcy	1·00	1·00
3433	**2605**	77p. Fanny Price	1·25	1·25
3434	**2606**	77p. Emma Woodhouse and Mr Knightley	1·25	1·25
3435	**2607**	£1·28 Catherine Morland	2·00	2·00
3436	**2608**	£1·28 Anne Elliot and Captain Wentworth	2·00	2·00
Set of 6			7·50	7·50
Set of 6 Gutter Pairs			15·00	
Set of 6 Traffic Light Gutter Pairs			32·00	
First Day Cover (Tallents House)				10·00
First Day Cover (Steventon, Basingstoke)				10·00
Presentation Pack (PO Pack No. 481)			9·00	
PHQ Cards (set of 6) (373)			2·40	9·25

2609 The Eleventh Doctor (Matt Smith, 2010-14)

2610 The Tenth Doctor (David Tennant, 2005-10)

2611 The Ninth Doctor (Christopher Eccleston, 2005)

2612 The Eighth Doctor (Paul McGann, 1996)

2613 The Seventh Doctor (Sylvester McCoy, 1987-9)

2614 The Sixth Doctor (Colin Baker, 1984-6)

2615 The Fifth Doctor (Peter Davison, 1982-4)

2616 The Fourth Doctor (Tom Baker, 1974-81)

2617 The Third Doctor (Jon Pertwee, 1970-4)

2618 The Second Doctor (Patrick Troughton, 1966-9)

2619 The First Doctor (William Hartnell, 1963-6)

2620 Tardis

2621 *Dr. Who* 1963-2013

(Des GBH. Litho Cartor (3437/47) and **MS**3451a
or gravure Walsall (3448/50) or Enschedé (**MS**3451))

2013 (26 Mar). *50th Anniv of Doctor Who* (TV programme) (1st issue). [MULTI COLOUR] 'All-over' phosphor.

(a) Ordinary gum. 'All-over' phosphor. Perf 14.

3437	**2609**	(1st) Matt Smith	1·00	1·00
		a. Horiz strip of 3. Nos. 3437/9	3·00	3·00
		b. Booklet pane. Nos. 3437/9	4·00	
3438	**2610**	(1st) David Tennant	1·00	1·00
3439	**2611**	(1st) Christopher Eccleston	1·00	1·00
3440	**2612**	(1st) Paul McGann	1·00	1·00
		a. Horiz strip of 4. Nos. 3440/3	4·00	4·00
		b. Booklet pane. Nos. 3440/3	4·25	
3441	**2613**	(1st) Sylvester McCoy	1·00	1·00
3442	**2614**	(1st) Colin Baker	1·00	1·00
3443	**2615**	(1st) Peter Davison	1·00	1·00
3444	**2616**	(1st) Tom Baker	1·00	1·00
		a. Horiz strip of 4. Nos. 3444/7	4·00	4·00
		b. Booklet pane. Nos. 3444/7	4·25	
3445	**2617**	(1st) Jon Pertwee	1·00	1·00
3446	**2618**	(1st) Patrick Troughton	1·00	1·00
3447	**2619**	(1st) William Hartnell	1·00	1·00
Set of 11			10·00	10·00
Set of 1 Gutter Strip of 3 and 2 Gutter Strips of 8			20·00	
First Day Covers (2) (Tallents House)				12·00
First Day Covers (2) (Cardiff)				12·00
Presentation Pack (PO Pack No. 482)				
(Nos. 3437/47 and **MS**3451)			15·00	
PHQ Cards (set of 17)			6·75	18·50

(b) Self-adhesive. One centre band (2nd) or two bands. Die-cut perf 14½ (2nd) or 14½×14 (with one elliptical hole in each vert side) (1st).

3448	**2609**	(1st) Matt Smith	4·50	4·50
		a. Booklet pane. No. 3448, 3449×4 and 3450	14·00	
3449	**2620**	(1st) Tardis	1·25	1·25
3450	**2619**	(1st) William Hartnell	4·50	4·50

MS3451 115×89 mm. **2621** *Dr. Who* 1963-2013 Dalek; (2nd) The Ood; (2nd) Weeping Angel; (2nd) Cyberman; (1st) TARDIS .... 4·00 4·25
a. Booklet pane. As No. **MS**3451 but 119×96 mm, with line of roulettes at left .... 8·00

First Day Cover (Tallents House) .... 5·00
First Day Cover (Cardiff) .... 5·00

Nos. 3437/9 were printed together, *se-tenant*, as horizontal strips of three stamps in sheets of 48 (2 panes 6×4).

Nos. 3440/3 and 3444/7 were each printed together, *se-tenant*, as horizontal strips of four stamps in sheets of 48 (2 panes 4×6).

Nos. 3448/50 were issued in stamp booklets, No. PM36, sold for £3·60.

The 1st class TARDIS stamp from the booklet pane **MS**3451a differs from the same design in the miniature sheet by being perforated 15 all round.

The *design area* of No. 3449 measures 17½×21½ mm, slightly larger than the same TARDIS design (Type **2620**) from the miniature sheet and premium booklet pane (**MS**3451/a) which measures 17×21mm. (All are 20×24 measured *perf to perf* edge).

The 1st class TARDIS stamp was also issued in sheets of 20, each stamp accompanied by a *se-tenant* label (LS85). These sheets were printed in lithography.

(Des GBH. Litho Cartor)

2013 (26 Mar). *50th Anniversary of Doctor Who* (TV programme) (2nd issue). As No. 3449 but ordinary gum. [MULTI COLOUR] Two phosphor bands. Perf 14½×14 with one elliptical hole in each vertical side

3452 **2620** (1st) Tardis .... 1·25 1·25
No. 3452 only comes from pane No. U3072a in the £13·37 premium booklet, No. DY6.

2622 Norman Parkinson (1913-90, portrait and fashion photographer)

2623 Vivien Leigh (1913-67, actress)

2624 Peter Cushing (1913-94, actor)

2625 David Lloyd George (1863-1945, Prime Minister 1916-22)

2626 Elizabeth David (1913-92, cookery writer)

2627 John Archer (1863-1932, politician and civil rights campaigner)

2628 Benjamin Britten
(1913-76, composer and pianist)

2629 Mary Leakey
(1913-96, archaeologist and
anthropologist)

2630 Bill Shankly (1913-81,
football player and manager)

2631 Richard Dimbleby
(1913-65, journalist and
broadcaster)

(Des Together Design. Litho Cartor)

2013 (16 Apr). *Great Britons*. |MULTI COLOUR| 'All-over' phosphor. Perf 14½.

3453	**2622**	(1st) Norman Parkinson	1·00	1·00
		a. Horiz strip of 5. Nos. 3453/7	4·50	4·50
3454	**2623**	(1st) Vivien Leigh	1·00	1·00
3455	**2624**	(1st) Peter Cushing	1·00	1·00
3456	**2625**	(1st) David Lloyd George	1·00	1·00
3457	**2626**	(1st) Elizabeth David	1·00	1·00
3458	**2627**	(1st) John Archer	1·00	1·00
		a. Horiz strip of 5. Nos. 3458/62	4·50	4·50
3459	**2628**	(1st) Benjamin Britten	1·00	1·00
3460	**2629**	(1st) Mary Leakey	1·00	1·00
3461	**2630**	(1st) Bill Shankly	1·00	1·00
3462	**2631**	(1st) Richard Dimbleby	1·00	1·00
Set of 10			9·00	9·00
Set of 2 Gutter Strips of 10			18·00	
First Day Cover (Tallents House)				11·00
First Day Cover (Great Ness, Shrewsbury)				11·00
Presentation Pack (PO Pack No. 483)			10·00	
PHQ Cards (set of 10) (375)			4·00	12·00

Nos. 3453/7 and 3458/62 were each printed together, *se-tenant*, as horizontal strips of five stamps in sheets of 50 (2 panes 5×5).

2632 Jimmy Greaves
(England)

2633 John Charles
(Wales)

2634 Gordon Banks
(England)

2635 George Best
(Northern Ireland)

2636 John Barnes
(England)

2637 Kevin Keegan
(England)

2638 Denis Law
(Scotland)

2639 Bobby Moore
(England)

2640 Bryan Robson
(England)

2641 Dave Mackay
(Scotland)

2642 Bobby Charlton
(England)

(Des Andrew Kinsman and True North. Litho Cartor (3463/74)
or gravure Walsall (3475/6))

2013 (9 May)–**14**. *Football Heroes* (1st issue). |MULTI COLOUR| 'All-over' phosphor.

(a) Ordinary gum. Perf 14½.

3463	**2632**	(1st) Jimmy Greaves	1·00	1·00
		a. Horiz strip of 5. Nos. 3463/7	4·50	4·50
3464	**2633**	(1st) John Charles	1·00	1·00
3465	**2634**	(1st) Gordon Banks	1·00	1·00
3466	**2635**	(1st) George Best	1·00	1·00
3467	**2636**	(1st) John Barnes	1·00	1·00
3468	**2637**	(1st) Kevin Keegan	1·00	1·00
		a. Horiz strip of 6. Nos. 3468/73	5·50	5·50
3469	**2638**	(1st) Denis Law	1·00	1·00
3470	**2639**	(1st) Bobby Moore	1·00	1·00
3471	**2640**	(1st) Bryan Robson	1·00	1·00
3472	**2641**	(1st) Dave Mackay	1·00	1·00
3473	**2642**	(1st) Bobby Charlton	1·00	1·00
Set of 11			10·00	10·00
Set of 1 Gutter Strip of 12 and 1 Gutter Strip of 10			20·00	
First Day Cover (Tallents House)				11·00
First Day Cover (Wembley, Middlesex)				11·00
Presentation Pack (PO Pack 484)			11·00	
PHQ Cards (set of 12) (376)			4·75	11·00
MS3474 192×74 mm. Nos. 3463/73			10·00	1·00
First Day Cover				12·00

(b) Self-adhesive. Die-cut perf 14½.

3475	**2635**	(1st) George Best	4·50	4·50
		a. Booklet pane. Nos. 3475/6 and U3022×4	10·00	
3476	**2639**	(1st) Bobby Moore	4·50	4·50
3477	**2633**	(1st) John Charles (20·2.14)	4·50	4·50
		a. Booklet pane. Nos. 3477/8 and U3022×4	10·00	
3478	**2641**	(1st) Dave Mackay (20·2.14)	4·50	4·50

Nos. 3463/7 were printed together, *se-tenant*, as horizontal strips of five stamps in sheets of 30 (5×6).

Nos. 3468/73 were printed together, *se-tenant*, as horizontal strips of six stamps in sheets of 30 (6×5).

Nos. 3475/6 and 3477/8 were issued in separate booklets, Nos. PM37 and PM41, both sold for £3·60.

Nos. 3463/89 commemorate the 150th anniversary of the Football Association and the 140th Anniversary of the Scottish Football Association.

(Litho Cartor)

2013 (9 May). *Football Heroes* (2nd issue). Self-adhesive. |MULTI COLOUR| 'All-over'. phosphor. Die-cut perf 14½×14.

3479	**2632**	(1st) Jimmy Greaves	1·60	1·60
		a. Booklet pane. Nos. 3479/83	7·25	7·25
3480	**2633**	(1st) John Charles	1·60	1·60
3481	**2637**	(1st) Kevin Keegan	1·60	1·60
3482	**2638**	(1st) Denis Law	1·60	1·60
3483	**2639**	(1st) Bobby Moore	1·60	1·60

3484	**2634**	(1st) Gordon Banks	1·60	1·60
		a. Booklet pane. Nos. 3484/9	8·75	8·75
3485	**2635**	(1st) George Best	1·60	1·60
3486	**2636**	(1st) John Barnes	1·60	1·60
3487	**2640**	(1st) Bryan Robson	1·60	1·60
3488	**2641**	(1st) Dave Mackay	1·60	1·60
3489	**2642**	(1st) Bobby Charlton	1·60	1·60
Set of 11			16·00	16·00

Nos. 3479/89 were issued in £11·11 premium booklets, No. DY7.

No. 3490 is vacant.

2646 Preliminary Oil Sketch for The Coronation of Queen Elizabeth II (*Terence Cuneo*), 1953

2647 Queen Elizabeth II in Garter Robes (*Nicky Philipps*), 2012

2648 Portrait by Andrew Festing, 1999

2649 Portrait by Pietro Annigoni, 1955

2650 Portrait by Sergei Pavlenko, 2000

2651 Her Majesty Queen Elizabeth II (Richard Stone), 1992

(Gravure Walsall)

2013 (30 May). *60th Anniversary of the Coronation.* Six Decades of Royal Portraits. MULTICOLOUR Phosphor band at left (2nd) or 'all-over' phosphor (others). Perf 14.

3491	**2646**	(2nd) Preliminary Oil Sketch for The Coronation of Queen Elizabeth II (Terence Cuneo), 1953	90	90
3492	**2647**	(1st) Queen Elizabeth II in Garter Robes (Nicky Philipps), 2012	1·00	1·00
3493	**2648**	78p. Portrait by Andrew Festing, 1999	1·10	1·10
3494	**2649**	88p. Portrait by Pietro Annigoni, 1955	1·45	1·45
3495	**2650**	£1·28 Portrait by Sergei Pavlenko, 2000	2·10	2·10
3496	**2651**	£1·88 Her Majesty Queen Elizabeth II (Richard Stone), 1992	3·00	3·00
Set of 6			8·50	8·50
Set of 6 Gutter Pairs			17·00	
Set of 6 Traffic Light Gutter Blocks of 4			36·00	
First Day Cover (Tallents House)				11·00
First Day Cover (London SW1)				11·00
Presentation Pack (PO Pack No. 485)			10·00	
PHQ Cards (set of 6) (377)			2·40	10·50
Commemorative Document (Nos. 3491/2) (2 June)			12·50	

2652 UTA Class W No. 103 *Thomas Somerset* with Belfast Express, Downhill, near Castlerock, c.1950

2653 Classic Locomotives of Northern Ireland

(Des Delaney Design Consultants. Gravure Walsall (3497) or litho Cartor (MS3498))

2013 (18 June). *Classic Locomotives* (3rd series). Northern Ireland. Black, grey and gold. 'All-over' phosphor.

(a) Self-adhesive. Die-cut perf 14

| 3497 | **2652** | (1st) UTA Class W No. 103 *Thomas Somerset* with Belfast Express | 1·25 | 1·25 |
| | | a. Booklet pane. No. 3497×2 and U3022×4 | 5·75 | |

(b) Ordinary gum. Sheet 180×74 mm. Perf 14

MS3498	**2653**	(1st) Classic Locomotives of Northern Ireland. As Type 2652; 78p. UTA SG3 No. 35; 88p. Peckett No. 2; £1·28 CDRJC Class 5 No. 4	5·00	5·25
First Day Cover (Tallents House)				6·50
First Day Cover (Belfast)				6·50
Presentation Pack (PO Pack No. 486)			6·25	
PHQ Cards (set of 5) (378)			2·00	6·50

No. 3497 was issued in booklets, No. PM38, sold for £3·60.

The five PHQ cards show the four individual stamps and the complete miniature sheet.

2654 Comma (*Polygonia c-album*)

2655 Orange-tip (*Anthocharis cardamines*)

2656 Small Copper (*Lycaena phlaeas*)

2657 Chalkhill Blue (*Polyommatus coridon*)

2658 Swallowtail (*Papilio machaon*)

2659 Purple Emperor (*Apatura iris*)

2660 Marsh Fritillary (*Euphydryas aurinia*)

2661 Brimstone (*Gonepteryx rhamni*)

2662 Red Admiral
(*Vanessa atalanta*)

2663 Marbled White
(*Melanargia galathea*)

(Des Richard Lewington and Marc & Anna. Litho Cartor (3499/508)
or gravure (3509/10) Walsall)

2013 (11 July). *Butterflies.* |MULTI COLOUR| 'All-over' phosphor.
(a) Ordinary paper. Perf 14×14½.

3499	**2654**	(1st) Comma	1·00	1·00
		a. Horiz strip of 5. Nos. 3499/503	4·50	4·50
3500	**2655**	(1st) Orange-tip	1·00	1·00
3501	**2656**	(1st) Small Copper	1·00	1·00
3502	**2657**	(1st) Chalkhill Blue	1·00	1·00
3503	**2658**	(1st) Swallowtail	1·00	1·00
3504	**2659**	(1st) Purple Emperor	1·00	1·00
		a. Horiz strip of 5. Nos. 3504/8	4·50	4·50
3505	**2660**	(1st) Marsh Fritillary	1·00	1·00
3506	**2661**	(1st) Brimstone	1·00	1·00
3507	**2662**	(1st) Red Admiral	1·00	1·00
3508	**2663**	(1st) Marbled White	1·00	1·00
Set of 10			9·00	9·00
Set of 2 Gutter Strips of 10			18·00	
First Day Cover (Tallents House)				12·00
First Day Cover (Lulworth Camp, Wareham, Dorset)				12·00
Presentation Pack (PO Pack No. 487)			11·00	
PHQ Cards (set of 10) (379)			4·00	11·00

(b) Self-adhesive. Die-cut perf 14×14½.

3509	**2657**	(1st) Chalkhill Blue (*Polyommatus coridon*). Multicoloured	1·50	1·50
		a. Booklet pane. Nos. 3509/10 and U3022×4	6·00	
3510	**2654**	(1st) Comma (*Polygonia c-album*). Multicoloured	1·50	1·50

Nos. 3499/503 and 3504/8 were each printed together, *se-tenant*, as horizontal strips of five stamps in sheets of 50 (2 panes 5×5).

Nos. 3509/10 were issued in stamp booklets, No. PM39, sold for £3·60.

2664 Andy Murray's Wimbledon Victory

(Litho Walsall)

2013 (8 Aug). *Andy Murray, Men's Singles Champion, Wimbledon.* Sheet 192×75 mm. |MULTI COLOUR| 'All-over' phosphor. Perf 14½.

MS3511	**2664**	Andy Murray's Wimbledon Victory		

(1st) Andy Murray kissing Wimbledon Trophy; (1st) Andy Murray serving; £1·28 In action; £1·28 Holding Trophy .. 5·25   5·50
First Day Cover (Tallents House) .... 7·00
First Day Cover (Wimbledon, SW19) .... 7·00
Presentation Pack (PO Pack No. M21) .... 6·50

2665 Jaguar E-Type, 1961

2667 Aston Martin DB5, 1963

2668 MG MGB, 1962

2669 Morgan Plus 8, 1968

2670 Lotus Esprit, 1976

BRITISH AUTO LEGENDS: THE WORKHORSES

2671 'The Workhorses'

(Des Why Not Associates (3512/17) or Robert Maude
and Sarah Davies (**MS**3518). Litho Cartor)

2013 (13 Aug). *British Auto Legends.* |MULTI COLOUR| 'All-over' phosphor. Perf 13½ (3512/17) or 14 (**MS**3518).

3512	**2665**	(1st) Jaguar E-Type, 1961	1·00	1·00
		a. Horiz strip of 3. Nos. 3512/14	3·00	3·00
3513	**2666**	(1st) Rolls-Royce Silver Shadow, 1965	1·00	1·00
3514	**2667**	(1st) Aston Martin DB5, 1963	1·00	1·00
3515	**2668**	£1·28 MG MGB, 1962	1·60	1·60
		a. Horiz strip of 3. Nos. 3515/17	4·75	4·75
3516	**2669**	£1·28 Morgan Plus 8, 1968	1·60	1·60
3517	**2670**	£1·28 Lotus Esprit, 1976	1·60	1·60
Set of 6			7·00	7·00
Set of 2 Gutter Strips of 6			14·00	
First Day Cover (Tallents House)				9·00
First Day Cover (Alwalton, Peterborough)				9·00
Presentation Pack (PO Pack No. 488) (Nos. 3512/7 and **MS**3518)			13·50	
PHQ Cards (set of 11) (380)			4·50	17·00

MS3518 180×74 mm. **2671** 'The Workhorses' (1st)×4 Morris Minor Royal Mail van (1953-71); Austin FX4 (1958-97) London taxi; Ford Anglia 105E (1959-67) police car; Coastguard Land Rover Defender 110 (from 1990) (all 40×30 mm) .... 4·00   4·00
First Day Cover (Tallents House) .... 4·50
First Day Cover (Alwalton, Peterborough) .... 4·50

Nos. 3512/14 and 3515/17 were each printed together, *se-tenant*, as horizontal strips of three stamps in sheets of 60 (2 panes 6×5).

The 1st value from **MS**3518 is inscr 'EUROPA'.

The complete miniature sheet is shown on one of the eleven PHQ cards with the others depicting individual stamps including those from the miniature sheet.

2672 East Indiaman *Atlas*, 1813

2673 Royal Mail Ship *Britannia*, 1840

2666 Rolls-Royce Silver Shadow, 1965

2674 Tea Clipper *Cutty Sark*, 1870

2675 Cargo Liner *Clan Matheson*, 1919

2676 Royal Mail Ship *Queen Elizabeth*, 1940

2677 Bulk Carrier *Lord Hinton*, 1986

(Des Silk Pearce. Litho Enschedé (booklet panes) or Cartor (others))

2013 (19 Sept). *Merchant Navy* (1st issue). [MULTI COLOUR] 'All-over' phosphor. Perf 14.

3519	**2672**	(1st) East Indiaman *Atlas*, 1813	1·00	1·00
		a. Booklet pane. Nos. 3519/21 with margins all round	4·00	
3520	**2673**	(1st) Royal Mail Ship *Britannia*, 1840	1·00	1·00
3521	**2674**	(1st) Tea Clipper *Cutty Sark*, 1870	1·00	1·00
3522	**2675**	£1·28 Cargo Liner *Clan Matheson*, 1919	1·60	1·60
		a. Booklet pane. Nos. 3522/4 with margins all round	5·00	
3523	**2676**	£1·28 Royal Mail Ship *Queen Elizabeth*, 1940	1·60	1·60
3524	**2677**	£1·28 Bulk Carrier *Lord Hinton*, 1986	1·60	1·60
Set of 6			7·00	7·00
Set of 6 Gutter Pairs			14·00	
First Day Cover (Tallents House)				9·00
First Day Cover (Clydebank)				9·00
Presentation Pack (PO Pack No. 489) (Nos. 3519/24 and MS3529)			13·50	
PHQ Cards (set of 11) (381)			4·50	17·00

Nos. 3519a and 3522a were only issued in the £11·19 Merchant Navy booklet, No DY8.

The complete miniature sheet is shown on one of the eleven PHQ cards with the others depicting individual stamps including those from **MS**3529.

2678 Destroyer HMS *Vanoc* escorting Atlantic Convoy

2679 Merchant Ship passing the Naval Control Base in the Thames Estuary

2680 Sailors clearing Ice from the Decks of HMS *King George V* in Arctic Waters

2681 Naval Convoy of 24 Merchant Ships in the North Sea

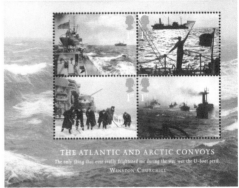

2682 Second World War Atlantic and Arctic Convoys

(Des Silk Pearce. Litho Enschedé)

2013 (19 Sept). *Merchant Navy* (2nd issue). [MULTI COLOUR] 'All-over' phosphor. Perf 14.

3525	**2678**	(1st) Destroyer HMS *Vanoc* escorting Atlantic Convoy	2·20	2·20
		a. Booklet pane. Nos. 3525/8	8·00	
3526	**2679**	(1st) Merchant Ship passing the Naval Control Base in the Thames Estuary	2·00	2·00
3527	**2680**	(1st) Sailors clearing Ice from the Decks of HMS *King George V* in Arctic Waters	2·20	2·20
3528	**2681**	(1st) Naval Convoy of 24 Merchant Ships in the North Sea	2·20	2·20
Set of 4			8·00	8·00
MS3529	**2682**	Second World War Atlantic and Arctic Convoys 115×89 mm. Nos. 3525/8	3·75	3·75
First Day Cover				4·50

Nos. 3525/8 were only issued in the £11·19 Merchant Navy booklet, No. DY8, and in **MS**3529.

2683 Royal Mail Van

(Gravure Walsall)

2013 (19 Sept). *Royal Mail Transport: By Land and Sea*. Self-adhesive booklet stamps. [MULTI COLOUR] Die-cut perf 14.

3530	**2683**	(1st) Royal Mail Van	5·50	5·50
		a. Nos. 3530/1 and No. U3022×4	14·00	
3531	**2673**	(1st) Royal Mail Ship *Britannia*, 1840. Multicoloured	5·50	5·50

The design of No. 3530 is as the Royal Mail van stamp within **MS**3518, and it is also inscr 'EUROPA'.

Nos. 3530/1 were only issued in booklets, No. PM40, originally sold for £3·60.

No. 3530 includes the 'EUROPA' emblem.

2684 Polacanthus

2685 Ichthyosaurus

2686 Iguanodon

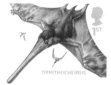

2687 Ornithocheirus

2688 Baryonyx

2689 Dimorphodon

2690 Hypsilophodon

2691 Cetiosaurus

2692 Megalosaurus

2693 Plesiosaurus

(Des John Sibbick (illustrator) and Why Not Associates. Gravure Walsall)

2013 (10 Oct). *Dinosaurs.* Self-adhesive. ⟨MULTI COLOUR⟩ 'All-over' phosphor. Die-cut perf 13½×14 (with no teeth around protruding parts at top or foot of the designs).

3532	2684	(1st) Polacanthus	1·00	1·00
		a. Horiz strip of 5. Nos. 3532/6	4·50	
3533	2685	(1st) Ichthyosaurus	1·00	1·00
3534	2686	(1st) Iguanodon	1·00	1·00
3535	2687	(1st) Ornithocheirus	1·00	1·00
3536	2688	(1st) Baryonyx	1·00	1·00
3537	2689	(1st) Dimorphodon	1·00	1·00
		a. Horiz strip of 5. Nos. 3537/41	4·50	
3538	2690	(1st) Hypsilophodon	1·00	1·00
3539	2691	(1st) Cetiosaurus	1·00	1·00
3540	2692	(1st) Megalosaurus	1·00	1·00
3541	2693	(1st) Plesiosaurus	1·00	1·00
Set of 10..			9·00	9·00
First Day Cover (Tallents House)				11·00
First Day Cover (Lyme Regis, Dorset)................				11·00
Presentation Pack (PO Pack 490)...................			10·00	
PHQ Cards (set of 10) (382)			4·00	11·00

Nos. 3532/6 and 3537/41 were each printed together as horizontal strips of five stamps in sheets of 50 (2 panes 5×5).

2694 Madonna and Child (Francesco Granacci)

2695 Virgin and Child with the Young St John the Baptist (detail) (Antoniazzo Romano)

2696 Madonna and Child (Francesco Granacci)

2697 St Roch Praying to the Virgin for an End to the Plague (detail) (Jacques-Louis David)

2698 Virgin and Child with the Young St John the Baptist (detail) (Antoniazzo Romano)

2699 La Vierge au Lys (William-Adolphe Bouguereau)

2700 Theotokos, Mother of God (Fadi Mikhail)

(Des Robert Maude and Sarah Davies. Gravure Walsall (3542a, 3543a) or De La Rue (others))

2013 (5 Nov). *Christmas. Madonna and Child Paintings.* ⟨MULTI COLOUR⟩ One centre band (3542) or two bands (others). Perf 14½×15.

(a) Self-adhesive.

3542	2694	(2nd) Madonna and Child	90	90
		a. Booklet pane. No. 3542×12	9·75	
3543	2695	(1st) Virgin and Child with the Young St John the Baptist (detail)......................	1·00	1·00
		a. Booklet pane. No. 3543×12..........	10·75	
3544	2696	(2nd Large) Madonna and Child................	1·10	1·10
3545	2697	88p. St Roch Praying to the Virgin for an End to the Plague (detail)...................	1·35	1·35
3546	2698	(1st Large) Virgin and Child with the Young St John the Baptist (detail)	1·40	1·40
3547	2699	£1·28 La Vierge au Lys..............................	2·00	2·00
3548	2700	£1·88 Theotokos, Mother of God...................	3·00	3·00
Set of 7..			9·50	9·50
First Day Cover (Tallents House).......................				12·50
First Day Cover (Bethlehem, Llandeilo)................				12·50
Presentation Pack (PO Pack No. 491)................			11·50	
PHQ Cards (set of 8) (383)			3·25	19·00

(b) Ordinary gum.

MS3549	146×74 mm. As Nos. 3542/8..........................	9·50	9·50
First Day Cover			12·50

The eight PHQ cards show the seven individual stamps and the complete miniature sheet.

The 2nd class, 1st class, 88p., £1·28 and £1·88 stamps were also issued in sheets of 20 containing eight 2nd class, eight 1st class, two 88p., one £1·28 and one £1·88 stamps, each stamp accompanied by a *se-tenant* label. These sheets were printed in lithography and sold for £13·62 each (LS88).

Separate sheets of 20 2nd, ten 1st, ten 88p. and ten £1·28 were available with personal photographs on the labels from Royal Mail, Edinburgh. These were sold at £14·50 for 20 2nd, £10·20 for ten 1st, £14·45 for ten 88p. and £18·50 for ten £1·28.

2701 Angels (Rosie Hargreaves)

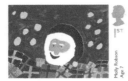

2702 *Santa* (Molly Robson)

(Gravure Walsall)

2013 (5 Nov). *Children's Christmas.* Self-adhesive. [MULTI COLOUR] One phosphor band at right (2nd) or two phosphor bands (1st). Die-cut perf 14½.

3550	**2701**	(2nd) *Angels*	1·00	1·00
3551	**2702**	(1st) *Santa*	1·25	1·25
First Day Cover (Tallents House)				4·25
First Day Cover (Bethlehem, Llandeilo)				4·25
Presentation Pack (PO Pack No. M22)			4·25	

Year Pack

2013 (5 Nov). Comprises Nos. 3423/9, 3431/47, **MS**3451, 3453/73, 3491/6, **MS**3498/508, **MS**3511/24, **MS**3529 and 3532/48
CP3551*a* Year Pack .... 145·00

Post Office Yearbook

2013 (5 Nov). Comprises Nos. 3423/9, 3431/47, **MS**3451, 3453/73, 3491/6, **MS**3498/508, **MS**3511/24, **MS**3529, 3532/48 and 3550/1
YB3551*a* Yearbook .... 155·00

Miniature Sheet Collection

2013 (5 Nov). Comprises Nos. **MS**3429, **MS**3451, **MS**3474, **MS**3498, **MS**3511, **MS**3518, **MS**3529 and **MS**3549
MS3551*a* Miniature Sheet Collection .... 45·00

2703 Andy Pandy

2704 Ivor the Engine

2705 Dougal (*The Magic Roundabout*)

2706 Windy Miller (*Camberwick Green*)

2707 Mr. Benn

2708 Great Uncle Bulgaria (*The Wombles*)

2709 Bagpuss

2710 Paddington Bear

2711 Postman Pat

2712 Bob the Builder

2713 Peppa Pig

2714 Shaun the Sheep

(Des Interabang. Gravure Walsall)

2014 (7 Jan). *Classic Children's TV.* Self-adhesive. [MULTI COLOUR] 'All-over' phosphor. Die-cut perf 15.

3552	**2703**	(1st) Andy Pandy	1·00	1·00
		a. Horiz strip of 6. Nos. 3552/7	5·50	
3553	**2704**	(1st) Ivor the Engine	1·00	1·00
3554	**2705**	(1st) Dougal (*The Magic Roundabout*)	1·00	1·00
3555	**2706**	(1st) Windy Miller (*Camberwick Green*)	1·00	1·00
3556	**2707**	(1st) Mr. Benn	1·00	1·00
3557	**2708**	(1st) Great Uncle Bulgaria (*The Wombles*)	1·00	1·00
3558	**2709**	(1st) Bagpuss	1·00	1·00
		a. Horiz strip of 6. Nos. 3558/63	5·50	
3559	**2710**	(1st) Paddington Bear	1·00	1·00
3560	**2711**	(1st) Postman Pat	1·00	1·00
3561	**2712**	(1st) Bob the Builder	1·00	1·00
3562	**2713**	(1st) Peppa Pig	1·00	1·00
3563	**2714**	(1st) Shaun the Sheep	1·00	1·00
Set of 12			11·00	11·00
Set of 2 Gutter Strips of 12			22·00	
First Day Cover (Tallents House)				13·50
First Day Cover (Wimbledon, London SW19)				13·50
Presentation Pack (PO Pack No. 493)			12·50	
PHQ Cards (set of 12) (384)			4·75	12·50

Nos. 3552/7 and 3558/63 were each printed together, *se-tenant*, in horizontal strips of six stamps in sheets of 60 (6×10).

2715 Riding for the Disabled Association

2716 The King's Troop Ceremonial Horses

2717 Dray Horses

2718 Royal Mews Carriage Horses

2719 Police Horses

2720 Forestry Horse

(Des Michael Denny and Harold Batten. Litho Cartor)

2014 (4 Feb). *Working Horses.* [MULTI COLOUR] 'All-over' phosphor. Perf 14.

3564	**2715**	(1st) Riding for the Disabled Association	1·00	1·00
3565	**2716**	(1st) The King's Troop Ceremonial Horses	1·00	1·00
3566	**2717**	88p. Dray Horses	1·40	1·40
3567	**2718**	88p. Royal Mews Carriage Horses	1·40	1·40
3568	**2719**	£1·28 Police Horses	2·10	2·10
3569	**2720**	£1·28 Forestry Horse	2·10	2·10
Set of 6			8·00	8·00
Set of 6 Gutter Pairs			16·00	
First Day Cover (Tallents House)				10·00
First Day Cover (Horseheath, Cambridge)				10·00
Presentation Pack (PO Pack No. 494)			9·50	
PHQ Cards (set of 6) (385)			2·40	9·50

2721 BR Dean Goods No. 2532

2722 BR D34 Nos. 62471 & 62496

2723 UTA Class W No. 103 *Thomas Somerset* with Belfast Express, Downhill, near Castlerock, *c.*1950

2724 LMS No. 7720

2725 Peckett R2 *Thor*

2726 BR D40 No. 62276

2727 UTA SG3 No. 35

2728 Hunslet No. 589 *Blanche*

2729 Classic Locomotives of Wales *(Illustration reduced)*

(Des Delaney Design Consultants. Litho Enschedé (booklet)

2014 (20 Feb). *Classic Locomotives* (4th and 5th series). Wales (**MS**3578) and United Kingdom. |MULTI|COLOUR 'All-over' phosphor. Perf 14.

3570	**2721**	(1st) BR Dean Goods No. 2532	2·75	2·75
		a. Booklet pane. Nos. 3570 and 3574, each×2 with margins all round	7·50	
3571	**2722**	(1st) BR D34 Nos. 62471 & 62496	2·75	2·75
		a. Booklet pane. Nos. 3571 and 3575, each×2 with margins all round	7·50	
3572	**2723**	(1st) UTA Class W No. 103 *Thomas Somerset* with Belfast Express	2·75	2·75
		a. Booklet pane. Nos. 3572 and 3576, each×2 with margins all round	7·50	
3573	**2724**	(1st) LMS No. 7720	2·75	2·75
		a. Booklet pane. Nos. 3573 and 3577, each×2 with margins all round	7·50	
3574	**2725**	60p. Peckett R2 *Thor*	2·75	2·75
3575	**2726**	68p. BR D40 No. 62276	2·75	2·75
3576	**2727**	78p. UTA SG3 No. 35	2·75	2·75
3577	**2728**	78p. Hunslet No. 589 *Blanche*	2·75	2·75
Set of 8			15·00	15·00

MS3578 180×74 mm. **2729** Classic Locomotives of Wales Nos. 3573; No. 3577; 88p. W&LLR No. 822 *The Earl*; £1·28 BR 5600 No. 5652 .... 5·00 5·25

First Day Cover (Tallents House) .... 6·50
First Day Cover (Porthmadog) .... 6·50
Presentation Pack (PO Pack No. 495) .... 6·00
PHQ *Cards* (set of 5) (386) .... 2·00 10·00

Nos. 3570/7 were issued only in £13·97 Classic Locomotives booklets, No. DY9, or also in **MS**3578 (Nos. 3573 and 3577).

The five PHQ cards show the four individual stamps and the complete miniature sheet.

2730 Roy Plomley (1914-85, broadcaster and writer)

2731 Barbara Ward (1914-81, economist and broadcaster)

2732 Joe Mercer (1914-90, football player and manager)

2733 Kenneth More (1914-82, stage and screen actor)

2734 Dylan Thomas (1914-53, poet and writer)

2735 Sir Alec Guinness (1914-2000, stage and screen actor)

2736 Noorunissa Inayat Khan (1914-44, SOE agent in occupied France)

2737 Max Perutz (1914-2002, molecular biologist and Nobel laureate)

2738 Joan Littlewood (1914-2002, theatre director and writer)

2739 Abram Games (1914-96, graphic designer)

(Des Purpose. Litho Cartor)

2014 (25 Mar). *Remarkable Lives.* |MULTI|COLOUR 'All-over' phosphor. Perf 14½.

3579	**2730**	(1st) Roy Plomley	1·00	1·00
		a. Horiz strip of 5. Nos. 3579/83	4·50	4·50
3580	**2731**	(1st) Barbara Ward	1·00	1·00
3581	**2732**	(1st) Joe Mercer	1·00	1·00
3582	**2733**	(1st) Kenneth More	1·00	1·00
3583	**2734**	(1st) Dylan Thomas	1·00	1·00
3584	**2735**	(1st) Sir Alec Guinness	1·00	1·00
		a. Horiz strip of 5. Nos. 3584/8	4·50	4·50
3585	**2736**	(1st) Noorunissa Inayat Khan	1·00	1·00
3586	**2737**	(1st) Max Perutz	1·00	1·00
3587	**2738**	(1st) Joan Littlewood	1·00	1·00
3588	**2739**	(1st) Abram Games	1·00	1·00
Set of 10			9·00	9·00
Set of 2 Gutter Strips of 10			18·00	

First Day Cover (Tallents House) .... 11·00
First Day Cover (Swansea) .... 11·00
Presentation Pack (PO Pack No. 496) .... 10·00
PHQ *Cards* (set of 10) (387) .... 4·00 11·00

Nos. 3579/83 and 3584/8 were each printed together, *se-tenant*, as horizontal strips of five stamps in sheets of 50 (2 panes 5×5).

2740 Buckingham Palace, 2014

2741 Buckingham Palace, *c.* 1862

2742 Buckingham Palace, 1846

2743 Buckingham House, 1819

2744 Buckingham House, 1714

2745 Buckingham House, *c.* 1700

2746 The Grand Staircase

2747 The Throne Room

(Des Howard Brown (sheet stamps). Litho ISP Cartor (3589/94) or Enschedé (booklet panes 3589b/94b) or gravure ISP Walsall (3595/6))

2014 (15 Apr). *Buckingham Palace, London* (1st issue). MULTI COLOUR 'All-over' phosphor'.

(a) Ordinary gum. Perf 14½.

3589	**2740**	(1st) Buckingham Palace, 2014.............	1·00	1·00
		a. Horiz strip of 3. Nos. 3589/91.......	2·75	2·75
		b. Perf 14×13½..	1·25	1·25

		ba. Booklet pane. Nos. 3589b and 3590b, each×2 with margins all round	5·00	
3590	**2741**	(1st) Buckingham Palace, *c.* 1862..	1·00	1·00
		b. Perf 14×13½	1·25	1·25
3591	**2742**	(1st) Buckingham Palace, 1846............	1·00	1·00
		b. Perf 14×13½	1·25	1·25
		ba. Booklet pane. Nos. 3591b/4b with margins all round...................	5·00	
3592	**2743**	(1st) Buckingham House, 1819............	1·00	1·00
		a. Horiz strip of 3. Nos. 3592/4.........	2·75	2·75
		b. Perf 14×13½	1·25	1·25
3593	**2744**	(1st) Buckingham House, 1714............	1·00	1·00
		b. Perf 14×13½	1·25	1·25
3594	**2745**	(1st) Buckingham House, *c.* 1700........	1·00	1·00
		b. Perf 14×13½	1·25	1·25
Set of 6 (Nos. 3589/94)			5·50	5·50
Set of 2 Gutter Strips of 6			11·00	
Set of 6 (Nos. 3589b/94b)			7·50	7·50
First Day Cover (Tallents House)				6·75
First Day Cover (London SW1)				6·75
Presentation Pack (PO Pack No. 497) Nos. 3589/94 and **MS**3601			10·00	
PHQ Cards (set of 11) (388)			4·50	13·00

(b) Self-adhesive. Die-cut perf 14.

3595	**2746**	(1st) The Grand Staircase	2·25	2·25
		a. Booklet pane. Nos. 3595/6 and U3022×4	5·50	
3596	**2747**	(1st) The Throne Room............................	2·25	2·25

Nos. 3589/91 and 3592/4 were each printed together, *se-tenant*, as horizontal strips of three stamps in sheets of 36 (2 panes 3×6).

Nos. 3589b/94b come from £11·39 premium booklets, No. DY10.

Nos. 3595/6 were issued in stamp booklets, No. PM42, originally sold for £3·72.

The complete miniature sheet is shown on one of the eleven PHQ cards with the others depicting individual stamps including those from **MS**3601.

2748 The Blue Drawing Room   **2749** The Green Drawing Room

2750 Buckingham Palace

(Des Robert Maude and Sarah Davies (**MS**3601). Litho Enschedé)

2014 (15 Apr). *Buckingham Palace, London* (2nd issue). MULTI COLOUR 'All-over' phosphor. Perf 14.

3597	**2747**	(1st) The Throne Room............................	1·00	1·00
		a. Booklet pane. Nos. 3597/3600 with margins all round and roulettes at left...................	3·50	
3598	**2746**	(1st) The Grand Staircase........................	1·00	1·00
3599	**2748**	(1st) The Blue Drawing Room................	1·00	1·00
3600	**2749**	(1st) The Green Drawing Room	1·00	1·00
Set of 4			3·50	3·50
MS3601 146×74 mm. **2750** Buckingham Palace Nos. 3597/3600			3·50	3·50
MS3601a *Imperf*			£12000	–
First Day Cover (Tallents House)				4·50
First Day Cover (London SW1)				4·50

Nos. 3597/3600 come from £11·39 premium booklets, No. DY10 and **MS**3601.

2751 *A Matter of Life and Death* (1946)

2752 *Lawrence of Arabia* (1962)

2753 *2001 A Space Odyssey* (1968)

2754 *Chariots of Fire* (1981)

2755 *Secrets and Lies* (1996)

2756 *Bend It Like Beckham* (2002)

2757 Films by GPO Film Unit

(Des Johnson Banks (3602/7) or Magpie Studio (**MS**3608). Litho ISP Cartor (3602/7) or Enschedé (**MS**3608))

2014 (13 May). *Great British Films.* |MULTI COLOUR| 'All-over' phosphor. Perf 14½ (3602/7) or 14 (**MS**3608).

3602	**2751**	(1st) *A Matter of Life and Death*	1·00	1·00
		a. Horiz strip of 3. Nos. 3602/4	3·00	3·00
3603	**2752**	(1st) *Lawrence of Arabia*	1·00	1·00
3604	**2753**	(1st) *2001 A Space Odyssey*	1·00	1·00
3605	**2754**	£1·28 *Chariots of Fire*	1·60	1·60
		a. Horiz strip of 3. Nos. 3605/7	4·75	4·75
3606	**2755**	£1·28 *Secrets and Lies*	1·60	1·60
3607	**2756**	£1·28 *Bend It Like Beckham*	1·60	1·60
Set of 6			7·00	7·00
Set of 2 Gutter Strips of 6			14·00	
First Day Cover (Tallents House)				10·00
First Day Cover (Blackheath London SE3)				10·00
Presentation Pack (PO Pack No. 498)				
(Nos. 3602/7 and **MS**3608)			14·00	
PHQ Cards (set of 11) (389)			4·50	18·00

MS3608 115×89 mm. **2757** Films by GPO Film Unit (1st)×4 *Night Mail* (1936) directed by Harry Watt and Basil Wright; *Love on the Wing* (1938) directed by Norman McLaren; *A Colour Box* (1935) directed by Len Lye; *Spare Time* (1939) directed by Humphrey Jennings................... 4·50 4·75

First Day Cover (Tallents House) .... 5·00
First Day Cover (Blackheath London SE3) .... 5·00

Nos. 3602/4 and 3605/7 were each printed together, *se-tenant*, as horizontal strips of three stamps in sheets of 36 (2 panes 3×6).

The complete miniature sheet is shown on one of the eleven PHQ cards with the others depicting individual stamps including those from **MS**3608.

2758 Herring

2759 Red Gurnard

2760 Dab

2761 Pouting

2762 Cornish Sardine

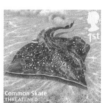

2763 Common Skate

2764 Spiny Dogfish

2765 Wolffish

2766 Sturgeon

2767 Conger Eel

(Des Kate Stephens. Litho ISP Cartor)

2014 (5 June). *Sustainable Fish* (Nos. 3609/13) *and Threatened Fish* (Nos. 3614/18). |MULTI COLOUR| 'All-over' phosphor. Perf 14×14½.

3609	**2758**	(1st) Herring	1·00	1·00
		a. Horiz strip of 5. Nos. 3609/13	4·50	4·50
3610	**2759**	(1st) Red Gurnard	1·00	1·00
3611	**2760**	(1st) Dab	1·00	1·00
3612	**2761**	(1st) Pouting	1·00	1·00
3613	**2762**	(1st) Cornish Sardine	1·00	1·00
3614	**2763**	(1st) Common Skate	1·00	1·00
		a. Horiz strip of 5. Nos. 3614/18	4·50	4·50
3615	**2764**	(1st) Spiny Dogfish	1·00	1·00
3616	**2765**	(1st) Wolffish	1·00	1·00
3617	**2766**	(1st) Sturgeon	1·00	1·00
3618	**2767**	(1st) Conger Eel	1·00	1·00
Set of 10			9·00	9·00
Set of 2 Gutter Strips of 10			18·00	
First Day Cover (Tallents House)				11·50
First Day Cover (Fishguard)				11·50
Presentation Pack (PO Pack No. 499)			10·50	
PHQ Cards (set of 10) (390)			4·00	11·00

Nos. 3609/13 and 3614/18 were each printed together, *se-tenant*, as horizontal strips of five in sheets of 50 (2 panes 5×5).

2768 Judo

2769 Swimming

2770 Marathon

2771 Squash

2772 Netball

2773 Para-athlete Cycling

(Des Nanette Hoogslag (illustration) and Howard Brown. Litho ISP Cartor (3619/24) or gravure ISP Walsall (3625))

2014 (17 July). *Commonwealth Games, Glasgow.* |MULTI COLOUR| One phosphor band (3619) or two bands (others).

(a) Ordinary gum. Perf 14×14½.

3619	**2768**	(2nd) Judo	90	90
3620	**2769**	(1st) Swimming	1·00	1·00
3621	**2770**	97p. Marathon	1·40	1·40
3622	**2771**	£1·28 Squash	1·80	1·80
3623	**2772**	£1·47 Netball	2·60	2·60
3624	**2773**	£2·15 Para-athlete Cycling	3·50	3·50
Set of 6			10·00	10·00
Set of 6 Gutter Pairs			20·00	
First Day Cover (Tallents House)				11·50

First Day Cover (Glasgow)				11·50
Presentation Pack (PO Pack No. 500)			10·50	
PHQ Cards (set of 6) (391)			2·40	11·50

(b) Self-adhesive. Die-cut perf 14×14½.

3625	**2769**	(1st) Swimming	1·50	1·50
		a. Booklet pane. Nos. 3625×2 and U3022×4	5·50	

The phosphor band on No. 3619 is at centre right of the stamps.
No. 3625 was issued in stamp booklets, No. PM43, originally sold for £3·72.

2774 Poppy (Fiona Strickland)

2775 Lines from *For the Fallen* (Laurence Binyon)

2776 Private William Cecil Tickle

2777 *A Star Shell* (C. R. W. Nevinson)

2778 *The Response* (sculpture by William Goscombe John)

2779 Princess Mary's Gift Box Fund

(Des Hat-trick Design. Litho ISP Cartor (3626/31) or Enschedé (booklet panes 3626a, 3629a))

2014 (28 July). *Centenary of the First World War* (1st issue). |MULTI COLOUR| 'All-over' phosphor (3627, 3629) or two bands (others). Perf 14½.

3626	**2774**	(1st) Poppy	1·00	1·00
		a. 'All-over' phosphor	1·25	1·50
		b. Booklet pane. Nos. 3626a, 3627, 3628a with margins all round	3·50	
3627	**2775**	(1st) Lines from *For the Fallen*	1·00	1·00
3628	**2776**	(1st) Private William Cecil Tickle	1·00	1·00
		a. 'All-over' phosphor	1·25	1·50
3629	**2777**	£1·47 *A Star Shell*	2·40	2·40
		b. Booklet pane. Nos. 3629, 3630a, 3631a with margins all round	9·00	
3630	**2778**	£1·47 *The Response*	2·40	2·40
		a. 'All-over' phosphor	3·25	3·50
3631	**2779**	£1·47 Princess Mary's Gift Box Fund	2·40	2·40
		a. 'All-over' phosphor	3·25	3·50
Set of 6			9·25	9·25
Set of 6 Gutter Pairs			18·50	
First Day Cover (Tallents House)				11·50
First Day Cover (Newcastle upon Tyne)				11·50
Presentation Pack (PO Pack No. 501)			10·50	
PHQ Cards (set of 6) (392)			2·40	10·50

Nos. 3626a, 3628a, 3630a and 3631a only come from premium booklets, No. DY11.

(Gravure ISP Walsall)

2014 (18 Aug). *Sustainable Fish and Threatened Fish* (2nd issue). Designs as Nos. 3613/14. Self-adhesive. |MULTI COLOUR| Die-cut perf 14×14½.

3632	**2763**	(1st) Common Skate. Multicoloured	1·50	1·60
		a. Booklet pane. Nos. 3632/3 and U3022×4	5·50	
3633	**2762**	(1st) Cornish Sardine. Multicoloured	1·50	1·60

Nos. 3632/3 were issued in stamp booklets, No. PM44, originally sold for £3·72.

(Gravure ISP Walsall)

2014 (18 Sept). *Classic Locomotives of Wales.* Booklet stamp as T **2724**. 'All-over' phosphor. Self-adhesive. |MULTI COLOUR Die-cut perf 14.

3634	**2724**	(1st) LMS No. 7720	1·50	1·60
		a. Booklet pane. No. 3634×2 and U3022×4	5·50	

No. 3634 was only issued in booklets, No. PM45, originally sold for £3·72.

2780 Eastbourne Bandstand

2781 Tinside Lido, Plymouth

2782 Bangor Pier

2783 Southwold Lighthouse

2784 Blackpool Pleasure Beach

2785 Bexhill-on-Sea Shelter

2786 British Piers

(Des Why Not Associates. Litho ISP Cartor (3635/40) or Enschedé (MS3641))

2014 (18 Sept). *Seaside Architecture.* |MULTI COLOUR Two bands (3635/40) or 'All-over' phosphor (**MS**3641). Perf 14.

3635	**2780**	(1st) Eastbourne Bandstand	1·00	1·00
3636	**2781**	(1st) Tinside Lido, Plymouth	1·00	1·00
3637	**2782**	97p. Bangor Pier	1·40	1·40
3638	**2783**	97p. Southwold Lighthouse	1·40	1·40
3639	**2784**	£1·28 Blackpool Pleasure Beach	2·10	2·10
3640	**2785**	£1·28 Bexhill-on-Sea Shelter	2·10	2·10
Set of 6			8·00	8·00
Set of 6 Gutter Pairs			16·00	
First Day Cover (Tallents House)				10·00
First Day Cover (Eastbourne)				10·00
Presentation Pack (PO Pack No. 502)				
(Nos. 3635/40 and **MS**3641)			16·00	
PHQ Cards (set of 11) (393)			4·50	19·00
MS3641 125×89 mm. **2786** British Piers (1st) Llandudno Pier; (1st) Worthing Pier; £1·28 Dunoon Pier; £1·28 Brighton Pier			5·25	5·50
First Day Cover (Tallents House)				7·00
First Day Cover (Eastbourne)				7·00

The complete miniature sheet is shown on one of the eleven PHQ cards with the others depicting individual stamps including those from the miniature sheet.

No. 3635 includes the 'EUROPA' emblem.

2787 Margaret Thatcher

2788 Harold Wilson

2789 Clement Attlee

2790 Winston Churchill

2791 William Gladstone

2792 Robert Peel

2793 Charles Grey

2794 William Pitt the Younger

(Des Together. Litho ISP Cartor)

2014 (14 Oct). *Prime Ministers.* |MULTI COLOUR 'All-over' phosphor. Perf 14½.

3642	**2787**	(1st) Margaret Thatcher	1·00	1·00
		a. Horiz strip of 4. Nos. 3642/5	4·00	4·00
3643	**2788**	(1st) Harold Wilson	1·00	1·00
3644	**2789**	(1st) Clement Attlee	1·00	1·00
3645	**2790**	(1st) Winston Churchill	1·00	1·00
3646	**2791**	97p. William Gladstone	1·60	1·60
		a. Horiz strip of 4. Nos. 3646/9	6·50	6·50
3647	**2792**	97p. Robert Peel	1·60	1·60
3648	**2793**	97p. Charles Grey	1·60	1·60
3649	**2794**	97p. William Pitt the Younger	1·60	1·60
Set of 8			9·50	9·50
Set of 2 Gutter strips of 4			19·00	
First Day Cover (Tallents House)				11·00
First Day Cover (London SW1)				11·00
Presentation Pack (PO Pack No. 503)			11·00	
PHQ Cards (set of 8) (394)			3·25	11·50

Nos. 3642/5 and 3646/9 were each printed together, *se-tenant*, as horizontal strips of four stamps in sheets of 48 (2 panes 4×6).

SELF-ADHESIVE STAMPS: Collectors are reminded that used self-adhesive stamps will no longer 'soak-off'. They should be collected with a neat margin of backing paper.

2795 Collecting the Christmas Tree

2796 Posting Christmas Cards

2797 Collecting the
Christmas Tree

2798 Posting Christmas
Cards

2799 Building a
Snowman

2800 Carol Singing

2801 Ice Skating

(Des True North. Gravure Walsall (3650a, 3651a) or De La Rue (others))

2014 (4 Nov). *Christmas.* Illustrations by Andrew Bannecker. |MULTI COLOUR| One centre band (3650) or two bands (others). Perf 14½×15.

(a) Self-adhesive

3650	**2795**	(2nd) Collecting the Christmas Tree	90	90
		a. Booklet pane. No. 3650×12...........	9·75	
3651	**2796**	(1st) Posting Christmas Cards................	1·00	1·00
		a. Booklet pane. No. 3651×12...........	10·75	
3652	**2797**	(2nd Large) Collecting the Christmas		
		Tree...	1·10	1·10
3653	**2798**	(1st Large) Posting Christmas Cards...	1·40	1·40
3654	**2799**	£1·28 Building a Snowman	2·00	2·00
3655	**2800**	£1·47 Carol Singing	2·50	2·50
3656	**2801**	£2·15 Ice Skating	3·25	3·25
Set of 7			11·00	11·00
First Day Cover (Tallents House)				14·00
First Day Cover (Bethlehem, Llandeilo)				14·00
Presentation Pack (PO Pack No. 504)......................			13·00	
PHQ Cards (set of 8) (395)			3·25	20·00

(b) Ordinary gum

MS3657 156×74 mm. Nos. 3650/6................		11·00	11·00
First Day Cover (Tallents House)			14·00
First Day Cover (Bethlehem, Llandeilo)			14·00

The 2nd class, 1st class, £1·28 and £1·47 stamps were also issued in sheets of 20 containing eight 2nd class, eight 1st class, two £1·28 and two £1·47 stamps, each stamp accompanied by a *se-tenant* label. These sheets were printed in lithography and sold for £15·20 per sheet (LS90).

Separate sheets of 20 2nd, 20 1st, ten 1st, ten £1·28 and ten £1·47 were available with personal photographs on the labels from Royal Mail, Edinburgh. These were sold at £14·50 for 20 2nd, £18·65 for 20 1st, £10·20 for ten 1st, £18·50 for ten £1·28 and £21·85 for ten £1·47.

Year Pack
2014 (4 Nov). Comprises Nos. 3552/69, **M**S3578/94, **M**S3601/24, 3626/31, 3635/56.

CP3657*a* Year Pack...	135·00	

Post Office Yearbook
2014 (4 Nov). Comprises Nos. 3552/69, **MS**3578/94, **MS**3601/24, 3626/31, 3635/56.

YB3657*a* Yearbook...	160·00	

Miniature Sheet Collection
2004 (4 Nov). Comprises Nos. **MS**3578, **MS**3601, **MS**3608, **MS**3641 and **MS**3657.

MS3657*a* Miniature Sheet Collection....................................	30·00	

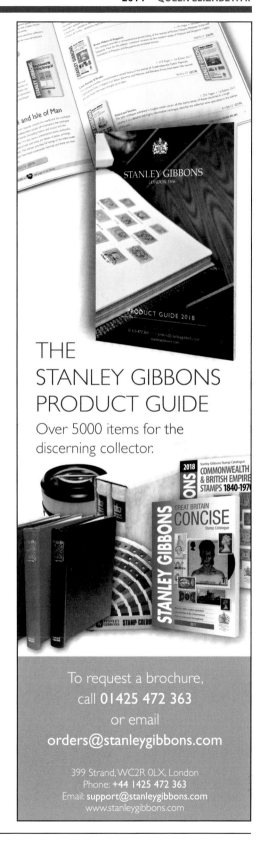

2802 The White Rabbit

2803 Down the Rabbit Hole

2804 Drink Me

2805 The White Rabbit's House

2806 The Cheshire-Cat

2807 A Mad Tea-Party

2808 The Queen of Hearts

2809 The Game of Croquet

2810 Alice's Evidence

2811 A Pack of Cards

(Grahame Baker-Smith (illustration) and Godfrey Design. Litho ISP Cartor (3658/67) or gravure ISP Walsall (3668/9))

2015 (6 Jan). *Alice in Wonderland.* |MULTI COLOUR One phosphor band at right (2nd) or two phosphor bands (others).

(a) Ordinary gum. Perf 14½

3658	**2802**	(2nd) The White Rabbit	90	90
		a. Vert pair. Nos. 3658/9	1·80	1·80
3659	**2803**	(2nd) Down the Rabbit Hole	90	90
3660	**2804**	(1st) Drink Me	1·00	1·00
		a. Vert pair. Nos. 3660/1	2·00	2·00
3661	**2805**	(1st) The White Rabbit's House	1·00	1·00
3662	**2806**	81p. The Cheshire-Cat	1·50	1·50
		a. Vert pair. Nos. 3662/3	3·00	3·00
3663	**2807**	81p. A Mad Tea-Party	1·50	1·50
3664	**2808**	£1·28 The Queen of Hearts	2·50	2·50
		a. Vert pair. Nos. 3664/5	5·00	5·00
3665	**2809**	£1·28 The Game of Croquet	2·50	2·50
3666	**2810**	£1·47 Alice's Evidence	3·25	3·25
		a. Vert pair. Nos. 3666/7	6·50	6·50
3667	**2811**	£1·47 A Pack of Cards	3·25	3·25
Set of 10			16·50	16·50
Set of 5 Gutter Strips of 4			35·00	
First Day Cover (Tallents House)				17·50
First Day Cover (Oxford)				17·50
Presentation Pack (PO Pack No. 506)			25·00	

PHQ Cards (Set of 10) (396)			5·00	18·00

(b) Self-adhesive. Die-cut perf 14½

3668	**2804**	(1st) Drink Me	5·00	5·00
		a. Booklet pane. Nos. 3668/9 and U3022×4	12·00	
3669	**2805**	(1st) The White Rabbit's House	5·00	5·00

Nos. 3658/9, 3660/1, 3662/3, 3664/5 and 3666/7 were each printed together, *se-tenant*, as vertical pairs in sheets of 60 (2 panes 5×6).

Nos. 3658/67 commemorate the 150th anniversary of the Publication of *Alice's Adventures in Wonderland* by Lewis Carroll.

Nos. 3668/9 were only issued in booklets, No. PM46, originally sold for £3·72

2812 Happy Birthday (NB Studio)

2813 Well Done (Webb & Webb Design Ltd)

2814 Wedding (Caroline Gardner Ltd)

2815 Love (Rebecca Sutherland)

2816 Mum (The Chase)

2817 New Baby (NB Studio)

2818 Grandparent (NB Studio)

2819 Dad (Webb & Webb Design Ltd)

(Des Jenny Bowers and NB Studio. Gravure ISP Walsall (3670/7) or litho ISP Cartor (**MS**3678))

2015 (20 Jan). *Smilers* (5th series). |MULTI COLOUR Two phosphor bands.

(a) Self-adhesive booklet stamps.
Die-cut perf 14½×14 (with one elliptical hole in each vert side)

3670	**2812**	(1st) Happy Birthday	1·85	1·85
		a. Booklet pane. Nos. 3670×2, 3671, 3672/3 each×2, 3674, 3675×2 and 3676/7	17·50	
3671	**2813**	(1st) Well Done	2·75	2·75
3672	**2814**	(1st) Wedding	1·85	1·85
3673	**2815**	(1st) Love	1·85	1·85
3674	**2816**	(1st) Mum	1·85	1·85
3675	**2817**	(1st) New Baby	1·85	1·85
3676	**2818**	(1st) Grandparent	1·85	1·85
3677	**2819**	(1st) Dad	1·85	1·85
Set of 8			13·50	13·50

(b) Ordinary gum. Perf 14½×14 (with one elliptical hole in each vert side)

MS3678	134×70 mm. As Nos. 3670/7		7·00	7·00
First Day Cover (Tallents House)				9·25
First Day Cover (Greetwell, Lincoln)				9·25
Presentation Pack (PO Pack No. M23)			8·25	
PHQ Cards (set of 9) (D34)			6·75	17·00

Nos. 3670/7 were issued in booklets of 12, No. QB1, originally sold for £7·44.

Nos. 3670/7 were also issued in sheets of 20 with *se-tenant* greetings labels, No. LS93, printed by Cartor in lithography and originally sold at £12·90 per sheet.

Sheets of 20 stamps of the same design were available with personal photographs on the labels from Royal mail, Tallents House.

The complete miniature sheet is shown on one of the nine PHQ cards with the others depicting individual stamps.

2820 Colossus - world's first electronic digital computer

2821 World Wide Web - revolutionary global communications system

2822 Catseyes - light-reflecting road safety innovation

2823 Fibre Optics - pioneering rapid-data-transfer technology

2824 Stainless Steel - non-corrosive, versatile, 100% recyclable alloy

2825 Carbon Fibre - high-strength, lightweight, composite material

2826 DNA Sequencing - revolution in understanding the genome

2827 i-LIMB - bionic hand with individually powered digits

(Des GBH. Litho ISP Cartor)

2015 (19 Feb). *Inventive Britain.* |MULTI COLOUR Two phosphor bands. Perf 14½.

3679	**2820**	(1st) Colossus	1·00	1·00
		a. Horiz pair. Nos. 3679/80	2·00	2·00
		b. Booklet pane. Nos. 3305, 3281×2 and 3679 with margins all round .	5·00	
		c. Booklet pane. Nos. 3679/80, 3683 and 3686	5·50	
3680	**2821**	(1st) World Wide Web	1·00	1·00
3681	**2822**	81p. Catseyes	1·10	1·10
		a. Horiz pair. Nos. 3681/2	2·20	2·20
		b. Booklet pane. Nos. 3681/2 and 3684/5 with margins all round	6·00	
3682	**2823**	81p. Fibre Optics	1·10	1·10
3683	**2824**	£1·28 Stainless Steel	1·80	1·80
		a. Horiz pair. Nos. 3683/4	3·75	3·75
3684	**2825**	£1·28 Carbon Fibre	1·80	1·80
3685	**2826**	£1·47 DNA Sequencing	2·25	2·25
		a. Horiz pair. Nos. 3685/6	4·50	4·50
3686	**2827**	£1·47 i-LIMB	2·25	2·25
Set of 8			11·25	11·25
Set of 4 Gutter Blocks of 4			23·00	
First Day Cover (Tallents House)				15·50
First Day Cover (Harlow)				15·50
Presentation Pack (PO Pack No. 507)			13·50	
PHQ Cards (397) (set of 8)			4·00	17·00

Nos. 3679/80, 3681/2, 3683/4 and 3685/6 were each printed together, *se-tenant*, as horizontal pairs in sheets of 60 (2 panes 6×5).

Nos. 3679b/c and 3681b were only issued in the £14·60 Inventive Britain booklet, No. DY12.

2828 Tarr Steps, River Barle

2829 Row Bridge, Mosedale Beck

2830 Pulteney Bridge, River Avon

2831 Craigellachie Bridge, River Spey

2832 Menai Suspension Bridge, Menai Strait

2833 High Level Bridge, River Tyne

2834 Royal Border Bridge, River Tweed

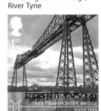

2835 Tees Transporter Bridge, River Tees

2836 Humber Bridge, River Humber

2837 Peace Bridge, River Foyle

(Des GBH. Litho ISP Cartor)

2015 (5 Mar). *Bridges.* |MULTI COLOUR Two phosphor bands. Perf 14½×14.

3687	**2828**	(1st) Tarr Steps, River Barle	1·00	1·00
		a. Horiz strip of 5. Nos. 3687/91	4·50	4·50
3688	**2829**	(1st) Row Bridge, Mosedale Beck	1·00	1·00
3689	**2830**	(1st) Pulteney Bridge, River Avon	1·00	1·00
3690	**2831**	(1st) Craigellachie Bridge, River Spey...	1·00	1·00
3691	**2832**	(1st) Menai Suspension Bridge, Menai Strait	1·00	1·00
3692	**2833**	(1st) High Level Bridge, River Tyne	1·00	1·00
		a. Horiz strip of 5. Nos. 3692/6	4·50	4·50
3693	**2834**	(1st) Royal Border Bridge, River Tweed	1·00	1·00
3694	**2835**	(1st) Tees Transporter Bridge, River Tees	1·00	1·00
3695	**2836**	(1st) Humber Bridge, River Humber	1·00	1·00
3696	**2837**	(1st) Peace Bridge, River Foyle	1·00	1·00
Set of 10			9·00	9·00
Set of 2 Gutter Strips of 10			18·00	
Set of 2 Traffic Light Gutter Strips of 10			25·00	
First Day Cover (Tallents House)				11·50

First Day Cover (Bridge, Canterbury).. 11·50
Presentation Pack (PO Pack No. 508).......................... 10·50
PHQ Cards (set of 10) (398).. 5·00   12·50
    Nos. 3687/91 and 3692/6 were each printed together, se-tenant, as horizontal strips of five stamps in sheets of 50 (2 panes 5×5).

2838 Spike Milligan   **2839** The Two Ronnies

2840 Billy Connolly   **2841** Morecambe and Wise

2842 Norman Wisdom   **2843** Lenny Henry

2844 Peter Cook and Dudley Moore   **2845** Monty Python

2846 French and Saunders   **2847** Victoria Wood

    (Des The Chase. Litho ISP Cartor (3697/3706) or gravure ISP Walsall 3707/8)

2015 (1 Apr). *Comedy Greats.* |MULTI COLOUR Two phosphor bands.

(a) Ordinary gum. Perf 14.

3697	2838	(1st) Spike Milligan	1·00	1·00
		a. Horiz strip of 5. Nos. 3697/701	4·50	4·50
3698	2839	(1st) The Two Ronnies..........................	1·00	1·00
3699	2840	(1st) Billy Connolly	1·00	1·00
3700	2841	(1st) Morecambe and Wise	1·00	1·00
3701	2842	(1st) Norman Wisdom..........................	1·00	1·00
3702	2843	(1st) Lenny Henry	1·00	1·00
		a. Horiz strip of 5. Nos. 3702/6..........	4·50	4·50
3703	2844	(1st) Peter Cook and Dudley Moore	1·00	1·00
3704	2845	(1st) Monty Python	1·00	1·00
3705	2846	(1st) French and Saunders	1·00	1·00
3706	2847	(1st) Victoria Wood	1·00	1·00

Set of 10 .... 9·00   9·00
Set of 2 Gutter Strips of 10 .... 18·00
First Day Cover (Tallents House).. 11·50
First Day Cover (Laughterton, Lincoln) .... 11·50
Presentation Pack (PO Pack No. 509)............................. 10·50
PHQ Cards (set of 10) (399).. 5·00   12·50

(b) Self-adhesive. Die-cut perf 14.

3707	2842	(1st) Norman Wisdom	3·50	3·50
		a. Booklet pane. Nos. 3707/8 and		
		U3022×4	9·00	
3708	2841	(1st) Morecambe and Wise	3·50	3·50

    Nos. 3697/701 and 3702/6 were each printed together, se-tenant, as horizontal strips of five stamps in sheets of 50 (2 panes 5×5).
    Nos. 3707/8 were issued in stamp booklets, No. PM47, sold for £3·72.

2848 Penny Black

2849 Penny Black and 1840 2d. blue

    (Des Sedley Place. Gravure ISP Walsall (3709) or litho ISP Cartor (MS3710))

2015 (6 May). *175th Anniversary of the Penny Black.* |MULTI COLOUR Two phosphor bands.

(a) Self-adhesive booklet stamps. Die-cut perf 14½×14 (with one elliptical hole in each vert side).

3709 **2848** (1st) Penny Black .... 2·00   2·00

(b) Ordinary gum. Perf 14½×14 (with one elliptical hole in each vert side).

MS3710 156×74 mm. **2849** (1st) Penny Black×2; (1st)
1840 2d. blue×2 .... 3·50   3·75
First Day Cover (Tallents House) .... 4·75
First Day Cover (Bath) .... 4·75
Presentation Pack (PO Pack No. 510)............................. 4·25
PHQ Cards (set of 3) (400)... 50   4·00
    No. 3709 was issued in booklets of six, No. MB13.
    The three PHQ cards show the two individual stamps and the complete miniature sheet.
    Designs as No. 3709 and (1st) Twopenny Blue as within **MS**3710 were also issued in sheets of 20 (No. LS94) containing ten 1st class Penny Black and ten 1st class Twopenny Blue, each stamp accompanied by a se-tenant label. These sheets were printed in lithography by ISP Cartor and originally sold for £12·90.
    Sheets of ten or 20 1st Penny Black were available with personal photographs on the labels from Royal Mail Edinburgh, sold for £10·20 (ten) or £18·65 (20).
    Miniature sheets as No. **MS**3710 with a special inscription were available only at Europhilex 2015 (Price £30).
    See also Nos. 3806/9.

2850 Poppies (Howard Hodgkin)   **2851** All the Hills and Vales Along (Charles Hamilton Sorley)

2852 Rifleman Kulbir Thapa   **2853** The Kensingtons at Laventie (Eric Kennington)

2854 'A British Soldier visits his Comrade's Grave on the Cliffs near Cape Helles', Gallipoli (posed photo by Ernest Brooks)

2855 London Irish Rifles' Football from Loos

(Des hat-trick design. Litho ISP Cartor)

2015 (14 May). *Centenary of the First World War* (2nd issue). MULTI COLOUR Two phosphor bands. Perf 14½.

3711	**2850**	(1st) *Poppies*........................	1·00	1·00
		a. Booklet pane. Nos. 3711/13 with margins all round	3·00	
3712	**2851**	(1st) All the Hills and Vales Alon	1·00	1·00
3713	**2852**	(1st) Rifleman Kulbir Thapa......................	1·00	1·00
3714	**2853**	£1·52 *The Kensingtons at Laventie*............	2·40	2·40
		a. Booklet pane. Nos. 3714/16 with margins all round	7·25	
3715	**2854**	£1·52 'A British Soldier visits his Comrade's Grave on the Cliffs near Cape Helles', Gallipoli	2·40	2·40
3716	**2855**	£1·52 London Irish Rifles' Football from Loos	2·40	2·40
Set of 6..			9·00	9·00
Set of 6 Gutter Pairs..................................			18·00	
First Day Cover (Tallents House).................				12·00
First Day Cover (Winchester)......................				12·00
Presentation Pack (PO Pack No. 511)........			10·75	
PHQ Cards (set of 6) (401)..........................			3·00	11·50

Nos. 3711*a* and 3714*a* were only issued in £13·96 premium booklets, No DY13.

(Des Hat-trick Design. Litho ISP Cartor)

2015 (14 May)–**2016**. *Centenary of the First World War*. Premium Booklet stamp. As No. 3414 but ordinary gum. MULTI COLOUR Two phosphor bands. Perf 14½×14 (with one elliptical hole in each vertical side).

3717	**2588**	(1st) Six Poppies on Barbed Wire Stems	1·50	1·50
		a. Booklet pane. Nos. 3717×4, EN51, NI95, S158 and W148 with margins all round (21·6.16).............	21·00	
First Day Cover (3717a) (Tallents House).......				7·50
First Day Cover (3717a) (Lyness, Stromness)				7·50

No. 3717 comes from pane No. U3070c in the £13·96 premium booklet, No. DY13, and pane No. 3717*a* from the £16·49 premium booklet, No. DY18.

MAGNA CARTA, 1215 ~ FOUNDATION OF LIBERTY

2856 Magna Carta, 1215

MAGNA CARTA, 1215 ~ FOUNDATION OF LIBERTY

2857 Simon de Montfort's Parliament, 1265

MAGNA CARTA, 1215 ~ FOUNDATION OF LIBERTY

2858 Bill of Rights, 1689

MAGNA CARTA, 1215 ~ FOUNDATION OF LIBERTY

2859 American Bill of Rights, 1791

MAGNA CARTA, 1215 ~ FOUNDATION OF LIBERTY

2860 Universal Declaration of Human Rights, 1948

MAGNA CARTA, 1215 ~ FOUNDATION OF LIBERTY

2861 Charter of the Commonwealth, 2013

(Des Howard Brown. Litho ISP Cartor)

2015 (2 June). *800th Anniversary of the Magna Carta*. MULTI COLOUR Two phosphor bands. Perf 14½.

3718	**2856**	(1st) Magna Carta	1·00	1·00
3719	**2857**	(1st) Simon de Montfort's Parliament	1·00	1·00
3720	**2858**	£1·33 Bill of Rights.........................	1·60	1·60
3721	**2859**	£1·33 American Bill of Rights......................	1·60	1·60
3722	**2860**	£1·52 Universal Declaration of Human Rights........................	3·00	3·00
3723	**2861**	£1·52 Charter of the Commonwealth........	3·00	3·00
Set of 6..			10·00	10·00
Set of 6 Gutter Pairs..................................			20·00	
First Day Cover (Tallents House).................				11·75
First Day Cover (London NW1)...................				11·75
Presentation Pack (PO Pack No. 512)........			13·00	
PHQ Cards (set of 6) (402)..........................			3·00	12·50

2862 The Defence of Hougoumont

2863 The Scots Greys during the Charge of the Union Brigade

2864 The French Cavalry's Assault on Allied Defensive Squares

2865 The Defence of La Haye Sainte by the King's German Legion

2866 The Capture of Plancenoit by the Prussians

2867 The French Imperial Guard's Final Assault

2870 92nd Gordon Highlanders, Anglo-Allied Army

2871 Grenadiers, Imperial Guard, French Army

2872 Soldiers and Battle of Waterloo Map

(Des Chris Collingwood (illustrations) and Webb and Webb Design Ltd. Litho ISP Cartor)

2015 (18 June). *Bicentenary of the Battle of Waterloo* (2nd issue). MULTI COLOUR Two phosphor bands. Perf 14.

3730	**2868**	(1st) 15th Infantry Regiment, IV Corps ...	1·50	1·50
		a. Booklet pane. Nos. 3730/3 with margins all round and roulettes at left	6·00	
3731	**2869**	(1st) Light Infantry, King's German Legion	1·50	1·50
3732	**2870**	£1·33 92nd Gordon Highlanders	1·50	1·75
3733	**2871**	£1·33 Grenadiers, Imperial Guard..............	1·50	1·75
MS3734	156×74 mm.	**2872** Soldiers and Battle of Waterloo Map Nos. 3730/3	5·50	5·75
First Day Cover (Tallents House)				7·50
First Day Cover (Waterloo, Liverpool)				7·50

Nos. 3730/3 come from £14·47 premium booklets, No. DY14, and **MS**3734.

2873 Battle of Britain

(Des Supple Studio (stamps) and The Team (miniature sheet). Litho ISP Cartor)

2015 (16 July). *75th Anniversary of the Battle of Britain.* MULTI COLOUR 'All-over' phosphor. Perf 14.

MS3735	190×74 mm. **2873** (1st) Pilots scramble to their Hurricanes; (1st) Supermarine Spitfires of 610 Squadron, Biggin Hill, on patrol; (1st) Armourer Fred Roberts replaces ammunition boxes on Supermarine Spitfire; £1·33 Spotters of the Auxiliary Territorial Service looking for enemy aircraft; £1·33 Operations Room at Bentley Priory; £1·33 Pilots of 32 Squadron await orders, RAF Hawkinge, Kent	8·25	8·25
First Day Cover (Tallents House)		11·00
First Day Cover (London NW9)...................................		11·00
Presentation Pack (PO Pack No. 514)........................	10·00	
PHQ Cards (set of 7) (404)......................................	80	13·50

The seven PHQ cards show the six individual stamps and the complete miniature sheet.

2868 15th Infantry Regiment, IV Corps, Prussian Army

2869 Light Infantry, King's German Legion, Anglo-Allied Army

(Des Silk Pearce. Litho ISP Cartor)

2015 (18 June). *Bicentenary of the Battle of Waterloo* (1st issue). MULTI COLOUR Two phosphor bands. Perf 14½.

3724	**2862**	(1st) The Defence of Hougoumont	1·00	1·00
		a. Booklet pane. Nos. 3724 and 3729 with margins all round	3·75	
3725	**2863**	(1st) The Scots Greys during the charge of the Union Brigade	1·00	1·00
		a. Booklet pane. Nos. 3725/8 with margins all round	6·25	
3726	**2864**	£1 The French Cavalry's assault on Allied defensive Squares....................	1·40	1·40
3727	**2865**	£1 The Defence of La Haye Sainte by the King's German Legion................	1·40	1·40
3728	**2866**	£1·52 The Capture of Plancenoit by the Prussians.......................................	2·40	2·40
3729	**2867**	£1·52 The French Imperial Guard's Final Assault..	2·40	2·40
Set of 6			8·50	8·00
Set of 6 Gutter Pairs			17·00	
First Day Cover (Tallents House).............................				11·75
First Day Cover (Waterloo, Liverpool)				11·75
Presentation Pack (PO Pack No. 513)			17·00	
(Nos. 3724/9 and **MS**3734)................................				
PHQ Cards (set of 11) (403)...................................			5·50	22·00

Nos. 3724*a* and 3725*a* were only issued in the £14·47 premium booklets, No. DY14

The eleven PHQ cards depict the individual stamps, including those from **MS**3734, and the complete miniature sheet.

2874 Scabious Bee (*Andrena hattorfiana*) on Field Scabious (*Knautia arvensis*)

2875 Great Yellow Bumblebee (*Bombus distinguendus*) on Bird's-foot Trefoil (*Lotus corniculatus*)

2876 Northern Colletes Bee (*Colletes floralis*) on Wild Carrot (*Daucus carota*)

2877 Bilberry Bumblebee (*Bombus monticola*) on Bilberry (*Vaccinium myrtillus*)

2878 Large Mason Bee (*Osmia xanthomelana*) on Horseshoe Vetch (*Hippocrepis comosa*)

2879 Potter Flower Bee (*Anthophora retusa*) on Ground Ivy (*Glechoma hederacea*)

2880 The Honeybee

(Des Richard Lewington (illustration) and Anna Ekelund (3736/41) or Andy English (illustration) and Interabang (MS3742). Litho ISP Cartor (3736/42) or gravure ISP Walsall (3743))

2015 (18 Aug). *Bees.* MULTI COLOUR

*(a) Ordinary gum. One centre band (3736), two phosphor bands (3737/41) or phosphor background (**MS**3742). Perf 14×14½.*

3736	**2874**	(2nd)	Scabious Bee on Field Scabious........	90	90
3737	**2875**	(1st)	Great Yellow Bumblebee on Bird's-foot Trefoil....................................	1·00	1·00
3738	**2876**	£1	Northern Colletes Bee on Wild Carrot..	1·50	1·50
3739	**2877**	£1·33	Bilberry Bumblebee on Bilberry........	1·80	1·80
3740	**2878**	£1·52	Large Mason Bee on Horseshoe Vetch..	2·25	2·25
3741	**2879**	£2·25	Potter Flower Bee on Ground Ivy......	3·75	3·75

Set of 6.. 10·00 10·00
Set of 6 Gutter Pairs... 20·00
First Day Cover (Tallents House)... 13·50
First Day Cover (St Bees).. 13·50
Presentation Pack (PO Pack No. 515)............. 19·00
(Nos. 3736/41 and **MS**3743)
PHQ Cards (set of 7) (405)......................... 3·50 18·00
MS3742 191×74 mm. **2880** (1st) Waggle dance; (1st) 5·50 5·75
Pollination; £1·33 Making honey; £1·33 Tending young
First Day Cover (Tallents House)... 6·00
First Day Cover (St Bees).. 6·00

(b) Self-adhesive. Two phosphor bands. Die-cut perf 14×14½.

3743	**2875**	(1st)	Great Yellow Bumblebee (*Bombus distinguendus*) on Bird's-foot Trefoil (*Lotus corniculatus*)....................	1·50	1·50

a. Booklet pane. Nos. 3743×2 and U3022×4 .... 5·75
No. 3743 was issued in stamp booklets, No. PM48, originally sold for £3·78.

The seven PHQ cards depict the six individual stamps and the complete miniature sheet.

2881 'Long to Reign Over Us'

(Des Sedley Place. Recess and gravure FNMT (Spain))

2015 (9 Sept) *Long to Reign Over Us* (2nd issue). MULTI COLOUR Two phosphor bands. Perf 14½×14 (with one elliptical hole in each vertical side) (Machin) or 14 (others).
MS3747 194×75 mm. **2881** 'Long to Reign Over Us' (1st) William Wyon's City Medal depicting Queen Victoria; (1st) Portrait of Queen Elizabeth II from photo by Dorothy Wilding; As No. U3747 (but printed gravure); £1·52 Badge of the House of Windsor depicting Round Tower of Windsor Castle; £1·52 Device from The Queen's Personal Flag .... 8·00 8·00
First Day Cover (Tallents House) .... 10·25
First Day Cover (Windsor) .... 10·25
Presentation Pack (PO Pack No. 516)................... 10·00
PHQ Cards (set of 6) (406).. 70 12·00
Stamps from **MS**3747 all have an iridescent overprint reading 'LONG TO REIGN OVER US'.
The 1st class bright lilac stamp from **MS**3747 has a source code 'REIGM' and date code 'O15R' within this iridescent overprint.
The PHQ cards depict the five individual stamps and the complete miniature sheet.

2882 Tackle

2883 Scrum

2884 Try

2885 Conversion

2886 Pass

2887 Drop Goal

2888 Ruck

2889 Line-Out

(Des Hat-trick design and Geoff Appleton (illustrations). Litho ISP Cartor (3748/55) or gravure ISP Walsall (3756/7))

2015 (18 Sept). *Rugby World Cup.* MULTI COLOUR One centre band (3748/9) or two bands (others)

(a) Ordinary gum. Perf 14.

3748	**2882**	(2nd)	Tackle..	90	90
			a. Horiz pair. Nos. 3748/9......................	1·80	1·80
3749	**2883**	(2nd)	Scrum..	90	90
3750	**2884**	(1st)	Try..	1·00	1·00

		a. Horiz pair. Nos. 3750/1	2·00	2·00
3751	2885	(1st) Conversion...	1·00	1·00
3752	2886	£1 Pass..	1·50	1·50
		a. Horiz pair. Nos. 3752/3	3·00	3·00
3753	2887	£1 Drop Goal..	1·50	1·50
3754	2888	£1·52 Ruck..	2·00	2·00
		a. Horiz pair. Nos. 3754/5	4·00	4·00
3755	2889	£1·52 Line-Out...	2·00	2·00

Set of 8... 9·75   9·75
Set of 4 Gutter Blocks of 4 .... 19·00
First Day Cover (Tallents House)... 12·50
First Day Cover (Rugby).. 12·50
Presentation Pack (PO Pack No. 517)............................ 12·50
PHQ Cards (set of 8) (407)... 4·00 13·00

(b) Self-adhesive. Die-cut perf 14.

3756	2884	(1st) Try	2·00	2·00
		a. Booklet pane. Nos. 3756/7 and		
		U3746×4	6·50	
3757	2885	(1st) Conversion...	2·00	2·00

Nos. 3748/9, 3750/1, 3752/3 and 3754/5 were each printed together, *se-tenant*, as horizontal pairs in sheets of 60 (2 panes 6×5).

Nos. 3756/7 were issued in stamp booklets, No. PM49, originally sold for £3·78.

2890 Darth Vader

2891 Yoda

2892 Obi-Wan Kenobi

2893 Stormtrooper

2894 Han Solo

2895 Rey

2896 Princess Leia

2897 The Emperor

2898 Luke Skywalker

2899 Boba Fett

2900 Finn

2901 Kylo Ren

2902 Star Wars

(Des Malcolm Tween (illustrations) and Interabang (3758/69) or GBH (**MS**3770). Litho ISP Cartor)

2015 (20 Oct-17 Dec). *Star Wars* (1st issue). Two phosphor bands and fluorescent emblems (3758/69) or 'All-over' phosphor (**MS**3770).

(a) Ordinary gum. Perf 14½.

3758	2890	(1st) Darth Vader..	1·00	1·00
		a. Horiz strip of 6. Nos. 3758/63..........	5·50	5·50
		b. Booklet pane. Nos. 3758, 3760,		
		3763 and 3767/9 with margins all		
		round (17 Dec)..	6·50	
3759	2891	(1st) Yoda...	1·00	1·00
		b. Booklet pane. Nos. 3759, 3761/2		
		and 3764/6 with margins all round		
		(17 Dec)	6·50	
3760	2892	(1st) Obi-Wan Kenobi.......................................	1·00	1·00
3761	2893	(1st) Stormtrooper..	1·00	1·00
3762	2894	(1st) Han Solo...	1·00	1·00
3763	2895	(1st) Rey..	1·00	1·00
3764	2896	(1st) Princess Leia..	1·00	1·00
		a. Horiz strip of 6. Nos. 3764/9...........	5·50	5·50
3765	2897	(1st) The Emperor...	1·00	1·00
3766	2898	(1st) Luke Skywalker..	1·00	1·00
3767	2899	(1st) Boba Fett..	1·00	1·00
3768	2900	(1st) Finn...	1·00	1·00
3769	2901	(1st) Kylo Ren...	1·00	1·00

Set of 12.. 11·00 11·00
Set of 2 Gutter Strips of 12... 22·00
First Day Cover (Tallents House)... 14·00
First Day Cover (Elstree, Borehamwood) .... 14·00
Presentation Pack (PO Pack No. 518)
(Nos. 3758/69 and **MS**3770).................................... 19·00
PHQ Cards (set of 19) (408).. 9·50 28·00

(b) Self-adhesive.

MS3770 204×75 mm. **2902** (1st) X-wing Starfighter (60×21 mm, perf 14½×14); (1st) TIE fighters (35×36 mm, perf 14); (1st) X-wing Starfighters (60×21 mm, perf 14½×14); (1st) AT-AT Walkers (41×30 mm, Perf 14); (1st) TIE fighters (27×37 mm, perf 14); (1st) Millennium Falcon (60×30 mm, perf 14½)................................ 6·50   6·50
First Day Cover (Tallents House)... 7·00
First Day Cover (Elstree, Borehamwood) .... 7·00

Nos. 3758/63 and 3764/9 were each printed together, *se-tenant*, as horizontal strips of six stamps in sheets of 60 (2 panes 6×5).

Nos. 3758/69 all show fluorescent emblems under UV light. Nos. 3758, 3761 and 3765 show the symbol of the Galactic Empire, Nos. 3759/60 show the Jedi Order symbol, 3762, 3764 and 3766 show the Rebel Alliance symbol, Nos. 3763 and 3768/9 show the logo for the new film *Star Wars The Force Awakens* and No. 3767 shows the Mandalorian Crest.

Nos 3758*b* and 3759*b* were only issued in £16·99 premium booklets, No. DY15.

The 19 PHQ cards depict the individual stamps including those from **MS**3770 and the complete miniature sheet.

Designs as Nos. 3758/9 and 3761/2 but self-adhesive were issued in sheets of ten with *se-tenant* labels showing film stills (No. LS96), each sheet containing Nos. 3758/9, each ×3, and Nos. 3761/2, each×2. These sheets were originally sold for £6·80 each.

The four designs were also available from Royal Mail, Edinburgh in separate sheets of ten with personal photographs on the labels, originally sold for £10·20 per sheet.

2903 The Journey to Bethlehem

2904 The Nativity

2905 The Journey to Bethlehem

2906 The Nativity

2907 The Animals of the Nativity

2908 The Shepherds

2909 The Three Wise Men

2910 The Annunciation

(Des David Holmes (illustrations) and Studio David Hillman. Gravure ISP Walsall (3771a, 3772a) or De La Rue (others))

2015 (3 Nov). *Christmas.* |MULTI COLOUR One centre band (3771) or two bands (others). Perf 14½×15.

(a) Self-adhesive.

3771	**2903**	(2nd) The Journey to Bethlehem	90	90
		a. Booklet pane. No. 3771×12	9·75	
3772	**2904**	(1st) The Nativity	1·00	1·00
		a. Booklet pane. No. 3772×12	10·75	
3773	**2905**	(2nd Large) The Journey to Bethlehem	1·10	1·10
3774	**2906**	(1st Large) The Nativity	1·40	1·40
3775	**2907**	£1·00 The Animals of the Nativity	1·80	1·80
3776	**2908**	£1·33 The Shepherds	2·10	2·10
3777	**2909**	£1·52 The Three Wise Men	2·50	2·50
3778	**2910**	£2·25 The Annunciation	3·50	3·50
Set of 8			12·75	12·75
First Day Cover (Tallents House)				16·75
First Day Cover (Bethlehem, Llandeilo)				16·75
Presentation Pack (PO Pack No. 519)			15·00	
PHQ Cards (set of 9) (409)			4·50	26·00

(b) Ordinary gum.

MS3779 190×74 mm. As Nos. 3771/8		12·75	12·75
First Day Cover (Tallents House)			16·75
First Day Cover (Bethlehem, Llandeilo)			16·75

The nine PHQ cards show the eight individual stamps and the complete miniature sheet.

The 2nd class, 1st class, £1, £1·33, £1·52 and £2·25 stamps were also issued in sheets of 20 (No. LS97) containing eight 2nd class, eight 1st class and one each of £1, £1·33, £1·52 and £2·25 stamps, each stamp accompanied by a *se-tenant* label with a verse from the King James Bible. These sheets were printed in lithography by ISP Cartor and originally sold for £15·96.

The design of the 1st class stamps in the Post office Label Sheet is enlarged compared with those from counter sheets and booklets, resulting in a much diminished grey foreground at lower left.

Year Pack
2015 (3 Nov). Comprises Nos. 3658/67, **MS**3678/706, **MS**3710/16, 3718/29. **MS**3734, **MS**3735/42, **MS**3747/55 and 3758/78
CP3779a Year Pack ....150·00

Post Office Yearbook
2015 (3 Nov). Comprises Nos. 3658/67, **MS**3678/706, **MS**3710/29, **MS**3734, **MS**3735/42, **MS**3747/55 and 3758/78
YB3779a Yearbook ....180·00

Miniature Sheet Collection
2015 (3 Nov).Comprises Nos. **MS**3678, **MS**3710, **MS**3734, **MS**3735, **MS**3742, **MS**3747, **MS**3770 and **MS**3779
MS3779a Miniature Sheet Collection.....................................56·00

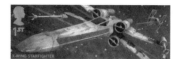

2911 X-wing Starfighter

2912 AT-AT Walkers

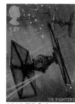 

2913 TIE fighters   **2914** TIE fighters

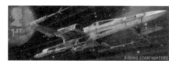

2915 X-wing Starfighters

2916 *Millennium Falcon*

(Des GBH. Litho ISP Cartor)

2015 (17 Dec). *Star Wars* (2nd issue). Self-adhesive. |MULTI COLOUR 'All-over' phosphor. Die-cut perf 14½×14 (3780, 3784), 14 (3781/3 or 14½ (3785).

3780	**2911**	(1st) X-wing Starfighter	1·00	1·00
		a. Booklet pane. Nos. 3780/2	3·25	
3781	**2912**	(1st) AT-AT Walkers	1·00	1·00
3782	**2913**	(1st) TIE fighters	1·00	1·00
3783	**2914**	(1st) TIE fighters	1·00	1·00
		a. Booklet pane. Nos. 3783/5	3·25	
3784	**2915**	(1st) X-wing Starfighters	1·00	1·00
3785	**2916**	(1st) *Millennium Falcon*	1·00	1·00
Set of 6			6·50	6·50

Nos. 3780/5 were only issued in £16·99 Star Wars booklets, No. DY15, or **MS**3770.

2917 Union Flag

(Litho ISP Cartor)

2015 (17 Dec). *Star Wars* (3rd issue). As No. 2570 but ordinary gum. |MULTI COLOUR| Two phosphor bands. Perf 14½×14 (with one elliptical hole in each vert side).

3786 **2917**   (1st) Union Flag.. 1·50 1·50

No. 3786 comes from booklet pane No. U3095*a* from £16·99 Star Wars booklet, No. DY15.

2918 Entering the Antarctic Ice, December 1914

2919 *Endurance* Frozen in Pack Ice, January 1915

2920 Striving to Free *Endurance*, February 1915

2921 Trapped in a Pressure Crack, October 1915

2922 Patience Camp, December 1915 – April 1916

2923 Safe Arrival at Elephant Island, April 1916

2924 Setting out for South Georgia, April 1916

2925 Rescue of *Endurance* Crew, August 1916

(Des Robert Maude and Sarah Davies. Litho ISP Cartor)

2016 (7 Jan). *Shackleton and the Endurance Expedition.* |MULTI COLOUR| Two phosphor bands. Perf 14×14½.

3787	**2918**	(1st) Entering the Antarctic Ice....................	1·00	1·00
		a. Horiz pair. Nos. 3787/8..........................	2·00	2·00
3788	**2919**	(1st) *Endurance* Frozen in Pack Ice.............	1·00	1·00
3789	**2920**	£1 Striving to Free *Endurance*	1·50	1·50
		a. Horiz pair. Nos. 3789/90........................	3·00	3·00
3790	**2921**	£1 Trapped in a Pressure Crack................	1·50	1·50
3791	**2922**	£1·33 Patience Camp..................................	1·80	1·80
		a. Horiz pair. Nos. 3791/2..........................	3·75	3·75
3792	**2923**	£1·33 Safe Arrival at Elephant Island	1·80	1·80
3793	**2924**	£1·52 Setting out for South Georgia.............	2·25	2·25
		a. Horiz pair. Nos. 3793/4..........................	4·50	4·50
3794	**2925**	£1·52 Rescue of *Endurance* Crew	2·25	2·25
Set of 8..			12·00	12·00
Set of 4 Gutter blocks of 4..			24·00	
First Day Cover (Tallents House)				16·00
First Day Cover (Plymouth)				16·00
Presentation Pack (PO Pack No. 521)................			15·00	
PHQ Cards (set of 8) (410)			4·00	15·00

Nos. 3787/8, 3789/90, 3791/2 and 3793/4 were each printed together, *se-tenant*, as horizontal pairs in sheets of 60 (2 panes 6×5).

2926 Sir Brian Tuke, Master of the Posts

2927 *Mail Packet off Eastbourne* (Capt Victor Howes)

2928 Penfold Pillar Box

2929 River Post

2930 Mail Coach

2931 Medway Mail Centre

2932 Classic GPO Posters

(Des Atelier Works (3795/800) or Purpose (**MS**3801). Litho ISP Cartor)

2016 (17-18 Feb). *Royal Mail 500* (1st issue). |MULTI COLOUR| Two phosphor bands. Perf 14½×14 (3795/800) or 14 (**MS**3801)

3795	**2926**	(1st) Sir Brian Tuke..	1·00	1·00
		a. Booklet pane. Nos. 3795 and 3797/8 with margins all round (18.2)	6·00	
3796	**2927**	(1st) *Mail Packet off Eastbourne*	1·00	1·00
		a. Booklet pane. Nos. 3796 and 3799/800 with margins all round (18.2)..	6·00	
3797	**2928**	(1st) Penfold Pillar Box.................................	1·00	1·00
3798	**2929**	£1·52 River Post..	2·50	2·50
3799	**2930**	£1·52 Mail Coach...	2·50	2·50
3800	**2931**	£1·52 Medway Mail Centre	2·50	2·50
Set of 6..			9·50	9·50
Set of 6 Gutter Pairs..			19·00	
Set of 6 Traffic light Gutter pairs (two stamps only in each pair)			20·00	
First Day Cover (Tallents House)				12·00
First Day Cover (London WC1)				12·00
Presentation Pack (PO Pack No. 522)				
(Nos. 3795/800 and **MS**3801)..............................			14·75	
PHQ Cards (set of 11) (411)......................			5·50	24·00

MS3801 125×89 mm. **2932** Classic GPO Posters (1st) 'QUICKEST WAY BY AIR MAIL' (Edward McKnight Kauffer, 1935); (1st) 'ADDRESS your letters PLAINLY' (Hans Schleger, 1942); £1·33 'pack your parcels carefully' (Hans Unger, 1950); £1·33 'STAMPS IN BOOKS SAVE TIME' (Harry Stevens, 1960)... 7·00 7·25

First Day Cover (Tallents House)		7·25
First Day Cover (London WC1).................................		7·25

Nos. 3795/**MS**3801 commemorate 500 years of a regular, organised postal service.

Nos. 3795*a* and 3796*a* come from £16·36 500 Years of Royal mail premium booklet No. DY16.

MS3801 additionally inscribed 'Spring Stampex, 17-20 February 2016' was only available at that exhibition (*Price £22*).

The complete miniature sheet is shown on one of the eleven PHQ cards with the others depicting individual stamps including those from the miniature sheet.

2933 'QUICKEST WAY BY AIR MAIL' (*Edward McKnight Kauffer, 1935*)

2934 'ADDRESS your letters PLAINLY' (*Hans Schleger, 1942*)

2935 'STAMPS IN BOOKS SAVE TIME' (*Harry Stevens, 1960*)

2936 'pack your parcels carefully' (*Hans Unger, 1950*)

(Litho ISP Cartor)

2016 (17-18 Feb). *Royal Mail 500* (2nd issue). |MULTI COLOUR Perf 14.

3802	**2933**	(1st) 'QUICKEST WAY BY AIR MAIL'.............	1·75	1·75
		a. Booklet pane. Nos. 3802/5 with margins all round and roulettes at left (*18 Feb*)	6·25	
3803	**2934**	(1st) 'ADDRESS your letters PLAINLY'........	1·75	1·75
3804	**2935**	£1·33 'STAMPS IN BOOKS SAVE TIME'.........	1·75	1·75
3805	**2936**	£1·33 'pack your parcels carefully'...............	1·75	1·75
Set of 4...			6·25	6·50

Nos. 3802/5 come from No. MS3801 and £16·36 premium booklets, No. DY16.

2937 Penny Red

2938 Two Pence Blue

(Gravure ISP Walsall)

2016 (18 Feb). *175th Anniversary of the Penny Red.* Self-adhesive. |MULTI COLOUR Two phosphor bands. Die-cut perf 14½×14 (with one elliptical hole in each vert side).

| 3806 | 2937 | (1st) Penny Red... | 1·50 | 1·50 |

No. 3806 comes from booklets of six, No. MB16.

No. 3806 was also issued in sheets of 20 with attached labels showing the 'Rainbow Trials' from which the Penny Red evolved (No. LS99). These sheets were printed in lithography by ISP Cartor and originally sold for £13·10 each.

Sheets of ten or 20 of these Penny Red stamps were available from Royal Mail with personal photographs on the labels for £10·20 (ten) or £18·65 (20).

(Des Atelier Works. Litho ISP Cartor)

2016 (18 Feb). *Royal Mail 500* (3rd issue). |MULTI COLOUR Two phosphor bands. 14½×14 (with one elliptical hole in each vert side).

3807	**2848**	(1st) Penny Black...	1.75	1.75
		a. Booklet pane. No. 3807x2 and Nos. 3808/9 eachx3 with central label and margins all round...........	11.00	
3808	**2937**	(1st) Penny Red...	1.50	1.50
3809	**2938**	(1st) Two Pence Blue	1.50	1.50

Nos. 3807/9 come from £16·36 500 Years of Royal Mail premium booklets, No. DY16.

2939 Nicholas Winton (1909-2015)

2940 Sue Ryder (1924-2000)

2941 John Boyd Orr (1880-1971)

2942 Eglantyne Jebb (1876-1928)

2943 Joseph Rowntree (1836-1925)

2944 Josephine Butler (1828-1906)

(Des Hat-trick Design. Litho ISP Cartor)

2016 (15 Mar). *British Humanitarians.* |MULTI COLOUR Two phosphor bands. Perf 14½.

3810	**2939**	(1st) Nicholas Winton.......................................	1·00	1·00
		a. Horiz strip of 3. Nos. 3810/12...............	3·00	3·00
3811	**2940**	(1st) Sue Ryder..	1·00	1·00
3812	**2941**	(1st) John Boyd Orr...	1·00	1·00
3813	**2942**	£1·33 Eglantyne Jebb......................................	2·00	2·00
		a. Horiz strip of 3. Nos. 3813/15...............	6·00	6·00
3814	**2943**	£1·33 Joseph Rowntree....................................	2·00	2·00
3815	**2944**	£1·33 Josephine Butler.....................................	2·00	2·00
Set of 6...			8·50	8·50
Set of 2 Gutter Strips of 6..			17·00	
First Day Cover (Tallents House).......................................				11·00
First Day Cover (Winton, Northallerton)............................				11·00
Presentation Pack (PO Pack No. 523)...............................			10·00	
PHQ Cards (set of 6) (412)...			3·00	11·00

Nos. 3810/12 and 3813/15 were each printed together, *se-tenant*, as horizontal strips of three stamps in sheets of 60 (2 panes 6×5).

2945 'to thine own self be true' (*Hamlet*)

2946 'cowards die many times before their deaths. The valiant never taste of death but once.' (*Julius Caesar*)

2947 'Love is a smoke made with the fume of sighs' (*Romeo and Juliet*)

2948 'The fool doth think he is wise, but the wise man knows himself to be a fool.' (*As You Like It*)

2949 'There was a star danced, and under that was I born.' (*Much Ado About Nothing*)

2950 'But if the while I think on thee, dear friend, all losses are restored and sorrows end.' (*Sonnet 30*)

2951 'LOVE comforteth like sunshine after rain' (*Venus and Adonis*)

2952 'We are such stuff as dreams are made on; and our little life is rounded with a sleep.' (*The Tempest*)

2953 'Life's but a walking shadow, a poor player That struts and frets his hour upon the stage' (*Macbeth*)

2954 'I wasted time, and now doth time waste me' (*Richard II*)

(Des The Chase. Litho ISP Cartor)

2016 (5 Apr). *400th Death Anniversary of William Shakespeare.* MULTICOLOUR Two phosphor bands. Perf 14½.

3816	**2945**	(1st) 'to thine own self be true'	1·00	1·00
		a. Horiz strip of 5. Nos. 3816/20	4·50	4·50
3817	**2946**	(1st) 'cowards die many times before their deaths. The valiant never taste of death but once.'	1·00	1·00
3818	**2947**	(1st) 'Love is a smoke made with the fume of sighs'	1·00	1·00
3819	**2948**	(1st) 'The fool doth think he is wise, but the wise man knows himself to be a fool.'	1·00	1·00
3820	**2949**	(1st) 'There was a star danced, and under that was I born'	1·00	1·00
3821	**2950**	(1st) 'But if the while I think on thee, dear friend, all losses are restored and sorrows end.'	1·00	1·00
		b. Horiz strip of 5. Nos. 3821/5	4·50	4·50
3822	**2951**	(1st) 'LOVE comforteth like sunshine after rain'	1·00	1·00
3823	**2952**	(1st) 'We are such stuff as dreams are made on; and our little life is rounded with a sleep.'	1·00	1·00
3824	**2953**	(1st) 'Life's but a walking shadow, a poor player That struts and frets his hour upon the stage'	1·00	1·00
3825	**2954**	(1st) 'I wasted time, and now doth time waste me' (*Richard II*)	1·00	1·00
3816/25 *Set of 10*			9·00	9·00
Set of 2 Gutter Strips of 10			18·00	
First Day Cover (Tallents House)				12·00
First Day Cover (Stratford-upon-Avon)				12·00
Presentation Pack (PO Pack No. 524)			11·00	
PHQ Cards (set of 10) (413)			5·00	12·00

Nos. 3816/20 and 3821/5 were each printed together, *se-tenant*, as horizontal strips of five stamps in sheets of 50 (2 panes 5×5).

2955 Princess Elizabeth and her Father the Duke of York (later King George VI), c. 1930

2956 Queen Elizabeth II at State Opening of Parliament, 2012

2957 Queen Elizabeth II with Prince Charles and Princess Anne, 1952

2958 Queen Elizabeth II on Visit to New Zealand, 1977

2959 Queen Elizabeth II and Duke of Edinburgh, 1957

2960 Queen Elizabeth II with Nelson Mandela, 1996

2961 Prince Charles, Queen Elizabeth II, Prince George and Prince William

2962 Prince Charles

2963 Queen Elizabeth II

2964 Prince George

2965 Prince William

(Des Kate Stephens (3826/31). Litho ISP Cartor (3826/MS3832) or Gravure ISP Walsall (3833/6))

2016 (21 Apr-9 June). *90th Birthday of Queen Elizabeth II.* MULTICOLOUR Two phosphor bands (3826/31) or 'all-over' phosphor (MS3832/b, 3833/6).

(a) Ordinary gum. Perf 14×14½ (3826/31) or 14 (MS3832).

3826	2955	(1st) Princess Elizabeth and her Father the Duke of York..............	1·00	1·00
		a. Horiz strip of 3. Nos. 3826/8..........	3·00	3·00
		b. Booklet pane. Nos. 3826/8 and 3831 with margins all round..........	5·50	
3827	2956	(1st) Queen Elizabeth II at State Opening of Parliament.........	1·00	1·00
3828	2957	(1st) Queen Elizabeth II with Prince Charles and Princess Anne.............	1·00	1·00
3829	2958	£1·52 Queen Elizabeth II on Visit to New Zealand	2·25	2·25
		a. Horiz strip of 3. Nos. 3829/31..........	6·75	6·75
		b. Booklet pane. Nos. 3829/30 with margins all round	4·25	
3830	2959	£1·52 Queen Elizabeth II and Duke of Edinburgh	2·25	2·25
3831	2960	£1·52 Queen Elizabeth II with Nelson Mandela	2·25	2·25
Set of 6..........................			8·75	8·75
Set of 2 Gutter Strips of 6.............			17·50	
First Day Cover (Tallents House)				11·50
First Day Cover (Windsor)......................				11·50
Presentation Pack (PO Pack No. 525)				
(Nos. 3826/31 and **MS**3832)			14·00	
PHQ Cards (set of 11) (414)...............			5·50	19·00

MS3832 189×75 mm. **2961** Prince Charles, Queen Elizabeth II, Prince George and Prince William (1st) multicoloured; (1st) multicoloured; (1st) multicoloured; (1st) multicoloured..................... 3·75 3·75

b Booklet pane. No. **MS**3832 but 150×95 mm with roulettes at left 3·75

First Day Cover (Tallents House) .... 4·75
First Day Cover (Windsor)...................... 4·75

(b) Self-adhesive. Die-cut perf 14.

3833	2962	(1st) Prince Charles	1·60	1·60
		a. Booklet pane. Nos. 3833/4 and U3746×4	5·75	
3834	2963	(1st) Queen Elizabeth II...............	1·60	1·60
3835	2964	(1st) Prince George (9.6)	1·60	1·60
		a. Booklet pane. Nos. 3835/6 and U3746×4	5·75	
3836	2965	(1st) Prince William (9.6)............	1·60	1·60
Set of 4.............................			6·00	6·00

Nos. 3826/8 and 3829/31 were each printed together, *se-tenant*, as horizontal strips of three stamps in sheets of 60 (2 panes 6×5)

Nos. 3826b, 3829b and **MS**3832b were issued in £15·11 90th Birthday of Queen Elizabeth II premium booklet, DY17.

Nos. 3833/6 were issued in stamp booklets, Nos. PM50/1, originally sold for £3·84 each.

2966 Animail

(Des Osborne Ross. Litho ISP Cartor)

2016 (17 May). *Animail*. Sheet 203×74 mm. |MULTI COLOUR| 'All-over' phosphor. Die-cut and die-cut perf 14.
MS3837 **2966** Animail (1st) Woodpecker; (1st) Snake; £1·05 Chimpanzee; £1·05 Bat; £1·33 Orangutan; £1·33 Koala......................... 8·50 8·75
First Day Cover (Tallents House) .... 11·25
First Day Cover (Playing Place, Truro) .... 11·25
Presentation Pack (PO Pack No. 526) 10·00
PHQ Cards (set of 7) (415)............... 3·50 15·00

The seven PHQ cards show the six individual stamps and the complete miniature sheet.

2967 *Battlefield Poppy* (Giles Revell)

2968 'Your battle wounds are scars upon my heart' (poem 'To My Brother', Vera Brittain)

2969 Munitions Worker Lottie Meade

2970 *Travoys Arriving with Wounded at a Dressing-Station at Smol, Macedonia, September 1916* (Stanley Spencer)

2971 Thiepval Memorial, Somme, France

2972 Captain A.C. Green's Battle of Jutland Commemorative Medal

(Des Hat-trick Design. Litho ISP Cartor)

2016 (21 June). *Centenary of the First World War* (3rd issue). |MULTI COLOUR| Two phosphor bands. Perf 14½.

3838	2967	(1st) *Battlefield Poppy*	1·00	1·00
		a. Booklet pane. Nos. 3838/40 with margins all round	3·00	
3839	2968	(1st) 'Your battle wounds are scars upon my heart'......................	1·00	1·00
3840	2969	(1st) Munitions Worker Lottie Meade ..	1·00	1·00
3841	2970	£1·52 *Travoys Arriving with Wounded at a Dressing-Station at Smol, Macedonia, September 1916*	2·50	2·50
		a. Booklet pane. Nos. 3841/3, with margins all round	7·50	
3842	2971	£1·52 Thiepval Memorial, Somme, France	2·50	2·50
3843	2972	£1·52 Captain A.C. Green's Battle of Jutland Commemorative Medal ..	2·50	2·50
Set of 6.............................			9·50	9·50
Set of 6 Gutter Pairs			19·00	
First Day Cover (Tallents House)				12·00
First Day Cover (Lyness, Stromness)............				12·00
Presentation Pack (PO Pack No. 527)				
(Nos. 3838/43 and **MS**3848)...............			17·50	
PHQ Cards (set of 11) (416)...............			5·50	26·00

Nos. 3838a and 3841a were issued in £16·49 premium booklets, No. DY18.

2973 The Post Office Rifles

2974 Writing a Letter from the Western Front

2975 Delivering the Mail on the Home Front

2976 Home Depot at Regent's Park, London

2977 The Post Office at War, 1914–18

(Des Hat-trick Design. Litho ISP Cartor)

2016 (21 June). *Centenary of the First World War* (3rd issue). MULTI COLOUR Perf 14.

3844	**2973**	(1st)	The Post Office Rifles.....................	1·60	1·60
		a.	Booklet pane. Nos. 3844/7 with margins all round		7·25
3845	**2974**	(1st)	Writing a Letter from the Western Front................................	1·60	1·60
3846	**2975**	£1·33	Delivering the Mail on the Home Front................................	2·40	2·40
3847	**2976**	£1·33	Home Depot at Regent's Park, London.............................	2·40	2·40
Set of 4..				7·25	7·25

MS3848   156×74 mm. **2977** The Post Office at War, 1914–18 Nos. 3844/7 .... 7·25 7·25
First Day Cover (Tallents House)................................ 8·50
First Day Cover (Lyness, Stromness) .... 8·25

Nos. 3844/7 were issued in £16·49 premium booklets, No. DY18, and in **MS**3848.

2978 *The Piper at the Gates of Dawn* (1967)

2979 *Atom Heart Mother* (1970)

2980 *The Dark Side of the Moon* (1973)

2981 *Animals* (1977)

2982 *Wish You Were Here* (1975)

2983 *The Endless River* (2014)

2984 Pink Floyd on Stage

(Gravure ISP Walsall (3849/54) or litho ISP Cartor (MS3855))

2016 (7 July). *Pink Floyd.* MULTI COLOUR

(a) Album Covers. Self-adhesive. Two phosphor bands. Die-cut perf 14½.

3849	**2978**	(1st)	The Piper at the Gates of Dawn (1967)	1·00	1·00
3850	**2979**	(1st)	Atom Heart Mother (1970)...............	1·00	1·00

3851	**2980**	(1st)	The Dark Side of the Moon (1973) ...	1·00	1·00
3852	**2981**	£1·52	Animals (1977).................................	2·50	2·50
3853	**2982**	£1·52	Wish You Were Here (1975).............	2·50	2·50
3854	**2983**	£1·52	The Endless River (2014)...................	2·50	2·50
Set of 6..				9·50	9·50

First Day Cover (Tallents House) .... 12·00
First Day Cover (Grantchester, Cambridge) .... 12·00
Presentation Pack (PO Pack No. 528)
(Nos. 3849/54 and **MS**3855) .... 18·00
PHQ Cards (set of 11) (417) .... 5·50 24·00

(b) Pink Floyd on Stage. Ordinary gum. Phosphor frame. Perf 14½.

MS3855 202×74 mm. **2984** Pink Floyd on Stage (1st) UFO Club, 1966; (1st) The Dark Side of the Moon Tour, 1973; £1·52 The Wall Tour, 1981; £1·52 The Division Bell Tour, 1994 .... 6·25 6·25
First Day Cover (Tallents House) .... 8·00
First Day Cover (Grantchester, Cambridge) .... 8·00

The right-hand edges of Nos. 3849/54 are all cut around to show the vinyl disc protruding from the open edge of the album cover.

A *Dark Side of the Moon* maxi sheet containing No. 3851×10 was sold at £12·95, a premium of £6·55 over face value.

The eleven PHQ cards depicts the individual stamps including those from **MS**3855 and the complete miniature sheet.

2985 Peter Rabbit

2986 Mrs. Tiggy-Winkle

2987 Squirrel Nutkin

2988 Jemima Puddle-Duck

2989 Tom Kitten

2990 Benjamin Bunny

(Des Charlie Smith Design. Litho ISP Cartor (3856/61) or gravure ISP Walsall (3862/3))

2016 (28 July). *150th Birth Anniversary of Beatrix Potter* (writer, illustrator and conservationist) (1st issue). MULTI COLOUR Two phosphor bands.

(a) Ordinary gum. Perf 14½×14.

3856	**2985**	(1st)	Peter Rabbit. Cobalt, greenish yellow, bright magenta, new blue and black	1·00	1·00
		a.	Horiz pair. Nos. 3856/7...........	2·00	2·00
		b.	Booklet pane. Nos. 3856, 3858 and 3861 with margins all round..		5·00
3857	**2986**	(1st)	Mrs. Tiggy-Winkle. Cobalt, greenish yellow, bright magenta, new blue and black	1·00	1·00
		b.	Booklet pane. Nos. 3857 and 3859/60 with margins all round ...		5·00
3858	**2987**	£1·33	Squirrel Nutkin	2·00	2·00
		a.	Horiz pair. Nos. 3858/9.............	4·00	4·00
3859	**2988**	£1·33	Jemima Puddle-Duck....................	2·00	2·00
3860	**2989**	£1·52	Tom Kitten...................................	2·25	2·25
		a.	Horiz pair. Nos. 3860/1..............	4·50	4·50
3861	**2990**	£1·52	Benjamin Bunny	2·25	2·25
Set of 6..				9·50	9·50

Set of 3 Gutter Pairs (two stamps only in each pair)..... 19·00
Set of 3 Traffic Light Gutter Pairs (two stamps only in each pair) .... 20·00
First Day Cover (Tallents House) .... 12·00
First Day Cover (Near Sawrey, Ambleside)............... 12·00

Presentation Pack (PO Pack No. 529)
(Nos. 3856/6 and **MS**3868).......................... 18·50
PHQ Cards (set of 11) (418)............................ 5·50 24·00

(b) *Self-adhesive. Die-cut perf* 14½×14.
3862	**2985**	(1st)	Peter Rabbit..........................	1·50	1·50
		a.	Booklet pane. Nos. 3862/3 and		
			U3746×4..........................	5·75	
3863	**2986**	(1st)	Mrs. Tiggy-Winkle..............	1·50	1·50

Nos. 3856/7, 3858/9 and 3860/1 were printed together, *se-tenant*, as horizontal pairs in sheets of 60 (2 panes 6×5).

Nos. 3862/3 were issued in stamp booklets, No. PM52, originally sold for £3·84.

The eleven PHQ cards depict the ten individual stamps including those from **MS**3868 and the complete miniature sheet.

2991 'Now run along, and don't get into mischief.'   **2992** 'And then, feeling rather sick, he went to look for some parsley.'

2993 'But Peter, who was very naughty, ran straight away to Mr. McGregor's garden, and squeezed under the gate!'   **2994** 'He slipped underneath the gate, and was safe at last?.'

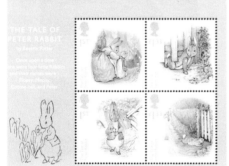

2995 Illustrations from The Tale of Peter Rabbit

(Des Magpie Studio (MS3868). Litho ISP Cartor)

2016 (28 July). *150th Birth Anniversary of Beatrix Potter (writer, illustrator and conservationist)* (2nd issue). |MULTI COLOUR Two phosphor bands. Perf 14½.
3864	**2991**	(1st)	'Now run along, and don't get into mischief.'...............	2·20	2·25
		a.	Booklet pane. Nos. 3864/7 with margins all round and roulettes at left........................	8·00	
3865	**2992**	(1st)	'And then, feeling rather sick, he went to look for some parsley.'.....	2·20	2·25
3866	**2993**	£1·33	'But Peter, who was very naughty, ran straight away to Mr. McGregor's garden, and squeezed under the gate!'..............	2·20	2·25
3867	**2994**	£1·33	'He slipped underneath the gate, and was safe at last?.'......................	2·20	2·25
Set of 4................				8·00	8·25

MS3868 125×89 mm. **2995** Illustrations from The Tale of Peter Rabbit (1st) multicoloured; (1st) multicoloured; £1·33 multicoloured; £1·33 multicoloured...................... 5·50 5·75
First Day Cover (Tallents House)............................ 7·50
First Day Cover (Near Sawrey, Ambleside).......................... 7·50

Nos. 3864/7 were issued in £15·37 The Tale of Beatrix Potter premium booklets, DY19, and in **MS**3868.

2996 Blenheim Palace   **2997** Longleat

2998 Compton Verney   **2999** Highclere Castle

3000 Alnwick Castle   **3001** Berrington Hall

3002 Stowe   **3003** Croome Park

(Des Robert Maude and Sarah Davies. Litho ISP Cartor (3869/76) or gravure ISP Walsall (3877/8))

2016 (16 Aug). *Landscape Gardens.* |MULTI COLOUR One centre band (2nd) or two phosphor bands (others).

(a) *Ordinary gum. Perf* 14.
3869	**2996**	(2nd)	Blenheim Palace................................	90	90
		a.	Horiz pair. Nos. 3869/70..................	1·80	1·80
3870	**2997**	(2nd)	Longleat............................	90	90
3871	**2998**	(1st)	Compton Verney......................	1·00	1·00
		a.	Horiz pair. Nos. 3871/2..................	2·00	2·00
3872	**2999**	(1st)	Highclere Castle.......................	1·00	1·00
3873	**3000**	£1·05	Alnwick Castle.......................	1·50	1·50
		a.	Horiz pair. Nos. 3873/4..................	3·00	3·00
3874	**3001**	£1·05	Berrington Hall......................	1·50	1·50
3875	**3002**	£1·33	Stowe............................	2·00	2·00
		a.	Horiz pair. Nos. 3875/6..................	4·00	4·00
3876	**3003**	£1·33	Croome Park...............	2·00	2·00
Set of 8................				10·00	10·00
Set of 4 Gutter Blocks of 4................				20·00	
First Day Cover (Tallents House)................					13·00
First Day Cover (Kirkharle, Newcastle)................					13·00
Presentation Pack (PO Pack No. 530)................				13·00	
PHQ Cards (set of 8) (419)................				4·00	12·00

(b) *Self-adhesive. Die-cut perf* 14.
3877	**2998**	(1st)	Compton Verney................................	1·50	1·50
		a.	Booklet pane. Nos. 3877/8 and U3746×4................	5·75	
3878	**2999**	(1st)	Highclere Castle................................	1·50	1·50

Nos. 3869/78 commemorate the 300th birth Anniversary of Capability Brown and show his landscape gardens.

Nos. 3869/70, 3871/2, 3873/4 and 3875/6 were each printed together, *se-tenant*, as horizontal pairs in sheets of 60 (2 panes 6×5).

Nos. 3877/8 were issued in stamp booklets, No. PM53, originally sold for £3·84.

3004 Fire Breaks Out in Bakery on Pudding Lane, and Thomas Farriner and his Daughter escape through a Window, Sunday 2nd September 1666

3005 The Fire Spreads Rapidly, and Many People Flee to the River with Their Possessions, Sunday 2nd September 1666

3006 Houses are Pulled Down to Create Breaks and Prevent the Fire from Spreading, Monday 3rd September 1666

3007 As the Fire reaches St Paul's Citizens witness the Cathedral's Destruction as Belongings stored inside Fuel the Flames, Tuesday 4th September 1666

3008 The Fire Dies Out, Many Gather at Moorfields and Temporary Food Markets are set up across London, Wednesday 5th September 1666

3009 Christopher Wren develops Plans for the Regeneration of the City and presents them to the King, Tuesday 11th September 1666

(Des John Higgins (artwork) and The Chase. Litho ISP Cartor)

2016 (2 Sept). *350th Anniversary of the Great Fire of London.* |MULTI COLOUR| Two phosphor bands. Perf 14½.

3879	**3004**	(1st)	Fire Breaks Out in Bakery on Pudding Lane	1·00	1·00
		a.	Horiz pair. Nos. 3879/80	2·00	2·00
3880	**3005**	(1st)	The Fire Spreads Rapidly	1·00	1·00
3881	**3006**	£1·05	Houses are Pulled Down to Create Breaks	1·60	1·60
		a.	Horiz pair. Nos. 3881/2	3·25	3·25
3882	**3007**	£1·05	As the Fire reaches St Paul's Citizens witness the Cathedral's Destruction	1·60	1·60
3883	**3008**	£1·52	The Fire Dies Out	2·25	2·35
		a.	Horiz pair. Nos. 3883/4	4·50	4·50
3884	**3009**	£1·52	Christopher Wren develops Plans for the Regeneration of the City	2·25	2·35
Set of 6				9·00	9·25
Set of 3 Gutter Blocks of 4				18·00	
First Day Cover (Tallents House)					12·00
First Day Cover (London EC3)					12·00
Presentation Pack (PO Pack No. 531)				11·00	
PHQ Cards (set of 6) (420)				3·00	11·00

Nos. 3879/80, 3881/2 and 3883/4 were each printed together, *se-tenant*, as horizontal pairs in sheets of 60 (2 panes 6×5).

3010 *Murder on the Orient Express*

3011 *And Then There Were None*

3012 *The Mysterious Affair at Styles*

3013 *The Murder of Roger Ackroyd*

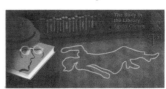

3014 *The Body in the Library*

3015 *A Murder is Announced*

(Des Studio Sutherl&. Litho ISP Cartor)

2016 (15 Sept). *40th Death Anniversary of Agatha Christie (writer).* |MULTI COLOUR| Two phosphor bands. Perf 14½.

3885	**3010**	(1st)	*Murder on the Orient Express*	1·00	1·00
		a.	Vert pair. Nos. 3885/6	2·00	2·00
3886	**3011**	(1st)	*And Then There Were None*	1·00	1·00
3887	**3012**	£1·33	*The Mysterious Affair at Styles*	2·00	2·00
		a.	Vert pair. Nos. 3887/8	4·00	4·00
3888	**3013**	£1·33	*The Murder of Roger Ackroyd*	2·00	2·00
3889	**3014**	£1·52	*The Body in the Library*	2·25	2·25
		a.	Vert pair. Nos. 3889/90	4·50	4·50
3890	**3015**	£1·52	*A Murder is Announced*	2·25	2·25
Set of 6				9·50	9·50
Set of 3 Gutter Pairs (two stamps in each gutter pair)				10·00	
First Day Cover (Tallents House)					13·00
First Day Cover (Torquay)					13·00
Presentation Pack (PO Pack No. 532)				12·00	
PHQ Cards (set of 6) (421)				3·00	11·00

Nos. 3885/6, 3887/8 and 3889/90 were each printed together, *se-tenant*, as vertical pairs in sheets of 48 (2 panes 4×6).

They all feature hidden secrets in the form of microtext, uv ink or thermochronic ink.

3016 Mr. Happy   3017 Little Miss Naughty

3018 Mr. Bump   3019 Little Miss Sunshine

3020 Mr. Tickle   3021 Mr. Grumpy

3022 Little Miss Princess   3023 Mr. Strong

3024 Little Miss Christmas   3025 Mr. Messy

(Des Supple Studio. Litho ISP Cartor (3891/900)
or gravure ISP Walsall (3901/2))

2016 (20 Oct). *Mr. Men and Little Miss* (children's books by Roger Hargreaves). |MULTI COLOUR Two phosphor bands.

(a) Ordinary gum. Perf 14½.

3891	3016	(1st) Mr. Happy	1·00	1·00
		a. Horiz strip of 5. Nos. 3891/5	4·50	4·50
3892	3017	(1st) Little Miss Naughty	1·00	1·00
3893	3018	(1st) Mr. Bump	1·00	1·00
3894	3019	(1st) Little Miss Sunshine	1·00	1·00
3895	3020	(1st) Mr. Tickle	1·00	1·00
3896	3021	(1st) Mr. Grumpy	1·00	1·00
		a. Horiz strip of 5. Nos. 3896/900	4·50	4·50
3897	3022	(1st) Little Miss Princess	1·00	1·00
3898	3023	(1st) Mr. Strong	1·00	1·00
3899	3024	(1st) Little Miss Christmas	1·00	1·00
3900	3025	(1st) Mr. Messy	1·00	1·00
Set of 10			9·00	9·00
Set of 2 Gutter Strips of 5			18·00	
First Day Cover (Tallents House)				11·00
First Day Cover (Cleckheaton)				11·75
Presentation Pack (PO Pack No. 533)			11·00	
PHQ Cards (set of 10) (422)			5·00	12·50

(b) Self-adhesive. Die-cut perf 14½.

3901	3016	(1st) Mr. Happy	1·50	1·50
		a. Booklet pane. Nos. 3901/2 and U3027×4	5·75	
3902	3020	(1st) Mr. Tickle	1·50	1·50

Nos. 3891/5 and 3896/900 were each printed together, *se-tenant*, as horizontal strips of five stamps in sheets of 50 stamps (2 panes 5×5).

Nos. 3901/2 were issued in stamp booklets, No. PM54, originally sold for £3·84.

Designs as Nos. 3891/900 but self-adhesive were issued in sheets of 10 with *se-tenant* labels, No. LS101, originally sold for £6·90.

Designs as Nos. 3891, 3893/4, 3896/7 and 3900 were also available in sheets of ten with personal photographs on the labels, originally sold for £10·20.

> **SELF-ADHESIVE STAMPS:** Collectors are reminded that used self-adhesive stamps will no longer 'soak-off'. They should be collected with a neat margin of backing paper.

3026 Snowman   3027 Robin

3028 Snowman   3029 Robin

3030 Christmas Tree   3031 Lantern

3032 Stocking   3033 Christmas
                                      Pudding

(Des Helen Musselwhite (illustrations) and The Chase. Gravure ISP Walsall (3903a, 3904a) or De La Rue (others))

2016 (8 Nov). *Christmas.* |MULTI COLOUR One centre band (3903) or two bands (others). Perf 14½×15.

(a) Self-adhesive.

3903	3026	(2nd) Snowman	90	90
		a. Booklet pane. No. 3903×12	9·75	
3904	3027	(1st) Robin	1·00	1·00
		a. Booklet pane. No. 3904×12	10·75	
3905	3028	(2nd Large) Snowman	1·10	1·10
3906	3029	(1st Large) Robin	1·40	1·40
3907	3030	£1·05 Christmas Tree	1·80	1·80
3908	3031	£1·33 Lantern	2·10	2·10
3909	3032	£1·52 Stocking	2·50	2·50
3910	3033	£2·25 Christmas Pudding	3·50	3·50
Set of 8			12·75	12·75
First Day Cover (Tallents House)				16·75
First Day Cover (Bethlehem, Llandeilo)				16·75
Presentation Pack (PO Pack No. 534)			16·75	
PHQ Cards (set of 9) (423)			4·50	28·00

(b) Ordinary gum.

MS3911	189×74 mm. As Nos. 3903/10	12·75	13·00
First Day Cover (Tallents House)			16·75
First Day Cover (Bethlehem, Llandeilo)			16·75

The nine PHQ cards show the eight individual stamps and the complete miniature sheet.

The 2nd class, 1st class, £1·05, £1·33, £1·52 and £2·25 values were also issued in sheets of 20 (LS102) containing eight 2nd class, eight 1st class and one each of the £1·05, £1·33, £1·52 and £2·25 stamps, each stamp accompanied by a *se-tenant* label showing paper cut out work by Helen Musselwhite forming a snowy landscape. These sheets were sold for £16·21.

Separate sheets of 20 2nd, 20 1st, ten 1st, ten £1·05, ten £1·33 and ten £1·52 were available with personal photographs on the labels. These were sold at £14·60 for 20 2nd, £18·65 for 20 1st, £10·20 for ten 1st, £14·45 for ten £1·05, £18·50 for ten £1·33 and £21·85 for ten £1·52. The 2nd class and 1st class values were also issued in sheets of 20 (LS103) 'Celebrating 50 Years of Christmas Stamps' containing ten 2nd class and ten 1st class stamps, each stamp accompanied by a greetings label. These sheets were sold at £12·40.

Year Pack
2016 (8 Nov). Comprises Nos. 3787/**MS**3801, 3810/**MS**3832, **MS**3837/43, **MS**3848/61, **MS**3868/76, 3879/900 and 3903/10
CP3911a Year Pack .... 160·00

Post Office Yearbook
2016 (8 Nov). Comprises Nos. 3787/**MS**3801, 3810/**MS**3832, MS3837/43, **MS**3848/61, **MS**3868/76, 3879/900 and 3903/10
YB3911a Yearbook.. 180·00

Miniature Sheet Collection
2016 (8 Nov). Comprises Nos. **MS**3801, **MS**3832, **MS**3837, **MS**3848, **MS**3855, **MS**3868 and **MS**3911
MS3911a Miniature Sheet Collection .... 50·00

3034 Battersea Shield, London, 350–50 BC

3035 Skara Brae Village, Orkney Islands, 3100–2500 BC

3036 Star Carr Headdress, Yorkshire, 9000 BC

3037 Maiden Castle Hill Fort, Dorset, 400 BC

3038 Avebury Stone Circles, Wiltshire, 2500 BC

3039 Drumbest Horns, County Antrim, 800 BC

3040 Grime's Graves Flint Mines, Norfolk, 2500 BC

3041 Mold Cape, Flintshire, 1900–1600 BC

(Des Rebecca Strickson (illustrations) and True North. Litho ISP Cartor)

2017 (17 Jan). *Ancient Britain.* MULTI COLOUR Two phosphor bands. Perf 14.

3912	**3034**	(1st) Battersea Shield	1·00	1·00
		a. Horiz pair. Nos. 3912/13....................	2·00	2·00
3913	**3035**	(1st) Skara Brae Village	1·00	1·00
3914	**3036**	£1·05 Star Carr Headdress	1·70	1·70
		a. Horiz pair. Nos. 3914/15....................	3·50	3·50
3915	**3037**	£1·05 Maiden Castle Hill Fort	1·70	1·70
3916	**3038**	£1·33 Avebury Stone Circles...................	2·00	2·00
		a. Horiz pair. Nos. 3916/17....................	4·00	4·00
3917	**3039**	£1·33 Drumbest Horns............................	2·00	2·00
3918	**3040**	£1·52 Grime's Graves Flint Mines	2·25	2·25
		a. Horiz pair. Nos. 3918/19	4·50	4·50

3919	**3041**	£1·52 Mold Cape............................	2·25	2·25
	Set of 8...		12·75	13·00
	Set of 4 Gutter Blocks of 4		25·50	
	First Day Cover (Tallents House)............................			17·00
	First Day Cover (Avebury, Marlborough)			17·00
	Presentation Pack (PO Pack No. 536)...................		15·50	
	PHQ Cards (set of 8) (424)..................................		4·00	15·00

Nos. 3912/13, 3914/15, 3916/17 and 3918/19 were each printed together, *se-tenant*, as horizontal pairs in sheets of 60 (2 panes 6×5).

3042 The Long Walk

3043 The Round Tower

3044 The Norman Gate

3045 St George's Hall

3046 The Queen's Ballroom

3047 The Waterloo Chamber

3048 St George's Chapel Nave: Sir Reginald Bray Roof Boss

3049 St George's Chapel Nave: Fan-vaulted Roof

(Des Up. Litho ISP Cartor (3920/5) or gravure ISP Walsall (3926/7))

2017 (15 Feb). *Windsor Castle* (1st issue). Two phosphor bands.

(a) Ordinary gum. Perf 14½.

3920	**3042**	(1st)	The Long Walk	1·00	1·00
		a.	Horiz strip of 3. Nos. 3920/2	3·00	3·00
		b.	Booklet pane. Nos. 3920 and 3923 with margins all round	4·00	
3921	**3043**	(1st)	The Round Tower	1·00	1·00
		b.	Booklet pane. Nos. 3921/2 and 3924/5 with margins all round	5·50	
3922	**3044**	(1st)	The Norman Gate	1·00	1·00
3923	**3045**	£1·52	St George's Hall	2·00	2·00
		a.	Horiz strip of 3. Nos. 3923/5	6·00	6·00
3924	**3046**	£1·52	The Queen's Ballroom	2·00	2·00
3925	**3047**	£1·52	The Waterloo Chamber	2·00	2·00

Set of 6	8·25	8·25
Set of 2 Gutter Strips of 3	16·50	
First Day Cover (Tallents House)		11·00
First Day Cover (Windsor)		11·00
Presentation Pack (PO Pack No. 537) (Nos. 3920/5 and MS3932)	17·50	
PHQ Cards (set of 11) (425)	5·50	23·00

(b) Self-adhesive. Die-cut perf 14½.

3926	**3048**	(1st)	Sir Reginald Bray Roof Boss	1·50	1·50
		a.	Booklet pane. Nos. 3926/7 and U3027×4	5·75	
3927	**3049**	(1st)	Fan-vaulted Roof	1·50	1·50

Nos. 3920/2 and 3923/5 were each printed together, *se-tenant*, as horizontal strips of three stamps in sheets of 60 (2 panes 6×5).

Nos. 3926/7 were issued in stamp booklets, No. PM55, originally sold for £3·84. The eleven PHQ cards show the individual stamps including those from **MS**3932 and the complete miniature sheet.

3050 St George's Chapel Quire: Garter Banners

3051 St George's Chapel Quire: St George's Cross Roof Boss

3052 St George's Chapel

(Des Up. Litho ISP Cartor)

2017 (15 Feb). *Windsor Castle* (2nd issue). Two phosphor bands. Perf 14½.

3928	**3048**	(1st)	Sir Reginald Bray Roof Boss	1·60	1·60
		a.	Booklet pane. Nos. 3928/31 with margins all round and roulettes at left	7·25	

3929	**3049**	(1st)	Fan-vaulted Roof	1·60	1·60
3930	**3050**	£1·33	Garter Banners	2·40	2·40
3931	**3051**	£1·33	St George's Cross Roof Boss	2·40	2·40

Set of 4	7·25	7·25
MS3932 125×89 mm. **3052** Nos. 3928/31	7·25	7·25
First Day Cover (Tallents House)		8·00
First Day Cover (Windsor)		8·00

Nos. 3928/31 come from **MS**3932 and £14·58 premium booklets, No. DY20.

3053 *Hunky Dory*

3054 *Aladdin Sane*

3055 *Heroes*

3056 *Let's Dance*

3057 *Earthling*

3058 *Blackstar*

3059 David Bowie Live

(Gravure ISP Walsall (3933/8) or litho ISP Cartor (**MS**3939))

2017 (14 Mar). *David Bowie (1947–2016, singer, songwriter and actor) Commemoration.* Two phosphor bands.

(a) Self-adhesive. Die-cut perf 14½

3933	**3053**	(1st)	*Hunky Dory*	1·00	1·00
3934	**3054**	(1st)	*Aladdin Sane*	1·00	1·00
		a.	Booklet pane. Nos. 3934/5 and U3027×4	5·75	
3935	**3055**	(1st)	*Heroes*	1·00	1·00
3936	**3056**	£1·52	*Let's Dance*	2·25	2·25
3937	**3057**	£1·52	*Earthling*	2·25	2·25
3938	**3058**	£1·52	*Blackstar*	2·25	2·25

Set of 6	8·75	8·75
First Day Cover (Tallents House)		11·50
First Day Cover (London SW9)		11·50
Presentation Pack (PO Pack No. 538) (Nos. 3933/8 and MS3939)	17·00	
PHQ Cards (set of 11) (426)	5·50	24·00

(b) Ordinary gum. Perf 14½

MS3939 126×89 mm. **3059** David Bowie Live (1st) The Ziggy Stardust Tour, 1973; (1st) The Serious Moonlight Tour, 1983; £1·52 The Stage Tour, 1978; £1·52 A Reality Tour, 2004	6·25	6·25
First Day Cover (Tallents House)		8·25
First Day Cover (London SW9)		8·25

Nos. 3933/8 were printed in separate sheets of 50 (2 panes 5×5).

Nos. 3934/5 were also issued in booklets, No. PM56, originally sold for £3·84.

The right-hand edges of Nos. 3933/8 are all cut around to show the vinyl disc protruding from the open edge of the album cover.

The eleven PHQ cards show the individual stamps including those from **MS**3939 and the complete miniature sheet.

Four 'Fan sheets', comprising the complete set. Types **3053/8**, Type **3054**×5 and Type **3055**×5, all printed on ordinary gummed paper, were available from Royal Mail at premium prices.

3060 Frankel

3061 Red Rum

3062 Shergar

3063 Kauto Star

3064 Desert Orchid

3065 Brigadier Gerard

3066 Arkle

3067 Estimate

(Des Michael Heslop (illustrations) and Together Design. Litho ISP Cartor)

2017 (6 Apr). *Racehorse Legends.* |MULTI COLOUR Two phosphor bands. Perf 14.

3940	3060	(1st) Frankel	1·00	1·00
3941	3061	(1st) Red Rum	1·00	1·00
3942	3062	£1·17 Shergar	1·75	1·75
3943	3063	£1·17 Kauto Star	1·75	1·75
3944	3064	£1·40 Desert Orchid	2·20	2·20
3945	3065	£1·40 Brigadier Gerard	2·20	2·20
3946	3066	£1·57 Arkle	2·60	2·60
3947	3067	£1·57 Estimate	2·60	2·60
Set of 8			13·50	13·50
Set of 8 Gutter Pairs			27·00	
First Day Cover (Tallents House)				17·50
First Day Cover (Newmarket)				17·50
Presentation Pack (PO Pack No. 539)			16·00	
PHQ Cards (set of 8) (427)			4·00	16·50

3068 Great Tit (*Parus major*)

3069 Wren (*Troglodytes troglodytes*)

3070 Willow Warbler (*Phylloscopus trochilus*)

3071 Goldcrest (*Regulus regulus*)

3072 Skylark (*Alaudia arvensis*)

3073 Blackcap (*Sylvia atricapilla*)

3074 Song Thrush (*Turdus philomelos*)

3075 Nightingale (*Luscinia megarhynchos*)

3076 Cuckoo (*Cuculus canorus*)

3077 Yellowhammer (*Emberiza citrinella*)

(Des Federico Gemma (illustrations) and Osborne Ross. Litho ISP Cartor)

2017 (4 May). *Songbirds.* |MULTI COLOUR Two phosphor bands. Perf 14½.

3948	3068	(1st) Great Tit	1·00	1·00
		a. Horiz strip of 5. Nos. 3948/52	4·50	4·50
3949	3069	(1st) Wren	1·00	1·00
3950	3070	(1st) Willow Warbler	1·00	1·00
3951	3071	(1st) Goldcrest	1·00	1·00
3952	3072	(1st) Skylark	1·00	1·00
3953	3073	(1st) Blackcap	1·00	1·00
		a. Horiz strip of 5. Nos. 3953/7	4·50	4·50
3954	3074	(1st) Song Thrush	1·00	1·00
3955	3075	(1st) Nightingale	1·00	1·00
3956	3076	(1st) Cuckoo	1·00	1·00
3957	3077	(1st) Yellowhammer	1·00	1·00
3948/57 Set of 10			9·00	9·00
Set of 2 Gutter Strips of 10			18·00	
First Day Cover (Tallents House)				12·00
First Day Cover (Warbleton, Heathfield)				12·00
Presentation Pack (PO Pack No. 540)			11·00	
PHQ Cards (set of 10) (428)			5·00	12·50

Nos. 3948/52 and 3953/7 were each printed together, *se-tenant*, as horizontal strips of five in sheets of 50 (2 panes 5×5).

3078 Preliminary sketch by Arnold Machin based on the Penny Black, January 1966

3079 Preparatory work by Arnold Machin using photograph of his coin mould, February 1966

3080 Essay with coinage head surrounded by Country symbols, April/May 1966

3081 Essay of Coinage head cropped and simplified, with only the denomination, October 1966

3082 Photo by John Hedgecoe with Queen Elizabeth II wearing the diadem, August 1966

3083 Essay of the first plaster cast of the Diadem Head, without corsage, October 1966

3084 The Machin definitive 50 Years of a design icon

3085 The Machin definitive Golden Anniversary celebration

3086 £1 gold foil Machin

(Des Atelier Works. Gravure and embossed ISP)

2017 (5 June). *50th Anniversary of the Machin Definitive* (1st issue). |MULTI COLOUR Two phosphor bands. Perf 14×15

3958	**3078**	(1st)	Preliminary sketch based on the Penny Black........................	1·25	1·25
		a.	Booklet pane. Nos. 3958/60 with margins all round	3·75	
3959	**3079**	(1st)	Preparatory work using photograph of his coin mould...	1·25	1·25
3960	**3080**	(1st)	Essay with coinage head surrounded by Country symbols, April/May 1966	1·25	1·25
3961	**3081**	(1st)	Essay of coinage head, with only the denomination	1·25	1·25
		a.	Booklet pane. Nos. 3961/63 with margins all round	3·75	
3962	**3082**	(1st)	Photo by John Hedgecoe...........	1·25	1·25
3963	**3083**	(1st)	Essay of the first plaster cast of the Diadem Head	1·25	1·25
Set of 6...				6·75	6·75

MS3964 202×74 mm. **3084** 6×(1st) Types 3078/3083 ... 6·75 6·75
MS3965 202×74 mm. **3085** No. X866; No. 1470; as Type **1116**; No. 2124; No. 2651; as No. U3067 (but MMIL code); as No. U3966 (but gravure).................... 6·75 6·75

First Day Cover (**MS**3964) (Tallents House) .... 8·00
First Day Cover (**MS**3964) (High Wycombe) .... 8·00
First Day Cover (**MS**3965) (Tallents House) .... 8·00
First Day Cover (**MS**3965) (High Wycombe) .... 8·00
Presentation Pack (**MS**3964/5) (PO Pack No. 541)........... 15·50
PHQ Cards (*Set of* 11) (429)................................... 5·50 21·00

Nos. 3958/63 were issued in £15·14 50th Anniversary of the Machin Definitive premium booklet, DY21, and in **MS**3964. The 5p, 20p and £1

stamps in **MS**3965 do not have an elliptical perforation hole in each vertical side.

On **MS**3965 only the £1 gold foil stamp is embossed.

(Litho and gold foil embossed. ISP)

2017 (5 June). *50th Anniversary of the Machin Definitive* Two narrow phosphor bands. Perf 14x14½.

U3966	**3086**	£1 gold		4·50	5·50
		a.	Booklet pane. Nos. U3966×4 with margins all round	13·50	

U3966 was embossed in gold foil, had the phosphor bands printed in litho and does not have an elliptical perforation hole on each vertical side. It was issued only in £15.59 booklet No. DY21.

> Please note that, for the convenience of collectors, Nos. **MS**3965 and U3966/a are also listed in the Machin section of this catalogue.

> For the 20p stamp as T **929** from the 50th Anniversary of the Machin booklet see No. 2133, pane No 1668sb.

3087 Nutley Windmill, East Sussex

3088 New Abbey Corn Mill, Dumfries and Galloway

3089 Ballycopeland Windmill, County Down

3090 Cheddleton Flint Mill, Staffordshire

3091 Woodchurch Windmill, Kent

3092 Felin Cochwillan Mill, Gwynedd

(Des Atelier Works. Litho ISP Cartor)

2017 (20 June). *Windmills and Watermills.* |MULTI COLOUR Two phosphor bands. Perf 14½×14

3967	**3087**	(1st)	Nutley Windmill, East Sussex......	1·00	1·00
		a.	Vert pair. Nos. 3967/68	2·00	2·00
3968	**3088**	(1st)	New Abbey Corn Mill, Dumfries and Galloway................	1·00	1·00
3969	**3089**	£1·40	Ballycopeland Windmill, County Down.........................	2·25	2·25
		a.	Vert pair. Nos. 3969/70	4·50	4·50
3970	**3090**	£1·40	Cheddleton Flint Mill, Staffordshire.....................................	2·25	2·25
3971	**3091**	£1·57	Woodchurch Windmill, Kent.......	2·50	2·50
		a.	Vert pair. Nos. 3971/72	5·00	5·00
3972	**3092**	£1·57	Felin Cochwillan Mill, Gwynedd	2·50	2·50
Set of 6..				10·50	10·50

Set of 3 Gutter Blocks of 4 .... 21·00
First Day Cover (Tallents House)................................... 12·00
First Day Cover (Old Mill, Callington)............................ 12·00
Presentation Pack (PO Pack No. 542)................................ 12·00
PHQ Cards (set of 6) (430).. 3·00 14·50

Nos. 3967/68, 3969/70 and 3971/72 were each printed together, *se-tenant*, as vertical pairs in sheets of 60 (2 panes 5×6).

3093 Aquatics Centre, Queen Elizabeth Olympic Park, London

3094 Library of Birmingham

3095 SEC Armadillo (formerly Clyde Auditorium), Glasgow

3096 Scottish Parliament, Edinburgh

3097 Giant's Causeway Visitor Centre, Co. Antrim

3098 National Assembly for Wales, Cardiff

3099 Eden Project, St Austell

3100 Everyman Theatre, Liverpool

3101 IWM (Imperial War Museum) North, Manchester

3102 Switch House, Tate Modern, London

(Des GBH. Litho ISP Cartor)

2017 (13 July). *Landmark Buildings.* ^{|MULTI|COLOUR} Two phosphor bands. Perf 14½

3973	**3093**	(1st) Aquatics Centre, Queen Elizabeth Olympic Park, London	1·00	1·00
		a. Horiz strip of 5. Nos. 3973/77	5·00	5·00
3974	**3094**	(1st) Library of Birmingham	1·00	1·00
3975	**3095**	(1st) SEC Armadillo (*formerly Clyde Auditorium*), Glasgow	1·00	1·00
3976	**3096**	(1st) Scottish Parliament, Edinburgh	1·00	1·00
3977	**3097**	(1st) Giant's Causeway Visitor Centre, Co. Antrim	1·00	1·00
3978	**3098**	(1st) National Assembly for Wales, Cardiff	1·00	1·00
		a. Horiz strip of 5. Nos. 3978/82	5·00	5·00
3979	**3099**	(1st) Eden Project, St Austell	1·00	1·00
3980	**3100**	(1st) Everyman Theatre, Liverpool	1·00	1·00
3981	**3101**	(1st) IWM (*Imperial War Museum*) North, Manchester	1·00	1·00
3982	**3102**	(1st) Switch House, Tate Modern, London	1·00	1·00
Set of 10			9·00	9·00
Set of 2 Gutter Strips of 5			18·00	
First Day Cover (Tallents House)				10·50
First Day Cover (St Austell)				10·50
Presentation Pack (PO Pack No. 543)			11·00	
PHQ Cards (set of 10) (431)			5·00	14·00

Nos. 3973/77 and 3978/82 were each printed together, *se-tenant*, as horizontal strips of five stamps in sheets of 50 (2 panes 5×5).

3103 *Shattered Poppy* (John Ross)

3104 *Dead Man's Dump* (Isaac Rosenberg)

3105 Nurses Elsie Knocker and Mairi Chisholm

3106 *Dry Docked for Sealing and Painting* (Edward Wadsworth)

3107 Tyne Cot Cemetery, Zonnebeke, Ypres Salient Battlefields, Belgium

3108 Private Lemuel Thomas Rees's Life-saving Bible

(Des hat-trick Design. Litho ISP Cartor)

2017 (31 July). *Centenary of the First World War* (4th issue). ^{|MULTI|COLOUR} Two phosphor bands. Perf 14½

3983	**3103**	(1st) *Shattered Poppy* (John Ross)	1·00	1·00
		a. Booklet pane. Nos. 3983/85 with margins all round	3·50	
3984	**3104**	(1st) *Dead Man's Dump*	1·00	1·00
3985	**3105**	(1st) Nurses Elsie Knocker and Mairi Chisholm	1·00	1·00
3986	**3106**	£1·57 *Dry Docked for Sealing and Painting*	2·50	2·50
		a. Booklet pane. Nos. 3986/88 with margins all round	9·00	
3987	**3107**	£1·57 Tyne Cot Cemetery, Belgium	2·50	2·50
3988	**3108**	£1·57 Private Lemuel Thomas Rees's Life-saving Bible	2·50	2·50
Set of 6			9·50	9·50
Set of 6 Gutter Pairs			19·00	
First Day Cover (Tallents House)				11·00
First Day Cover (Blaenannerch, Aberteifi-Cardigan)				11·00
Presentation Pack (PO Pack No. 544)			11·50	
PHQ Cards (set of 6) (431)			3·00	12·50

Nos. 3983a and 3786a were only issued in £15·41 Centenary of the First World War (4th issue). premium booklet, No DY22.

3109 The Merrythought Bear

3110 Sindy Weekender Doll

3111 Spirograph

3112 Stickle Bricks Super Set House

3113 Herald Trojan Warriors

3114 Spacehopper

3115 Fuzzy-Felt Farm Set

3116 Meccano Ferris Wheel

3117 Action Man Red Devil Parachutist

3118 Hornby Dublo Electric Train and TPO Mail Van

(Des Interabang. Litho ISP Cartor)

2017 (22 Aug). *Classic Toys*. |MULTI COLOUR Two phosphor bands. Perf 14½

3989	**3109**	(1st)	The Merrythought Bear	1·00	1·00
			a. Horiz strip of 5. Nos. 3989/93	5·00	5·00
3990	**3110**	(1st)	Sindy Weekender Doll	1·00	1·00
3991	**3111**	(1st)	Spirograph	1·00	1·00
3992	**3112**	(1st)	Stickle Bricks Super Set House	1·00	1·00
3993	**3113**	(1st)	Herald Trojan Warriors	1·00	1·00
3994	**3114**	(1st)	Spacehopper	1·00	1·00
			a. Horiz strip of 5. Nos. 3994/98	5·00	5·00
3995	**3115**	(1st)	Fuzzy-Felt Farm Set	1·00	1·00
3996	**3116**	(1st)	Meccano Ferris Wheel	1·00	1·00
3997	**3117**	(1st)	Action Man Red Devil Parachutist	1·00	1·00
3998	**3118**	(1st)	Hornby Dublo Electric Train and TPO Mail Van	1·00	1·00
Set of 10				9·00	9·00
Set of 2 Gutter Strips of 5				18·00	
First Day Cover (Tallents House)					10·50
First Day Cover (Toys Hill, Edenbridge)					10·50
Presentation Pack (PO Pack No. 545)				11·00	
PHQ Cards (set of 10) (433)				5·00	14·00

Nos. 3989/93 and 3994/98 were each printed together, *se-tenant*, as horizontal strips of five stamps in sheets of 50 (2 panes 5×5).

3119 'The Story of Nelson', 'The Story of the First Queen Elizabeth' and 'Florence Nightingale' (Adventures from History)

3120 'The Gingerbread Boy, Cinderella' and 'The Elves and the Shoemaker' (Well-loved Tales)

3121 'We have fun, Look at this' and 'Things we do' (Key Words Reading Scheme)

3122 'Piggly Plays Truant, Tootles the Taxi and Other Rhymes' and 'Smoke and Fluff' (Early Tales and Rhymes)

3123 'Things to Make', 'How it works: The Telephone' and 'Tricks and Magic' (Hobbies and How it Works)

3124 'The Nurse', 'The Postman' and 'The Fireman' (People at Work)

3125 'British Wild Flowers', 'Wild Life in Britain' and 'Garden Flowers' (Nature and Conservation)

3126 'The Story of Ships', 'The Story of the Motor Car' and 'The Story of Metals' (Achievements)

(Des True North. Litho ISP Cartor)

2017 (14 Sept). *Ladybird Books*. |MULTI COLOUR One centre band (Nos. 3999/4000) or two bands (others). Perf 14

3999	**3119**	(2nd)	Adventures from History	90	90
			a. Horiz pair. Nos. 3999/4000	1·80	1·80
4000	**3120**	(2nd)	Well-loved Tales	90	90
4001	**3121**	(1st)	Key Words Reading Scheme	1·00	1·00
			a. Horiz pair. Nos. 4001/02	2·00	2·00
4002	**3122**	(1st)	Early Tales and Rhymes	1·00	1·00
4003	**3123**	£1·40	Hobbies and How it Works	2·25	2·25
			a. Horiz pair. Nos. 4003/04	4·50	4·50
4004	**3124**	£1·40	People at Work	2·25	2·25
4005	**3125**	£1·57	Nature and Conservation	2·50	2·50
			a. Horiz pair. Nos. 4005/06	5·00	5·00
4006	**3126**	£1·57	Achievements	2·50	2·50
Set of 8				12·00	12·00
Set of 4 Gutter Blocks of 4				24·00	
First Day Cover (Tallents House)					13·50
First Day Cover (Loughborough)					13·50
Presentation Pack (PO Pack No. 546)				14·00	
PHQ Cards (Set of 8) (434)				4·00	16·00

Nos. 3999/4000, 4001/02, 4003/04 and 4005/06 were each printed together, *se-tenant*, as horizontal pairs in sheets of 60 (2 panes 6×5).

3127 Maz Kanata

3128 Chewbacca

3129 Supreme Leader Snoke

3130 Porg

3131 BB-8

3132 R2-D2

3133 C-3PO

3134 K-2SO

(Des Malcolm Tween (illustrations) and Interabang.
Litho ISP Cartor (4007/14) or gravure Walsall (4015/18))

2017 (12 Oct-14 Dec). *Star Wars* (4th issue). *Aliens and Droids.* MULTI COLOUR Two phosphor bands

(a) Ordinary gum. Perf 14½

4007	**3127**	(1st)	Maz Kanata	1·00	1·00
		a.	Horiz strip of 4. Nos. 4007/10	4·00	4·00
4008	**3128**	(1st)	Chewbacca	1·00	1·00
		a.	Booklet pane. Nos. 4008, 4010/11 and 4014 with margins all round (14.12.17)	6·00	
4009	**3129**	(1st)	Supreme Leader Snoke	1·00	1·00
4010	**3130**	(1st)	Porg	1·00	1·00
4011	**3131**	(1st)	BB-8	1·00	1·00
		a.	Horiz strip of 4. Nos. 4011/14	4·00	4·00
4012	**3132**	(1st)	R2-D2	1·00	1·00
4013	**3133**	(1st)	C-3PO	1·00	1·00
4014	**3134**	(1st)	K-2SO	1·00	1·00
			Set of 8	7·25	7·25
			Set of 2 Gutter Strips of 4	14·50	
			First Day Cover (Tallents House)		9·00
			First Day Cover (Wookey, Wells)		9·00
			Presentation Pack (PO Pack No. 547)	9·25	
			PHQ Cards (Set of 8) (435)	4·00	11·50

(b) Self-adhesive. Die-cut perf 14½

4015	**3127**	(1st)	Maz Kanata	1·50	1·50
		a.	Booklet pane. Nos. 4015/16 and U3027×4	10·00	
4016	**3128**	(1st)	Chewbacca	1·50	1·50
4017	**3131**	(1st)	BB-8	1·50	1·50
		a.	Booklet pane. Nos. 4017/18 and U3027×4	10·00	
4018	**3132**	(1st)	R2-D2	1·50	1·50

Nos. 4007/10 and 4011/14 were each printed together, *se-tenant*, as horizontal strips of four stamps in sheets of 48 (2 panes 4×6).

No. 4008*b* was only issued in £14·32 Star Wars: The Making of the Droids, Aliens and Creatures premium booklet, No DY23.

Nos. 4015/16 and 4017/18 were each issued in stamp booklets with 4×1st bright scarlet stamps, PM57/58, originally sold for £3·90 each.

3135 *Virgin and Child* (attributed to Gerard David)

3136 *The Madonna and Child* (William Dyce)

3137 *Virgin and Child* (attributed to Gerard David)

3138 *The Madonna and Child* (William Dyce)

3139 *Virgin Mary with Child* (attributed to Quinten Massys)

3140 *The Small Cowper Madonna* (Raphael)

3141 *The Sleep of the Infant Jesus* (Giovanni Battista Sassoferrato)

3142 *St Luke painting the Virgin* (detail) (Eduard Jakob von Steinle)

(Gravure De La Rue or ISP Walsall (4019a/b, 4020a/b),
Litho by ISP Cartor (**MS**4027))

2017 (7 Nov). *Christmas. Madonna and Child.* MULTI COLOUR One centre phosphor band (4019) or two bands

(a) Self-adhesive. Die-cut perf 14½×15

4019	**3135**	(2nd)	Virgin and Child (attributed to Gerard David)	90	90
		a.	Booklet pane. Nos. 4019 and 4028, each ×6	9·75	
		b.	Booklet pane. No. 4019×12	9·75	
4020	**3136**	(1st)	The Madonna and Child (William Dyce)	1·00	1·00
		a.	Booklet pane. Nos. 4020 and 4029, each ×6	10·75	
		b.	Booklet pane. No. 4020×12	10·75	
4021	**3137**	(2nd Large)	Virgin and Child (attributed to Gerard David)	1·10	1·10
4022	**3138**	(1st Large)	The Madonna and Child (William Dyce)	1·40	1·40
4023	**3139**	£1·17	Virgin Mary with Child (attributed to Quinten Massys)	1·80	1·80
4024	**3140**	£1·40	The Small Cowper Madonna (Raphael)	2·25	2·25
4025	**3141**	£1·57	The Sleep of the Infant Jesus (Giovanni Battista Sassoferrato)	2·50	2·50
4026	**3142**	£2·27	St Luke painting the Virgin (detail) (Eduard Jakob von Steinle)	3·50	3·50
			Set of 8	13·00	13·00
			First Day Cover (Nos. 4019/26 and 4028/31) (Tallents House)		14·50
			First Day Cover (Nos. 4019/26 and 4028/31) (Bethlehem, Llandeilo)		15·00
			Presentation Pack (PO Pack No. 548)	15·00	
			PHQ Cards (set of 13) (436)	6·50	19·50

(b) Ordinary gum. Perf 14½×15

MS4027	189×74 mm. As nos. 4019/26		13·00	13·00

Nos. 4019 and 4028, 4020 and 4029, 4021 and 4030 and 4022 and 4031 were printed together in sheets of 50 (5×10), the upper 25 stamps being Nos. 4019, 4020, 4021 or 4022 and the lower 25 stamps Nos. 4028, 4029, 4030 or 4031. Nos. 4023/26 were printed individually in sheets of 50 (5×10).

The presentation pack (No. 548) contains Nos. 4019/26 and 4028/31.

The 13 PHQ cards show the 12 individual stamps and **MS**4027.

The 2nd class (No. 4019), 1st class (No. 4020), £1·17, £1·40, £1·57 and £2·27 values were also issued in sheets of 20 containing eight 2nd class, eight 1st class and one each of the £1·17, £1·40, £1·57 and £2·27 values, each stamp accompanied by a *se-tenant* label.

Arwen Wilson, age 9

3143 *Snow Family* (Arwen Wilson)

Ted Lewis-Clark, age 10

3144 *Santa Claus on his sleigh on a starry night* (Ted Lewis-Clark)

Arwen Wilson, age 9
Ted Lewis-Clark, age 10

3145 *Snow Family* (Arwen Wilson)

3146 *Santa Claus on his sleigh on a starry night* (Ted Lewis-Clark)

(Gravure De La Rue)

2017 (7 Nov). *Children's Christmas.* |MULTI COLOUR One centre phosphor band (No. 4028) or two bands. Self-adhesive. Die-cut perf 14½×15

4028	**3143**	(2nd)	*Snow Family (Arwen Wilson)*............	90	90
4029	**3144**	(1st)	*Santa Claus on his sleigh on a starry night (Ted Lewis-Clark)*..........	1·00	1·00
4030	**3145**	(2nd Large)	*Snow Family (Arwen Wilson)*............	1·10	1·10
4031	**3146**	(1st Large)	*Santa Claus on his sleigh on a starry night (Ted Lewis-Clark)*	1·40	1·40
Set of 4................				4·00	4·00

3147 Platinum Anniversary

(Litho ISP)

2017 (20 Nov). *Royal Platinum Wedding Anniversary of Queen Elizabeth II and Duke of Edinburgh.* |MULTI COLOUR Two phosphor bands. Perf 14

MS4032 200×67 mm **3147** (1st) Engagement of Princess Elizabeth and Lt. Philip Mountbatten; (1st) Princess Elizabeth and Duke of Edinburgh after their wedding at Westminster Abbey; (1st) Princess Elizabeth and Duke of Edinburgh looking at wedding photographs during their honeymoon; £1·57 Engagement photograph; £1·57 Princess Elizabeth and Duke of Edinburgh on their wedding day; £1·57 Princess Elizabeth and Duke of Edinburgh on honeymoon at Broadlands................... 10·00 10·00

First Day Cover (Tallents House)................		12·00
First Day Cover (London SW1)................		12·00
Presentation Pack (PO Pack No. 549)................	12·00	
PHQ Cards (set of 7) (437)................	3·50	13·50
Souvenir Pack................		15·00

A Limited Edition Pack of 5,000 was available at £14·99.

Collectors Pack

2017 (20 Nov). Comprises Nos. 3912/25, MS3932/3957, MS3964/65, 3967/4014, 4019/29 and MS4032

CP4031a Collectors Pack................ £250

Post Office Yearbook

2017 (20 Nov). Comprises Nos. 3912/25, MS3932/3957, MS3964/65, 3967/4014, 4019/31 and MS4032

YB4031a Yearbook................ £325

Miniature Sheet Collection

2017 (20 Nov). Comprises Nos. MS3932, MS3939, MS3964/65, MS4027 and MS4032

Miniature Sheet Collection................ 85·00

3148 *Sansa Stark* (Sophie Tucker

3149 *Jon Snow* (Kit Harington)

3150 *Eddard Stark* (Sean Bean)

3151 *Olenna Tyrell* (Dianna Rigg

3152 *Tywin Lannister* (Charles Dance)

3153 *Tyrion Lannister* (Peter Dinklage)

3154 *Cersei Lannister* (Lena Headey)

3155 *Arya Stark* (Maisie Williams)

3156 *Jaime Lannister* (Nicolaj Coster-Waldau)

3157 *Daenerys Targaryen* (Emilia Clarke)

(Des GBH, Litho Cartor)

2018 (23 Jan) *Game of Thrones* (1st issue). |MULTI COLOUR Two phosphor bands. Perf 14½×14.

4033	**3148**	(1st)	*Sansa Stark (Sophie Tucker)*............	1·00	1·00
		a.	Horiz strip of 5. Nos. 4033/4037....	7·50	7·00
		b.	Booklet pane Nos. 4033/4035, 4038/4040................	9·00	
4034	**3149**	(1st)	*Jon Snow (Kit Harington)*	1·00	1·00
4035	**3150**	(1st)	*Eddard Stark (Sean Bean)*............	1·00	1·00
4036	**3151**	(1st)	*Olenna Tyrell (Dianna Rigg)*.	1·00	1·00
		b.	Booklet pane Nos. 4036/4037, 4041/4042................	9·00	
4037	**3152**	(1st)	*Tywin Lannister (Charles Dance)*............	1·00	1·00
4038	**3153**	(1st)	*Tyrion Lannister (Peter Dinklage)*............	1·00	1·00
		a.	Horiz strip of 5. Nos. 4038/4042............	7·50	7·00
4039	**3154**	(1st)	*Cersei Lannister (Lena Headey)*............	1·00	1·00
4040	**3155**	(1st)	*Arya Stark (Maisie Williams)*............	1·00	1·00
4041	**3156**	(1st)	*Jaime Lannister (Nicolaj Coster-Waldau)*	1·00	1·00
4042	**3157**	(1st)	*Daenerys Targaryen (Emilia Clarke)*................	1·00	1·00
Set of 10................				9·00	9·00
Set of 2 Gutter Strips of 10................				18·00	
First Day Cover (Tallents House)				10·50	
First Day Cover (Belfast)				10·50	
Presentation Pack (PO Pack No. 551)................				11·00	
PHQ Cards (set of 16) (438)................				8·00	23·00

Nos. 4033/4037 and 4038/4042 were each printed together, se-tenant, as horizontal strips of five stamps in sheets of 60 (2 panes 5×6).

The presentation pack (No. 549) contains Nos. 4033/4042 and MS4043.

Nos. 4033b and 4036b were only issued in £13·95 Game of Thrones premium booklet, No DY24.

The 16 PHQ cards show the 15 individual stamps and MS4043.

3158 Game of Thrones non-human characters

(Des GBH, Litho ISP Cartor)

2018 (23 Jan) Game of Thrones (2nd issue). |MULTI COLOUR Two phosphor bands. Self-adhesive die cut perf 14½×14 (with one elliptical hole in each vert side) (as No. 4044) or 14½

MS4043 204×74 mm **3158** As Nos. 4044/4048.............			7·50	7·50
First Day Cover (Tallents House)				8·50
First Day Cover (Belfast)				8·50

3159 The Iron Throne

3160 The Night King and White Walkers

3161 Giants

3162 Direwolves

3163 Dragons

(Des GBH, Litho ISP Cartor)

2018 (23 Jan) Game of Thrones (3rd issue). |MULTI COLOUR Two phosphor bands. Perf 14½×14 (with one elliptical hole in each vert side) (No. 4044) or 14½

4044	3159	(1st) The Iron Throne.............................	1·50	1·40
4045	3160	(1st) The Night King and White		
		Walkers...	1·50	1·40
		a. Booklet pane Nos. 4045/48...........	6·00	
4046	3161	(1st) Giants..	1·50	1·40
4047	3162	(1st) Direwolves....................................	1·50	1·40
4048	3163	(1st) Dragons...	1·50	1·40

Nos. 4044/4048 were issued in £13·95 Game of Thrones premium booklets, No. DY24.

Self-adhesive stamps as No. 4044 were additionally available from **MS**4043 and stamp booklets, No. MB20 while those as Nos.4045/4048 were additionally available only from **MS**4043.

(Des GBH, Gravure Walsall)

2018 (23 Jan) Game of Thrones (4th issue). |MULTI COLOUR Two phosphor bands. Self-adhesive die cut Perf 14½×14 (with one elliptical hole in each vert side)

4049	3159	(1st) The Iron Throne.............................	1·50	1·40
		a. Booklet pane Nos. 4043×6...........	9·00	

No. 4049 was issued in stamp booklets, No. MB20, sold for £3·90.

3164 The Lone Suffragette in Whitehall, c.1908

3165 The Great Pilgrimage of Suffragists, 1913

3166 Suffragette Leaders at Earl's Court, 1908

3167 Women's Freedom League poster parade, c.1907

3168 Welsh Suffragettes, Coronation Procession, 1911

3169 Leigh and New Released from Prison, 1908

3170 Sophia Duleep Singh sells The Suffragette, 1913

3171 Suffragette Prisoners' Pageant, 1911

(Des Supple Studio, Litho ISP)

2018 (15 Feb) Votes for Women. |MULTI COLOUR One phosphor band (4050/51) or two bands. Perf 14½×14.

4050	3164	(2nd) The Lone Suffragette in		
		Whitehall......................................	90	90
		a. Horiz pair. Nos. 4050/51................	1·80	1·80
4051	3165	(2nd) The Great Pilgrimage of		
		Suffragists....................................	90	90
4052	3166	(1st) Suffragette Leaders at		
		Earl's Court...................................	1·00	1·00
		a. Horiz pair. Nos. 4052/53	2·00	2·00
4053	3167	(1st) Women's Freedom League poster		
		parade...	1·00	1·00
4054	3168	£1.40 Welsh Suffragettes, Coronation		
		Procession.....................................	2·25	2·25
		a. Horiz pair. Nos. 4054/55................	4·50	4·50
4055	3169	£1.40 Leigh and New Released from		
		Prison..	2·25	2·25
4056	3170	£1.57 Sophia Duleep Singh sells The		
		Suffragette....................................	2·50	2·50
		a. Horiz pair. Nos. 4056/57................	5·00	5·00
4057	3171	£1.57 Suffragette Prisoners' Pageant......	2·50	2·50
Set of 8..			12·00	12·00
Set of 4 Gutter Blocks of 4..			24·00	
First Day Cover (Tallents House)....................................				14·00
First Day Cover (London SW1)..				14·00
Presentation Pack (PO Pack No. 552)............................			15·00	
PHQ Cards (set of 8) (439)...			4·00	16·00

Nos. 4050/51, 4052/53, 4054/55 and 4056/57 were each printed together, se-tenant, as horizontal pairs in sheets of 60 (2 panes 6×5).

3172 Lightning F6

3173 Hawker Hurricane Mk.I

3174 Vulcan B2

3175 Typhoon FGR4

3176 Sopwith Camel F.1   **3177** Nimrod MR2

(Des Royal Mail Group Ltd with illustrations by Michael Turner, Litho ISP Cartor (4058/63, MS4064) or gravure ISP Walsall (4065/66))

2018 (20 March) *RAF Centenary* (1st issue). |MULTI COLOUR| Two phosphor bands.

(a) Ordinary gum. Perf 14½×14.

4058	3172	(1st)	Lightning F6	1·50	1·40
		a.	Horiz pair. Nos. 4058/59	3·00	2·75
		b.	Booklet Pane Nos. 4058×2,		
			4061×2	6·00	
4059	3173	(1st)	Hurricane Mk.I	1·50	1·40
		b.	Booklet pane Nos. 4059/60,		
			4062/63	12·00	
4060	3174	£1.40	Vulcan B2	3·25	3·25
		a.	Horiz pair. Nos. 4060/61	6·50	6·50
4061	3175	£1.40	Typhoon FGR4	3·25	3·25
4062	3176	£1.57	Sopwith Camel F.1	3·75	3·75
		a.	Horiz pair. Nos. 4062/63	7·50	7·50
4063	3177	£1.57	Nimrod MR2	3·75	3·75
Set of 6				15·00	15·00
Set of 3 Gutter Blocks of 4				30·00	
First Day Cover (Tallents House)					16·00
First Day Cover (Cranwell, Sleaford)					16·00
Presentation Pack (PO Pack No. 553)				25·00	
PHQ Cards (set of 11) (440)				10·00	25·00
MS4064 192×74 mm **3178** Nos. 4067/4070				9·50	9·50
First Day Cover (Tallents House)					10·50
First Day Cover (Cranwell, Sleaford)					10·50

(b) Self-adhesive. Die-cut perf 14½.

4065	3172	(1st)	Lightning F6	1·50	1·40
		a.	Booklet pane. Nos. 4065/66 and		
			U3027×4		
4066	3173	(1st)	Hurricane Mk.I	1·50	1·40

Nos. 4058/59, 4060/61 and 4062/63 were each printed together, *se-tenant*, as horizontal pairs in sheets of 60 (2 panes 6×5).

Nos 4058*b* and 4059*b* were issued in £18·69 RAF Centenary premium booklet, No. DY25.

Nos. 4065/66 were issued in stamp booklets, No. PM59, originally sold for £3·90.

The eleven PHQ cards show the individual stamps including those from **MS**4070 and the complete miniature sheet.

(Des Turner Duckworth, Litho International Security Printers)

2018 (20 March) *RAF Centenary* (2nd issue). *Red Arrows.* |MULTI COLOUR| Two phosphor bands. Perf 14½×14.

4067	3178	(1st)	Red Arrows, Flypast	1·50	1·50
		a.	Booklet pane Nos. 4066/69	9·50	
4068	3179	(1st)	Red Arrows, Swan	1·50	1·50
4069	3180	£1.40	Red Arrows, Syncro pair	3·25	3·25
4070	3181	£1.40	Red Arrows, Python	3·25	3·25

Nos. 4067/70 come from **MS**4064 and £18·69 RAF Centenary premium booklets, No. DY25.

3183 Pilots scramble to their Hurricanes

3184 Supermarine Spitfires of 610 Squadron, Biggin Hill, on patrol

3185 Armourer Fred Roberts replaces ammunition boxes on Supermarine Spitfire

(Des Supple Studio (stamps) and Royal Mail Group, Supple Studio. Litho ISP Cartor)

2018 (20 March) *RAF Centenary* (3rd issue). *Battle of Britain.* |MULTI COLOUR| Two phosphor bands. Perf 14½×14.

4071	3183	(1st)	Pilots scramble	1·50	1·50
		a.	Booklet pane Nos. 4071, 4072×2,		
			4073	6·00	
4072	3184	(1st)	Spitfires	1·50	1·50
4073	3185	(1st)	Armourer replaces ammunition		
			boxes	1·50	1·50

Nos. 4071/73 come from £18·69 premium booklets, No. DY25. The images on these three stamps were previously used in **MS**3735 issued on 16 July 2015 to commemorate the 75th Anniversary of the Battle of Britain; those stamps were 'all-over' phosphor, Perf 14.

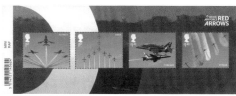

3178 Royal Air Force RED ARROWS

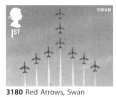

3179 Red Arrows, Flypast   **3180** Red Arrows, Swan

3181 Red Arrows, Syncro pair   **3182** Red Arrows, Python

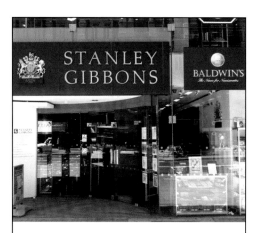

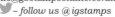

Decimal Machin Definitives

Denominated stamps, PVA, PVAD or gum arabic, 'standard' perforations

356a   **357** (Value redrawn)

(Des after plaster cast by Arnold Machin. Recess B.W.)

1970 (17 June)–**72**. Decimal Currency. Chalk-surfaced paper or phosphorised paper (10p.). Perf 12.

829	**356a**	10p. cerise	50	50
830		20p. olive-green	60	20
		Ea. Thinner uncoated paper*		
831		50p. deep ultramarine	1·25	25
		Ea. Thinner uncoated paper*	60·00	
831*b*	**357**	£1 bluish black (6.12.72)	2·25	40
Set of 4			3·25	1·20
First Day Cover (829/31)				2·00
First Day Cover (831b)				2·50
Presentation Pack No. 18 (829/31)				8·00
Presentation Pack No. 38 (790 (or 831b), 830/1)				12·50

* These are not as apparent as uncoated photogravure issues where there is normally a higher degree of chalk-surfacing. The 20p. is known only as a block of four with Plate No. 5. The 50p. comes from Plate No. 9.

The 10p. on phosphorised paper continued the experiments which started with the Machin 1s.6d. When the experiment had ended a quantity of the 50p. value was printed on the phosphorised paper to use up the stock. These stamps were issued on 1 February 1973, but they cannot be distinguished from No. 831 by the naked eye. (*Price* £2).

A £1 was also issued in 1970, but it is difficult to distinguish it from the earlier No. 790. In common with the other 1970 values it was issued in sheets of 100.

A whiter paper was introduced in 1973. The £1 appeared on 27 Sept. 1973, the 20p. on 30 Nov. 1973 and the 50p. on 20 Feb. 1974.

Imperforate examples of No. 831*b* are believed to be printer's waste.

Special First Day of Issue Postmarks

British Philatelic Bureau, Edinburgh (Type C) (Nos. 829/31)	3·00
Windsor, Berks (Type C) (Nos. 829/31)	6·50
Philatelic Bureau, Edinburgh (Type E) (No. 831*b*)	3·00
Windsor, Berks (Type E) (No. 831*b*)	8·00

"X" NUMBERS. The following definitive series has been allocated "X" prefixes to the catalogue numbers to avoid renumbering all subsequent issues.

NO VALUE INDICATED. Stamps as Types **367/a** inscribed "2nd" or "1st" are listed as Nos. 1445/52, 1511/16, 1664/72, 2039/40 and 2295.

ELLIPTICAL PERFORATIONS. These were introduced in 1993 and stamps showing them will be found listed as Nos. Y1667 etc.

367   **367a**

Printing differences

Litho   Gravure

(*Illustrations enlarged*×6)

Litho. Clear outlines to value and frame of stamp.

Gravure. Uneven lines to value and frame formed by edges of screen.

Two types of the 3p., 10p. and 26p. (Nos. X930/c, X886/b and X971/b)

I   II

I   II

I   II

Figures of face value as I (all ptgs of 3p. bright magenta except the multi-value coil No. 930cl and sheets from 21.1.92 onwards, 10p. orange-brown except 1984 "Christian Heritage" £4 booklet and 26p. rosine except 1987 £1.04 barcode booklet).

Figures of face value narrower as in II (from coil No. X930cl in sheets from 21.1.92 (3p.), 1984 "Christian Heritage" £4 booklet (10p.) or 1987 £1.04 barcode booklet (26p.)). This catalogue includes changes of figure styles on these stamps where there is no other listable difference. Similar changes have also taken place on other values, but only in conjuction with listed colour, paper or perforation changes.

1971 (15 Feb)–**96**. Decimal Currency. T **367**. Chalk-surfaced paper.

(*a*) *Photo Harrison (except for some printings of Nos. X879 and X913 in sheets produced by Enschedé and issued on 12 Dec. 1979 (8p.) and 19 Nov. 1991 (18p.)). With phosphor bands. P* 15×14.

X841	½p. turquoise-blue (2 bands)		10	10
	a. Imperf (pair)†		£3500	
	Ey. Phosphor omitted		4·00	
	l. Booklet pane. No. X841×2 *se-tenant* vert with X849×2		6·00	
	lEy. Booklet pane. Phosphor omitted		£225	
	la. Booklet pane. No. X841×2 *se-tenant* horiz with X849×2 (14.7.71)		1·00	
	laEy. Booklet pane. Phosphor omitted		£375	
	m. Booklet pane. No. X841×5 plus label		2·75	
	mEy. Booklet pane. Phosphor omitted		£120	
	n. Coil strip. No. X849Eg, X841Eg×2 and X844Eg×2		3·50	
	nEy. Coil strip. Phosphor omitted		45·00	
	nEv. Coil strip. PVA gum. No. X849, X841×2 and X844×2 (4.74)		80	
	nEvy. Coil strip. Phosphor omitted		18·00	
	o. Booklet pane. No. X841, X851, X852, X852Ea, each×3 (24.5.72)		13·00	
	oEy. Booklet pane. Phosphor omitted		£1600	
	p. Booklet pane. No. X841×3, X842 and X852×2 (24.5.72)		60·00	
	pEy. Booklet pane. Phosphor omitted			
	q. Coil strip. No. X870, X849, X844 and X841×2 (3.12.75)		1·00	
	r. Booklet pane. No. X841×2, X844×3 and X870 (10.3.76)		75	
	s. Booklet pane. No. X841×2, X844×2, X873×2 and X881×4 (8½p. values at right) (26.1.77)		3·00	
	sa. Ditto, but No. X873Ea and 8½p. values at left		3·00	
	t. Booklet pane. No. X841, X844, X894×3 and X902 (14p. value at right) (26.1.81)		2·00	
	tEy. Booklet pane. Phosphor omitted		65·00	
	ta. Booklet pane. No. X841, X844, X894Ea×3 and X902 (14p. value at left)		1·90	
	taEy. Booklet pane. Phosphor omitted		65·00	
	u. Booklet pane. No. X841, X857×4 and X899×3 (12½p. values at left) (1.2.82)		3·00	
	ua. Ditto, but No. X899Ea and 12½p. values at right		3·00	
	Eg. Gum arabic (from coil strip, and on 22.9.72 from sheets)		40	
	Egy. Phosphor omitted		70·00	

X842	½p. turquoise-blue (1 side band at left) (24.5.72)	55·00	25·00
X843	½p. turquoise-blue (1 centre band) (14.12.77)	40	25
	l. Coil strip. No. X843×2, X875 and X845×2 (14.12.77)	85	
	m. Booklet pane. No. X843×2, X845×2 and X875 plus label (8.2.78)	60	
	mEy. Booklet pane. Phosphor omitted	45·00	
X844	1p. crimson (2 bands)	10	10
	a. Imperf (vert coil)		
	b. Pair, one imperf 3 sides (vert coil)		
	c. Imperf (pair)	£1700	
	Ey. Phosphor omitted	5·00	
	l. Booklet pane. No. X844×2 *se-tenant* vert with X848×2	6·00	
	m. Ditto, but *se-tenant* horiz (14.7.71)	1·00	
	mEy. Booklet pane. Phosphor omitted	£300	
	n. Booklet pane. No. X844×2, X876×3 and X883×3 (9p. values at right) (13.6.77)	4·75	
	na. Ditto, but No. X876Ea and 9p. values at left	2·75	
	Eg. Gum arabic (from coil strip)	50	
	Egy. Phosphor omitted	70·00	
X845	1p. crimson (1 centre band) (14.12.77)	35	30
	l. Booklet pane. No. X879 and X845×2 plus label (17.10.79)	60	
	m. Coil strip. No. X879 and X845×2 plus 2 labels (16.1.80)	85	
	n. Booklet pane. No. X845×2, X860 and X898 each×3 (5.4.83)	6·50	
	nEy. Booklet pane. Phosphor omitted	22·00	
	p. Booklet pane. No. X845×2, X863×2 and X900×3 (3.9.84)	4·00	
	pEy. Booklet pane. Phosphor omitted	£250	
	q. Booklet pane. No. X845×2 and X896×4 (29.7.86)	9·00	
	s. Booklet pane. No. X845, X867×2 and X900×3 (20.10.86)	6·00	
	sa. Ditto, but with vertical edges of pane imperf (29.9.87)	3·00	
	saEy. Booklet pane. Phosphor omitted	£225	
X846	1p. crimson ("all-over") (10.10.79)	30	30
X847	1p. crimson (1 side band at left) (20.10.86)	1·75	1·75
	Ea. Band at right (3.3.87)	4·50	4·50
	l. Booklet pane. No. X847, X901 and X912×2 (20.10.86)	4·00	
	lEy. Booklet pane. Phosphor omitted	£110	
	m. Booklet pane. No. X847Ea, X901×2, X912×5 and X918 with margins all round (3.3.87)	12·50	
X848	1½p. black (2 bands)	20	20
	a. Uncoated paper*	£130	
	b. Imperf (pair)		
	c. Imperf 3 sides (horiz pair)		
	Ey. Phosphor omitted	60·00	
X849	2p. myrtle-green (2 bands)	15	15
	a. Imperf (horiz pair)	£3500	
	Ey. Phosphor omitted	12·00	
	l. Booklet pane. No. X849×2, X880×2 and X886×3 plus label (10p. values at right) (28.8.79)	2·50	
	la. Ditto, but No. X880Ea and 10p. values at left	2·50	
	m. Booklet pane. No. X849×3, X889×2 and X895×2 plus label (12p. values at right) (4.2.80)	2·50	
	mEy. Booklet pane. Phosphor omitted	55·00	
	ma. Booklet pane. No. X849×3, X889Ea×2 and X895×2 plus label (12p. values at left)	2·50	
	maEy. Booklet pane. Phosphor omitted	55·00	
	n. Booklet pane. No. X849, X888×3, X889Ea and X895×4 with margins all round (16.4.80)	4·25	
	nEy. Booklet pane. Phosphor omitted	55·00	
	o. Booklet pane. No. X849×6 with margins all round (16.4.80)	1·40	
	oEy. Booklet pane. Phosphor omitted	60·00	
	p. Booklet pane. No. X849, X857, X898, X899×3 and X899Ea×3 with margins all round (19.5.82)	6·00	
	pEy. Booklet pane. Phosphor omitted	£150	
	Eg. Gum arabic (from coil strip)	2·25	
	Egy. Phosphor omitted	£225	
X850	2p. myrtle-green ("all-over") (10.10.79)	25	25
X851	2½p. magenta (1 centre band)	20	15
	a. Imperf (pair)†	£375	
	Ey. Phosphor omitted	10·00	
	l. Booklet pane. No. X851×5 plus label	4·50	
	lEy. Booklet pane. Phosphor omitted	5·00	
	m. Booklet pane. No. X851×4 plus two labels	5·00	
	mEy. Booklet pane. Phosphor omitted	£425	

	n. Booklet pane. No. X851×3, X852Ea×3 and X855×6 (24.5.72)	8·00	
	nEy. Booklet pane. Phosphor omitted		
	Eg. Gum arabic (13.9.72)	30	
X852	2½p. magenta (1 band at left)	1·50	1·50
	l. Booklet pane. No. X852×2 and X855×4.	6·00	
	lEy. Booklet pane. Phosphor omitted	£160	
	Ea. Band at right (24.5.72)	1·50	1·50
X853	2½p. magenta (2 bands) (21.5.75)	1·00	1·00
X854	2½p. rose-red (2 bands) (26.8.81)	55	75
	l. Booklet pane. No. X854×3, X862×2 and X894×3 (11½p. values at left)	5·25	
	la. Ditto, but No. X894Ea and 11½p. values at right	7·00	
X855	3p. ultramarine (2 bands)	20	20
	a. Imperf (coil strip of 5)	£3000	
	b. Imperf (pair)†	£400	
	c. Uncoated paper*	45·00	
	Ey. Phosphor omitted	5·00	
	l. Booklet pane. No. X855×5 plus label	2·50	
	lEy. Booklet pane. Phosphor omitted	£375	
	n. Booklet pane. No. X855×12 (24.5.72)	5·00	
	nEy. Booklet pane. Phosphor omitted	£250	
	Eg. Gum arabic (23.8.72)	1·00	
	Egy. Phosphor omitted	10·00	
X856	3p. ultramarine (1 centre band) (10.9.73)	15	15
	a. Imperf (pair)†	£350	
	b. Imperf between (vert pair)†	£475	
	c. Imperf horiz (vert pair)†	£300	
	Eg. Gum arabic	50	
X857	3p. bright magenta (Type I) (2 bands) (1.2.82)	35	35
	Ey. Phosphor omitted	£160	
X858	3½p. olive-grey (2 bands) (*shades*)	40	40
	a. Imperf (pair)	£600	
	Ey. Phosphor omitted	12·00	
	Eb. *Bronze-green* (18.7.73)	1·25	1·25
	Eby. Phosphor omitted	12·00	
X859	3½p. olive-grey (1 centre band) (24.6.74)	30	30
X860	3½p. purple-brown (1 centre band) (5.4.83)	1·50	1·50
	Ey. Phosphor omitted	10·00	
X861	4p. ochre-brown (2 bands)	40	40
	a. Imperf (pair)†	£2400	
	Ey. Phosphor omitted	38·00	
	Eg. Gum arabic (1.11.72)	75	
X862	4p. greenish blue (2 bands) (26.8.81)	2·00	2·00
X863	4p. greenish blue (1 centre band) (3.9.84)	1·25	1·25
	Ey. Phosphor omitted	90·00	
X864	4p. greenish blue (1 band at right) (8.1.85).	4·50	4·50
	Ea. Band at left	4·50	4·50
	l. Booklet pane. No. X864, X864Ea, X901×2, X901Ea×2, X909×2 and X920 with margins all round (8.1.85)	15·00	
	lEy. Booklet pane. Phosphor omitted	£2600	
X865	4½p. grey-blue (2 bands) (24.10.73)	25	25
	a. Imperf (pair)	£525	
	Ey. Phosphor omitted	11·00	
X866	5p. pale violet (2 bands)	20	20
	Ey. Phosphor omitted	£240	
X867	5p. claret (1 centre band) (20.10.86)	1·00	1·00
	Ey. Phosphor omitted	85·00	
X868	5½p. violet (2 bands) (24.10.73)	55	55
X869	5½p. violet (1 centre band) (17.3.75)	25	25
	a. Uncoated paper*	£400	
	Ey. Phosphor omitted	22·00	
X870	6p. light emerald (2 bands)	25	25
	a. Uncoated paper*	20·00	
	Ey. Phosphor omitted	75·00	
	Eg. Gum arabic (6.6.73)	2·50	
X871	6½p. greenish blue (2 bands) (4.9.74)	70	70
X872	6½p. greenish blue (1 centre band) (24.9.75).	25	20
	a. Imperf (vert pair)	£450	
	b. Uncoated paper*	£225	
	Ey. Phosphor omitted	15·00	
X873	6½p. greenish blue (1 band at right) (26.1.77)	80	80
	Ea. Band at left	80	80
X874	7p. purple-brown (2 bands) (15.1.75)	30	30
	a. Imperf (pair)	£1200	
	Ey. Phosphor omitted	4·00	
X875	7p. purple-brown (1 centre band) (13.6.77).	25	25
	a. Imperf (pair)	£140	
	l. Booklet pane. No. X875 and X883, each×10 (15.11.78)	4·50	
X876	7p. purple-brown (1 band at right) (13.6.77)	80	80
	Ea. Band at left	80	80
X877	7½p. pale chestnut (2 bands)	30	30
	Ey. Phosphor omitted	22·00	
X878	8p. rosine (2 bands) (24.10.73)	30	30
	a. Uncoated paper*	15·00	

X879	8p. rosine (1 centre band) (20.8.79)................	30	30
	a. Uncoated paper*..................................	£900	
	b. Imperf (pair)..	£1400	
	Ey. Phosphor omitted...............................	£475	
	l. Booklet pane. No. X879 and X886, each×10 (14.11.79).........................	5·00	
X880	8p. rosine (1 band at right) (28.8.79)............	1·10	1·10
	Ea. Band at left.......................................	1·10	1·10
X881	8½p. light yellowish green (2 bands) (*shades*) (24.9.75).......................................	30	30
	a. Imperf (pair)..	£1700	
	Eb. *Yellowish green* (24.3.76)................	35	35
	Ey. Phosphor omitted...............................	6·00	
X882	9p. yellow-orange and black (2 bands)	45	45
	Ey. Phosphor omitted...............................	£110	
X883	9p. deep violet (2 bands) (25.2.76)	35	30
	a. Imperf (pair)..	£325	
	Ey. Phosphor omitted...............................	4·50	
X884	9½p. purple (2 bands) (25.2.76)	75	75
	Ey. Phosphor omitted...............................	24·00	
X885	10p. orange-brown and chestnut (2 bands) (11.8.71)...	35	35
	a. Orange-brown omitted	£200	
	b. Imperf (horiz pair).............................	£4000	
	Ey. Phosphor omitted...............................	12·00	
X886	10p. orange-brown (Type I) (2 bands) (25.2.76)...	35	30
	a. Imperf (pair)..	£375	
	Ey. Phosphor omitted...............................	3·00	
	b. Type II (4.9.84)..................................	14·00	14·00
	bEy. Phosphor omitted...............................	£2000	
	bl. Booklet pane. No. X886b, X901Ea and X909×7 with margins all round.........	16·00	
	blEy. Booklet pane. Phosphor omitted.............	£4000	
X887	10p. orange-brown (Type I) ("all-over") (3.10.79)...	35	35
X888	10p. orange-brown (Type I) (1 centre band) (4.2.80)..	35	25
	a. Imperf (pair)..	£375	
	l. Booklet pane. No. X888×9 with margins all round (16.4.80).................	3·75	
	lEy. Booklet pane. Phosphor omitted.............	55·00	
	m. Booklet pane. No. X888 and X895, each×10 (12.11.80).........................	5·50	
X889	10p. orange-brown (Type I) (1 band at right) (4.2.80)..	1·10	1·10
	Ea. Band at left.......................................	1·00	1·00
X890	10½p. yellow (2 bands) (25.2.76)	60	60
X891	10½p. deep dull blue (2 bands) (26.4.78)	80	80
X892	11p. brown-red (2 bands) (25.2.76)	40	40
	a. Imperf (pair)..	£3750	
	Ey. Phosphor omitted...............................	5·00	
X893	11½p. drab (1 centre band) (14.1.81)..............	40	35
	a. Imperf (pair)..	£340	
	Ey. Phosphor omitted...............................	7·00	
	l. Booklet pane. No. X893 and X902, each×10 (11.11.81).........................	8·50	
X894	11½p. drab (1 band at right) (26.1.81)	65	65
	Ea. Band at left.......................................	65	65
	l. Booklet pane. No. X894/Ea, each×2 and X902×6 (6.5.81)...............................	6·50	
X895	12p. yellowish green (2 bands) (4.2.80).........	55	55
	Ey. Phosphor omitted...............................	8·00	
	l. Booklet pane. No. X895×9 with margins all round (16.4.80).................	4·00	
	lEy. Booklet pane. Phosphor omitted.............	65·00	
X896	12p. bright emerald (1 centre band) (29.10.85)..	45	45
	a. Imperf (pair)..	£2200	
	Ey. Phosphor omitted...............................	12·00	
	l. Booklet pane. No. X896×9 with margins all round (18.3.86).................	4·75	
	lEy. Booklet pane. Phosphor omitted.............	£225	
	Eu. Underprint Type 4 (29.10.85)..........	55	
X897	12p. bright emerald (1 band at right) (14.1.86)...	80	80
	Ea. Band at left.......................................	80	80
	l. Booklet pane. No. X897/Ea, each×2 and X909×6 (12p. values at left) (14.1.86)...	6·00	
	la. Ditto, but 12p. values at right...........	6·00	
	m. Booklet pane. No. X897/Ea, each×3, X909×2 and X919 with margins all round (18.3.86).....................................	23·00	
	mEy. Booklet pane. Phosphor omitted.............	£1800	
X898	12½p. light emerald (1 centre band) (27.1.82) .	45	40
	a. Imperf (pair)..	£120	
	Ey. Phosphor omitted...............................	6·50	
	Eu. Underprint Type 1 (10.11.82)..........	60	
	Euy. Phosphor omitted...............................	75·00	
	Ev. Underprint Type 2 (9.11.83)............	60	

	l. Booklet pane. No. X898Eu and X907Eu, each×10 (10.11.82).......................	10·00	
X899	12½p. light emerald (1 band at right) (1.2.82)..	70	70
	Ea. Band at left.......................................	70	70
	l. Booklet pane. No. X899/Ea, each×2 and X907×6 (1.2.82)††........................	5·00	
	lEy. Booklet pane. Phosphor omitted.............	£3600	
	m. Booklet pane. No. X899/Ea, each×3 with margins all round (19.5.82).........	3·25	
	mEy. Booklet pane. Phosphor omitted.............	45·00	
	n. Booklet pane. No. X899/Ea, each×2, and X908×6 (12½p. values at left) (5.4.83)..	8·50	
	na. Ditto, but 12½p. values at right.........	8·00	
X900	13p. pale chestnut (1 centre band) (28.8.84).	40	40
	a. Imperf (pair)..	£775	
	Eu. Underprint Type 2 (2.12.86)............	60	
	Ey. Phosphor omitted...............................	6·50	
	l. Booklet pane. No. X900×9 with margins all round (8.1.85)...................	4·50	
	lEy. Booklet pane. Phosphor omitted.............	£425	
	m. Booklet pane. No. X900×6 with margins all round (3.3.87)...................	3·75	
	n. Booklet pane. No. X900×4 with margins all round (4.8.87)...................	3·00	
	o. Booklet pane. No. X900×10 with margins all round (4.8.87)...................	7·00	
X901	13p. pale chestnut (1 band at right) (3.9.84).	65	65
	Ea. Band at left.......................................	65	65
	l. Booklet pane. No. X901/Ea, each×2, and X909×6 (13p. values at left)††.......	5·00	
	la. Ditto, but 13p. values at right...........	5·00	
	m. Booklet pane. No. X901/Ea, each×3 with margins all round (4.9.84)...........	4·50	
	mEy. Booklet pane. Phosphor omitted.............	£325	
	n. Booklet pane. No. X901Ea and X912×5 (20.10.86)...	4·50	
	na. Ditto, but with vertical edges of pane imperf (29.9.87).................................	4·75	
X902	14p. grey-blue (2 bands) (26.1.81)................	90	90
	Ey. Phosphor omitted...............................	30·00	
X903	14p. deep blue (1 centre band) (23.8.88).......	45	45
	a. Imperf (pair)..	£500	
	Ey. Phosphor omitted...............................	9·00	
	l. Booklet pane. No. X903×4 with margins all round..................................	6·00	
	lEy. Booklet pane. Phosphor omitted.............	£110	
	m. Booklet pane. No. X903×10 with margins all round..................................	9·50	
	n. Booklet pane. No. X903×4 with horizontal edges of pane imperf (11.10.88)..	6·50	
	p. Booklet pane. No. X903×10 with horizontal edges of pane imperf (11.10.88)..	9·00	
	pEy. Booklet pane. Phosphor omitted.............	£160	
	q. Booklet pane. No. X903×4 with three edges of pane imperf (24.1.89)............	32·00	
	qEy. Booklet pane. Phosphor omitted.............	35·00	
X904	14p. deep blue (1 band at right) (5.9.88) ..	4·00	4·00
	l. Booklet pane. No. X904 and X914×2 plus label...	8·00	
	lEy. Booklet pane. Phosphor omitted.............	15·00	
	m. Booklet pane. No. X904×2 and X914×4 with vertical edges of pane imperf........	6·50	
	mEy. Booklet pane. Phosphor omitted.............	£850	
X905	15p. bright blue (1 centre band) (26.9.89)......	65	65
	a. Imperf (pair)..	£625	
	Ey. Phosphor omitted...............................	14·00	
X906	15p. brt blue (1 band at left) (2.10.89)...........	3·00	3·00
	Ea. Band at right (20.3.90).....................	5·00	5·00
	l. Booklet pane. No. X906×2 and X916 plus label...	8·50	
	lEy. Booklet pane. Phosphor omitted.............	£550	
	m. Booklet pane. No. X906Ea, X916, X922, 1446, 1448, 1468Ea, 1470 and 1472 plus label with margins all round (20.3.90)...	15·00	
X907	15½p. pale violet (2 bands) (1.2.82).................	70	70
	aEy. Phosphor omitted...............................	7·00	
	Eu. Underprint Type 1 (10.11.82)..........	60	
	l. Booklet pane. No. X907×6 with margins all round (19.5.82).................	4·00	
	lEy. Booklet pane. Phosphor omitted.............	85·00	
	m. Booklet pane. No. X907×9 with margins all round (19.5.82).................	5·25	
	mEy. Booklet pane. Phosphor omitted.............	50·00	
X908	16p. olive-drab (2 bands) (5.4.83)	1·50	1·50
	Ey. Phosphor omitted...............................	£110	
X909	17p. grey-blue (2 bands) (3.9.84)	60	60
	aEy. Phosphor omitted...............................	£240	
	Eu. Underprint Type 4 (4.11.85)............	60	
	Euy. Phosphor omitted...............................	22·00	

	l. Booklet pane. No. X909Eu×3 plus label (4.11.85)	2·50		
	lEy. Booklet pane. Phosphor omitted	65·00		
	Ela. Booklet pane. No. X909×3 plus label (12.8.86)	3·00		
X910	17p. deep blue (1 centre band) (4.9.90)	80	80	
	a. Imperf (pair)	£1700		
X911	17p. deep blue (1 band at right) (4.9.90)	12·00	12·00	
	Ea. Band at left	2·00	2·00	
	Ey. Phosphor omitted	12·00		
	l. Booklet pane. No. X911 and X911Ea×2 plus label	16·00		
	lEy. Booklet pane. Phosphor omitted	55·00		
	m. Booklet pane. No. X911×2 and X917×3 plus three labels with vertical edges of pane imperf	4·25		
	mEy. Booklet pane. Phosphor omitted	75·00		
X912	18p. deep olive-grey (2 bands) (20.10.86)	80	80	
	Ey. Phosphor omitted	30·00		
X913	18p. bright green (1 centre band) (10.9.91)	60	60	
	a. Imperf (pair)	£525		
	Ey. Phosphor omitted	28·00		
X914	19p. brt orange-red (2 bands) (5.9.88)	1·50	1·50	
	Ey. Phosphor omitted	4·00		
X915	20p. dull purple (2 bands) (25.2.76)	1·20	1·20	
X916	20p. brownish black (2 bands) (2.10.89)	2·00	2·00	
	Ey. Phosphor omitted	£550		
X917	22p. brt orange-red (2 bands) (4.9.90)	1·60	1·60	
	Ey. Phosphor omitted	22·00		
X917a	25p. rose-red (2 bands) (6.2.96)	12·00	12·00	
X918	26p. rosine (Type I) (2 bands) (3.3.87)	8·00	8·00	
X919	31p. purple (2 bands) (18.3.86)	15·00	15·00	
	Ey. Phosphor omitted	£1600		
X920	34p. ochre-brown (2 bands) (8.1.85)	6·00	6·00	
	Ey. Phosphor omitted	£1600		
X921	50p. ochre-brown (2 bands) (2.2.77)	1·80	1·80	
X922	50p. ochre (2 bands) (20.3.90)	3·75	3·75	

(b) Photo Harrison. On phosphorised paper. P 15×14.

X924	½p. turquoise-blue (10.12.80)	20	20	
	a. Imperf (pair)	£150		
	l. Coil strip. No. X924 and X932×3 (30.12.81)	75		
X925	1p. crimson (12.12.79)	10	10	
	a. Imperf (pair)	£1600		
	l. Coil strip. No. X925 and X932Ea×3 (14.8.84)	90		
	m. Booklet pane. No. X925 and X969, each×2 (10.9.91)	2·00		
X926	2p. myrtle-green (face value as T **367**) (12.12.79)	15	15	
	a. Imperf (pair)	£3000		
X927	2p. deep green (face value as T **367a**) (26.7.88)	25	25	
	a. Imperf (pair)	£3000		
	l. Booklet pane. No. X927×2 and X969×4 plus 2 labels with vert edges of pane imperf (10.9.91)	3·25		
X928	2p. myrtle-green (face value as T **367a**) (5.9.88)	10·00	10·00	
	l. Coil strip. No. X928 and X932Ea×3	10·50		
X929	2½p. rose-red (14.1.81)	25	25	
	l. Coil strip. No. X929 and X930×3 (6.81)	1·00		
X930	3p. brt magenta (Type I) (22.10.80)	20	20	
	a. Imperf (horiz pair)	£2000		
	b. Booklet pane. No. X930, X931×2 and X949×6 with margins all round (14.9.83)	6·50		
	c. Type II (10.10.89)	1·20	1·20	
	cl. Coil strip. No. X930c and X933×3	2·25		
X931	3½p. purple-brown (30.3.83)	60	60	
X932	4p. greenish blue (30.12.81)	45	45	
	Ea. Pale greenish blue (14.8.84)	45	45	
X933	4p. new blue (26.7.88)	20	20	
	a. Imperf (pair)	£3000		
	l. Coil strip. No. X933×3 and X935 (27.11.90)	1·40		
	m. Coil strip. No. X933 and X935, each×2 (1.10.91)	1·00		
	n. Coil strip. No. X933 and X935×3 (31.1.95)	1·25		
X934	5p. pale violet (10.10.79)	55	55	
X935	5p. dull red-brown (26.7.88)	25	25	
	a. Imperf (pair)	£5000		
X936	6p. yellow-olive (10.9.91)	30	30	
X937	7p. brownish red (29.10.85)	1·50	1·50	
X938	8½p. yellowish green (24.3.76)	50	50	
X939	10p. orange-brown (Type I) (11.79)	35	35	
X940	10p. dull orange (Type II) (4.9.90)	40	35	
X941	11p. brown-red (27.8.80)	90	90	
X942	11½p. ochre-brown (15.8.79)	65	65	
X943	12p. yellowish green (30.1.80)	45	45	
X944	13p. olive-grey (15.8.79)	90	90	

X945	13½p. purple-brown (30.1.80)	90	90	
X946	14p. grey-blue (14.1.81)	50	50	
X947	15p. ultramarine (15.8.79)	60	60	
X948	15½p. pale violet (14.1.81)	60	50	
	a. Imperf (pair)	£300		
X949	16p. olive-drab (30.3.83)	55	55	
	a. Imperf (pair)	£200		
	Eu. Underprint Type 3 (10.8.83)	60		
	l. Booklet pane. No. X949×9 with margins all round (14.9.83)	5·00		
X950	16½p. pale chestnut (27.1.82)	90	90	
X951	17p. light emerald (30.1.80)	90	90	
X952	17p. grey-blue (30.3.83)	45	45	
	a. Imperf (pair)	£400		
	Eu. Underprint Type 3 (5.3.85)	60		
	l. Booklet pane. No. X952×6 with margins all round (4.9.84)	4·50		
	m. Booklet pane. No. X952×9 with margins all round (8.1.85)	6·00		
X953	17½p. pale chestnut (30.1.80)	1·25	1·25	
X954	18p. deep violet (14.1.81)	80	80	
X955	18p. deep olive-grey (28.8.84)	75	60	
	a. Imperf (pair)	£150		
	l. Booklet pane. No. X955×9 with margins all round (3.3.87)	7·50		
	m. Booklet pane. No. X955×4 with margins all round (4.8.87)	3·50		
	n. Booklet pane. No. X955×10 with margins all round (4.8.87)	8·00		
X956	19p. bright orange-red (23.8.88)	80	60	
	a. Imperf (pair)	£500		
	l. Booklet pane. No. X956×4 with margins all round	7·00		
	m. Booklet pane. No. X956×10 with margins all round	12·00		
	n. Booklet pane. No. X956×4 with horizontal edges of pane imperf (11.10.88)	8·50		
	o. Booklet pane. No. X956×10 with horizontal edges of pane imperf (11.10.88)	12·00		
	q. Booklet pane. No. X956×4 with three edges of pane imperf (24.1.89)	32·00		
X957	19½p. olive-grey (27.1.82)	2·00	2·00	
X958	20p. dull purple (10.10.79)	1·00	1·00	
X959	20p. turquoise-green (23.8.88)	75	70	
X960	20p. brownish black (26.9.89)	75	75	
	a. Imperf (pair)	£1100		
	l. Booklet pane. No. X960×5 plus label with vertical edges of pane imperf (2.10.89)	6·25		
X961	20½p. ultramarine (30.3.83)	1·40	1·40	
	a. Imperf (pair)	£2200		
X962	22p. blue (22.10.80)	1·20	1·20	
	a. Imperf (pair)	£325		
X963	22p. yellow-green (28.8.84)	1·00	1·00	
	a. Imperf (horiz pair)	£2700		
X964	22p. bright orange-red (4.9.90)	90	80	
	a. Imperf (pair)	£875		
X965	23p. brown-red (30.3.83)	1·25	1·25	
	a. Imperf (horiz pair)	£2000		
X966	23p. bright green (23.8.88)	1·25	1·25	
X967	24p. violet (28.8.84)	1·50	1·50	
X968	24p. Indian red (26.9.89)	2·00	2·00	
	a. Imperf (horiz pair)	£4000		
X969	24p. chestnut (10.9.91)	80	80	
	a. Imperf (pair)	£280		
X970	25p. purple (14.1.81)	1·00	1·00	
X971	26p. rosine (Type I) (27.1.82)	1·00	1·00	
	a. Imperf (horiz pair)	£975		
	b. Type II (4.8.87)	4·50	4·50	
	bl. Booklet pane. No. X971b×4 with margins all round	18·00		
X972	26p. drab (4.9.90)	1·25	1·25	
X973	27p. chestnut (23.8.88)	1·25	1·25	
	l. Booklet pane. No. X973×4 with margins all round	8·00		
	m. Booklet pane. No. X973×4 with horizontal edges of pane imperf (11.10.88)	30·00		
X974	27p. violet (4.9.90)	1·25	1·25	
X975	28p. deep violet (30.3.83)	1·25	1·25	
	a. Imperf (pair)	£2400		
X976	28p. ochre (23.8.88)	1·25	1·25	
X977	28p. deep bluish grey (10.9.91)	1·25	1·25	
	a. Imperf (pair)	£3000		
X978	29p. ochre-brown (27.1.82)	2·25	2·25	
X979	29p. deep mauve (26.9.89)	1·75	1·75	
X980	30p. deep olive-grey (26.9.89)	1·25	1·25	
X981	31p. purple (30.3.83)	1·25	1·25	
	a. Imperf (pair)	£1900		
X982	31p. ultramarine (4.9.90)	1·50	1·50	

X983	32p. greenish blue (23.8.88)	1·50	1·50
	a. Imperf (pair)	£3000	
X984	33p. light emerald (4.9.90)	1·50	1·50
X985	34p. ochre-brown (28.8.84)	1·75	1·75
X986	34p. deep bluish grey (26.9.89)	1·75	1·75
X987	34p. deep mauve (10.9.91)	1·50	1·50
X988	35p. sepia (23.8.88)	1·40	1·40
	a. Imperf (pair)	£3000	
X989	35p. yellow (10.9.91)	1·40	1·40
X990	37p. rosine (26.9.89)	1·50	1·50
X991	39p. bright mauve (10.9.91)	1·75	1·75
X991*a*	50p. ochre (21.1.92)	9·00	9·00
	ab. Imperf (pair)	£2600	

(c) Photo Harrison. On ordinary paper. P 15×14.

X992	50p. ochre-brown (21.5.80)	1·75	1·75
	a. Imperf (pair)	£875	
X993	50p. ochre (13.3.90)	4·00	4·00
X994	75p. grey-black (face value as T **367a**) (26.7.88)	4·50	4·50

(d) Litho J.W. P 14.

X996	4p. greenish blue (2 bands) (30.1.80)	50	50
	Ey. Phosphor omitted	£1600	
X997	4p. greenish blue (phosphorised paper) (11.81)	45	40
X998	20p. dull purple (2 bands) (21.5.80)	1·25	1·25
X999	20p. dull purple (phosphorised paper) (11.81)	1·25	1·25

(e) Litho Questa. P 14 (Nos. X1000, X1003/4 and X1023) or 15×14 (others).

X1000	2p. emerald-green (face value as T **367**) (phosphorised paper) (21.5.80)	40	40
	a. Perf 15×14 (10.7.84)	35	35
X1001	2p. brt green and dp green (face value as T **367a**) (phosphorised paper) (23.2.88)	1·00	1·00
X1002	4p. greenish blue (phosphorised paper) (13.5.86)	80	80
X1003	5p. light violet (phosphorised paper) (21.5.80)	60	60
X1004	5p. claret (phosphorised paper) (27.1.82)	75	75
	a. Perf 15×14 (21.2.84)	65	60
X1005	13p. pale chestnut (1 centre band) (9.2.88)	1·00	1·00
	l. Booklet pane. No. X1005×6 with margins all round	4·75	
X1006	13p. pale chestnut (1 side band at right) (9.2.88)	75	75
	Ea. Band at left	75	75
	l. Booklet pane. No. X1006/Ea each×3, X1010, X1015 and X1021 with margins all round	22·00	
	lEa. Grey-green (on 18p.) ptg double	£3800	
X1007	14p. deep blue (1 centre band) (11.10.88)	1·80	1·80
X1008	17p. deep blue (1 centre band) (19.3.91)	1·00	1·00
	Ey. Phosphor omitted	£240	
	l. Booklet pane. No. X1008×6 with margins all round	5·00	
	lEy. Booklet pane. Phosphor omitted	£1400	
X1009	18p. deep olive-grey (phosphorised paper) (9.2.88)	1·00	1·00
	l. Booklet pane. No. X1009×9 with margins all round	10·00	
	m. Booklet pane. No. X1009×6 with margins all round	5·50	
X1010	18p. deep olive-grey (2 bands) (9.2.88)	7·50	7·50
X1011	18p. bright green (1 centre band) (27.10.92)	1·00	1·00
	l. Booklet pane. No. X1011×6 with margins all round	5·00	
X1012	18p. bright green (1 side band at right) (27.10.92)	1·80	1·80
	Ea. Band at left (10.8.93)	1·80	1·80
	Ey. Phosphor omitted	£850	
	l. Booklet pane. No. X1012×2, X1018×2, X1022×2, 1451a, 1514a and centre label with margins all round	12·00	
	lEa. Bright blue (on 2nd) ptg treble	£7000	
	lEy. Phosphor omitted	£7000	
	m. Booklet pane. No. X1012Ea, X1020, X1022 and 1451aEb, each×2, with centre label and margins all round (10.8.93)	13·00	
	mEy. Booklet pane. Phosphor omitted	£4000	
X1013	19p. bright orange-red (phosphorised paper) (11.10.88)	2·00	2·00
X1014	20p. dull purple (phosphorised paper) (13.5.86)	1·75	1·75
X1015	22p. yellow-green (2 bands) (9.2.88)	7·50	7·50
X1016	22p. bright orange-red (phosphorised paper) (19.3.91)	1·00	90
	l. Booklet pane. No. X1016×9 with margins all round	9·00	
	m. Booklet pane. No. X1016×6, X1019×2 and centre label with margins all round	10·00	

X1017	24p. chestnut (phosphorised paper) (27.10.92)	90	90
	l. Booklet pane. No. X1017×6 with margins all round	5·50	
X1018	24p. chestnut (2 bands) (27.10.92)	2·00	2·00
	Ey. Phosphor omitted	£950	
X1019	33p. light emerald (phosphorised paper) (19.3.91)	2·00	2·00
X1020	33p. lt emerald (2 bands) (25.2.92)	2·00	2·00
	Ey. Phosphor omitted	£750	
X1021	34p. bistre-brown (2 bands) (9.2.88)	7·50	7·50
X1022	39p. brt mauve (2 bands) (27.10.92)	2·00	2·00
	Ey. Phosphor omitted	£950	
X1023	75p. black (face value as T **367**) (ordinary paper) (30.1.80)	3·00	3·00
	a. Perf 15×14 (21.2.84)	4·00	4·00
X1024	75p. brownish grey and black (face value as T **367a**) (ordinary paper) (23.2.88)	9·00	9·00

(f) Litho Walsall. P 14.

X1050	2p. deep green (phosphorised paper) (9.2.93)	1·50	1·50
	l. Booklet pane. No. X1050×2 and X1053×4 plus 2 labels with vert edges of pane imperf	7·50	
X1051	14p. deep blue (1 side band at right) (25.4.89)	3·25	3·25
	Ey. Phosphor omitted	£280	
	l. Booklet pane. No. X1051×2 and X1052×4 with vertical edges of pane imperf	14·00	
	lEy. Phosphor omitted	£975	
X1052	19p. bright orange-red (2 bands) (25.4.89)	2·00	2·00
	Ey. Phosphor omitted	£240	
X1053	24p. chestnut (phosphorised paper) (9.2.93)	1·40	1·40
X1054	29p. dp mauve (2 bands) (2.10.89)	3·00	3·00
	l. Booklet pane. No. X1054×4 with three edges of pane imperf	12·00	
X1055	29p. deep mauve (phosphorised paper) (17.9.90)	3·00	3·00
	l. Booklet pane. No. X1055×4 with three edges of pane imperf	12·00	
X1056	31p. ultramarine (phosphorised paper) (17.9.90)	1·50	1·50
	l. Booklet pane. No. X1056×4 with horizontal edges of pane imperf	6·00	
X1057	33p. light emerald (phosphorised paper) (16.9.91)	1·50	1·50
	l. Booklet pane. No. X1057×4 with horiz edges of pane imperf	6·00	
X1058	39p. bright mauve (phosphorised paper) (16.9.91)	2·00	2·00
	l. Booklet pane. No. X1058×4 with horiz edges of pane imperf	8·00	

* See footnote after No. 744.

† These come from sheets with gum arabic.

†† Examples of Booklet panes Nos. X899l, X901l and X901la are known on which the phosphor bands were printed on the wrong values in error with the result that the side bands appear on the 15½p. or 17p. and the two bands on the 12½p. or 13p. Similarly examples of the 1p. with phosphor band at right instead of left and of the 13p. with band at left instead of right, exist from 50p. booklet pane No. X847l.

Nos. X844a/b come from a strip of eight of the vertical coil. It comprises two normals, one imperforate at sides and bottom, one completely imperforate, one imperforate at top, left and bottom and partly perforated at right due to the bottom three stamps being perforated twice. No. X844b is also known from another strip having one stamp imperforate at sides and bottom.

Nos. X848b/c come from the same sheet, the latter having perforations at the foot of the stamps only.

Multi-value coil strips Nos. X924l, X925l, X928l, X929l, X930cl and X933l/n were produced by the Post Office for use by a large direct mail marketing firm. From 2 September 1981 No. X929l was available from the Philatelic Bureau, Edinburgh, and, subsequently from a number of other Post Office counters. Later multi-value coil strips were sold at the Philatelic Bureau and Post Office philatelic counters.

In addition to booklet pane No. X1012m No. X1020 also comes from the *se-tenant* pane in the Wales £6 booklet. This pane is listed under No. W49a in the Wales Regional section.

PANES OF SIX FROM STITCHED BOOKLETS. Nos. X841m, X851l/m and X855l include one or two printed labels showing commercial advertisements. These were originally perforated on all four sides, but from the August 1971 editions of the 25p. and 30p. booklets (Nos. DH42, DQ59) and December 1971 edition of the 50p. (No. DT4) the line of perforations between the label and the binding margin was omitted. Similar panes, with the line of perforations omitted, exist for the 3p., 3½p. and 4½p. values (Nos. X856, X858 and X865), but these are outside the scope of this listing as the labels are blank.

PART-PERFORATED SHEETS. Since the introduction of the "Jumelle" press in 1972 a number of part perforated sheets, both definitives and commemoratives, have been discovered. It is believed that these occur when the operation of the press is interrupted. Such sheets invariably show a number of "blind" perforations, where the pins have failed to cut the paper. Our listings of imperforate errors from these sheets are for pairs showing no traces whatsoever of the perforations. Examples showing "blind" perforations are outside the scope of this catalogue.

In cases where perforation varieties affect *se-tenant* stamps, fuller descriptions will be found in Vols. 4 and 5 of the *G.B. Specialised Catalogue.*

WHITE PAPER. From 1972 printings appeared on fluorescent white paper giving a stronger chalk reaction than the original ordinary cream paper.

PHOSPHOR OMITTED ERRORS. It should be noted that several values listed with phosphor omitted errors also exist on phosphorised paper. These errors can only be identified with certainty by checking for an "afterglow", using a short-wave ultraviolet lamp.

"ALL-OVER" PHOSPHOR. To improve mechanised handling most commemoratives from the 1972 Royal Silver Wedding 3p. value to the 1979 Rowland Hill Death Centenary set had the phosphor applied by printing cylinder across the entire surface of the stamp, giving a matt effect. Printings of the 1, 2 and 10p. definitives, released in October 1979, also had "all-over" phosphor, but these were purely a temporary expedient pending the adoption of phosphorised paper. Nos. X883, X890 and X921 have been discovered with "all-over" phosphor in addition to the normal phosphor bands. These errors are outside the scope of this catalogue.

PHOSPHORISED PAPER. Following the experiments on Nos. 743c and 829 a printing of the 4½p. definitive was issued on 13 November 1974, which had, in addition to the normal phosphor bands, phosphor included in the paper coating. Because of difficulties in identifying this phosphorised paper with the naked eye this printing is not listed separately in this catalogue.

No. X938 was the first value printed on phosphorised paper without phosphor bands and was a further experimental issue to test the efficacy of this system. From 15 August 1979 phosphorised paper was accepted for use generally, this paper replacing phosphor bands on values other than those required for the second-class rate.

Stamps on phosphorised paper show a shiny surface instead of the matt areas of those printed with phosphor bands or the overall matt appearance of "All-over" phosphor.

DEXTRIN GUM. From 1973 printings in photogravure appeared with PVA gum to which dextrin had been added. Because this is virtually colourless a bluish green colouring matter was added to distinguish it from the earlier pure PVA.

The 4p., 5p. (light violet), 20p. and 75p. printed in lithography exist with PVA and PVAD gum. From 1988 Questa printings were with PVAD gum, but did not show the bluish green additive.

VARNISH COATING. Nos. X841 and X883 exist with and without a varnish coating. This cannot easily be detected without the use of an ultra-violet lamp as it merely reduces the fluorescent paper reaction.

POSTAL FORGERIES. In mid-1993 a number of postal forgeries of the 24p. chestnut were detected in the London area. These forgeries, produced by lithography, can be identified by the lack of phosphor in the paper, screening dots across the face value and by the perforations which were applied by a line machine gauging 11.

First Day Covers

15.2.71	½p., 1p., 1½p., 2p., 2½p., 3p., 3½p., 4p., 5p., 6p., 7½p., 9p. (X841, X844, X848/9, X851, X855, X858, X861, X866, X870, X877, X882) (Covers carry "POSTING DELAYED BY THE POST OFFICE STRIKE 1971" cachet)	2·50
11.8.71	10p. (X885)	1·00
24.5.72	Wedgwood *se-tenant* pane ½p., 2½p. (X841p)	25·00
24.10.73	4½p., 5½p., 8p. (X865, X868, X878)	1·00
4.9.74	6½p. (X871)	1·00
15.1.75	7p. (X874)	1·00
24.9.75	8½p. (X881)	1·00
25.2.76	9p., 9½p., 10p., 10½p., 11p., 20p. (X883/4, X886, X890, X892, X915)	2·50
2.2.77	50p. (X921)	1·00
26.4.78	10½p. (X891)	1·00
15.8.79	11½p., 13p., 15p. (X942, X944, X947)	1·00
30.1.80	4p., 12p., 13½p., 17p., 17½p., 75p. (X996, X943, X945, X951, X953, X1023)	2·00
16.4.80	Wedgwood *se-tenant* pane 2p., 10p., 12p. (X849n)	1·25
22.10.80	3p., 22p. (X930, X962)	1·00
14.1.81	2½p., 11½p., 14p., 15½p., 18p., 25p. (X929, X893, X946, X948, X954, X970)	1·25
27.1.82	5p., 12½p., 16½p., 19½p., 26p., 29p. (X1004, X898, X950, X957, X971, X978)	2·00
19.5.82	Stanley Gibbons *se-tenant* pane 2p., 3p., 12½p. (X849p)	2·00
30.3.83	3½p., 16p., 17p., 20½p., 23p., 28p., 31p. (X931, X949, X952, X961, X965, X975, X981)	2·75
14.9.83	Royal Mint *se-tenant* pane 3p., 3½p., 16p. (X930b)	2·50
28.8.84	13p., 18p., 22p., 34p. (X900, X955, X963, X967, X985)	2·00
4.9.84	Christian Heritage *se-tenant* pane 10p., 13p., 17p. (X886bl)	8·50
8.1.85	*The Times se-tenant* pane 4p., 13p., 17p., 34p. (X864l)	4·00
29.10.85	7p., 12p. (X937, X896)	2·00
18.3.86	British Rail *se-tenant* pane 12p., 17p., 31p. (X897m)	5·50
3.3.87	P&O *se-tenant* pane 1p., 13p., 18p., 26p. (X847m)	4·00

9.2.88	*Financial Times se-tenant* pane 13p., 18p., 22p., 34p. (X1006l)	6·00
23.8.88	14p., 19p., 20p., 23p., 27p., 28p., 32p., 35p. (X903, X956, X959, X966, X973, X976, X983, X988)	3·50
26.9.89	15p., 20p., 24p., 29p., 30p., 34p., 37p. (X905, X960, X968, X979/80, X986, X990)	3·00
20.3.90	London Life *se-tenant* pane 15p., (2nd), 20p., (1st), 15p., 20p., 29p. (X906m)	4·00
4.9.90	10p., 17p., 22p., 26p., 27p., 31p., 33p. (X910, X940, X964, X972, X974, X982, X984)	3·00
19.3.91	Alias Agatha Christie *se-tenant* pane 22p., 33p. (X1016m)	4·00
10.9.91	6p., 18p., 24p., 28p., 34p., 35p., 39p. (X936, X913, X969, X977, X987, X989, X991)	3·25
27.10.92	Tolkien *se-tenant* pane 18p., (2nd), 24p., (1st), 39p. (X1012l)	4·00
10.8.93	Beatrix Potter *se-tenant* pane 18p., (2nd), 33p., 39p. (X1012m)	5·50

Post Office Presentation Packs

15.2.71	PO Pack No. 26. ½p. (2 bands), 1p. (2 bands), 1½p. (2 bands), 2p. (2 bands), 2½p. magenta (1 centre band), 3p. ultramarine (2 bands), 3½p. olive-grey (2 bands), 4p. ochre-brown (2 bands), 5p. pale violet (2 bands), 6p. light emerald (2 bands), 7½p. (2 bands), 9p. yellow-orange and black (2 bands). (*Nos.* X841, X844, X848/9, X851, X855, X858, X861, X866, X870, X877, X882)	9·00
15.4.71**	"Scandinavia 71". Contents as above	25·00
25.11.71	PO Pack No. 37. ½p. (2 bands), 1p. (2 bands), 1½p. (2 bands), 2p. (2 bands), 2½p. magenta (1 centre band), 3p. ultramarine (2 bands) or (1 centre band), 3½p. olive-grey (2 bands) or (1 centre band), 4p. ochre-brown (2 bands), 4½p. (2 bands), 5p. pale violet (2 bands), 5½p. (2 bands) or (1 centre band), 6p. (2 bands), 6½p. (2 bands) or (1 centre band), 7p. (2 bands), 7½p. (2 bands), 8p (2 bands), 9p. yellow-orange and black (2 bands), 10p. orange-brown and chestnut (2 bands). (*Nos.* X841, X844, X848/9, X851, X855 or X856, X858 or X859, X861, X865/6, X868 or X869, X870, X871 or X872, X874, X877/8, X882, X885)	30·00
	Later issues of this Pack contained the alternatives	
2.2.77	PO Pack No. 90. ½p. (2 bands), 1p. (2 bands), 1½p. (2 bands), 2p. (2 bands), 2½p. magenta (1 centre band), 3p. ultramarine (1 centre band), 5p. pale violet (2 bands), 6½p. (1 centre band), 7p. (2 bands) or (1 centre band), 7½p. (2 bands), 8p. (2 bands), 8½p. (2 bands), 9p. deep violet (2 bands), 9½p. (2 bands), 10p. orange-brown (2 bands), 10½p. yellow (2 bands), 11p. (2 bands), 20p. dull purple (2 bands), 50p. ochre-brown (2 bands). (*Nos.* X841, X844, X848/9, X851, X856, X866, X872, X874 or X875, X877/8, X881, X883/4, X886, X890, X892, X915, X921)	5·00
28.10.81	PO Pack No. 129a. 10½p. deep dull blue (2 bands), 11½p. (1 centre band), 2½p. (phos paper), 3p. (phos paper), 11½p. (phos paper), 12p. (phos paper), 13p. (phos paper), 13½p. (phos paper), 14p. (phos paper), 15p. (phos paper), 15½p. (phos paper), 17p. light emerald (phos paper), 17½p. (phos paper), 18p. deep violet (phos paper), 22p. blue (phos paper), 25p. (phos paper), 4p. greenish blue (litho, 2 bands), 75p. (litho) (*Nos.* X891, X893, X929/30, X942/8, X951, X953/4, X962, X970, X996, X1023).	15·00
3.8.83	PO Pack No. 1. 10p. orange-brown (1 centre band), 12½p. (1 centre band), ½p. (phos paper), 1p. (phos paper), 3p. (phos paper), 3½p. (phos paper), 16p. (phos paper), 16½p. (phos paper), 17p. grey-blue (phos paper), 20½p. (phos paper), 23p. brown-red (phos paper), 26p. prosine (phos paper), 28p. deep violet (phos paper), 31p. purple (phos paper), 50p (ord paper), 2p. (litho phos paper), 4p. (litho phos paper), 5p. claret (litho phos paper), 20p. (litho phos paper), 75p. (litho) (*Nos.* X888, X898, X924/5, X930/1, X949/50, X952, X961, X965, X971, X975, X981, X992, X997, X999, X1000, X1004, X1023)	32·00
23.10.84	PO Pack No. 5. 13p. (1 centre band), ½p. (phos paper), 1p. (phos paper), 3p. (phos paper), 10p. orange-brown (phos paper), 16p. (phos paper), 17p. grey-blue (phos paper), 18p. dp olive-grey (phos paper), 22p. yellow-green (phos paper), 24p. violet (phos paper), 26p. rosine (phos paper), 28p. deep violet (phos paper), 31p. purple (phos paper), 34p. ochre-brown (phos paper), 50p. (ord paper), 2p. (litho phos paper), 4p. (litho phos paper), 5p. claret (litho phos paper), 20p. (litho phos paper), 75p. (litho) (*Nos.* X900, X924/5, X930, X939, X949, X952, X955, X963, X967, X971, X975, X981, X985, X992, X1000a, X997, X1004a, X999, X1023a)	25·00

3.3.87　PO Pack No. 9. 12p. (1 centre band), 13p. (1 centre band), 1p. (phos paper), 3p. (phos paper), 7p. (phos paper), 10p. orange-brown (phos paper), 17p. grey-blue (phos paper), 18p. dp olive-grey (phos paper), 22p. yellow-green (phos paper), 24p. violet (phos paper), 26p. rosine (phos paper), 28p. deep violet (phos paper), 31p. purple (phos paper), 34p. ochre-brown (phos paper), 50p. (ord paper), 2p. (litho phos paper), 4p. (litho phos paper), 5p. claret (litho phos paper), 20p. (litho phos paper), 75p. (litho) (*Nos.* X896, X900, X925, X930, X937, X939, X952, X955, X963, X967, X971, X975, X981, X985, X992, X1000a, X997, X1004a, X999, X1023a).. 30·00

23.8.88　PO Pack No. 15. 14p. (1 centre band), 19p. (phos paper), 20p. turquoise-green (phos paper), 23p. bright green (phos paper), 27p. chestnut (phos paper), 28p. ochre (phos paper), 32p. (phos paper), 35p. sepia (phos paper) (*Nos.* X903, X956, X959, X966, X973, X976, X983, X988).. 9·00

26.9.89　PO Pack No. 19. 15p. (centre band), 20p. brownish black (phos paper), 24p. Indian red (phos paper), 29p. deep mauve (phos paper), 30p. (phos paper), 34p. deep bluish grey (phos paper), 37p. (phos paper) (*Nos.* X905, X960, X968, X979/80, X986, X990)............. 7·00

4.9.90　PO Pack No. 22. 10p. dull orange (phos paper), 17p. (centre band), 22p. bright orange-red (phos paper), 26p. drab (phos paper), 27p. violet (phos paper), 31p. ultramarine (phos paper), 33p. (phos paper) (*Nos.* X940, X910, X964, X972, X974, X9 82, X984) .... 7·00

14.5.91　PO Pack No. 24. 1p. (phos paper), 2p. (phos paper), 3p. (phos paper), 4p. new blue (phos paper), 5p. dull red-brown (phos paper), 10p. dull orange (phos paper), 17p. (centre band), 20p. turquoise-green (phos paper), 22p. bright orange-red (phos paper), 26p. drab (phos paper), 27p. violet (phos paper), 30p. (phos paper), 31p. ultramarine (phos paper), 32p. (phos paper), 33p. (phos paper), 37p. (phos paper), 50p. (ord paper), 75p. (ord paper). (*Nos.* X925, X927, X930, X933, X935, X940, X910, X959, X964, X972, X974, X980, X982/4, X990, X993/4)..................... 30·00

10.9.91　PO Pack No. 25. 6p (phos paper), 18p. (centre band), 24p. chestnut (phos paper), 28p. deep bluish grey (phos paper), 34p. deep mauve (phos paper), 35p. yellow (phos paper), 39p. (phos paper) (*Nos.* X913, X936, X969, X977, X987, X989, X991).............................. 7·00

** The "Scandinavia 71" was a special pack produced for sale during a visit to six cities in Denmark, Sweden and Norway by a mobile display unit between 15 April and 20 May 1971. The pack gives details of this tour and also lists the other stamps which were due to be issued in 1971, the text being in English. A separate insert gives translations in Danish, Swedish and Norwegian. The pack was also available at the Philatelic Bureau, Edinburgh.

For stamps of this design inscribed "2nd" and "1st" see Nos. 1445/52 and 1511/16, and for stamps with one elliptical perforation hole on each vertical side see Nos. 1664/72, Y1667/1803, 2039/40, 2295/8, 2650/7, U2941/74 and 3271/8.

508

1977 (2 Feb)–**87**. Perf 14×15.

1026	**508**	£1 brt yellow-green and blackish olive	3·00	25
		a. Imperf (pair)..	£1700	
1026*b*		£1.30 pale drab and deep greenish blue (3.8.83)..	5·50	6·00
1026*c*		£1.33 pale mauve and grey-black (28.8.84)...	7·50	8·00
1026*d*		£1.41 pale drab and deep greenish blue (17.9.85)	8·50	8·50
1026*e*		£1.50 pale mauve and grey-black (2.9.86)..	6·00	5·00
1026*f*		£1.60 pale drab and deep greenish blue (15.9.87)	6·50	7·00
1027		£2 light emerald and purple-brown	9·00	50
		a. Imperf (pair)...	£4000	
1028		£5 salmon and chalky blue......................	22·00	3·00
		a. Imperf (vert pair)...................................	£15000	
Set of 8			60·00	32·00
Set of 8 Gutter Pairs...			£125	

Set of 8 Traffic Light Gutter Pairs.. £150

	Gutter pairs	
	Plain	Traffic Light
1026, 1027/8	70·00	75·00
1026*b*	13·00	20·00
1026*c*	16·00	22·00
1026*d*	18·00	25·00
1026*e*	13·00	17·00
1026*f*	14·00	18·00

Presentation Pack (*P.O. Pack No.* 91 (small size)) (1026, 1027/8)... 38·00
Presentation Pack (*P.O. Pack No.* 13 (large size)) (1026, 1027/8)... £170
Presentation Pack (*P.O. Pack No.* 14) (large size) (1026*f*) 22·00

Special First Day of Issue Postmarks
(for illustrations see Introduction)

Philatelic Bureau, Edinburgh (Type F) (£1, £2, £5)	10·00
Windsor, Berks (Type F) (£1, £2, £5)	12·00
Philatelic Bureau, Edinburgh (Type F) (£1.30)	6·50
Windsor, Berks (Type F) (£1.30)	6·50
British Philatelic Bureau, Edinburgh (Type F) (£1.33)	8·50
Windsor, Berks (Type F) (£1.33)...	8·50
British Philatelic Bureau, Edinburgh (Type G) (£1.41)	9·00
Windsor, Berks (Type G) (£1.41)	9·00
British Philatelic Bureau, Edinburgh (Type G) (£1.50)	5·50
Windsor, Berks (Type G) (£1.50)	5·50
British Philatelic Bureau, Edinburgh (Type G) (£1.60)	7·50
Windsor, Berks (Type G) (£1.60)..	7·50

Decimal Machin Index

(Denominated stamps with 'standard' perforations)

Those booklet stamps shown below with an * after the catalogue number do not exist with perforations on all four sides, but show one or two sides imperforate.

Value.	Process	Colour	Phosphor	Cat. No.	Source
½p.	photo	turquoise-blue	2 bands	X841/Fg	(a) with P.V.A. gum—sheets, 5p. m/v coil (X841nEv), 10p.m/v coil (X841q), 10p. booklets (DN46/75, FA1/3), 25p. booklets (DH39/52), 50p. booklets (DT1/12, FB1, FB14/16, FB19/23), £1 Wedgwood booklet (DX1)
					(b) with gum arabic—sheets, 5p. m/v coil (X841n)
½p.	photo	turquoise-blue	1 band at left	X842	£1 Wedgwood booklet (DX1)
½p.	photo	turquoise-blue	1 centre band	X843	10p. m/v coil (X843l), 10p. booklets (FA4/9)
½p.	photo	turquoise-blue	phos paper	X924	sheets, 12½p. m/v coil (X924l)
1p.	photo	crimson	2 bands	X844/Eg	(a) with P.V.A. gum—sheets, vertical coils, 5p. m/v coil (X841nEv), 10p. m/v coil (X841q), 10p. booklets (DN46/75, FA1/3), 50p. booklets (FB1/8, FB14/16)
					(b) with gum arabic—vertical coils, 5p. m/v coil (X841n)
1p.	photo	crimson	1 centre band	X845	10p. m/v coils (X843l, X845m), 10p. booklets (FA4/11), 50p. booklets (FB24/30, 34/36, 43/6, 48, 50)
1p.	photo	crimson	"all-over"	X846	sheets
1p.	photo	crimson	phos paper	X925	sheets, horizontal and vertical coils, 13p. m/v coil (X925l), 50p. booklet (FB59/66)
1p.	photo	crimson	1 band at left	X847	50p. booklets (FB37/42, 47, 49)
1p.	photo	crimson	1 band at right	X847Ea	£5 P. & O. booklet (DX8)
1½p.	photo	black	2 bands	X848	sheets, 10p. booklets (DN46/75)
2p.	photo	myrtle-green	2 bands	X849/Eg	(a) with P.V.A. gum—sheets, 5p. m/v coil (X841nEv), 10p. m/v coil (X841q), 10p. booklets (DN46/75), 50p. booklets (FB9/13), £3 Wedgwood booklet (DX2), £4 SG booklet (DX3)
					(b) with gum arabic—5p. m/v coil (X841n)
2p.	photo	myrtle-green	"all-over"	X850	sheets
2p.	photo	myrtle-green	phos paper	X926	sheets
2p.	photo	myrtle-green	phos paper	X928	14p. m/v coil (X928l)
2p.	litho	emerald-green	phos paper	X1000/a	sheets
2p.	litho	brt grn and dp grn	phos paper	X1001	sheets
2p.	photo	dp green	phos paper	X927	sheets, £1 booklets (FH23/7)
2p.	litho	dp green	phos paper	X1050*	£1 booklets (FH28/30)
2½p.	photo	magenta	1 centre band	X851/Eg	(a) with P.V.A. gum—sheets, horizontal and vertical coils, 25p. booklets (DH39/52), 50p. booklets (DT1/12), £1 Wedgwood booklet (DX1)
					(b) with gum arabic—sheets, horizontal coils
2½p.	photo	magenta	1 side band	X852/Ea	(a) band at left—50p. booklets (DT1/12), £1 Wedgwood booklet (DX1)
					(b) band at right—£1 Wedgwood booklet (DX1)
2½p.	photo	magenta	2 bands	X853	sheets
2½p.	photo	rose-red	phos paper	X929	sheets, 11½p. m/v coil (X929l)
2½p.	photo	rose-red	2 bands	X854	50p. booklets (FB17/18)
3p.	photo	ultramarine	2 bands	X855/Eg	(a) with P.V.A. gum—sheets, horizontal and vertical coils, 30p. booklets (DQ56/72), 50p. booklets (DT1/12), £1 Wedgwood booklet (DX1)
					(b) with gum arabic—sheets, horizontal coils
3p.	photo	ultramarine	1 centre band	X856/Eg	(a) with P.V.A. gum—sheets, horizontal and vertical coils, 30p. booklets (DQ73/4), 50p. booklets (DT13/14)
					(b) with gum arabic—sheets
3p.	photo	brt magenta	phos paper	X930	Type I. sheets, 11½p. m/v coil (X929l), £4 Royal Mint booklet (DX4)
3p.	photo	brt magenta	phos paper	X930c	Type II. sheets (from 21.1.92), 15p. m/v coil (X930cl)
3p.	photo	brt magenta	2 bands	X857	Type I. 50p. booklets (FB19/23), £4 SG booklet (DX3)
3½p.	photo	olive-grey	2 bands	X858/Eb	sheets, horizontal and vertical coils, 35p. booklets (DP1/3), 50p. booklets (DT13/14)
3½p.	photo	olive-grey	1 centre band	X859	sheet, horizontal coils, 35p. booklet (DP4), 85p. booklet (DW1)
3½p.	photo	purple-brown	phos paper	X931	sheets, £4 Royal Mint booklet (DX4)
3½p.	photo	purple-brown	1 centre band	X860	50p. booklets (FB24/6)
4p.	photo	ochre-brown	2 bands	X861/Eg	(a) with P.V.A. gum—sheets.
					(b) with gum arabic—sheets
4p.	litho	greenish blue	2 bands	X996	sheets
4p.	photo	greenish blue	2 bands	X862	50p. booklets (FB17/18)
4p.	litho	greenish blue	phos paper	X997	sheets J.W. ptg.
				X1002	sheets Questa ptg.
4p.	photo	greenish blue	phos paper	X932	12½p. m/v coil (X924l)
				X932Ea	13p. m/v coil (X925l), 14p. m/v coil (X928l)
4p.	photo	greenish blue	1 centre band	X863	50p. booklets (FB27/30)
4p.	photo	greenish blue	1 side band	X864/Ea	(a) band at right—£5 *The Times* booklet (DX6)
					(b) band at left—£5 *The Times* booklet (DX6)
4p.	photo	new blue	phos paper	X933	sheets, 15p. m/v coil (X930cl), 17p. m/v coil (X933l), 18p. m/v coil (X933m), 19p m/v coil (X933n)
4½p.	photo	grey-blue	2 bands	X865	sheets, horizontal coils, 45p. booklets (DS1/2), 85p. booklet (DW1)
5p.	photo	pale violet	2 bands	X866	sheets
5p.	photo	pale violet	phos paper	X934	sheets
5p.	litho	lt violet	phos paper	X1003	sheets
5p.	litho	claret	phos paper	X1004/a	sheets
5p.	photo	claret	1 centre band	X867	50p. booklets (FB35/36, 43/6, 48, 50)

Value.	Process	Colour	Phosphor	Cat. No.	Source
5p.	photo	dull red-brown	phos paper	X935	sheets, 17p. m/v coil (X933l), 18p. m/v coil (X933m), 19p m/v coil (X933n)
5½p.	photo	violet	2 bands	X868	sheets
5½p.	photo	violet	1 centre band	X869	sheets
6p.	photo	lt emerald	2 bands	X870/Eg	(a) with P.V.A. gum—sheets, 10p. m/v coil (X841q), 10p. booklets (FA1/3)
					(b) with gum arabic—sheets
6p.	photo	yellow-olive	phos paper	X936	sheets
6½p.	photo	greenish blue	2 bands	X871	sheets
6½p.	photo	greenish blue	1 centre band	X872	sheets, horizontal and vertical coils, 65p. booklet (FC1)
6½p.	photo	greenish blue	1 side band	X873/Ea	(a) band at right—50p. booklet (FB1A).
					(b) band at left—50p. booklet (FB1B)
7p.	photo	purple-brown	2 bands	X874	sheets
7p.	photo	purple-brown	1 centre band	X875	sheets, horizontal and vertical coils, 10p. m/v coil (X843l), 10p. booklets (FA4/9), 70p. booklets (FD1/8), £1.60 Christmas booklet (FX1)
7p.	photo	purple-brown	1 side band	X876/Ea	(a) band at right—50p. booklets (FB2A/8A)
					(b) band at left—50p. booklets (FB2B/8B)
7p.	photo	brownish red	phos paper	X937	sheets
7½p.	photo	pale chestnut	2 bands	X877	sheets
8p.	photo	rosine	2 bands	X878	sheets
8p.	photo	rosine	1 centre band	X879	sheets, vertical coils, 10p. m/v coil (X845m), 10p. booklets (FA10/11), 80p. booklet (FE1), £1.80 Christmas booklet (FX2)
8p.	photo	rosine	1 side band	X880/Ea	(a) band at right—50p. booklets (FB9A/10A)
					(b) band at left—50p. booklets (FB9B/10B)
8½p	photo	lt yellowish green	2 bands	X881/b	sheets, horizontal and vertical coils, 50p. booklet (FB1), 85p. booklet (FF1)
8½p	photo	yellowish green	phos paper	X938	sheets
9p.	photo	yellow-orange and black	2 bands	X882	sheets
9p.	photo	dp violet	2 bands	X883	sheets, horizontal and vertical coils, 50p. booklets (FB2/8), 90p. booklets (FG1/8), £1.60 Christmas booklet (FX1)
9½p	photo	purple	2 bands	X884	sheets
10p.	recess	cerise	phos paper	829	sheets
10p.	photo	orange-brown and chestnut	2 bands	X885	sheets
10p.	photo	orange-brown	2 bands	X886	Type I. sheets, 50p. booklets (FB9/10), £1.80 Christmas booklet (FX2)
10p.	photo	orange-brown	2 bands	X886b	Type II. £4 Christian Heritage booklet (DX5)
10p.	photo	orange-brown	"all-over"	X887	Type I. sheets, vertical coils, £1 booklet (FH1)
10p.	photo	orange-brown	phos paper	X939	Type I. sheets
10p.	photo	orange-brown	1 centre band	X888	Type I. sheets, vertical coils, £1 booklets (FH2/4), £2.20 Christmas booklet (FX3), £3 Wedgwood booklet (DX2)
10p.	photo	orange-brown	1 side band	X889/Ea	Type I. (a) band at right—50p. booklets (FB11A/13A)
					(b) band at left—50p. booklets (FB11B/13B), £3 Wedgwood booklet (DX2)
10p.	photo	dull orange	phos paper	X940	sheets
10½p.	photo	yellow	2 bands	X890	sheets
10½p.	photo	dp dull blue	2 bands	X891	sheets
11p.	photo	brown-red	2 bands	X892	sheets
11p.	photo	brown-red	phos paper	X941	sheets
11½p	photo	ochre-brown	phos paper	X942	sheets
11½p	photo	drab	1 centre band	X893	sheets, vertical coils, £1.15 booklets (FI1/4), £2.55 Christmas booklet (FX4)
11½p.	photo	drab	1 side band	X894/Ea	(a) band at right—50p. booklets (FB14A/18A), £1.30 booklets (FL1/2)
					(b) band at left—50p. booklets FB14B/18B), £1.30 booklets (FL1/2)
12p.	photo	yellowish green	phos paper	X943	sheets, vertical coils, £1.20 booklets (FJ1/3)
12p.	photo	yellowish green	2 bands	X895	50p. booklets (FB11/13), £2.20 Christmas booklet (FX3), £3 Wedgwood booklet (DX2)
12p.	photo	brt emerald	1 centre band	X896	sheets, horizontal and vertical coils, 50p. booklet (FB34), £1.20 booklets (FJ4/6), £5 British Rail booklet (DX7)
12p.	photo	brt emerald	1 side band	X897/ Ea	(a) band at right—£1.50 booklets (FP1/3), £5 British Rail booklet (DX7)
					(b) band at left—£1.50 booklets (FP1/3), £5 British Rail booklet (DX7)
12p.	photo	brt emerald	1 centre band Underprint T.4	X896Eu	sheets
12½p.	photo	lt emerald	1 centre band	X898	sheets, vertical coils, 50p. booklets (FB24/6), £1.25 booklets (FK1/8), £4 SG booklet (DX3)
12½p.	photo	lt emerald	1 centre band Underprint T.1	X898Eu	£2.80 Christmas booklet (FX5)
12½p.	photo	lt emerald	1 centre band Underprint T.2	X898Ev	£2.50 Christmas booklet (FX6)
12½p.	photo	lt emerald	1 side band	X899/Ea	(a) band at right—50p. booklets (FB19A/23A), £1.43 booklets (FN1/6), £1.46 booklets (FO1/3), £4 SG booklet (DX3), £4 Royal Mint booklet (DX4)
					(b) band at left—50p. booklets (FB19B/23B), £1.43 booklets (FN1/6), £1.46 booklets (FO1/3), £4 SG booklet (DX3), £4 Royal Mint booklet (DX4)
13p.	photo	olive-grey	phos paper	X944	sheets
13p.	photo	pale chestnut	1 centre band	X900	sheets, horizontal and vertical coils, 50p. booklets (FB27/30, 35/6, 43/6, 48, 50), 52p. booklet (GA1), £1.30 booklets (FL3/14, Gl1), £5 *The Times* booklet (DX6), £5 P & O booklet (DX8)
13p.	photo	pale chestnut	1 centre band Underprint T.2	X900Eu	£1.30 Christmas booklet (FX9)
13p.	photo	pale chestnut	1 side band	X901/Ea	(a) band at right—50p. booklets (FB37/42, 47, 49), £1.54 booklets (FQ1/4), £4 Christian Heritage booklet (DX5), £5 *The Times* booklet (DX6), £5 P & O booklet (DX8)
					(b) band at left—£1 booklets (FH6/13), £1.54 booklets (FQ1/4), £4 Christian Heritage booklet (DX5), £5 *The Times* booklet (DX6)
13p.	litho	pale chestnut	1 centre band	X1005	£5 *Financial Times* booklet (DX9)
13p.	litho	pale chestnut	1 side band	X1006/Ea	£5 *Financial Times* booklet (DX9)
13½p.	photo	purple-brown	phos paper	X945	sheets
14p.	photo	grey-blue	phos paper	X946	sheets, vertical coils, £1.40 booklets (FM1/4)
14p.	photo	grey-blue	2 bands	X902	50p. booklets (FB14/16), £1.30 booklets (FL1/2), £2.55 Christmas booklet (FX4)

Value.	Process	Colour	Phosphor	Cat. No.	Source
14p.	photo	dp blue	1 centre band	X903	sheets, horizontal and vertical coils, 56p. booklets (GB1/4), £1.40 booklets (FM5/6, GK1, 3)
14p.	photo	dp blue	1 band at right	X904	50p. booklets (FB51/4), £1 booklets (FH14/15 and 17)
14p.	litho	dp blue	1 centre band	X1007	£1.40 booklets (GK2, 4)
14p.	litho	dp blue	1 band at right	X1051*	£1 booklet (FH16)
15p.	photo	ultramarine	phos paper	X947	sheets
15p.	photo	brt blue	1 centre band	X905	sheets, horizontal and vertical coils
15p.	photo	brt blue	1 side band	X906/Ea	(a) band at left—50p. booklet (FB55) (b) band at right—£5 London Life booklet (DX11)
15½p.	photo	pale violet	phos paper	X948	sheets, vertical coils, £1.55 booklets (FR1/4)
15½p.	photo	pale violet	2 bands	X907	£1.43 booklets (FN1/6), £4 SG booklet (DX3)
15½p.	photo	pale violet	2 bands Underprint T.1	X907Eu	£2.80 Christmas booklet (FX5)
16p.	photo	olive-drab	phos paper	X949	sheets, vertical coils, £1.60 booklets (FS1, 3/4), £4 Royal Mint booklet (DX4)
16p.	photo	olive-drab	phos paper Underprint T.3	X949Eu	£1.60 booklet (FS2)
16p.	photo	olive-drab	2 bands	X908	£1.46 booklets (FO1/3)
16½p.	photo	pale chestnut	phos paper	X950	sheets
17p.	photo	lt emerald	phos paper	X951	sheets
17p.	photo	grey-blue	phos paper	X952	sheets, vertical coils, £1 booklet (FH5), £1.70 booklets (FT1, 3 & 5/7), £4 Christian Heritage booklet (DX5), £5 *The Times* booklet (DX6), £5 British Rail booklet (DX7)
17p.	photo	grey-blue	phos paper Underprint T.3	X952Eu	£1.70 booklet (FT2)
17p.	photo	grey-blue	2 bands	X909	50p. booklet (FB33a), £1.50 booklets (FP1/3), £1.54 booklets (FQ1/4), £4 Christian Heritage booklet (DX5), £5 *The Times* booklet (DX6), £5 British Rail booklet (DX7)
17p.	photo	grey-blue	2 bands Underprint T.4	X909Eu	50p. booklets (FB31/3)
17p.	photo	dp blue	1 centre band	X910	sheets, vertical coils
17p.	photo	dp blue	1 side band	X911/Ea	(a) band at right—50p. booklet (FB57/8), £1 booklet (FH21/2) (b) band at left—50p. booklet (FB57/8)
17p.	litho	dp blue	1 centre band	X1008	£6 Alias Agatha Christie booklet (DX12)
17½p	photo	pale chestnut	phos paper	X953	sheets
18p.	photo	dp violet	phos paper	X954	sheets
18p.	photo	dp olive-grey	phos paper	X955	sheets, vertical coils, 72p. booklet (GC1), £1.80 booklets (FU1/8, GO1), £5 P & O booklet (DX8)
18p.	photo	dp olive-grey	2 bands	X912	50p. booklets (FB37/42, 47, 49), £1 booklet (FH6/13), £5 P & O booklet (DX8)
18p.	litho	dp olive-grey	phos paper	X1009	£5 *Financial Times* booklet (DX9)
18p.	litho	dp olive-grey	2 bands	X1010	£5 *Financial Times* booklet (DX9)
18p.	photo/gravure	brt green	1 centre band	X913	sheets, vertical coils
18p.	litho	brt green	1 centre band	X1011	£6 Tolkien booklet (DX14)
18p.	litho	brt green	1 side band	X1012/Ea	(a) band at right—£6 Tolkien booklet (DX14). (b) band at left—£6 (£5.64) Beatrix Potter booklet (DX15)).
19p.	photo	brt orange-red	phos paper	X956	sheets, vertical coils, 76p. booklets (GD1/4), £1.90 booklets (FV1/2, GP1, 3)
19p.	photo	brt orange-red	2 bands	X914	50p. booklets (FB51/4), £1 booklets (FH14/15, 17)
19p.	litho	brt orange-red	phos paper	X1013	£1.90 booklets (GP2, 4)
19p.	litho	brt orange-red	2 bands	X1052*	£1 booklet (FH16)
19½p	photo	olive-grey	phos paper	X957	sheets
20p.	recess	olive-green	none	830	sheets
20p.	photo	dull purple	2 bands	X915	sheets
20p.	photo	dull purple	phos paper	X958	sheets
20p.	litho	dull purple	2 bands	X998	sheets
20p.	litho	dull purple	phos paper	X999	sheets J.W. ptg.
				X1014	sheets Questa ptg.
20p.	photo	turquoise-green	phos paper	X959	sheets
20p.	photo	brownish black	phos paper	X960	sheets, horizontal and vertical coils, £1 booklet (FH18)
20p.	photo	brownish black	2 bands	X916	50p. booklet (FB55), £5 London Life booklet (DX11)
20½p.	photo	ultramarine	phos paper	X961	sheets
22p.	photo	blue	phos paper	X962	sheets
22p.	photo	yellow-green	phos paper	X963	sheets
22p.	litho	yellow-green	2 bands	X1015	£5 *Financial Times* booklet (DX9)
22p.	photo	brt orange-red	2 bands	X917*	£1 booklet (FH21/2)
22p.	photo	brt orange-red	phos paper	X964	sheets, vertical coils
22p.	litho	brt orange-red	phos paper	X1016	£6 Alias Agatha Christie booklet (DX12)
23p.	photo	brown-red	phos paper	X965	sheets
23p.	photo	brt green	phos paper	X966	sheets
24p.	photo	violet	phos paper	X967	sheets
24p.	photo	Indian red	phos paper	X968	sheets
24p.	photo	chestnut	phos paper	X969	sheets, vertical coils, 50p. booklets (FB59/66), £1 booklets (FH23/7)
24p.	litho	chestnut	phos paper	X1017	£6 Tolkien booklet (DX14) (Questa ptg)
				X1053*	£1 booklet (FH28/30) Walsall ptg
24p.	litho	chestnut	2 bands	X1018	£6 Tolkien booklet (DX14)
25p.	photo	purple	phos paper	X970	sheets
25p.	photo	rose-red	2 bands	X917a	horizontal coils
26p.	photo	rosine	phos paper	X971	Type I. sheets
26p.	photo	rosine	2 bands	X918	Type I. £5 P & O booklet (DX8)
26p.	photo	rosine	phos paper	X971b	Type II. £1.04 booklet (GE1)
26p.	photo	drab	phos paper	X972	sheets
27p.	photo	chestnut	phos paper	X973	sheets, £1.08 booklets (GF1/2)
27p.	photo	violet	phos paper	X974	sheets
28p.	photo	dp violet	phos paper	X975	sheets
28p.	photo	ochre	phos paper	X976	sheets
28p.	photo	dp bluish grey	phos paper	X977	sheets
29p.	photo	ochre-brown	phos paper	X978	sheets

Value.	Process	Colour	Phosphor	Cat. No.	Source
29p.	photo	dp mauve	phos paper	X979	sheets
29p.	litho	dp mauve	2 bands	X1054*	£1.16 booklet (GG1)
29p.	litho	dp mauve	phos paper	X1055*	£1.16 booklet (GG2)
30p.	photo	dp olive-grey	phos paper	X980	sheets
31p.	photo	purple	phos paper	X981	sheets
31p.	photo	purple	2 bands	X919	£5 British Rail booklet (DX7)
31p.	photo	ultramarine	phos paper	X982	sheets
31p.	litho	ultramarine	phos paper	X1056*	£1.24 booklet (GH1)
32p.	photo	greenish blue	phos paper	X983	sheets
33p.	photo	lt emerald	phos paper	X984	sheets, vertical coils
33p.	photo	lt emerald	phos paper	X1019	£6 Alias Agatha Christie booklet (DX12)
33p.	litho	lt emerald	phos paper	X1057*	£1.32 booklet (GJ1)
33p.	litho	lt emerald	2 bands	X1020	£6 Wales booklet (DX13), £6 (£5.64) Beatrix Potter booklet (DX15)
34p.	photo	ochre-brown	phos paper	X985	sheets
34p.	photo	ochre-brown	2 bands	X920	£5 *The Times* booklet (DX6)
34p.	litho	bistre-brown	2 bands	X1021	£5 *Financial Times* booklet (DX9)
34p.	photo	dp bluish grey	phos paper	X986	sheets
34p.	photo	dp mauve	phos paper	X987	sheets
35p.	photo	sepia	phos paper	X988	sheets
35p.	photo	yellow	phos paper	X989	sheets
37p.	photo	rosine	phos paper	X990	sheets
39p.	photo	brt mauve	phos paper	X991	sheets, vertical coils
39p.	litho	brt mauve	phos paper	X1058*	78p. booklet (GD4*a*), £1.56 booklet (GM1)
39p.	litho	brt mauve	2 bands	X1022	£6 Tolkien booklet (DX14), £6 (£5.64) Beatrix Potter booklet (DX15)
50p.	recess	dp ultramarine	none or phos paper	831/Ea	sheets
50p.	photo	ochre-brown	2 bands	X921	sheets
50p.	photo	ochre-brown	none	X992	sheets
50p.	photo	ochre	2 bands	X922	£5 London Life (DX11)
50p.	photo	ochre	none	X993	sheets
50p.	photo	ochre	phos paper	X991a	sheets
75p.	litho	black	none	X1023/a	sheets
75p.	litho	brownish grey and black	none	X1024	sheets
75p.	photo	grey-black	none	X994	sheets
£1	recess	bluish black	none	831b	sheets
£1	photo	brt yellow-green and blackish olive	none	1026	sheets
£1.30	photo	drab and dp greenish blue	none	1026b	sheets
£1.33	photo	pale mauve and grey-black	none	1026c	sheets
£1.41	photo	drab and dp greenish blue	none	1026d	sheets
£1.50	photo	pale mauve and grey-black	none	1026e	sheets
£1.60	photo	pale drab and dp greenish blue	none	1026f	sheets
£2	photo	lt emerald and purple-brown	none	1027	sheets
£5	photo	salmon and chalky blue	none	1028	sheets

For 1st and 2nd class no value indicated (NVI) stamps, see Nos. 1445/52, 1511/16 and 1664/71.

For table covering Machin stamps with elliptical perforations see after Nos. Y1667, etc, in 1993.

Photo/Gravure stamps were printed from both photogravure and computer engraved (Gravure) cylinders.

DECIMAL MACHIN MULTI-VALUE COIL INDEX

The following is a simplified checklist of horizontal multi-value coils, to be used in conjunction with the main listing as details of stamps listed there are not repeated.

Strip Value	Date	Contents	Cat No.
5p.	15.2.71	½p.×2, 1p.×2, 2p.	X841n
10p.	3.12.75	½p.×2, 1p., 2p., 6p.	X841q
10p.	14.12.77	½p.×2, 1p.×2, 7p.	X843l
10p.	16.1.80	1p.×2, 8p. plus 2 labels	X845m
11½p.	6.81	2½p., 3p.×3	X929l
12½p.	30.12.81	½p., 4p.×3	X924l
13p.	14.8.84	1p., 4p.×3	X925l
14p.	5.9.88	2p., 4p.×3	X928l
15p.	10.10.89	3p., 4p.×3	X930cl
17p.	27.11.90	4p.×3, 5p.	X933l
18p.	1.10.91	4p.×2, 5p.×2	X933m
19p.	31.1.95	4p., 5p.×3	X933n

Abbreviations used in the diagrams: 2B = 2 bands, CB = centre band, LB = left band and RB = right band. The shaded squares represent printed labels.
Panes completed by unprinted white labels are outside the scope of this catalogue.

Unless otherwise stated the panes were printed in photogravure. Some panes exist in photogravure and lithography and these are separately identified and listed. Imperforate or straight edges are described under the appropriate illustration.

2	2
½	½

X841l
(2 bands)

2	½
2	½

X841la
(2 bands)

½	½	½
(label)	½	½

X841m
(2 bands)

2½ RB	½ 2B	2½ LB	2½ CB
2½ RB	½ 2B	2½ LB	2½ CB
2½ RB	½ 2B	2½ LB	2½ CB

X841o
£1 Wedgwood (DX 1)

½ 2B	2½ LB
½ 2B	2½ LB
½ 2B	½ LB

X841p
£1 Wedgwood (DX 1)

½	½
6	1
1	1

X841r
(2 bands)

½ 2B	½ 2B
1 2B	8½ 2B
1 2B	8½ 2B
6½ RB	8½ 2B
6½ RB	8½ 2B

X841s

½ 2B	½ 2B
8½ 2B	1 2B
8½ 2B	1 2B
8½ 2B	6½ LB
8½ 2B	6½ LB

X841sa

11½ RB	½ 2B
11½ RB	1 2B
11½ RB	14 2B

X841t

½ 2B	11½ LB
1 2B	11½ LB
14 2B	11½ LB

X841ta

½ 2B	3 2B
12½ RB	3 2B
12½ RB	3 2B
12½ RB	3 2B

X841u

3 2B	½ 2B
3 2B	12½ LB
3 2B	12½ LB
3 2B	12½ LB

X841ua

½	(label)
½	1
7	1

X843m
(centre band)

1	1
1½	1½

X844l
(2 bands)

1½	1
1½	1

X844m
(2 bands)

1 2B	1 2B
7 RB	9 2B
7 RB	9 2B
7 RB	9 2B

X844n

1 2B	1 2B
9 2B	7 LB
9 2B	7 LB
9 2B	7 LB

X844na

(label)	1
8	1

X845l

1	1
3½	12½
3½	12½
3½	12½

X845n
(centre band)

1	1
1	13
4	13
4	13

X845p
(centre band)

1	1
12	12
12	12

X845q
(centre band)

1	13
5	13
5	13

X845s/sa
(centre band)
X845sa imperf
at left and
right

1 LB	13 RB
18 2B	18 2B

X847l

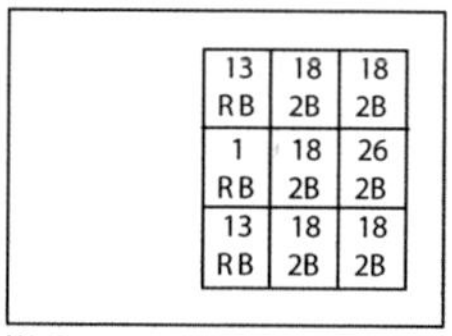

13 RB	18 2B	18 2B
1 RB	18 2B	26 2B
13 RB	18 2B	18 2B

X847m
£5 P & O
(DX 8)

(label)	2 2B
2 2B	10 2B
8 RB	10 2B
8 RB	10 2B

X849l

2 2B	(label)
10 2B	2 2B
10 2B	8 LB
10 2B	8 LB

X849la

(label)	2 RB
2 2B	2 2B
10 RB	12 2B
10 RB	12 2B

X849m

2 2B	(label)
2 2B	2 2B
12 2B	10 LB
12 2B	10 LB

X849ma

12 2B	10 LB	10 CB
12 2B	2 2B	10 CB
12 2B	12 2B	10 CB

X849n
£3 Wedgwood (DX 2)

2	2
2	2
2	2

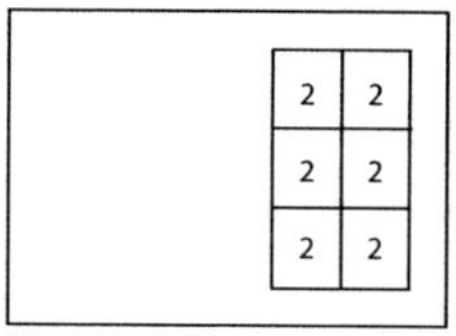

X849o (2 bands)
£3 Wedgwood (DX 2)

12½ RB	12½ LB	12½ CB
12½ RB	3 2B	12½ LB
12½ RB	2 2B	12½ LB

X849p
£4 Stanley Gibbons (DX 3)

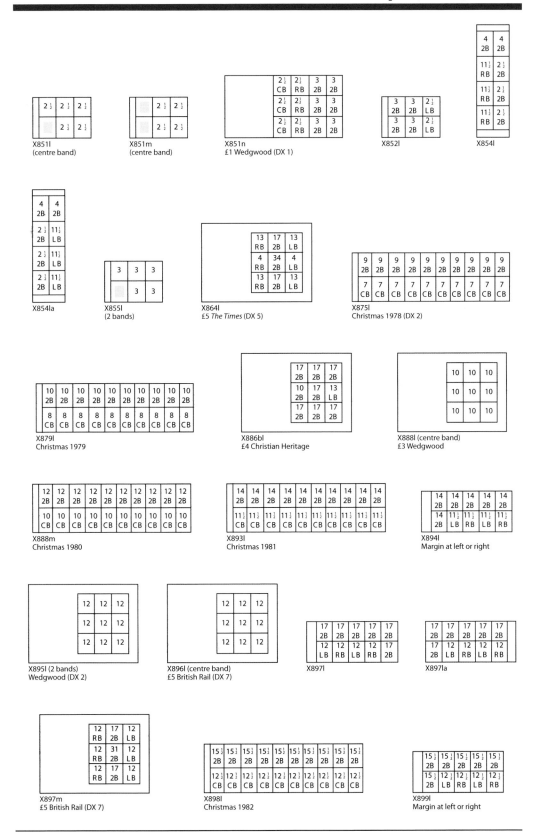

X851l
(centre band)

X851m
(centre band)

X851n
£1 Wedgwood (DX 1)

X852l

X854l

X854la

X855l
(2 bands)

X864l
£5 *The Times* (DX 5)

X875l
Christmas 1978 (DX 2)

X879l
Christmas 1979

X886bl
£4 Christian Heritage

X888l (centre band)
£3 Wedgwood

X888m
Christmas 1980

X893l
Christmas 1981

X894l
Margin at left or right

X895l (2 bands)
Wedgwood (DX 2)

X896l (centre band)
£5 British Rail (DX 7)

X897l

X897la

X897m
£5 British Rail (DX 7)

X898l
Christmas 1982

X899l
Margin at left or right

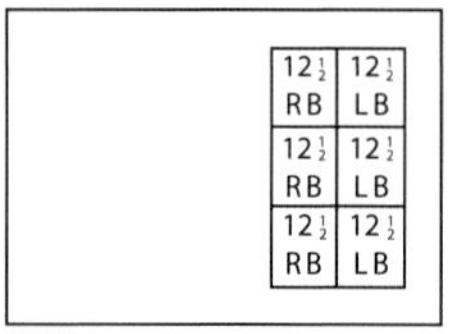
12½ 12½
RB LB
12½ 12½
RB LB
12½ 12½
RB LB

X899m
£4 Stanley Gibbons (DX 3)
£4 Royal Mint (DX 4)

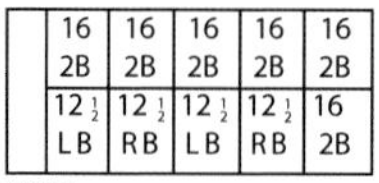
16 16 16 16 16
2B 2B 2B 2B 2B
12½ 12½ 12½ 12½ 16
LB RB LB RB 2B

X899n

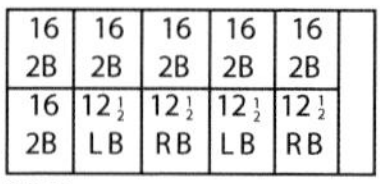
16 16 16 16 16
2B 2B 2B 2B 2B
16 12½ 12½ 12½ 12½
2B LB RB LB RB

X899na

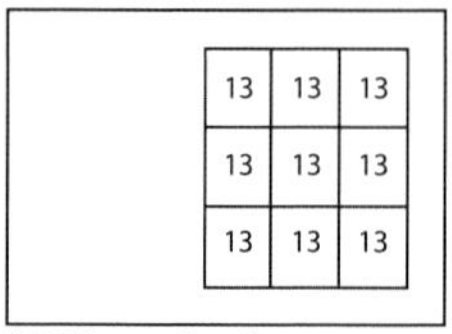
13 13 13
13 13 13
13 13 13

X900l (centre band)
£5 *The Times* (DX 6)
£5 P & O (DX 8)

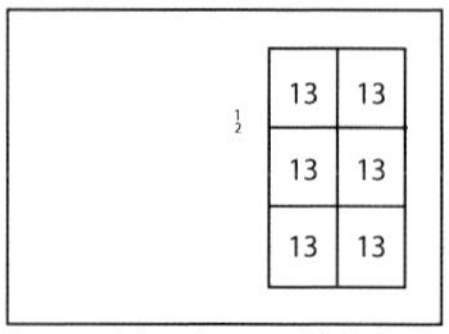
13 13
13 13
13 13

X900m, (photo), X1005l (litho)
(centre band)
£5 P & O (DX900m)
£5 Financial times (X 1005l) (DX 9)

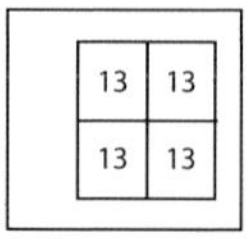
13 13
13 13

X900n (centre band)
52p. Barcode booklet

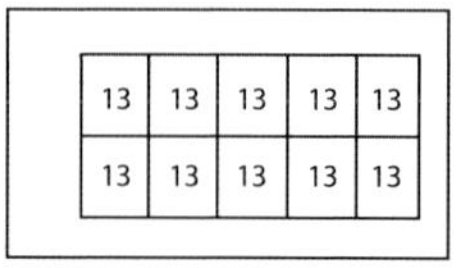
13 13 13 13 13
13 13 13 13 13

X900o (centre band)
£1.30 Barcode Booklet

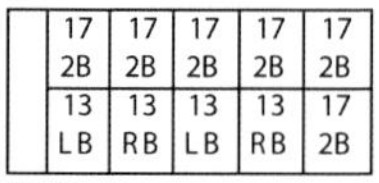
17 17 17 17 17
2B 2B 2B 2B 2B
13 13 13 13 17
LB RB LB RB 2B

X901l

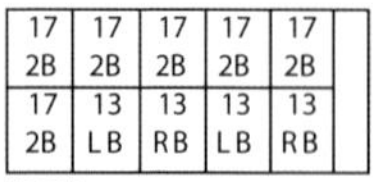
17 17 17 17 17
2B 2B 2B 2B 2B
17 13 13 13 13
2B LB RB LB RB

X901la

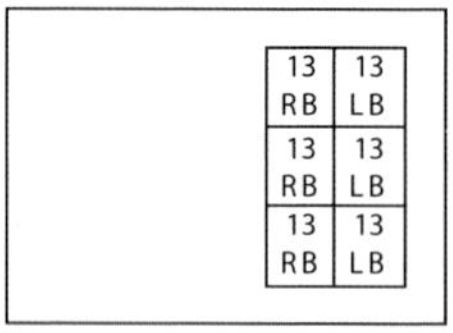
13 13
RB LB
13 13
RB LB
13 13
RB LB

X901m
£4 Christian Heritage
(DX 5)

13 18
LB 2B
18 18
2B 2B
18 18
2B 2B

X901n/na
901na imperf
at left and right

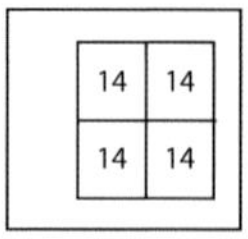
14 14
14 14

X903l (centre band)
56p. Barcode Booklet

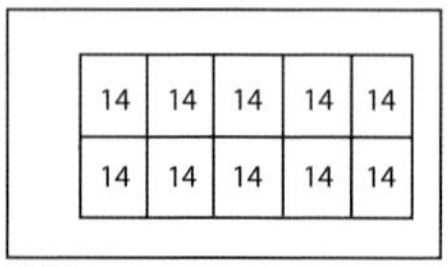
14 14 14 14 14
14 14 14 14 14

X903m
(centre band)
£1.40 Barcode Booklet

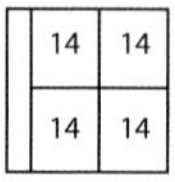
14 14
14 14

X903n, X903q
(centre band)
56p. Barcode Booklet
X903n imperf at top
and bottom
X903q imperf 3 sides

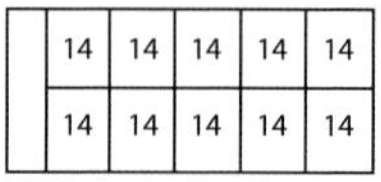
14 14 14 14 14
14 14 14 14 14

X903p (centre band)
£1.40 Barcode Booklet
Imperf at top and bottom

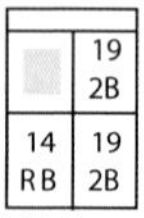
19
2B
14 19
RB 2B

X904l

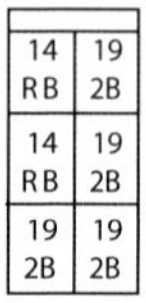
14 19
RB 2B
14 19
RB 2B
19 19
2B 2B

X904m (photo)
X1051l (litho)
Imperf at left
and right

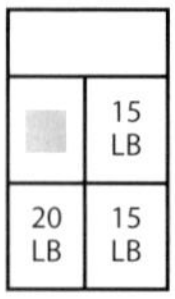
15
LB
20 15
LB LB

X906l

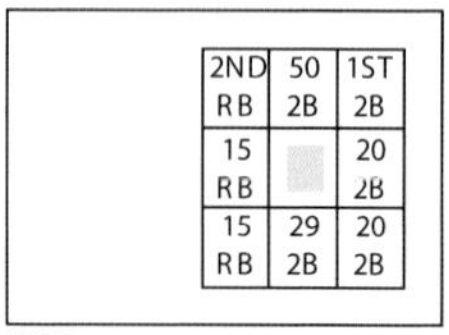
2ND 50 1ST
RB 2B 2B
15 20
RB 2B
15 29 20
RB 2B 2B

X906m
£5 London Life (DX 11)
The stamps in the bottom row are
Penny Black Anniversary definitives
(Nos 1468Ea,1470 and 1472)

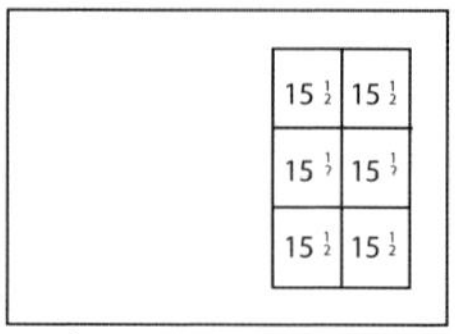
15½ 15½
15½ 15½
15½ 15½

X907l
(2 bands)
£4 Stanley Gibbons
(DX 3)

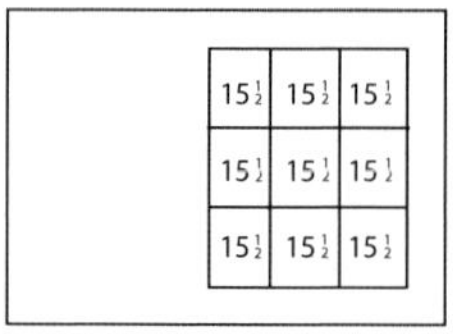
15½ 15½ 15½
15½ 15½ 15½
15½ 15½ 15½

X907m
(2 bands)
£4 Stanley Gibbons
(DX 3)

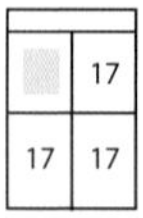
17
17 17

X909l (2 bands)
and underprint
X909Ela (as
X909l but with-
out underprint)

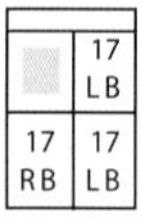
17
LB
17 17
RB LB

X911l

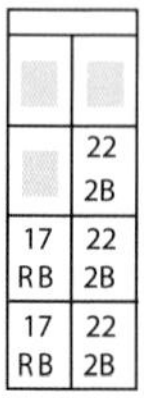
22
2B
17 22
RB 2B
17 22
RB 2B

X911m
Imperf at left
and right

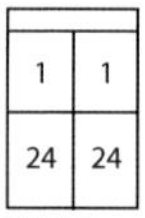
1 1
24 24

X925m
(phosphorised
paper)

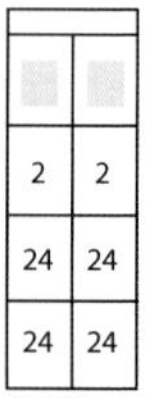
2 2
24 24
24 24

X927l (photo)
X1050l (litho)
(phosphorised
paper) Imperf
at left and right

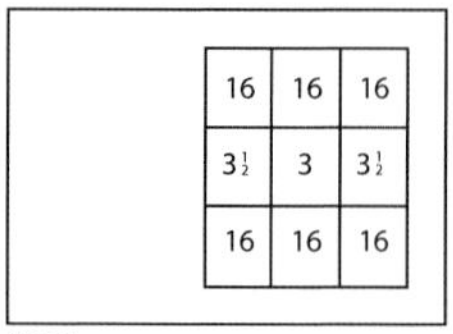
16 16 16
3½ 3 3½
16 16 16

X930b
(phosphorised paper)
£4 Royal mint
(DX 4)

X949l
(phosphorised paper)
£4 Royal Mint
(DX 4)

X952l
(phosphorised paper)
£4 Christian Heritage (DX 5)
£5 *The Times* £5 British Rail (DX 7)
X1008l (centre band)
£6 Agatha Christie (DX 12)

X952m
(phosphorised paper)
£5 *The Times* (DX 6)
£5 British Rail (DX 7)

X955l (photo), X1009l (litho)
(phosphorised paper)
£5 P & O (X955l) (DX 8)
£5 *Financial Times* (X1009l) (DX 9)

X955m
(phosphorised paper)
72p. Barcode Booklet

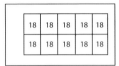

X955n
(phosphorised paper)
£1.80 Barcode Booklet

X956l
(phosphorised paper)
76p. Barcode Booklet

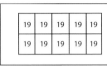

X956m
(phosphorised paper)
£1.90 Barcode Booklet

X956n, X956q
(phosphorised paper)
76p. Barcode Booklet
X956n imperf at top
and bottom
X956q imperf on
three sides

X956o
(phosphorised paper)
£1.90 Barcode Booklet Imperf
at top and bottom

X960l
(phosphorised
paper)
Imperf at left
and right

X971bl
(phosphorised paper)
£1.04 Barcode Booklet

X973l
(phosphorised paper)
£1.08 Barcode
Booklet

X973m
(phosphorised
paper)
£1.08 Barcode
Booklet
Imperf at top and
bottom

X1006l (litho)
£5 *Financial Times*
(DX 9)

X1009m (litho)
(phosphorised paper)
£5 *Financial Times* (DX 9)
X1011l (litho) (centre band)
£6 Tolkien
(DX 14)

X1012l (litho)
£6 Tolkien
(DX 14)

X1012m (litho)
£6 (£5.64) Beatrix Potter
(DX 15)

X1016l (litho)
(phosphorised paper)
£6 Agatha Christie (DX 12)

X1016m (litho)
(phosphorised paper)
£6 Agatha Christie (DX 12)

X1017l (litho)
(phosphorised paper)
£6 Tolkien (DX 14)

X1054l (litho), X1055l (litho)
(X1054l 2 bands)
(X1055l phosphorised paper)
£1.16 Barcode Booklet
Imperf on three sides

X1056l (litho)
(phosphorised paper)
£1.24 Barcode Booklet
Imperf top and bottom

X1057l
(phosphorised paper)
£1.32 Barcode Booklet
Imperf top and bottom

X1058l
(phosphorised paper)
£1.56 Barcode Booklet
Imperf top and bottom

N.V.I. stamps, PVA gum, "standard" perforations

913   914

1989 (22 Aug)–**1993**. Booklet Stamps.

(a) Photo Harrison. P 15×14.

1445	913	(2nd) brt blue (1 centre band)...................	1·25	1·25
		a. Booklet pane. No. 1445×10 with horizontal edges of pane imperf....	12·50	
		b. Booklet pane. No. 1445×4 with three edges of pane imperf (28.11.89)................................	23·00	
1446		(2nd) brt blue (1 band at right) (20.3.90)	3·50	3·50
1447	914	(1st) brownish black (phosphorised paper)..	1·75	1·50
		a. Booklet pane. No. 1447×10 with horizontal edges of pane imperf....	15·00	
		b. Booklet pane. No. 1447×4 with three edges of pane imperf (5.12.89)................................	35·00	
1448		(1st) brownish black (2 phosphor bands) (20.3.90)........................	3·75	3·75

(b) Litho Walsall. P 14.

1449	913	(2nd) brt blue (1 centre band)...................	1·00	1·00
		a. Imperf between (vert pair)..............		
		b. Booklet pane. No. 1449×4 with three edges of pane imperf..............	7·00	
		c. Booklet pane. No. 1449×4 with horiz edges of pane imperf (6.8.91)................................	3·50	
		d. Booklet pane. No. 1449×10 with horiz edges of pane imperf (6.8.91)................................	7·50	
1450	914	(1st) blackish brown (2 phosphor bands)	2·50	2·50
		a. Booklet pane. No. 1450×4 with three edges of pane imperf..............	8·50	
		Ey. Phosphor omitted............................	£650	

(c) Litho Questa. P 15×14.

1451	913	(2nd) brt blue (1 centre band) (19.9.89) ..	1·00	1·00
		Ey. Phosphor omitted............................	£160	
1451*a*		(2nd) brt blue (1 band at right) (25.2.92)	2·00	2·00
		a*Eb*. Band at left (10.8.93).....................	2·50	2·50
		a*l*. Booklet pane. Nos. 1451aEb and 1514a, each×3, with margins all round (10.8.93)................................	14·00	
		Ey. Phosphor omitted............................	£950	
1452	914	(1st) brownish black (phosphorised paper) (19.9.89).........................	2·50	2·50

First Day Cover (Nos. 1445, 1447)..................................... 4·50

Nos. 1445, 1447 and 1449/52 were initially sold at 14p. (2nd) and 19p. (1st), but these prices were later increased to reflect new postage rates.

Nos. 1446 and 1448 come from the *se-tenant* pane in the London Life £5 Booklet. This pane is listed under No. X906m in the Decimal Machin section.

No. 1451a comes from the *se-tenant* panes in the Wales and Tolkien £6 booklet. These panes are listed under Nos. X1012l and W49a (Wales Regionals). No. 1451aEb comes from the £6 (£5.64) Beatrix Potter booklet.

Nos. 1445, 1447 and 1449/50 do not exist perforated on all four sides, but come with either one or two adjacent sides imperforate.

No. 1450Ey comes from a pane in which one stamp was without phosphor bands due to a dry print.

For illustrations showing the differences between photogravure and lithography see above Type **367**.

For similar designs, but in changed colours, see Nos. 1511/16, for those with elliptical perforations, Nos. 1664/71, and for self-adhesive versions Nos. 2039/40 and 2295.

Special First Day of Issue Postmarks
(for illustrations see Introduction)

Philatelic Bureau Edingburgh (Type G) (in red)..................................... 4·50
Windsor, Berks (Type G) (in red)..................................... 4·50

1990 (7 Aug)–**92**. Booklet stamps. As *T* **913/14**, but colours changed.

(a) Photo Harrison. P 15×14.

1511	913	(2nd) deep blue (1 centre band)...............	1·50	1·50
		a. Booklet pane. No. 1511×10 with horiz edges of pane imperf................	12·00	
1512	914	(1st) brt orange-red (phosphorised paper)	1·50	1·50
		a. Booklet pane. No. 1512×10 with horiz edges of pane imperf................	10·00	

(b) Litho Questa. P 15×14.

1513	913	(2nd) deep blue (1 centre band)...................	2·50	2·50
1514	914	(1st) brt orange-red (phosphorised paper)	1·50	1·00

1514*a*		(1st) brt orange-red (2 bands) (25.2.92)...	2·00	2·00
		a*Ey*. Phosphor omitted............................	£775	

(c) Litho Walsall. P 14.

1515	913	(2nd) deep blue (1 centre band)...................	1·50	1·20
		a. Booklet pane. No. 1515×4 with horiz edges of pane imperf..............	3·75	
		b. Booklet pane. No. 1515×10 with horiz edges of pane imperf..............	8·50	
1516	914	(1st) brt orange-red (phosphorised paper)	1·20	1·20
		a. Booklet pane. No. 1516×4 with horiz edges of pane imperf..............	4·00	
		b. Booklet pane. No. 1516×10 with horiz edges of pane imperf..............	8·00	
		c. Perf 13..	4·00	4·00
		ca. Booklet pane. No. 1516c×4 with horiz edges of pane imperf..............	16·00	

First Day Cover (Nos. 1515/16)..................................... 3·00

Nos. 1511/14 and 1515/16 were initially sold at 15p. (2nd) and 20p. (1st), but these prices were later increased to reflect new postage rates.

No. 1514a comes from the *se-tenant* panes in the £6 Wales, £6 Tolkien and £5.64 Beatrix Potter booklets. These panes are listed under Nos. X1012l, 1451al and W49a (Wales Regionals).

No. 1516c was caused by the use of an incorrect perforation comb.

Nos. 1511/12 and 1515/16 do not exist with perforations on all four sides, but come with either the top or the bottom edge imperforate.

For similar stamps with elliptical perforations see Nos. 1664/72.

Special First Day of Issue Postmarks
(For illustration see Introduction)

Philatelic Bureau, Edinburgh (Type G)..................................... 3·00
Windsor, Berks (Type G)..................................... 3·50

FLUORESCENT PHOSPHOR BANDS. Following the introduction of new automatic sorting machinery in 1991 it was found necessary to substantially increase the signal emitted by the phosphor bands. This was achieved by adding a fluorescent element to the phosphor which appears yellow under U.V. light. This combination was first used on an experimental sheet printing of the 18p., No. X913, produced by Enschedé in 1991. All values with phosphor bands from the elliptical perforations issue, including the No Value Indicated design, originally showed this yellow fluor.

From mid-1995 printings of current sheet and booklet stamps began to appear with the colour of the fluorescent element changed to blue. As such differences in fluor colour can only be identified by use of a U.V. lamp they are outside the scope of this catalogue, but full details will be found in the *Great Britain Specialised Catalogue Volume 4.*

The first commemorative/special stamp issue to show the change to blue fluor was the Centenary of Rugby League set, Nos. 1891/5.

COMPUTER-ENGRAVED CYLINDERS. In 1991 Enschedé introduced a new method of preparing photogravure cylinders for Great Britain stamps. This new method utilised computer-engraving instead of the traditional acid-etching and produced cylinders without the minor flaws which had long been a feature of the photogravure process. Such cylinders were first used on Great Britain stamps for the printing of the 18p. released on 19 November 1991 (see No. X913).

Harrison and Sons continued to use the acid-etching method until mid-1996 after which most Machin values, including N.V.I.'s, were produced from computer-engraved cylinders using a very similar process to that of Enschedé. Some values exist in versions from both cylinder production methods and can often be identified by minor differences. Such stamps are, however, outside the scope of this listing, but full details can be found in the current edition of the *Great Britain Specialised Catalogue Volume 4.*

For commemorative stamps the first Harrison issue to use computer-engraved cylinders was the Centenary of Cinema set (Nos. 1920/4).

When Walsall introduced photogravure printing in 1997 their cylinders were produced using a similar computer-engraved process.

N.V.I. stamps, PVA gum, elliptical perforations

1093a

1993 (6 Apr)–**2017**. *As T* **913/14**, *and* **1093a**. Perf 14 (No. 1665) or 15×14 (others) (both with one elliptical hole in each vertical side).

(a) *Photo/gravure*
Harrison – No. 1666
Questa – Nos. 1664a, 1667a
Walsall/ISP Walsall – Nos. 1665, 1668s
Harrison/De La Rue, Questa or Walsall– No. 1667
Harrison/De La Rue, Enschedé, Questa
or Walsall/ISP Walsall – Nos. 1664, 1668, 1669

1664	**913**	(2nd) brt blue (1 centre band) (7.9.93)	1·50	1·30
		a. Perf 14 (1.12.98)	1·50	1·30
		b. Imperf (pair)..	£1400	
		l. Booklet pane. Nos. 1664 and 1667×3 plus 4 labels ("postcode" on top right label) (27.4.00)......................	4·50	
		la. As No. 1664l, but inscr "postcodes" on top right label (17.4.01)......	5·50	
		m. Booklet pane. Nos. 1664×2 and 1667×6 (27.4.00)	12·00	
		n. Booklet pane. Nos. 1664 and 1669, each×4, with central label and margins all round (6.2.02)...................	12·00	
		o. Booklet pane. Nos. 1664 and 1668, each×4, with central label and margins all round (2.6.03)...................	11·00	
		p. Booklet pane. Nos. 1664×4, Y1709×2 and Y1715×2, with central label and margins all round (24.2.05)...................................	10·00	
1665		(2nd) bright blue (1 band at right) (13.10.98)..	2·00	2·00
		Ec. Band at left..	2·00	2·00
		l. Booklet pane. Nos. 1665×3 and NI81b, S91a and W80a with margins all round	7·50	
1666	**914**	(1st) brt orange-red (phosphor paper)	1·80	1·50
1667		(1st) brt orange-red (2 phosphor bands) (4.4.95)..	1·80	1·30
		Ey. Phosphor omitted...............................	£225	
		a. Perf 14 (1.12.98)	2·00	1·80
		l. Booklet pane. No. 1667×8 with centre label and margins all round (16.2.99)..	12·00	
		m. Booklet pane. No. 1667×4 plus commemorative label at right (12.5.99)..	4·50	
1668		(1st) gold (2 phosphor bands) (21.4.97)...	1·60	1·60
		a. Imperf (pair)	£175	
		l. Booklet pane. Nos. 1668 and Y1692, each×4, and centre label with margins all round (23.9.97)	9·00	
		m. Booklet pane. Nos. 1668/9, each×4, with centre label and margins all round (24.9.02)................................	12·00	
		o. Booklet pane. Nos. 1668 and Y1704, each×4, with centre label and margins all round (16.3.04)	10·00	
		p. Booklet pane. Nos. 1668×4, Y1715×2 and Y1723×3, with centre label and margins all round (25.5.04)	9·75	
		q. Booklet pane. Nos. 1668×4, Y1726×2 and Y1736×2, with centre label and margins all round (18.10.05).......................................	9·50	
		r. Booklet pane. Nos. 1668×4, Y1701×2 and Y1711×2, with centre label and margins all round (23.2.06)..	9·50	
1668s		(1st) brownish black (2 phosphor bands) (5.6.17)..	1·50	1·50
		sb. Booklet pane. No. 1668s, 2133×2, 1667/8, 2124, 2651 and U3067 with central label and margins all round ..	8·00	
1669	**1093a**	(E) deep blue (2 phosphor bands) (19.1.99)	2·25	2·25

(b) *Litho Questa or Walsall (1670), Enschedé, Questa or Walsall (1671*) *or De La Rue or Walsall (1672).*

1670	**913**	(2nd) brt blue (1 centre band)......................	1·50	90
		Ey. Phosphor omitted	£175	
		l. Booklet pane. Nos. 1670 and 1672, each×4, with central label and margins all round (18.9.08)................	5·75	
1671	**914**	(1st) brt orange-red (2 phosphor bands)	1·80	1·00
		Ey. Phosphor omitted..................................	£200	
		l. Booklet pane. No. 1671×4 plus commemorative label at left (27.7.94)	8·50	
		la. Ditto, but with commemorative label at right (16.5.95).........................	6·00	
		lEy. Phosphor omitted...............................	£400	
		m. Pane. No. 1671 with margins all round (roul 8 across top corners of pane) (Boots logo on margin) (17.8.94)..	2·50	
		mEy. Phosphor omitted............................	£1500	
		ma. Without Boots logo above stamp (11.9.95)..	1·25	
		mb. Ditto, but roul 10 across top corners of pane (20.2.97)......................................	2·00	
		n. Booklet pane. No. 1671×9 with margins all round (16.2.99)................	9·00	
1672		(1st) gold (2 phosphor bands) (8.1.08)......	2·00	2·00
		Ey. Phosphor omitted.................................	£1800	
		l. Booklet pane. No. 1672×8 with centre label and margins all round (8.1.08)..	15·00	

For details of sheets, booklets, etc containing these stamps see Decimal Machin Index following the "Y" numbers.

Nos. 1664/71 were issued in booklet panes showing perforations on all four edges.

On 6 September 1993 Nos. 1670/71 printed in lithography by Questa were made available in sheets from post offices in Birmingham, Coventry, Falkirk and Milton Keynes. These sheet stamps became available nationally on 5 October 1993. On 29 April 1997 No. 1664 printed in photogravure by Walsall became available in sheets. On the same date Nos. 1664 and 1667 were issued in coils printed by Harrison. Sheets of No. 1667 were printed by Walsall from 18 November 1997.

No. 1665 exists with the phosphor band at the left or right of the stamp from separate panes of the £6.16 Speed stamp booklet No. DX21. For pane containing No. 1665Ec see No. Y1676al.

No. 1668 was originally printed by Harrisons in booklets and Walsall in sheets and booklets for The Queen's Golden Wedding and issued on 21 April 1997. It was printed in coils by Enschedé (5.10.02), when gold became the accepted colour for 1st class definitives, and later in sheets and coils by De La Rue.

Booklet pane No. 1668m was issued on 24 September 2002 in the £6.83 "Across the Universe" booklet, No. DX29. It was issued again with a different central label on 25 February 2003 in the £6.99 "Microcosmos" booklet, No. DX30.

No. 1669 was intended for the basic European air mail rate, initially 30p., and was at first only available from Barcode booklet No. HF1, printed by Walsall. It appeared in sheets printed by De La Rue on 5 October 1999.

No. 1671m, printed by Questa, was provided by the Royal Mail for inclusion in single pre-packed greetings cards. The pane shows large margins at top and sides with lines of roulette gauging 8 stretching from the bottom corners to the mid point of the top edge. Examples included with greetings cards show the top two corners of the pane folded over. Unfolded examples were available from the British Philatelic Bureau and from other Post Office philatelic outlets. The scheme was originally limited to Boots and their logo appeared on the pane margin. Other card retailers subsequently participated and later supplies omitted the logo.

A further printing by Enschedé in 1997 showed the roulettes gauging 10 (No. 1671mb). Blank pieces of gummed paper have been found showing the perforation and rouletting of No. 1671mb, but no printing.

No. 1672 was only issued in the following booklets: £7.40 Ian Fleming's "James Bond" (DX41), "Pilot to Plane" (DX42) and "Charles Darwin" (DX45).

For illustration of differences between lithography and gravure see below Types **367** and **367a**.

For self-adhesive stamps in these colours see Nos. 2039/40 and 2295/6.

POSTAL FORGERIES. In mid-1994 a number of postal forgeries of the 2nd bright blue printed in lithography were detected after having been rejected by the sorting equipment. These show the Queen's head in bright greenish blue, have a fluorescent, rather than a phosphor, band and show matt, colourless gum on the reverse. These forgeries come from booklets of ten which also have forged covers.

COMMEMORATIVE BOOKLET PANES. Booklets of four 1st Class stamps with *se-tenant* commemorative label were issued for the following anniversaries or events:
300th Anniversary of the Bank of England (No. 1671l)
Birth Centenary of R. J. Mitchell (No. 1671la)
70th Birthday of Queen Elizabeth II (No. 1671la)
"Hong Kong '97" International Stamp Exhibition (No. 1671la)
Commonwealth Heads of Government Meeting, Edinburgh (No. 1671la)
50th Birthday of Prince of Wales (No. 1671la)
50th Anniversary of Berlin Airlift (No. 1667m)
Rugby World Cup (No. 1667m)

First Day Covers
21.4.97 1st (No. 1668), 26p. (Y1692) (Type G) (Philatelic Bureau or Windsor) .... 3·25

23.9.97	B.B.C. label pane 1st×4, 26p×4 (No. 1668l), (Philatelic Bureau or London W1)..	9·00
19.1.99	E (No. 1669) (Type G) (Philatelic Bureau or Windsor).....	2·75
16.2.99	"Profile on Print" label pane 1st×8 (No. 1671n) (see Nos. 2077/9) (Philatelic Bureau or London SW1)	5·50
6.2.02	"A Gracious Accession" label pane 2nd×4 and E×4 (No. 1664n) (see Nos. 2253/7) (Tallents House or Windsor)	5·00
24.9.02	"Across the Universe" label pane 1st×4, E×4 (No. 1668m) (Tallents House or Star, Glenrothes)	5·00
25.2.03	"Microcosmos" label pane 1st×4, E×4 (No. 1668n) (Tallents House or Cambridge)	5·00
2.6.03	"A Perfect Coronation" label pane 2nd×4, 1st×4 (No. 1664o) (Tallents House or London SW1)	4·00
16.3.04	"Letters by Night: A Tribute to the Travelling Post Office" label pane 1st×4, 37p×4 (No. 1668o) (Tallents House or London NW10)	8·00
25.5.04	"The Glory of the Garden" label pane 1st×4, 42p×2, 47p×2 (No. 1668p) (Tallents House or Wisley, Woking	7·00
24.2.05	The Brontë Sisters label pane 2nd×4, 39p.×2, 42p.×2 (No. 1664p) (Tallents House or Haworth, Keighley)	5·00
18.10.05	Bicentenary of the Battle of Trafalgar label pane 1st×4, 50p.×2 and 68p.×2 (No. 1668q) (Tallents House and Portsmouth)	7·00
23.2.06	Birth Bicentenary of Isambard Kingdom Brunel label pane 1st×4, 35p.×2 and 40p.×2 (No. 1668r) (Tallents House or Bristol)	7·00
8.1.08	James Bond label pane 1st×8 (No. 1672l) (Tallents House or London SE1)	12·00
18.9.08	"Pilot to Plane" RAF Uniforms label pane 2nd×4 and 1st×4 (No.1670l) (Tallents House or Hendon, London NW9)..	5·00

1390

1999 (16 Feb).

(a) Embossed and litho Walsall. Self-adhesive.
Die-cut perf 14×15.

2077	**1390**	(1st) grey (face value) (Queen's head in colourless relief) (phosphor background around head)................	2·75	2·75
		l. Booklet pane. No. 2077×4 with margins all round..................................	10·00	

(b) Eng C. Slania. Recess Enschedé. P 14×14½.

2078	**1390**	(1st) grey-black (2 phosphor bands)........	2·75	2·75
		l. Booklet pane. No. 2078×4 with margins all round..................................	10·00	

(c) Typo Harrison. P 14×15.

2079	**1390**	(1st) black (2 phosphor bands)	2·75	2·75
		Ey. Phosphor omitted...................................	£1800	
		l. Booklet pane. No. 2079×4 with margins all round..................................	10·00	
		LEy. Booklet pane.Phosphor omitted		

Set of 3 .... 7·50   7·50
First Day Covers (3 covers with Nos. 2077l, 2078l, 2079l) (Philatelic Bureau) .... 9·50
First Day Covers (3 covers with Nos. 2077l, 2078l, 2079l) (London SW1) .... 9·50

    Nos. 2077/9 were only issued in the £7.54 "Profile on Print" booklet, No. DX22.

NVI Stamps. Panes with "standard" perforations

2nd	2nd	2nd	2nd	2nd
2nd	2nd	2nd	2nd	2nd

1445a (bright blue, photo)
Imperf at top and bottom

2nd	2nd
2nd	2nd

1445b (bright blue, photo)
Imperf at top and bottom

2nd	2nd
2nd	2nd

1449b (bright blue, litho)
Imperf at top and bottom and right

2nd	2nd
2nd	2nd

1449c (bright blue, litho)
Imperf at top and bottom

2nd	2nd	2nd	2nd	2nd
2nd	2nd	2nd	2nd	2nd

1449d (bright blue, litho)
Imperf at top and bottom

2nd	2nd	2nd	2nd	2nd
2nd	2nd	2nd	2nd	2nd

1511a (deep blue, photo)
Imperf at top and bottom

2nd	2nd
2nd	2nd

1515a (deep blue, litho)
Imperf at top and bottom

2nd	2nd	2nd	2nd	2nd
2nd	2nd	2nd	2nd	2nd

1515b (deep blue, litho)
Imperf at top and bottom

1st	1st	1st	1st	1st
1st	1st	1st	1st	1st

1447a (black, photo)
Imperf at top and bottom

1st	1st
1st	1st

1447b (black, litho)
Imperf at top and bottom

1st	1st
1st	1st

1450a (black, litho)
Imperf at top and bottom and right

1st	2nd
1st	2nd
1st	2nd

1451al (litho)
£6 (£5.64) Beatrix Potter

1st	1st	1st	1st	1st
1st	1st	1st	1st	1st

1512a (orange, photo)
Imperf at top and bottom

1st	1st
1st	1st

1516a (orange, litho P 14)
Imperf at top and bottom

1st	1st
1st	1st

1516a (orange, litho, P 13))
Imperf at top and bottom

1st	1st	1st	1st	1st
1st	1st	1st	1st	1st

1516b (orange, litho)
Imperf at top and bottom

NVI Stamps. Panes with **elliptical perforations** the shaded squares represent printed labels.

	post-code
2nd	1st
1st	1st

1664l

	post-codes
2nd	1st
1st	1st

1664la

2nd	2nd
1st	1st
1st	1st
1st	1st

1664m

E	2nd	E
2nd		2nd
E	2nd	E

1664n
£7.29 A Gracious Accession
(DX 28)

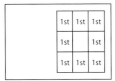

1st	1st	1st
1st		1st
1st	1st	1st

1667l
£7.54 Profile in Print
(DX 22)

1667m (photo)

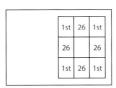

1668l
£6.15 Celebrating 75 Years of the BBC
(DX 19)

1st	E	1st
E		E
1st	E	1st

1668m
£6.83 Across the Universe
(DX 29)

37	1st	37
1st		1st
37	1st	37

1668o (photo)
£7.44 Letters by Night
(DX 32)

1st	42	1st
47		47
1st	42	1st

1668p
£7.23 The Glory of the Garden
(DX 33)

1st	50	1st
68		68
1st	50	1st

1668q
£7.26 Bicentenary of the Battle of Trafalgar
(DX 35)

1st	35	1st
40		40
1st	35	1st

1668r
£7.40 Isambard Kingdom Brunel
(DX 36)

1st	20	1st
1st		1st
1st	20	1st

1668sb
£15.14 50th Anniversary of the Machin
(DY 21)

1st	2nd	1st
2nd		2nd
1st	2nd	1st

1670l
£7.15 Pilot to Plane
(DX 42)

Label	1st	1st
	1st	1st

1671l

1st	1st	Label
1st	1st	

1671la (litho)

1st	1st	1st
1st	1st	1st
1st	1st	1st

1671n
£7.54 Profile on Print
(DX 22)

1st	1st	1st
1st		1st
1st	1st	1st

1672l
£7.40 Ian Fleming's James Bond
(DX 41)

Denominated stamps, PVA gum, elliptical perforations

II Normal figures of face value   III Open '4' and open lower curve of '5'

1993 (27 Apr)–**2017**. As Nos. X**841**, etc, but Perf 15×14 (with one elliptical hole in each vertical side).

(a) Photo/gravure

Enschedé – 20p. (Y1684), 29p., 35p. (Y1698), 36p., 38p. (Y1706), 41p. (Y1712), 43p. (Y1716)
Harrison:– 20p. (Y1686), 25p. (Y1689), 26p. (Y1692), 35p. (Y1699), 41p. (Y1713), 43p. (Y1717)
Walsall:– 10p. (Y1676a), 19p. (Y1683), 38p. (Y1707a), 43p. (Y1717a).
Enschedé or Harrison/De La Rue:– 4p., 5p., 6p., 25p. (Y1690), 31p., 39p. (Y1708), £1 (Y1743)
Enschedé, Harrison/De La Rue, Questa or ISP Walsall:– 1p.
Enschedé, Harrison/De La Rue, Questa or Walsall:– 2p.
Enschedé, Harrison/De La Rue or Walsall:– 10p. (Y1676), 30p., 37p. (Y1703), 42p., 50p. (Y1726), 63p.
Harrison/De La Rue or Questa:– 19p. (Y1682), 20p. (Y1685), 26p. (Y1691)
De La Rue or Walsall:– 38p. (Y1707), 39p. (Y1709), 40p. (Y1710), 64p., 65p., 68p.
De La Rue:– 7p., 8p., 9p., 12p., 14p., 15p., 16p., 17p., 20p. (Y1687), 22p., 33p., 34p., 35p. (Y1700), 37p. (Y1704/5), 41p. (Y1714), 43p. (Y1718), 44p., 45p., 48p., 49p., 50p., (Y1727), 56p., 60p., 62p., 67p., 72p., 78p., 81p., 88p., 90p., 97p., £1 (Y1744), £1.46, £1.50, £2, £3, £5
Enschedé or De La Rue:– 35p. (Y1701), 40p. (Y1711), 46p., 47p., 54p.

Y1667	**367**	1p. crimson (2 bands) (8.6.93)	30	25
		l. Booklet pane. Nos. Y1667×2, Y1685 and Y1691×3 plus 2 labels (1.12.98)	20·00	
		m. Booklet pane. Nos. Y1667/8, Y1682 and Y1691×3 plus 2 labels (26.4.99)	6·50	
		n. Booklet pane. Nos. Y1667×4, Y1682×3 and Y1691 with central label and margins all round (21.9.99)	5·50	
		o. Booklet pane. Nos. Y1667×2, Y1722×4 and Y1728×2 with central label and margins all round (20.9.07)	6·00	
		p. Booklet pane. Nos. Y1667, Y1668, Y1670, Y1676, Y1687, Y1727, 1664 and U3061, with central label and margins all round (5.6.17)	5·00	
Y1668		2p. dp green (2 bands) (11.4.95)	30	30
		a. Imperf (pair)	£2500	
		l. Booklet pane. Nos. Y1668×4 and Nos. Y1722 and Y1724, each×2 with centre label and margins all round (5.6.07)	4·25	
		m. Booklet pane. Nos. Y1668×2, Y1676×2 and U3060×4 with central label and margins all round (10.1.12)	12·00	
Y1669		4p. new blue (2 bands) (14.12.93)	30	30
		a. Imperf	£1700	
Y1670		5p. dull red-brown (Type II) (2 bands) (8.6.93)	30	35
		l. Booklet pane. Nos. Y1670 and 2651, each×4, with centre label and margins all round (1.3.07)	5·50	
Y1671		6p. yellow-olive (2 bands)	50	50
		Ey. Phosphor omitted	£180	
Y1672		7p. grey (2 bands) (20.4.99)	2·75	2·75
		a. Imperf (pair)		
Y1673		7p. bright magenta (2 bands) (1.4.04)	1·20	1·20
		a. Imperf (pair)	£200	
Y1674		8p. yellow (2 bands) (25.4.00)	35	35
Y1675		9p. yellow-orange (2 bands) (5.4.05)	30	20
Y1676		10p. dull orange (2 bands) (8.6.93)	35	35
		aa. Imperf pair	£1400	
		a. Perf 14 (13.10.98)	1·75	1·75
		al. Booklet pane. Nos. Y1676a×2, 1665Ec and Y1717a, each×3, with centre label and margins all round	12·00	
Y1677		12p. greenish blue (2 bands) (1.8.06)	70	70
Y1678		14p. rose-red (2 bands) (1.8.06)	75	90
Y1679		15p. bright magenta (2 bands) (1.4.08)	70	85
Y1680		16p. pale cerise (2 bands) (27.3.07)	70	85

Y1681	17p. brown-olive (2 bands) (31.3.09)	75	75
	a. Imperf (pair)	£2600	
Y1682	19p. bistre (1 centre band) (26.10.93)	40	45
	a. Imperf (pair)	£550	
	l. Booklet pane. Nos. Y1682 and Y1691×7 (26.4.99)	13·00	
	lEy. Phosphor omitted	£140	
Y1683	19p. bistre (1 band at right) (*p* 14) (15.2.00)	1·75	1·75
	l. Booklet pane. Nos. Y1683×4 and Y1707a×2 with margins all round	15·00	
Y1684	20p. turquoise-green (2 bands) (14.12.93)	80	80
Y1685	20p. brt green (1 centre band) (25.6.96)	50	50
	a. Imperf (horiz pair)	£275	
	l. Booklet pane. Nos. Y1685 and Y1691×7 (1.12.98)	22·00	
Y1686	20p. brt green (1 band at right) (23.9.97)	2·00	2·00
	l. Booklet pane. Nos. Y1686 and Y1691, each×3 with margins all round	6·00	
Y1687	20p. brt green (2 bands) (20.4.99)	75	75
	a. Imperf (pair)	£375	
Y1688	22p. drab (2 bands) (31.3.09)	1·00	1·00
Y1689	25p. rose-red (phosphorised paper) (26.10.93)	70	70
	a. Imperf (pair)	£1000	
	l. Booklet pane. No. Y1689×2 plus 2 labels (1.11.93)	2·00	
Y1690	25p. rose-red (2 bands) (20.12.94)	70	70
	Ey. Phosphor omitted	24·00	
	l. Booklet pane. No. Y1690×2 plus 2 labels (6.6.95)	3·50	
Y1691	26p. red-brown (2 bands) (25.6.96)	70	70
	a. Imperf (pair)	£650	
Y1692	26p. gold (2 bands) (21.4.97)	90	90
	ba. Imperf (horiz pair)	£2750	
Y1693	29p. grey (2 bands) (26.10.93)	1·00	1·00
Y1694	30p. dp olive-grey (2 bands) (27.7.93)	90	90
	a. Imperf (pair)	£1400	
Y1695	31p. dp mauve (2 bands) (25.6.96)	1·20	1·20
Y1696	33p. grey-green (2 bands) (25.4.00)	1·20	1·00
Y1697	34p. yellow-olive (2 bands) (6.5.03)	4·50	4·50
Y1698	35p. yellow (2 bands) (17.8.93)	1·25	1·25
Y1699	35p. yellow (phosphorised paper) (1.11.93)	7·50	7·50
Y1700	35p. sepia (2 bands) (1.4.04)	1·30	1·30
	a. Imperf (pair)	£275	
Y1701	35p. yellow-olive (5.4.05) (1 centre band)	1·10	1·10
Y1702	36p. brt ultramarine (2 bands) (26.10.93)	1·30	1·30
Y1703	37p. brt mauve (2 bands) (25.6.96)	1·40	1·40
Y1704	37p. grey-black (2 bands) (4.7.02)	1·50	1·50
Y1705	37p. brown-olive (1 centre band) (28.3.06)	1·50	1·50
Y1706	38p. rosine (2 bands) (26.10.93)	1·50	1·50
	a. Imperf (pair)	£375	
Y1707	38p. ultramarine (2 bands) (20.4.99)	4·00	4·00
	a. Perf 14 (15.2.00)	8·00	8·00
Y1708	39p. brt magenta (2 bands) (25.6.96)	1·50	1·50
	a. Imperf (pair)	£1700	
Y1709	39p. grey (2 bands) (1.4.04)	1·50	1·50
	a. Imperf (pair)	£275	
Y1710	40p. dp azure (2 bands) (25.4.00)	1·50	1·50
Y1711	40p. turquoise-blue (2 bands) (1.4.04)	1·50	1·50
	a. Imperf (pair)	£350	
Y1712	41p. grey-brown (2 bands) (26.10.93)	1·50	1·50
Y1713	41p. drab (phosphorised paper) (1.11.93)	7·50	7·50
Y1714	41p. rosine (2 bands) (25.4.00)	1·50	1·50
Y1715	42p. dp olive-grey (2 bands) (4.7.02)	1·50	1·50
Y1716	43p. dp olive-brown (2 bands) (25.6.96)	1·75	1·75
Y1717	43p. sepia (2 bands) (8.7.96)	4·00	4·00
	a. Perf 14 (13.10.98)	2·00	2·00
Y1718	43p. emerald (2 bands) (1.4.04)	1·75	1·75
	a. Imperf (pair)	£275	
Y1719	44p. grey-brown (2 bands) (20.4.99)	4·00	4·00
Y1720	44p. deep bright blue (2 bands) (28.3.06)	1·50	1·50
Y1721	45p. brt mauve (2 bands) (25.4.00)	1·50	1·50
Y1722	46p. yellow (2 bands) (5.4.05)	1·50	1·50
Y1723	47p. turquoise-green (2 bands) (4.7.02)	1·75	1·75
Y1724	48p. bright mauve (2 bands) (27.3.07)	1·75	1·75
Y1725	49p. red-brown (2 bands) (28.3.06)	2·00	2·00
Y1726	50p. ochre (2 bands) (14.12.93)	1·75	1·75
	a. Imperf (pair)	£2750	
Y1727	50p. grey (2 bands) (27.3.07)	1·75	1·75
Y1728	54p. brown (Type II) (2 bands) (27.3.07)	1·75	1·75
Y1729	56p. yellow-olive (2 bands) (1.4.08)	1·75	1·75
Y1730	60p. light emerald (2 bands) (30.3.10)	1·75	1·75
Y1731	62p. rosine (2 bands) (31.3.09)	1·80	1·80

Y1732		63p. lt emerald (2 bands) (25.6.96)	1·80	1·80
Y1733		64p. turquoise-green (2 bands) (20.4.99) ...	1·80	1·80
Y1734		65p. greenish blue (2 bands) (25.4.00) ...	1·80	1·80
Y1735		67p. bright mauve (2 bands) (30.3.10).....	1·80	1·80
Y1736		68p. grey-brown (2 bands) (4.7.02)..........	2·00	2·00
Y1737		72p. rosine (2 bands) (28.3.06)	2·25	2·25
Y1738		78p. emerald (2 bands) (27.3.07)...............	1·75	1·75
Y1739		81p. turquoise-green (2 bands) (1.4.08) ...	2·00	2·00
Y1740		88p. bright magenta (2 bands) (30.3.10) ...	2·00	2·00
Y1741		90p. ultramarine (2 bands) (31.3.09)	2·00	2·00
Y1742		97p. violet (2 bands) (30.3.10)...................	2·25	2·25
Y1743		£1 bluish violet (2 bands) (22.8.95)	2·50	2·50
		a. Imperf (horiz pair)	£1800	
Y1744		£1 magenta (2 bands) (5.6.07)...............	2·00	2·00
		l. Booklet pane. No. Y1744×2 with centre label and margins all round	4·50	
Y1745		£1.46 greenish blue (2 bands) (30.3.10) ...	3·00	3·00
Y1746		£1.50 brown-red (2 bands) (1.7.03)..........	3·50	3·50
Y1747		£2 deep blue-green (2 bands) (1.7.03)	5·00	5·00
		a. Missing "£" in value (R. 18/1, Cyl D1 no dot)......................................	£250	
Y1748		£3 deep mauve (2 bands) (1.7.03).......	7·00	7·00
Y1749		£5 azure (2 bands) (1.7.03)...................	12·00	12·00

*(b) Litho Cartor (*1p. (Y1761)), 5p. (Y1763/5), 10p. (Y1768), 16p., 17p., 20p., (Y1773), 22p., 50p., 54p., 60p. (Y1785), 62p., 67p., 90p., 97p. *De La Rue* (5p. (Y1762)), *Questa, De La Rue or Cartor* (10p. (Y1767)), *Questa or Walsall* (25p., 35p.,), *Walsall* (37p., 41p. (Y1780) 60p. (Y1784), 63p.), *De La Rue* (48p.), *Questa (others).*

Y1760	**367**	1p. lake (2 bands) (8.7.96)....................	80	80
		Ey. Phosphor omitted.............................	£500	
		l. Booklet pane. Nos. Y1760×2, Y1772 and Y1776×3 plus 2 labels	5·00	
		lEy. Booklet pane. Phosphor omitted ..	£1200	
Y1761		1p. reddish purple (2 bands) (17.9.09)	2·50	2·50
		l. Booklet pane. Nos. Y1761×2, Y1770×4 and Y1789×3 with central label and margins all round	20·00	
Y1762		5p. chocolate (2 bands)(Type II) (12.2.09)	3·25	3·25
		Ey. Phosphor omitted.............................	£1800	
		l. Booklet pane. Nos. 1672, Y1762, Y1767 and Y1781, each×2 with central label...	18·00	
Y1763		5p. Red-brown (*shades*) (13.5.10)	2·50	2·50
		l. Booklet pane. Nos. Y1763×4, Y1767×2 and Y1785×2, with central label and margins all round	22·00	
		m. Booklet pane. Nos. Y1763×4, U3096×2 and U3078×2 with central label and margins all round (9.9.11)..	30·00	
Y1764		5p. Lake-brown (22.3.11).......................	2·50	2·50
		l. Booklet pane. Nos. Y1764×3, Y1767×3, Y1788 and Y1790, with central label and margins all round	22·00	
Y1765		5p. red-brown (2 bands) (Type III) (7.1.10)	3·00	3·00
		l. Booklet pane. Nos. Y1765×2, Y1768×5 and Y1774×2 with margins all round	18·00	
Y1766		6p. yellow-olive (2 bands) (26.7.94)	8·00	8·00
		l. Booklet pane. Nos. Y1766, Y1771 and Y1775×4 with margins all round.............................	8·00	
		la. 6p. value misplaced............................	£4000	
Y1767		10p. dull orange (*shades*) (2 bands) (25.4.95)...	3·00	3·00
		Ey. Phosphor omitted.............................	18·00	
		l. Booklet pane. Nos. Y1767, Y1771/a, Y1775×2, Y1777/8, Y1780a and centre label with margins all round.......................	12·00	
Y1768		10p. Pale brownish orange (7.1.10)	3·00	3·00
Y1769		16p. pale cerise (2 bands) (13.1.09)	2·50	2·50
		l. Booklet pane. Nos. Y1769 and Y1782, each×4, with central label .	22·00	
Y1770		17p. bistre (2 bands) (18.8.09)	2·50	2·50
		l. Booklet pane. Nos. Y1770×4, Y1774×2 and Y1786×2 with central label and margins all round	20·00	
Y1771		19p. bistre (1 band at left) (26.7.94)........	1·50	1·50
		a. Band at right (25.4.95)	1·50	1·50
		l. Booklet pane. Nos. Y1771/a, each×3 with margins all round (25.4.95)...	7·50	
Y1772		20p. brt yellow-green (1 centre band) (8.7.96)..	1·25	1·25
		Ey. Phosphor omitted.............................	£125	
		l. Booklet pane. Nos. Y1772 and Y1776×7...................................	7·00	
		lEy. Booklet pane. Phosphor omitted ..	£200	
Y1773		20p. light green (2 bands) (7.1.10)	3·00	3·00

		l. Booklet pane. Nos. Y1773×4, Y1783×2 and Y1786×2 with central label and margins all round	20·00	
Y1774		22p. olive-brown (2 bands) (18.8.09)	3·50	3·50
		l. Booklet pane. Nos. Y1774 and Y1783, each×4 with central label and margins all round (25.2.10)	18·00	
Y1775		25p. red (2 bands) (1.11.93)....................	1·10	1·10
		l. Booklet pane. Nos. Y1775, NI72, S84 and W73, each×2, with centre label and margins all round (14.5.96)..	7·50	
Y1776		26p. chestnut (2 bands) (8.7.96)...............	1·00	1·00
		Ey. Phosphor omitted.............................	10·00	
Y1777		30p. olive-grey (2 bands) (25.4.95)...........	3·00	3·00
Y1778		35p. yellow (2 bands) (1.11.93).................	1·25	1·25
Y1779		37p. brt mauve (2 bands) (8.7.96)	2·50	2·50
Y1780		41p. drab (2 bands) (1.11.93)....................	1·75	1·75
		a. Grey-brown (25.4.95)..........................	2·50	2·50
		Ey. Phosphor omitted.............................	£800	
Y1781		48p. bright mauve (2 bands) (12.2.09).	3·00	3·00
		Ey. Phosphor omitted.............................	£1800	
Y1782		50p. grey (2 bands) (13.1.09)	3·75	3·75
Y1783		54p. chestnut (2 bands) (Type III) (7.1.10)	3·50	3·50
Y1784		60p. dull blue-grey (2 bands) (9.8.94)	1·75	1·75
Y1785		60p. emerald (2 bands) (13.5.10)	6·00	6·00
Y1786		62p. rosine (2 bands) (18.8.09)	3·75	3·75
Y1787		63p. lt emerald (2 bands) (8.7.96)	3·50	3·50
		Ey. Phosphor omitted.............................	£525	
Y1788		67p. bright mauve (2 bands) (22.3.11)....	8·00	8·00
Y1789		90p. bright blue (2 bands) (17.9.09)	4·00	4·00
Y1790		97p. bluish violet (2 bands) (22.3.11)......	9·00	9·00

(c) Eng C. Slania. Recess Enschedé (until Mar 2000) or De La Rue (from 11 Apr 2000)

Y1800	**367**	£1.50 red (9.3.99)...................................	4·50	2·00
Y1801		£2 dull blue (9.3.99).............................	5·00	2·25
Y1802		£3 dull violet (9.3.99)...........................	7·00	3·00
Y1803		£5 brown (9.3.99).................................	12·00	5·00
		a. Imperf (pair)......................................	£950	

P.H.Q. Card (No. Y1725) (D7) .... 0·50 8·00
P.H.Q. Cards (Nos. 1664, 1668, Y1667/8, Y1670, Y1675/6, Y16779/80, Y1687, Y1724, Y1727, Y1729, Y1739, Y1744, Y1746/9, 2357a, 2652/3, 2358/9 (D30) .... 7·00

Nos. Y1743/9 are printed in Iriodin ink which gives a shiny effect to the solid part of the background behind the Queen's head.

A gravure-printed £5 stamp, as No. Y1749 but in sepia is believed to have come from stock stolen from the printer. Both unused and used examples are known.

No. Y1766la shows the 6p. value printed 22 mm to the left so that its position on the booklet pane is completely blank except for the phosphor bands. Other more minor misplacements exist.

The De La Rue printings of the high values, Nos. Y1800/3 cannot easily be identified from the original Enschedé issue as single stamps.

For self-adhesive versions of the 42p. and 68p. see Nos. 2297/8.

First Day Covers

26.10.93	19p., 25p., 29p., 36p., 38p., 41p. (Y1682, Y1689, Y1693, Y1702, Y1706, Y1712)	6·00	
9.8.94	60p. (Y1784)	2·00	
25.4.95	National Trust *se-tenant* pane 10p., 19p., 25p., 30p., 35p., 41p. (Y1767l)	10·00	
22.8.95	£1 (Y1743)	3·00	
14.5.96	European Football Championship *se-tenant* pane 25p.×8 (Y1775l)	6·00	
25.6.96	20p., 26p., 31p., 37p., 39p., 43p., 63p. (Y1685, Y1691, Y1695, Y1703, Y1708, Y1716, Y1732)	8·00	
13.10.98	Speed *se-tenant* pane 10p., 2nd, 43p. (Y1676al)	8·00	
9.3.99	£1.50, £2, £3, £5 (Y1800/3) (Type G) (Philatelic Bureau or Windsor)	15·00	
20.4.99	7p., 38p., 44p., 64p. (Y1672, Y1707, Y1719, Y1733) (Type G) (Philatelic Bureau or Windsor)	5·00	
21.9.99	World Changers *se-tenant* pane 1p.,19p., 26p. (Y1667n) (Philatelic Bureau or Downe, Orpington)	4·00	
25.4.00	8p., 33p., 40p., 41p., 45p., 65p. (Y1674, Y1696, Y1710, Y1714, Y1721, Y1734) (Type G) (Philatelic Bureau or Windsor)...	5·00	
4.7.02	37p., 42p., 47p., 68p. (Y1704, Y1715, Y1722, Y1736) (Type K) (Tallents House or Windsor)	5·00	
6.5.03	34p., (Y1697) (Type K) (Tallents House or Windsor)	4·50	
1.7.03	£1.50, £2, £3, £5 (*Nos*. Y1746/9) (Type K) (Tallents House or Windsor)...	25·00	
1.4.04	7p., 35p., 39p., 40p., 43p. Worldwide postcard (Y1673, Y1700, Y1709, Y1711, Y1718, 2357a) (Type K) (Tallents House or Windsor)...................................	9·00	
5.4.05	9p., 35p., 46p. (*Nos*. Y1675, Y1701, Y1722) (Type K) (Tallents House or Windsor)...................................	2·20	
28.3.06	37p., 44p., 49p., 72p. (Y1703, Y1725, Y1737) (Type K) (Tallents House or Windsor)...................................	4·25	
1.3.07	World of Invention label pane 5p., 1st (Y1670l) (Tallents House or Menai Bridge, Gwynedd)................	5·00	

27.3.07	16p., 48p., 50p., 54p., 78p. (Y1680, Y1724, Y1727/8, Y1738) (Type K) (Tallents House or Windsor)	6·00
5.6.07	Machin Anniversary *se-tenant* pane 2p., 46p., 48p. (Y1668l) (Tallents House, Windsor or Stoke-on-Trent) .	4·00
20.9.07	Army Uniforms *se-tenant* pane 1p., 46p., 54p. (Y1667o) (Tallents House or Boot, Holmrook, Cumbria)	7·00
1.4.08	15p., 56p., 81p. (Y1679, Y1727, Y1739) (Type K) (Tallents House or Windsor)	4·50
13.1.09	British Design Classics *se-tenant* pane 16p., 50p. (Y1769l) (Tallents House or Longbridge, Birmingham)	20·00
12.2.09	Charles Darwin *se-tenant* pane 5p., 10p., 1st, 48p. (Y1762l) (Tallents House or Shrewsbury)	16·00
31.3.09	17p., 22p., 62p., 90p. (Y1681, Y1688, Y1731, Y1741) (Type K) (Tallents House or Windsor)	6·00
18.8.09	"Treasures of the Archive" *se-tenant* pane 17p., 22p., 62p., (Y1770l) (Tallents House or London EC1)	20·00
17.9.09	Royal Navy Uniforms *se-tenant* pane 1p., 17p., 90p. (Y1761l) (Tallents House or Portsmouth)	22·00
7.1.10	Classic Album Covers *se-tenant* pane 20p., 54p., 52p. (Y1773l) (Tallents House or Oldfield, Keighley)	20·00
25.2.10	Royal Society *se-tenant* pane 22p., 54p. (Y1774l) (Tallents House or London SW1)	18·00
30.3.10	60p., 67p., 88p., 97p., £1.46, Europe up to 20 grams, Worldwide up to 20 grams (Y1730, Y1735, Y1740, Y1742, Y1745, 2357b, 2358a (Type K) (Tallents House or Windwor)	20·00
13.5.10	"Britain Alone" *se-tenant* pane 5p., 10p., 60p., (Y1763l) (Tallents House or Dover, Kent)	5·50
22.3.11	WWF *se-tenant* pane 5p., 10p., 67p., 97p. (Y1764l) (Tallents House or Godalming, Surrey)	20·00
9.9.11	Aerial Post Centenary *se-tenant* pane 5p., 1st, 76p. (Y1763m) (Tallents House or Hendon, London NW4) ..	25·00
10.1.12	Roald Dahl *se-tenant* pane 2p., 10p., 68p. (Y1668c) (Tallents House or Great Missenden, Bucks)	10·00

For first day covers for Nos. Y1677/8 see under Nos. 2650/7.

Post Office Presentation Packs

26.10.93	PO Pack No. 30. 19p. (1 centre band), 25p. (phos paper), 29p., 36p., 38p. rosine, 41p. grey-brown (*Nos.* Y1682, Y1689, Y1693, Y1702, Y1706, Y1712)	6·00
21.11.95	PO Pack No. 34. 1p. (photo), 2p., 4p., 5p., 6p. (photo), 10p. (photo), 19p. (1 centre band), 20p. turquoise-green, 25p. (photo) (2 bands), 29p., 30p. (photo), 35p. (photo) (2 bands), 36p., 38p. rosine, 41p. grey-brown, 50p., 60p., £1 (*Nos.* Y1667/71, Y1676, Y1682, Y1684, Y1690, Y1693/4, Y1698, Y1702, Y1706, Y1712, Y1726, Y1743, Y1784)	35·00
25.6.96	PO Pack No. 35. 20p. brt green (1 centre band), 26p. (photo), 31p., 37p. (photo), 39p., 43p. deep olive brown, 63p. (photo) (*Nos.* Y1685, Y1691, Y1695, Y1703, Y1708, Y1716, Y1732)	8·00
21.4.97	PO Pack No. 38. 1st, 26p. gold (*Nos.* 1668, Y1692)	6·00
20.10.98	PO Pack No. 41. 2nd brt blue (1 centre band), 1st brt orange-red (2 phosphor bands), 1p., 2p., 4p., 5p., 6p., 10p., 20p. brt green (1 centre band), 26p., 31p., 37p., 39p., 43p. sepia, 50p., 63p., £1 (*Nos.* 1664, 1667, Y1667/71, Y1676, Y1685, Y1691, Y1694/5, Y1703, Y1708, Y1717, Y1726, Y1732)	18·00
9.3.99	PO Pack No. 43 or 43a. £1·50, £2, £3, £5 (*Nos.* Y1800/3)	38·00
20.4.99	PO Pack No. 44. 7p., 19p., 38p. ultramarine, 44p., 64p. (*Nos.* Y1672, Y1682, Y1707, Y1719, Y1733)	9·50
25.4.00	PO Pack No. 49. 8p., 33p., 40p., 41p. rosine, 45p., 65p. (*Nos.* Y1674, Y1696, Y1710, Y1714, Y1721, Y1734)	8·50
12.3.02	PO Pack No. 57. 2nd, 1st, E, 1p., 2p., 4p., 5p., 8p., 10p., 20p., 33p., 40p., 41p., 45p., 50p., 65p., £1 (*Nos.* 1664, 1667, 1669, Y1667/70, Y1674, Y1676, Y1687, Y1696, Y1710, Y1714, Y1721, Y1726, Y1734, Y1743)	16·00
4.7.02	PO Pack No. 58. 37p., 42p., 47p., 68p. (*Nos.* Y1704, Y1715, Y1723, Y1736)	6·50
1.7.03	PO Pack No. 62. £1·50, £2, £3, £5 (*Nos.* Y1746/9)	25·00
1.4.04	PO Pack No. 67. 1st gold (DLR ptg), 7p., 35p., 39p., 40p., 43p. Worldwide postcard (*Nos.* 1668, Y1673, Y1700, Y1709, Y1711, Y1718, 2357a)	10·00
6.9.05	PO Pack No. 71. 1p., 2p., 5p., 9p., 10p., 20p., 35p., 40p., 42p., 46p., 47p., 50p., 68p., £1., 2nd, 1st, Worldwide postcard, Europe up to 40 grams, Worldwide up to 40 grams (*Nos.* Y1667/8, Y1670, Y1675/6, Y1687, Y1701, Y1711, Y1715, Y1722/3, Y1726, Y1736, Y1743, 2039, 2295, 2357a, 2358, 2359)	50·00
28.3.06	PO Pack No. 72. 37p., 44p., 49p., 72p. (*Nos.* Y1705, Y1720, Y1725, Y1737)	11·00
27.3.07	PO Pack No. 75. 16p., 48p., 50p., 54p., 78p. (*Nos.* Y1680, Y1724, Y1727, Y1728, Y1738)	10·00
5.6.07	PO Pack No. 77. 2nd, 1st, 1p., 2p., 5p., 10p., 14p., 16p., 20p., 46p., 48p., 50p., 54p., 78p., £1, Worldwide postcard, Europe up to 40 grams, 2nd Large, 1st Large (*Nos.* 1664, 1668, Y1667/8, Y1670, Y1676, Y1678/9, Y1687, Y1722, Y1724, Y1727/8, Y1744, 2357a, 2358, 2359, 2652/3)	45·00
1.4.08	P.O. Pack. No. 78. 15p., 56p., 81p. (Nos. Y1679, Y1729, Y1739)	5·00
31.3.09	PO Pack No. 84 17p., 22p., 62p., 90p. (Nos. Y1681, Y1688, Y1731, Y1741)	8·50

30.3.10	PO Pack No. 86. 60p. 67p., 88p., 97p., £1.46, Europe up to 20 grams, Worldwide up to 20 grams, 1st Recorded Signed For, 1st Large Recorded Signed For (Nos. Y1730, Y1735, Y1740, Y1742, Y1745, 2357b, 2358a, U2981/2)	28·00
8.5.10	PO Pack No. 88. 2nd, 1st, 1p., 2p., 5p., 9p., 10p., 20p., 50p., 60p., 67p., 88p., 97p., £1, £1.46, Worldwide postcard, Europe up to 20 grams Worldwide up to 20 grams, Europe up to 40 grams, Worldwide up to 40 grams, 2nd Large, 1st Large, 1st Recorded Signed For, 1st Large Recorded Signed For (Nos. 1664, 1668, Y1667, Y1668, Y1670, Y1675, Y1676, Y1727, Y1730, Y1735, Y1740, Y1742, Y1744, Y1745, 2357a/9, 2652/3 and U2981/2)	50·00

In 2002 a 'master' presentation pack entitled 'Royal Mail Definitive Stamps Collection' was released, containing packs 43a, 53, 54, 55, 56 and 57 (*Price* £120).

1917 (Illustration reduced. Actual size 127×72 mm)

(Des Katja Thielan. Gravure De La Rue)

2006 (31 Aug). *70th Anniversary of the Year of Three Kings*. Sheet 127×72 mm containing No. Y1748. Multicoloured. Two phosphor bands. Perf 15×14 (with one elliptical hole in each vertical side).

MS2658	**1917** £3 deep mauve	5·25	5·25
First Day Cover (Tallents House)			5·50
First Day Cover (Threekingham, Sleaford, Lincs)			5·50

Decimal Machin Index

(stamps with elliptical perforations, including (N.V.Is)

Value	Process	Colour	Phosphor	Cat. No.	Source
2nd	litho Questa or Walsall	brt blue	1 centre band	1670	sheets (Questa), booklets of 4 (Walsall – HA6, Walsall HA9/11), booklets of 10 (Questa – HC11, HC13, HC16, HC18, HC20, Walsall – HC12), $7.15 "Pilot to Plane" booklet (Walsall - DX42)
2nd	photo/gravure Harrison/De La Rue), Enschedé, Questa or Walsall	brt blue	1 centre band	1664	sheets (Walsall, De La Rue), horizontal coil (Harrison/De La Rue), vertical coils (Harrison/De La Rue or Enschedé) booklets of 4 (Harrison – HA7/8, Walsall – HA12), booklets of 10 (Harrison/De La Rue – HC14/15, HC17, HC19, HC21), £1 booklet (Questa – FH44/a), £2 booklet (Questa – FW12), £7.29 "A Gracious Accession" booklet (Enschedé – DX28), £7.46 "A Perfect Coronation" booklet (Walsall – DX31), £7.43 The Brontë Sisters booklet (Walsall – DX34)
2nd	gravure Walsall (p 14)	brt blue	1 band at right	1665	£6.16 British Land Speed Record Holders booklet (DX21)
2nd	gravure Walsall (p 14)	brt blue	1 band at left	1665Ec	£6.16 British Land Speed Record Holders booklet (DX21)
2nd	gravure Questa (p 14)	brt blue	1 centre band	1664a	booklets of 10 (HC22)
1st	litho Enschedé, Questa or Walsall	brt orange-red	2 bands	1671	sheets (Questa), greetings card panes Questa – Y1671m/ma, Enschedé – Y1671mb), booklets of 4 (Walsall – HB6, HB8/13, HB15/16, Questa – HB7), booklets of 10 Walsall – HD10, HD12/19, HD22/3, HD25, HD28, HD34, HD36/8, HD40, Questa – HD11, HD21, HD26, HD50), £7.54 "Profile on Print" booklet (Questa – DX22)
1st	photo Harrison	brt orange-red	phos paper	1666	booklets of 4 (HB5), booklets of 10 (HD9, HD20)
1st	photo/gravure Harrison/De La Rue, Questa or Walsall/ISP Walsall	brt orange-red	2 bands	1667	sheets (Walsall), horizontal and vertical coils (Harrison, De La Rue), booklets of 4 (Walsall – HB14, HB17/18), booklets of 8 with 2 Millennium commems (Walsall – HBA1/2), booklets of 10 (Harrison/De La Rue – HD24, HD27, HD29/33, HD35, HD39, HD45/9, Walsall – HD44), £1 booklet (Questa – FH44/a), £2 booklet (Questa – FW12), £7.54 "Profile on Print" booklet (De La Rue – DX22), £15.14 "50th Anniversary of the Machin" booklet (ISP Walsall – DY21)
1st	gravure Questa (p 14)	brt orange-red	2 bands	1667a	booklets of 10 (HD51)
1st	gravure De La Rue, Enschedé, Harrison, Questa or Walsall/ISP Walsall	gold	2 bands	1668	sheets (Walsall, De La Rue), vertical coils (Enschedé, De La Rue), booklets of 10 (Harrison – HD41, HD43, Walsall – HD42), £6.15 B.B.C. booklet (Harrison – DX19), £6.83 "Across the Universe" booklet (Questa – DX29, £6.99 "Microcosmos" booklet (Enschedé – DX30), £7.46 "A Perfect Coronation" booklet (Walsall – DX31), £7.44 "Letters by Night" booklet (De La Rue – DX32), £7.23 "The Glory of the Garden" booklet (Enschedé – DX33), £7.26 Trafalgar booklet (Walsall – DX35), £7.40 Brunel booklet (Enschedé – DX36), £15.14 "50th Anniversary of the Machin" booklet (ISP Walsall – DY21)
1st	gravure ISP Walsall	brownish black	2 bands	1668s	£15.14 "50th Anniversary of the Machin" booklet (ISP Walsall – DY21)
1st	litho De La Rue or Walsall	gold	2 bands	1672	£7.40 Ian Fleming's James Bond booklet (De La Rue – DX41), £7.15 "Pilot to Plane" booklet (Walsall - DX42)
E	gravure De La Rue, Enschedé, Questa or Walsall	deep blue	2 bands	1669	sheets (De La Rue), booklets of 4 (Walsall – HF1), £7.29 "A Gracious Accession" booklet (Enschedé – DX28), £6.83 "Across the Universe" booklet (Questa – DX29), £6.99 "Microcosmos" booklet (Enschedé – DX30)
1p.	photo/gravure De La Rue, Enschedé, Harrison, Questa or ISP Walsall	crimson	2 bands	Y1667	sheets, £1 booklets (Questa – FH42/3), £6.91 World Changers booklet (Questa – DX23) , £7.66 British Army Uniforms booklet (Enschedé – DX40), £15.14 "50th Anniversary of the Machin" booklet (ISP Walsall – DY21)
1p.	litho Questa	lake	2 bands	Y1760	£1 booklet (FH41)
1p.	litho Cartor	reddish purple	2 bands	Y1761	£7.93 Royal Navy Uniforms booklet (DX47)
2p.	photo/gravure De La Rue, Enschedé, Harrison, Questa or Walsall/ISP Walsall	dp green	2 bands	Y1668	sheets, £1 booklet (Questa – FH43), £7.66 "The Machin" booklet (De La Rue – DX39), £11.47 Roald Dahl booklet (Walsall – DY3), £15.14 "50th Anniversary of the Machin" booklet (ISP Walsall – DY21)
4p.	photo/gravure De La Rue, Enschedé or Harrison	new blue	2 bands	Y1669	sheets
4p.	gravure De La Rue	new blue	phos paper	MS2146	Jeffery Matthews Colour Palette miniature sheet
5p.	photo/gravure De La Rue, Enschedé, Harrison or ISP Walsall	dull red-brown	2 bands	Y1670	sheets , £7.49 World of Invention booklet (De La Rue – DX38), £15.14 "50th Anniversary of the Machin" booklet (ISP Walsall – DY21)
5p.	gravure De La Rue	dull red-brown	phos paper	MS2146	Jeffery Matthews Colour Palette miniature sheet
5p.	litho De La Rue	chocolate	2 bands	Y1762	£7.75 Charles Darwin booklet (DX45)
5p.	litho Cartor	red-brown	2 bands	Y1763	£9.76 Great Britain Alone booklet (DX51), £9.97 Aerial Post Centenary booklet (DY2)
5p.	litho Cartor	lake-brown	2 bands	Y1764	£9.05 WWF booklet (DX52)
5p.	litho Cartor	red-brown	2 bands	Y1765	Type III. £8.06 Classic Album Covers booklet (DX48)

Value	Process	Colour	Phosphor	Cat. No.	Source
6p.	photo/gravure Enschedé or Harrison	yellow-olive	2 bands	Y1671	sheets
6p.	litho Questa	yellow-olive	2 bands	Y1766	£6.04 Northern Ireland booklet (DX16)
6p.	gravure De La Rue	yellow-olive	phos paper	**MS**2146	Jeffery Matthews Colour Palette miniature sheet
7p.	gravure De La Rue	grey	2 bands	Y1672	sheets
7p.	gravure De La Rue	bright magenta	2 bands	Y1673	sheets
8p.	gravure De La Rue	yellow	2 bands	Y1674	sheets
9p.	gravure De La Rue	yellow-orange	2 bands	Y1675	sheets
10p.	photo/gravure De La Rue, Enschedé, Harrison or Walsall/ ISP Walsall	dull orange	2 bands	Y1676	sheets, £11.47 Roald Dahl booklet (Walsall – DY3), £15.14 "50th Anniversary of the Machin" booklet (ISP Walsall – DY21)
10p.	litho Questa, De La Rue or Cartor	dull orange	2 bands	Y1767	£6 National Trust booklet (Questa - DX17), £7.75 Charles Darwin booklet (De La Rue - DX45), £9.76 "Britain Alone" booklet (Cartor - DX51), £9.05 WWF booklet (Cartor - DX52)
10p.	litho Cartor	pale brownish orange	2 bands	Y1768	£8.06 Classic Album Covers booklet (DX48)
10p.	gravure Walsall (*p* 14)	dull orange	2 bands	Y1676a	£6.16 British Land Speed Record Holders booklet (DX21)
10p.	gravure Walsall	dull orange	phos paper	**MS**2146	Jeffery Matthews Colour Palette miniature sheet
12p.	gravure De La Rue	greenish blue	2 bands	Y1677	sheets
14p.	gravure De La Rue	rose-red	2 bands	Y1678	sheets
15p.	gravure De La Rue	bright magenta	2 bands	Y1679	sheets
16p.	gravure De La Rue	pale cerise	2 bands	Y1680	sheets
16p.	litho Cartor	pale cerise	2 bands	Y1769	£7.75 British Design Classics booklet (DX44)
17p.	gravure De La Rue	brown-olive	2 bands	Y1681	sheets
17p.	litho Cartor	bistre	2 bands	Y1770	£8.18 "Treasures of the Archive" booklet (DX46) and £7.93 Royal Navy Uniforms booklet (DX47)
19p.	photo/gravure Harrison or Questa	bistre	1 centre band	Y1682	sheets, vertical coils, £1 booklet (Questa – FH43), £2 booklet (Questa – FW11), £6.99 World Changers booklet (Questa – DX23)
19p.	litho Questa	bistre	1 band at left	Y1771	£6.04 Northern Ireland booklet (DX16), £6 National Trust booklet (DX17)
19p.	litho Questa	bistre	1 band at right	Y1771a	£6 National Trust booklet (DX17)
19p.	gravure Walsall (*p* 14)	bistre	1 band at right	Y1683	£7.50 "Special by Design" booklet (DX24)
20p.	gravure Enschedé	turquoise-green	2 bands	Y1684	sheets
20p.	photo/gravure Harrison or Questa	brt green	1 centre band	Y1685	sheets, £1 booklet (Questa – FH42), £2 booklet (Questa – FW10)
20p.	litho Questa	brt yellow-green	1 centre band	Y1772	£1 booklet (FH41), £2 booklet (FW9)
20p.	gravure Harrison	brt green	1 band at right	Y1686	£6.15 B.B.C. booklet (DX19)
20p.	gravure De La Rue or ISP Walsall	brt green	2 bands	Y1687	sheets, £15.14 "50th Anniversary of the Machin" booklet (ISP Walsall – DY21)
20p.	litho Cartor	light green	2 bands	Y1773	£8.06 Classic Album Covers booklet (DX48)
22p.	gravure De La Rue	drab	2 bands	Y1688	sheets
22p.	litho Cartor	olive-brown	2 bands	Y1774	£8.18 "Treasures of the Archive" booklet (DX46), £8.06 Classic Album Covers booklet (DX48) and £7.72 Royal Society booklet (DX49)
25p.	photo Harrison	rose-red	phos paper	Y1689	sheets, vertical coils, 50p booklets (FB67/73), £1 booklets (FH33/7), £2 booklets (FW1/5)
25p.	litho Walsall or Questa	red	2 bands	Y1775	£1 booklets (Walsall – FH31/2), (Questa – FH40), £2 booklet (Questa – FW8), £6.04 Northern Ireland booklet (Questa – DX16), £6 National Trust booklet (Questa – DX17), £6.84 European Football Championship (Questa – DX18)
25p.	photo/gravure Harrison or Enschedé	rose-red	2 bands	Y1690	sheets (Harrison or Enschedé), vertical coils (Harrison), 50p booklets (Harrison – FB74/5), £1 booklets (Harrison – FH38/9)), £2 booklets (Harrison – FW6/7)
26p.	photo/gravure Harrison or Questa	red-brown	2 bands	Y1691	sheets, £1 booklets (Questa – FH42/3), £2 booklets (Questa – FW10/11), £6.15 B.B.C. booklet (Harrison – DX19), £6.99 World Changers booklet (Questa – DX23)
26p.	litho Questa	chestnut	2 bands	Y1776	£1 booklet (FH41), £2 booklet (FW9)
26p.	gravure Harrison	gold	2 bands	Y1692	sheets, £6.15 B.B.C. booklet (Harrison – DX19)
29p.	gravure Enschedé	grey	2 bands	Y1693	sheets
30p.	photo/gravure Enschedé, Harrison or Walsall	dp olive-grey	2 bands	Y1694	sheets, £1.20 booklets (Walsall – GGAI/2)
30p.	litho Questa	olive-grey	2 bands	Y1777	£6 National Trust booklet (DX17)
31p.	photo/gravure Enschedé or Harrison	dp mauve	2 bands	Y1695	sheets
31p.	gravure De La Rue	dp mauve	phos paper	**MS**2146	Jeffery Matthews Colour Palette miniature sheet
33p.	gravure De La Rue	grey-green	2 bands	Y1696	sheets
34p.	gravure De La Rue	yellow-olive	2 bands	Y1697	sheets
35p.	gravure Enschedé	yellow	2 bands	Y1698	sheets
35p.	photo Harrison	yellow	phos paper	Y1699	vertical coils
35p.	litho Walsall or Questa	yellow	2 bands	Y1778	£1.40 booklets (Walsall – GK5/7), £6 National Trust booklet (Questa – DX17)
35p.	gravure De La Rue	sepia	2 bands	Y1700	sheets
35p.	gravure Enschedé or De La Rue	yellow-olive	1 centre band	Y1701	sheets, £7.40 Brunel booklet (Enschedé – DX36)
36p.	gravure Enschedé	brt ultramarine	2 bands	Y1702	sheets
37p.	photo/gravure Enschedé, Harrison or Walsall	brt mauve	2 bands	Y1703	sheets (Enschedé or Harrison), vertical coils (Harrison), £1.48 booklets (Walsall – GL3/4)
37p.	litho Walsall	brt mauve	2 bands	Y1779	£1.48 booklets (GL1/2)

Value	Process	Colour	Phosphor	Cat. No.	Source
37p.	gravure De La Rue	grey-black	2 bands	Y1704	sheets, £7.44 "Letters by Night" booklet (De La Rue – DX32)
37p.	gravure De La Rue	brown-olive	1 centre band	Y1705	sheets
38p.	gravure Enschedé	rosine	2 bands	Y1706	sheets
38p.	gravure De La Rue or Walsall	ultramarine	2 bands	Y1707	sheets (D.L.R.), £1.52 booklet (Walsall – GLAl)
38p.	gravure Walsall (p 14)	ultramarine	2 bands	Y1707a	£7.50 "Special by Design" booklet (DX24)
39p.	photo/gravure Enschedé or Harrison	brt magenta	2 bands	Y1708	sheets
39p.	gravure De La Rue	brt magenta	phos paper	**MS**2146	Jeffery Matthews Colour Palette miniature sheet
39p.	gravure De La Rue or Walsall	grey	2 bands	Y1709	sheets (De La Rue), £7.43 The Brontë Sisters booklet (Walsall – DX34)
40p.	gravure De La Rue or Walsall	deep azure	2 bands	Y1710	sheets (D.L.R.), £1.60 booklet (Walsall – GMA1)
40p.	gravure De La Rue or Enschedé	turquoise-blue	2 bands	Y1711	sheets (D.L.R.), £7.40 Brunel booklet (Enschedé – DX36)
41p.	gravure Enschedé	grey-brown	2 bands	Y1712	sheets
41p.	photo Harrison	drab	phos paper	Y1713	vertical coils
41p.	gravure De La Rue	rosine	2 bands	Y1714	sheets
41p.	litho Walsall	drab	2 bands	Y1780	£1.64 booklets (GN1/3)
41p.	litho Questa	grey-brown	2 bands	Y1780a	£6 National Trust booklet (DX17)
42p.	gravure De La Rue, Enschedé or Walsall	dp olive-grey	2 bands	Y1715	sheets (De La Rue), £7.23 "The Glory of the Garden" booklet (Enschedé – DX33), £7.43 The Brontë Sisters booklet (Walsall – DX34)
43p.	gravure Enschedé	dp olive-brown	2 bands	Y1716	sheets
43p.	photo Harrison	sepia	2 bands	Y1717	sheets, vertical coils
43p.	gravure Walsall (p 14)	sepia	2 bands	Y1717a	£6.16 British Land Speed Record Holders booklet (DX21)
43p.	gravure De La Rue	emerald	2 bands	Y1718	sheets
44p.	gravure De La Rue	grey-brown	2 bands	Y1719	sheets
44p.	gravure De La Rue	bright blue	2 bands	Y1720	sheets
45p.	gravure De La Rue	brt mauve	2 bands	Y1721	sheets
46p.	gravure De La Rue or Enschedé	yellow	2 bands	Y1722	sheets (De La Rue), £7.66 "The Machin" booklet (De La Rue – DX39), £7.66 British Army Uniforms booklet (Enschedé – DX40)
47p.	gravure De La Rue or Enschedé	turquoise-green	2 bands	Y1723	sheets (De La Rue), £7.23 "The Glory of the Garden" booklet (Enschedé – DX33)
48p.	gravure De La Rue	bright mauve	2 bands	Y1724	sheets, £7.66 "The Machin" booklet (DX39)
48p.	litho De La Rue	bright mauve	2 bands	Y1781	£7.75 Charles Darwin booklet (DX45)
49p.	gravure De La Rue	red-brown	2 bands	Y1725	sheets
50p.	photo/gravure Enschedé, Harrison or Walsall	ochre	2 bands	Y1726	sheets (Enschedé or Harrison), £7.26 Trafalgar booklet (Walsall–DX35), £7.44 Victoria Cross booklet (Enschedé – DX37)
50p.	gravure De La Rue	grey	2 bands	Y1727	sheets
50p.	litho Cartor	grey	2 bands	Y1782	£7.68 British Design Classics Booklet (DX44)
54p.	gravure De La Rue or Enschedé	red-brown	2 bands	Y1728	sheets (D.L.R.), £7.66 British Army Uniforms booklet (Enschedé – DX40)
54p.	litho Cartor	chestnut	2 bands	Y1783	Type III. £8.06 Classic Album Covers booklet (DX48) and £7.72 Royal Society booklet (DX49)
56p.	gravure De La Rue	yellow-olive	2 bands	Y1729	sheets
60p.	litho Walsall	dull blue-grey	2 bands	Y1784	£2.40 booklets (GQ1/4)
60p.	gravure De La Rue	light emerald	2 bands	Y1730	sheets
60p.	litho Cartor	emerald	2 bands	Y1785	"Britain Alone" booklet (DX51)
62p.	gravure De La Rue	rosine	2 bands	Y1731	sheets
62p.	litho Cartor	rosine	2 bands	Y1786	£8.18 "Treasures of the Archive" booklet (DX46) and £8.06 Classic Album Covers booklet (DX48)
63p.	photo/gravure Enschedé, Harrison or Walsall	lt emerald	2 bands	Y1732	sheets (Enschedé or Harrison), vertical coils (Harrison) £2.52 booklets (Walsall – GR3/4)
63p.	litho Walsall	lt emerald	2 bands	Y1787	£2.52 booklets (GR1/2)
64p.	gravure De La Rue or Walsall	turquoise-green	2 bands	Y1733	sheets (D.L.R.), £2.56 booklet (Walsall – GS1)
64p.	gravure De La Rue	turquoise-green	phos paper	**MS**2146	Jeffery Matthews Colour Palette miniature sheet
65p.	gravure De La Rue or Walsall	greenish blue	2 bands	Y1734	sheets (D.L.R.), £2.60 booklet (Walsall – GT1)
67p.	gravure De La Rue	bright mauve	2 bands	Y1735	sheets
67p.	litho Cartor	bright mauve	2 bands	Y1788	£9.05 WWF booklet (DX52)
68p.	gravure De La Rue or Walsall	grey-brown	2 bands	Y1736	sheets (D.L.R.), £7.26 Trafalgar booklet (Walsall – DX35)
72p.	gravure De La Rue	rosine	2 bands	Y1737	sheets
78p.	gravure De La Rue	emerald	2 bands	Y1738	sheets
81p.	gravure De La Rue	turquoise-green	2 bands	Y1739	sheets
88p.	gravure De La Rue	bright magenta	2 bands	Y1740	sheets
90p.	gravure De La Rue	ultramarine	2 bands	Y1741	sheets
90p.	litho Cartor	bright blue	2 bands	Y1789	£7.93 Royal Navy Uniforms booklet (DX47)
97p.	gravure De La Rue	violet	2 bands	Y1742	sheets
97p.	litho Cartor	bluish violet	2 bands	Y1790	£9.05 WWF booklet (DX52)
£1	gravure Enschedé, Harrison or De la Rue	bluish violet	2 bands	Y1743	sheets, **MS**2743 (D.L.R.)
£1	gravure De La Rue	magenta	2 bands	Y1744	sheets, £7.66 "The Machin" booklet (DX39), **MS**2743
£1	gravure De La Rue	bluish violet	phos paper	**MS**2146	Jeffery Matthews Colour Palette miniature sheet
£1.46	gravure De La Rue	greenish blue	2 bands	Y1745	sheets
£1.50	recess	red	—	Y1800	sheets (Enschedé then D.L.R.)
£1.50	gravure De La Rue	brown-red	2 bands	Y1746	sheets
£2	recess	dull blue	—	Y1801	sheets (Enschedé then D.L.R.)
£2	gravure De La Rue	deep blue-green	2 bands	Y1747	sheets
£3	recess	dull violet	—	Y1802	sheets (Enschedé then D.L.R.)

Value	Process	Colour	Phosphor	Cat. No.	Source
£3	gravure De La Rue	deep mauve	2 bands	Y1748	sheets, **MS**2658
£5	recess	brown	—	Y1803	sheets (Enschedé then D.L.R.)
£5	gravure De La Rue	azure	2 bands	Y1749	sheets

Note. Harrison and Sons became De La Rue Security Print on 8 September 1997.

Photo/gravure stamps were printed from both photogravure and computor engraved (gravure) cylinders.

Decimal Machin Booklet Pane Guide (ordinary gum) ("Y" numbers) the shaded squares represent printed labels.

1	1
20	26
26	26

Y1667l
(photo)

1	2
19	26
26	26

Y1667m

1	19	1
26		19
1	19	1

Y1667n
£6.99 World Changers
(DX 23)

1	46	54
46		46
54	46	1

Y1667o
£7.66 British Army Uniforms
(DX 40)

1	2	5
10		20
50	2nd	£1.00

Y1667p
£15.14 50th Anniversary of the
Machin Definitive (DY21)

2	48	2
46		46
2	48	2

Y1668l
£7.66 Machin, Making of a Masterpiece
(DX 39)

68	10	68
2		2
68	10	68

Y1668m
£11.47 Roald Dahl: Master Storyteller
(DY 3)

1st	5	1st
5		5
1st	5	1st

Y1670l
£7.49 World of Invention
(DX 38)

43	10	2nd
43		2nd
43	10	2nd

Y1676al
£6.16 Breaking Barriers
(DX 21)

19	26
26	26
26	26
26	26

Y1682l

19	19
19	19
38	38

Y1683l
£7.50 Special by Design
(DX 24)

20	26
26	26
26	26
26	26

Y1685l
(photo)

20	26
20	26
20	26

Y1686l
£6.15 Celebrating 75 years of the BBC
(DX 19)

25	25

Y1689l
(2 bands)

25	25

Y1690l
(phosphorised)

£1
£1

Y1744l
£7.66 Machin, Making of a Masterpiece
(DX 39)

1	1
20	26
26	26

Y1760l
(litho)

17	1	17
90		90
17	1	17

Y1761l
£7.93 Royal Navy Uniforms
(DX 47)

5	10	48
1st		1st
48	10	5

Y1762l
£7.75 Charles Darwin
(DX 45)

5	60	5
10		10
5	60	5

Y1763l
£9.76 Britain Alone
(DX 51)

1st	5	76
5		5
76	5	1st

Y1763m
£9.97 First United Kingdom
Aerial Post (DY 2)

10	67	5
5		10
10	97	5

Y1764l
£9.05 50th Anniv of WWF
(DX 52)

10	22	10
5	10	5
10	22	10

Y1765l
£8.06 Classic Album Covers
(DX 48)

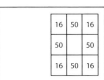

	6	19
	25	25
	25	25

Y1766I
£6.04 Northern Ireland
(DX 43)

19	10	19
25		25
30	35	41

Y1767I
£6.00 The National Trust
(DX 17)

16	50	16
50		50
16	50	16

Y1769I
£7.68 British Design Classics
(DX 44)

17	22	17
62		62
17	22	17

Y1770I
£8.18 Treasures of the Archive
(DX 46)

19	19
19	19
19	19

Y1771I
£6.00 The National Trust
(DX 17)

20	26
26	26
26	26
26	26

Y1772I
(litho)

20	62	20
54		54
20	62	20

Y1773I
£8.06 Classic Album Covers
(DX 48)

54	22	54
22		22
54	22	54

Y1774I
£7.72 350th Anniv of the Royal Society
(DX 49)

25 S	25 W	25 NI
25		25
25 S	25 W	25 NI

Y1775I
£6.48 European Football Championship
(DX 18)

SELF-ADHESIVE MACHIN INDEX

Value	Format	Process	Colour	Phosphor	Cat. No.	Source
2nd	horizontal	photo	bright blue	1 centre band	1976	coils
2nd	vertical	photo	bright blue	1 centre band	2039	rolls, sheets, booklets
1st	horizontal	litho	orange-red	2 bands	1789	booklets
1st	horizontal	photo	brt orge-red	2 bands	1977	coils
1st	vertical	photo	brt orge-red	2 bands	2040	coils, sheets, booklets
1st	vertical	photo	gold	2 bands	2295	booklets, sheets
E	vertical	photo	deep blue	2 bands	2296	booklets
42p.	vertical	photo	dp olive-grey	2 bands	2297	booklets
68p.	vertical	photo	grey-brown	2 bands	2298	booklets

N.V.I. stamps, self-adhesive gum, elliptical perforations

1116

(Des J. Matthews. Litho Walsall)

1993 (19 Oct). *Self-adhesive*. Two phosphor bands. Die-cut Perf 14×15 (with one elliptical hole on each vertical side).

1789	**1116**	(1st) orange-red	1·50	1·50
		Ey. Phosphor omitted	£260	
First Day Cover (No. 1789)				2·50
Presentation Pack (booklet of 20) (P.O. Pack No. 29)			15·00	
PHQ Card (D6)			40	2·50

No. 1789 was initially sold at 24p. which was increased to 25p. from November 1993.

It was only issued in booklets containing 20 stamps, each surrounded by die-cut perforations.

For similar 2nd and 1st designs printed in photogravure by Enschedé see Nos. 1976/7.

Special First Day of Issue Postmarks

British Philatelic Bureau, Edinburgh	2·50
Newcastle upon Tyne	2·50

1301	**1302**

(Des J. Matthews. Gravure Enschedé)

1997 (18 Mar). *Self-adhesive*. One centre phosphor band (2nd) or two phosphor bands (1st). Perf 14×15 die-cut (with one elliptical hole in each vertical side).

1976	**1301**	(2nd) bright blue	1·40	1·40
1977	**1302**	(1st) bright orange-red	1·40	1·40
Set of 2			2·75	2·75
First Day Cover				2·75
Presentation Pack (P.O. Pack No. 37)			3·50	

Nos. 1976/7, which were sold at 20p. and 26p., were in rolls of 100 with the stamps separate on the backing paper.

No. 1976 exists with the printed image in two sizes; the normal stamp is 21.25 mm×17.25 mm, while the scarcer second version is 21.75×17.75 mm.

Special First Day of Issue Postmarks

British Philatelic Bureau, Edinburgh	2·75
Glasgow	2·75

(Gravure Enschedé, Questa or Walsall)

1998 (6 Apr)–**2001**. *Self-adhesive*. Designs as T **913/14**. One centre phosphor band (2nd), or two phosphor bands (1st). Perf 15×14 die-cut (with one elliptical hole in each vertical side).

2039	(2nd) bright blue		1·00	1·00
	a. Imperf (pair, 6mm. gap) (1998)	£275		
	ab. Imperf (pair, 4mm. gap) (2000)	£100		
	b. Perf 14½×14 die-cut (22.6.98)	£300		
2040	(1st) bright orange-red		1·25	1·25
	a. Imperf (pair, 6mm. gap) (1998)	£275		
	ab. Imperf (pair, 4mm. gap) (2000)	£100		
	b. Perf 14½×14 die-cut (22.6.98)	£300		
	Ey. Phosphor omitted	£125		
	l. Booklet pane. No. 2040×6 plus commemorative label at left (29.1.01)	11·50		

Nos. 2039/40, initially sold for 20p. and 26p., were in rolls of 200 printed by Enschedé with the surplus self-adhesive paper removed.

2nd and 1st self-adhesive stamps as Nos. 2039/40 were issued in sheets, printed in photogravure by Walsall Security Printers, on 22 June 1998. These are similar to the previous coil printings, but the sheets retain the surplus self-adhesive paper around each stamp. Stamps from these sheets have square perforation tips instead of the rounded versions to be found on the coils.

No. 2039 exists die-cut through the backing paper from Presentation Pack No. 71.

No. 2039 was issued in rolls of 10,000, printed by Enschedé on yellow backing paper with the surplus self-adhesive paper removed. A number appears on the back of every tenth stamp in the roll.

2039a/40a come from business sheets printed by Walsall and show a 6mm. space between the stamps. 2039ab/40ab come from business sheets printed by Walsall and Questa respectively and have a 4mm space between stamps. 4mm. pairs also exist from booklets, but are much scarcer from this source.

Nos. 2039b and 2040b come from initial stocks of these Walsall sheet printings sent to the Philatelic Bureau and supplied to collectors requiring single stamps.

They can be indentified by the pointed perforation tips in the corners of the stamp, as illustrated below.

Nos. 2039/40	Nos. 2039b/40b

A further printing in sheets appeared on 4 September 2000 printed by Walsall (2nd) or Questa (1st). These sheets were slightly re-designed to provide a block of 4, rather than a strip, in the top panel. Individual stamps cannot be identified as coming from these new sheets as they have rounded perforation tips similar to those on the original coil printings.

The sheets of 100 were re-issued on 9 May 2002 printed by Enschedé in the same format as used in September 2000. The individual stamps are similar to the Enschedé coil printings of April 1998. A further printing of No. 2039 in sheets of 100 appeared on 4 July 2002 printed by Enschedé. On this printing the top panel reverted to a strip of 4 with the typography on the label matching that of contemporary stamp booklets.

No. 2039 was issued on 18 March 2003 in stripped matrix sheets of 100, printed by Walsall.

The sheets of 100 were again issued but without the strapline "The Real Network" on 15 June 2004. The stamps in stripped matrix sheets of 100 had rounded perforations and were printed by Walsall.

Both values appeared in stamp booklets from 29 January 2001. No. 2040l comes from self-adhesive booklet No. MB2. The label commemorates the death centenary of Queen Victoria.

See also Nos. 2295/8.

"Millennium" Machins

1437 Queen Elizabeth II

(Des A. Machin, adapted R. Scholey. Gravure De La Rue, Questa or Walsall/ISP Walsall (No. 2124), Walsall (Nos. 2124bl, 2124dl), Questa or Walsall (No. 2124d))

2000 (6 Jan–Aug). *New Millennium*. Two phosphor bands. Perf 15×14 (with one elliptical hole in each vertical side).

2124	**1437**	(1st) olive-brown	1·25	1·25
		a. Imperf (pair)	£900	
		bl. Booklet pane. No. 2124×4 plus commemorative label at right (21.3.00)	3·00	
		bm. Booklet pane. No. 2124×9 with margins all round (4 Aug)	6·50	
		cEy. Phosphor omitted	£500	
		d. Perf 14	1·25	1·25
		dEa. Phosphor omitted	20·00	
		dl. Booklet pane. No. 2124d×8 with central label and margins all round (15.2.00)	6·00	
First Day Cover (No. 2124) (Philatelic Bureau) (Type G, see Introduction)				2·00
First Day Cover (No. 2124) (Windsor) (Type G)				2·00
First Day Cover (No. 2124bm) (Philatelic Bureau)				6·00
First Day Cover (No. 2124bm) (London SW1)				6·00
First Day Cover (No. 2124dl) (Philatelic Bureau)				6·00
First Day Cover (No. 2124dl) (London SW5)				6·00
Presentation Pack (P.O. Pack No. 48)			2·50	
PHQ Card (23 May) (D16)			0·40	2·50

No. 2124d comes from stamp booklets printed by Questa. Similar booklets produced by Walsall have the same perforation as the sheet stamps. The labels on booklet pane No. 2124bl show either Postman Pat, publicising "The Stamp Show 2000", or the National Botanic Garden of Wales.

EXHIBITION SOUVENIR

1459

(Des J. Matthews. Gravure De La Rue)

2000 (22 May). *Stamp Show 2000 International Stamp Exhibition, London.* Jeffery Matthews Colour Palette. Sheet, 124×70 mm. Phosphorised paper. Perf 15×14 (with one elliptical hole in each vertical side).

MS2146 **1459** 4p. new blue; 5p. dull red-brown; 6p. yellow-olive; 10p. dull orange; 31p. deep mauve; 39p. bright magenta; 64p. turquoise-green; £1 bluish violet		15·00	15·00
First Day Cover (Philatelic Bureau)			15·00
First Day Cover (Earls Court, London SW5)			15·00
Exhibition Card (wallet, sold at £4.99, containing one mint sheet and one cancelled on postcard)		30·00	

The £1 value is printed in Iriodin ink which gives a shiny effect to the solid part of the background behind the Queen's head.

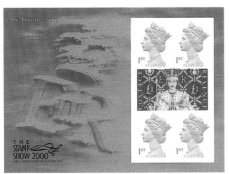

1459a

(Des Delaney Design Consultants. Gravure De La Rue)

2000 (23 May). *Stamp Show 2000 International Stamp Exhibition, London. Her Majesty's Stamps.* Sheet 121×89 mm. Phosphorised paper. Perf 15×14 (with one elliptical hole in each vertical side of stamps as *T* **1437**).

MS2147 **1459a** (1st) olive-brown (Type **1437**)×4; £1 slate-green (as Type **163**)		9·00	9·00
First Day Cover (Philatelic Bureau)			9·25
First Day Cover (City of Westminster, London SW1)			9·25
Presentation Pack (P.O. Pack no. M03)		40·00	
PHQ Cards (set of 2) (PSM03)		—	15·00

The £1 value is an adaptation of the 1953 Coronation 1s.3d. stamp originally designed by Edmund Dulac. It is shown on one of the PHQ cards with the other depicting the complete miniature sheet.

N.V.I. and denominated stamps, self-adhesive gum, elliptical perforations

(Gravure Questa, Walsall, Enschedé or De La Rue (1st), Walsall (others))

2002 (5 June–4 July). *Self-adhesive.* Two phosphor bands. Perf 15×14 die-cut (with one elliptical hole in each vertical side).

2295	**914**	(1st) gold	1·25	1·25
		a. Imperf (pair)	£1100	
		Ey. Phosphor omitted	£225	
2296	**1093a**	(E) deep blue (4 July)	2·25	2·25
2297	**367a**	42p. deep olive-grey (4 July)	4·50	4·50
2298		68p. grey-brown (4 July)	5·00	5·00
Set of 4			12·50	12·50
PHQ Card (No. 2295) (Walsall) (D22) (27.3.03)			0·40	1·10

No. 2295, sold for 27p., was initially only available in booklets of 6 or 12, printed by Questa or Walsall, with the surplus self-adhesive paper around each stamp removed. Later booklets were also printed by De La Rue. Nos. 2296/8 were only issued in separate booklets, each containing six stamps with the surplus self-adhesive paper around each stamp removed.

No. 2295 exists die-cut through the backing paper from Presentation Pack No. 71

No. 2295 was issued in rolls of 10,000, printed by Enschedé on yellow backing paper with the surplus self-adhesive paper removed. A number appears on the back of every tenth stamp in the roll.

A further printing of No. 2295 in sheets of 100 appeared on 4 July 2002 produced by Enschedé and on 18 March 2003 in stripped matrix sheets of 100 printed by Walsall. The top panel shows a strip of four with the typography of the label matching that of booklet Type ME 2.

POSTAL FORGERIES. A postal forgery of No. 2295 exists, produced in booklets of 12 with a varnish band printed across the centre of the stamps to mimic phosphor bands. A similar forgery is known with the wavy 'perforations', gauge 10.

Overseas Booklet Stamps

1655

(Des Sedley Place. Gravure Walsall)

2003 (27 Mar)–**10**. *Overseas Booklet Stamps.* Self-adhesive. As T **1655** Two phosphor bands. Perf 15×14 die-cut with one elliptical hole in each vertical side.

2357a	(Worldwide postcard) grey-black, rosine and ultramarine (1.4.04)	1·85	1·85
2357b	(Europe up to 20 grams) deep blue-green, new blue and rosine (30.3.10)	2·00	2·00
2358	(Europe up to 40 grams) new blue and rosine	2·00	2·00
2358a	(Worldwide up to 20 grams) deep mauve, new blue and rosine (30.3.10)	2·25	2·25
2359	(Worldwide up to 40 grams) rosine and new blue	3·00	3·00
Set of 5		11·00	11·00
First Day Cover (Nos. 2358, 2359) (Tallents House) (Type K, see Introduction)			5·00
First Day Cover (Nos. 2358, 2359) (Windsor) (Type K)			5·00
Presentation Pack (Nos. 2358, 2359) (P.O. Pack No. 60)		5·00	
PHQ Card (No. 2358) (D23)		40·00	5·00

No. 2357a was intended to pay postcard rate to foreign destinations (43p.).

Nos. 2357b and 2358a were intended to pay postage on mail up to 20 grams to either Europe (initially 56p.) or to foreign destinations outside Europe (90p.).

They were only available in separate booklets of four (Nos. MI3 and MJ3) initially sold at £2.24 and £3.60, with the surplus self-adhesive paper around each stamp removed.

Nos. 2358/9 were intended to pay postage on mail up to 40 grams to either Europe (52p.) or to foreign destinations outside Europe (£1.12).

Operationally they were only available in separate booklets of 4 (Nos. MI1, MJ1 and MJA1), initially sold at £1.72, £2.08 and £4.48, with the surplus self-adhesive paper around each stamp removed.

No. 2357a was available from philatelic outlets as a single stamp or in P.O. Packs Nos. 67 and 71 together with other definitive stamps. These single stamps were die-cut through the white backing paper.

For listings of first day covers (together with definitives issued on the same day) and presentation packs for Nos. 2357a/b and 2358a see after No. Y1803.

Single examples of Nos. 2358/9 were available from philatelic outlets as sets of two or in P.O. Pack No 60. These stamps were die-cut through the backing paper on the back and showed parts of the booklet covers. Nos. 2358a and 2358/9 from packs 67 (2357a only), 71 and 77 were die-cut through on plain white paper, while 2357b and 2358a in pack 86 and all five values in pack 88 were guillotined to show an area of margin surrounding the stamps.

> The purchase prices of NVI stamps are shown in the introduction to this catalogue.

Pricing in Proportion

1915

1916

(Des J. Matthews)

2006 (1st Aug)-**2007**. *Pricing in Proportion* Perf 15×14 (with one elliptical hole in each vertical side).

(a) Ordinary gum. Gravure De La Rue, ISP Walsall or Enschedé (No. 2651a).

(i) As *T* **1915**.

2650	(2nd) bright blue (1 centre band)............	1·00	1·00
	a. Booklet pane. Nos. 2650/1, and Nos. 2652/3 each×2, with centre label and margins all round (5.6.07)............	5·75	
2651	(1st) gold (2 bands)............	1·25	1·25
	a. Booklet pane. Nos. 2651 and Y1726, each×4, with centre label and margins all round (21.9.06)............	5·50	

(ii) As *T* **1916**.

2652	(2nd Large) bright blue (2 bands)............	1·50	1·50
2653	(1st Large) gold (2 bands)............	1·85	1·85

(b) Self-adhesive. Gravure Walsall or Enschedé. (2654) or Walsall

(i) As *T* **1915**.

2654	(2nd) bright blue (one centre band) (12.9.06).	1·00	1·00
	a. Imperf (pair)............	£280	
2655	(1st) gold (2 bands) (12.9.06)............	1·25	1·25
	Ey. Phosphor omitted............	£250	

(ii) As *T* **1916**.

2656	(2nd Large) bright blue (2 bands) (15.8.06).......	1·50	1·50
2657	(1st Large) gold (2 bands) (15.8.06)............	1·85	1·85
First Day Cover (Nos. Y1677/8, 2650/3) (Type K, see Introduction)............		5·75	
First Day Cover (Nos. Y1677/8, 2650/3) (Windsor) (Type K)............		5·75	
First Day Cover (Victoria Cross label pane 1st×4, 50p.×4 (No. 2651a) (Tallents House or Cuffley, Potters Bar, Herts)............		5·75	
Presentation Pack (Nos. Y1677/8, 2650/3) (P.O. Pack No. 74)............		6·00	

No. 2650 was issued in sheets (1 August) and coils of 500 (15 August).

Nos. 2654/5 were available in separate booklets of six (No. RC1, sold at £1.92) or twelve (Nos. RD1 and RE1, sold at £2.76 or £3.84 respectively) and in business sheets of 100.

Nos. 2656/7 were initially only available in separate booklets of four (Nos. RA1 and RB1), sold at £1.48 and £1.76.

All these booklets had the surplus self-adhesive paper around each stamp removed.

Nos. 2656/7 were issued in sheets of 50, printed by Walsall, on 27 March 2007.

No. 2654 was issued in rolls of 10,000, printed by Enschedé on yellow backing paper with the surplus self-adhesive paper removed. A number appears on the back of every tenth stamp in the roll.

A postal forgery similar to No. 2651 exists with wavy 'perforations' (gauge 10).

For PHQ cards for Nos. 2652/3 see below No. Y1803.

Security Machins

Please note that the "U" numbers in this section are temporary and subject to change.

On 17 February 2009 a new form of Machin definitive appeared, incorporating additional security features to combat the re-use of uncancelled stamps.

The stamps no longer included a water-soluble layer of gum between the paper and the self-adhesive to prevent them being 'soaked off' envelope paper; in addition, four U-shaped slits were die-cut into the stamps to prevent them being peeled off paper and, to make forgery more difficult, an overall iridescent multiple 'ROYALMAIL' overprint was incorporated into the design.

In May 2010 2nd and 1st class stamps were issued in rolls with iridescent overprint but printed on paper with ordinary gum and without U-shaped slits. These are listed as U3065/66. Other values in this form subsequently appeared in prestige booklets.

USED STAMPS: Because the self-adhesive stamps in this section do not include a water-soluble layer of gum, we recommend that used stamps are retained on their backing paper and trimmed with a uniform border of 1-2 mm around all sides, taking care not to cut into the perforations.

Source Codes: In March 2009 stamps were issued with "codes" incorporated into the iridescent overprint which allowed the source to be identified. The codes may be seen in the words 'ROYALMAIL', usually at the top right of the stamp, although some later Large Letter issues have it at the bottom right (marked 'BR' in the list below) or just to the front of the Queen's hair (marked 'FOH' in the list below).

The codes are:

2nd and 1st
MAIL — (ie without code letter) – counter sheets
MBIL — Business sheets
MCIL — 'Custom' booklets, which include special stamps
MMIL — Miniature sheet (**MS**3222/**MS**3965) (not listed as individual stamps)
MPIL — Prestige booklet panes
MRIL — Rolls
MSIL — standard booklets of Six
MTIL — booklets of Twelve

2nd and 1st Large
ROYALMAIL — (ie without code letter) – counter sheets
YBLM — Business sheets (2009)
MBI — Business sheets (2010)
BIL — Business sheets (2011-13) (BR)
MBIL — Business sheets (2014-18) (FOH)
FOYAL — booklets of Four (2009)
MFI — booklets of Four (2010)
FIL — booklets of Four (2011-13) (BR)
MFIL — booklets of Four (2014-18) (FOH)

For the Diamond Jubilee definitive with source codes, which are behind The Queen's head, the end of 'DIAMOND' is adjusted to:
MBND — Business sheets
MCND — 'Custom' booklets of six
MMND — Miniature sheet (**MS**3272) (not listed as individual stamps)
MPND — Prestige booklet pane
MSND — standard booklet of Six
MTND — booklets of Twelve

And for Large Letter stamps with source codes the end of "JUBILEE" is adjusted to :
LBE — Business sheets
LFE — booklets of Four

For the Long to Reign Over Us definitives with source codes, which are behind The Queen's neck, the end of 'REIGN' is adjusted to:
GC — 'Custom' booklets of six
GM — Miniature sheet (**MS**3747) (not listed as individual stamp)
GP — Prestige booklet pane
GS — standard booklet of Six

Year Codes: From 2010 a year code (also sometimes referred to as a date code) was added to the iridescent overprint. Generally it appears in the upper left corner of the stamp, in front of the crown or The Queen's forehead or eye, but on later Large Letter stamps it appears lower down, above the "ge" of "Large". Stamps are listed without or with year codes, and the different codes known are given in checklists at the end of this section. Note that year dates given within the listings are years of issue, not year codes.

Note that, where stamps exist with more that one year code, the issue date given is for the first release, but prices are for the cheapest code.

U-Shaped slits: The first issue featured U-shaped die-cut slits without a break in the middle of each 'U', but subsequent issues have incorporated a break to prevent the stamps tearing while being removed from the backing paper on which they were issued. We no longer list these as separate varieties but details are provided in the checklists at the end of this section.

A 1st gold stamp with U-slits but without iridescent overprint was supplied only to bulk mailing houses.

'ROYALMAIL' printed backing paper: As an additional security measure, in early 2016 the backing paper on certain booklets appeared with a repeated undulating 'ROYALMAIL' background in two sizes of grey text printed upright on the front of the backing paper (Type PB-Up). This feature extended to business sheets and counter sheets during 2016 and 2017. In early 2017 the background was changed, so that alternate pairs of lines of the repeated 'ROYALMAIL' text were inverted in relation to each other. The pairs of lines can appear with the Large lettering above the small (Type PB-Ls), or with the small above the Large (Type PB-sL). These differences are not listed in this catalogue, unless the stamps themselves are different. Their existence is, however, noted under the sections in which they occur and in the checklists at the end of this section. For illustrations and further details please refer to the checklists. Booklets with 'ROYALMAIL' security text are listed in the relevant section of this catalogue.

Details of known source and year-code combinations, and different year code changes, are provided in the series of tables following the listings. For the convenience of collectors, the printer of each combination is also given.

We are grateful to John M. Deering for compiling these tables.

2009 (17 Feb)–**2018** Self-adhesive. Designs as T**367**. Two phosphor bands. Iridescent overprint. U-shaped slits. Die-cut *Perf* 14½×14 (with one elliptical hole in each vertical side).

(a) Without source or year codes, gravure De La Rue

U2911	50p. grey	2·00	2·00
U2912	£1 magenta	3·50	3·50
U2913	£1.50 brown-red	3·25	3·25
U2914	£2 deep blue-green	5·00	5·00
U2915	£3 deep mauve	6·25	6·25
U2916	£5 azure	10·50	10·50

(b) With source and year codes, gravure Walsall

U2917	50p. grey (MPIL) (8.5.10)	3·00	3·00
	a. Booklet pane Nos. U2917×2, U3011×2 and U3017×4, with central label and margins all round	16·00	

*(c) Without source code, with year code, gravure Walsall/ISP Walsall or De La Rue (U2928, U2931, U2953, U2957), ISP Walsall (U**2938**, U**2943**, U**2947**, U**2963**) or De La Rue (others)*

U2920	1p. deep crimson (3.1.13)	50	50
U2921	2p. deep green (3.1.13)	50	50
U2922	5p. dull red-brown (3.1.13)	60	60
U2923	10p. dull orange (3.1.13)	60	60
U2924	20p. bright green (3.1.13)	70	70
U2925	50p. slate (3.1.13)	1·70	1·70
U2926	68p. deep turquoise-green (29.3.11)	2·60	2·60
U2927	76p. bright rose (29.3.11)	2·70	2·70
U2928	78p. deep mauve (27.3.13)	2·40	2·40
U2929	81p. emerald (26.3.14)	2·40	2·40
U2930	87p. yellow-orange (25.4.12)	4·75	4·75
U2931	88p. orange-yellow (27.3.13)	3·00	3·00
U2932	97p. bluish violet (26.3.14)	3·25	3·25
U2933	£1 magenta (10.10.11)	7·75	7·75
U2934	£1 bistre-brown (3.1.13)	3·25	2·90
U2935	£1.05 grey-olive (22.3.16)	2·70	2·70
U2936	£1.10 yellow-olive (29.3.11)	3·75	3·75
U2937	£1.17 orange-red (21.3.17)	2·70	2·70
U2938	£1.25 emerald (20.3.18)	2·50	2·50
U2939	£1.28 orange-yellow (25.4.12)	5·50	5·50
U2940	£1.33 orange-yellow (24.3.15)	3·25	3·25
U2941	£1.40 grey-green (21.3.17)	3·25	3·25
U2943	£1.45 lavender-grey (20.3.18)	2·80	2·80
U2945	£1.47 lavender-grey (26.3.14)	3·75	3·75
U2946	£1.52 bright mauve (24.3.15)	3·75	3·75
U2947	£1.55 greenish blue (20.3.18)	3·00	3·00
U2948	£1.57 yellow-olive (21.3.17)	3·75	3·75
U2950	£1.65 grey-olive (29.3.11)	4·75	4·75
U2953	£1.88 dull ultramarine (27.3.13)	5·25	5·25
U2954	£1.90 bright mauve (25.4.12)	5·75	5·75
U2955	£2 deep blue-green (4.13)	9·00	9·00
U2956	£2.15 greenish blue (26.3.14)	5·25	5·25
U2957	£2.25 deep violet (24.3.15)	3·50	3·50

U2958	£2.27 bistre (21.3.17)	5·00	5·00
U2961	£2.45 bluish green (24.3.15)	6·00	6·00
U2962	£2.55 deep rose-red (21.3.17)	5.50	5.50
U2963	£2.65 bluish violet (20.3.18)	4.00	4.00
U2968	£3.15 turquoise-blue (24.3.15)	6·50	6·50
U2969	£3.30 bright magenta (24.3.15)	6·75	6·75
U2920/69 Set of 39		£135	£135

No. U2917 was first issued in £11.15 booklets, No. DX50 with 'MA10' year code. It was issued again in £9.99 premium booklets, No. DY1, with 'M11L' year code.

Nos. U2911/17, U2926/33, U2935/36, U2939/40, U2945/46 U2950, U2953/56, U2961, and U2968/69 only exist on plain backing paper.

Nos. U2920/25, U2937, U2941, U2948, U2957/58 and U2962 were originally issued on plain backing paper, but later appeared on paper with repeating 'ROYALMAIL' text, with alternate pairs of lines inverted.

At the time of publication, No. U2934 only exists on plain backing paper.

Nos. U2938, U2943, U2947 and U2963 only exist on backing paper with repeating 'ROYALMAIL' text, with alternate pairs of lines inverted.

> Please note that the 'missing' numbers in this and subsequent listings in this section have been left for future additions to this series.

2009 (17 Feb)–**2017.** Self-adhesive. Designs as T913/**14** or *T* **1916**. One centre band (U2975, U2979/81, U2995 and U3010/13) two bands (others). U-shaped slits. Iridescent overprint. Die-cut *Perf* 14½×14 (with one elliptical hole in each vertical side).

(a) Without source or year codes, gravure De La Rue

U2975	(2nd) bright blue	3·50	3·50
U2976	(1st) gold	3·50	3·50
U2977	(2nd Large) bright blue	3·75	3·75
U2978	(1st Large) gold	4·00	4·00

(b) With source code, without year code, gravure De La Rue (U2979/80, U2982, U2984, U2987, U2989) or Walsall (others)

U2979	(2nd) bright blue (MBIL) (31.3.09)	3·75	3·75
U2980	(2nd) bright blue (MRIL) (7.09)	4·50	4·50
U2981	(2nd) bright blue (MTIL) (31.3.09)	2·30	2·30
U2982	(1st) gold (MBIL) (31.3.09)	3·75	3·75
U2983	(1st) gold (MCIL) (10.3.09)	2·20	2·20
U2984	(1st) gold (MRIL) (7.09)	5·00	5·00
U2985	(1st) gold (MSIL) (31.3.09)	4·50	4·50
U2986	(1st) gold (MTIL) (31.3.09)	2·50	2·50
U2987	(2nd Large) bright blue (YBLM) (31.3.09)	3·75	3·75
U2988	(2nd Large) bright blue (FOYAL) (31.3.09)	3·75	3·75
U2989	(1st Large) gold (YBLM) (31.3.09)	3·75	3·75
U2990	(1st Large) gold (FOYAL) (31.3.09)	4·50	4·50

(c) Without source code, with year code, gravure De La Rue

U2995	(2nd) bright blue (1.7.10)	1·60	1·30
U2996	(1st) gold (20.5.10)	3·50	3·50
U2997	(1st) vermilion (3.1.13)	2·00	2·00
U2998	(1st) bright scarlet (11.4.17)	1·80	1·50
U3000	(2nd Large) bright blue (26.1.11)	2·00	1·70
U3001	(1st Large) gold (3.11.10)	3·25	3·25
U3002	(1st Large) vermilion (3.1.13)	2·70	2·70
U3003	(1st Large) bright scarlet (11.4.17)	2·20	1·90

(d) With source and year codes, gravure De La Rue or Walsall (U3010 and U3031), De La Rue or Enschedé (U3018), De La Rue, Enschedé or Walsall (U3012), Enschedé or Walsall (U3023), De La Rue (U3015 and U3034) or Walsall (others)

U3010	(2nd) bright blue (MBIL) (3.10)	2·10	1·90
U3011	(2nd) bright blue (MPIL) (8.5.10)	3·25	3·25
U3012	(2nd) bright blue (MRIL) (6.12)	4·25	4·25
U3013	(2nd) bright blue (MTIL) (2.10)	1·80	1·60
U3015	(1st) gold (MBIL) (6.10)	4·50	4·50
U3016	(1st) gold (MCIL) (25.2.10)	2·70	2·70
U3017	(1st) gold (MPIL) (8.5.10)	2·20	2·20
U3018	(1st) gold (MRIL) (15.7.11)	4·75	4·75
U3019	(1st) gold (MSIL) (26.1.10)	2·70	2·70
U3020	(1st) gold (MTIL) (2.10)	3·50	3·50
U3021	(1st) vermilion (3.1.13)	2·80	2·80
U3022	(1st) vermilion (MCIL) (9.1.13)	2·20	2·20
U3023	(1st) vermilion (MRIL) (3.1.13)	3·00	3·00
U3024	(1st) vermilion (MSIL) (3.1.13)	2·60	2·60
U3025	(1st) vermilion (MTIL) (3.1.13)	2·60	2·60
U3026	(1st) bright scarlet (MBIL) (20.10.16)	2·20	2·00
U3027	(1st) bright scarlet (MCIL) (20.10.16)	1·50	1·30
U3028	(1st) bright scarlet (MSIL) (20.10.16)	1·70	1·70
U3029	(1st) bright scarlet (MTIL) (20.10.16)	2·00	1·80
U3031	(2nd Large) bright blue (MBI/BIL/MBIL) (3.11)	2·70	2·70
U3032	(2nd Large) bright blue (MFI/FIL/MFIL) (8.5.10)	2·50	2·50
U3034	(1st Large) gold (MBI/BIL) (6.10)	4·50	4·50
U3035	(1st Large) gold (MFI/FIL) (8.5.10)	3·25	3·25
U3036	(1st Large) vermilion (BIL/MBIL) (3.1.13)	4·00	4·00
U3037	(1st Large) vermilion (FIL/MFIL) (3.1.13)	3·25	3·25
U3038	(1st Large) bright scarlet (MBIL) (20.10.16)	3.00	3.00
U3039	(1st Large) bright scarlet (MFIL) (20.10.16)	2.80	2.80

Nos. U2975/90, U2996/97, U3001/02, U3011/12, U3015/20, U3022/23 and U3034/35 only exist on plain backing paper.

Nos. U3021, U3024/25 and U3036/37 were originally issued on plain backing paper, but later appeared on paper with repeating 'ROYALMAIL' text the same way up.

Nos. U2995 and U3000 were originally issued on plain backing paper, but later appeared on paper with repeating 'ROYALMAIL' text, with alternate pairs of lines inverted.

Nos. U3010, U3013, U3031 and U3032 were originally issued on plain backing paper, but later appeared on paper with repeating 'ROYALMAIL' text the same way up, and subsequently with alternate pairs of lines inverted.

Nos. U3026/29 and U3038/39 were originally issued on backing paper with repeating 'ROYALMAIL' text the same way up, but later appeared with alternate pairs of lines inverted.

Nos. U2998 and U3003 only exist on backing paper with repeating 'ROYALMAIL' text, with alternate pairs of lines inverted.

For full details of which stamps and year codes exist on different backing papers, please see the checklists at the end of this section of the catalogue.

2132a	2132b
2132c	2132d

(Gravure De La Rue)

2009 (17 Nov)–**13.** Self-adhesive. Designs as T2132a/**d**. Two phosphor bands. U-shaped slits. Iridescent overprint. Die-cut *Perf* 14 (U3046, U3048/50) or 14½×14 (others) (all with one elliptical hole in each vertical side).

(a) Without source or year codes, gravure De La Rue

U3045	(Recorded Signed for 1st) bright orange-red and lemon	6·50	6·50
U3046	(Recorded Signed for 1st Large) bright orange-red and lemon	8·00	8·00

(b) Without source code, with year code, gravure De La Rue

U3047	(Recorded Signed for 1st) bright orange-red and lemon (11.4.11)	14·00	14·00
U3048	(Recorded Signed for 1st Large) bright orange-red and lemon (11.4.11)	16·00	16·00
U3049	(Royal Mail Signed for 1st) bright orange-red and lemon (27.3.13)	4·75	4.25
U3050	(Royal Mail Signed for 1st Large) bright orange-red and lemon (27.3.13)	5.75	5.25
U3051	(Special delivery up to 100g) blue and silver (26.10.10)	13·50	10·00
U3052	(Special delivery up to 500g) blue and silver (26.10.10)	15·50	12·50

Nos. U3047/48 have "MA10" year codes

Nos. U3049/50 exist with "MA13", "M15L", "M16L" and "M17L" year codes.

No. U3051 exists with "MA10", "M14L", "M15L", "M16L" and "M17L" year codes.

No. U3052 exists with "MA10", "M14L" and "M16L" year codes.

No. U3045 was originally sold for £1.14 (£1.15 from 6 April 2010 and £1.23 from 4 April 2011).

No. U3046 was originally sold for £1.36 (£1.40 from 6 April 2010 and £1.52 from 4 April 2011).

No. U3047 was originally sold for £1.23 (£1.55 from 30 April 2012).

No. U3048 was originally sold for £1.52 (£1.85 from 30 April 2012).

No. U3049 was originally sold for £1.55 (£1.70 from 2 April 2013, £1.72 from 31 March 2014, £1.73 from 30 March 2015, £1.74 from 29 March 2016, £1.75 from 27 March 2017 and £1.77 from 26 March 2018).

No. U3050 was originally sold for £1.85 (£2 from 2 April 2013, £2.03 from 31 March 2014, £2.05 from 30 March 2015, £2.06 from 29 March 2016, £2.08 from 27 March 2017 and £2.11 from 26 March 2018).

No. U3051 was originally sold for £5.05 (£5.45 from 4 April 2011, £5.90 from 30 April 2012, £6.22 from 2 April 2013, £6.40 from 31 March 2014, £6.45 from 30 March 2015 and £6.50 from 26 March 2018).

No. U3052 was originally sold for £5.50 (£5.90 from 4 April 2011, £6.35 from 30 April 2012, £6.95 from 2 April 2013, £7.15 from 31 March 2014, £7.25 from 30 March 2015 and £7.30 from 26 March 2018).

Nos. U3045/48 only exist on plain backing paper.

Nos. U3049 and U3051 were originally issued on plain backing paper, but later appeared on paper with repeating 'ROYALMAIL' text, with alternate pairs of lines inverted.

At the time of publication, No. U3050 and U3052 only exist on plain backing paper.

(Gravure De La Rue or Walsall (U3057/58) or De La Rue (others))

2011 (8 Mar–5 May). Self-adhesive. Designs as T**367**. Two phosphor bands. U-shaped slits. No iridescent overprint. Die-cut *Perf* 14½×14 (with one elliptical hole in each vertical side).

U3055	1p. crimson	80	80
U3056	2p. deep green	50	50
U3057	5p. dull red-brown	60	60
	a. Booklet pane. Nos. U3057×4, U3058×2 and U2917×2 with central label and margins all round (5.5.11)	10·50	
U3058	10p. dull orange	70	70
U3059	20p. bright green	1·00	1·00
U3055/59 Set of 5		3·25	3·25

2010 (13 May)–**18**. Ordinary gum. Designs as T367 and T913/**14**. Without U-shaped slits. Iridescent overprint. One centre phosphor band (U3065 and U3095) or two bands (others). *Perf* 14½×14 (with one elliptical hole in each vertical side).

(a) With source and year codes, gravure Walsall/ISP Walsall)

U3060	68p turquoise-green (MPIL) (10.1.12)	4·00	4·00
U3061	£1 magenta (MPIL) (5.6.17)	4·00	4·00

(b) NVIs with source and year codes, gravure De La Rue (U3065/66) or ISP Walsall (U3067)

U3065	(2nd) bright blue (MRIL) (13.5.10)	4·75	4·75
U3066	(1st) gold (MRIL) (13.5.10)	4·75	4·75
U3067	(1st) vermilion (MPIL) (5.6.17)	3·00	3·00

(c) With source and year codes, litho Enschedé (U3073, U3076), Cartor/ISP Cartor or Enschedé (U3071/75, U3082) or Cartor/ISP Cartor (others)

U3070	1p. crimson (MPIL) (9.5.13)	1·20	1·20
	a. Booklet pane. Nos. U3070×2, U3097×2, EN51, NI95, S158 and W148 with central label and margins all round (9.5.13)	16·00	
	b. Booklet pane. Nos. U3070×2, U3071×3, U3079 and U3081×2 with central label and margins all round (19.2.15)	17·00	
	c. Booklet pane. Nos. U3070, U3072c, U3085 and 3717, each×2 with central label and margins all round (14.5.15)	14·00	
U3071	2p. deep green (MPIL) (9.5.13)	1·20	1·20
	a. Booklet pane. Nos. U3071/72 and U3074, each×2 (9.5.13)	6·50	
	b. Booklet pane. Nos. U3071/72, each×2, and Nos. EN51, NI95, S158 and W148 with central label and margins all round (20.2.14)	14·50	
	c. Booklet pane. Nos. U3071×2, U3074×2, U3098×3 and U3083 with central label and margins all round (15.2.17)	13·50	
	d. source code without P (M IL) (20.3.18)	1·00	1·00
	e. Booklet pane. Nos. U3071d×3, U3072f x3 and U3084a x2 with central label and margins all round (20.3.18)	11·00	
U3072	5p. red-brown (MPIL) (26.3.13)	1·20	1·20
	a. Booklet pane. Nos. U3072, U3074/75 U3080, and 3452×4 with central label and margins all round (26.3.13)	16·00	
	b. Booklet pane. Nos. U3072, U3074, U3077 and U3082, each×2 with central label and margins all round (18.6.15)	15·00	
	c. *deep red-brown* (MPIL) (14.5.15)	2·20	2·20
	d. Booklet pane. Nos. U3072×3, U3074×2 and U3083×3 with central label and margins all round (28.7.16)	12·50	
	e. Booklet pane. Nos. U3072×2, U3075, U3084, NI94x2 and 4044×2 with central label and margins all round (23.1.18)	10·75	
	f. source code without P (M IL) (20.3.18)	1·00	1·00
U3073	5p. red-brown (MPIL). Ellipses toward top of stamp (19.9.13)	2·00	2·00
	a. Booklet pane. Nos. U3073 and U3076, each×4 with central label and margins all round (19.9.13)	12·00	
U3074	10p. dull orange (MPIL) (26.3.13)	1·40	1·40
	a. Booklet pane. Nos. U3074×2, U3075×4 and U3082×2 with central label and margins all round (15.4.14)	10·00	
	b. Booklet pane. Nos. U3074×2, U3075×4, EN30, NI95, S131 and W122×1 with central label and margins all round (28.7.14)	9·50	
U3075	20p. bright green (MPIL) (26.3.13)	1·50	1·50
U3076	50p. slate-blue (MPIL). Ellipses toward top of stamp (19.9.13)	2·80	2·80

U3077	50p. slate-blue (MPIL) (18.6.15)	2·70	2·70
U3078	76p. bright rose (MPIL) (9.9.11)	5·50	5·50
U3079	81p. deep turquoise-green (MPIL) (19.2.15)	8·00	8·00
U3080	87p. yellow-orange (MPIL) (26.3.13)	6·00	6·00
U3081	97p. bluish violet (MPIL) (19.2.15)	3·75	3·75
U3082	£1 sepia (MPIL) (15.4.14)	3·25	3·25
	a. Booklet pane. No. U3082 with eight reproduction King George V 1d. stamps all round (28.7.14)	6·25	
U3083	£1.05 grey-olive (MPIL) (28.7.16)	3·00	3·00
U3084	£1.17 bright orange (MPIL) (28.1.18)	3·50	3·50
	a. source code without P (M IL) (20.3.18)	3·00	3·00
U3085	£1.33 orange-yellow (MPIL) (14.5.15)	3·50	3·50
U3086	£1.40 grey-green (MPIL) (14.12.17)	3·50	3·50

(d) NVIs with source and year codes, litho Cartor/ISP Cartor

U3095	(2nd) bright blue (MPIL) (17.12.15)	2·50	2·50
	a. Booklet pane. Nos. U3095, and U3097, each×2 and 3786×4 with central label and margins all round (17.12.15)	15·00	
	b. Booklet pane. Nos. U3095×2, U3097×4 and U3086×2 with central label and margins all round (14.12.17)	15·75	
U3096	(1st) gold (MPIL) (9.9.11)	5·25	5·25
U3097	(1st) vermilion (MPIL) (9.5.13)	2·20	2·20
	a. Booklet pane. Nos. U3097×2, U3747×2, EN30, NI95, S131 and W122 with central label and margins all round (14.4.16)	16·00	
U3098	(1st) bright scarlet (MPIL) (15.2.17)	2·50	2·50

No. U3060 comes from pane Y1668m in No. DY3 Roald Dahl's Children's Stories premium booklet, and has a "M11L" year code.

No. U3061 comes from pane Y1667p in No. DY21 50th Anniversary of the Machin Definitive premium booklet, and has a "M17L" year code.

Nos. U3065/3066 were issued in separate coils of 500 or 1000, and have "MA10" year codes.

No. U3066 also exists from Birth Centenary of Arnold Machin miniature sheet MS3222, from which it has source code "MMIL" (and "AM11" year code).

No. U3067 comes from pane 3966ba in No. DY21 50th Anniversary of the Machin Definitive premium booklet, and has a "M17L" year code.

No. U3067 also exists printed gravure from *50th Anniversary of the Machin Definitive* miniature sheet MS3965, from which it has source code "MMIL" and year code "M17L", but is not separately listed.

Nos. U3070/3098 were all issued in premium booklets.
No. U3070 comes from No. DY7, DY12 and DY13.
No. U3071 comes from No. DY7, DY9, DY12 and DY20.
No. U3071d comes from No. DY25.
No. U3072 comes from No. DY6, DY7 DY9, DY14, DY19 and DY24.
No. U3072c comes from No. DY13.
No. U3072f comes from No. DY25.
No. U3073 comes from No. DY8, and has the elliptical holes toward the top of the stamp.
No. U3074 comes from No. DY6, DY7, DY10, DY11, DY14, DY19 and DY20.
No. U3075 comes from Nos. DY6, DY10, DY11 and DY24.
No. U3076 comes from No. DY8, and has the elliptical holes toward the top of the stamp.
No. U3077 comes from No. DY14.
Nos. U3078 comes from pane Y1763m in No. DY2.
No. U3079 comes from No. DY12.
No. U3080 comes from No. DY6.
No. U3081 comes from No. DY12.
No. U3082 comes from Nos. DY10, DY11 and DY14.
No. U3082a comes from DY11 and contains one U3082 with year code MA14, and eight reproduction King George V 1d. stamps.
No. U3083 comes from Nos. DY19 and DY20.
No. U3084 comes from No. DY24.
No. U3084a comes from No. DY25.
No. U3085 comes from No. DY13.
No. U3086 comes from No. DY23.
No. U3095 comes from No. DY15 and DY23.
No. U3096 comes from comes from pane Y1763m in No. DY2
No. U3097 comes from Nos. DY7, DY15, DY17 and DY23.
No. U3098 comes from No. DY20.
For additional information see Security Machin source and year code tables at the end of this section.

First Day Covers

17.2.09	Nos. U2911/12 and U2975/78 (Type K, see introduction)	14·00
	Nos. U2911/12 and U2975/78 (Windsor, Type K)	14·00
	Nos. U2913/16 (Type K)	30·00
	Nos. U2913/16 (Windsor)	30·00
17.11.09	Nos. U3045/46 (Type K)	6·75
	Nos. U3045/46 (Windsor)	6·75
8.5.10	King George V Accession Centenary, *se-tenant* pane (No. U2917a) (Tallents House or London N1)	10·00
26.10.10	Nos. U3051/52 (Type K)	25·00

	Nos. U3051/52 (Windsor)	25·00
8.3.11	Nos. U3055/59 (Type K)	3·50
	Nos. U3055/59 (Windsor)	3·50
29.3.11	Nos. U2926/27, U2936, U2950 (Type K)	10·50
	Nos. U2926/27, U2936, U2950 (Windsor) ...	10·50
5.5.11	Morris & Co, *se-tenant* pane (U3057a) (Tallents House or Walthamstow)	5·00
25.4.12	Nos. U2930, U2939, U2954, U3271 and U3276 (Type K)	14·00
	Nos. U2930, U2939, U2954, U3271 and U3276 (Windsor) ...	14·00
3.1.13	Nos. U2920/25, U2934, U2997 and U3002 (Type K)	10·00
	Nos. U2920/25, U2934, U2997 and U3002 (Windsor)	10·00
26.3.13	Dr. Who *se-tenant* pane (U3072a) (Tallents House or Cardiff)	11·00
27.3.13	Nos. U2928, U2931, U2953, U3048 and U3050 (Type K) ...	16·00
	Nos. U2928, U2931, U2953, U3048 and U3050 (Windsor).	16·00
9.5.13	Football Heroes *se-tenant* pane (U3070a) (Tallents House, Wembley, Middlesex) ...	11·50
19.9.13	Merchant Navy *se-tenant* pane (U3073a) (Tallents House or Clydebank)	9·00
20.2.14	Classic Locomotives *se-tenant* pane (U3071b) (Tallents House or Newcastle upon Tyne)	9·00
26.3.14	Nos. U2929, U2932, U2945 and U2956 (Type K)	17·00
	Nos. U2929, U2932, U2945 and U2956 (Windsor)	17·00
15.4.14	Buckingham Palace *se-tenant* pane (U3074a) (Tallents House or London SW1)	16·00
28.7.14	First World War Centenary *se-tenant* pane (U3074b) (Tallents House or Newcastle upon Tyne)	11·50
19.2.15	Inventive Britain *se-tenant* pane (U3070b) (Tallents House or Harlow)	16·00
24.3.15	Nos. U2940, U2946, U2957, U2961 and U2967/68 (Type K)	40·00
	Nos. U2940, U2946, U2957, U2961 and U2967/68 (Windsor)	40·00
14.5.15	First World War Centenary (2nd issue) *se-tenant* pane (U3070c) (Tallents House or Winchester)	15·00
18.6.15	Battle of Waterloo Bicentenary *se-tenant* pane (U3072b) (Tallents House or Elstree, Borehamwood)	19·00
17.12.15	Star Wars *se-tenant* pane (U3095a) (Tallents House or Elstree, Borehamwood)	13·00
22.3.16	No. U2935 (Type K)	3·00
	No. U2935 (Windsor)	3·00
21.4.16	90th Birthday of Queen Elizabeth II *se-tenant* pane (Tallents House or Windsor)	13·00
28.7.16	150th Birth Anniversary of Beatrix Potter *se-tenant* pane (U3072d) (Tallents House or Near Sawrey, Ambleside)	11·00
15.2.17	Windsor Castle *se-tenant* pane (U3071c) (Tallents House or Windsor)	10·00
21.3.17	Nos. U2937, U2941, U2948, U2958 and U2962 (Type K) ...	25·00
	Nos. U2937, U2941, U2948, U2958 and U2962 (Windsor).	25·00
14.12.17	Star Wars (4th issue) Aliens and Droids *se-tenant* pane No. U3095b (Tallents House or Wookey, Wells)	10·00
23.1.18	Game of Thrones *se-tenant* pane No. U3072e (Tallents House or Belfast)	8·00
20.3.18	Nos. U2938, U2943, U2947 and U2963 (Type K)	13·00
	Nos. U2938, U2943, U2947 and U2963 (Windsor)	13·00
20.3.18	RAF Centenary *se-tenant* pane No. U3071e (Tallents House or Cranwell, Sleaford)	11·00

Presentation Packs

17.2.09	Nos. U2911/12 and U2975/76 (PO Pack No. 82) ...	10·00
17.2.09	Nos. U2913/16 (PO Pack No. 83)	30·00
26.10.10	Nos. U3051/52 (PO Pack No. 89)	30·00
23.3.11	Nos. U2926/27, U2936, U2950 and U3055/59 (PO Pack No. 90)	17·00
25.4.12	Nos. U2930, U2939, U2954, U3271 and U3276 (PO Pack No. 94)	13·50
3.1.13	Nos. U2920/25, U2934, U2997 and U3002 (PO Pack No. 96)	9·00
27.3.13	Nos. U2928, U2931, U2953, U3048 and U3050 (PO Pack No. 97)	18·00
26.3.14	Nos. U2929, U2932, U2945 and U2956 (PO Pack No. 99)	14·00
24.3.15	Nos. U2940, U2946, U2957, U2961 and U2967/68 (PO Pack No. 101)	35·00
22.3.16	No. U2935 (PO Pack No. 103)	3·00
21.3.17	Nos. U2937, U2941, U2948, U2958 and U2962 (PO Pack No. 106)	22·00
20.3.18	Nos. U2938, U2943, U2947 and U2963 (P.O.Pack No. 108)	15·00

For presentation pack containing Nos. U3045/6 see after No. Y1803.

London 2010 Exhibition Miniature Sheet

EXHIBITION SOUVENIR

2268 (Illustration reduced. Actual size 104×95 mm)

(Litho Cartor)

2010 (8 May). *London 2010 Festival of Stamps.* Jeffery Matthews Colour Palette. Sheet 104×95 mm containing stamps as T367 with a label. Two phosphor bands. *Perf* 15×14 (with one elliptical hole in each vertical side).

MS3073 **2268** 1p. reddish purple; 2p. deep grey-green; 5p. reddish-brown; 9p. bright orange; 10p. orange; 20p. light green; 60p. emerald; 67p. bright mauve; 88p. bright magenta; 97p. bluish violet; £1.46 turquoise-blue .... 30·00 | 30·00

First Day Cover .... | 32·00

> For details of known source and year-code combinations, and the different year codes, please refer to the tables following these listings.

In June 1967 Royal Mail introduced a new definitive stamp design. Arnold Machin's bas-relief portrait of HM The Queen has been acknowledged as a classic icon of British design.

2408 (Illustration reduced. Actual size 124×71 mm)

(Gravure Walsall)

2011 (14 Sept). *Birth Centenary of Arnold Machin.* Sheet 124×71 mm containing stamps as No. U3066×10 but with source code "MMIL" and year code "AM11". Two phosphor bands. *Perf* 14½×14 (with one elliptical hole in each vertical side).

MS3222 **2408** (1st) gold×10 .... 13·00 | 13·50

First Day Cover (Stoke on Trent) .... | 15·00

First Day Cover (Piccadilly, London 1) .... | 15·00

(Photo De La Rue (U3271, U3276), Walsall (U3272, U3274/75, U3277/79) or De La Rue and Walsall (U3273))

2012 (6 Feb–1 Oct). *Diamond Jubilee.* (1st issue). Self-adhesive. Two phosphor bands. U-shaped slits. Iridescent overprint reading 'DIAMOND JUBILEE'. Die-cut *perf* 14½×14 (with one elliptical hole in each vertical side).

(a) As T914. (i) Without source code

U3271	(1st) slate-blue	2·00	2·00

(ii) With source code

U3272	(1st) slate-blue (MTND)	2·00	2·00
U3273	(1st) slate-blue (MBND)	3·50	3·50
U3274	(1st) slate-blue (MCND) (31.5.12)	2·20	2·20
U3275	(1st) slate-blue (MSND) (1.10.12)	2·70	2·70

(b) As T1916. (i) Without source code

U3276	(1st Large) slate-blue (25.4.12)	2·70	2·70

(ii) With source code

U3277	(1st Large) slate-blue (LFE) (25.4.12)	3·25	3·25
U3278	(1st Large) slate-blue (LBE) (25.4.12)	3·50	3·50

(c) Ordinary gum. Without U-shaped slits. With source code

U3279	(1st) slate-blue (MPND) (31.5.12)......................	3.75	3·75
	a. Booklet pane. Nos. U3279/3329, each×4, with central label and margins all round	14·00

Nos. U3271 and U3276 are from counter sheets.

No. U3272 is from booklets of 12, No. MF6.

Nos. U3273 and U3278 are from business sheets.

No. U3274 is from booklet PM33 and PM34.

No. U3275 is from booklets of 6, No. MB11.

No. U3277 is from booklets of 4, No. RB3.

No. U3279 is from premium booklet No. DY4.

No. U3279 also exists from *Diamond Jubilee* miniature sheet MS3272, from which it has source code "MMND", but is not separately listed.

For first day cover for No. U3276 and presentation pack for Nos. U3271 and U3276 see under No. U3098.

(Gravure De La Rue (U3744) or ISP Walsall (U3745/6), or litho ISP Cartor (U3747))

2015 (9 Sept)–**2016**. *Long to Reign Over Us* (1st issue). As T**914**. Self-adhesive. Two phosphor bands. U-shaped slits. Iridescent overprint reading 'LONG TO REIGN OVER US'. *Die-cut perf* 14½×14 (with one elliptical hole in each vertical side).

(a) Without source code, with year code

U3744	(1st) bright lilac	2.00	2.00

(b) With source and year codes

U3745	(1st) bright lilac (REIGS)	2·30	2·30
U3746	(1st) bright lilac (REIGC) (18.9.15)	2·30	2·30

(c) Ordinary gum. Without U-shaped slits. With source and year codes

U3747	(1st) bright lilac (REIGP) (21.4.16)	3.50	3.50

No. U3744 comes from counter sheets printed by De La Rue and exists with both 015R and 016R year code.

No. U3745 comes from booklets of six, No. MB14, printed by ISP Walsall. Initial printings had a 015R year code and the front of the self-adhesive backing paper was unprinted. Later printings have repeating 'ROYALMAIL' wording printed on the front of the self-adhesive backing paper and exist with 015R and 016R year code.

No. U3746 comes from booklets Nos. PM49/53, printed by ISP Walsall, and has 015R (PM49) or 016R (PM50/3) year code.

No. U3747 was issued in £15.11 premium stamp booklets, No. DY17 and has 015R year code.

No. U3747 also exists printed gravure (by FNMT Spain) from *Long to Reign Over Us* miniature sheet MS3747, from which it has source code REIGM and year code 015R, but is not separately listed.

(Des Atelier Works. Gravure and gold foil embossed. ISP Walsall)

2017 (5 June). *50th Anniversary of the Machin Definitive* Two phosphor bands. *Perf* 14x14½ (Type **1116**) and U3966 or 14½x14 (others).

MS3965 **3085** No. X866; No. 1470; as Type **1116**; No. 2124; No. 2651; as No. U3067 (but MMIL source code); as No. U3966 (but gravure)..............................	6.00	6.75
First Day Cover (MS3965) (Tallents House)...............................		7.75
First Day Cover (MS3965) (High Wycombe).............................		7.75
Presentation Pack (MS3964/5) (P.O.Pack No. 541).................	13.50

On **MS**3965 only the £1 gold foil stamp is embossed.

The 5p, 20p and £1 stamps in **MS**3965 do not have an elliptical perforation hole in each vertical side.

3086

(Litho and gold foil embossed. ISP)

2017 (5 June). *50th Anniversary of the Machin Definitive* Two narrow phosphor bands. *Perf* 14x14½.

3966	**3086**	£1 gold	4.50	5.50
		a. Booklet pane. Nos. U3966×4 with margins all round	13.50

3966 was embossed in gold foil, has the phosphor bands printed in litho and does not have an elliptical perforation hole on each vertical side. It was issued only in £15.59 booklet No. DY21.

> Please note that, for the convenience of collectors, Nos. **MS**3965 and U3966/a are also listed in the main section of this catalogue.

> For the 20p stamp as T **929** from the 50th Anniversary of the Machin booklet see No. 2133, pane No 1668sb.

3041a

(Gravure ISP Walsall)

2017 (6 Feb). *65th Anniversary of Accession of Queen Elizabeth II.* As T**3041a**. Two phosphor bands. Iridescent overprint reading '65TH ANNIVERSARY OF ACCESSION' with year code 'ACCE17ION'. *Perf* 14×14½.

U3920	£5 ultramarine	10·00	10·00
First Day Cover (Tallents House)		12·00
First Day Cover (Windsor)..		12·00
Presentation Pack (PO Pack No. 105)	11·00

No. U3920 does not have an elliptical perforation hole on each vertical side.

3085 (Illustration reduced. Actual size 202×74 mm)

Decimal Machin Booklet pane Guide ("U" numbers)

1st	2nd	1st
50		50
1st	2nd	1st

U2917a
£11.15 Accession of King George V
(DX50)

5	10	5
50		50
5	10	5

U3057a
£9.99 Morris and Company
(DY1)

1	1st	1
1st E		1st
1st S	1st W	1st NI

U3070a
£11.11 Football Heroes
(DY7)

2	81	2
1		1
97	2	97

U3070b
£14.60 Inventive Britain
(DY12)

5	£1.33	1
1st ✿		1st ✿
1	£1.33	5

U3070c
£13.96 Centenary of the First World War
(2nd Issue) (DY13) ✿ = Poppy

5	10
10	2
2	5

U3071a
£11.11 Football Heroes
(DY7)

1st E	5	1st S
2		2
1st NI	5	1st W

U3071b
£13.97 Classic Locomotives
(DY9)

1st	£1.05	1st
10		10
2	1st	2

U3071c
£14.58 Windsor Castle
(DY20)

5	2	5
£1.17		£1.17
2	5	2

U3071e
£18.69 Centenary of the RAF
(DY25)

1st ❖	10	1st ❖
5		20
1st ❖	87	1st ❖

U3072a
£13.77 Doctor Who (DY6)
❖ = Tardis

5	50	10
£1		£1
10	50	5

U3072b
£14.47 Bicentenary of the
Battle of Waterloo (DY14)

5	£1.05	5
10		10
£1.05	5	£1.05

U3072d
£15.37 The Tale of Beatrix Potter
(DY19)

1st GoT	20	2nd NI
5		5
2nd NI	£1.17	1st GoT

U3072e
£13.95 *Game of Thrones*
(DY24)

5	50	5
50		50
5	50	5

U3073a
£11.19 Merchant Navy
(DY8)

20	£1	20
10		10
20	£1	20

U3074a
£11.39 Buckingham Palace
(DY10)

20	1st E	10
1st W		1st S
10	1st NI	20

U3074b
£11.30 Centenary of the
First World War (1st Issue) (DY11)

	£1	

U3082a
£11.30 Centenary of the
First World War (1st Issue) (DY11)

✠ 1st	2nd	✠ 1st
1st		1st
✠ 1st	2nd	✠ 1st

U3095a
£16.99 The Making of Star Wars (DY15)
✠ = Union Flag

1st	£1.40	1st
2nd		2nd
1st	£1.40	1st

U3095b
£15.99 *Star Wars*: The making of
the Droids, Aliens and Creatures (DY23)

1st E	1st	1st S
1st		1st
1st NI	1st	1st W

U3097a
£15.11 90th Birthday of
Queen Elizabeth II (DY17)

1st	W 1st	1st
W 1st		W 1st
1st	W 1st	1st

U3279a
£12.77 Diamond Jubilee (DY4)
W = Wilding

'U' Numbers – conversion table

Please note that ALL the 'U' Numbers used are shown in the table. From U2911 to U2928 the orginal and revised numbers are the same; from that point onwards the changes are shown.
   There are a number of 'U' numbers not utilised – these are for future additions to the series – to overcome the extensive usage of suffix letters.

Original	Revised	Original	Revised	Original	Revised
U2911	**U2911**	U2943	**U2977**	U2973	**U3036**
U2912	**U2912**	U2944	**U2978**	U2974	**U3037**
U2913	**U2913**	U2945	**U2979**	U2975	**U3038**
U2914	**U2914**	U2946	**U2980**	U2976	**U3039**
U2915	**U2915**	U2947	**U2981**		
U2916	**U2916**	U2948	**U2982**	U2981	**U3045**
		U2949	**U2983**	U2982	**U3046**
U2917	**U2917**	U2950	**U2984**	U2983	**U3047**
		U2951	**U2985**	U2984	**U3048**
U2920	**U2920**	U2952	**U2986**	U2983a	**U3049**
U2921	**U2921**	U2953	**U2987**	U2984a	**U3050**
U2922	**U2922**	U2954	**U2988**	U2985	**U3051**
U2923	**U2923**	U2955	**U2989**	U2986	**U3052**
U2924	**U2924**	U2956	**U2990**		
U2925	**U2925**			U2991	**U3055**
U2926	**U2926**	U2957	**U2995**	U2992	**U3056**
U2927	**U2927**	U2958	**U2996**	U2993	**U3057**
U2928	**U2928**	U2958a	**U2997**	U2994	**U3058**
U2928a	**U2929**	U2958b	**U2998**	U2995	**U3059**
U2929	**U2930**	U2959	**U3000**		
U2930	**U2931**	U2960	**U3001**	U3005	**U3060**
U2930a	**U2932**	U2960a	**U3002**	U3007	**U3061**
U2931	**U2933**	U2960b	**U3003**	U3001	**U3065**
U2932	**U2934**			U3002	**U3066**
U2932a	**U2935**	U2961	**U3010**	U3003	**U3067**
U2933	**U2936**	U2962	**U3011**		
U2933a	**U2937**	U2962a	**U3012**	U3010	**U3070**
U2934	**U2939**	U2963	**U3013**	U3011	**U3071**
U2934a	**U2940**	U2964	**U3015**	U3012	**U3072**
U2934ab	**U2941**	U2965	**U3016**	U3012c	**U3072c**
U2934b	**U2945**	U2966	**U3017**	U3012g	**U3073**
U2934c	**U2946**	U2966a	**U3018**	U3013	**U3074**
U2934ca	**U2948**	U2967	**U3019**	U3014	**U3075**
U2935	**U2950**	U2968	**U3020**	U3017	**U3076**
U2936	**U2953**	U2968a	**U3021**	U3017a	**U3077**
U2937	**U2954**	U2968b	**U3022**	U3019	**U3078**
U2938	**U2955**	U2968c	**U3023**	U3019a	**U3079**
U2939	**U2956**	U2968d	**U3024**	U3020	**U3080**
U2940	**U2957**	U2968e	**U3025**	U3020a	**U3081**
U2940aa	**U2958**	U2968f	**U3026**	U3021	**U3082**
U2940a	**U2961**	U2968g	**U3027**	U3021b	**U3083**
U2940ab	**U2962**	U2968h	**U3028**	U3022	**U3085**
U2940b	**U2968**	U2968i	**U3029**	U3023	**U3086**
U2940c	**U2969**	U2969	**U3031**	U3014a	**U3095**
		U2970	**U3032**	U3015	**U3096**
U2941	**U2975**	U2971	**U3034**	U3016	**U3097**
U2942	**U2976**	U2972	**U3035**	U3016b	**U3098**

The following series of tables gives details of all source and year-code combinations reported at the time of going to press. Each is related to its printer and variations in the U-shaped slits are also noted. These tables are copyright John M Deering and are reproduced with his permission.

'ROYALMAIL' printed backing paper: From early 2016 self-adhesive Security Machins appeared with a repeated undulating 'ROYALMAIL' background in two sizes of grey text printed on the front of the backing paper. Initially the two sizes of grey text were printed upright: Type PB-Up (Printed Backing Upright). In early 2017 the background was changed so that alternate pairs of lines of the repeated 'ROYALMAIL' text were inverted in relation to each other. The pairs of lines can appear with the Large lettering above the small (Type PB-Ls), or with the small above the Large (Type PB-sL). Where they exist these differences are noted in the following tables, and where a stamp is known with both Type PB-Ls and Type PB-sL the price noted is for the cheaper of the two, whichever that is. Type PB-Up are noted and priced separately.

Type PB-Up

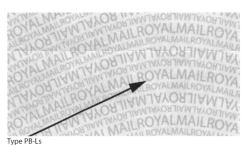

Type PB-Ls

Type PB-sL

SG No.	DESCRIPTION	

Denominated self-adhesive Security Machins, with source and year code *(b)*.

(The source code is at top right, and the year code is to the left of the front of The Queen's forehead.)

(The 'U'-shaped slits are broken.)

U2917	**50p** grey Walsall 'MPIL'	
	('U'-shaped slits with break at bottom only)	
	'MA10' (from DX50)	3·00
	50p grey Walsall 'MPIL'	
	('U'-shaped slits with break at top & bottom)	
	'MA10' (from DX50)	7·75
	50p grey Walsall 'MPIL' 'M11L'	
	(from DY1 premium booklet)	4·75

SG No.	DESCRIPTION	

Denominated self-adhesive Security Machins, no source code (as from counter sheets), with year code *(c)*.

(Unless noted, front of self-adhesive backing is plain.)

(All have the year code to the left of the front of The Queen's crown.)

(The 'U'-shaped slits are broken.)

U2920	**1p** DLR 'MAIL' (no source code) 'M12L'	0·50
	1p DLR 'MAIL' (no source code) 'M15L'	0·50
	1p DLR 'MAIL' (no source code) 'M16L'	0·50
	1p DLR 'MAIL' (no source code) 'M17L', Type PB-Ls	0.50
U2921	**2p** DLR 'MAIL' (no source code) 'M12L'	0·60
	2p DLR 'MAIL' (no source code) 'M14L'	0·60
	2p DLR 'MAIL' (no source code) 'M15L'	0·60
	2p DLR 'MAIL' (no source code) 'M16L'	0·60
	2p DLR 'MAIL' (no source code) 'M17L',	0·60
	2p DLR 'MAIL' (no source code) 'M17L', Type PB-Ls	0·50
U2922	**5p** DLR 'MAIL' (no source code) 'M12L'	0·60
	5p DLR 'MAIL' (no source code) 'M14L'	0·60
	5p DLR 'MAIL' (no source code) 'M15L'	0·60
	5p DLR 'MAIL' (no source code) 'M16L'	0·60
	5p DLR 'MAIL' (no source code) 'M17L', Type PB-Ls/sL	0.60
U2923	**10p** DLR 'MAIL' (no source code) 'M12L'	0·70
	10p DLR 'MAIL' (no source code) 'MA13'	0·70
	10p DLR 'MAIL' (no source code) 'M14L'	0·80
	10p DLR 'MAIL' (no source code) 'M15L'	0·80
	10p DLR 'MAIL' (no source code) 'M16L'	0·80
	10p DLR 'MAIL' (no source code) 'M17L'	0·70
	10p DLR 'MAIL' (no source code) 'M17L', Type PB-sL	0·60
U2924	**20p** DLR 'MAIL' (no source code) 'M12L'	1·20
	20p DLR 'MAIL' (no source code) 'MA13'	1·40
	20p DLR 'MAIL' (no source code) 'M14L'	1·30
	20p DLR 'MAIL' (no source code) 'M15L'	1·00
	20p DLR 'MAIL' (no source code) 'M16L'	0·80
	20p DLR 'MAIL' (no source code) 'M17L', Type PB-Ls	0·70
U2925	**50p** slate DLR 'MAIL' (no source code) 'M12L'	2·20
	50p slate DLR 'MAIL' (no source code) 'M17L', Type PB-Ls	1.70
U2926	**68p** DLR 'MAIL' (no source code) 'M11L'	2·60
	68p DLR 'MAIL' (no source code) 'M12L'	8·00
U2927	**76p** DLR 'MAIL' (no source code) 'M11L'	2·70
	76p DLR 'MAIL' (no source code) 'M12L'	7·75
U2928	**78p** Walsall 'MAIL' (no source code) 'M13L'	2·40
	78p DLR 'MAIL' (no source code) 'MA13'	4·50
U2929	**81p** DLR 'MAIL' (no source code) 'M14L'	2·40
U2930	**87p** DLR 'MAIL' (no source code) 'M12L'	4·75
U2931	**88p** Walsall 'MAIL' (no source code) 'M13L'	3·00
	88p DLR 'MAIL' (no source code) 'MA13'	4·75
U2932	**97p** DLR 'MAIL' (no source code) 'M14L'	3·25
U2933	**£1·00** magenta DLR 'MAIL' (no source code) 'M11L'	7·75

SG No.	DESCRIPTION	
	£1·00 magenta DLR 'MAIL' (no source code) 'M12L'	7·75
U2934	£1·00 bistre-brown DLR 'MAIL' (no source code) 'M12L'	5·25
	£1·00 bistre-brown DLR 'MAIL' (no source code) 'M14L'	4·00
	£1·00 bistre-brown DLR 'MAIL' (no source code) 'M15L'	3·25
	£1·00 bistre-brown DLR 'MAIL' (no source code) 'M16L'	4·50
U2935	£1·05 DLR 'MAIL' (no source code) 'M16L'	2·70
U2936	£1·10 DLR 'MAIL' (no source code) 'M11L'	3·75
U2937	£1·17 DLR 'MAIL' (no source code) 'M17L'	2·70
	£1·17 DLR 'MAIL' (no source code) 'M17L', Type PB-Ls/sL	3·00
U2938	£1·25 ISP Walsall 'MAIL' (no source code) 'M18L' Type PB-Ls	2.50
U2939	£1·28 DLR 'MAIL' (no source code) 'M12L'	6·00
	£1·28 DLR 'MAIL' (no source code) 'MA13'	6·00
	£1·28 DLR 'MAIL' (no source code) 'M14L'	5·50
U2940	£1·33 DLR 'MAIL' (no source code) 'M15L'	3·25
	£1·33 DLR 'MAIL' (no source code) 'M16L'	3·75
U2941	£1·40 DLR 'MAIL' (no source code) 'M17L'	3·25
	£1·40 DLR 'MAIL' (no source code) 'M17L', Type PB-Ls	3·25
U2943	£1·45 ISP Walsall 'MAIL' (no source code) 'M18L' Type PB-Ls	2.80
U2945	£1·47 DLR 'MAIL' (no source code) 'M14L'	3·75
U2946	£1·52 DLR 'MAIL' (no source code) 'M15L'	3·75
U2947	£1·55 ISP Walsall 'MAIL' (no source code) 'M18L' Type PB-Ls/sL	3·00
U2948	£1·57 DLR 'MAIL' (no source code) 'M17L'	3·75
	£1·57 DLR 'MAIL' (no source code) 'M17L' Type PB-Ls/sL	3·75
U2950	£1·65 DLR 'MAIL' (no source code) 'M11L'	4·75
U2953	£1·88 Walsall 'MAIL' (no source code) 'M13L'	5·25
	£1·88 DLR 'MAIL' (no source code) 'MA13'	7·00
U2954	£1·90 DLR 'MAIL' (no source code) 'M12L'	5·75
U2955	£2·00 DLR 'MAIL' (no source code) 'MA13'	9·00
U2956	£2·15 DLR 'MAIL' (no source code) 'M14L'	5·25
U2957	£2·25 DLR 'MAIL' (no source code) 'M15L'	5·00
	£2·25 DLR 'MAIL' (no source code) 'M16L'	5·50
	£2·25 ISP Walsall 'MAIL' (no source code) 'M18L' Type PB-Ls	3.50
U2958	£2·27 DLR 'MAIL' (no source code) 'M17L'	5·00
	£2·27 DLR 'MAIL' (no source code) 'M17L' Type PB-Ls/sL	5·00
U2961	£2·45 DLR 'MAIL' (no source code) 'M15L'	6·00
U2962	£2·55 DLR 'MAIL' (no source code) 'M17L'	5·50
	£2·55 DLR 'MAIL' (no source code) 'M17L' Type PB-Ls	5·50
U2963	£2·65 ISP Walsall 'MAIL' (no source code) 'M18L' Type PB-Ls	4.00
U2968	£3·15 DLR 'MAIL' (no source code) 'M15L'	6·50
U2969	£3·30 DLR 'MAIL' (no source code) 'M15L'	6.75

SG No.	DESCRIPTION	

2nd (bright blue) and 1st (as noted) self-adhesive Security Machins, no source code (as from counter sheets), with year code (c).

(Unless noted, front of self-adhesive backing is plain.)

(All have the year code to the left of the front of The Queen's forehead or crown, or for the 'Large' issues from MA11 onwards it is above the 'ge' of 'Large'.)

(The 'U'-shaped slits are broken.)

SG No.	DESCRIPTION	
U2995	2nd DLR 'MAIL' (no source code) 'MA10'	4·25
	2nd DLR 'MAIL' (no source code) 'M11L'	3·50
	2nd DLR 'MAIL' (no source code) 'M12L'	2·60
	2nd DLR 'MAIL' (no source code) 'MA13'	2·60
	2nd DLR 'MAIL' (no source code) 'M14L'	2·60
	2nd DLR 'MAIL' (no source code) 'M15L'	2·40
	2nd DLR 'MAIL' (no source code) 'M16L'	2·40
	2nd DLR 'MAIL' (no source code) 'M17L'	3·00
	2nd DLR 'MAIL' (no source code) 'M17L', Type PB-Ls/sL	1·60
U2996	1st gold DLR 'MAIL' (no source code) 'MA10'	3·75

SG No.	DESCRIPTION	
	1st gold DLR 'MAIL' (no source code) 'M11L'	3·50
U2997	1st vermilion DLR 'MAIL' (no source code) 'M12L'	2·00
	1st vermilion DLR 'MAIL' (no source code) 'MA13'	2·60
	1st vermilion DLR 'MAIL' (no source code) 'M14L'	2·60
	1st vermilion DLR 'MAIL' (no source code) 'M15L'	2·60
	1st vermilion DLR 'MAIL' (no source code) 'M16L'	2·70
U2998	1st bright scarlet DLR 'MAIL' (no source code) 'M16L', Type PB-sL	6.00
	1st bright scarlet DLR 'MAIL' (no source code) 'M17L', Type PB-Ls/sL	1.80
U3000	2nd Large DLR 'ROYAL' (no source code) 'MA10'	6·00
	2nd Large DLR 'ROYAL' (no source code) 'MA11'	3·00
	2nd Large DLR 'ROYAL' (no source code) 'MA12'	3·00
	2nd Large DLR 'ROYAL' (no source code) 'MA13'	3·00
	2nd Large DLR 'ROYAL' (no source code) 'M14L'	2·80
	2nd Large DLR 'ROYAL' (no source code) 'M15L'	2·80
	2nd Large DLR 'ROYAL' (no source code) 'M16L'	2·80
	2nd Large DLR 'ROYAL' (no source code) 'M17L', Type PB-Ls/sL	2·00
U3001	1st Large, gold, DLR 'ROYAL' (no source code) 'MA10'	5·25
	1st Large, gold, DLR 'ROYAL' (no source code) 'MA11'	3·25
U3002	1st Large, vermilion, DLR 'ROYAL' (no source code) 'MA12'	3·00
	1st Large, vermilion, DLR 'ROYAL' (no source code) 'MA13'	3·00
	1st Large, vermilion, DLR 'ROYAL' (no source code) 'M14L'	3·00
	1st Large, vermilion, DLR 'ROYAL' (no source code) 'M15L'	2·70
	1st Large, vermilion, DLR 'ROYAL' (no source code) 'M16L'	2·70
U3003	1st Large, bright scarlet, DLR 'ROYAL' (no source code) 'M17L', Type PB-Ls/sL	2·20

SG No.	DESCRIPTION	

2nd (bright blue) and 1st (as noted) self-adhesive Security Machins, with source and year code (d).

(Unless noted, the source code is at top right, the year code is to the left of the front of The Queen's forehead or crown, or for the 'Large' issues from MA11 onwards it is above the 'ge' of 'Large'.)

(The 'U'-shaped slits are broken.)

SG No.	DESCRIPTION	
U3010	2nd DLR 'MBIL' 'MA10'	6·75
	2nd DLR 'MBIL' 'M11L'	5·00
	2nd Walsall 'MBIL' 'M12L'	2·60
	2nd Walsall 'MBIL' 'M13L'	2·60
	2nd Walsall 'MBIL' 'M14L'	2·60
	2nd Walsall 'MBIL' 'M15L'	2·60
	2nd Walsall 'MBIL' 'M15L' Type PB-Up	3·75
	2nd Walsall 'MBIL' 'M16L' Type PB-Up	2·40
	2nd Walsall 'MBIL' 'M16L' Type PB-sL	2·40
	2nd Walsall 'MBIL' 'M17L' Type PB-Ls/sL	2·10
	2nd Walsall 'MBIL' 'M18L' Type PB-sL	2·10
U3011	2nd Walsall 'MPIL' 'MA10' ('U'-shaped slits with break at bottom only) (from DX50)	3.25
	2nd Walsall 'MPIL' 'MA10' ('U'-shaped slits with break at top & bottom) (from DX50)	7·75
U3012	2nd DLR 'MRIL' 'MA10'; only known USED from mail posted by bulk mailing houses. *Please note that the 2nd class stamp with these codes on ordinary gummed paper and without U-shaped slits is No. U3065.*	—
	2nd Enschedé 'MRIL' 'MA12'	4·75
	2nd Walsall 'MRIL' 'M12L'	5·25
	2nd Walsall 'MRIL' 'M15L'	4·25
U3013	2nd Walsall 'MTIL' 'MA10'	5·00
	2nd Walsall 'MTIL' 'M11L'	3·25
	2nd Walsall 'MTIL' 'M12L'	2·40

SG No.	DESCRIPTION	
	2nd Walsall 'MTIL''M13L'	2·20
	2nd Walsall 'MTIL''M14L'	2·20
	2nd Walsall 'MTIL''M15L',	2·40
	2nd Walsall 'MTIL''M15L' Type PB-Up	8·50
	2nd Walsall 'MTIL''M16L' Type PB-Up	2·20
	2nd Walsall 'MTIL''M16L', Type PB-sL	2·20
	2nd Walsall 'MTIL''M17L', Type PB-Ls/sL	1·80
U3015	**1st** gold DLR 'MBIL''MA10'	8·00
	1st gold DLR 'MBIL''M11L'	4·50
U3016	**1st** gold Walsall 'MCIL''MA10'	3·00
	1st gold Walsall 'MCIL''M11L'	2·70
U3017	**1st** gold Walsall 'MPIL''MA10' ('U'-shaped slits with break at bottom only) (from DX50)	2·20
	1st gold Walsall 'MPIL''MA10' ('U'-shaped slits with break at top & bottom) (from DX50)	6·00
U3018	**1st** gold DLR 'MRIL''MA10'	5·75
	1st gold Enschedé 'MRIL''MA12'	4·75
U3019	**1st** gold Walsall 'MSIL''MA10'	2·70
	1st gold Walsall 'MSIL''M11L'	3·75
U3020	**1st** gold Walsall 'MTIL''MA10'	5·00
	1st gold Walsall 'MTIL''M11L'	3·50
	1st gold Walsall 'MTIL''M12L'	6·75
U3021	**1st** vermilion Walsall 'MBIL''M12L'	3·00
	1st vermilion Walsall 'MBIL''M13L'	6·25
	1st vermilion Walsall 'MBIL''M14L'	3·00
	1st vermilion Walsall 'MBIL''M15L'	2·80
	1st vermilion Walsall 'MBIL''M15L' Type PB-Up	3·75
	1st vermilion Walsall 'MBIL''M16L' Type PB-Up	3·00
U3022	**1st** vermilion Walsall 'MCIL''M12L'	2·70
	1st vermilion Walsall 'MCIL''M13L'	2·20
	1st vermilion Walsall 'MCIL''M14L'	2·20
	1st vermilion Walsall 'MCIL''M15L'	2·20
U3023	**1st** vermilion Enschedé 'MRIL''MA12'	3·00
	1st vermilion Walsall 'MRIL''M13L'	3·00
U3024	**1st** vermilion Walsall 'MSIL''M12L'	2·60
	1st vermilion Walsall 'MSIL''M13L'	3·50
	1st vermilion Walsall 'MSIL''M14L'	2·80
	1st vermilion Walsall 'MSIL''M15L'	3·50
	1st vermilion Walsall 'MSIL''M16L' Type PB-Up	2·80
U3025	**1st** vermilion Walsall 'MTIL''M12L'	2·60
	1st vermilion Walsall 'MTIL''M13L'	2·60
	1st vermilion Walsall 'MTIL''M14L'	2·60
	1st vermilion Walsall 'MTIL''M15L'	2·70
	1st vermilion Walsall 'MTIL''M15L' Type PB-Up	5·25
	1st vermilion Walsall 'MTIL''M16L' Type PB-Up	2·80
U3026	**1st** bright scarlet Walsall 'MBIL''M16L' Type PB-Up	2·60
	1st bright scarlet Walsall 'MBIL''M16L' Type PB-sL	3.50
	1st bright scarlet Walsall 'MBIL''M17L' Type PB-Ls/sL	2.20
U3027	**1st** bright scarlet Walsall 'MCIL''M16L' Type PB-Up	2·10
	1st bright scarlet Walsall 'MCIL''M17L' Type PB-Up	2·10
	1st bright scarlet Walsall 'MCIL''M17L' Type PB-Ls/sL	1·50
	1st bright scarlet Walsall 'MCIL''M18L' Type PB-Ls/sL	1·50
U3028	**1st** bright scarlet Walsall 'MSIL''M16L' Type PB-Up	2·40
	1st bright scarlet Walsall 'MSIL''M16L' Type PB-Ls/sL	2·60
	1st bright scarlet Walsall 'MSIL''M17L' Type PB-Up	1·70
	1st bright scarlet Walsall 'MSIL''M17L' Type PB-Ls/sL	2·00
U3029	**1st** bright scarlet Walsall 'MTIL''M16L' Type PB-Up	2·40
	1st bright scarlet Walsall 'MTIL''M16L' Type PB-Ls/sL	2·60

SG No.	DESCRIPTION	
	1st bright scarlet Walsall 'MTIL''M17L' Type PB-Ls/sL	2·00
U3031	**2nd Large** DLR 'MBI''MA10'	24·00
	2nd Large DLR 'BIL''MA11' (source code bottom right)	3·50
	2nd Large Walsall 'BIL''MA12' (source code bottom right) (The 'U' slits do not have breaks in them)	3·50
	2nd Large Walsall 'BIL''MA13' (source code bottom right)	4·25
	2nd Large Walsall 'BIL''MA13' (source code bottom right) (The 'U' slits do not have breaks in them)	4·25
	2nd Large Walsall 'MBIL''MA14' (source code in front of hair)	3·25
	2nd Large Walsall 'MBIL''MA15' (source code in front of hair)	3·50
	2nd Large Walsall 'MBIL''M16L' (not MA16) (source code in front of hair) Type PB-Up	3·25
	2nd Large Walsall 'MBIL''M17L' (source code in front of hair) Type PB-Ls/sL	2·70
U3032	**2nd Large** Walsall 'MFI''MA10'	19·00
	2nd Large Walsall 'FIL''MA11' (source code bottom right)	3·00
	2nd Large Walsall 'FIL''MA12' (source code bottom right)	4·25
	2nd Large Walsall 'FIL''MA13' (source code bottom right)	4·00
	2nd Large Walsall 'MFIL''MA14' (source code in front of hair)	3·00
	2nd Large Walsall 'MFIL''MA15' (source code in front of hair)	3·75
	2nd Large Walsall 'MFIL''M16L' (not MA16) (source code in front of hair) Type PB-Up	3·00
	2nd Large Walsall 'MFIL''M17L' (source code in front of hair) Type PB-Ls	2.50
U3034	**1st Large**, gold, DLR 'MBI''MA10'	8·75
	1st Large, gold, DLR 'BIL''MA11' (source code bottom right)	4·50
U3035	**1st Large**, gold, Walsall 'MFI''MA10'	8·00
	1st Large, gold, Walsall 'FIL''MA11' (source code bottom right)	3·25
U3036	**1st Large**, vermilion, Walsall 'BIL''MA12' (source code bottom right) (The 'U' slits do not have breaks in them)	4·00
	1st Large, vermilion, Walsall 'BIL''MA13' (source code bottom right)	4·75
	1st Large, vermilion, Walsall 'BIL''MA13' (source code bottom right) (The 'U' slits do not have breaks in them)	4·75
	1st Large, vermilion, Walsall 'MBIL''MA14' (source code in front of hair)	4·00
	1st Large, vermilion, Walsall 'MBIL''MA15' (source code in front of hair)	4·00
	1st Large, vermilion, Walsall 'MBIL''MA15' (source code in front of hair) Type PB-Up	5·75
	1st Large, vermilion, Walsall 'MBIL''M16L' (not MA16) (source code in front of hair) Type PB-Up	4·00
U3037	**1st Large**, vermilion, Walsall 'FIL''MA12' (source code bottom right)	3.25
	1st Large, vermilion, Walsall 'FIL''MA13' (source code bottom right)	4·00
	1st Large, vermilion, Walsall 'MFIL''MA14' (source code in front of hair)	3·25
	1st Large, vermilion, Walsall 'MFIL''MA15' (source code in front of hair)	3·75
	1st Large, vermilion, Walsall 'MFIL''MA15' (source code in front of hair) Type PB-Up	3·75
	1st Large, vermilion, Walsall 'MFIL''M16L' (not MA16) (source code in front of hair) Type PB-Up	3·50
U3038	**1st Large**, bright scarlet, Walsall 'MBIL''M16L' (source code in front of hair) Type PB-Up	3·75
	1st Large, bright scarlet, Walsall 'MBIL''M17L' (source code in front of hair) Type PB-Ls/sL	3·00

SG No.	DESCRIPTION	
U3039	**1st Large**, bright scarlet, Walsall 'MFIL''M16L' (source code in front of hair) Type PB-Up	3·00
	1st Large, bright scarlet, Walsall 'MFIL''M17L' (source code in front of hair) Type PB-Ls/sL	2·80

Note. Where Walsall is stated as the printer, for later year codes the printer is more accutaly ISP Walsall. However; being one and the same, later year codes are simply noted here as Walsall. ISP stands for 'International Security Printers' which encompasses both Cartor and Walsall.

SG No.	DESCRIPTION	

'Recorded Signed For', 'Royal Mail Signed For', and 'Special Delivery' self-adhesive Security Machins, no source code (as from counter sheets), with year code *(b)*.

(Unless noted, front of self-adhesive backing is plain.)

(Unless noted, the year code is to the left of the front of The Queen's forehead or crown.)

(The U-shaped slits are broken.)

U3047	**'Recorded Signed For' 1st** DLR 'MAIL' (no source code) 'MA10'	14·00
U3048	**'Recorded Signed For' 1st Large** DLR 'MAIL' (no source code) 'MA10'	16·00
U3049	**'Royal Mail Signed For' 1st** DLR (Note. The service name was revised in March 2013.) 'MAIL' (no source code) 'MA13'	5·25
	'Royal Mail Signed For' 1st DLR 'MAIL' (no source code) 'M15L' (not MA15)	6·00
	'Royal Mail Signed For' 1st DLR 'MAIL' (no source code) 'M16L'	5·25
	'Royal Mail Signed For' 1st DLR 'MAIL' (no source code) 'M17L' Type PB-Ls/sL	4·75
U3050	**'Royal Mail Signed For' 1st Large** DLR (Note. The service name was revised in March 2013.) 'MAIL' (no source code) 'MA13' (date code is above the 'ge' of 'Large')	5·75
	'Royal Mail Signed For' 1st Large DLR 'MAIL' (no source code) 'M15L' (not MA15) (date code is above the 'ge' of 'Large')	7·25
	'Royal Mail Signed For' 1st Large DLR 'MAIL' (no source code) 'M16L' (date code is above the 'ge' of 'Large')	7·25
	'Royal Mail Signed For' 1st Large DLR 'MAIL' (no source code) 'M17L' (date code is above the 'ge' of 'Large')	5·75
U3051	**'Special Delivery up to 100g'** DLR 'MAIL' (no source code) 'MA10'	13·50
	'Special Delivery up to 100g' DLR 'MAIL' (no source code) 'M14L'	19·25
	'Special Delivery up to 100g' DLR 'MAIL' (no source code) 'M15L'	17·25
	'Special Delivery up to 100g' DLR 'MAIL' (no source code) 'M16L'	16·75
	'Special Delivery up to 100g' DLR 'MAIL' (no source code) 'M17L'	16·75
	'Special Delivery up to 100g' DLR 'MAIL' (no source code) 'M17L' Type PB-Ls	16·75
U3052	**'Special Delivery up to 500g'** DLR 'MAIL' (no source code) 'MA10'	15·50
	'Special Delivery up to 500g' DLR 'MAIL' (no source code) 'M14L'	20·00
	'Special Delivery up to 500g' DLR 'MAIL' (no source code) 'M16L'	17·75

SG No.	DESCRIPTION	

Denominated ordinary gummed (i.e. not self-adhesive) Security Machins, with source and date code *(c)*.

No 'U'-shaped slits. Printed litho.

U3070	**1p** Cartor 'MPIL''M13L' (from DY7 premium booklet)	1·60
	1p ISP Cartor 'MPIL''M14L' (from DY12 premium booklet)	1·40
	1p ISP Cartor 'MPIL''M15L' (from DY13 premium booket)	1·20
U3071	**2p** Cartor 'MPIL''M13L' (from DY7 premium booklet)	1·40
	2p Enschedé 'MPIL''M13L' (from DY9 premium booklet)	1·40
	2p ISP Cartor 'MPIL''M14L' (from DY12 premium booklet)	1·40
	2p ISP Cartor 'MPIL''M16L' (from DY20 premium booklet)	1·20
U3071d	**2p** ISP Cartor 'M IL''M18L' i.e. source code without P (from DY25 premium booklet)	1·00
U3072	**5p** Cartor 'MPIL''M12L' (from DY6 premium booklet)	2·20
	5p Cartor 'MPIL''M13L' (from DY7 premium booklet)	1·50
	5p Enschedé 'MPIL''M13L' (from DY9 premium booklet)	1·50
	5p ISP Cartor 'MPIL''M15L' (from DY14 premium booklet)	1·50
	5p ISP Cartor 'MPIL''M16L' (from DY19 premium booklet)	1·50
	5p ISP Cartor 'MPIL''M17L' (from DY24 premium booklet)	1·20
U3072c	**5p** *Deep red-brown*, ISP Cartor 'MPIL''M15L' (from DY13 premium booklet)	2·20
U3072f	**5p** ISP Cartor 'M IL''M18L' i.e. source code without P (from DY25 premium booklet)	1·00
U3073	**5p** Enschedé 'MPIL''M13L'; ellipse toward top of sides of stamp (from DY8 premium booklet)	2·00
U3074	**10p** Cartor 'MPIL''M12L' (from DY6 premium booklet)	2·20
	10p Cartor 'MPIL''M13L' (from DY7 premium booklet)	1·60
	10p Enschedé 'MPIL''M14L' (from DY10 and DY11 premium booklets)	1·60
	10p ISP Cartor 'MPIL''M15L' (from DY14 premium booklet)	1·50
	10p ISP Cartor 'MPIL''M16L' (from DY19 and DY20 premium booklets)	1·40
U3075	**20p** Cartor 'MPIL''M12L' (from DY6 premium booklet)	3·75
	20p Enschedé 'MPIL''M14L' (from DY10 and DY11 premium booklets)	1·50
	20p Enschedé 'MPIL''M17L' (from DY24 premium booklet)	1·70
U3076	**50p** slate-blue, Enschedé 'MPIL''M13L'; ellipse toward top of sides of stamp (from DY8 premium booklet)	2·80
U3077	**50p** slate-blue, ISP Cartor 'MPIL''M15L' (from DY14 premium booklet)	2·70
U3078	**76p** Cartor 'MPIL''M11L' (from DY2 premium booklet)	5·50
U3079	**81p** ISP Cartor 'MPIL''M14L' (from DY12 premium booklet)	8·00
U3080	**87p** Cartor 'MPIL''M12L' (from DY6 premium booklet)	6·00
U3081	**97p** ISP Cartor 'MPIL''M14L' (from DY12 premium booklet)	3·75
U3082	**£1·00** Enschedé 'MPIL''M14L' (from DY10 and DY11 premium booklets)	3·25
	£1·00 ISP Cartor 'MPIL''M15L' (from DY14 premium booklet)	3·25
U3083	**£1·05** ISP Cartor 'MPIL''M16L' (from DY19 and DY20 premium booklets)	3·00
U3084	**£1·17** ISP Cartor 'MPIL''M17L' (from DY24 premium booklet)	3·50
U3084a	**£1·17** ISP Cartor 'M IL''M18L' i.e. source code without P (from DY25 premium booklet)	3·00
U3085	**£1·33** ISP Cartor 'MPIL''M15L' (from DY13 premium booklet)	3·50

SG No.	DESCRIPTION	
U3086	**£1·40** ISP Cartor 'MPIL' 'M17L'	
	(from DY23 premium booklet)	3·50

NVI ordinary gummed (i.e. not self-adhesive) Security Machins, with source and date code (d).

No 'U'-shaped slits. Printed litho.

U3095	**2nd** ISP Cartor 'MPIL' 'M15L'	
	(from DY15 premium booklet)	3·50
	2nd ISP Cartor 'MPIL' 'M17L'	
	(from DY23 premium booklet)	2·50
U3096	**1st** gold, Cartor 'MPIL' 'M11L'	
	(from DY2 premium booklet)	5·25
U3097	**1st** vermilion, Cartor 'MPIL' 'M13L'	
	(from DY7 premium booklet)	2·80
	1st vermilion, ISP Cartor 'MPIL' 'M15L'	
	(from DY15 premium booklet)	3·60
	1st vermilion, ISP Cartor 'MPIL' 'M16L'	
	(from DY17 premium booklet)	3·50
	1st vermilion, ISP Cartor 'MPIL' 'M17L'	
	(from DY23 premium booklet)	2·20
U3098	**1st** bright scarlet, ISP Cartor 'MPIL' 'M16L'	
	(from DY20 premium booklet)	2·50

Note. ISP stands for 'International Security Printers' which encompasses both Cartor and Walsall.

SG No.	DESCRIPTION	

1st 'Long to Reign Over Us' self-adhesive Security Machins, no source code (as from counter sheets), with date code (a).

(All have the date code to the left of The Queen's neck, just above the front of the necklace.)

(The 'U'-shaped slits are broken.)

U3744	**1st** bright lilac DLR	
	'REIGN' (no source code) '015R'	2·00
	1st bright lilac DLR	
	'REIGN' (no source code) '016R'	2·30

SG No.	DESCRIPTION	

1st 'Long to Reign Over Us' self-adhesive Security Machins, with source and date code (b).

(Unless noted, front of self-adhesive backing is plain.)

(All have the source code behind the back of the Queen's hair at the bottom, the year code is to the left of The Queen's neck, just above the front of the necklace.)

(The 'U'-shaped slits are broken.)

U3745	**1st** bright lilac ISP Walsall 'REIGS' '015R'	2·30
	1st bright lilac ISP Walsall 'REIGS' '015R'	
	Type PB-Up	—
	1st bright lilac ISP Walsall 'REIGS' '016R'	
	Type PB-Up	3·00
U3746	**1st** bright lilac ISP Walsall 'REIGC' '015R'	2·60
	1st bright lilac ISP Walsall 'REIGC' '016R'	
	Type PB-Up	2·30

Note. ISP stands for 'International Security Printers' which encompasses both Cartor and Walsall.

SG No.	DESCRIPTION	

1st 'Long to Reign Over Us' ordinary gum (i.e. not self-adhesive) Security Machin, with source and year code (c).
No 'U'-shaped slits. Printed litho.

(Source code behind the back of the Queen's hair at the bottom, year code is to the left of The Queen's neck, just above the front of the necklace.)

U3747	**1st** bright lilac ISP Cartor 'REIGP' '016R'	
	(from DY17 premium booklet)	3·50

Note. ISP stands for 'International Security Printers' which encompasses both Cartor and Walsall. 1st bright lilac with ordinary gum but gravure (by FNMT Spain), with source code REIGM and year code 015R, exists from the *Long to Reign Over Us* miniature sheet **MS**3747, but is not separately listed.

ROYAL MAIL POSTAGE LABELS

These imperforate labels were issued as an experiment by the Post Office. Special microprocessor controlled machines were installed at post offices in Cambridge, London, Shirley (Southampton) and Windsor to provide an after-hours sales service to the public. The machines printed and dispensed the labels according to the coins inserted and the buttons operated by the customer. Values were initially available in ½p. steps to 16p. and in addition, the labels were sold at philatelic counters in two packs containing either 3 values (3½, 12½, 16p.) or 32 values (½p. to 16p.).

From 28 August 1984 the machines were adjusted to provide values up to 17p. After 31 December 1984 labels including ½p. values were withdrawn. The machines were taken out of service on 30 April 1985.

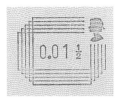

Machine postage-paid impression in red on phosphorised paper with grey-green background design. No watermark. Imperforate.

1984 (1 May–28 Aug).

Set of 32 (½p. to 16p.)	15·00	22·00
Set of 3 (3½p., 12½p., 16p.)	2·50	3·00
Set of 3 on First Day Cover (1.5.84)		6·50
Set of 2 (16½p., 17p.) (28.8.84)	4·00	3·00

ROYAL MAIL POST & GO STAMPS

Following trials of a number of self-service machines capable of dispensing postage labels, Royal Mail began installing "Post & Go" machines, manufactured by Wincor Nixdorf, in larger post offices. The first machines were sited at the Galleries post office in Bristol and came into use on 8 October 2008. In addition to postage labels, the machines dispense ready to use stamps, from rolls which have the design and background pre-printed in gravure, by thermally printing a two-line service indicator and a four-part code that represents the branch in which the machine is sited, the machine number within the branch, and session and transaction numbers.

A new series of machines, manufactured by NCR, made their appearance from 28 February 2014, dispensing Type IIA stamps (see below).

Large and small typeface (Wincor): when the machines were first installed they were programmed to dispense five denominations and the service indicator lines were in a large size typeface (Type I), as Type FT **1**. The large typeface remained current until September 2010 when the first pictorial Post & Go stamps, depicting British Birds, were released. The larger pictorial element in the new design necessitated machines to be upgraded to print the service indicator both repositioned to the left and in a reduced size (Type II). The four-part code was also significantly reduced in size. Initially the pictorials were only available from 30 offices nationwide, and because the upgrading was phased over many months, the early pictorial issues had limited availability. The Machin design ran concurrently with the pictorials and started appearing with the smaller service indicator from 8 September 2010, when machines in London were the first to be upgraded in advance of the first pictorial issue. The smaller service indicator became the norm after all machines were upgraded.

Tariff changes: in the autumn of 2011 a new value, "Worldwide up to 40g", was added to the range and began to appear whilst Birds (4th series) was current. The Machin design was the first to be seen with it though, having been trialled in one London office from 13 October. Birds (4th series) appeared with "Worldwide up to 40g" later in the year and due to the late use of earlier Birds issues they too are known with it, although it is not included in set prices for Birds, series 1 to 3. Second class stamps were introduced to the range on 20 February 2013 but only in Special Packs, and from Hytech machines at Spring Stampex 2013. They were finally released at a postal location (a mobile "pop-up" post shop in Newcastle-upon-Tyne) on 20 November 2013.

Worldwide up to 10g and Worldwide up to 40g stamps were withdrawn on 31 March 2014 and both Europe and Worldwide 60g. stamps were withdrawn on 30 March 2015, to be replaced by new 100g. versions.

Special Packs: 1st stamps of the different "Post & Go" pictorial designs are available in Special Packs from Tallents House. For the Birds series these packs contained sheetlets of the six designs which were printed in gravure and had the two lines of the service indicator "1st Class" and "up to 100g" printed much closer together (2mm). From Farm Animals onwards the sheetlets were replaced by strips of six thermally printed from Hytech machines which also had the two lines of the service indicator printed closer together (3mm). First day covers sold by Tallents House use these types of stamps.

Unintentional use of large typeface: after upgrading machines to produce the smaller service indicator, some machines experienced software glitches resulting in the unintentional part reversion to the large typeface, or a semi corrupted version of it, and in some instances a mixture of both large and small on the same denomination. Machines at varying locations were affected and some went unchanged for many months, or were amended and then simply reverted again. Such glitches seem to have continued on and off until December 2012 when all machines nationwide seemed to be functioning correctly.

Digitally-printed stamps: Since November 2015 for the Hong Kong World Stamp Exhibition certain designs have been produced in single-design rolls, digitally printed rather than printed by gravure. To date, these have been available from exhibitions and from a machine at The Postal Museum (and locations outside the scope of this catalogue). Details may be found in the relevant tables.

Figure 1

Figure 2

Figure 3

There were two main types of part reversion: the first resulted in the "Worldwide up to 10g" having the "Up to 10g" in the larger typeface whilst "Worldwide" was still in the smaller typeface (*Fig. 1*). At the same time and although still in the smaller typeface, the "1st Class", "1st Large" and "Europe" were also affected by the glitch and had the service indicator lines positioned a little too far to the right. The "Worldwide up to 20g" was similarly affected which results in the "e" of Worldwide being printed on the pictorial design. All five values show the four-part code incorrectly spaced so that there is a large gap between the branch and machine number. The "Worldwide up to 40g" had not been introduced at this point. The second type of reversion is more significant and is of a complete return to the large typeface across the five original denominations, but with the "Worldwide Up to 10g" stamp having the second line, "Up to 10g", completely missing (*Fig. 2*). The problems continued after the introduction of the "Worldwide up to 40g" which when affected had the "Worldwide" in the large typeface whilst the "up to 40g" was in the small typeface, and so is the opposite of the "Worldwide up to 10g" from the first type of reversion (*Fig. 3*).

Hytech/Royal Mail Series II machines: since Spring Stampex 2011, Post & Go machines manufactured by Hytech International have been sited at stamp exhibitions by Royal Mail. Stamps from Hytech machines are identifiable from the Wincor versions because the two lines of the service indicator are printed much closer together, whilst those from Wincor machines are 4mm apart. There are other minor differences. Marking particular events, from autumn 2011, some Hytech machines at exhibitions have produced stamps with special inscriptions. Owing to their restricted availability, Hytech versions from exhibitions with and without inscriptions are not listed separately, although details are provided in tables following the Royal Mail Post & Go stamps listings. The British Postal Museum & Archive, London, have a permanently available machine (originally Hytech, later Royal Mail Series II) which can be used by members of the public. Stamps from this machine initially bore the inscription "The B.P.M.A.". For commemorative inscriptions on BPMA (rebranded The Postal Museum in February 2016) stamps, see the tables at the end of this section.

In November 2012 "next generation" Hytech machines appeared at a new type of post office, a temporary, pop-up, Christmas Post Shop in Camden, London. The installation of Hytech machines at this office resulted in the first publicly available Hytech versions in a post office location. Both the Machins and 2012 Robin designs were on sale at this post office, and differ from Wincor versions through the two lines of the service indicator being printed much closer together (2.6 mm) (Type III).

From Spring Stampex 2014 Hytech Machines were replaced by Royal Mail Series II Machines.

Enquiry Offices: Royal Mail Series II machines installed at Royal Mail enquiry offices from December 2014 dispense stamps with a Type IIIA service indicator. These are given full listing.

Year codes: codes first appeared on the 2012 Robin issue where there is an "MA12" in the background to the left of the main pictorial design. The February 2013 2nd class stamps also have an MA12 year code and the year code became a standard feature from 2013

OPEN VALUE LABELS In February 2014, "Open Value labels", previously dispensed from Post & Go machines printed on white self-adhesive paper began to appear on the same illustrated background labels as Post & Go stamps. These show a service indicator "1L" (1st Letter), "2SP" (2nd Small Parcel), etc and the price. These are outside the scope of this catalogue, but on 7 July 2014 Royal Mail released a special pack containing five such labels in the Machin Head design, as Types FT **1** and FT **14** (P&G 15) (*Price* £8).

Five Types of Post & Go service indicator, including subtypes of Types II and III:

FT **1** (Type I)

Type I: As Type FT **1**, with large, bold service indicator and four-part code consisting entirely of numerals (Wincor)

Type II

Type II: Smaller service indicator with lines 4mm apart and code consisting entirely of numerals (Wincor)

Type IIA

Type IIA: Similar to Type II but with service indicator and code in changed typeface and ranged left with service indicator lines 3.3 mm apart and code consisting entirely of numerals (NCR)

Type III

Type III: Smaller service indicator with lines 2.6mm apart and code consisting of letters and numerals (Hytech "next generation").

Type IIIA

Type IIIA: As Type III, with the code being a mixture of letters and numerals and all wording ranged left. However, the top line of the service indicator is noticeably smaller and slightly further away from the second line, at 2.7mm (Royal Mail Series II with revised typeface).

(Gravure Walsall, thermally printed service indicator)

2008 (8 Oct)–**15**. Type FT **1**. Self-adhesive. Olive-brown background. Two phosphor bands. Perf 14×14½.

FS1	(1st Class Up to 100g) (Type I)	9·00	9·00
	a. Type II (8.9.10)	3·25	3·25
	b. Type III (17.11.12)	10·50	10·50
	c. Type IIA (6.14)	6·50	6·50
	d. Type IIIA (3.6.15)	5·25	5·25
FS2	(1st Large Up to 100g) (Type I)	9·75	9·75
	a. Type II (8.9.10)	3·50	3·50
	b. Type III (17.11.12)	11·00	11·00
	c. Type IIA (6.14)	7·00	7·00
	d. Type IIIA (3.6.15)	5·50	5·50
FS3	(Europe Up to 20g)(Type I)	9·75	9·75
	a. Type II (8.9.10)	4·00	4·00
	b. Type III (17.11.12)	11·50	11·50
FS3c	Euro 20g World 10g (TIIA) (6.14)	7·00	7·00
	ca. Type II (20.10.14)	8·50	8·50
	cb. Type IIIA (3.6.15)	5·50	5·50
FS3d	Europe up to 60g (Type II) (31.3.14)	9·75	9·75
	dc. Type IIA (6.14)	8·50	8·50
FS3e	Europe up to 100g (Type IIA) (4.15)	9·75	9·75
	ea. Type IIIA (3.6.15)	8·50	8·50
FS4	(Worldwide Up to 10g) (Type I) (9.10.08)	11·00	11·00
	a. Type II (8.9.10)	6·00	6·00
	b. Type III (17.11.12)	11·50	11·50
FS5	(Worldwide Up to 20g) (Type I)	11·00	11·00
	a. Type II (8.9.10)	4·75	4·75
	b. Type III (17.11.12)	12·00	12·00
	c. Type IIA (6.14)	7·25	7·25
	d. Type IIIA (3.6.15)	6·00	6·00
FS5e	(Worldwide Up to 40g) (Type II) (13.10.11)	13·00	13·00
	eb. Type III (17.11.12)	14·00	14·00
FS5f	Worldwide Up to 60g (Type II) (31.3.14)	10·50	10·50
	fc. Type IIA (6.14)	9·25	9·25
FS5g	Worldwide Up to 100g (Type IIA) (4.15)	10·50	10·50
	ga. Type IIIA (3.6.15)	9·25	9·25
FS1/5 *Set* of 5 (Type I)		45·00	45·00
FS1a/3a, 4a, 5a, 5e *Set* of 6 (Type II)		32·00	32·00
FS1b/3b, 4b, 5b, 5eb *Set* of 6 (Type III)		65·00	65·00
FS1c, 2c, 3c, 3dc, 5c, 5fc *Set* of 6 (Type IIA)		42·00	42·00
FS1d, 2d, 3cb, 3fa, 5d, 5ga *Set* of 6 (Type IIIA)		35·00	35·00

Special Pack (As Nos. FS1/5 but service indicator and code lines in gravure) (Type I) £100

Although the very first Post & Go machines went live at the Galleries post office, Bristol, on 8 October 2008, one particular machine function had not been properly enabled and the "Worldwide Up to 10g" version was not available until 9 October.

The five stamps from the special pack and first day cover sold by Tallents House differ from machine-printed stamps in having the service indicator and branch code printed in gravure and have a narrow gap between the two lines of the service indicator. Also, they are easily identified through the code lines which are unique to the gravure printing: 020511 1-08445-01 (to -05).

Smaller service indicator versions similar to Type II were available from Hytech machines at Spring Stampex 2011. Subsequently, versions similar to Type II or Type III were available from Hytech machines with additional inscriptions at other events. Details are provided in separate tables at the end of this section. Versions with various inscriptions have been available at the BPMA (now the PM) since December 2012.

FS1/5e are known printed unintentionally from Wincor machines with the typeface varieties resulting from software glitches causing a reversion to the large typeface; see notes to 'Unintentional use of large typeface'.

Nos. FS4a and FS5e were replaced on 31 March 2014 by FS3d and FS5f.

Nos. FS3a was replaced on 20 October 2014 by FS3ca.

Nos. FS3dc and FS5fc were replaced on in April 2015 by FS3e and FS5g.

All Wincor machines, producing Type II stamps, were decommissioned before the 30 March 2015 tariff change.

For full details of Post & Go stamps dispensed from machines at locations other than post offices and post shops, please refer to the tables following these listings

FT **2** Blue Tit

(Des Robert Gillmor and Kate Stephens. Gravure Walsall, thermally printed service indicator).

2010 (17 Sept)–**14**. *Birds of Britain (1st series)*. Self-adhesive. Two phosphor bands. MULTI COLOUR Perf 14×14½.

FS6	(1st Class up to 100g) (Type II)	9·00	9·00
FS7	(1st Large up to 100g) (Type II)	9·50	9·50
FS8	(Europe up to 20g) (Type II)	9·50	9·50
FS8a	(Europe up to 60g) (Type II) (5.14)	90·00	90·00
FS9	(Worldwide up to 10g) (Type II)	18·00	18·00
FS10	(Worldwide up to 20g) (Type II)	13·00	13·00
FS10a	(Worldwide up to 40g) (Type II) (2.12)	60·00	60·00
FS10b	(Worldwide up to 60g) (Type II) (5.14)	90·00	90·00
FS6/8, 9, 10 *Set* of 5 (Type II)		55·00	55·00
First Day Cover (No. FS6 in 6 designs)			20·00

Special Pack (No. FS6 in sheetlet of 6 gravure designs) (Type II) .... 24·00

Nos. FS6/10b were each available in six different designs: Type FT **2**, Goldfinch, Wood Pigeon, Robin, House Sparrow and Starling.

Nos. FS6/10 were available from Post & Go terminals, initially in 30 post offices.

FS6/10 are known printed unintentionally from Wincor machines with both typeface varieties resulting from software glitches causing a reversion to the large typeface; see notes to 'Unintentional use of large typeface'.

FS8a, 10a, 10b resulted from the late use of old stock.

FT **3** Blackbird

(Des Robert Gillmor and Kate Stephens. Gravure Walsall, thermally printed service indicator)

2011 (24 Jan)–**14**. *Birds of Britain (2nd series)*. Self-adhesive. Two phosphor bands. MULTI COLOUR Perf 14×14½.

FS11	(1st class up to 100g) (Type II)	4·00	4·00
FS12	(1st Large up to 100g) (Type II)	4·25	4·25
FS13	(Europe up to 20g) (Type II)	4·25	4·25
FS13a	(Europe up to 60g) (Type II) (4.14)	26·00	26·00
FS14	(Worldwide up to 10g) (Type II)	9·00	9·00
FS15	(Worldwide up to 20g) (Type II)	4·75	4·75
FS15a	(Worldwide up to 40g) (Type II) (12.11)	32·00	32·00
FS15b	(Worldwide up to 60g) (Type II) (4.14)	27·00	27·00
FS11/13, 14, 15 *Set* of 5 (Type II)		24·00	24·00
First Day Cover (No. FS11 in 6 designs)			20·00

Special Pack (No. FS11 in sheetlet of 6 gravure designs) (Type II) .... 45·00

Nos. FS11/15b were each available in six different designs: Type FT **3**, two Magpies, Long-tailed Tit, Chaffinch, Collared Dove and Greenfinch.

FS11/15a are known printed unintentionally from Wincor machines with the first type of software glitch causing a part reversion to the large typeface on "Up to 10g". The issue is also known printed with the large typeface because a roll was supplied to an office yet to have its machine upgraded for the smaller service indicator. See notes to "Unintentional use of large typeface".

FS13a, 15a, 15b resulted from the late use of old stock.

FT **4** Mallard

(Des Robert Gillmor and Kate Stephens.
Gravure Walsall, thermally printed service indicator)

2011 (19 May)–**14**. *Birds of Britain (3rd series).* Self-adhesive. Two phosphor bands. Perf 14×14½.

FS16	(1st Class up to 100g) (Type II)	3·50	3·50
FS17	(1st Large up to 100g) (Type II)	4·00	4·00
FS18	(Europe up to 20g) (Type II)	4·00	4·00
FS18a	(Europe up to 60g) (Type II) (4.14)	40·00	40·00
FS19	(Worldwide up to 10g) (Type II)	6·00	6·00
FS20	(Worldwide up to 20g) (Type II)	4·50	4·50
FS20a	(Worldwide up to 40g) (Type II) (12.11)	14·00	14·00
FS20b	(Worldwide up to 60g) (Type II) (4.14)	40·00	40·00
FS16/18, 19, 20 *Set of 5* (Type II)		20·00	20·00
First Day Cover (No. FS16 in 6 designs)			8·75

Special Pack (No. FS16 in sheetlet of 6 gravure designs)
(Type II) .... 10·00

Nos. FS16/20b were each available in six different designs: Type FT **4**, Greylag Goose, Kingfisher, Moorhen, Mute Swan and Great Crested Grebe.

FS16/20 are known printed unintentionally from Wincor machines with both typeface varieties resulting from software glitches causing a reversion to the large typeface; see notes to "Unintentional use of large typeface".

FS18a, 20a, 20b resulted from the late use of old stock.

FT **5** Puffin

(Des Robert Gillmor and Kate Stephens.
Gravure Walsall, thermally printed service indicator)

2011 (16 Sept)–**14**. *Birds of Britain (4th series).* Self-adhesive. Two phosphor bands. Perf 14×14½.

FS21	(1st class up to 100g) (Type II)	2·75	2·75
FS22	(1st Large up to 100g) (Type II)	3·25	3·25
FS23	(Europe up to 20g) (Type II)	3·25	3·25
FS23a	(Europe up to 60g) (Type II) (31.3.14)	12·00	12·00
FS24	(Worldwide up to 10g) (Type II)	5·25	5·25
FS25	(Worldwide up to 20g) (Type II)	4·00	4·00
FS26	(Worldwide up to 40g) (17.10.11) (Type II)	11·00	11·00
FS26a	(Worldwide up to 60g) (Type II) (31.3.14)	13·00	13·00
FS21/23, 24/26 *Set of 6* (Type II)		26·00	26·00
First Day Cover (FS21 in 6 designs)			7·25

Special Pack (No. FS21 in sheetlet of 6 gravure designs)
(Type II) .... 10·00

Nos. FS21/26a were each available in six different designs: Type FT **5**, Gannet, Oystercatcher, Ringed Plover, Cormorant and Arctic Tern.

FS21/25 are known printed unintentionally from Wincor machines with both typeface varieties resulting from software glitches causing a reversion to the large typeface. Additionally FS26 is known with the second type mixing both sizes of typeface; see notes to "Unintentional use of large typeface".

FS23a, 26a resulted from the late use of old stock.

FT **6** Welsh Mountain Badger Face

(Des Robert Gillmor and Kate Stephens. Gravure,
thermally printed service indicator Walsall)

2012 (24 Feb)–**14**. *British Farm Animals (1st series).* Sheep. Self-adhesive. Two phosphor bands. Perf 14×14½.

FS27	(1st Class up to 100g) (Type II)	2·75	2·75
FS28	(1st Large up to 100g) (Type II)	3·25	3·25
FS29	(Europe up to 20g) (Type II)	3·25	3·25
FS29a	(Euro 20g World 10g) (Type II) (10.14)	10·00	10·00
FS29b	(Europe up to 60g) (Type II) (31.3.14)	12·00	12·00
FS30	(Worldwide up to 10g) (Type II)	5·25	5·25
FS31	(Worldwide up to 20g) (Type II)	4·00	4·00
FS32	(Worldwide up to 40g) (Type II)	5·75	5·75
FS32b	(Worldwide up to 60g) (Type II) (31.3.14)	13·00	13·00
FS27/29, 30/32 *Set of 6* (Type II)		22·00	22·00
First Day Cover (FS27 in 6 designs)			8·75

Special Pack (FS27 in strip of 6 designs) (Type II) (P&G 6) 10·00

Nos. FS27/32b were each available in six different designs: Type FT **6**, Dalesbred, Jacob, Suffolk, Soay, Leicester Longwool.

FS27/32 are known printed unintentionally from Wincor machines with the second typeface variety resulting from software glitches causing a reversion to the large typeface; see notes to "Unintentional use of large typeface".

FS29a, 29b, 32b resulted from the late use of old stock.

FT **7** Berkshire

(Des Robert Gillmor and Kate Stephens. Gravure Walsall,
thermally printed service indicator)

2012 (24 Apr)–**14**. *British Farm Animals (2nd series).* Pigs. Multicoloured. Self-adhesive. Two phosphor bands. Perf 14×14½.

FS33	(1st class up to 100g) (Type II)	2·75	2·75
FS34	(1st Large up to 100g) (Type II)	3·25	3·25
FS35	(Europe up to 20g) (Type II)	3·25	3·25
FS35a	(Euro 20g World 10g) (Type II) (10.14)	8·75	8·75
FS35b	(Europe up to 60g) (Type II) (31.3.14)	13·00	13·00
FS36	(Worldwide up to 10g) (Type II)	5·25	5·25
FS37	(Worldwide up to 20g) (Type II)	4·00	4·00
FS38	(Worldwide up to 40g) (Type II)	5·75	5·75
FS38b	(Worldwide up to 60g) (Type II) (31.3.14)	13·00	13·00
FS33/35, 36/38 *Set of 6* (Type II)		22·00	22·00
First Day Cover (No. FS33 in 6 designs)			8·50

Special Pack (FS33 in strip of 6 designs) (Type II) (P&G 7) 10·00

Nos. FS33/38b were each available in six different designs: Type FT **7**, Gloucestershire Old Spots, Oxford Sandy and Black, Welsh, Tamworth, British Saddleback.

FS33/38 are known printed unintentionally from Wincor machines with the second typeface variety resulting from software glitches causing a reversion to the large typeface; see notes to "Unintentional use of large typeface".

FS35a, 35b, 38b resulted from the late use of old stock.

FT **8**

(Des Anton Morris and Dick Davies.
Gravure Walsall, thermally printed service indicator)

2012 (21 May)–**15**. *Union Flag* Type FT **8**. Self-adhesive. Two phosphor bands. [MULTI COLOUR] Perf 14×14½.

FS39	(1st Class up to 100g) (Type II)	2·75	2·75
	a. Type IIA	3·00	3·00
FS40	(1st Large up to 100g) (Type II)	3·25	3·25
	a. Type IIA	3·25	3·25
FS41	(Europe up to 20g) (Type II)	3·50	3·50
FS41*a*	(Euro 20g World 10g) (Type IIA) (7.14)	3·50	3·50
	ab. Type II (10.14)	9·00	9·00
FS41*b*	(Europe up to 60g) (Type II) (31.3.14)	9·75	9·75
	ba. Type IIA (7.14)	11·50	11·50
FS41*c*	(Europe up to 100g) (Type IIA) (30.3.15)	9·50	9·50
FS42	(Worldwide up to 10g) (Type II)	5·25	5·25
FS43	(Worldwide up to 20g) (Type II)	4·50	4·50
	a. Type IIA (7.14)	4·50	4·50
FS44	(Worldwide up to 40g) (Type II)	6·00	6·00
FS44*b*	(Worldwide up to 60g) (Type II) (31.3.14)	10·50	10·50
	ba. Type IIA (7.14)	12·50	12·50
FS44*c*	(Worldwide up to 100g) (Type IIA) (30.3.15)	10·50	10·50
FS39/41, 42/44 *Set of 6* (Type II)		23·00	23·00
FS39a, 40a, 41*a*, 41ba, 43a, 44ba *Set of 6* (Type IIA)		35·00	35·00
First Day Cover (No. FS39 only)			2·50
Special Pack (No. FS39 only) (Type IIA) (P&G 8)		3·00	

When first printed the Special Pack stamps had the upper service indicator line, 1st Class, in a slightly larger typeface and ranged left with the code line, and are therefore a Type II sub-type (*Price* £3.50). A reprint of the Special Packs has stamps in a smaller typeface, with all lines ranged left, and are therefore similar to Type IIA.

FS39/44 are known printed unintentionally from Wincor machines with the second typeface variety resulting from software glitches causing a reversion to the large typeface; see notes to "Unintentional use of large typeface".

FT **8** is known thermally printed with 2nd Class up to 100g and 2nd Large up to 100g, Type IIA, when put in machine's second class unit due to standard second class FT **14** stock being temporarily unavailable.

All Wincor machines, producing Type II stamps, were decommissioned before the 30 March 2015 tariff change.

FT **9** Irish Moiled

(Des Robert Gillmor and Kate Stephens.
Gravure Walsall, thermally printed service indicator)

2012 (28 Sept)–**14**. *British Farm Animals (3rd series). Cattle.* Self-adhesive. Two phosphor bands. [MULTI COLOUR] Perf 14×14½.

FS45	(1st Class up to 100g) (Type II)	4·00	4·00
FS46	(1st Large up to 100g) (Type II)	4·75	4·75
FS47	(Europe up to 20g) (Type II)	5·00	5·00
FS47*a*	(Euro 20g World 10g) (Type II) (10.14)	10·00	10·00
FS47*b*	(Europe up to 60g) (Type II) (31.3.14)	12·00	12·00
FS48	(Worldwide up to 10g) (Type II)	6·00	6·00
FS49	(Worldwide up to 20g) (Type II)	5·25	5·25
FS50	(Worldwide up to 40g) (Type II)	7·00	7·00
FS50*b*	(Worldwide up to 60g) (Type II) (31.3.14)	13·00	13·00
FS45/47, 48/50 *Set of 6* (Type II)		29·00	29·00
First Day Cover (No. FS45 in 6 designs) (Type III)			8·50
Special Pack (FS45 in strip of 6 designs) (Type III) (P&G 9)		10·00	

Nos. FS45/50*b* were each available in six different designs: Type FT **9**, Welsh Black, Highland, White Park, Red Poll, Aberdeen Angus.

FS45/50 are known printed unintentionally from Wincor machines with the second typeface variety resulting from software glitches causing a reversion to the large typeface; see notes to "Unintentional use of large typeface".

FS47*a*, 47*b*, 50*b* resulted from the late use of old stock.

FT **10** Robin

(Des. Robert Gillmor and Kate Stephens.
Gravure Walsall, thermally printed service indicator)

2012 (6 Nov)–**15**. *Christmas Robin* with year code in background. Type FT **10**. Self-adhesive. Two phosphor bands. [MULTI COLOUR] Perf 14×14½.

FS51	(1st Class up to 100g) (Type II)	2·75	2·75
	a. Type III (17.11.12)	4·25	4·25
	b. Type IIA (7.14)	4·50	4·50
FS52	(1st Large up to 100g) (Type II)	3·25	3·25
	a. Type III (17.11.12)	4·75	4·75
	b. Type IIA (7.14)	5·00	5·00
FS53	(Europe up to 20g) (Type II)	3·50	3·50
	a. Type III (17.11.12)	5·25	5·25
FS53*c*	(Euro 20g World 10g) (Type IIA) (7.14)	5·00	5·00
	ca. Type II (20.10.14)	9·00	9·00
FS53*d*	(Europe up to 60g) (Type II) (4.14)	10·00	10·00
	da. Type IIA (7.14)	9·00	9·00
FS53*e*	(Europe up to 100g) (Type IIA) (4.15)	13·00	13·00
FS54	(Worldwide up to 10g) (Type II)	4·00	4·00
	a. Type III (17.11.12)	5·25	5·25
FS55	(Worldwide up to 20g) (Type II)	4·50	4·50
	a. Type III (17.11.12)	5·50	5·50
	b. Type IIA (7.14)	5·25	5·25
FS56	(Worldwide up to 40g) (Type II)	5·75	5·75
	a. Type III (17.11.12)	6·50	6·50
FS56*d*	(Worldwide up to 60g) (Type II) (4.14)	11·00	11·00
	da. Type IIA (7.14)	9·75	9·75
FS56*e*	(Worldwide up to 100g) (Type IIA) (4.15)	14·00	14·00
FS51/53, 54/56 *Set of 6* (Type II)		22·00	22·00
FS51a/56a *Set of 6* (Type III)		29·00	29·00
FS51b, 52b, 53*c*, 53da, 55b, 56da *Set of 6* (Type IIA)		35·00	35·00

FS51/56 are known printed unintentionally from Wincor machines with the second typeface variety resulting from software glitches causing a reversion to the large typeface; see notes to "Unintentional use of large typeface".

FS51/56, FS53ca, 53*d* and 56*d* exist with both MA12 and MA13 year codes (Type II).

FS51a/56a exist with both MA12 and MA13 year codes (Type III).

FS51b, 52b, 53*c*, 53da, 53*e*, 55b, 56da and 56*e* are MA13 (Type IIA).

FS53*c*, 53*d*, 56*d* resulted from the late use of old stock.

FT **10** is known thermally printed with 2nd Class up to 100g and 2nd Large up to 100g, Type IIA, MA13, when put in machine's second class unit because standard second class (new blue Machin) FT **14** stock was temporarily unavailable and it was deemed necessary to use alternative stock.

All Wincor machines, producing Type II stamps, were decommissioned before the 30 March 2015 tariff change.

Nos. 57 and 58 are vacant

FT **11** Lesser Silver Water Beetle

(Des Kate Stephens. Illustrations by Chris Wormell.
Gravure Walsall, thermally printed service indicator)

2013 (22 Feb)–**14**. *Freshwater Life (1st series). Ponds.* Self-adhesive. Two phosphor bands. [MULTI COLOUR] Perf 14×14½.

FS59	(1st Class up to 100g) (Type II)	3·50	3·50
FS60	(1st Large up to 100g) (Type II)	3·75	3·75
FS61	(Europe up to 20g) (Type II)	4·00	4·00
FS61*a*	(Euro 20g World 10g) (Type II) (10.14)	10·00	10·00
FS61*b*	(Europe up to 60g) (Type II) (4.14)	11·00	11·00
FS62	(Worldwide up to 10g) (Type II)	5·00	5·00
FS63	(Worldwide up to 20g) (Type II)	4·25	4·25
FS64	(Worldwide up to 40g) (Type II)	6·00	6·00
FS64*b*	(Worldwide up to 60g) (Type II) (4.14)	12·00	12·00
FS59/61, 62/64 *Set of 6* (Type II)		24·00	24·00
First Day Cover (FS59 in 6 designs) (Type III)			9·50
Special Pack (FS59 in strip of 6 designs) (Type III) (P&G 11)		10·00	

Nos. FS59/64*b* were each available in six different designs: Type FT **11**, Three-spined Stickleback, Smooth Newt, Fairy Shrimp, Emperor Dragonfly and Glutinous Snail.

FS61*a*, 61*b*, 64*b* resulted from the late use of old stock.

FT **12** Perch

(Des Kate Stephens. Illustrations by Chris Wormell.
Gravure Walsall, thermally printed service indicator)

2013 (25 June)–**14**. *Freshwater Life (2nd series). Lakes.* Self-adhesive. Two
phosphor bands. Perf 14×14½.

FS65	(1st Class up to 100g) (Type II)	4·00	4·00
FS66	(1st Large up to 100g) (Type II)	4·75	4·75
FS67	(Europe up to 20g) (Type II)	5·00	5·00
FS67*a*	(Euro 20g World 10g) (Type II) (10.14)	9·00	9·00
FS67*b*	(Europe up to 60g) (Type II) (31.3.14)	12·00	12·00
FS68	(Worldwide up to 10g) (Type II)	6·00	6·00
FS69	(Worldwide up to 20g) (Type II)	5·25	5·25
FS70	(Worldwide up to 40g) (Type II)	7·00	7·00
FS70*b*	(Worldwide up to 60g) (Type II) (31.3.14)	13·00	13·00
FS65/67, 68/70 *Set of 6* (Type II)		29·00	29·00
First Day Cover (FS65 in 6 designs) (Type III)			9·50
Special Pack (FS65 in strip of 6 designs) (Type III) (P&G 12)		11·00	

Nos. FS65/70*b* were each available in six different designs: Type
FT 12, European Eel, Crucian Carp, Caddis Fly Larva, Arctic Char and
Common Toad.

FS67*a*, 67*b*, 70*b* resulted from the late use of old stock.

FT **13** Minnow

(Des Kate Stephens. Illustrations by Chris Wormell.
Gravure Walsall, thermally printed service indicator)

2013 (20 Sept)–**14**. *Freshwater Life (3rd series). Rivers.* Self-adhesive. Two
phosphor bands. Perf 14×14½.

FS71	(1st Class up to 100g) (Type II)	3·25	3·25
FS72	(1st Large up to 100g) (Type II)	3·50	3·50
FS73	(Europe up to 20g) (Type II)	3·75	3·75
FS73*a*	(Euro 20g World 10g) (Type II) (10.14)	9·00	9·00
FS73*b*	(Europe up to 60g) (Type II) (31.3.14)	10·50	10·50
FS74	(Worldwide up to 10g) (Type II)	5·75	5·75
FS75	(Worldwide up to 20g) (Type II)	4·50	4·50
FS76	(Worldwide up to 40g) (Type II)	6·25	6·25
FS76*b*	(Worldwide up to 60g) (Type II) (31.3.14)	11·50	11·50
FS71/73, 74/76 *Set of 6* (Type II)		24·00	24·00
First Day Cover (FS71 in 6 designs) (Type III)			9·50
Special Pack (FS71 in strip of 6 designs) (Type III) (P&G 13)		10·00	

Nos. FS71/76*b* were each available in six different designs: Type
FT 13, Atlantic Salmon, White-clawed Crayfish, River Lamprey, Blue-
winged Olive Mayfly Larva, Brown Trout.

FS73*a* resulted from the late use of old stock.

NOTE: From FS77 onwards all Post & Go stamps incorporated a year
code, unless otherwise stated.

(Gravure Walsall, thermally printed service indicator)

2013 (19 Nov)–**15**. Type FT **1** with year code in background. Olive-brown
background. Self-adhesive. Two phosphor bands. Perf 14×14½.

FS77	(1st Class up to 100g) (Type II)	3·50	3·50
	a. Type IIA (28.2.14)	2·50	2·50
	b. Type IIIA (30.3.15)	3·50	3·50
FS78	(1st Large up to 100g) (Type II)	3·75	3·75
	a. Type IIA (28.2.14)	3·00	3·00
	b. Type IIIA (30.3.15)	4·00	4·00
FS79	(Europe up to 20g) (Type II)	5·50	5·50
	a. Type IIA (28.2.14)	8·00	8·00
FS79*b*	(Euro 20g World 10g) (Type II) (20.10.14)	8·00	8·00
	ba. Type IIA (5.6.14)	3·25	3·25
	bb. Type IIIA (30.3.15)	4·25	4·25
FS80	(Europe up to 60g) (Type II) (31.3.14)	6·50	6·50
	a. Type IIA (1.4.14)	6·00	6·00
FS80*c*	(Europe up to 100g) (Type IIA) (30.3.15)	4·25	4·25
	ca. Type IIIA (30.3.15)	5·50	5·50
FS81	(Worldwide up to 10g) (Type II)	—	—
	a. Type IIA (28.2.14)	—	—
FS82	(Worldwide up to 20g) (Type II)	5·00	5·00
	a. Type IIA (28.2.14)	3·75	3·75
	b. Type IIIA (30.3.15)	4·75	4·75
FS83	(Worldwide up to 40g) (Type II)	—	—
	a. Type IIA (28.2.14)	—	—
FS84	(Worldwide up to 60g) (Type II) (31.3.14)	7·50	7·50
	a. Type IIA (1.4.14)	7·00	7·00
FS84*c*	(Worldwide up to 100g) (Type IIA) (30.3.15)	5·75	5·75
	ca. Type IIIA (30.3.15)	6·75	6·75
FS77/80, 82, 84 *Set of 6* (Type II)		29·00	29·00
FS77a, 78a, 79ba, 80c, 82a, 84c *Set of 6* (Type IIA)		20·00	20·00
FS77b, 78b, 79bb, 80ca, 82b, 84ca *Set of 6* (Type IIIA)		27·00	27·00

FS77/79, 79*b*, 80, 81, 82, 83 and 84 are year code MA13 (Type II).

FS77a, 78a, 79ba, 80*c*, 82a and 84*c* exist year code MA13, MA14,
MA15 and MA16 (Type IIA).

FS80a and 84a exist year code MA13 and MA14 (Type IIA).

FS79a, 81a and 83a are year code MA13 (Type IIA).

FS77b, 78b, 79bb, 80ca, 82b and 84ca are year code MA13 and
MA15 (Type IIIA).

Nos. FS81 and FS83 were replaced on 31 March 2014 by FS80 and
FS84.

Nos. FS81a and FS83a were replaced on 1 April 2014 by FS80a and
FS84a.

Nos. FS79a was replaced on 5 June 2014 by FS79ba.

Nos. FS79 was replaced on 20 October 2014 by FS79*b*.

Nos. FS80a and FS84a were replaced on 30 March 2015 by FS80*c*
and FS84*c*.

Type FT **1** (olive-brown) with year code MA14 and MA16 are known
thermally printed with 2nd Class up to 100g and 2nd Large up to
100g, Type IIA, when put in machine's second class unit. This may
have occurred because they were mistakenly put in the wrong unit,
or because standard second class (new blue Machin) FT **14** stock
was temporarily unavailable and it was deemed necessary to use
alternative stock.

All Wincor machines, producing Type II stamps, were
decommissioned before the 30 March 2015 tariff change.

(Gravure Walsall, thermally printed service indicator)

2013 (17 Nov)–**16**. *Union Flag* Type FT **8** with year code in background. Multicoloured. Self-adhesive. Two phosphor bands. Perf 14×14½.

FS85	(1st Class up to 100g) (Type II)	—	—
	a. Type IIA (10.8.16)	4·00	4·00
FS86	(1st Large up to 100g) (Type II)	—	—
	a. Type IIA (10.8.16)	4·25	4·25
FS87	(Europe up to 20g) (Type II)	—	—
FS87a	(Euro 20g World 10g) (Type IIA) (10.8.16)	4·50	4·50
FS88	(Europe up to 60g) (Type II) (31.3.14)	20·00	20·00
FS88a	(Europe up to 100g) (Type IIA) (10.8.16)	5·50	5·50
FS89	(Worldwide up to 10g) (Type II)	—	—
FS90	(Worldwide up to 20g) (Type II)	—	—
	a. Type IIA (10.8.16)	4·75	4·75
FS91	(Worldwide up to 40g) (Type II)	—	—
FS92	(Worldwide up to 60g) (Type II) (31.3.14)	21·00	21·00
FS92a	(Worldwide up to 100g) (Type IIA) (10.8.16)	6·75	6·75
FS85/87, 89/91 *Set of 6* (Type II)		27·00	27·00
FS85a, 86a, 87a, 88a, 90a, 92a *Set of 6* (Type IIA)		27·00	27·00

FS85/92a are MA13.

FS85, 86, 87, and 90 are known from the Ludgate Circus post office in late 2013, and from Harrogate and Dorchester post offices following the 31 March 2014 tariff change.

FS89 and 91 are only known from Ludgate Circus post office in late 2013.

(Worldwide up to 10g) and (Worldwide up to 40g) were replaced on 31 March 2014 by (Europe up to 60g) and (Worldwide up to 60g).

All Wincor machines, producing Type II stamps, were decommissioned before the 30 March 2015 tariff change.

Type FT **8** with year code in background is known thermally printed with 2nd Class up to 100g and 2nd Large up to 100g, Type IIA, when put in machine's second class unit. This may have occurred because it was mistakenly put in the wrong unit, or because standard second class (new blue Machin) FT **14** stock was temporarily unavailable and it was deemed necessary to use alternative stock.

FT **14**

(Gravure Walsall, thermally printed service indicator)

2013 (20 Nov)–**15**. Type FT **14** with background text reading "ROYALMAIL" in alternate lines of large and small lettering with year code in background. New blue background. Self-adhesive. One phosphor band (over the Queen's head). Perf 14×14½.

FS93	(2nd Class up to 100g) (Type III)	3·50	3·50
	a. Type IIA (2.14)	2·50	2·50
	b. Type IIIA (30.3.15)	3·50	3·50
FS94	(2nd Large up to 100g) (Type III)	4·00	4·00
	a. Type IIA (2.14)	2·75	2·75
	b. Type IIIA (30.3.15)	3·75	3·75
Special Pack (As Nos. FS93/94 but weight line inset at left) (Type III) (P&G 10)		10·00	

Post & Go stamps as Type FT **14** were issued by Tallents House on 20 February 2013 in packs and on first day covers (price £7·00 per pack and £3·00 on first day cover). They were sold from Hytech Next Generation machines at Spring Stampex 2013 but were not made available through post offices until November 2013.

FS93/94 exist MA12 from Special Pack and Spring Stampex 2013, and MA12/MA13 from Christmas Post Shop.

FS93a/94a exist MA12, MA13, MA14 and MA15 (Type IIA)

FS93b/94b are MA12 and MA15 (Type IIIA).

Type FT **14** with year code MA12 is known thermally printed with 1st Class up to 100g, 1st Class Large up to 100g, Euro 20g World 10g, Europe up to 60g, Worldwide up to 20g and Worldwide up to 60g, Type IIA, when mistakenly put in machine's first class unit.

For the 2nd Class Machin design with the background text reading "2ndCLASS" in large lettering, alternating with "ROYALMAIL" in small lettering, see Nos. FS157/158.

FT **15** Primrose

(Des Kate Stephens. Illustrations by Julia Trickey. Gravure ISP Walsall, thermally printed service indicator)

2014 (19 Feb)–**15**. *British Flora (1st series). Spring Blooms.* Two phosphor bands. Perf 14×14½.

FS95	(1st Class up to 100g) (Type II)	4·50	4·50
	a. Type IIA (5.14)	4·50	4·50
FS96	(1st Large up to 100g) (Type II)	5·25	5·25
	a. Type IIA (5.14)	5·25	5·25
FS97	(Europe up to 20g) (Type II)	5·50	5·50
	a. Type IIA (5.14)	15·00	15·00
FS97b	(Euro 20g World 10g) (Type IIA) (5.6.14)	6·00	6·00
	ba. Type II (10.14)	8·50	8·50
FS98	(Europe up to 60g) (Type II) (31.3.14)	10·00	10·00
	a. Type IIA (5.14)	7·50	7·50
FS98b	(Europe up to 100g) (Type IIA) (30.3.15)	11·50	11·50
FS99	(Worldwide up to 10g) (Type II)	6·50	6·50
FS100	(Worldwide up to 20g) (Type II)	5·75	5·75
	a. Type IIA (5.14)	5·75	5·75
FS101	(Worldwide up to 40g) (Type II)	7·50	7·50
FS102	(Worldwide up to 60g) (Type II) (31.3.14)	11·00	11·00
	a. Type IIA (5.14)	8·50	8·50
FS102b	(Worldwide up to 100g) (Type IIA)	12·50	12·50
FS95/97 and FS99/101 *Set of 6* (Type II)		32·00	32·00
FS95a, 96a, 97b, 98a, 100a, 102a *Set of 6* (Type IIA)		35·00	35·00
First Day Cover (FS95 in 6 designs) (Type III)			9·50
Special Pack (FS95 in strip of 6 designs) (Type III) (P&G 14)		10·00	

Nos. FS95 through to FS102b were each available in six different designs: Type FT **15**, Snowdrop, Lesser Celandine, Dog Violet, Wild Daffodil, Blackthorn.

Nos. FS95 through to FS102b have year code MA14.

There was a late reprint of the Special Packs containing Type IIIA stamps (*Price* £20).

Nos. FS97a was replaced on 5 June 2014 by FS97b.

FS98b and 102b resulted from the late use of old stock.

All Wincor machines, producing Type II stamps, were decommissioned before the 30 March 2015 tariff change.

FT **16** Forget-me-not

FT **17** Common Ivy

(Des Kate Stephens. Illustrations by Julia Trickey.
Gravure ISP Walsall, thermally printed service indicator)

2014 (17 Sept)–**15**. *British Flora (2nd series). Symbolic Flowers*. Self-adhesive. Two phosphor bands. 🄼🄲 Perf 14×14½

FS103	(1st Class up to 100g) (Type IIA)	3·00	3·00
	a. Type II (17.9.14)	5·25	5·25
FS104	(1st Large up to 100g) (Type IIA)	3·25	3·25
	a. Type II (17.9.14)	5·50	5·50
FS104*b*	Europe up to 20g (Type II) (17.9.14)	25·00	25·00
FS105	(Euro 20g World 10g) (Type IIA)	3·50	3·50
	a. Type II (20.10.14)	9·25	9·25
FS106	(Europe up to 60g) (Type IIA)	6·75	6·75
	a. Type II (17.9.14)	6·75	6·75
FS106*b*	(Europe up to 100g) (Type IIA) (30.3.15)	10·00	10·00
FS107	(Worldwide up to 20g) (Type IIA)	4·50	4·50
	a. Type II (17.9.14)	6·00	6·00
FS108	(Worldwide up to 60g) (Type IIA)	7·25	7·25
	a. Type II (17.9.14)	7·25	7·25
FS108*b*	(Worldwide up to 100g) (Type IIA) (30.3.15)	11·00	11·00
FS103/104, 105/106, 107/108 *Set of 6* (Type IIA)		26·00	26·00
FS103a, 104a, 104b, 106a, 107a, 108a *Set of 6* (Type II)		50·00	50·00
First Day Cover (FS103 in 6 designs) (Type IIIA)			9·50
Special Pack (FS103 in strip of 6 designs) (Type IIIA)			
(P&G 16)			10·00

Nos. FS103/108*b* were each available in six different designs (all with year code MA14): Type FT **16**, Common Poppy, Dog Rose, Spear Thistle, Heather and Cultivated Flax.

Nos. FS104*b* was replaced on 20 October 2014 by FS105a.

Nos. FS106 and FS108 were replaced on 30 March 2015 by FS106*b* and FS108*b*.

Wincor machines, producing Type II stamps, were decommissioned before the 30 March 2015 tariff change.

In the run-up to Remembrance Sunday 2014, for the first time the Common Poppy design was made available in single-design rolls for use in post offices (for a limited time from 21 October 2014). When distributed to post offices in 2014 the single-design roll stock had year code MA14. Nos. FS103/108 (Type IIA) and FS103a/108a (Type II) exist in this form.

The annual tradition of reissuing the Common Poppy in single-design rolls for a short time continues, and it was dispensed in post offices from 19 October 2015 (Type IIA only), both from MA14 stock and also from newly-printed stock with year code MA15. Nos. FS103/105, 106*b*, 107 and 108*b*. From 24 October 2016 the Common Poppy was again reissued, and newly distributed stock at this time had MA16, and from 24 October 2017 with R17Y (Nos. FS103/105, 106*b*, 107 and 108*b*, Type IIA only). See also FS137/142.

Type FT **16**, Common Poppy, Dog Rose, Spear Thistle, Heather and Cultivated Flax are each known thermally printed with 2nd Class up to 100g and 2nd Large up to 100g, Type IIA, when mistakenly put in machine's second class unit. Single-design rolls of the Common Poppy, code MA14, are known thermally printed with 2nd Class up to 100g and 2nd Large up to 100g, Type IIA, when put in machine's second class unit due to standard second class (new blue Machin) FT **14** stock being temporarily unavailable.

(Des Kate Stephens. Illustrations by Julia Trickey.
Gravure ISP Walsall, thermally printed service indicator)

2014 (13 Nov)–**15**. *British Flora (3rd series). Winter Greenery*. Blue background with one phosphor band at right (FS109/b and FS110/b) or olive-brown background with two phosphor bands (others). Self-adhesive. 🄼🄲 Perf 14×14½

FS109	(2nd Class up to 100g) (Type IIA)	3·50	3·50
	b. Type IIIA (3.12.14)	4·50	4·50
FS110	(2nd Large up to 100g) (Type IIA)	4·00	4·00
	b. Type IIIA (3.12.14)	5·00	5·00
FS111	(1st Class up to 100g) (Type IIA)	3·50	3·50
	a. Type II (13.11.14)	7·25	7·25
	b. Type IIIA (3.12.14)	4·75	4·75
FS112	(1st Large up to 100g) (Type IIA)	4·00	4·00
	a. Type II (13.11.14)	7·50	7·50
	b. Type IIIA (3.12.14)	5·25	5·25
FS113	(Euro 20g World 10g) (Type IIA)	4·00	4·00
	a. Type II (13.11.14)	7·75	7·75
	b. Type IIIA (3.12.14)	5·50	5·50
FS113*c*	(Europe up to 20g) (Type II) (12.14)	25·00	25·00
FS114	(Europe up to 60g) (Type IIA)	4·50	4·50
	a. Type II (13.11.14)	8·25	8·25
	b. Type IIIA (3.12.14)	6·00	6·00
FS114*c*	(Europe up to 100g) (Type IIA) (5.15)	10·00	10·00
FS115	(Worldwide up to 20g) (Type IIA)	4·25	4·25
	a. Type II (13.11.14)	8·00	8·00
	b. Type IIIA (3.12.14)	5·75	5·75
FS116	(Worldwide up to 60g) (Type IIA)	5·75	5·75
	a. Type II (13.11.14)	9·00	9·00
	b. Type IIIA (3.12.14)	6·75	6·75
FS116*c*	(Worldwide up to 100g) (Type IIA) (5.15)	11·00	11·00
FS109/113, 114, 115, 116 *Set of 8* (Type IIA)		30·00	30·00
FS111a/113a, 114a, 115a, 116a *Set of 6* (Type II)		45·00	45·00
FS109b/113b, 114b, 115b, 116b *Set of 8* (Type IIIA)		40·00	40·00
First Day Cover (FS109b/112b; 4 designs) (Type IIIA)			9·50
Special Pack (FS109b/112b; 4 designs as two pairs)			
(Type IIIA) (P&G 17)			8·00

Nos. FS109/b and 110/b were each available in two different designs: Type FT **17** and Mistletoe.

Nos. FS111/b through to 116c were each available in two different designs: Butcher's Broom and Holly.

Nos. FS109 through to FS116b have year code MA14.

Defining their intended second class status, Type FT **17** and Mistletoe have repeating background "ROYAL MAIL" wording in blue and a single phosphor band placed at the right-hand side.

Nos. FS113*c*, 114*c* and 116*c* were also each available in two different designs: Butcher's Broom and Holly.

Nos. FS113*c*, 114*c* and 116*c* also have year code MA14.

The Special Pack stamps are FS109b FT **17**, 110b Mistletoe, 111b Butcher's Broom, and 112b Holly.

FS113*c* only came from a single Wincor machine in Keighley during December 2014.

Nos. FS109b/116b came from Royal Mail Series II machines situated at Royal Mail enquiry offices, and the stamps are easily identified by the code being a mixture of letters and numerals.

All Wincor machines, producing Type II stamps, were decommissioned before the 30 March 2015 tariff change.

Type FT **17** and Mistletoe are also each known thermally printed with 1st Class up to 100g, 1st Class Large up to 100g, Euro 20g World 10g, Europe up to 60g, Worldwide up to 20g and Worldwide up to 60g, Type II, having been mistakenly sent to post offices using Wincor machines. Wincor machines did not dispense 2nd Class and 2nd Large.

For Type FT **17** and the Mistletoe design with the blue background text reading "2ndCLASS" in large lettering, alternating with "ROYALMAIL" in small lettering, see Nos. FS191/a and FS192/a.

For Butcher's Broom and Holly with the background text in greenish grey, see Nos. FS193/a and FS198/a.

FT **18** Falcon

FT **20** Dover

(Des Osborne Ross.
Gravure ISP Walsall, thermally printed service indicator)

2015 (18 Feb-30 Mar). *Working Sail.* Self-adhesive. Two phosphor bands.
[MULTI COLOUR] Perf 14×14½

FS117	(1st Class up to 100g) (Type IIA)	3·75	3·75
FS118	(1st Large up to 100g) (Type IIA)	4·25	4·25
FS119	(Euro 20g World 10g) (Type IIA)	4·50	4·50
FS120	(Europe up to 60g) (Type IIA)	7·50	7·50
FS121	(Europe up to 100g) (Type IIA) (30.03.15)	14·00	14·00
FS122	(Worldwide up to 20g) (Type IIA)	5·25	5·25
FS123	(Worldwide up to 60g) (Type IIA)	8·25	8·25
FS124	(Worldwide up to 100g) (Type IIA) (30.03.15)	15·00	15·00
FS117/120, 122, 123 *Set of 6* (Type IIA)		30·00	30·00

First Day Cover (FS117 in 6 designs) (Type IIIA) .... 9·50
Special Pack (FS117 in strip of 6 designs) (Type IIIA)
(P&G 18) .... 8·00

Nos. FS117/124 were each available in six different designs: Type
FT **18**, *Briar, Harry, Margaret, Stag, Nell Morgan.*

FS117/124 have year code MA15.

Nos. FS120 and FS123 were replaced on 30 March 2015 by FS121
and FS124.

Type FT **18**, *Briar, Harry, Margaret, Stag* and *Nell Morgan* are each
known thermally printed with 2nd Class up to 100g and 2nd Large up
to 100g, Type IIA, when put in machine's second class unit. This may
have occurred because the issue was mistakenly put in the wrong
unit, or because standard second class (new blue Machin) FT **14** stock
was temporarily unavailable and it was deemed necessary to use
alternative stock.

FT **19** Lion

(Des Osborne Ross. Illustrations by Chris Wormell,
Gravure ISP Walsall, thermally printed service indicator)

2015 (13 May). *Heraldic Beasts* Self-adhesive. Two phosphor bands. [MULTI COLOUR]
Perf 14×14½

FS125	(1st Class up to 100g) (Type IIA)	3·75	3·75
FS126	(1st Large up to 100g) (Type IIA)	4·25	4·25
FS127	(Euro 20g World 10g) (Type IIA)	4·50	4·50
FS128	(Europe up to 100g) (Type IIA)	5·50	5·50
FS129	(Worldwide up to 20g) (Type IIA)	5·25	5·25
FS130	(Worldwide up to 100g) (Type IIA)	6·75	6·75
FS125/130, *Set of 6* (Type IIA)		27·00	27·00

First Day Cover (FS125 in 6 designs) (Type IIIA) .... 9·50
Special Pack (FS125 in strip of 6 designs) (Type IIIA)
(P&G 19) .... 8·00

Nos. FS125/130 were each available in six different designs: Type
FT **19**, *Unicorn, Yale, Dragon, Falcon* and *Griffin.*

FS125/130 have year code MA15.

Type FT **19**, *Unicorn, Yale, Dragon, Falcon* and *Griffin* are each
known thermally printed with 2nd Class up to 100g and 2nd Large up
to 100g, Type IIA, when put in machine's second class unit. This may
have occurred because the issue was mistakenly put in the wrong
unit, or because standard second class (new blue Machin) FT **14** stock
was temporarily unavailable and it was deemed necessary to use
alternative stock.

(Des Osborne Ross. Illustrations by Andy Tuohy,
Gravure ISP Walsall, thermally printed service indicator)

2015 (16 Sept). *Sea Travel.* Self-adhesive. Two phosphor bands. [MULTI COLOUR]
Perf 14×14½

FS131	(1st Class up to 100g) (Type IIA)	3·75	3·75
FS132	(1st Large up to 100g) (Type IIA)	4·25	4·25
FS133	(Euro 20g World 10g) (Type IIA)	4·50	4·50
FS134	(Europe up to 100g) (Type IIA)	5·50	5·50
FS135	(Worldwide up to 20g) (Type IIA)	5·25	5·25
FS136	(Worldwide up to 100g) (Type IIA)	6·75	6·75
FS131/136, *Set of 6*		27·00	27·00

First Day Cover (FS131 in 6 designs) (Type IIIA) .... 9·50
Special Pack (FS131 in strip of 6 designs) (Type IIIA)
(P&G 20) .... 8·00

Nos. FS131/136 were each available in six different designs: Type
FT **20**, Hong Kong, Sydney, Ha Long Bay, New York City and Venice.

FS131/136 have year code MA15.

FT **21** Common Poppy

(Des Kate Stephens. Illustrations by Julia Trickey.
Gravure ISP Walsall, thermally printed service indicator)

2015 (19 Oct). *Common Poppy* in Type IIIA. Self-adhesive. Two phosphor
bands. [MULTI COLOUR] Perf 14×14½

FS137	(1st Class up to 100g) (Type IIIA)	3·75	3·75
FS138	(1st Large up to 100g) (Type IIIA)	4·25	4·25
FS139	(Euro 20g World 10g) (Type IIIA)	4·50	4·50
FS140	(Europe up to 100g) (Type IIIA)	5·50	5·50
FS141	(Worldwide up to 20g) (Type IIIA)	5·25	5·25
FS142	(Worldwide up to 100g) (Type IIIA)	6·75	6·75
FS137/142 *Set of 6* (Type IIIA)		27·00	27·00

Nos. FS137/142 came from Royal Mail Series II machines situated at
Royal Mail enquiry offices, and the stamps are easily identified by the
code being a mixture of letters and numerals.

In the run-up to Remembrance Sunday 2015 the Common Poppy
design was for the first time offered through Royal Mail enquiry offices
in single-design rolls. The annual tradition of reissuing the Common
Poppy in single-design rolls continues, with short-term availability from
Royal Mail enquiry offices from 24 October 2016 and 14 October 2017.

Nos. FS137/142 only exist with year code MA15.

See also FS103/108b.

FT **22** Mountain Hare

(Des Osborne Ross. Illustrations by Robert Gillmor.
Gravure ISP Walsall, thermally printed service indicator)

2015 (16 Nov). *Winter Fur and Feathers*. Self-adhesive. One phosphor band at right (FS143/a and FS144/a) or two phosphor bands (others). |MULTI COLOUR| Perf 14×14½

FS143	(2nd Class up to 100g) (Type IIA)	2·25	2·25
	a. Type IIIA (16.11.15)	4·00	4·00
FS144	(2nd Large up to 100g) (Type IIA)	3·00	3·00
	a. Type IIIA (16.11.15)	4·25	4·25
FS145	(1st Class up to 100g) (Type IIA)	3·75	3·75
	a. Type IIIA (16.11.15)	4·25	4·25
FS146	(1st Large up to 100g) (Type IIA)	4·25	4·25
	a. Type IIIA (16.11.15)	4·50	4·50
FS147	(Euro 20g World 10g) (Type IIA)	4·50	4·50
	a. Type IIIA (16.11.15)	5·25	5·25
FS148	(Europe up to 100g) (Type IIA)	5·50	5·50
	a. Type IIIA (16.11.15)	6·50	6·50
FS149	(Worldwide up to 20g) (Type IIA)	5·25	5·25
	a. Type IIIA (16.11.15)	6·25	6·25
FS150	(Worldwide up to 100g) (Type IIA)	6·75	6·75
	a. Type IIIA (16.11.15)	7·50	7·50
FS143/150, *Set of 8* (Type IIA)		28·00	28·00
FS143a/150a, *Set of 8* (Type IIIA)		38·00	38·00
First Day Cover (FS143a/146a; 4 designs) (Type IIIA)			8·00
Special Pack (FS143a/146a; 4 designs as two pairs) (Type IIIA) (P&G 21)			7·00

Nos. FS143/a and 144/a were each available in two different designs: Type FT 22 and Redwing.

Nos. FS145/a through to 150/a were each available in two different designs: Red Fox and Squirrel.

Defining their intended second class status, FT **22** and Redwing have repeated background text in blue, reading "2ndCLASS" (large typeface) and "ROYALMAIL" (small typeface) in alternate lines and a single phosphor band placed at the right-hand side.

The Special Pack stamps are FS143a FT **22**, 144a Redwing, 145a Red Fox, and 146a Red Squirrel.

Nos. FS143/a and 144/a have year code CL15S.

Nos. FS145/a through to 150/a have year code MA15.

Nos. FS143a/150a came from Royal Mail machines situated at Royal Mail enquiry offices, and the stamps are easily identified by the code being a mixture of letters and numerals.

FT **22** and Redwing are also both known thermally printed with 1st Class up to 100g, 1st Class Large up to 100g, Euro 20g World 10g, Europe up to 100g, Worldwide up to 20g and Worldwide up to 100g, Type IIA, when mistakenly put in machine's first class unit.

FT **23** Post boy

(Des Howard Brown. Illustrations by Andrew Davidson.
Gravure ISP Walsall, thermally printed service indicator)

2016 (17 Feb). *Royal Mail Heritage: Transport*. Self-adhesive. Two phosphor bands. |MULTI COLOUR| Perf 14×14½

FS151	(1st Class up to 100g) (Type IIA)	3·25	3·25
FS152	(1st Large up to 100g) (Type IIA)	3·50	3·50
FS153	(Euro 20g World 10g) (Type IIA)	3·75	3·75
FS154	(Europe up to 100g) (Type IIA)	4·50	4·50
FS155	(Worldwide up to 20g) (Type IIA)	4·25	4·25
FS156	(Worldwide up to 100g) (Type IIA)	6·25	6·25
FS151/156, *Set of 6* (Type IIA)		23·00	23·00
First Day Cover (FS151 in 6 designs) (Type IIIA)			9·50
Special Pack (FS151 in strip of 6 designs) (Type IIIA) (P&G 22)			8·00

Nos. FS151/156 were each available in six different designs: Type FT **23**; Mail coach, 1790s; Falmouth packet ship, 1820s; Travelling Post Office, 1890s; Airmail, 1930s and Royal Mail Minivan, 1970s.

FS151/156 have year code MA16.

2016 (5 Aug). Type FT **14** with background text reading, alternately, "2ndCLASS" in large lettering and "ROYALMAIL" in small lettering, with year code. New blue background. Self-adhesive. One phosphor band (over the Queen's head). Perf 14×14½.

FS157	(2nd Class up to 100g) (Type IIA)	2·50	2·50
FS158	(2nd Large up to 100g) (Type IIA)	2·75	2·75

FS157/8 have year code CL16S, with the code positioned half-way between the left edge of the stamp and The Queen's nose.

FT **24** Seven-spot Ladybird

(Des Osborne Ross. Illustrations by Chris Wormell,
Gravure ISP Walsall, thermally printed service indicator)

2016 (14 Sept.) *Ladybirds*. Self-adhesive. Two phosphor bands. |MULTI COLOUR| Perf 14×14½

FS159	(1st Class up to 100g) (Type IIA)	2·50	2·50
	a. Type IIIA	4·25	4·25
FS160	(1st Large up to 100g) (Type IIA)	2·75	2·75
	a. Type IIIA	4·50	4·50
FS161	(Euro 20g World 10g) (Type IIA)	3·00	3·00
	a. Type IIIA	4·75	4·75
FS162	(Europe up to 100g) (Type IIA)	3·75	3·75
	a. Type IIIA	5·50	5·50
FS163	(Worldwide up to 20g) (Type IIA)	3·50	3·50
	a. Type IIIA	5·25	5·25
FS164	(Worldwide up to 100g) (Type IIA)	5·75	5·75
	a. Type IIIA	7·50	7·50
FS159/164, *Set of 6* (Type IIA)		20·00	20·00
FS159a/164a, *Set of 6* (Type IIIA)		29·00	29·00
First Day Cover (FS159a in 6 designs) (Type IIIA)			9·50
Special Pack (FS159a in strip of 6 designs) (Type IIIA) (P&G 23)			6·50

Nos. 159/164a were each available in six different designs: Type FT **24**, Fourteen-spot Ladybird, Orange Ladybird, Heather Ladybird, Striped Ladybird and Water Ladybird.

Nos. FS159 through to FS164a hav year code MA16.

Type FT **24**, Fourteen-spot Ladybird, Orange Ladybird, Heather Ladybird, Striped Ladybird and Water Ladybird are each known thermally printed ih 2nd Class up to 100g and 2nd Large up to 100g, Type IIA, when put in machine's second class unit. This may have occurred because the issue was mistakenly put in the wrong unit, or because standard second class (new blue Machin) FT **14** stock was temporarily unavailable and it was deemed necessary to use alternative stock.

Nos. FS159a/164 (Type IIIA) come from Royal Mail Series II machines situated at Royal Mail enquiry offices. These may be identified by the code "M00" at the beginning of the second group of data within the code line at the foot of the stamp. Stamps with codes other than "M00" either come from machines at stamp exhibitions (see tables), or in the case of No. FS173a with code "C00" come from special packs.

FT **25** Hedgehog

(Des Osborne Ross. Illustrations by Chris Wormell,
Gravure ISP Walsall, thermally printed service indicator)

2016 (14 Nov.) *Hibernating Animals*. Self-adhesive. One phosphor band
at right (FS165/a and FS166/a) or two phosphor bands (others).
|MULTI COLOUR| Perf 14×14½

FS165	(2nd Class up to 100g) (Type IIA)	2·50	2·50
	a. Type IIIA	3·00	3·00
FS166	(2nd Large up to 100g) (Type IIA)	2·75	2·75
	a. Type IIIA	3·25	3·25
FS167	(1st Class up to 100g) (Type IIA)	2·75	2·75
	a. Type IIIA	4·25	4·25
FS168	(1st Large up to 100g) (Type IIA)	3·00	3·00
	a. Type IIIA	4·50	4·50
FS169	(Euro 20g World 10g) (Type IIA)	3·25	3·25
	a. Type IIIA	4·75	4·75
FS170	(Europe up to 100g) (Type IIA)	4·50	4·50
	a. Type IIIA	5·50	5·50
FS171	(Worldwide up to 20g) (Type IIA)	4·25	4·25
	a. Type IIIA	5·25	5·25
FS172	(Worldwide up to 100g) (Type IIA)	6·00	6·00
	a. Type IIIA	7·50	7·50
FS165/172, *Set of 8* (Type IIA)		25·00	25·00
FS165a/172a, *Set of 8* (Type IIIA)		32·00	32·00
First Day Cover (FS165a/FS168a in 4 designs) (Type IIIA)			8·00
Special Pack (FS165a/FS168a; 4 designs as two pairs) (Type IIIA) (P&G 24)		6·50	

Nos. FS165/a and 166/a were each available in two different
designs: Type FT **25** or Grass Snake.

Nos. FS167/a through to 172/a were each available in two different
designs: Dormouse or Brown Long-eared Bat.

Defining their intended second class status, FT **25** and Grass Snake
have repeated background text in blue, reading "2ndCLASS" (large
typeface) and "ROYALMAIL" (small typeface) in alternate lines and a
single phosphor band placed at the right-hand side.

The Special Pack stamps are FS165a FT **25**, 166a Grass Snake, 167a
Dormouse, and 168a Long-eared Bat.

Nos. FS165/a and 166/a have year code CL16S.

Nos. FS167/a through to 172/a have year code MA16.

Dormouse and Brown Long-eared Bat are each known thermally
printed with 2nd Class up to 100g and 2nd Large up to 100g, Type
IIA, when put in machine's second class unit. This may have occurred
because they were mistakenly put in the wrong unit, or because Type
FT **25** and Grass Snake or standard second class (new blue Machin) FT
14 stock were not available, and it was deemed necessary to use the
other design instead.

FS165a/172a (Type IIIA) come from Royal Mail Series II machines
situated at Royal Mail enquiry offices. These may be identified by the
code "M00" at the beginning of the second group of data within the
code line at the foot of the stamp.

No. FS165a with code "C00" come from special packs

FT **26** Travelling Post Office: bag exchange

(Des Osborne Ross.
Gravure ISP Walsall, thermally printed service indicator)

2017 (15 Feb.) *Royal Mail Heritage: Mail by Rail*. Self-adhesive. Two
phosphor bands.|MULTI COLOUR| Perf 14×14½

FS173	(1st Class up to 100g) (Type IIA)	2·50	2·50
	a. Type IIIA	4·25	4·25
FS174	(1st Large up to 100g) (Type IIA)	2·75	2·75
	a. Type IIIA	4·50	4·50
FS175	(Euro 20g World 10g) (Type IIA)	3·00	3·00
	a. Type IIIA	4·75	4·75
FS176	(Europe up to 100g) (Type IIA)	3·75	3·75
	a. Type IIIA	5·50	5·50
FS177	(Worldwide up to 20g) (Type IIA)	3·50	3·50
	a. Type IIIA	5·25	5·25
FS178	(Worldwide up to 100g) (Type IIA)	5·75	5·75
	a. Type IIIA	7·50	7·50
FS173/178, *Set of 6* (Type IIA)		20·00	20·00
FS173a/178a, *Set of 6* (Type IIIA)		27·00	27·00
First Day Cover (FS173a in 6 designs) (Type IIIA)			7·50
Special Pack (FS173a in strip of 6 designs) (Type IIIA) (P&G 25)		6·50	

Nos. FS173/178a were each available in six different designs (all
MA17): Type FT **26**; Post Office (London) Railway; Night Mail: poster;
Travelling Post Office: loading; Travelling Post Office: sorting and
Travelling Post Office: on the move.

Nos. FS173/178a have year code MA17.

Nos. FS173a/178a (Type IIIA) come from Royal Mail Series II machines
situated at Royal Mail enquiry offices. These may be identified by the
code "M00" at the beginning of the second group of data within the
code line at the foot of the stamp. Stamps with codes other than "M00"
either come from machines at stamp exhibitions (see tables), or in the
case of No. FS173a with code "C00" come from special packs.

FT **27** Machin Commemorative Head

(Gravure ISP Walsall, thermally printed service indicator)

2017 (5 June) *Machin Anniversary 1967-2017*. Self-adhesive.
Two phosphor bands. |MULTI COLOUR| Perf 14×14½

FS179	(1st Class up to 100g) (Type IIA)	2·30	2·30
	a. Type IIIA	3·30	3·30
FS180	(1st Large up to 100g) (Type IIA)	2·70	2·70
	a. Type IIIA	3·70	3·70
FS181	(Euro 20g World 10g) (Type IIA)	3·00	3·00
	a. Type IIIA	4·00	4·00
FS182	(Europe up to 100g) (Type IIA)	3·50	3·50
	a. Type IIIA	4·50	4·50
FS183	(Worldwide up to 20g) (Type IIA)	3·25	3·25
	a. Type IIIA	4·25	4·25
FS184	(Worldwide up to 100g) (Type IIA)	5·25	5·25
	a. Type IIIA	6·25	6·25
FS179/184, *Set of 6* (Type IIA)		19·00	19·00
FS179a/184a, *Set of 6* (Type IIIA)		23·00	23·00
First Day Cover (FS179a in 6 designs) (Type IIIA)			7.50
Special Pack (FS179a in strip of 6 designs) (Type IIIA) (P&G 26)		6·50	

Nos. FS179/184a were each available in six different colours:
Type FT **27**, light olive, violet, deep sepia, bright emerald and drab.

Nos. FS179/184a do not have a year code as such, but have repeated
background text, reading "MACHIN ANNIVERSARY, 1967 - 2017" (large
typeface) and "ROYALMAIL" (small typeface) in alternate lines.

Type FT **27**, light olive, violet, deep sepia, bright emerald and drab
are each known thermally printed with 2nd Class up to 100g and 2nd
Large up to 100g, Type IIA, when put in machine's second class unit.
This may have occurred because the issue was mistakenly put in the
wrong unit, or because standard second class (new blue Machin) FT **14**
stock was temporarily unavailable and it was deemed necessary to use
alternative stock.

Nos. FS179a/184a (Type IIIA) come from Royal Mail Series II
machines situated at Royal Mail enquiry offices. These may be
identified by the code "M00" at the beginning of the second group of
data within the code line at the foot of the stamp. Stamps with codes
other than "M00" either come from machines at stamp exhibitions (see
tables), or in the case of No. FS179a with code "C00" come from special
packs.

FT **28** First UK Aerial Mail, 1911

Des Osborne Ross. Illustrations by Andrew Davidson.
Gravure ISP Walsall, thermally printed service indicator)

2017 (13 Sept.) *Royal Mail Heritage: Mail by Air.* Self-adhesive. Two
phosphor bands. |MULTI COLOUR Perf 14×14½

FS185	(1st Class up to 100g) (Type IIA)	2·30	2·30
	a. Type IIIA	3.30	3.30
FS186	(1st Large up to 100g) (Type IIA)	2·70	2·70
	a. Type IIIA	3.70	3.70
FS187	(Euro 20g World 10g) (Type IIA)	3·00	3·00
	a. Type IIIA	4.00	4.00
FS188	(Europe up to 100g) (Type IIA)	3·50	3·50
	a. Type IIIA	4.50	4.50
FS189	(Worldwide up to 20g) (Type IIA)	3·25	3·25
	a. Type IIIA	4.25	4.25
FS190	(Worldwide up to 100g) (Type IIA)	5·25	5·25
	a. Type IIIA	6.25	6.25
FS185/190, *Set of 6* (Type IIA)		18.00	18.00
FS185a/190a, *Set of 6* (Type IIIA)		22.00	22.00
First Day Cover (FS185a in 6 designs) (Type IIIA)			7.50
Special Pack (FS185a in strip of 6 designs) (Type IIIA)			
(P&G 27)			6.50

Nos. FS185/190a were each available in six different designs: Type
FT **28**; Military Mail Flight, 1919; International Airmail, 1933; Domestic
Airmail, 1934; Flying Boat Airmail, 1937 and Datapost Service, 1980s.

Nos. FS185/190a have year code R17Y.

Nos. FS185a/190a (Type IIIA) come from Royal Mail Series II
machines situated at Royal Mail enquiry offices. These may be
identified by the code "M00" at the beginning of the second group of
data within the code line at the foot of the stamp. Stamps with codes
other than "M00" either come from machines at stamp exhibitions (see
tables), or in the case of No. FS185a with code "C00" come from special
packs.

(Des Kate Stephens. Illustrations by Julia Trickey.
Gravure ISP Walsall, thermally printed service indicator)

2017 (13 Nov.) British Flora (3rd series). Winter Greenery,
2017 reissue. Type FT **17** with blue background text reading, alternately,
"2ndCLASS" in large lettering and ROYALMAIL in small lettering, with one
phosphor band at right (FS191/a and FS192/a), or greenish grey
repeated 'ROYALMAIL' background, with two phosphor bands
(others). Self-adhesive. |MULTI COLOUR Perf 14×14½.

FS191	(2nd Class up to 100g) (Type IIA)	2.20	2.20
	a. Type IIIA	2.50	2.50
FS192	(2nd Large up to 100g) (Type IIA)	2·40	2·40
	a. Type IIIA	2.70	2.70
FS193	(1st Class up to 100g) (Type IIA)	2·30	2·30
	a. Type IIIA	2.70	2.70
FS194	(1st Large up to 100g) (Type IIA)	2·70	2·70
	a. Type IIIA	3.25	3.25
FS195	(Euro 20g World 10g) (Type IIA)	3.50	3.50
	a. Type IIIA	4.00	4.00
FS196	(Europe up to 100g) (Type IIA)	3·75	3·75
	a. Type IIIA	4.25	4.25
FS197	(Worldwide up to 20g) (Type IIA)	3·50	3·50
	a. Type IIIA	4.25	4.25
FS198	(Worldwide up to 100g) (Type IIA)	5·25	5·25
	a. Type IIIA	5.75	5.75
FS191/198, *Set of 8* (Type IIA)		24.00	24.00
FS191a/198a, *Set of 8* (Type IIIA)		26.00	26.00

Nos. FS191/a and FS192/a were each available in two different
designs: Type FT **17** and Mistletoe.

FS193/a through to FS198a were each available in two different
designs: Butcher's Broom and Holly.

Nos. FS191 through to FS198a are a reissue of the 13 November
2014 designs, but with differences necessitating a separate listing.

For the 2014 issue see FS109 through to FS116c.

Nos. FS191/a and FS192/a may be differentiated from the 2014
issue through their repeated blue background text, reading "2ndCLASS"
(large typeface) and "ROYALMAIL" (small typeface) in alternate lines.

Nos. FS191/a and FS192/a may also be differentiated through the
year code which is CL17S (the 2014 issue has year code MA14).

Nos. FS193 through to FS198a may be differentiated from the 2014
issue through their greenish grey background text (the 2014 issue has
olive-brown background text).

Nos. FS193 through to FS198a may also be differentiated through
the year code which is R17Y (the 2014 issue has year code MA14).

Nos. FS191a/198a (Type IIIA) come from Royal Mail Series II
machines situated at Royal Mail enquiry offices. These may be
identified by the code "M00" at the beginning of the second group of
data within the code line at the foot of the stamp.

FT **29** *The Iron Throne* – Ice

(Design GBH. Illustrations by Rob Ball. Gravure ISP Walsall, thermally printed service indicator)

2018 (23 Jan.) *Game of Thrones*. Self-adhesive. One phosphor band at right (FS199/a and 200/a) or two phosphor bands (others). |MULTI COLOUR Perf 14×14½

FS199	(2nd Class up to 100g) (Type IIA)	2·00	2·00
	a. Type IIIA	2.20	2.20
FS200	(2nd Large up to 100g) (Type IIA)	2·40	2·40
	a. Type IIIA	2.60	2.60
FS201	(1st Class up to 100g) (Type IIA)	2·30	2·30
	a. Type IIIA	2.70	2.70
FS202	(1st Large up to 100g) (Type IIA)	2·70	2·70
	a. Type IIIA	3.00	3.00
FS203	(Euro 20g World 10g) (Type IIA)	3·00	3·00
	a. Type IIIA	3.50	3.50
FS204	(Europe up to 100g) (Type IIA)	3·50	3·50
	a. Type IIIA	4.00	4.00
FS205	(Worldwide up to 20g) (Type IIA)	3·25	3·25
	a. Type IIIA	3.75	3.75
FS206	(Worldwide up to 100g) (Type IIA)	5·25	5·25
	a. Type IIIA	5.75	5.75
FS199/206, *Set* of 8 (Type IIA)		22.00	22.00
FS199a/206a, *Set* of 8 (Type IIIA)		24·00	24·00
First Day Cover (FS199a and FS201a) (Type IIIA)			4.00
Special Pack (FS199a and FS201a) (Type IIIA) (P&G 28)		3.00	

Nos. FS199/a and FS200/a were each available in one blue design: Type FT **29**.

Nos. FS201/a through to FS206/a were each available in one yellow-orange design depicting *The Iron Throne* – Fire.

The Special Pack stamps are FS199a FT **29** and FS201a *The Iron Throne* – Fire.

Defining their intended second class status, FT **29** has repeated background text in blue, reading "2ndCLASS" (large typeface) and 'ROYALMAIL' (small typeface) in alternate lines, and a single phosphor band placed at the right-hand side.

Nos. FS201/a through to FS206/a have repeated background text in yellow-orange with 'ROYALMAIL' in alternate lines of large and small typeface.

Nos. FS199/a and FS200/a have year code CL18S.

Nos. FS201/a through to 206/a have year code R18Y.

Nos. FS199a/206a (Type IIIA) come from Royal Mail Series II machines situated at Royal Mail enquiry offices. These may be identified by the code "M00" at the beginning of the second group of data within the code line at the foot of the stamp.

No. FS199a and 201a with code "C00" come from special packs.

FT **30** Packet *Antelope*, 1780

(Illustrations Andrew Davidson. Gravure ISP Walsall, thermally printed service indicator)

2018 (14 Feb.) *Royal Mail Heritage: Mail by Sea*. Self-adhesive. Two phosphor bands. |MULTI COLOUR Perf 14×14½

FS207	(1st Class up to 100g) (Type IIA)	2·30	2·30
	a. Type IIIA	3.30	3.30
FS208	(1st Large up to 100g) (Type IIA)	2·70	2·70
	a. Type IIIA	3.70	3.70
FS209	(Euro 20g World 10g) (Type IIA)	3·00	3·00
	a. Type IIIA	4.00	4.00
FS210	(Europe up to 100g) (Type IIA)	3·50	3·50
	a. Type IIIA	4.50	4.50
FS211	(Worldwide up to 20g) (Type IIA)	3·25	3·25
	a. Type IIIA	4.25	4.25
FS212	(Worldwide up to 100g) (Type IIA)	5·25	5·25
	a. Type IIIA	6.25	6.25
FS207/212 *Set* of 6 (Type IIA)		18.00	18.00
FS207a/212a *Set* of 6 (Type IIIA)		22·00	22·00
First Day Cover (FS207a in 6 designs) (Type IIIA)			7.50
Special Pack (FS207a in strip of 6 designs) (Type IIIA) (P&G 29)		6.50	

Nos. FS207/212a were each available in six different designs: Type FT 30; SS *Great Western*, 1838; SS *Britannia*, 1887; RMS *Olympic*, 1911; RMS *Queen Mary*, 1936; RMS *St Helena*, 1990.

Nos. FS207a/212a have year code R18Y.

Nos. FS207a/212a come from Royal Mail Series II machines situated at Royal Mail enquiry offices. These may be identified by the code "M00" at the beginning of the second group of data within the code line at the foot of the stamp.

No. FS207a with code "C00" come from special packs.

Post & Go tables. The tables on the next few pages list Post & Go stamps with inscriptions from the following primary locations: UK and international stamp exhibitions, the UK's national Postal Museum (formerly The BPMA, and since 1 February 2016, The Postal Museum), Royal Mail Enquiry Offices and the Armed Forces' museums which have (or had) Post & Go machines. Inscriptions from other (secondary) locations are not within the scope of these tables. The final table lists Post & Go stamps from exhibitions and stamp fairs which were generated without inscriptions.

The tables have been compiled from information available at time of going to press. Note that the lists of dates of availability/duration are not exhaustive and are merely intended as a guide to the availability of the inscriptions. However, if you have additional relevant information (or spot any mistakes) please do get in touch in the usual way. The tables are intended to be a simplified record and do not attempt to list Post & Go stamps from the specified locations with errors, as such items are beyond the scope of this particular listing. Note that some of the catalogue numbers shown are provisional and may be subject to change. 2018 is the first year that these tables have included prices. The prices shown are provided for the information of collectors and indicate what one might expect to pay for the said items in the retail market place. They are for collectors' strips. (These tables are copyright John M Deering are reproduced   in catalogue style with his permission for the convenience of collectors.)

Post & Go stamps – the different exhibition issues with inscriptions to May 2018: a simplified checklist

Post and Go stamps – the inscriptions from UK and international stamp exhibitions, September 2011–May 2018:
A simplified checklist of the Machin, Union Flag and Common Poppy issues

Inscription	Year code	Name/location of dispensing machine Date/duration/details of inscription (dates are inclusive)	Cat. No. of stamp issue without inscription, or closest match	Price
Machin, 1st/1stL/E-20g/WW-10g/WW-20g/WW-40g:				
Arnold Machin 1911–1999	None	Autumn Stampex 2011 14–17 September 2011	FS1a/3a, 4a, 5a & 5e (Type II)	17.00
Diamond Jubilee 1952–2012	None	Spring Stampex 2012 22–25 February 2012	FS1a/3a, 4a, 5a & 5e (Type II)	15.00
Perth 2012 19–22 October	None	The National Philatelic Exhibition, Perth, Scotland Note: Only available to non-delegates on 19–20 October 2012	FS1b/3b, 4b, 5b & 5eb (Type III)	40.00
The Coronation 60th Anniversary (both lines ranged left)	None	Spring Stampex 2013 20–23 February 2013	FS1b/3b, 4b, 5b & 5eb (Type III)	15.00
– as above but with first line slightly inset	None	Spring Stampex 2013 20–23 February 2013 Note: Only available from stock produced in advance for sale at Royal Mail exhibition stand	FS1b/3b, 4b, 5b & 5eb (Type III)	20.00
84th Scottish Congress 2013	None	The Annual Congress of Scottish Philatelic Societies, Perth, Scotland 19–20 April 2013	FS1b/3b, 4b, 5b & 5eb (Type III)	20.00
Australia 2013 World Stamp Expo GB version (with the word 'World' included, only available from stock produced in advance of the exhibition, and specifically for sale in the UK from Royal Mail via Tallents House)	None	Australia International Stamp Exhibition, Melbourne, Australia 10–15 May 2013	FS1b/3b, 4b, 5b & 5eb (Type III)	18.00
Australia 2013 Stamp Expo AU version (without the word 'World', only available from machines at the exhibition: 'World' omitted unintentionally	None	Australia International Stamp Exhibition, Melbourne, Australia 10–15 May 2013	FS1b/3b, 4b, 5b & 5eb (Type III)	28.00
Stampex 2014 19–22 February	None	Spring Stampex 2014 19–22 February 2014	FS1b/3b, 4b, 5b & 5eb (Type III)	23.00
	MA13	Note: Sometimes when the machine was re-filled, stock bearing MA13 was used	FS77/79, 81/83 (but Type III)	25.00
Machin, 1st/1stL/E-20g/E-60g/WW-20g/WW-60g:				
85th Scottish Congress 2014	None	The Annual Congress of Scottish Philatelic Societies, Perth, Scotland 11–12 April 2014	FS1b/3b, 3d, 5b, 5f (but Type III)	30.00
	MA13	Note: Sometimes when the machine was re-filled, stock bearing MA13 was used	FS77/80, 82 & 84 (but Type III)	28.00
Machin, 1st/1stL/E-20g WW-10g/E-60g/WW-20g/WW-60g:				
Philakorea 2014 World Stamp Expo	None	Philakorea World Stamp Exhibition, Seoul, Korea 7–12 August 2014	FS1d, 2d, 3cb, 3d, 5d & 5f (Type IIIA)	18.00
	MA13	Note: • Stock for sale in the UK from Royal Mail via Tallents House was produced in advance of the exhibition • Stocks without a year code and with an MA13 were used in machines both in the UK and at the exhibition	FS77b, 78b, 79bb, 80, 82b & 84 (Type IIIA)	20.00

Post and Go stamps – the inscriptions from UK and international stamp exhibitions, September 2011–May 2018:
A simplified checklist of the Machin, Union Flag and Common Poppy issues

Inscription	Year code	Name/location of dispensing machine Date/duration/details of inscription (dates are inclusive)	Cat. No. of stamp issue without inscription, or closest match	Price
Machin, 1st/1stL/E-20g WW-10g/E-100g/WW-20g/WW-100g:				
86th Scottish Congress 2015 (i.e. with '2015' after the word Congress. Only stock produced from machines at the exhibition has '2015')	MA13	The Annual Congress of Scottish Philatelic Societies, Perth, Scotland 17–18 April 2015	FS77b, 78b, 79bb, 80ca, 82b & 84ca (Type IIIA)	23.00
	None	Note: Sometimes when the machine was re-filled, stock that did not have a year code was used	FS1d, 2d, 3cb, 3ea, 5d & 5ga (Type IIIA)	25.00
86th Scottish Congress (i.e. without '2015' after the word Congress. Only stock produced in advance of the exhibition is without '2015')	MA13	The Annual Congress of Scottish Philatelic Societies, Perth, Scotland 17–18 April 2015	FS77b, 78b, 79bb, 80ca, 82b & 84ca (Type IIIA)	40.00
	None	Note: From stock produced in advance of the exhibition only a small part did not have a year code	FS1d, 2d, 3cb, 3ea, 5d & 5ga (Type IIIA)	80.00
Europhilex London Penny Black 175	MA13	Europhilex Stamp Exhibition, London 2015 13–16 May 2015	FS77b, 78b, 79bb, 80ca, 82b & 84ca (Type IIIA)	15.00
	None	Note: Sometimes when the machine was re-filled, stock that did not have a year code was used	FS1d, 2d, 3cb, 3ea, 5d & 5ga (Type IIIA)	19.00
Singpex 2015 World Stamp Expo	MA13	Singpex World Stamp Exhibition, Singapore 14–19 August 2015 Note: Stock for sale in the UK from Royal Mail via Tallents House was produced in advance of the exhibition; only stock with MA13 was used at the exhibition	FS77b, 78b, 79bb, 80ca, 82b & 84ca (Type IIIA)	19.00
	None	Note: Sometimes when the machine at Tallents House was re-filled, stock that did not have a year code was used	FS1d, 2d, 3cb, 3ea, 5d & 5ga (Type IIIA)	18.00
Queen Elizabeth II Longest Reign	None	Autumn Stampex 2015 16–19 September 2015	FS1d, 2d, 3cb, 3ea, 5d & 5ga (Type IIIA)	15.00
	MA13	Note: Stock bearing MA13 was only available for a very short period, apparently from one roll only	FS77b, 78b, 79bb, 80ca, 82b & 84ca (Type IIIA)	30.00
500 Years of Royal Mail	None	Spring Stampex 2016 17–20 February 2016	FS1d, 2d, 3cb, 3ea, 5d & 5ga (Type IIIA)	15.00
	MA13	Note: Sometimes when the machine was re-filled, stock bearing MA13 was used	FS77b, 78b, 79bb, 80ca, 82b & 84ca (Type IIIA)	22.00
87th Scottish Congress 2016 ('Dual' value correctly shown as 'Euro 20g World 10g'. Only available from machines at the exhibition)	MA13	The Annual Congress of Scottish Philatelic Societies, Perth, Scotland 15–16 April 2016 Note: MA13 is only known from stock used at the exhibition	FS77b, 78b, 79bb, 80ca, 82b & 84ca (Type IIIA)	23.00
87th Scottish Congress 2016 ('Dual' value without 20g weight, and instead shown as 'Euro World 10g'. Only available from stock produced in advance of the exhibition)	None	The Annual Congress of Scottish Philatelic Societies, Perth, Scotland 15–16 April 2016 Note: Stock without a year code is only known without the 20g weight and is from the material produced in advance of the exhibition	FS1d, 2d, 3cb, 3ea, 5d & 5ga (Type IIIA)	60.00
65th Anniversary of HM The Queen's Accession	MA14	Spring Stampex 2017 15–18 February 2017	FS77b, 78b, 79bb, 80ca, 82b & 84ca (Type IIIA)	16.00
	MA13	Note: MA13 is only known from a very small part of the stock produced in advance of the exhibition	FS77b, 78b, 79bb, 80ca, 82b & 84ca (Type IIIA)	40.00
Machin Anniversary 1967–2017	MA14	Spring Stampex 2017 15–18 February 2017	FS77b, 78b, 79bb, 80ca, 82b & 84ca (Type IIIA)	16.00
	None	Note: Stock without a year code was only available for a very short period, apparently from one roll only	FS1d, 2d, 3cb, 3ea, 5d & 5ga (Type IIIA)	42.00
88th Scottish Congress (i.e. without '2017' after the word Congress. Only stock produced from machines at the exhibition is without '2017')	MA15	The Annual Congress of Scottish Philatelic Societies, Perth, Scotland 21–22 April 2017	FS77b, 78b, 79bb, 80ca, 82b & 84ca (Type IIIA)	35.00
	None	Note: Sometimes when the machine was re-filled, stock that did not have a year code was used	FS1d, 2d, 3cb, 3ea, 5d & 5ga (Type IIIA)	35.00
	MA13	Note: MA13 is only known from a very small part of the stock produced during the exhibition	FS77b, 78b, 79bb, 80ca, 82b & 84ca (Type IIIA)	—

Post and Go stamps – the inscriptions from UK and international stamp exhibitions, September 2011–May 2018:
A simplified checklist of the Machin, Union Flag and Common Poppy issues

Inscription	Year code	Name/location of dispensing machine Date/duration/details of inscription (dates are inclusive)	Cat. No. of stamp issue without inscription, or closest match	Price
50th Anniversary Machin design in six different colours, 1st/1stL/E-20g WW-10g/E-100g/WW-20g/WW-100g:				
88th Scottish Congress 2017 (i.e. with '2017' after the word Congress. Only stock produced in advance of the exhibition has '2017')	N/A	The Annual Congress of Scottish Philatelic Societies, Perth, Scotland 21–22 April 2017 Note: The standard Machin design was not used for stock produced in advance of the exhibition; instead, the 50th Anniversary Machin design, not for issue until 5 June, was used by mistake. The Anniversary design was not available at the exhibition	FS179a/184a (Type IIIA)	95.00
50th Anniversary Machin design, 1st x 6 different colours:				
Autumn Stampex 2017	N/A	Autumn Stampex 2017 13–16 September 2017	F5179a/184a (Type IIIA)	9.00
Union Flag, 1st/1stL/E-20g/WW-10g/WW-20g/WW-40g:				
Diamond Jubilee 1952–2012	None	Autumn Stampex 2012 26–29 September 2012	FS39/44 (but Type III)	15.00
Perth 2012 19–22 October	None	The National Philatelic Exhibition, Perth, Scotland Note: Only available to non-delegates on 19–20 October 2012	FS39/44 (but Type III)	45.00
84th Scottish Congress 2013	None	The Annual Congress of Scottish Philatelic Societies, Perth, Scotland 19–20 April 2013	FS39/44 (but Type III)	20.00
Australia 2013 World Stamp Expo GB version (with the word 'World' included, only available from stock produced in advance of the exhibition, and specifically for sale in the UK from Royal Mail via Tallents House)	None	Australia International Stamp Exhibition, Melbourne, Australia 10–15 May 2013	FS39/44 (but Type III)	18.00
Australia 2013 Stamp Expo AU version (without the word 'World', only available from machines at the exhibition; 'World' omitted unintentionally)	None	Australia International Stamp Exhibition, Melbourne, Australia 10–15 May 2013	FS39/44 (but Type III)	28.00
The Coronation 60th Anniversary	MA13	Autumn Stampex 2013 18–21 September 2013	FS85/7 & 89/91 (but Type III)	15.00
Union Flag, 1st/1stL/E-20g/E-60g/WW-20g/WW-60g:				
85th Scottish Congress 2014	MA13	The Annual Congress of Scottish Philatelic Societies, Perth, Scotland 11–12 April 2014	FS85/8, 90 & 92 (but Type III)	30.00
	None	Note: Sometimes when the machine was re-filled, stock that did not have a year code was used	FS39/41, 41b, 43 & 44b (but Type III)	27.00
Union Flag, 1st/1stL/E-20g WW-10g/E-60g/WW-20g/WW-60g:				
Philakorea 2014 World Stamp Expo	None	Philakorea World Stamp Exhibition, Seoul, Korea 7–12 August 2014 Note: Stock for sale in the UK from Royal Mail via Tallents House was produced in advance of the exhibition	FS39, 40, 41a, 41b, 43 & 44b (but Type IIIA)	18.00
	MA13	Note: MA13 is only known from a very small part of the stock produced in advance of the exhibition)	FS85/6, 87a, 88, 90 & 92 (but Type IIIA)	125.00
Spring Stampex February 2015	None	Spring Stampex 2015 18–21 February 2015	FS39, 40, 41a, 41b, 43 & 44b (but Type IIIA)	15.00

Post and Go stamps – the inscriptions from UK and international stamp exhibitions, September 2011–May 2018:
A simplified checklist of the Machin, Union Flag and Common Poppy issues

Inscription	Year code	Name/location of dispensing machine Date/duration/details of inscription (dates are inclusive)	Cat. No. of stamp issue without inscription, or closest match	Price
Union Flag, 1st/1stL/E-20g WW-10g/E-100g/WW-20g/WW-100g:				
86th Scottish Congress 2015 (i.e. with '2015' after the word Congress. Only stock produced from machines at the exhibition has '2015')	None	The Annual Congress of Scottish Philatelic Societies, Perth, Scotland 17–18 April 2015	FS39, 40, 41*a*, 41*c*, 43 & 44*c* (but Type IIIA)	20.00
86th Scottish Congress (i.e. without '2015' after the word Congress. Only stock produced in advance of the exhibition is without '2015')	None	The Annual Congress of Scottish Philatelic Societies, Perth, Scotland 17–18 April 2015	FS39, 40, 41*a*, 41*c*, 43 & 44*c* (but Type IIIA)	40.00
Singpex 2015 World Stamp Expo	None	Singpex World Stamp Exhibition, Singapore 14–19 August 2015 Note: Stock for sale in the UK from Royal Mail via Tallents House was produced in advance of the exhibition	FS39, 40, 41*a*, 41*c*, 43 & 44*c* (but Type IIIA)	17.00
Hong Kong November 2015	None	Hong Kong World Stamp Exhibition 20–23 November 2015 Note: Stock for sale in the UK from Royal Mail via Tallents House was produced in advance of the exhibition	FS39, 40, 41*a*, 41*c*, 43 & 44*c* (but Type IIIA)	16.00
87th Scottish Congress 2016 ('Dual' value correctly shown as 'Euro 20g World 10g'. Only available from machines at the exhibition)	None	The Annual Congress of Scottish Philatelic Societies, Perth, Scotland 15–16 April 2016	FS39, 40, 41*a*, 41*c*, 43 & 44*c* (but Type IIIA)	20.00
87th Scottish Congress 2016 ('Dual' value without 20g weight, and instead shown as 'Euro World 10g'. Only available from stock produced in advance of the exhibition)	None	The Annual Congress of Scottish Philatelic Societies, Perth, Scotland 15–16 April 2016	FS39, 40, 41*a*, 41*c*, 43 & 44*c* (but Type IIIA)	40.00
World Stamp Show NY2016	None	New York World Stamp Exhibition 28 May–4 June 2016 Note: Stock for sale in the UK from Royal Mail via Tallents House was produced in advance of the exhibition	FS39, 40, 41*a*, 41*c*, 43 & 44*c* (but Type IIIA)	15.00
Poppy, 1st/1stL/E-20g WW-10g/E-60g/WW-20g/WW-60g:				
First World War Centenary	MA14	Autumn Stampex 2014 17–20 September 2014	FS103, 104, 105, 106, 107 & 108 (but Type IIIA)	18.00
Poppy, 1st/1stL/E-20g WW-10g/E-100g/WW-20g/WW-100g:				
The Battle of the Somme + tank logo	MA15	Autumn Stampex 2016 14–17 September 2016	FS137/142 (Type IIIA)	19.00
WWI Battle of Passchendaele	MA15	Autumn Stampex 2017 13–16 September 2017	FS137/142 (Type IIIA)	16.00
Hong Kong Sea Travel, 1st/1stL/E-20g WW-10g/E-100g/WW-20g/WW-100g:				
Hong Kong November 2015	MA15	Hong Kong World Stamp Exhibition 20–23 November 2015 Note: Stock for sale in the UK from Royal Mail via Tallents House was produced in advance of the exhibition	FS131/136 (but Type IIIA & digitally printed)	16.00
New York Sea Travel, 1st/1stL/E-20g WW-10g/E-100g/WW-20g/WW-100g:				
World Stamp Show NY2016	MA15	New York World Stamp Exhibition 28 May–4 June 2016 Note: Stock for sale in the UK from Royal Mail via Tallents House was produced in advance of the exhibition	FS131/136 (but Type IIIA & digitally printed)	15.00

Post and Go stamps – the inscriptions from UK and international stamp exhibitions, September 2011–May 2018:
A simplified checklist of the Machin, Union Flag and Common Poppy issues

Inscription	Year code	Name/location of dispensing machine Date/duration/details of inscription (dates are inclusive)	Cat. No. of stamp issue without inscription, or closest match	Price
Lion (Heraldic Beast), 1st/1stL/E-20g WW-10g/E-100g/WW-20g/WW-100g:				
87th Scottish Congress 2016 ('Dual' value correctly shown as 'Euro 20g World 10g'. Only available from machines at the exhibition)	MA15	The Annual Congress of Scottish Philatelic Societies, Perth, Scotland 5–16 April 2016	FS125/130 (but Type IIIA)	20.00
87th Scottish Congress 2016 ('Dual' value without 20g weight, and instead shown as 'Euro World 10g'. Only available from stock produced in advance of the exhibition)	MA15	The Annual Congress of Scottish Philatelic Societies, Perth, Scotland 5–16 April 2016	FS125/130 (but Type IIIA)	36.00
88th Scottish Congress 2017 (i.e. with '2017' after the word Congress. Only stock produced in advance of the exhibition has '2017')	MA15	The Annual Congress of Scottish Philatelic Societies, Perth, Scotland 21–22 April 2017	FS125/130 (but Type IIIA)	50.00
88th Scottish Congress (i.e. without '2017' after the word Congress. Only stock produced from machines at the exhibition is without '2017')	MA15	The Annual Congress of Scottish Philatelic Societies, Perth, Scotland 21–22 April 2017	FS125/130 (but Type IIIA)	—
Thistle (Symbolic Flower), 1st/1stL/E-20g WW-10g/E-100g/WW-20g/WW-100g:				
88th Scottish Congress 2017 (i.e. with '2017' after the word Congress. Only stock produced in advance of the exhibition has '2017')	MA17	The Annual Congress of Scottish Philatelic Societies, Perth, Scotland 21–22 April 2017	FS103, 104, 105, 106b, 107, 108b (but Type IIIA & digitally printed)	50.00
88th Scottish Congress (i.e. without '2017' after the word Congress. Only stock produced from machines at the exhibition is without '2017')	MA17	The Annual Congress of Scottish Philatelic Societies, Perth, Scotland 21–22 April 2017	FS103, 104, 105, 106b, 107, 108b (but Type IIIA & digitally printed)	—

Post & Go stamps – the different issues and inscriptions from 'The Postal Museum' (formerly 'The BPMA'), to May 2018: a simplified checklist

Post and Go stamps – the inscriptions from The Postal Museum (formerly 'The BPMA'), December 2012–May 2018: A simplified checklist of the Machin, Union Flag and pictorial issues

Inscription	Year code	Name/location of dispensing machine Date/duration/details of inscription (dates are inclusive)	Cat. No. of stamp issue without inscription, or closest match	Price
Machin, 1st/1stL/E-20g/WW-10g/WW-20g/WW-40g:				
The B.P.M.A. (low set; inscription is immediately above code line)	None	3 December 2012–18 February 2014	FS1b/3b, 4b, 5b & 5eb (Type III)	17.00
The B.P.M.A. Postage Due 1914	None	19 February–29 March 2014	FS1b/3b, 4b, 5b & 5eb (Type III)	23.00
	MA13	Note: Sometimes the machine was refilled with stock bearing MA13. An RMS II machine has been used since 24 March 2014, and the stamps from it have a subtly different typeface. Between 24–29 March 2014 only stamps bearing MA13 were dispensed.	FS77/79, 81/83 (but Type III)	30.00
Machin, 1st/1stL/E-20g/E-60g/WW-20g/WW-60g:				
The B.P.M.A. Postage Due 1914	MA13	31 March–25 April 2014	FS77/80, 82 & 84 (but Type III)	25.00
Machin, 1st/1stL/E-20g WW-10g/E-60g/WW-20g/WW-60g:				
The B.P.M.A. (high set; inscription is immediately below service indicator)	MA13	28 April–19 August 2014 Note: E-20g WW-10g in large typeface.	FS77, 78, 79b, 80, 82 & 84 (but Type III)	30.00
The B.P.M.A. Inland Airmail 1934 (+ Airmail logo)	None	20 August–20 October 2014	FS1d, 2d, 3cb, 3*d*, 5d & 5*f* (Type IIIA)	23.00
	MA13	Note: Sometimes the machine was refilled with stock bearing MA13.	FS77b, 78b, 79bb, 80, 82b & 84 (Type IIIA)	20.00
The B.P.M.A. (low set; inscription is immediately above code line)	None	21 October 2014–17 Februray 2015 Note: All six values have a revised (smaller) typeface.	FS1d, 2d, 3cb, 3*d*, 5d & 5*f* (Type IIIA)	23.00
The B.P.M.A. Trollope 200 (+ Postbox logo)	MA13	18 February–28 March 2015	FS77b, 78b, 79bb, 80, 82b & 84 (Type IIIA)	19.00
Machin, 1st/1stL/E-20g WW-10g/E-100g/WW-20g/WW-100g:				
The B.P.M.A. Trollope 200 (+ Postbox logo)	MA13	30 March–30 April 2015	FS77b, 78b, 79bb, 80ca, 82b & 84ca (Type IIIA)	30.00
The B.P.M.A. (low set; inscription is immediately above code line)	MA13	1–5 May 2015 8 August 2015–29 January 2016 Note: All six values have a revised (smaller) typeface.	FS77b, 78b, 79bb, 80ca, 82b & 84ca (Type IIIA)	22.00
The B.P.M.A. Penny Black 175 (+ Maltese Cross logo)	MA13	6 May–7 August 2015	FS77b, 78b, 79bb, 80ca, 82b & 84ca (Type IIIA)	18.00
The Postal Museum Note: Positioned before the wording is a small format version of the museum's envelope logo	MA13	1 February–13 September 2016 14 November 2016–2 June 2017 Note: Initially the 'envelope' logo was inset at the left, but from 15 February 2016, it was re-positioned so as to be ranged left	FS77b, 78b, 79bb, 80ca, 82b & 84ca (Type IIIA)	19.00
	MA15	Note: From 14 November 2016 the machine mostly dispensed stock bearing MA15	FS77b, 78b, 79bb, 80ca, 82b & 84ca (Type IIIA)	19.00
The Postal Museum King Edward VIII 1936 (+ ERI VIII Cypher) Note: Positioned before the wording is a small format version of the museum's envelope logo	None	14 September–11 November 2016	FS1d, 2d, 3cb, 3ea, 5d & 5ga	19.00
	MA15	Note: From early November and until 11 November 2016, the machine dispensed stock bearing MA15	FS77b, 78b, 79bb, 80ca, 82b & 84ca (Type IIIA)	23.00
50th Anniversary Machin design, 1st x 6 different colours:				
The Postal Museum Note: Positioned before the wording is a small format version of the museum's envelope logo	N/A	5 June–12 July 2017	FS179a/184a (Type IIIA)	9.00
The Postal Museum Official Opening 2017	N/A	25 July 2017 28 July–12 September 2017	FS179a/184a (Type IIIA)	9.50
The Postal Museum	N/A	13 September–23 October 2017 2–22 January 2018 From 14 February 2018	FS179a/184a (Type IIIA)	8.50

Post and Go stamps – the inscriptions from The Postal Museum (formerly 'The BPMA'), December 2012–May 2018: A simplified checklist of the Machin, Union Flag and pictorial issues

Inscription	Year code	Name/location of dispensing machine Date/duration/details of inscription (dates are inclusive)	Cat. No. of stamp issue without inscription, or closest match	Price
Machin, 2nd/2ndL:				
The B.P.M.A. Inland Airmail 1934 (+ Airmail logo)	MA12	20 August–20 October 2014	FS93b/94b (Type IIIA)	10.00
Note: On 16 September 2014, due to software glitch, some (blue-coloured FT **14**) second class stock was printed 1st/1stL.	MA12	16 September 2014	FT 14 in 1st/1stL (Type IIIA)	50.00
The B.P.M.A. (low set; inscription is immediately above code line)	MA12	21 October–12 November 2014 29 December 2014–17 February 2015 1–5 May 2015 8 August–13 November 2015 4–29 January 2016	FS93b/94b (Type IIIA)	6.50
The B.P.M.A. Trollope 200 (+ Postbox logo)	MA12	18 February–30 April 2015	FS93b/94b (Type IIIA)	6.50
The B.P.M.A. Penny Black 175 (+ Maltese Cross logo)	MA13	6 May–7 August 2015	FS93b/94b (Type IIIA)	6.50
	MA12	Note: During August the machine was re-filled with stock bearing MA12. All examples with MA12 have their year code obscured owing to the Maltese Cross being set slightly lower and to the right, the result of a software upgrade.	FS93b/94b (Type IIIA)	13.00
The Postal Museum Note: Positioned before the wording is a small format version of the museum's envelope logo	MA12	1 February–13 September 2016 3 January–4 June 2017 Note: Initially the 'envelope' logo was inset at the left, but from 15 February 2017 it was re-positioned so as to be ranged left	FS93b/94b (Type IIIA)	5.50
	CL16	Note: From 25 January 2017 the machine dispensed stock bearing CL16	FS157/8 (but Type IIIA)	5.50
The Postal Museum King Edward VIII 1936 (+ ERI VIII Cypher) Note: Positioned before the wording is a small format version of the museum's envelope logo	MA12	14 September–11 November 2016	FS93b/94b (Type IIIA)	5.50
The Postal Museum Official Opening 2017	CL16	25 July 2017 28 July–12 September 2017	FS157/158 (Type IIIA)	6.00
	MA15		FS93b/94b (Type IIIA)	6.00
The Postal Museum	MA15	From 13 September 2017	FS93b/94b (Type IIIA)	6.00
Union Flag, 1st/1stL/E-20g/WW-10g/WW-20g/WW-40g:				
The B.P.M.A. (low set; inscription is immediately above code line)	None	21 February–4 November 2013 30 December 2013–18 February 2014	FS39/44 (but Type III)	17.00
The B.P.M.A. Postage Due 1914	None	19 February–29 March 2014	FS39/44 (but Type III)	23.00
	MA13	Note: Between 19–21 February 2014 the machine dispensed stock bearing MA13. An RMS II machine has been used since 24 March 2014, and the stamps from it have a subtly different typeface. Only stamps without a year code were dispensed between 24–29 March 2014.	FS85/7 & 89/91 (but Type III)	55.00
Union Flag, 1st/1stL/E-20g/E-60g/WW-20g/WW-60g:				
The B.P.M.A. Postage Due 1914	None	31 March–25 April 2014	FS39/41, 41b, 43 & 44b (but Type III)	20.00
Union Flag, 1st/1stL/E-20g WW-10g/E-60g/WW-20g/WW-60g:				
The B.P.M.A. (high set; inscription is immediately below service indicator)	None	28 April–19 August 2014 Note: E-20g WW-10g in large typeface.	FS39, 40, 41a, 41b, 43 & 44b (but Type III)	25.00
The B.P.M.A. (low set; inscription is immediately above code line)	None	21 October 2014–17 February 2015 Note: All six values have a revised (smaller) typeface.	FS39, 40, 41a, 41b, 43 & 44b (but Type IIIA)	25.00
The B.P.M.A. (high set; inscription is immediately below service indicator)	None	18 February–28 March 2015 Note: All six values have a revised (smaller) typeface.	FS39, 40, 41a, 41b, 43 & 44b (but Type IIIA)	45.00

Post and Go stamps – the inscriptions from The Postal Museum (formerly 'The BPMA'), December 2012–May 2018:
A simplified checklist of the Machin, Union Flag and pictorial issues

Inscription	Year code	Name/location of dispensing machine Date/duration/details of inscription (dates are inclusive)	Cat. No. of stamp issue without inscription, or closest match	Price
Union Flag, 1st/1stL/E-20g WW-10g/E-100g/WW-20g/WW-100g:				
The B.P.M.A. (low set; inscription is immediately above code line)	None	30 March 2015–29 January 2016 Note: All six values have a revised (smaller) typeface.	FS39, 40, 41a, 41c, 43 & 44c (but Type IIIA)	25.00
The Postal Museum Note: Positioned before the wording is a large format version of the museum's envelope logo	None	From 1 February 2016	FS39, 40, 41a, 41c, 43 & 44c (but Type IIIA)	19.00
The Postal Museum Official Opening 2017	None	25 July 2017 28 July–12 September 2017	FS39, 40, 41a, 41c, 43 & 44c (but Type IIIA)	19.00
Robin, 1st/1stL/E-20g/WW-10g/WW-20g/WW-40g:				
The B.P.M.A.	MA12	3 December 2012–20 February 2013	FS51a/56a (Type III)	20.00
	MA13	5 November–24 December 2013	FS51a/56a (Type III)	18.00
Poppy, 1st/1stL/E-20g WW-10g/E-60g/WW-20g/WW-60g:				
The B.P.M.A.	MA14	21 October–12 November 2014	FS103, 104, 105, 106, 107 & 108 (but Type IIIA)	20.00
Poppy, 1st/1stL/E-20g WW-10g/E-100g/WW-20g/WW-100g:				
The B.P.M.A.	MA15	19 October–13 November 2015	FS137/142 (Type IIIA)	20.00
The Postal Museum Note: Positioned before the wording is a large format version of the museum's envelope logo	MA15	24 October–11 November 2016	FS137/142 (Type IIIA)	20.00
The Postal Museum	MA15	24 October–10 November 2017	FS137/142 (Type IIIA)	19.00
Winter Greenery, 2nd/2ndL, and 1st/1stL/E-20g WW-10g/E-60g/WW-20g/WW-60g:				
The B.P.M.A. (low set; inscription is immediately above code line)	MA14	13 November–23 December 2014	FS109b/116b (Type IIIA) Set of 16	44.00
Lion (Heraldic Beast), 1st/1stL/E-20g WW-10g/E-100g/WW-20g/WW-100g:				
The B.P.M.A. (low set; inscription is immediately above code line)	MA15	16 September–16 October 2015 4–29 January 2016	FS125/130 (but Type IIIA)	20.00
The Postal Museum Note: Positioned before the wording is a large format version of the museum's envelope logo	MA15	1–16 February 2016	FS125/130 (but Type IIIA)	19.00
Fur & Feathers, 2nd/2ndL, and 1st/1stL/E-20g WW-10g/E-100g/WW-20g/WW-100g:				
The B.P.M.A. (low set; inscription is immediately above code line)	CL15/ MA15	16 November–31 December 2015	FS143a/150a (Type IIIA) Set of 16 Set of 16	44.00
Royal Mail Heritage: Transport, 1st × 6 designs:				
The Postal Museum Note: Positioned before the wording is a large format version of the museum's envelope logo	MA16	17 February–31 March 2016	FS151×6 (but Type IIIA)	9.00
Royal Mail Heritage: Mail Coach design, 1st/1stL/E-20g WW-10g/E-100g/WW-20g/WW-100g:				
The Postal Museum Note: Positioned before the wording is a large format version of the museum's envelope logo	MA16	1 April 2016–12 July 2017	FS151/156 (but Type IIIA & digitally printed)	19.00
The Postal Museum Official Opening 2017	MA16	25 July, and 28 July–12 September 2017	FS151/156 (but Type IIIA & digitally printed)	19.00
The Postal Museum	MA16	From 13 September 2017	FS151/156 (but Type IIIA & digitally printed)	19.00
Hibernating Animals, 2nd/2ndL, and 1st/1stL/E-20g WW-10g/E-100g/WW-20g/WW-100g:				
The Postal Museum Note: Positioned before the wording is a large format version of the museum's envelope logo	CL16 / MA16	14 November–30 December 2016	FS165a/172a (Type IIIA) Set of 16:	44.00

**Post and Go stamps – the inscriptions from The Postal Museum (formerly 'The BPMA'), December 2012–May 2018:
A simplified checklist of the Machin, Union Flag and pictorial issues**

Inscription	Year code	Name/location of dispensing machine Date/duration/details of inscription (dates are inclusive)	Cat. No. of stamp issue without inscription, or closest match	Price
Royal Mail Heritage: Mail by Rail, 1st × 6 designs:				
The Postal Museum Note: Positioned before the wording is a large format version of the museum's envelope logo	MA17	15 February–31 March 2017	FS173a x6 (Type IIIA)	8.75
Royal Mail Heritage: Post Office (London) Railway design, 1st/1stL/E-20g WW-10g/E-100g/WW-20g/WW-100g:				
The Postal Museum Note: Positioned before the wording is a large format version of the museum's envelope logo	MA17	From 3 April–12 July 2017	FS173a/178a (Type IIIA but digitally printed)	19.00
The Postal Museum Official Opening 2017	MA17	25 July, and 28 July–12 September 2017	FS173a/178a (Type IIIA but digitally printed)	19.00
The Postal Museum	MA17	From 13 September 2017	FS173a/178a (Type IIIA but digitally printed)	19.00
Royal Mail Heritage: Mail by Air, 1st × 6 designs:				
The Postal Museum	R17Y	13 September 2017–13 February 2018	FS185a x6 (Type IIIA)	9.00
Winter Greenery 2017 issue, 2nd/2ndL, and 1st/1stL/E-20g WW-10g/E-100g/WW-20g/WW-100g:				
The Postal Museum	CL17/ R17Y	13 November 2017–1 January 2018	FS191/198a (Type IIIA) Set of 16:	46.00
***Game of Thrones*, 2nd/2ndL, and 1st/1stL/E-20g WW-10g/E-100g/WW-20g/WW-100g:**				
The Postal Museum	CL18/ R18Y	23 January–13 February 2018	FS199a/206a (Type IIIA) Set of 8:	24.00
Royal Mail Heritage: Mail by Sea, 1st × 6 designs:				
The Postal Museum	R18Y	14 February–28 March 2018	FS207a x6 (Type IIIA)	9.00
Voices from the Deep The Postal Museum	R18Y	From 29 March 2018	FS207a x6 (Type IIIA)	9.00

Post & Go stamps – the different issues and inscriptions from Royal Mail Enquiry Offices to 29 March 2015: a simplified checklist

Post and Go stamps – the inscriptions from Royal Mail Enquiry Offices, February 2015–March 2015: A simplified checklist of the Machin issues				
Inscription	Year code	Name/location of dispensing machine Date/duration/details of inscription (dates are inclusive)	Cat. No. of stamp issue without inscription, or closest match	Price
Machin, 1st/1stL/E-20g WW-10g/E-60g/WW-20g/WW-60g				
Bradford N	MA13	Bradford North Royal Mail Enquiry Office 9 February–28 March 2015 Note: This inscription was the result of a two-office trial which ended very quickly, and Enquiry Office inscriptions ceased	FS77b, 78b, 79bb, 80?, 82b, & 84? (Type IIIA)	23.00
Crewe	MA13	Crewe Royal Mail Enquiry Office 9 February–28 March 2015 Note: This inscription was the result of a two-office trial which ended very quickly, and Enquiry Office inscriptions ceased	FS77b, 78b, 79bb, 80?, 82b, & 84? (Type IIIA)	23.00
Machin, 2nd/2ndL:				
Bradford N	MA12	Bradford North Royal Mail Enquiry Office 9 February–28 March 2015 Note: This inscription was the result of a two-office trial which ended very quickly, and Enquiry Office inscriptions ceased	FS93b/94b (Type IIIA)	10.00
Crewe	MA12	Crewe Royal Mail Enquiry Office 9 February–28 March 2015 Note: This inscription was the result of a two-office trial which ended very quickly, and Enquiry Office inscriptions ceased	FS93b/94b (Type IIIA)	10.00

Post & Go stamps – the different issues and inscriptions from the Armed Forces museums to May 2018: a simplified checklist

Post and Go stamps – the inscriptions from The National Museum Royal Navy, July 2014–May 2018: A simplified checklist of the Machin, Union Flag and Common Poppy issues

Inscription	Year code	Name/location of dispensing machine Date/duration/details of inscription (dates are inclusive)	Cat. No. of stamp issue without inscription, or closest match	Price
Machin, 1st/1stL/E-20g WW-10g/E-60g/WW-20g/WW-60g:				
The NMRN	None	National Museum Royal Navy 28 July–20 October 2014 14 November 2014–29 March 2015	FS1d, 2d, 3cb, 3d, 5d & 5f (Type IIIA)	20.00
Machin, 1st/1stL/E-20g WW-10g/E-100g/WW-20g/WW-100g:				
The NMRN	MA13	National Museum of the Royal Navy, Portsmouth[1] 30 March–18 October 2015	FS77b, 78b, 79bb, 80ca, 82b & 84ca (Type IIIA)	20.00
	None	For a short while the machine dispensed stock that did not have a year code	FS1d, 2d, 3cb, 3ea, 5d & 5ga (Type IIIA)	50.00
Royal Navy + large circle logo (generic inscription revised so words replace acronym, and large logo introduced)	MA13	National Museum of the Royal Navy, Portsmouth 16 November 2015–30 May 2016 1 July 2016–18 August 2017	FS77b, 78b, 79bb, 80ca, 82b & 84ca (Type IIIA)	19.00
	None	The Explosion Museum of Naval Firepower, Gosport[4] 16 August 2016–18 May 2017 19 June–18 August 2017 Note: No year code, MA13 and MA15 dispensed at various times	FS1d, 2d, 3cb, 3ea, 5d and 5ga (Type IIIA)	20.00
	MA15	The only version to be dispensed from the machines at: HMS *Caroline*, Belfast[2] 1 July 2016–spring/summer 2017 HMS *Trincomalee*, Hartlepool[3] 1 July 2016–15 June 2017	FS77b, 78b, 79bb, 80ca, 82b & 84ca (Type IIIA)	20.00
Royal Navy Battle of Jutland + large circle logo	None	National Museum of the Royal Navy, Portsmouth 31 May–30 June 2016	FS1d 2d, 3cb, 3ea, 5d and 5ga (Type IIIA)	20.00
	MA13	Dispensed from the machine for a few hours on 31 May 2016	FS77b, 78b, 79bb, 80ca, 82b & 84ca (Type IIIA)	—
	MA15	The only version to be dispensed from the machines at HMS *Caroline*, Belfast, and HMS *Trincomalee*, Hartlepool 1–30 June 2016 (Note: Not 31 May)	FS77b, 78b, 79bb, 80ca, 82b & 84ca (Type IIIA)	20.00
Heligoland 'Big Bang' 1947 + large circle logo	MA15	The Explosion Museum of Naval Firepower, Gosport 19 May–18 June 2017	FS77b, 78b, 79bb, 80ca, 82b & 84ca (Type IIIA)	20.00
HMS Trincomalee 200 Years + large circle logo	MA15	National Museum of the Royal Navy, Hartlepool – HMS *Trincomalee* 16 June–18 August 2017	FS77b, 78b, 79bb, 80ca, 82b & 84ca (Type IIIA)	20.00
Royal Navy Queen Elizabeth II Carrier + small circle logo	MA15	National Museum of the Royal Navy, Portsmouth 19–28 August 2017 The carrier is named *Queen Elizabeth* and not *Queen Elizabeth II*. From 29 August 2017, the erroneous 'II' was removed	FS77b, 78b, 79bb, 80ca, 82b & 84ca (Type IIIA)	23.00
Royal Navy Queen Elizabeth Carrier 2017 + small circle logo	MA15	National Museum of the Royal Navy, Portsmouth 29 August–17 September 2017 At the same time the erroneous 'II' was removed from the inscription the date '2017' was added	FS77b, 78b, 79bb, 80ca, 82b & 84ca (Type IIIA)	23.00
HMS Trincomalee 200 Years + small circle logo	MA14	National Museum of the Royal Navy, Hartlepool – HMS *Trincomalee* 19 August–19 October 2017	FS77b, 78b, 79bb, 80ca, 82b & 84ca (Type IIIA)	22.00
	MA15	Dispensed from the machine initially and only for a short while	FS77b, 78b, 79bb, 80ca, 82b & 84ca (Type IIIA)	40.00
Royal Navy' + small circle logo (generic inscription revised through introduction of small logo)	MA15	The Explosion Museum of Naval Firepower, Gosport August–19 October 2017 National Museum of the Royal Navy, Portsmouth From 19 September 2017	FS77b, 78b, 79bb, 80ca, 82b & 84ca (Type IIIA)	20.00
HMS Trincomalee 12th Oct 1817 + small circle logo	MA14	National Museum of the Royal Navy, Hartlepool – HMS *Trincomalee* 20 October–31 December 2017	FS77b, 78b, 79bb, 80ca, 82b & 84ca (Type IIIA)	20.00
	MA15	National Museum of the Royal Navy, Hartlepool – HMS *Trincomalee* 20 October–31 December 2017	FS77b, 78b, 79bb, 80ca, 82b & 84ca (Type IIIA)	40.00

Post and Go stamps – the inscriptions from The National Museum Royal Navy, July 2014–May 2018:
A simplified checklist of the Machin, Union Flag and Common Poppy issues

Inscription	Year code	Name/location of dispensing machine Date/duration/details of inscription (dates are inclusive)	Cat. No. of stamp issue without inscription, or closest match	Price
Machin, 1st/1stL/E-20g WW-10g/E-100g/WW-20g/WW-100g: (cont.)				
HMS Trincomalee 19th Oct 1817 + small circle logo (19th Oct in error for a very short time on the first day of the Oct 1817 inscription)	MA14	National Museum of the Royal Navy, Hartlepool – HMS *Trincomalee* 20 October 2017	FS77b, 78b, 79bb, 80ca, 82b & 84ca (Type IIIA)	50.00
HMS Trincomalee + small circle logo	MA14	National Museum of the Royal Navy, Hartlepool – HMS *Trincomalee* From 2 January 2017	FS77b, 78b, 79bb, 80ca, 82b & 84ca (Type IIIA)	20.00
Union Flag, 1st/1stL/E-20g WW-10g/E-60g/WW-20g/WW-60g:				
The NMRN	None	The National Museum Royal Navy 28 July–20 October 2014, 11 November 2014–29 March 2015	FS39, 40, 41*a*, 41*b*, 43 & 44*b* (but Type IIIA)	20.00
The NMRN Trafalgar Day	None	The National Museum Royal Navy 21 October–10 November 2014	FS39, 40, 41*a*, 41*b*, 43 & 44*b* (but Type IIIA)	30.00
Union Flag, 1st/1stL/E-20g WW-10g/E-100g/WW-20g/WW-100g:				
The NMRN	None	National Museum of the Royal Navy, Portsmouth[1] 30 March–7 May 2015 30 May–18 October 2015	FS39, 40, 41*a*, 41*c*, 43 and 44*c* (but Type IIIA)	25.00
The NMRN V.E. Day 70	None	National Museum of the Royal Navy, Portsmouth 8–29 May 2015	FS39, 40, 41a, 41c, 43 and 44c (but Type IIIA)	20.00
Royal Navy Trafalgar Day (words replace acronym)	None	National Museum of the Royal Navy, Portsmouth 19 October–15 November 2015 23 September–23 October 2016 – all sites	FS39, 40, 41a, 41c, 43 and 44c (but Type IIIA)	20.00
Royal Navy (generic inscription revised so words replace acronym)	None	National Museum of the Royal Navy, Portsmouth 16 November 2015–30 May 2016 14 November 2016–18 August 2017 From 18 September 2017 1 July–22 September 2016 – all sites National Museum of the Royal Navy, Belfast – HMS *Caroline*[2] 1 July 2016–spring/summer 2017 National Museum of the Royal Navy, Hartlepool – HMS *Trincomalee*[3] 1 July 2016–15 June 2017 The Explosion Museum of Naval Firepower, Gosport[4] 16 August 2016–18 May 2017 From 19 June 2017	FS39, 40, 41a, 41c, 43 and 44c (but Type IIIA)	20.00
Royal Navy Battle of Jutland	None	National Museum of the Royal Navy, Portsmouth 31 May–30 June 2016 1–30 June 2016 – all sites	FS39, 40, 41a, 41c, 43 and 44c (but Type IIIA)	20.00
Heligoland 'Big Bang' 1947	None	The Explosion Museum of Naval Firepower, Gosport 19 May–18 June 2017	FS39, 40, 41a, 41c, 43 and 44c (but Type IIIA)	20.00
HMS Trincomalee 200 Years	None	National Museum of the Royal Navy, Hartlepool – HMS *Trincomalee* From 16 June 2017	FS39, 40, 41a, 41c, 43 and 44c (but Type IIIA)	20.00
Royal Navy QE II Carrier	None	National Museum of the Royal Navy, Portsmouth 19–28 August 2017 The Carrier is named *Queen Elizabeth* and not *Queen Elizabeth II*. From 29 August 2017 the erroneous 'II' was removed	FS39, 40, 41a, 41c, 43 and 44c (but Type IIIA)	23.00
Royal Navy QE Carrier 2017	None	National Museum of the Royal Navy, Portsmouth 29 August–17 September 2017 At the same time the erroneous 'II' was removed from the inscription the date '2017' was added	FS39, 40, 41a, 41c, 43 and 44c (but Type IIIA)	23.00
HMS Trincomalee 12th Oct 1817	None	National Museum of the Royal Navy, Hartlepool – HMS *Trincomalee* 20 November–31 December 2017	FS39, 40, 41a, 41c, 43 and 44c (but Type IIIA)	20.00
HMS Trincomalee	None	National Museum of the Royal Navy, Hartlepool – HMS *Trincomalee* From 2 January 2018	FS39, 40, 41a, 41c, 43 and 44c (but Type IIIA)	20.00

Post and Go stamps – the inscriptions from The National Museum Royal Navy, July 2014–May 2018:
A simplified checklist of the Machin, Union Flag and Common Poppy issues

Inscription	Year code	Name/location of dispensing machine Date/duration/details of inscription (dates are inclusive)	Cat. No. of stamp issue without inscription, or closest match	Price
Poppy, 1st/1stL/E-20g WW-10g/E-60g/WW-20g/WW-60g:				
The NMRN Remembrance	MA14	The National Museum Royal Navy 21 October–13 November 2014	FS103, 104, 105, 106, 107 & 108 (but Type IIIA)	30.00
Poppy, 1st/1stL/E-20g WW-10g/E-100g/WW-20g/WW-100g:				
Royal Navy	MA15	The National Museum Royal Navy 19 October–15 November 2015 24 October–13 November 2016 20 October–19 November 2017 – all sites	FS137, 138, 139, 140, 141 &142 (Type IIIA)	20.00
HMS Trincomalee 12 Oct 1817 (Unintentional issue owing to part roll being left in machine in error)	MA15	National Museum of the Royal Navy, Hartlepool – HMS *Trincomalee* 20 November 2017	FS137, 138, 139, 140, 141 &142 (Type IIIA)	40.00

Post & Go machines at Royal Navy Museums and the dates they were available from:

[1] National Museum of the Royal Navy (NMRN), Portsmouth – from 28 July 2014

[2] National Museum of the Royal Navy, Belfast – HMS Caroline – from 1 June 2016–spring/summer 2017
(Note: Machine taken out of service with no plans for it to be reinstated)

[3] National Museum of the Royal Navy, Hartlepool – HMS Trincomalee – from 1 June 2016

[4] The Explosion Museum of Naval Firepower, Gosport – from 16 August 2016

The machines at all the National Museum Royal Navy sites dispense stamps with the same generic inscription, although sometimes a particular site will mark a specific event through a unique inscription that is only available for a limited period.

Post & Go stamps – the different issues and inscriptions from the Armed Forces museums to May 2018: a simplified checklist

Post and Go stamps – the inscriptions from The Royal Marines Museum, January 2015–February 2017: A simplified checklist of the Machin, Union Flag and Common Poppy issues

Inscription	Year code	Name/location of dispensing machine Date/duration/details of inscription (dates are inclusive)	Cat. No. of stamp issue without inscription, or closest match	Price
Machin, 1st/1stL/E-20g WW-10g/E-60g/WW-20g/WW-60g:				
The RMM	MA13	The Royal Marines Museum 13 January–29 March 2015	FS77b, 78b, 79bb, 80, 82b & 84 (Type IIIA)	19.00
	None	Note: For a short while the machine was filled with stock that did not have a year code	FS1d, 2d, 3cb, 3d, 5d & 5f (Type IIIA)	75.00
Machin, 1st/1stL/E-20g WW-10g/E-100g/WW-20g/WW-100g:				
The RMM	MA13	The Royal Marines Museum 30 March–18 October 2015	FS77b, 78b, 79bb, 80ca, 82b & 84ca (Type IIIA)	25.00
Royal Marines + large circle logo (generic inscription revised so words replace acronym, and large circle logo introduced)	MA13	The Royal Marines Museum 16 November 2015–30 May 2016 1 July 2016–24 February 2017 after which the machine was relocated owing to the imminent 3-year closure of the museum	FS77b, 78b, 79bb, 80ca, 82b & 84ca (Type IIIA)	19.00
Royal Marines Battle of Jutland + large circle logo	MA13	The Royal Marines Museum 31 May–30 June 2016	FS77b, 78b, 79bb, 80ca, 82b & 84ca (Type IIIA)	20.00
Union Flag, 1st/1stL/E-20g WW-10g/E-60g/WW-20g/WW-60g:				
The RMM	None	The Royal Marines Museum 13 January–29 March 2015	FS39, 40, 41a, 41b, 43 & 44b (but Type IIIA)	19.00
Union Flag, 1st/1stL/E-20g WW-10g/E-100g/WW-20g/WW-100g:				
The RMM	None	The Royal Marines Museum 30 March–7 May 2015 1 June–18 October 2015	FS39, 40, 41a, 41c, 43 & 44c (but Type IIIA)	25.00
The RMM V.E. Day 70	None	The Royal Marines Museum 8–31 May 2015	FS39, 40, 41a, 41c, 43 & 44c (but Type IIIA)	20.00
Royal Marines Trafalgar Day (generic inscription revised so words replace acronym)	None	The Royal Marines Museum 19 October–15 November 2015 23 September–23 October 2016	FS39, 40, 41a, 41c, 43 & 44c (but Type IIIA)	20.00
Royal Marines (generic inscription revised so words replace acronym)	None	The Royal Marines Museum 16 November 2015–30 May 2016 1 July–22 September 2016 14 November 2016–24 February 2017 after which the machine was relocated owing to the imminent 3-year closure of the museum	FS39, 40, 41a, 41c, 43 & 44c (but Type IIIA)	19.00
Royal Marines Battle of Jutland	None	The Royal Marines Museum 31 May–30 June 2016	FS39, 40, 41a, 41c, 43 & 44c (but Type IIIA)	19.00
Poppy, 1st/1stL/E-20g WW-10g/E-100g/WW-20g/WW-100g:				
Royal Marines	MA15	The Royal Marines Museum 19 October–15 November 2015 24 October–13 November 2016	FS137, 138, 139, 140, 141 &142 (Type IIIA)	20.00

Post & Go stamps – the different issues and inscriptions from the Armed Forces museums to May 2018: a simplified checklist

Post and Go stamps – the inscriptions from The Royal Navy Submarine Museum, July 2015–May 2018: A simplified checklist of the Machin, Union Flag and Common Poppy issues

Inscription	Year code	Name/location of dispensing machine Date/duration/details of inscription (dates are inclusive)	Cat. No. of stamp issue without inscription, or closest match	Price
Machin, 1st/1stL/E-20g WW-10g/E-100g/WW-20g/WW-100g:				
The RNSM	MA13	The Royal Navy Submarine Museum , Gosport 28 July–18 October 2015	FS77b, 78b, 79bb, 80ca, 82b & 84ca (Type IIIA)	20.00
RN Submarine + large circle logo (generic inscription revised: 'Submarine' replaces acronym and large logo introduced)	MA13	The Royal Navy Submarine Museum , Gosport 16 November 2015–30 May 2016 1 July 2016–18 May 2017	FS77b, 78b, 79bb, 80ca, 82b & 84ca (Type IIIA)	19.00
	MA15	From 19 June 2017	FS77b, 78b, 79bb, 80ca, 82b & 84ca (Type IIIA)	
		Note: MA15 was first dispensed on 1 July 2016		20.00
RN Submarine Battle of Jutland + large circle logo	MA15	The Royal Navy Submarine Museum , Gosport 31 May–30 June 2016	FS77b, 78b, 79bb, 80ca, 82b & 84ca (Type IIIA)	20.00
HMS Alliance 14th May 1947 + large circle logo	MA15	The Royal Navy Submarine Museum , Gosport 19 May–18 June 2017	FS77b, 78b, 79bb, 80ca, 82b & 84ca (Type IIIA)	23.00
	MA13		FS77b, 78b, 79bb, 80ca, 82b & 84ca (Type IIIA)	20.00
Union Flag, 1st/1stL/E-20g WW-10g/E-100g/WW-20g/WW-100g:				
The RNSM	None	The Royal Navy Submarine Museum , Gosport 28 July–18 October 2015	FS39, 40, 41a, 41c, 43 & 44c (but Type IIIA)	20.00
RN Submarine (generic inscription revised: 'Submarine' replaces acronym)	None	The Royal Navy Submarine Museum , Gosport 19 October 2015–30 May 2016 1 July–23 October 2016 14 November 2016–18 May 2017 19 June–19 October 2017 From 20 November 2017	FS39, 40, 41a, 41c, 43 & 44c (but Type IIIA)	19.00
RN Submarine Battle of Jutland	None	The Royal Navy Submarine Museum , Gosport 31 May–30 June 2016	FS39, 40, 41a, 41c, 43 & 44c (but Type IIIA)	19.00
HMS Alliance 14th May 1947	None	The Royal Navy Submarine Museum , Gosport 19 May–18 June 2017	FS39, 40, 41a, 41c, 43 & 44c (but Type IIIA)	20.00
Poppy, 1st/1stL/E-20g WW-10g/E-100g/WW-20g/WW-100g:				
RN Submarine	MA15	The Royal Navy Submarine Museum , Gosport 19 October–15 November 2015 24 October–13 November 2016 20 October–19 November 2017	FS137, 138, 139, 140, 141 &142 (Type IIIA)	20.00

Post & Go stamps – the different issues and inscriptions from the Armed Forces museums to May 2018: a simplified checklist

Post and Go stamps – the inscriptions from The Royal Navy Fleet Air Arm Museum and The Royal Signals Museum, April 2015–May 2018: A simplified checklist of the Machin, Union Flag and Common Poppy issues

Inscription	Year code	Name/location of dispensing machine Date/duration/details of inscription (dates are inclusive)	Cat. No. of stamp issue without inscription, or closest match	Price
Machin, 1st/1stL/E-20g WW-10g/E-100g/WW-20g/WW-100g:				
The FAAM	MA13	Royal Navy Fleet Air Arm Museum 14 April–18 October 2015	FS77b, 78b, 79bb, 80ca, 82b & 84ca (Type IIIA)	20.00
Fleet Air Arm + large circle logo (generic inscription revised so words replace acronym, and large logo introduced)	MA13	Royal Navy Fleet Air Arm Museum 16 November 2015–30 May 2016 1 July–2 December 2016 4 January–18 July 2017 and from 22 August 2017	FS77b, 78b, 79bb, 80ca, 82b & 84ca (Type IIIA)	19.00
	MA15	Note: MA15 was dispensed for a short time in early January 2017, and then MA13 returned	FS77b, 78b, 79bb, 80ca, 82b & 84ca (Type IIIA)	20.00
Fleet Air Arm Battle of Jutland + small circle logo	MA13	Royal Navy Fleet Air Arm Museum 31 May–30 June 2016	FS77b, 78b, 79bb, 80ca, 82b & 84ca (Type IIIA)	20.00
Royal Corps of Signals + Jimmy logo	None	Royal Signals Museum From 3 November 2016	FS1d, 2d, 3cb, 3ea, 5d & 5ga (Type IIIA)	20.00
	MA13	Note: At different times, no year code and MA13 have been dispensed	FS77b, 78b, 79bb, 80ca, 82b & 84ca (Type IIIA)	25.00
Fleet Air Arm LZ551/G 1st Jet Carrier Landing	MA13	Royal Navy Fleet Air Arm Museum 3 December 2016–3 January 2017	FS77b, 78b, 79bb, 80ca, 82b & 84ca (Type IIIA)	35.00
	MA15	Note: MA13 was only dispensed for a short time on 3 December 2017	FS77b, 78b, 79bb, 80ca, 82b & 84ca (Type IIIA)	20.00
Fleet Air Arm Sea King ZA298 Junglie + large circle logo	MA15	Royal Navy Fleet Air Arm Museum 19 July–21 August 2017	FS77b, 78b, 79bb, 80ca, 82b & 84ca (Type IIIA)	20.00
Union Flag, 1st/1stL/E-20g WW-10g/E-100g/WW-20g/WW-100g:				
The FAAM	None	Royal Navy Fleet Air Arm Museum 14 April–7 May 2015 30 May–18 October 2015	FS39, 40, 41a, 41c, 43 & 44c (but Type IIIA)	20.00
The FAAM V.E. Day 70	None	Royal Navy Fleet Air Arm Museum 8–29 May 2015	FS39, 40, 41a, 41c, 43 & 44c (but Type IIIA)	20.00
Fleet Air Arm (generic inscription revised so words replace acronym)	None	Royal Navy Fleet Air Arm Museum 19 October 2015–30 May 2016 1 July–23 October 14 November–2 December 2016 4 January–18 July 2017 22 August–19 October 2017 From 20 November 2017	FS39, 40, 41a, 41c, 43 & 44c (but Type IIIA)	19.00
Fleet Air Arm Battle of Jutland	None	Royal Navy Fleet Air Arm Museum 31 May–30 June 2016	FS39, 40, 41a, 41c, 43 & 44c (but Type IIIA)	19.00
Royal Corps of Signals	None	Royal Signals Museum 3 November 2016–8 June 2017 From 20 November 2017	FS39, 40, 41a, 41c, 43 & 44c (but Type IIIA)	20.00
Fleet Air Arm LZ551/G 03Dec45	None	Royal Navy Fleet Air Arm Museum 3 December 2016–3 January 2017	FS39, 40, 41a, 41c, 43 & 44c (but Type IIIA)	20.00
– as above but with second line of inscription slightly inset	None	Note: Only available on 3 December 2016 and then corrected	FS39, 40, 41a, 41c, 43 & 44c (but Type IIIA)	25.00
Royal Signals White Helmets + Motorcycle logo	None	Royal Signals Museum 9 June–19 October 2017	FS39, 40, 41a, 41c, 43 & 44c (but Type IIIA)	20.00
Fleet Air Arm GR9A Harrier ZD433	None	Royal Navy Fleet Air Arm Museum 19 July–21 August 2017	FS39, 40, 41a, 41c, 43 & 44c (but Type IIIA)	19.00
Poppy, 1st/1stL/E-20g WW-10g/E-100g/WW-20g/WW-100g:				
Fleet Air Arm	MA15	Royal Navy Fleet Air Arm Museum 19 October–15 November 2015 24 October–13 November 2016 20 October–19 November 2017	FS137, 138, 139, 140, 141 &142 (Type IIIA)	20.00
Royal Corps of Signals	MA15	Royal Signals Museum 20 October–19 November 2017	FS137, 138, 139, 140, 141 &142 (Type IIIA)	19.00

Post & Go stamps – the different HYTECH & ROYAL MAIL 'SERIES II' printings from exhibitions and Stamp Fairs in the United Kingdon but without inscriptions (February 2011 - May 2018): a simplified checklist

Stamp design, values and machine type	Format produced		Event the stamps were available from, the date and duration (all the dates are inclusive)	Main distinguishing features			Catalogue No. of standard issue or closest match
				Space between service indicator lines	Code string consisting of		
	CS	Set of 36			Numerals only (Type II)	Letters & numerals (Type III)	
Machin, 1st/1stL/E-20g/WW-10g/WW-20g without date code (N.B. five values only):							
Hytech Postal Vision (N.B. a trial machine) († weight line inset)	✓		Spring Stampex 2011 (23 - 26 February: 4 days)	3mm	yes		FS1a/5a
Machin, 1st/1stL/E-20g/WW-10g/WW-20g/WW-40g without date code:							
Hytech 'next generation'	✓		York Stamp Fair (18 - 19 January 2013: 2 days) Salisbury Stamp Fair (15 - 16 March 2013: 2 days) Midpex Exhibition (6 July 2013: 1 day) (N.B. similar stamps were first issued in November 2012 from a pop-up Christmas Post Shop in Camden, London)	2.6mm		yes	FS1b/3b, 4b, 5b & 5eb
Royal Mail 'Series II'	✓		Salisbury Stamp Fair (14 - 15 March 2014: 2 days)	2.4mm		yes	FS1b/3b, 4b, 5b & 5eb
Machin, 1st/1stL/E-20g/WW-10g/WW-20g/WW-40g with MA13 date code:							
Hytech 'next generation'	✓		York Stamp Fair (19 - 20 July 2013: 2 days) Autumn Stampex 2013 (18 - 21 September: 4 days) Stafford Stamp Fair (8 - 9 November 2013: 2 days) York Stamp Fair (17 - 18 January 2014: 2 days)	2.6mm		yes	FS77/79, 81/83 (but Type III)
Royal Mail 'Series II'	✓		Salisbury Stamp Fair (14 - 15 March 2014: 2 days)	2.4mm		yes	FS77/79, 81/83 (but Type III)
Machin, 1st/1stL/E-20g WW-10g/E-60g/WW-20g/WW-60g without date code:							
Royal Mail 'Series II' (Euro 20g in a large typeface)	✓		York Stamp Fair (18 - 19 July 2014: 2 days)	2.4mm		yes	FS1b, 2b, 3c, 3d, 5d, 5f
Royal Mail 'Series II' (all values with smaller (revised) typeface)	✓		Autumn Stampex 2014 (17 - 20 September: 4 days) Stafford Stamp Fair (7 - 8 November 2014: 2 days) Spring Stampex 2015 (18 - 21 February: 4 days) (N.B. limited availablilty and only known from stock produced in advance of the exhibition)	2.7mm		yes (Type IIIA)	FS1d, 2d, 3cb, 3d, 5d & 5f
Machin, 1st/1stL/E-20g WW-10g/E-60g/WW-20g/WW-60g with MA13 date code:							
Royal Mail 'Series II' (Euro 20g in a large typeface)	✓		York Stamp Fair (18 - 19 July 2014: 2 days)	2.4mm		yes	FS77/78, 79b, 80, 82 & 84 (but Type III)
Royal Mail 'Series II' (all values with smaller (revised) typeface)	✓		Autumn Stampex 2014 (17 - 20 September: 4 days) Stafford Stamp Fair (7 - 8 November 2014: 2 days) Spring Stampex 2015 (18 - 21 February: 4 days)	2.7mm		yes (Type IIIA)	FS77b, 78b, 79bb, 80, 82b & 84
Machin, 1st/1stL/E-20g WW-10g/E-100g/WW-20g/WW-100g without date code:							
Royal Mail 'Series II' (all values with smaller (revised) typeface)	✓		Midpex Exhibition (4 July 2015: 1 day) (N.B. similar stamps were (officially) issued on 3 June 2015 from Royal Mail Enquiry offices)	2.7mm		yes (Type IIIA)	FS1d, 2d, 3cb, 3ea, 5d & 5ga

Stamp design, values and machine type	Format produced		Event the stamps were available from, the date and duration (all the dates are inclusive)	Main distinguishing features			
				Space between service indicator lines	Code string consisting of		Catalogue No. of standard issue or closest match
	CS	Set of 36			Numerals only (Type II)	Letters & numerals (Type III)	

Machin, 1st/1stL/E-20g WW-10g/E-100g/WW-20g/WW-100g with MA13 date code:

| Royal Mail 'Series II' (all values with smaller (revised) typeface) | ✓ | | **Midpex Exhibition** (4 July 2015: 1 day) (N.B. similar stamps were (officially) issued on 30 March 2015 from Royal Mail Enquiry offices) | 2.7mm | | yes (Type IIIA) | FS77b, 78b, 79bb, 80ca, 82b & 84ca |

Machin, 2nd/2ndL with MA12 date code:

| Hytech 'next generation' | ✓ | | **Spring Stampex** 2013 (20 - 23 February: 4 days) (N.B. similar stamps, but not identical, were (officially) issued in November 2013 from a travelling pop-up Christmas post office) | 2.6mm | | yes | FS93, 94 |

Union Flag, 1st/1stL/E-20g/WW-10g/WW-20g/WW-40g without date code:

| Hytech 'next generation' | ✓ | | **Autumn Stampex** 2012 (26 - 29 September: 4 days) **York Stamp Fair** (18 - 19 January 2013: 2 days) **Salisbury Stamp Fair** (15 - 16 March 2013: 2 days) **Midpex Exhibition** (6 July 2013: 1 day) | 2.6mm | | yes | FS39/44 (but Type III) |
| Royal Mail 'Series II' | ✓ | | **Spring Stampex** 2014 (19 - 22 February: 4 days) (N.B. only available on 21/22 February: 2 days) **Salisbury Stamp Fair** (14 - 15 March 2014: 2 days) | 2.4mm | | yes | FS39/44 (but Type III) |

Union Flag, 1st/1stL/E-20g/WW-10g/WW-20g/WW-40g with MA13 date code:

| Hytech 'next generation' | ✓ | | **York Stamp Fair** (19 - 20 July 2013: 2 days) **York Stamp Fair** (17 - 18 January 2014: 2 days) | 2.6mm | | yes | FS85/90 (but Type III) |
| Royal Mail 'Series II' | ✓ | | **Spring Stampex** 2014 (19 - 22 February: 4 days) **Salisbury Stamp Fair** (14 - 15 March 2014: 2 days) | 2.4mm | | yes | FS85/90 (but Type III) |

Union Flag, 1st/1stL/E-20g/E-60g/WW-20g/WW-60g without date code:

| Royal Mail 'Series II' | ✓ | | **The Annual Congress of Scottish Philatelic Societies**, Perth, Scotland (11 - 12 April 2014: 2 days) | 2.4mm | | yes | FS39/41, 41b, 43, 44b (but Type III) |

Union Flag, 1st/1stL/E-20g/E-60g/WW-20g/WW-60g with MA13 date code:

| Royal Mail 'Series II' | ✓ | | **The Annual Congress of Scottish Philatelic Societies**, Perth, Scotland (11 - 12 April 2014: 2 days) | 2.4mm | | yes | FS85/91 (but Type III) |

Union Flag, 1st/1stL/E-20g WW-10g/E-60g/WW-20g/WW-60g without date code :

| Royal Mail 'Series II' (Euro 20g in a large typeface) | ✓ | | **York Stamp Fair** (18 - 19 July 2014: 2 days) | 2.4mm | | yes | FS39, 40, 41a, 41b, 43, 44b (but Type III) |
| Royal Mail 'Series II' (all values with smaller (revised) typeface) | ✓ | | **Autumn Stampex** 2014 (17 - 20 September: 4 days) **Stafford Stamp Fair** (7 - 8 November 2014: 2 days) | 2.7mm | | yes (Type IIIA) | FS39, 40, 41a, 41b, 43, 44b (but Type IIIA) |

Union Flag, 1st/1stL/E-20g WW-10g/E-100g/WW-20g/WW-100g without date code :

| Royal Mail 'Series II' (all values with smaller (revised) typeface) | ✓ | | **Europhilex** 2015 (13 - 16 May: 4 days) **Midpex Exhibition** (4 July 2015: 1 day) **Autumn Stampex** 2015 (16 - 19 September: 4 days) | 2.7mm | | yes (Type IIIA) | FS39, 40, 41a, 41c, 43 & 44c (but Type IIIA) |

Stamp design, values and machine type	Format produced		Event the stamps were available from, the date and duration (all the dates are inclusive)	Space between service indicator lines	Code string consisting of		Catalogue No. of standard issue or closest match
	CS	Set of 36			Numerals only (Type II)	Letters & numerals (Type III)	
Robin, 1st/1stL/E-20g/WW-10g/WW-20g/WW-40g with MA13 date code:							
Hytech 'next generation'	✓		Stafford Stamp Fair (8 - 9 November 2013: 2 days) (N.B. similar MA13 stamps were (officially) issued later in November 2013 from a travelling pop-up Christmas post office)	2.6mm		yes	FS51a/56a
Birds of Britain 3rd series, 1st/1stL/E-20g/WW-10g/WW-20g/1st (N.B. only produced in collectors' strips of six with additional '1st Class' value at bottom so all six designs represented):							
Hytech 'version 1' († weight line inset)	✓		Autumn Stampex 2011 (14 - 17 September: 4 days) (N.B. only available on 14 September: 1 day)	3mm	yes		FS16/20
Birds of Britain 4th series, 1st/1stL/E-20g/WW-10g/WW-20g/WW-40g:							
Hytech 'version 1' († weight line inset)	✓	✓	Autumn Stampex 2011 (14 - 17 September: 4 days) (N.B. only available on 16/17 September: 2 days) Spring Stampex 2012 (22 - 25 February: 4 days) (N.B. only available on 22/23 September: 2 days)	3mm	yes		FS21/26
Sheep (British Farm Animals 1st series), 1st/1stL/E-20g/WW-10g/WW-20g/WW-40g:							
Hytech 'version 1' († weight line inset)	✓	✓	Spring Stampex 2012 (22 - 25 February: 4 days) (N.B. only available on 24/25 February: 2 days)	3mm	yes		FS27/32
Pigs (British Farm Animals 2nd series), 1st/1stL/E-20g/WW-10g/WW-20g/WW-40g:							
Hytech 'next generation'	✓	✓	Autumn Stampex 2012 (26 - 29 September: 4 days) (N.B. only available on 26/27 September: 2 days)	2.6mm		yes	FS33/38 (but Type III)
Cattle (British Farm Animals 3rd series), 1st/1stL/E-20g/WW-10g/WW-20g/WW-40g:							
Hytech 'next generation'	✓	✓	Autumn Stampex 2012 (26 - 29 September: 4 days) (N.B. only available on 28/29 September: 2 days)	2.6mm		yes	FS45/50 (but Type III)
Ponds (Freshwater Life 1st series), 1st/1stL/E-20g/WW-10g/WW-20g/WW-40g:							
Hytech 'next generation'	✓	✓	Spring Stampex 2013 (20 - 23 February: 4 days) (N.B. only available on 22/23 February: 2 days)	2.6mm		yes	FS59/64 (but Type III)
Lakes (Freshwater Life 2nd series), 1st/1stL/E-20g/WW-10g/WW-20g/WW-40g:							
Hytech 'next generation'	✓	✓	Midpex Exhibition (06 July 2013: 1 day) York Stamp Fair (19 - 20 July 2013: 2 days)	2.6mm		yes	FS65/70 (but Type III)
Rivers (Freshwater Life 3rd series), 1st/1stL/E-20g/WW-10g/WW-20g/WW-40g:							
Hytech 'next generation'	✓	✓	Autumn Stampex 2013 (18 - 21 September: 4 days) (N.B. only available on 20/21 September: 2 days) Stafford Stamp Fair (08 - 09 November 2013: 2 days)	2.6mm		yes	FS71/76 (but Type III)
Spring Blooms (British Flora 1st series), 1st/1stL/E-20g/WW-10g/WW-20g/WW-40g:							
Royal Mail 'Series II'	✓	✓	Spring Stampex 2014 (19 - 22 February: 4 days)	2.4mm		yes	FS95/97, 99/101 (but Type III)
Symbolic Flowers (British Flora 2nd series), 1st/1stL/E-20g WW-10g/E-60g/WW-20g/WW-60g:							
Royal Mail 'Series II'	✓	✓	Autumn Stampex 2014 (17 - 20 September: 4 days)	2.7mm		yes (Type IIIA)	FS103/108 (but Type IIIA)

Stamp design, values and machine type	Format produced		Event the stamps were available from, the date and duration (all the dates are inclusive)	Space between service indicator lines	Main distinguishing features		Catalogue No. of standard issue or closest match
					Code string consisting of		
	CS	Set of 36			Numerals only (Type II)	Letters & numerals (Type III)	

Working Sail, 1st/1stL/E-20g WW-10g/E-60g/WW-20g/WW-60g:

| Royal Mail 'Series II' | ✓ | ✓ | Spring Stampex 2015 (18 - 21 February: 4 days) | 2.7mm | | yes (Type IIIA) | FS117/120, 122/123 (but Type IIIA) |

Heraldic Beasts, 1st/1stL/E-20g WW-10g/E-100g/WW-20g/WW-100g:

| Royal Mail 'Series II' | ✓ | ✓ | Europhilex 2015 (13 - 16 May: 4 days) | 2.7mm | | yes (Type IIIA) | FS125/130 (but Type IIIA) |

Lion design (from Heraldic Beasts issue) in single design rolls, 1st/1stL/E-20g WW-10g/E-100g/WW-20g/WW-100g:

| Royal Mail 'Series II' (stamps gravure printed) | ✓ | | Autumn Stampex 2015 (16 - 19 September: 4 days) | 2.7mm | | yes (Type IIIA) | FS125/130 (but Type IIIA) |

Sea Travel, 1st/1stL/E-20g WW-10g/E-100g/WW-20g/WW-100g:

| Royal Mail 'Series II' | ✓ | ✓ | Autumn Stampex 2015 (16 - 19 September: 4 days) | 2.7mm | | yes (Type IIIA) | FS131/136 (but Type IIIA) |

Royal Mail Heritage: Transport, 1st/1stL/E-20g WW-10g/E-100g/WW-20g/WW-100g:

| Royal Mail 'Series II' (stamps gravure printed) | ✓ | ✓ | Spring Stampex 2016 (17 - 20 February: 4 days) | 2.7mm | | yes (Type IIIA) | FS151/156 (but Type IIIA) |

Locomotive design (from Royal Mail Heritage: Transport issue) from single-design rolls, 1st/1stL/E-20g WW-10g/E-100g/WW-20g/WW-100g:

| Royal Mail 'Series II' (stamps digitally printed) | ✓ | ✓ | Spring Stampex 2016 (17 - 20 February: 4 days) Spring Stampex 2017 (15 - 18 February: 4 days) | 2.7mm | | yes (Type IIIA) | FS151/156 (but Type IIIA) |

Ladybirds, 1st/1stL/E-20g WW-10g/E-100g/WW-20g/WW-100g:

| Royal Mail 'Series II' (stamps gravure printed) | ✓ | ✓ | Autumn Stampex 2016 (14 - 17 September: 4 days) | 2.7mm | | yes (Type IIIA) | FS159a/164a |

Royal Mail Heritage: Mail by Rail, 1st/1stL/E-20g WW-10g/E-100g/WW-20g/WW-100g:

| Royal Mail 'Series II' (stamps gravure printed) | ✓ | ✓ | Spring Stampex 2017 (15 - 18 February: 4 days) | 2.7mm | | yes (Type IIIA) | FS173a/178a |

Royal Mail Heritage: Mail by Air, 1st/1stL/E-20g WW-10g/E-100g/WW-20g/WW-100g:

| Royal Mail 'Series II' (stamps gravure printed) | ✓ | ✓ | Autumn Stampex 2017 (13 - 16 February: 4 days) | 2.7mm | | yes (Type IIIA) | FS185a/195a |

Hytech Postal Vision was a trial machine introduced at Spring Stampex 2011. Machines referred to as Hytech version 1 were used at Autumn Stampex 2011 and Spring Stampex 2012. From Autumn Stampex 2012 modified machines were instead brought into use, sometimes referred to as Hytech 'next generation', Hytech version 2, and also Royal Mail Series I. At Spring Stampex 2014 a new machine was brought into use and it is classified as a Royal Mail 'Series II' (although it is sometimes referred to as Royal Mail Series B).

† = stamps generated from Hytech Postal Vision and Hytech version I machines have their weight lines inset, whereas Hytech 'next generation' and Royal Mail 'Series II' stamps have their weight lines ranged left. From Autumn Stampex 2014, Royal Mail 'Series II' machines at exhibitions produced stamps with a smaller typeface. In place of gravure, digital printing is sometimes used for some single-design rolls. Stamps produced by this process are very shiny and have poor background definition, especially in the repeating "ROYALMAIL" wording.

CS = collectors' strips: the Machins from the Hytech Postal Vision trial machine are in strips of five, the Machin 2nds are in pairs, and all other collectors' strips are of six stamps. Sets of 36 (from and including Birds of Britain 4th series): all six denominations were available in all six designs making a complete set 36 stamps. Some of the catalogue numbers shown are provisional and may be subject to change

Regional Issues

PRINTERS (£.s.d. stamps of all regions): Photo Harrison & Sons. Portrait by Dorothy Wilding Ltd.
DATES OF ISSUE. Conflicting dates of issue have been announced for some of the regional issues, partly explained by the stamps being released on different dates by the Philatelic Bureau in Edinburgh or the Philatelic Counter in London and in the regions. We have adopted the practice of giving the earliest known dates, since once released the stamps could have been used anywhere in the United Kingdom.

CHANNEL ISLANDS

GENERAL ISSUE

C **1** Gathering Vraic   C **2** Islanders gathering Vraic

Broken Wheel (R. 20/5)

(Des J R R Stobie (1d.) or from drawing by Edmund Blampied (2½d.). Photo Harrison)

1948 (10 May). *Third Anniversary of Liberation. W* **127** *of Great Britain.* Perf 15×14.

C1	C **1**	1d. scarlet	25	55
C2	C **2**	2½d. ultramarine	25	60
		a. Broken wheel	75·00	

First Day Cover .... 35·00

I. ENGLAND

"Emblem" Regional colours. Where the Queen's head has been printed in a black screen, this appears as grey, which is the colour given in the description.

EN **1** Three lions of England

EN **2** Crowned lion, supporting the shield of St George

EN **3** English oak tree

EN **4** English Tudor rose

(Des Sedley Place, from sculptures by David Dathan. Gravure Questa(No. EN1b) or De La Rue (others))

2001 (23 Apr)–**02**. One centre phosphor band (2nd) or two phosphor bands (others). Perf 15×14 (with one elliptical hole in each vertical side). All heads Type I

EN1	EN **1**	(2nd) Three lions of England	1·25	1·00
		a. Imperf (pair)		
		b. Booklet pane. Nos. EN1/2, each×4, and No. S95, with margins all round (24.9.02)	8·50	
		ba. Imperf pane	†	—
EN2	EN **2**	(1st) Lion and shield	1·50	1·00
		a. Imperf pair	£350	
EN3	EN **3**	(E) English oak tree	2·00	2·00
EN4	EN **4**	65p. English Tudor rose	2·10	2·10
EN5		68p. English Tudor rose (4.7.02)	2·10	2·10
Presentation Pack (PO Pack No. 54) (Nos. EN1/4)			7·00	
PHQ Cards (set of 4) (D20) (Nos. EN1/4)			1·20	7·00

Nos. EN1/3 were initially sold at 19p., 27p. and 36p., the latter representing the basic European airmail rate.

First Day Covers

23.4.01	2nd, 1st, E, 65p. (EN1/4)		
	Philatelic Bureau (Type G, see Introduction)		2·50
	Windsor		2·00
4.7.02	68p. (EN5) Tallents House (Type K, see Introduction)		2·50
	London (as Windsor)		1·50

Combined Presentation Pack for England, Northern Ireland, Scotland and Wales

4.7.02	PO Pack No. 59. 68p. (Nos. EN5, NI93, S99, W88)	8·50

Two Types of Head
Type I Ribbon at back of the head appears as two separate and distinct strands
Type II Ribbon solid and firmly joined to the head

2003 (14 Oct)–**16**. As Nos. EN1/3 and EN5, and new values, but with white borders. One centre phosphor band (2nd) or two phosphor bands (others). Type I heads unless otherwise stated. Perf 15×14 (with one elliptical hole in each vertical side).

(a) (Gravure Walsall (No. EN6l) Walsall or De La Rue (No. EN10) or De La Rue (others))

EN6	EN **1**	(2nd) Three lions of England. Type II	1·25	1·00
		a. Imperf (pair)	£175	
		l. Booklet pane. Nos. EN6 and EN9, each×2, with central label and margins all round (24.2.05)	4·75	
		b. Type I (2006)	5·50	5·50
EN7	EN **2**	(1st) Lion and shield. Type II	1·50	1·25
		a. Imperf (pair)	£250	
		b. Type I (2006)	5·50	5·50
EN8	EN **3**	(E) English oak tree. Type II	2·00	2·00
EN9		40p. English oak tree (11.5.04). Type II	1·25	1·25
EN10		42p. English oak tree (5.4.05). Type II	1·80	1·80
EN11		44p. English oak tree (28.3.06). Type II	1·25	1·25
		a. Imperf (pair)	£1600	
		b. Type I (2006)	40·00	40·00
EN12		48p. English oak tree (27.3.07)	1·00	1·00
EN13		50p. English oak tree (1.4.08)	1·25	1·25
EN14		56p. English oak tree (31.3.09)	1·25	1·25
EN15		60p. English oak tree (31.3.10)	1·50	1·50
EN16	EN **4**	68p. English Tudor rose. Type II	1·75	1·75
EN17		72p. English Tudor rose (28.3.06). Type II	1·75	1·75

EN18		a. Type I (2006)..	25·00	25·00
EN19		78p. English Tudor rose (27.3.07)...................	2·00	2·00
EN20		81p. English Tudor rose (1.4.08)....................	2·00	2·00
EN21		90p. English Tudor rose (31.3.09)..................	2·25	2·25
		97p. English Tudor rose (31.3.10)..................	2·50	2·50

(b) Litho Enschedé or ISP Cartor (EN30) or ISP Cartor (others).
Queen's head in grey (Nos. EN29, EN30b and EN36) or silver (others)

EN29	EN **1**	(2nd) Three lions of England (1.2013).......	1·25	1·00
EN30	EN **2**	(1st) Lion and shield (Queen's head silver) (20.9.07)....................	1·50	1·25
		al. Booklet pane. Nos. EN30, NI95 S131 and W122 with five labels and margins all round	14·00	
EN30*b*		(1st) Lion and shield (Queen's head grey) (5.2016).........................	2·00	1·75
EN31	EN **3**	68p. English oak tree (29.3.11)	1·75	1·75
EN32		87p. English oak tree (25.4.12)	2·25	2·25
EN33		88p. English oak tree (27.3.13)	2·25	2·10
EN34		97p. English oak tree (26.3.14)	2·10	2·00
EN35		£1 English oak tree (24.3.15)	2·40	2·40
EN36		£1·05 English oak tree (22.3.16)	2·50	2·50
EN41	EN **4**	£1·10 English Tudor rose (29.3.11)	2·50	2·50
EN43		£1·28 English Tudor rose (25.4.12)	2·50	2·50
EN44		£1·33 English Tudor rose (24.3.15)	2·75	2·75
Presentation Pack (PO Pack No. 63) (Nos. EN6/8, EN16)....			6·00	
PHQ Cards (set of 4) (D24) (Nos. EN6/8, EN16)...................			1·20	6·50

The 72p stamp from the 2006 "Lest We Forget" miniature sheet, **MS**2685, has the Type I head. The price for No. EN17a is for the Type I stamp from counter sheets. **Collectors should obtain this stamp from a reliable source.**

No. EN6I comes from booklet No. DX34.

Stamps as Nos. EN18/19 but printed in lithography were only issued within **MS**2796 (EN18) or **MS**2886 (EN19).

No. EN30 was first issued for £7·66 stamp booklets, No. DX40, printed by Enschedé. It was issued in sheets printed by ISP Cartor in January 2013.

A design as No. EN30 but self-adhesive was issued on 23 April 2007 in sheets of 20, each stamp accompanied by a *se-tenant* label showing an English scene (LS38). These sheets were printed in lithography by Cartor, perforated 15×14 without the elliptical holes, and sold at £7·35 each. They were also available with personalised photographs on the labels at £14·95 from the Royal Mail in Edinburgh.

Stamps as Nos. EN30, NI95, S131 and W122 but self-adhesive were issued on 29 September 2008 in sheets of 20 containing five of each design with *se-tenant* labels (LS49). These sheets were printed in lithography by Cartor and perforated 15×14 with one elliptical hole on each vertical side.

First Day Covers

14.10.03	2nd, 1st, E, 68p. (EN6/8, EN16)		
	Tallents House (Type K, see Introduction)	5·50	
	London (as Windsor)..	5·50	
11.5.04	40p. (EN9) Tallents House (Type K).................................	2·00	
	London (as Windsor)..	2·00	
5.4.05	42p. (EN10) Tallents House (Type K)...............................	2·00	
	London (as Windsor)..	2·00	
28.3.06	44p., 72p., (EN11, EN17) Tallents House (Type K)	3·50	
	London (as Windsor)..	3·50	
27.3.07	48p., 78p., (EN12, EN18) Tallents House (Type K)	3·00	
	London (as Windsor)..	3·00	
1.4.08	50p., 81p., (EN13, EN19) Tallents House (Type K)	3·00	
	London (as Windsor)..	3·00	
31.3.09	56p., 90p. (EN14, EN20) Tallents House (Type K)	3·50	
	London (as Windsor)..	3·50	
30.3.10	60p., 97p. (EN15, EN21) Tallents House (Type K)	4·00	
	London (as Windsor)..	4·00	
29.3.11	68p., £1·10 (EN31, EN41) Tallents House (Type K).......	4·50	
	London (as Windsor)..	4·50	
25.4.12	87p., £1·28 (EN32, EN43) Tallents House (Type K).......	4·75	
	London (as Windsor)..	4·75	
27.3.13	88p. (EN33) Tallents House (Type K)..............................	2·25	
	London (as Windsor)..	2·25	
26.3.14	97p. (EN34) Tallents House (Type K)..............................	2·25	
	London (as Windsor)..	2·25	
24.3.15	£1, £1·33 (EN35, EN44) Tallents House (Type K)...........	5·50	
	London (as Windsor)..	5·50	
22.3.16	£1·05 (EN36) Tallents House (Type K)............................	2·50	
	London (as Windsor)..	2·50	

Combination Presentation Packs for England, Northern Ireland, Scotland and Wales

11.5.04	PO Pack No. 68. 40p. (Nos. EN9, NI97, S112, W101)	6·50	
5.4.05	PO Pack No. 70. 42p. (Nos. EN10, NI98, S113, W102)..	6·25	
28.3.06	PO Pack No. 73. 44p. and 72p. (Nos. EN11, EN17, NI99, NI102, S114, S120, W103, W109)................	10·00	
27.3.07	PO Pack No. 76. 48p. and 78p. (Nos. EN12, EN18, NI124, NI128, S115, S121, W104, and W110)	10·00	
1.4.08	P.O. Pack. No. 79. 50p. and 81p. (Nos. EN13, EN19, NI125, NI129, S116, S122, W105, W111)................	10·00	
29.9.08	PO Pack No. 81. 2nd, 1st, 50p. and 81p. (Nos. EN6/7, EN13, EN19, NI122/3, NI125, NI129, S109/10, S116, S122, W98/9, W105, W111).................................	40·00	

31.3.09	PO Pack No. 85. 56p. and 90p. (Nos. EN14, EN20, NI126, NI130, S117, S123, W106, W112).....................	13·00	
30.3.10	PO Pack No. 87. 60p. and 97p. (Nos. EN15, EN21, NI127, NI131, S118, S124, W107, W113).....................	14·00	
29.3.11	PO Pack No. 91. 68p. and £1·10 (Nos. EN31, EN41, NI101, NI111, S132, S138 W123, W129)......................	15·00	
25.4.12	PO Pack No. 95. 87p. and £1·28 (Nos. EN32, EN43, NI103, NI113, S133, S143, W124, W134)...................	17·50	
27.3.13	PO. Pack No. 98. 88p. (Nos. EN33, NI104, S134, W125)...	8·50	
26.3.14	PO Pack No. 100. 97p. (Nos. EN34, NI105, S135, W126)...	8·50	
24.3.15	PO Pack No. 102 £1 and £1·33 (Nos. EN35, EN44, NI106, NI114, S136, S144, W127, W135)...................	17·50	
22.3.16	PO Pack No. 104. £1·05 (Nos. EN36, NI 107, S137 and W128)...	10·00	

EN **5** *(Illustration reduced.)*

(Des Peter Crowther, Clare Melinsky and Silk Pearce. Gravure De La Rue)

2007 (23 Apr). *Celebrating England.* Sheet 123×70 mm. Two phosphor bands. Perf 15×14 (with one elliptical hole in each vertical side) (1st) or 15×14½ (78p.).

MSEN50	EN **5**	(1st) No. EN7b; (1st) St George's flag; 78p. St George; 78p. Houses of Parliament, London	4·00	4·00
First Day Cover (Tallents House)				4·50
First Day Cover (St Georges, Telford)				4·50
Presentation Pack (PO Pack No. M15)................................			5·00	
PHQ Cards (set of 5) (CGB2)...			2·00	8·00

MSEN50 was on sale at post offices throughout the UK.

The five PHQ cards show the four individual stamps and the complete miniature sheet.

Stamps as the 1st class St George's flag stamp within **MS**EN50 but self-adhesive were issued on 23 April 2009 in sheets of 20 with *se-tenant* labels showing English Castles, No. LS59. These sheets were printed in lithography by Cartor and sold for £8·35 each.

EN **6**
St George's Flag

(Des Peter Crowther and Silk Pierce. Litho ISP Cartor (EN51) or Enschedé (EN51a))

2013 (9 May)–**14**. *England Flag.* Two phosphor bands. Perf 14½×14 (with one elliptical hole in each vertical side).

EN51	EN **6**	(1st) St George's Flag (Queen's head silver)............................	4·50	4·50
		a. St George's Flag (Queen's head grey) (20.2.14)	4·50	4·50

No. EN51 was issued in £11·11 Football Heroes booklets (No. DY7, booklet pane no. U3010a) and £16.49 Centenary of the First World War (3rd issue) booklets (No. DY18, booklet pane no. 3717a), and EN51a was issued in £13·97 Classic Locomotives booklets (No. DY9, booklet pane no. U3011b).

EN **7** Three lions   EN **8** Crowned lion,
of England   supporting the
                     shield of St George

EN **9** English
oak tree

EN **10** English
Tudor rose

(Des Sedley Place, from sculptures by David Dathan.
Litho ISP Cartor)

2017 (21 Mar)–**18**. As previous set but with value indicated in revised typeface. One centre band (EN52) or two phosphor bands. Perf 15×14 (with one elliptical hole in each vertical side).

EN52	EN **7**	(2nd)	Three lions of England (20.3.18) ...	1·00	75
EN53	EN **8**	(1st)	Lion and shield (20.3.18)........	1·25	75
EN54	EN **9**	£1·17	English oak tree (21.3.17)...............	2·75	2·75
EN55		£1·25	English oak tree (20.3.18)...........	2·75	2·75
EN60	EN **10**	£1·40	English Tudor rose (21.3.17)..........	3·00	3·00
EN61		£1·45	English Tudor rose (20.3.18)...........	3·25	3·25

Numbers have been left for possible additions to the above definitive series.

First Day Covers

21.3.17	£1.17, £1.40. (EN54, EN60) Tallents House (Type K).......	6·00
	London (as Windsor)	6·00
20.3.18	2nd, 1st, £1.25, £1.45. (EN52/53, EN55, EN61)	
	Tallents House (Type K)	9·00
	London (as Windsor)	9·00

**Combination Presentation Packs for England, Northern Ireland,
Scotland and Wales**

21.3.17	PO Pack No. 107. £1·17 and £1·40 (Nos. EN54, EN60, NI159, NI165, S161, S167, W151, W157)............	22·00
20.3.18	PO Pack No. 109. 2nd, 1st, £1.25, £1.45 (Nos. EN52/53, EN55, EN61, NI157/58, NI160, NI166, S159/60, S162, S168, W149/50, W152, W158)................	25·00

II. NORTHERN IRELAND

N **1** 　　　　N **2** 　　　　N **3**

(Des W Hollywood (3d., 4d., 5d.), L Pilton (6d., 9d.),
T Collins (1s.3d., 1s.6d.))

1958–67. W *179*. Perf 15×14.

NI1	N **1**	3d. deep lilac (18.8.58)................	15	15
		p. One centre phosphor band (9.6.67)................	25	25
NI2		4d. ultramarine (7.2.66)	15	15
		p. Two phosphor bands (10.67)..........	15	15
NI3	N **2**	6d. deep claret (29.9.58)................	50	50
NI4		9d. bronze-green (2 phosphor bands) (1.3.67)................	40	40
NI5	N **3**	1s.3d. green (29.9.58)................	50	50
NI6		1s.6d. grey-blue (2 phosphor bands) (1.3.67)................	40	40
		Ey. Phosphor omitted................	£225	

First Day Covers

18.8.58	3d. (NI1)................	30·00
29.9.58	6d., 1s.3d. (NI3, NI5)	35·00
7.2.66	4d. (NI2)	7·00
1.3.67	9d., 1s.6d. (NI4, NI6)	4·00

For Nos. NI1, NI3 and NI5 in Presentation Pack, see below Wales No. W6.

1968–69. No watermark. Chalk-surfaced paper. One centre phosphor band (Nos. NI8/9) or two phosphor bands (others). Gum arabic (No. NI7) or PVA gum (others). Perf 15×14.

NI7	N **1**	4d. deep bright blue (27.6.68)	25	25
		Ev. PVA gum* (23.10.68)............	30·00	
NI8		4d. olive-sepia (4.9.68)	25	25
		Ey. Phosphor omitted................		
NI9		4d. bright vermilion (26.2.69)................	30	30
		Ey. Phosphor omitted................	4·50	
NI10		5d. royal blue (4.9.68)................	40	40
		Ey. Phosphor omitted................	25·00	
NI11	N **3**	1s.6d. grey-blue (20.5.69)................	1·50	1·50
		Ey. Phosphor omitted................	£500	

4.9.68	*First Day Cover* (NI8, NI10)	3·00
9.12.70	*Presentation Pack* (PO Pack No. 25)	
	Nos. NI1p, NI4/6, NI8/10................	3·50

* No. NI7Ev was never issued in Northern Ireland. After No. NI7 (gum arabic) had been withdrawn from Northern Ireland but while still on sale at the philatelic counters elsewhere, about fifty sheets with PVA gum were sold over the London Philatelic counter on 23 October, 1968, and some were also on sale at the British Philatelic Exhibition Post Office.

There was no post office first day cover for No. NI9.

N **4**

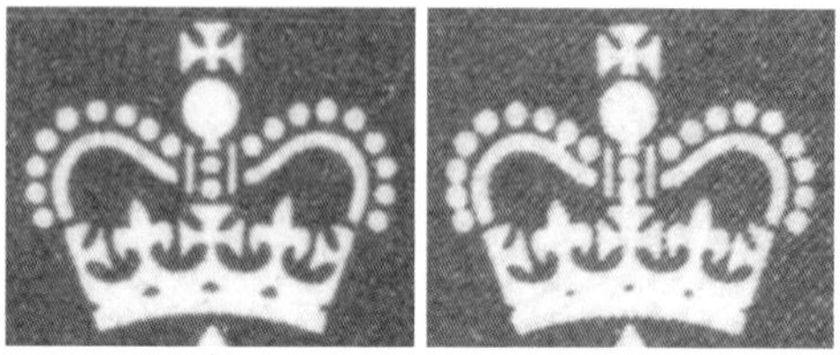

I　　　　　　　　　II

Redrawn design of Type N 4 (litho printings)
Two Types of Crown

Type I Crown with all pearls individually drawn.

Type II Crown with clear outlines, large pearls and strong white line below them. First 3 pearls at left are joined, except on Nos. NI39 and NI49.

The following stamps printed in lithography show a screened background behind and to the left of the emblem: 11½p., 12½p., 14p. (No. NI38), 15½p., 16p., 18p. (No. NI45), 19½p., 22p. (No. NI53) and 28p. (No. NI62). The 13p. and 17p. (No. NI43) also showed screened backgrounds in Type I, but changed to solid backgrounds for Type II. The 31p. had a solid background in Type I, but changed to a screened background for Type II. All other values printed in lithography have solid backgrounds.

(Des Jeffery Matthews after plaster cast by Arnold Machin)

1971 (7 July)–**93**. *Decimal Currency*. Chalk-surfaced paper. Type N 4.

(a) Photo Harrison. With phosphor bands. Perf 15×14.

NI12	2½p. bright magenta (1 centre band)................	60	60
NI13	3p. ultramarine (2 bands)................	30	30
	Ey. Phosphor omitted................	50·00	
NI14	3p. ultramarine (1 centre band) (23.1.74)................	20	20
NI15	3½p. olive-grey (2 bands) (23.1.74)................	20	20
NI16	3½p. olive-grey (1 centre band) (6.11.74)........	40	40
NI17	4½p. grey-blue (2 bands) (6.11.74)................	30	30
NI18	5p. reddish violet (2 bands)................	90	90
NI19	5½p. violet (2 bands) (23.1.74)................	25	25
	Ey. Phosphor omitted................	£250	
NI20	5½p. violet (1 centre band) (21.5.75)................	25	25
NI21	6½p. greenish blue (1 centre band) (14.1.76).	20	20
NI22	7p. purple-brown (1 centre band) (18.1.78).	30	30
NI23	7½p. chestnut (2 bands)................	1·25	1·25
	Ey. Phosphor omitted................	£100	
NI24	8p. rosine (2 bands) (23.1.74)................	40	40
	Ey. Phosphor omitted................	75·00	
NI25	8½p. yellow-green (2 bands) (14.1.76)................	40	40
NI26	9p. deep violet (2 bands) (18.1.78)................	40	40
	Ey. Phosphor omitted................	25·00	
NI27	10p. orange-brown (2 bands) (20.10.76)................	40	40
NI28	10p. orange-brown (1 centre band) (23.7.80)	40	40
NI29	10½p. steel-blue (2 bands) (18.1.78)................	50	50
NI30	11p. scarlet (2 bands) (20.10.76)................	50	50
	Ey. Phosphor omitted................	5·00	

(b) Photo Harrison. On phosphorised paper. Perf 15×14.

NI31	12p. yellowish green (23.7.80)................	50	50
NI32	13½p. purple-brown (23.7.80)................	60	60
NI33	15p. ultramarine (23.7.80)................	60	60

(c) Litho Questa (Type II, unless otherwise stated). Perf 14 (11½p., 12½p., 14p. (No. NI38), 15½p., 16p., 18p. (No. NI45), 19½p., 20½p., 22p. (No. NI53), 26p. (No. NI60), 28p. (No. NI62)) or 15×14 (others).

NI34	11½p. drab (1 side band) (8.4.81)................	85	85
NI35	12p. bright emerald (1 side band) (7.1.86)................	90	90
NI36	12½p. light emerald (Type I) (1 side band) (24.2.82)................	50	50
	a. Perf 15×14 (28.2.84)................	3·50	3·50
NI37	13p. pale chestnut (Type I) (1 side band) (23.10.84)................	60	60
	Ea. Type II (28.11.86)................	1·10	1·10
	Ey. Phosphor omitted (Type I)................	£375	

NI38	14p. grey-blue (Type I)			
	(phosphorised paper) (8.4.81)...................	60	60
NI39	14p. deep blue (1 centre band) (8.11.88)........	50	50
NI40	15p. bright blue (1 centre band) (28.11.89) ...	60	60
NI41	15½p. pale violet (Type I)		
	(phosphorised paper) (24.2.82).................	80	80
NI42	16p. drab (Type I)		
	(phosphorised paper) (27.4.83).................	1·00	1·00
	a. Perf 15×14 (28.2.84).......................	5·00	5·00
NI43	17p. grey-blue (Type I)		
	(phosphorised paper) (23.10.84)................	80	80
	Ea. Type II (9.9.86)...........................	£175	£150
NI44	17p. deep blue (1 centre band) (4.12.90).......	60	60
NI45	18p. deep violet (Type I)		
	(phosphorised paper) (8.4.81).................	80	80
NI46	18p. deep olive-grey		
	(phosphorised paper) (6.1.87).................	80	80
NI47	18p. bright green (1 centre band) (3.12.91)...	80	80
	a. Perf 14 (31.12.92*).........................	6·50	6·50
NI48	18p. bright green (1 side band) (10.8.93).......	1·50	1·50
	l. Booklet pane. Nos. NI48, NI59, S61, S71,		
	W49Eb and W60 with margins all round....	9·00	
NI49	19p. bright orange-red		
	(phosphorised paper) (8.11.88).................	80	80
NI50	19½p. olive-grey (Type I)		
	(phosphorised paper) (24.2.82).................	1·50	1·50
NI51	20p. brownish black		
	(phosphorised paper) (28.11.89)................	80	80
NI52	20½p. ultramarine (Type I)		
	(phosphorised paper) (27.4.83).................	2·75	2·75
NI53	22p. blue (Type I)		
	(phosphorised paper) (8.4.81).................	80	80
NI54	22p. yellow-green (Type I)		
	(phosphorised paper) (23.10.84)................	80	80
NI55	22p. bright orange-red		
	(phosphorised paper) (4.12.90).................	80	80
NI56	23p. bright green		
	(phosphorised paper) (8.11.88).................	80	80
NI57	24p. Indian red		
	(phosphorised paper) (28.11.89)................	90	90
NI58	24p. chestnut		
	(phosphorised paper) (3.12.91).................	80	80
NI59	24p. chestnut (2 bands) (10.8.93)...............	1·50	1·50
NI60	26p. rosine (Type I)		
	(phosphorised paper) (24.2.82).................	90	90
	a. Perf 15×14 (Type II) (27.1.87)..............	2·00	2·00
NI61	26p. drab (phosphorised paper) (4.12.90).......	1·25	1·25
NI62	28p. deep violet-blue (Type I)		
	(phosphorised paper) (27.4.83).................	1·00	1·00
	a. Perf 15×14 (Type II) (27.1.87)..............	90	90
NI63	28p. deep bluish grey		
	(phosphorised paper) (3.12.91).................	1·00	1·00
NI64	31p. bright purple (Type I)		
	(phosphorised paper) (23.10.84)................	1·40	1·40
	Ea. Type II (14.4.87).........................	1·80	1·80
NI65	32p. greenish blue		
	(phosphorised paper) (8.11.88).................	1·40	1·40
NI66	34p. deep bluish grey		
	(phosphorised paper) (28.11.89)................	1·40	1·40
NI67	37p. rosine		
	(phosphorised paper) (4.12.90).................	1·50	1·50
NI68	39p. bright mauve		
	(phosphorised paper) (3.12.91).................	1·40	1·40

* Earliest known date of use.

No. NI47a was caused by the use of a reserve perforating machine for some printings in the second half of 1992.

Nos. NI48 and NI59 only come from booklets.

From 1972 printings were made on fluorescent white paper and from 1973 most printings had dextrin added to the PVA gum (see notes after 1971 Decimal Machin issue).

First Day Covers

7.7.71	2½p., 3p., 5p., 7½p. (NI12/13, NI18, NI23)	2·50
23.1.74	3p., 3½p., 5½p., 8p. (NI14/15, NI19, NI24)	2·00
6.11.74	4½p. (NI17)	80
14.1.76	6½p., 8½p., 9p. (NI21, NI25)	80
20.10.76	10p., 11p. (NI27, NI30)	90
18.1.78	7p., 9p., 10½p. (NI22, NI26, NI29)	90
23.7.80	12p., 13½p., 15p. (NI31/3)	1·50
8.4.81	11½p., 14p., 18p., 22p. (NI34, NI38, NI45, NI53)...	1·20
24.2.82	12½p., 15½p., 19½p., 26p. (NI36, NI41, NI50, NI60) ..	2·00
27.4.83	16p., 20½p., 28p. (NI42, NI52, NI62)	2·00
23.10.84	13p., 17p., 22p., 31p. (NI37, NI43, NI54, NI64) ...	2·25
7.1.86	12p. (NI35)	90
6.1.87	18p. (NI46)	90
8.11.88	14p., 19p., 23p., 32p. (NI39, NI49, NI56, NI65) ...	2·50
28.11.89	15p., 20p., 24p., 34p. (NI40, NI51, NI57, NI66) ...	3·00
4.12.90	17p., 22p., 26p., 37p. (NI44, NI55, NI61, NI67) ...	3·00
3.12.91	18p., 24p., 28p., 39p. (NI47, NI58, NI63, NI68) ...	3·00

Presentation Packs

7.7.71	PO Pack No. 29. 2½p., 3p. (2 bands) 5p., 7½p. (Nos. NI12/13, NI18, NI23)..................	2·00
29.5.74	PO Pack No. 61. 3p. (1 centre band), 3½p. (2 bands) or (1 centre band), 5½p. (2 bands) or (1 centre band), 8p. (Nos. NI14, NI15 or NI16, NI19 or NI20, NI24). The 4½p. (No. NI17) was added later............	3·00
20.10.76	PO Pack No. 84. 6½p., 8½p., 10p. (2 bands), 11p. (Nos. NI21, NI25, NI27, NI30)......................	1·50
28.10.81	PO Pack No. 129d. 7p., 9p., 10½p., 12p. (gravure), 13½p., 15p. (gravure), 11½p., 14p. grey-blue, 18p. dp violet, 22p. blue (Nos. NI22, NI26, NI29, NI31/4, NI38, NI45, NI53)...................................	7·00
3.8.83	PO Pack No. 4. 10p. (1 centre band), 12½p., 16p., 20½p., 26p. rosine, 28p. dp violet-blue (Nos. NI28, NI36, NI42, NI52, NI60, NI62)..................	15·00
23.10.84	PO Pack No. 8. 10p. (1 centre band), 13p., 16p., 17p. grey-blue, 22p. yellow-green, 26p. rosine, 28p. dp violet-blue, 31p. (Nos. NI28, NI37, NI142a, NI43, NI54, NI60, NI62, NI64).............................	12·50
3.3.87	PO Pack No. 12. 12p. (litho), 13p., 17p. grey-blue, 18p. dp olive-grey, 22p. yellow-green, 26p. rosine, 28p. dp violet-blue, 31p. (Nos. NI35, NI37, NI43, NI46, NI54, NI60a, NI62a, NI64).......................	16·00

Presentation Packs for Northern Ireland, Scotland and Wales

8.11.88	PO Pack No. 17. 14p. dp blue, 19p., 23p., 32p. (Nos. NI39, NI49, NI56, NI65), 14p. (1 centre band), 19p. (phosphorised paper), 23p. (phosphorised paper), 32p. (Nos. S54, S62, S67, S77), 14p. dp blue, 19p., 23p., 32p. (Nos. W40, W50, W57, W66)..................	12·50
28.11.89	PO Pack No. 20. 15p. (litho), 20p., 24p. Indian red, 34p. (Nos. NI40, NI51, NI57, NI66), 15p. (litho), 20p., 24p. Indian red, 34p. (Nos. S56, S64, S69, S78), 15p. (litho), 20p., 24p. Indian red, 34p. (Nos. W41, W52, W58, W67)...................................	12·00
4.12.90	PO Pack No. 23. 17p. dp blue, 22p. brt orange-red, 26p. drab, 37p., (Nos. NI44, NI55, NI61, NI67), 17p. dp blue, 22p. brt orange-red, 26p. drab, 37p. (Nos. S58, S66, S73, S79), 17p. dp blue, 22p. brt orange-red, 26p. drab, 37p. (Nos. W45, W56, W62, W68)..........	12·00
3.12.91	PO Pack No. 26. 18p. brt green, 24p. chestnut, 28p. dp bluish grey, 39p. (Nos. NI47, NI58, NI63, NI68), 18p. brt green, 24p. chestnut, 28p. dp bluish grey, 39p. (Nos. S60, S70, S75, S80), 18p. brt green, 24p. chestnut, 28p. dp bluish grey, 39p. (Nos. W48, W59, W64, W69)...	12·00

(Des Jeffery Matthews after plaster cast by Arnold Machin)

1993 (7 Dec)–**2000**. Chalk-surfaced paper.

(a) Litho Questa. Perf 15×14 *(with one elliptical hole in each vert side).*

NI69	**N 4**	19p. bistre (1 centre band)..................	80	80
NI70		19p. bistre (1 band at left) (26.7.94)	1·25	1·25
		Ey. Phosphor omitted......................	£1000	
		a. Booklet pane. Nos. NI70×2, NI72×4, NI74, NI76 and centre label with margins all round............	5·00	
		b. Booklet pane. Nos. NI70, NI72, NI74 and NI76 with margins all round....	3·50	
		bEy. Booklet pane. Phosphor omitted.....	£4000	
		Ec. Band at left (25.4.95).................	1·80	1·80
		d. Booklet pane. Nos. NI70Ec, NI72, S82, S84, W71 and W73 with margins all round (25.4.95)..............	5·00	
		da. Part perf pane*........................	£4250	
NI71		20p. bright green (1 centre band) (23.7.96).......................................	1·25	1·25
NI72		25p. red (2 bands)...........................	75	75
		Ey. Phosphor omitted......................	£1000	
NI73		26p. red-brown (2 bands) (23.7.96)........	1·50	1·50
NI74		30p. deep olive-grey (2 bands)............	1·10	1·10
		Ey. Phosphor omitted......................	£1000	
NI75		37p. bright mauve (2 bands) (23.7.96)....	2·25	2·25
NI76		41p. grey-brown (2 bands).................	1·50	1·50
		Ey. Phosphor omitted......................	£950	
NI77		63p. light emerald (2 bands) (23.7.96)....	3·50	3·50

(b) Gravure Walsall (19p., 20p., 26p. (No. NI81b), 38p., 40p., 63p., 64p., 65p.), Harrison or Walsall (26p. (No. NI81), 37p.). Perf 14 (No. NI80) or 15×14 (others) (both with one elliptical hole in each vertical side).

NI78	**N 4**	19p. bistre (1 centre band) (8.6.99)........	2·50	2·50
NI79		20p. bright green (1 centre band) (1.7.97).......................................	2·25	2·25
NI80		20p. bright green (1 side band at right) (13.10.98)...................................	3·00	3·00
		al. Booklet pane. Nos. NI80, S90a, W79a and Y1717a×3 with margins all round............................	7·50	
NI81		26p. chestnut (2 bands) (1.7.97)...........	1·50	1·50
		al. Booklet pane. Nos. NI81/2, S91/2 and W80/1 with margins all round (23.9.97)................................	6·00	
		b. Perf 14 (13.10.98)	3·00	3·00
NI82		37p. bright mauve (2 bands) (1.7.97)......	1·90	1·90

NI83	38p. ultramarine (2 bands) (8.6.99)	5·50	5·50
NI84	40p. deep azure (2 bands) (25.4.00)...........	3·50	3·50
NI85	63p. light emerald (2 bands) (1.7.97).......	3·50	3·50
NI86	64p. turquoise-green (2 bands) (8.6.99).	6·50	6·50
NI87	65p. greenish blue (2 bands) (25.4.00)....	3·00	3·00

* No. NI70da, which comes from the 1995 National Trust £6 booklet, shows the top two values in the pane of 6 (Nos. S82, S84) completely imperforate and the two Wales values below partly imperforate.

Nos. NI70, NI80 and NI81b only come from booklets.
The listed booklet panes come from the following Sponsored Booklets:

NI70a/b	Booklet DX16
NI70d	Booklet DX17
NI80al	Booklet DX21
NI81al	Booklet DX19

First Day Covers

7.12.93	19p., 25p., 30p., 41p. (NI69, NI72, NI74, NI76)	4·00
26.7.94	Northern Ireland *se-tenant* pane 19p., 25p., 30p., 41p. (NI70a)..	5·00
23.7.96	20p., 26p., 37p., 63p. (NI71, NI73, NI75, NI77)	5·00
8.6.99	38p., 64p. (NI81, NI86)..................................	10·00
25.4.00	1st, 40p., 65p. (NI84, NI87, NI88b)........................	12·50

Presentation Packs

8.6.99	PO Pack No. 47. 19p., 26p., 38p., 64p. (Nos. NI78, NI81, NI83, NI86)..	15·00
25.4.00	PO Pack No. 52. 1st, 40p., 65p. (Nos. NI88b, NI84, NI87)	16·00

Presentation Packs for Northern Ireland, Scotland and Wales

7.12.93	PO Pack No. 31. 19p., 25p., 30p., 41p., each×3 (Nos. NI69, NI72, NI74, NI76, S81, S84, S86, S88, W70, W73, W75, W77)...	20·00
23.7.96	PO Pack No. 36. 20p., 26p., 37p., 63p., each×3 (Nos. NI71, NI73, NI75, NI77, S83, S85, S87, S89, W72, W74, W76, W78)...	16·00
20.10.98	PO Pack No. 42. 20p. (1 centre band), 26p., 37p., 63p., each×3 (Nos. NI79, NI81/2, NI85, S90/3, W79/82)......	18·00

N **5**

(Des Jeffery Matthews. Gravure Walsall)

2000 (15 Feb–25 Apr). Type N **4** redrawn with *1st* face value as Type N **5**. Two phosphor bands. Perf 14 (with one elliptical hole in each vertical side).

NI88	N **5**	(1st) bright orange-red	2·00	2·00
		al. Booklet pane. Nos. NI88, S108 and W97, each×3 with margins all round	13·00	
		b. Perf 15×14 (25.4.00)...................	7·00	7·00

First Day Cover (*se-tenant* pane No. NI88al) (Philatelic Bureau) .... 7·00
First Day Cover (*se-tenant* pane No. NI88al) (London SW5) 7·00
No. NI88 was issued in £7·50 stamp booklets (No. DX24) and No NI88b in sheets.

N **6** Basalt columns, Giant's Causeway

N **7** Aerial view of patchwork fields

N **8** Linen pattern

N **9** Vase pattern from Belleek

(Des Rodney Miller Associates (Basalt columns), Richard Cooke (Aerial view of fields), David Pauley (Linen pattern), Tiff Hunter (Vase pattern). Litho Walsall or Enschedé (1st, 2nd), De La Rue or Walsall (E), Walsall (65p.), De La Rue (68p.))

2001 (6 Mar)–**03**. One centre phosphor band (2nd) or two phosphor bands (others). Perf 15×14 (with one elliptical hole in each vertical side).

NI89	N **6**	(2nd) Basalt columns, Giant's Causeway ..	1·25	1·25
		a. Booklet pane. No. NI89x5 and No. NI90×4 with margins all round (25.2.03)	7·00	
		Ey. Phosphor omitted....................	£625	
NI90	N **7**	(1st) Aerial view of patchwork fields	1·50	1·50
		Ey. Phosphor omitted....................	35·00	
NI91	N **8**	(E) Linen pattern............................	2·00	2·00
NI92	N **9**	65p. Vase pattern from Belleek.................	2·25	2·25
NI93		68p. Vase pattern from Belleek (4.7.02)..	2·50	2·50

Presentation Pack (PO Pack No. 53) (Nos. NI89/92).......... 6·00
PHQ Cards (set of 4) (D19) (Nos. NI89/92)........................... 1·20 7·50

Nos. NI89, NI90 and NI91 were initially sold at 19p., 27p. and 36p., the latter representing the basic European airmail rate. A new printing of No. NI91, produced by De La Rue instead of Walsall, was issued on 15 October 2002. Stamps from this printing do not differ from those produced by Walsall. Booklet pane No. NI89a was printed by Enschedé. For combined presentation pack for all four Regions, see under England.

First Day Covers

6.3.01	2nd, 1st, E, 65p. (NI89/92) Philatelic Bureau	2·75
	Belfast..	3·00
4.7.02	68p. (NI93) Tallents House (Type K, see Introduction)	2·50
	Belfast..	2·75

2003 (14 Oct)–**17**. *As Nos. NI89/91 and* NI93, *and new values, but with white borders.* One centre phosphor band (2nd) or two phosphor bands (others). Perf 15×14 (with one elliptical hole in each vertical side).

(a) (Litho Walsall (NI98), De La Rue or Enschedé (NI95), Cartor (NI101 and NI103/15) or De La Rue (others))

NI94	N **6**	(2nd) Basalt columns, Giant's Causeway ..	1·25	1·25
NI95	N **7**	(1st) Aerial view of patchwork fields	1·50	1·50
		a. black omitted............................	£6000	
NI96	N **8**	(E) Linen pattern...........................	2·25	2·25
NI97		40p. Linen pattern (11.5.04).........................	1·60	1·60
NI98		42p. Linen pattern (5.4.05)		
		bluish grey and black.....................	2·25	2·25
		a. Linen pattern (26.7.05)		
		olive-grey and black.....................	2·50	2·50
NI99		44p. Linen pattern (28.3.06).........................	1·25	1·25
NI100	N **9**	68p. Vase pattern from Belleek.................	2·50	2·50
NI101	N **8**	68p. Linen pattern (29.3.11).........................	1·80	1·80
NI102	N **9**	72p. Vase pattern from Belleek (28.3.06)	2·75	2·75
NI103	N **8**	87p Linen pattern (25.4.12).........................	2·25	2·25
NI104		88p. Linen pattern (27.3.13).........................	2·25	2·25
NI105		97p. Linen pattern (26.3.14).........................	2·25	2·25
NI106		£1 Linen pattern (24.3.15)..............................	2·25	2·25
NI107		£1·05 Linen pattern (22.3.16).......................	2·50	2·50
NI111	N **9**	£1·10 Vase pattern from Belleek (29.3.11)	2·50	2·50
NI113		£1·28 Vase pattern from Belleek (25.4.12)	2·75	2·75
NI114		£1·33 Vase pattern from Belleek (24.3.15)	2·75	2·75

(b) Gravure De La Rue

NI122	N **6**	(2nd) Basalt columns, Giant's Causeway (20.9.07)	1·25	1·25
NI123	N **7**	(1st) Aerial view of patchwork fields (20.9.07)	1·50	1·50
NI124	N **8**	48p. Linen pattern (27.3.07).........................	1·20	1·20
NI125		50p. Linen pattern (1.4.08)...........................	1·20	1·20
NI126		56p. Linen pattern (31.3.09).........................	1·25	1·25
NI127		58p. Linen pattern (30.3.10).........................	1·40	1·40
NI128	N **9**	78p. Vase pattern from Belleek (27.3.07)	1·60	1·60
NI129		81p. Vase pattern from Belleek (1.4.08)..	2·00	2·00
NI130		90p. Vase pattern from Belleek (31.3.09)	2·25	2·25
NI131		97p. Vase pattern from Belleek (30.3.10)	2·50	2·50

Presentation Pack (PO Pack No. 66) (Nos. NI94/6, NI100) 7·50
PHQ Cards (set of 4) (D27) (Nos. NI94/6, NI100) 1·20 10·00

No. NI95 was printed in sheets and in £9·72 booklets, No. DX43 by De La Rue and was also issued in £7·66 booklets, No. DX40, printed by Enschedé and in premium booklets DY7 and DY18 (ISP Cartor) and DY9 and DY11 (Enschedé).
NI95a originates from an example of booklet pane NI154m with a progressive dry print of black.
No NI98 (Walsall printing) appears bluish grey and No. NI98a (De La Rue printing) appears olive-grey.
Nos. NI122/3 went on philatelic sale on 20 September 2007. They went on sale in Northern Ireland post offices as supplies of Nos. NI94/95 were used up.
* The bright magenta used on the 68p. is fluorescent.
A stamp as No. NI102 but printed in gravure was only issued within **MS**2685.
Stamps as Nos. NI128/9 but printed in lithography were only issued within **MS**2796 (NI128) or **MS**2886 (NI129).
A design as No. NI95 but self-adhesive was issued on 11 March 2008 in sheets of 20, each stamp accompanied by a *se-tenant* label showing a Northern Ireland scene (LS46). These sheets, perforated 15×14 without the elliptical holes, were printed in lithography by Cartor and sold at £7·35 each. They were also available with

personalised photographs on the labels at £14·95 from the Royal Mail in Edinburgh.

Stamps as EN30, NI95, S131 and W122 but self-adhesive were issued on 29 September 2008 in sheets of 20 containing five of each design with *se-tenant* labels (LS49).

Stamps as NI95 but self-adhesive were issued again on 17 March 2009 in sheets of 20 with *se-tenant* labels showing Northern Ireland Castles, LS58. These sheets were printed in lithography by Cartor and originally sold at £7·74 each (£8·35 from 6 April 2009).

First Day Covers

14.10.03	2nd, 1st, E, 68p. (NI94/6, NI100)		
	Tallents House (Type K, see Introduction)		3·25
	Belfast		3·25
11.5.04	40p. (NI97) Tallents House (Type K)		1·75
	Belfast		1·75
5.4.05	42p. (NI198) Tallents House (Type K)		2·25
	Belfast		2·25
28.3.06	44p., 72p. (NI99, NI102) Tallents House (Type K)		3·50
	Belfast		3·50
27.3.07	48p., 78p. (NI124, NI128) Tallents House (Type K)		2·50
	Belfast		2·50
1.4.08	50p., 81p. (NI125, NI129) Tallents House (Type K)		3·00
	Belfast		3·00
31.3.09	56p., 90p. (NI126, NI130) Tallents House(Type K)		3·50
	Belfast		3·50
30.3.10	60p., 97p. (NI127, NI131) Tallents House (Type K)		4·00
	Belfast		4·00
29.3.11	68p., £1·10 (NI101, NI111) Tallents House (Type K)		4·25
	Belfast		4·25
25.4.12	87p., £1·28 (NI103, NI113) Tallents House (Type K)		5·00
	Belfast		5·00
27.3.13	88p. (NI104) Tallents House (Type K)		2·25
	Belfast		2·25
26.3.14	97p. (NI105) Tallents House (Type K)		2·25
	Belfast		2·25
24.3.15	£1, £1·33 (NI106, NI114) Tallents House (Type K)		5·00
	Belfast		5·00
22.3.16	£1·05 (NI107) Tallents House (Type K)		2·50
	Belfast		2·50

N **10** *(Illustration reduced.)*

(Des David Lyons, Clare Melinsky, Ric Ergenhright and Silk Pearce. Litho De La Rue)

2008 (11 Mar). *Celebrating Northern Ireland.* Sheet 123×70 mm. Two phosphor bands. Perf 15×14½ (with one elliptical hole in each vertical side) (1st) or 15×14½ (78p).

MSNI152 N **10**	(1st) Carrickfergus Castle; (1st) Giant's Causeway; 78p. St Patrick; 78p. Queen's Bridge and *Angel of Thanksgiving* sculpture, Belfast	4·00	4·00
First Day Cover (Tallents House)			4·75
First Day Cover (Downpatrick, Co. Down)			4·75
Presentation Pack (PO Pack No. 410)		5·00	
PHQ Cards (set of 5) (CGB3)		60	7·00

MSNI152 was on sale at post offices throughout the UK.
The five PHQ cards depict the complete miniature sheet and the four stamps within it.

N **11** *(Illustration reduced.)*

(Des Sedley Place. Gravure De La Rue)

2008 (29 Sept). *50th Anniversary of the Country Definitives.* Sheet 124×70 mm, containing designs as Nos. NI1, NI3, NI5, S1, S3, S5, W1, W3 and W5 (regional definitives of 1958) but inscribed 1st and printed on pale cream. Two phosphor bands. Perf 15×14 (with one elliptical hole in each vertical side).

MSNI153 N **11** (1st)×9 As No. W1; As No. S1; As No. W5; As No. S5; As No. NI1; As No. W3; As No. S3; As No. NI3; As No. NI5		7·00	7·00
First Day Cover (Tallents House)			9·25
First Day Cover (Gloucester)			9·25
Presentation Pack (PO Pack No. 80)		10·00	
PHQ Cards (set of 10)		1·20	12·50

MSNI153 was on sale at post offices throughout the UK.
The ten PHQ cards show the nine individual stamps and the complete sheet.

(Litho De La Rue)

2008 (29 Sept). *50th Anniversary of the Country Definitives* (2nd issue). As Nos. NI1, NI3 and NI5 (definitives of 1958) but inscribed 1st. Two phosphor bands. Perf 15×14½ (with one elliptical hole in each vertical side).

NI154	N **1**	(1st) deep lilac	1·60	1·60
		l. Booklet pane. Nos. NI154/6, S154/6 and W144/6	15·00	
		m. Booklet pane. Nos. NI154/6 and NI95×3	6·50	
NI155	N **3**	(1st) green	1·60	1·60
NI156	N **2**	(1st) deep claret	1·60	1·60
First Day Cover (No. NI154l) (Tallents House)				6·00
First Day Cover (No. NI154l) (Gloucester)				6·00

Nos. NI154/6 come from £9·72 booklets, No. DX43.

N **12** Basalt columns, Giant's Causeway

N **13** Aerial view of patchwork fields

N **14** Linen pattern

N **15** Vase pattern from Belleek

(Des Rodney Miller Associates (Basalt columns), Richard Cooke (Aerial view of fields), David Pauley (Linen pattern), Tiff Hunter (Vase pattern). Litho ISP Cartor.)

2017 (21 Mar)–**2018**. As previous set but with value indicated in revised typeface. One centre band (2nd) or two phosphor bands. Perf 15×14 (with one elliptical hole in each vertical side).

NI157	N **12**	(2nd) Basalt columns, Giant's Causeway (20.3.18)	1·00	75
NI158	N **13**	(1st) Aerial view of patchwork fields (20.3.18)	1·25	75
NI159	N **14**	£1·17 Linen pattern (21.3.17)	2·50	2·50
NI160		£1·25 Linen pattern (20.3.18)	2·75	2·75
NI165	N **15**	£1·40 Vase pattern from Belleek (21.3.17)	3·00	3·00
NI166		£1·45 Vase pattern from Belleek (20.3.18)	3·25	3·25

Numbers have been left for possible additions to the above definitive series.

First Day Covers

21.3.17	£1.17, £1.40. (NI159, NI165) Tallents House (Type K)		6·00
	Belfast		6·00
20.3.18	2nd, 1st, £1.25, £1.45. (NI157/58, NI160, NI166) Tallents House (Type K)		9·00
	Belfast		9·00

III. SCOTLAND

S **1**    S **2**    S **3**

(Des. G. Huntly (3d., 4d., 5d.), J. Fleming (6d., 9d.),
A. Imrie (1s.3d., 1s.6d.))

1958–67. *W* **179**. Perf 15×14.

S1	S **1**	3d. deep lilac (18.8.58)		15	15
		p. Two phosphor bands (29.1.63)		7·50	6·00
		pa. One phosphor band at right (30.4.65)		25	25
		pb. Band at left		25	25
		pc. Horizontal pair. Nos. S1pa/pb		60	75
		pd. One centre phosphor band (9.11.67)		15	15
S2		4d. ultramarine (7.2.66)		20	20
		p. Two phosphor bands		20	20
S3	S **2**	6d. deep claret (29.9.58)		25	25
		p. Two phosphor bands (29.1.63)		25	25
S4		9d. bronze-green (2 phosphor bands) (1.3.67)		40	40
S5	S **3**	1s.3d. green (29.9.58)		40	40
		p. Two phosphor bands (29.1.63)		50	50
S6		1s.6d. grey-blue (2 phosphor bands) (1.3.67)		60	60

First Day Covers

18.8.58	3d. (S1)	17·00
29.9.58	6d., 1s.3d. (S3, S5)	25·00
7.2.66	4d. (S2)	7·00
1.3.67	9d., 1s.6d. (S4, S6)	6·00

The one phosphor band on No. S1pa was produced by printing broad phosphor bands across alternate vertical perforations. Individual stamps show the band at right or left (same prices either way).

For Nos. S1, S3 and S5 in Presentation Pack, see below Wales No. W6.

1967–70. No watermark. Chalk-surfaced paper. One centre phosphor band (Nos. 7, S9/10) or two phosphor bands (others). Gum arabic (Nos. S7, S8) or PVA gum (others). Perf 15×14.

S7	S **1**	3d. deep lilac (16.5.68)		15	15
		Ey. Phosphor omitted		7·00	
		Ev. PVA gum		10	
		Eya. Phosphor omitted (No. S7Ev)		4·00	
S8		4d. deep bright blue (28.11.67)		30	30
		Ey. Phosphor omitted		10·00	
		Ev. PVA gum (25.7.68)		10	
S9		4d. olive-sepia (4.9.68)		15	15
		Ey. Phosphor omitted		3·00	
S10		4d. bright vermilion (26.2.69)		15	15
		Ey. Phosphor omitted		2·50	
S11		5d. royal blue (4.9.68)		25	25
		Ey. Phosphor omitted		55·00	
S12	S **2**	9d. bronze-green (28.9.70)		4·00	4·00
		Ey. Phosphor omitted		£275	
S13	S **3**	1s.6d. grey-blue (12.12.68)		1·25	1·25
		Ey. Phosphor omitted		£125	

There was no Post Office first day cover for No. S10.

4.9.68	*First Day Cover* (S9, S11)	3·00
9.12.70	*Presentation Pack* (PO Pack No. 23) Nos. S3, S5p., S7, S9/13)	8·00

S **4**

I   II

Redrawn design of Type S 4 (litho printings.)

The introduction of the redrawn lion took place in 1983 when Wadding-ton's had the contract and therefore the 13, 17, 22 and 31p. exist in both

types and perforated 14. The Questa printings, perforated 15×14, are all Type II.

The Types of Lion.

Type I: The eye and jaw appear larger and there is no line across the bridge of the nose.

Type II: The tongue is thick at the point of entry to the mouth and the eye is linked to the background by a solid line.

The following stamps printed in lithography show a screened background behind and to the left of the emblem: 12½p., 15½p., 16p., 19½p., 28p. (Nos. S50 and S74) and 31p. (Nos. S51 and S76). The 13p. and 17p. (No. S43) also showed screened backgrounds for both Type I and II of the John Waddington printings, but changed to solid backgrounds for the Questa Type II. All other values printed in lithography have solid backgrounds.

(Des Jeffery Matthews after plaster cast by Arnold Machin)

1971 (7 July)–**93**. *Decimal Currency. Chalk-surfaced paper. Type S* **4**.

(a) Photo Harrison. With phosphor bands. Perf 15×14.

S14	2½p. bright magenta (1 centre band)	25	20
	Ey. Phosphor omitted	10·00	
	Eg. Gum arabic (22.9.72)	30	
	Egy. Phosphor omitted	20·00	
S15	3p. ultramarine (2 bands)	25	15
	Ey. Phosphor omitted	17·00	
	Eg. Gum arabic (14.12.72)	30	
	Ega. Imperf (pair)	£800	
	Egy. Phosphor omitted	50·00	
S16	3p. ultramarine (1 centre band) (23.1.74)	15	15
S17	3½p. olive-grey (2 bands) (23.1.74)	20	20
	Ey. Phosphor omitted	50·00	
S18	3½p. olive-grey (1 centre band) (6.11.74)	20	20
S19	4½p. grey-blue (6.11.74)	25	25
S20	5p. reddish violet (2 bands)	90	90
S21	5½p. violet (2 bands) (23.1.74)	25	25
S22	5½p. violet (1 centre band) (21.5.75)	20	25
	a. Imperf (pair)	£650	
S23	6½p. greenish blue (1 centre band) (14.1.76)	20	25
S24	7p. purple-brown (1 centre band) (18.1.78)	25	25
S25	7½p. chestnut (2 bands)	90	90
	Ey. Phosphor omitted	7·00	
S26	8p. rosine (2 bands) (23.1.74)	35	35
S27	8½p. yellow-green (2 bands) (14.1.76)	35	35
S28	9p. deep violet (2 bands) (18.1.78)	35	35
S29	10p. orange-brown (2 bands) (20.10.76)	35	35
S30	10p. orange-brown (1 centre band) (23.7.80)	35	35
S31	10½p. steel-blue (2 bands) (18.1.78)	45	45
S32	11p. scarlet (2 bands) (20.10.76)	40	40
	Ey. Phosphor omitted	3·50	

(b) Photo Harrison. On phosphorised paper. Perf 15×14.

S33	12p. yellowish green (23.7.80)	45	45
S34	13½p. purple-brown (23.7.80)	60	60
S35	15p. ultramarine (23.7.80)	50	50

(c) Litho Waddington. (Type I unless otherwise stated). One side phosphor band (11½p., 12p., 12½p., 13p.) or phosphorised paper (others). Perf 14.

S36	11½p. drab (8.4.81)	55	55
	Ey. Phosphor omitted	£1000	
S37	12p. bright emerald (Type II) (7.1.86)	1·25	1·25
S38	12½p. light emerald (24.2.82)	45	45
S39	13p. pale chestnut (Type I) (23.10.84)	75	75
	Ey. Phosphor omitted	£1000	
	Ea. Type II (1.85)	8·00	8·00
	Eay. Phosphor omitted	£1000	
S40	14p. grey-blue (8.4.81)	45	45
S41	15½p. pale violet (24.2.82)	50	50
S42	16p. drab (Type II) (27.4.83)	50	50
S43	17p. grey-blue (Type I) (23.10.84)	1·25	1·25
	Ea. Type II (1.85)	1·10	1·10
S44	18p. deep violet (8.4.81)	70	70
S45	19½p. olive-grey (24.2.82)	1·25	1·25
S46	20½p. ultramarine (Type II) (27.4.83)	2·25	2·25
S47	22p. blue (8.4.81)	75	75
S48	22p. yellow-green (Type I) (23.10.84)	2·25	2·25
	Ea. Type II (1.86)	28·00	28·00
S49	26p. rosine (24.2.82)	70	70
S50	28p. deep violet-blue (Type II) (27.4.83)	70	70
S51	31p. bright purple (Type I) (23.10.84)	1·50	1·50
	Ea. Type II (11.85*)	£180	£180

(d) Litho Questa (Type II). Perf 15×14.

S52	12p. bright emerald (1 side band) (29.4.86)	1·25	1·25
S53	13p. pale chestnut (1 side band) (4.11.86)	70	70
S54	14p. deep blue (1 centre band) (8.11.88)	45	45
	I. Booklet pane. No. S54×6 with margins all round (21.3.89)	2·00	
S55	14p. deep blue (1 side band) (21.3.89)	50	50
	I. Booklet pane. No. S55×5, S63×2, S68 and centre label with margins all round	10·00	
	Ia. Error. Booklet pane imperf	£2600	
S56	15p. bright blue (1 centre band) (28.11.89)	50	50
	a. Imperf (three sides) (block of four)	£275	

S57	17p. grey-blue (phosphorised paper) (29.4.86)	2·40	2·40
S58	17p. deep blue (1 centre band) (4.12.90)	70	70
S59	18p. deep olive-grey (phosphorised paper) (6.1.87)	70	70
S60	18p. bright green (1 centre band) (3.12.91)	60	60
	a. *Perf 14* (26.9.92*)	1·00	1·00
	aEy. Phosphor omitted	£1250	
S61	18p. bright green (1 side band) (10.8.93)	1·40	1·40
S62	19p. bright orange-red (phosphorised paper) (8.11.88)	50	50
	l. Booklet pane. No. S62×9 with margins all round (21.3.89)	3·00	
	m. Booklet pane. No. S62×6 with margins all round (21.3.89)	2·25	
S63	19p. bright orange-red (2 bands) (21.3.89)	1·40	1·40
S64	20p. brownish black (phosphorised paper) (28.11.89)	70	70
S65	22p. yellow-green (phosphorised paper) (27.1.87)	1·10	1·10
S66	22p. bright orange-red (phosphorised paper) (4.12.90)	60	60
S67	23p. bright green (phosphorised paper) (8.11.88)	80	80
S68	23p. bright green (2 bands) (21.3.89)	9·00	9·00
S69	24p. Indian red (phosphorised paper) (28.11.89)	1·00	1·00
S70	24p. chestnut (phosphorised paper) (3.12.91)	75	75
	a. *Perf 14* (10.92*)	8·00	8·00
S71	24p. chestnut (2 bands) (10.8.93)	1·40	1·40
S72	26p. rosine (phosphorised paper) (27.1.87)	2·25	2·25
S73	26p. drab (phosphorised paper) (4.12.90)	1·00	1·00
S74	28p. deep violet-blue (phosphorised paper) (27.1.87)	1·00	1·00
S75	28p. deep bluish grey (phosphorised paper) (3.12.91)	1·00	1·00
	a. *Perf 14* (18.2.93*)	9·00	9·00
S76	31p. bright purple (phosphorised paper) (29.4.86)	1·50	1·50
S77	32p. greenish blue (phosphorised paper) (8.11.88)	1·00	1·00
S78	34p. deep bluish grey (phosphorised paper) (28.11.89)	1·20	1·75
S79	37p. rosine (phosphorised paper) (4.12.90)	1·25	1·25
S80	39p. bright mauve (phosphorised paper) (3.12.91)	1·50	1·50
	a. *Perf 14* (11.92)	12·50	12·50

* Earliest known date of use.

Nos. S55, S61, S63, S68 and S71 only come from booklets.
The listed booklet panes come from the Sponsored Booklet DX10; S54l, S55l, S62l/m.

No. S56a occured in the second vertical row of two sheets. It is best collected as a block of four including the left-hand vertical pair imperforate on three sides.

Nos. S60a, S70a, S75a and S80a were caused by the use of a reserve perforating machine for some printings in the second half of 1992.

From 1972 printings were on fluorescent white paper. From 1973 most printings had dextrin added to the PVA gum (see notes after the 1971 Decimal Machin issue).

First Day Covers

7.7.71	2½p., 3p., 5p., 7½p. (S14/15, S20, S25)	1·50
23.1.74	3p., 3½p., 5½p., 8p. (S16/17, S21, S26)	1·20
6.11.74	4½p. (S19)	1·00
14.1.76	6½p., 8½p. (S23, S27)	1·00
20.10.76	10p., 11p. (S29, S32)	1·00
18.1.78	7p., 9p., 10½p. (S24, S28, S31)	1·00
23.7.80	12p., 13½p., 15p. (S33/5)	1·50
8.4.81	11½p., 14p., 18p., 22p. (S36, S40, S44, S47)	1·50
24.2.82	12½p., 15½p., 19½p., 26p. (S38, S41, S45, S49)	1·80
27.4.83	16p., 20½p., 28p. (S42, S46, S50)	2·00
23.10.84	13p., 17p., 22p., 31p. (S39, S43, S48, S51)	2·00
7.1.86	12p. (S37)	1·00
6.1.87	18p. (S59)	1·00
8.11.88	14p., 19p., 23p., 32p. (S54, S62, S67, S77)	2·00
21.3.89	Scots Connection *se-tenant* pane 14p., 19p., 23p. (S55l)	10·00
28.11.89	15p., 20p., 24p., 34p. (S56, S64, S69, S78)	2·50
4.12.90	17p., 22p., 26p., 37p. (S58, S66, S73, S79)	2·50
3.12.91	18p., 24p., 28p., 39p. (S60, S70, S75, S80)	2·50

Presentation Packs

7.7.71	PO Pack No. 27. 2½p., 3p. (2 bands), 5p., 7½p. (Nos. S14/15, S20, S25)	2·00
29.5.74	PO Pack No. 62. 3p. (1 centre band), 3½p. (2 bands) or (1 centre band), 5½p. (2 bands) or (1 centre band), 8p. (Nos. S16, S17 or S18, S21 or S22, S26). The 4½p. (No. S19) was added later	2·00
20.10.76	PO Pack No. 85. 6½p., 8½p., 10p. (2 bands), 11p. (Nos. S23, S27, S29, S32)	1·50

28.10.81	PO Pack No. 129b. 7p., 9p., 10½p., 12p. (gravure), 13½p., 15p. (gravure), 11½p., 14p. grey-blue, 18p. dp violet, 22p. blue (Nos. S24, S28, S31, S33/6, S40, S44, S47)	6·00
3.8.83	PO Pack No. 2. 10p. (1 centre band), 12½p., 16p., 20½p., 26p. (J.W.), 28p. (J.W.), (Nos. S30, S38, S42, S46, S49/50)	14·00
23.10.84	PO Pack No. 6. 10p. (1 centre band), 13p. (J.W.), 16p., 17p. (J.W.), 22p. yellow-green, 26p. (J.W.), 28p. (J.W.), 31p. (J.W.), (Nos. S30, S39, S42/3, S48/51)	12·00
3.3.87	PO Pack No. 10. 12p. (litho), 13p. (Questa), 17p. grey-blue (Questa), 18p. dp olive-grey, 22p. yellow-green, 26p. rosine (Questa), 28p. dp violet-blue (Questa), 31p. (Questa) (Nos. S52/3, S57, S59, S65, S72, S74, S76)	15·00

Presentation Packs containing stamps of Northern Ireland, Scotland and Wales are listed after those for Northern Ireland.

1977–78 EXPERIMENTAL MACHINE PACKETS. These are small cartons containing loose stamps for sale in vending machines. The experiment was confined to the Scottish Postal Board area, where six vending machines were installed, the first becoming operational in Dundee about February 1977.

The cartons carry labels inscribed "ROYAL MAIL STAMPS", their total face value (30p. or 60p.) and their contents.

At first the 30p. packet contained two 6½p. and two 8½p. Scottish Regional stamps and the 60p. packet had four of each. The stamps could be in pairs or blocks, but also in strips or singles.

With the change in postal rates on 13 June 1977 these packets were withdrawn on 11 June and on 13 June the contents were changed, giving three 7p. and one 9p. for the 30p. packet and double this for the 60p. packet. However, this time ordinary British Machin stamps were used. Moreover the Edinburgh machine, situated in an automatic sorting area, was supplied with 7p. stamps with two phosphor bands instead of the new centre band 7p. stamps, despite instructions having been given to withdraw the two band stamps. However, the demand for these packets was too great to be filled and by 27 June the machine was closed down. It was brought back into use on 16 August 1977, supplying 7p. stamps with the centre band.

The 6½p. and 8½p. Scottish Regional packets were put on sale at the Edinburgh Philatelic Bureau in June 1977 and withdrawn in April 1978. The packets with the 7p. and 9p. Machin stamps were put on sale at the Bureau in June 1977 and withdrawn in December 1978.

Such machine packets are outside the scope of this catalogue.

(Des Jeffery Matthews after plaster cast by Arnold Machin)

1993 (7 Dec)–**98.** Chalk-surfaced paper.

(a) Litho Questa. Perf 15×14 (with one elliptical hole in each vert side).

S81	S 4	19p. bistre (1 centre band)	70	70
S82		19p. bistre (1 band at right) (25.4.95)	2·00	2·00
S83		20p. bright green (1 centre band) (23.7.96)	1·25	1·25
S84		25p. red (2 bands)	80	80
S85		26p. red-brown (2 bands) (23.7.96)	1·40	1·40
S86		30p. deep olive-grey (2 bands)	1·25	1·25
S87		37p. bright mauve (2 bands) (23.7.96)	1·75	1·75
S88		41p. grey-brown (2 bands)	1·25	1·25
		Ey. Phosphor omitted	£325	
S89		63p. light emerald (2 bands) (23.7.96)	2·50	2·50

(b) Gravure Walsall (20p., 26p. (No. S91a), 63p.), Harrison or Walsall (26p. (No. S91), 37p.). Perf 14 (No. S90a) or 15×14 (others) (both with one elliptical hole in each vertical side).

S90	S 4	20p. bright green (1 centre band) (1.7.97)	1·00	1·00
S90a		20p. bright green (1 side band at right) (13.10.98)	3·00	3·00
S91		26p. chestnut (2 bands) (1.7.97)	1·40	1·40
		a. *Perf 14* (13.10.98)	3·00	3·00
S92		37p. bright mauve (2 bands) (1.7.97)	1·60	1·60
S93		63p. light emerald (2 bands) (1.7.97)	3·50	3·50

Nos. S82, S90a and S91a only come from booklets. The Harrison printings of Nos. S91/2 come from booklet pane No. NI81al.

First Day Covers

7.12.93	19p., 25p., 30p., 41p. (S81, S84, S86, S88)	3·50
23.7.96	20p. 26p., 37p., 63p. (S83, S85, S87, S89)	4·00

For Presentation Pack containing stamps of Northern Ireland, Scotland and Wales see after No. NI87 of Northern Ireland.

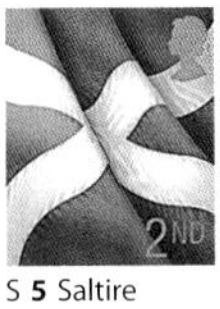

S **5** Saltire

S **6** Lion Rampant of Scotland

S **7** Thistle   S **8** Tartan

(Des Anton Morris (Saltire), Frank Pottinger (Lion Rampant of Scotland), Tim Chalk (Thistle) and Tartan, supplied by Kinloch Anderson; adapted by Tayburn of Edinburgh. Gravure Questa (Nos. S94a, S95a), De La Rue (No. S99), De La Rue or Walsall (Nos. S94/5), Walsall (others))

1999 (8 June)–**2002**. One centre phosphor band (2nd) or two phosphor bands (others). Perf 15×14 (with one elliptical hole in each vertical side).

S94	S **5**	(2nd) Saltire	1·25	1·25
		a. Booklet pane. Nos. S94×6 and S98×2 with centre label and margins all round (4.8.00)	6·00	
S95	S **6**	(1st) Lion Rampant of Scotland	1·50	1·50
		a. Booklet pane. Nos. S95/6, each×4, with centre label and margins all round (22.10.01)	7·50	
S96	S **7**	(E) Thistle	2·25	2·25
S97	S **8**	64p. Tartan	5·50	5·50
S98		65p. Tartan (25.4.00)	2·00	2·00
S99		68p. Tartan (4.7.02)	2·60	2·60

Presentation Pack (PO Pack No. 45)
(2nd, 1st, E, 64p.) (Nos. S94/7) .... 9·50
Presentation Pack (PO Pack No. 50) (65p.) (No. S98) .... 10·00
Presentation Pack (PO Pack No. 55)
(2nd, 1st, E, 65p.) (Nos. S94/6, S98) .... 15·00
PHQ Cards (set of 4) (D12) (Nos. S94/7) .... 1·20   10·00

Nos. S94, S95 and S96 were initially sold at 19p, 26p. and 30p., the latter representing the basic European airmail rate.

New printings of Nos. S94/5, produced by De La Rue instead of Walsall were issued on 5 June 2002. Stamps from this printing do not differ from those produced by Walsall.

No. S94a comes from booklet No. DX25.

No. S95a comes from booklet No. DX27.

For combined presentation pack for all four Regions, see under England.

First Day Covers

8.6.99	2nd, 1st, E, 64p. (S94/7) Philatelic Bureau		3·50
	Edinburgh		4·00
25.4.00	65p. (S98) Philatelic Bureau		2·50
	Edinburgh		2·50
4.8.00	Queen Elizabeth the Queen Mother *se-tenant* pane 2nd, 65p. (S94a) Philatelic Bureau (as for Nos. 2160/1)		4·75
	London SW1 (as for Nos. 2160/1)		4·75
22.10.01	Unseen and Unheard *se-tenant* pane (1st), E, (S95a) Philatelic Bureau (as for **MS**2206)		7·00
	Rosyth, Dunfermline (as for **MS**2206)		7·00
4.7.02	68p. (S99) Tallents House (Type K) (see Introduction)		2·00
	Edinburgh		2·00

S **9**

(Des Jeffery Matthews. Gravure Walsall)

2000 (15 Feb). Type S **4** redrawn with *1st* face value as Type S **9**. Two phosphor bands. Perf 14 (with one elliptical hole in each vertical side).

S108	S **9**	(1st) bright orange-red	2·00	2·00

No. S108 was only issued in £7·50 stamp booklets (No. DX24).

2003 (14 Oct)–**17**. As Nos. S 94/6 and S 99, and new values, but with white borders. One centre phosphor band (2nd) or two phosphor bands (others). Perf 15×14 (with one elliptical hole in each vertical side).

(a) Gravure Walsall or De La Rue (42p.) or De La Rue (others)

S109	S **5**	(2nd) Saltire	1·25	1·25
		l. Booklet pane. Nos. S109 and EN16, each×3, with margins all round (16.3.04)	5·50	
		m. Booklet pane. Nos. S109 and W103, each×3, with margins all round (1.3.07)	5·00	
S110	S **6**	(1st) Lion Rampant of Scotland	1·50	1·50
S111	S **7**	(E) Thistle	2·10	2·10
S112		40p. Thistle (11.5.04)	1·40	1·40
S113		42p. Thistle (5.4.05)	1·75	1·75

S114		44p. Thistle (28.3.06)	1·40	1·40
S115		48p. Thistle (27.3.07)	1·25	1·25
S116		50p. Thistle (1.4.08)	1·25	1·25
S117		56p. Thistle (31.3.09)	1·40	1·40
S118		60p. Thistle (30.3.10)	1·50	1·50
S119	S **8**	68p. Tartan	1·60	1·60
S120		72p. Tartan (28.3.06)	1·75	1·75
S121		78p. Tartan (27.3.07)	1·75	1·75
S122		81p. Tartan (1.4.08)	2·00	2·00
S123		90p. Tartan (31.3.09)	2·25	2·25
S124		97p. Tartan (30.3.10)	2·40	2·40

(b) Litho Enschedé, De La Rue or ISP Cartor (1st) or ISP Cartor (others). Queen's head in grey (Nos. S130a and S131a) or silver (others)

S130	S **5**	(2nd) Saltire (27.6.12)	1·25	1·25
S130a		Saltire (5.16)	1·75	2·50
S131	S **6**	(1st) Lion Rampant of Scotland (20.9.07)	1·50	1·50
S131a		Lion Rampant of Scotland (5.16)	2·00	2·00
S132	S **7**	68p. Thistle (29.3.11)	1·80	1·80
S133		87p. Thistle (25.4.12)	2·10	2·10
S134		88p. Thistle (27.3.13)	2·10	2·10
S135		97p. Thistle (26.3.14)	2·40	2·40
S136		£1 Thistle (24.3.15)	2·40	2·40
S137		£1·05 Thistle (22.3.16)	2·60	2·60
S138	S **8**	£1·10 Tartan (29.3.11)	2·40	2·40
S143		£1·28 Tartan (25.4.12)	2·60	2·60
S144		£1·33 Tartan (24.3.15)	2·75	2·75

Presentation Pack (PO Pack No. 64) (Nos. S109/11, S119) .... 6·00
PHQ Cards (set of 4) (D25) (Nos. S109/11, S119) .... 6·50

No. S109l comes from booklet No. DX32 and S109m from booklet DX38. The Walsall printing of No. S113 was issued on 5 April 2005, and the De La Rue printing on 24 May 2005.

Stamps as No. S121/2 but printed in lithography were only issued within **MS**2796 (S121) or **MS**2886 (S122).

No. S131 was issued on 20 September 2007 in £7·66 stamp booklets printed by Enschedé, No. DX40 and on 29 September 2008 in £9·72 booklets (DX43) printed by De La Rue. It was issued in sheets printed by ISP Cartor on 27 June 2012

A design as No. S131 but self-adhesive was issued on 30 November 2007 in sheets of 20, each stamp accompanied by a *se-tenant.* label showing a Scottish scene (LS44). These sheets were printed in lithography by Cartor, perforated 15×14 without the elliptical holes, and sold at £7·35. They were also available with personalised photographs on the labels at £14·95 from the Royal Mail in Edinburgh.

Stamps as Nos. EN30, NI95, S131 and W122 but self-adhesive were issued on 29 September 2008 in sheets of 20 containing five of each design with *se-tenant* labels (LS49).

Numbers have be left for possible additions to this definitive series.

First Day Covers

14.10.03	2nd, 1st, E, 68p. (S109/11, S119) Tallents House (Type K, see Introduction)	2·00
	Edinburgh	2·00
11.5.04	40p. (S112) Tallents House (Type K)	1·50
	Edinburgh	1·50
5.4.05	42p. (S113) Tallents House (Type K)	1·75
	Edinburgh	1·75
28.3.06	44p., 72p. (S114, S120) Tallents House (Type K)	3·00
	Edinburgh	3·00
27.3.07	48p., 78p. (S115, S121) Tallents House (Type K)	3·00
	Edinburgh	3·00
1.4.08	50p., 81p. (S116, S122) Tallents House (Type K)	3·25
	Edinburgh	3·25
31.3.09	56p., 90p. (S117, S123) Tallents House (Type K)	3·50
	Edinburgh	3·50
30.3.10	60p., 97p. (S118, S124) Tallents House (Type K)	3·75
	Edinburgh	3·75
29.3.11	68p., £1·10 (S132, S138) Tallents House (Type K)	4·25
	Edinburgh	4·25
25.4.12	87p., £1·28 (S133, S143) Tallents House (Type K)	4·50
	Edinburgh	4·50
27.3.13	88p. (S134) Tallents House (Type K)	2·00
	Edinburgh	2·00
26.3.14	97p. (S135) Tallents House (Type K)	2·25
	Edinburgh	2·25
24.3.15	£1, £1·33 (S136, S144) Tallents House (Type K)	5·25
	Edinburgh	5·25
22.3.16	£1·05 (S137) Tallents House (Type K)	2·50
	Edinburgh	2·50

S **9a** *(Illustration reduced.)*

(Des Howard Brown. Gravure De La Rue)

2004 (5 Oct). *Opening of New Scottish Parliament Building, Edinburgh.* Sheet 123×70 mm. Printed in gravure by De La Rue. One centre phosphor band (2nd) or two phosphor bands (others). Perf 15×14 (with one elliptical hole in each vertical side).

MSS152 S **9a** Nos. S109, S110×2 and S112×2		5·00	5·00	
First Day Cover (Tallents House)			5·00	
First Day Cover (Edinburgh)			5·00	

S **10** *(Illustration reduced.)*

(Des Peter Crowther, Clare Melinsky and Silk Pearce. Gravure De La Rue)

2006 (30 Nov). *Celebrating Scotland.* Sheet 124×71 mm. Two phosphor bands. Perf 15×14 (with one elliptical hole in each vertical side) (1st) or 14½×14 (72p).

MSS153 S **10** (1st) As No. S110; (1st) Saltire; 72p. St Andrew; 72p. Edinburgh Castle		4·00	4·00	
First Day Cover (Tallents House)			4·25	
First Day Cover (St Andrews, Fife)			4·75	
Presentation Pack (PO Pack No. M14)		5·25		
PHQ Cards (set of 5) (CGB1)		1·50	4·00	

MSS153 was on sale at post offices throughout the UK.

The five PHQ cards depict the complete miniature sheet and the four stamps within it.

Stamps as the 1st class Saltire stamp within **MS**S153 but self-adhesive were issued on 30 November 2009 in sheets of 20 with *se-tenant* labels showing Scottish Castles, No. LS68. These sheets were printed in lithography by Cartor and sold for £8·35 each.

(Litho De La Rue)

2008 (29 Sept). *50th Anniversary of the Country Definitives.* As Nos. S1, S3 and S5 (definitives of 1958) but inscribed 1st. Two phosphor bands. Perf 15×14½ (with one elliptical hole in each vertical side).

S154	S **1**	(1st) deep lilac	1·60	1·60
		I. Booklet pane. Nos. S154/6 and S131×3	6·50	
S155	S **3**	(1st) green	1·60	1·60
S156	S **2**	(1st) deep claret	1·60	1·60

Nos. S154/6 come from £9·72 booklets, No. DX43.

S **11** *(Illustration reduced.)*

(Des Tayburn. Gravure Enschedé)

2009 (22 Jan). *250th Birth Anniversary of Robert Burns (Scottish poet).* Sheet 145×74 mm. One centre phosphor band (2nd) or two phosphor bands (others). Perf 14½ (size 34×34 mm) or 15×14 (with one elliptical hole in each vertical side) (others).

MSS157 S **11** (2nd) No. S109; (1st) *"A Man's a Man for a' that"* and Burns ploughing (detail) (James Sargent Storer) (34×34 mm); (1st) No. S110; (1st) Portrait of Burns (Alexander Nasmyth) (34×34 mm); 50p. No. S116; 81p. S122	5·00	5·00
First Day Cover (Tallents House)		5·25
First Day Cover (Alloway, Ayr)		5·25
Presentation Pack (PO Pack No. 422)	6·00	
PHQ Cards (set of 3) (319)	90	7·00

MSS157 was on sale at post offices throughout the UK.

The three PHQ cards show the two 34×34 mm Robert Burns stamps and the complete miniature sheet.

S **12** Saltire

Des Peter Crowther (illustration) and Silk Pierce.
Litho ISP Cartor or Enschedé

2013 (9 May). *Scotland Flag.* Two phosphor bands. Perf 14½×14 (with one elliptical hole in each vertical side).

S158	S **12**	(1st) Saltire	3·50	3·50

No. S158 was issued in £11·11 Football Heroes booklets (No. DY7, booklet pane No. U3010*a*), £13·97 Classic Locomotives booklets (No. DY9, booklet pane No. U3011*b*) and £16·49 Centenary of the First World War (3rd issue) booklets (No. DY18, booklet pane 3717*a*).

S **13** Saltire   S **14** Lion Rampant of Scotland

S **15** Thistle   S **16** Tartan

(Des Des Anton Morris (Saltire), Frank Pottinger (Lion Rampant of Scotland), Tim Chalk (Thistle) and Tartan, supplied by Kinloch Anderson; adapted by Tayburn of Edinburgh. Litho ISP Cartor)

2017 (21 Mar)–**2018**. As previous set but with value indicated in revised typeface. One centre band (2nd) or two phosphor bands. Perf 15×14 (with one elliptical hole in each vertical side).

S159	S **12**	(2nd) Saltire (20.3.18)	1·00	75
S160	S **13**	(1st) Lion Rampant of Scotland (20.3.18)	1·25	75
S161	S **14**	£1·17 Thistle (21.3.17)	2·40	2·40
S162		£1·25 Thistle (20.3.18)	2·75	2·75
S167	S **15**	£1·40 Tartan (21.3.17)	2·75	2·75
S168		£1·45 Tartan (20.3.18)	3·25	3·25

Numbers have been left for possible additions to the above definitive series.

First Day Covers

21.3.17	£1.17, £1.40. (S161, S167) Tallents House (Type K)	5·00	
	Edinburgh	5·00	
20.3.18	2nd, 1st, £1.25, £1.45. (S159/60, S162, S168)		
	Tallents House (Type K)	9·00	
	Edinburgh	9·00	

IV. WALES

From the inception of the Regional stamps, the Welsh versions were tendered to members of the public at all Post Offices within the former County of Monmouthshire but the national alternatives were available on request. By August 1961 the policy of "dual stocking" of definitive stamps was only maintained at Abergavenny, Chepstow, Newport and Pontypool. Offices with a Monmouthshire postal address but situated outside the County, namely Beachley, Brockweir, Redbrook, Sedbury, Tutshill, Welsh Newton and Woodcroft, were not supplied with the Welsh Regional stamps. With the re-formation of Counties, Monmouthshire became known as Gwent and was also declared to be part of Wales. From 1 July 1974, therefore, except for the offices mentioned above, only Welsh Regional stamps were available at the offices under the jurisdiction of Newport, Gwent.

| **W 1** | **W 2** | **W 3** |

(Des Reynolds Stone)

1958–67. *W* **179.** Perf 15×14.

W1	W **1**	3d. deep lilac (18.8.58)	15	15
		p. One centre phosphor band (16.5.67)	20	15
W2		4d. ultramarine (7.2.66)	20	20
		p. Two phosphor bands (10.67)	20	20
W3	W **2**	6d. deep claret (29.9.58)	35	35
W4		9d. bronze-green (2 phosphor bands) (1.3.67)	35	35
		Ey. Phosphor omitted	£375	
W5	W **3**	1s.3d. green (29.9.58)	40	40
W6		1s.6d. grey-blue (2 phosphor bands) (1.3.67)	40	40
		Ey. Phosphor omitted	50·00	

First Day Covers

18.8.58	3d. (W1)	12·00
29.9.58	6d., 1s.3d. (W3, W5)	25·00
7.2.66	4d. (W2)	7·00
1.3.67	9d., 1s.6d. (W4, W6)	4·00
	Presentation Pack*	£100

* This was issued in 1960 and comprises Guernsey No. 7, Jersey No. 10, Isle of Man No. 2, Northern Ireland Nos. NI1, NI3 and NI5, Scotland Nos. S1, S3 and S5 and Wales Nos. W1, W3 and W5 together with a 6-page printed leaflet describing the stamps. There exist two forms: (a) inscribed "7s.3d." for sale in the U.K.; and (b) inscribed "$1.20" for sale in the USA.

1967–69. No wmk. Chalk-surfaced paper. One centre phosphor band (Nos. W7, W9/10) or two phosphor bands (others). Gum arabic (3d.) or PVA gum (others). Perf 15×14.

W7	W **1**	3d. deep lilac (6.12.67)	15	15
		Ey. Phosphor omitted	70·00	
W8		4d. ultramarine (21.6.68)	15	15
W9		4d. olive-sepia (4.9.68)	15	15
W10		4d. bright vermilion (26.2.69)	15	15
		Ey. Phosphor omitted	2·00	
W11		5d. royal blue (4.9.68)	15	15
		Ey. Phosphor omitted	3·00	
W12	W **3**	1s.6d. grey-blue (1.8.69)	2·00	2·00

There was no Post Office first day cover for No. W10.

4.9.68	First Day Cover (W9, W11)	3·00
9.12.70	Presentation Pack (PO Pack No. 24) Nos. W4, W6/7, W9/11	5·50

W 4 With "p"

| I |  II |

Redrawn design of Type W 4 (litho ptgs.)

Two Types of Dragon

Type I: The eye is complete with white dot in the centre. Wing-tips, tail and tongue are thin.

Type II: The eye is joined to the nose by a solid line. Tail, wing-tips, claws and tongue are wider than in Type I.

The following stamps printed in lithography show a screened background behind and to the left of the emblem: 11½p., 12½p., 14p. (No. W39), 15½p., 16p., 18p. (No. W46), 19½p. (No. W54) and 28p. (No. W63). The 13p. and 17p. (No. W44) also show screened backgrounds in Type I, but changed to solid backgrounds for Type II. All other values printed in lithography have solid backgrounds.

Two Types of 5½p.

| Cyl. 1 (W21) | Cyl. 2 (W21b) |

(Des Jeffery Matthews after plaster cast by Arnold Machin)

1971 (7 July)–**93.** *Decimal Currency. Chalk-surfaced paper. Type W* 4.

(a) Gravure Harrison. With phosphor bands. Perf 15×14.

W13	2½p. bright magenta (1 centre band)	20	20
	Ey. Phosphor omitted	7·50	
	Eg. Gum arabic (22.9.72)	20	
	Ega. Imperf (pair)	£800	
W14	3p. ultramarine (2 bands)	25	20
	Ey. Phosphor omitted	30·00	
	Eg. Gum arabic (6.6.73)	25	
	Eya. Phosphor omitted (No. W14Eg)	12·00	
W15	3p. ultramarine (1 centre band) (23.1.74)	25	25
W16	3½p. olive-grey (2 bands) (23.1.74)	20	30
W17	3½p. olive-grey (1 centre band) (6.11.74)*	20	20
W18	4½p. grey-blue (2 bands) (6.11.74)	25	25
W19	5p. reddish violet (2 bands)	80	80
	Ey. Phosphor omitted	20·00	
W20	5½p. violet (2 bands) (23.1.74)	25	25
	Ey. Phosphor omitted	£180	
W21	5½p. violet (1 centre band) (21.5.75)	25	25
	a. Imperf (pair)	£700	
	b. Low emblem and value (cyl. 2) (1977)	£225	£225
W22	6½p. greenish blue (1 centre band) (14.1.76)	20	20
W23	7p. purple-brown (1 centre band) (18.1.78)	25	25
W24	7½p. chestnut (2 bands)	1·25	1·25
	Ey. Phosphor omitted	95·00	
W25	8p. rosine (2 bands) (23.1.74)	30	30
	Ey. Phosphor omitted	£850	
W26	8½p. yellow-green (2 bands) (14.1.76)	35	35
W27	9p. deep violet (2 bands) (18.1.78)	35	35
W28	10p. orange-brown (2 bands) (20.10.76)	35	35
W29	10p. orange-brown (1 centre band) (23.7.80)	35	35
W30	10½p. steel-blue (2 bands) (18.1.78)	45	45
W31	11p. scarlet (2 bands) (20.10.76)	40	40

(b) Gravure Harrison. On phosphorised paper. Perf 15×14.

W32	12p. yellowish green (23.7.80)	45	45
W33	13½p. purple-brown (23.7.80)	55	55
W34	15p. ultramarine (23.7.80)	55	55

(c) Litho Questa (Type II unless otherwise stated). Perf 14 (11½p., 12½p., 14p. (No. W39), 15½p., 16p., 18p. (No. W46), 19½p., 20½p., 22p. (No. W54), 26p. (No. W61), 28p. (No. W63)) or 15×14 (others).

W35	11½p. drab (Type I) (1 side band) (8.4.81)	70	70
W36	12p. bright emerald (1 side band) (7.1.86)	1·00	1·00
W37	12½p. light emerald (Type I) (1 side band) (24.2.82)	50	50
	a. Perf 15×14 (Type I) (10.1.84)	2·75	2·75
W38	13p. pale chestnut (Type I) (1 side band) (23.10.84)	50	50
	Ea. Type II (1.87)	1·40	1·40
W39	14p. grey-blue (Type I) (phosphorised paper) (8.4.81)	55	55
W40	14p. deep blue (1 centre band) (8.11.88)	55	55
W41	15p. bright blue (1 centre band) (28.11.89)	60	60
	Ey. Phosphor omitted	£140	
W42	15½p. pale violet (Type I) (phosphorised paper) (24.2.82)	70	70
W43	16p. drab (Type I) (phosphorised paper) (27.4.83)	1·10	1·10
	a. Perf 15×14 (Type I) (10.1.84)	1·10	1·10
W44	17p. grey-blue (Type I) (phosphorised paper) (23.10.84)	80	80
	Ea. Type II (18.8.86)	50·00	50·00
W45	17p. deep blue (1 centre band) (4.12.90)	60	60
	Ey. Phosphor omitted	18·00	
W46	18p. deep violet (Type I) (8.4.81)	80	80
W47	18p. deep olive-grey (phosphorised paper) (6.1.87)	80	80
W48	18p. bright green (1 centre band) (3.12.91)	55	55
	Ey. Phosphor omitted	£225	
	a. Booklet pane. No. W48×6 with margins all round (25.2.92)	1·80	

	aEy. Phosphor omitted........................	7·50	7·50
	b. Perf 14 (12.1.93*)		
W49	18p. bright green (1 side band at right) (25.2.92)	1·75	1·75
	a. Booklet pane. No. X1020×2, 1451a, 1514a, W49×2, W60×2 and centre label with margins all round	8·50	
	aEy. Phosphor omitted........................	£225	
	Eb. Band at left (10.8.93)	1·60	1·60
W50	19p. bright orange-red (phosphorised paper) (8.11.88)	70	70
W51	19½p. olive-grey (Type I) (phosphorised paper) (24.2.82)	1·25	1·25
W52	20p. brownish black (phosphorised paper) (28.11.89)	70	70
W53	20½p. ultramarine (Type I) (phosphorised paper) (27.4.83)	2·50	2·50
W54	22p. blue (Type I) (phosphorised paper) (8.4.81)	80	80
W55	22p. yellow-green (Type I) (phosphorised paper) (23.10.84)	80	80
W56	22p. bright orange-red (phosphorised paper) (4.12.90)	80	80
W57	23p. bright green (phosphorised paper) (8.11.88)	80	80
W58	24p. Indian red (phosphorised paper) (28.11.89)	90	90
W59	24p. chestnut (phosphorised paper) (3.12.91)	70	70
	a. Booklet pane. No. W59×6 with margins all round (25.2.92)	2·50	
	b. Perf 14 (14.9.92*)	7·50	7·50
W60	24p. chestnut (2 bands) (25.2.92)	90	90
W61	26p. rosine (Type I) (phosphorised paper) (24.2.82)	80	80
	a. Perf 15×14 (Type II) (27.1.87)	3·00	3·00
W62	26p. drab (phosphorised paper) (4.12.90)	1·25	1·25
W63	28p. deep violet-blue (Type I) (phosphorised paper) (27.4.83)	90	90
	a. Perf 15×14 (Type II) (27.1.87)	1·30	1·30
W64	28p. deep bluish grey (phosphorised paper) (3.12.91)	80	80
W65	31p. bright purple (Type I) (phosphorised paper) (23.10.84)	1·00	1·00
W66	32p. greenish blue (phosphorised paper) (8.11.88)	1·20	1·20
W67	34p. deep bluish grey (phosphorised paper) (28.11.89)	1·20	1·20
W68	37p. rosine (phosphorised paper) (4.12.90)	1·25	1·25
W69	39p. bright mauve (phosphorised paper) (3.12.91)	1·25	1·25

* Earliest known date of use.
Nos. W48b and W59b were caused by the use of a reserve perforating machine for some printings in the second half of 1992.
Nos. W49, W49Eb and W60 only come from booklets.
The listed booklet panes come from the Sponsored Booklet DX13; W48a, W49a, W59a.
No. W60 exists with the phosphor omitted, but cannot be identified without the use of ultraviolet light (*Price* £375 *unused*).
From 1972 printings were on fluorescent white paper. From 1973 most printings had dextrin added to the PVA gum (see notes after 1971 Decimal Machin issue).

First Day Covers

7.7.71	2½p., 3p., 5p., 7½p., (W13/14, W19, W24)	2·00	
23.1.74	3p., 3½p., 5½p., 8p. (W15/16, W20, W25)	1·50	
6.11.74	4½p. (W18)	80	
14.1.76	6½p., 8½p. (W22, W26)	80	
20.10.76	10p., 11p. (W28, W31)	80	
18.1.78	7p., 9p., 10½p. (W23, W27, W30)	1·00	
23.7.80	12p., 13½p., 15p. (W32/4)	2·00	
8.4.81	11½p., 14p., 18p., 22p. (W35, W39, W46, W54)	2·00	
24.2.82	12½p., 15½p., 19½p., 26p. (W37, W42, W51, W61)	2·50	
27.4.83	16p., 20½p., 28p. (W43, W53, W63)	2·50	
23.10.84	13p., 17p., 22p., 31p. (W38, W44, W55, W65)	3·00	
7.1.86	12p. (W36)	1·00	
6.1.87	18p. (W47)	1·00	
8.11.88	14p., 19p., 23p., 32p. (W40, W50, W57, W66)	3·00	
28.11.89	15p., 20p., 24p., 34p. (W41, W52, W58, W67)	4·00	
4.12.90	17p., 22p., 26p., 37p (W45, W56, W62, W68)	4·00	
3.12.91	18p., 24p., 28p., 39p. (W48, W59, W64, W69)	4·25	
25.2.92	Cymru-Wales *se-tenant* pane 18p. (*2nd*), 24p. (*1st*), 33p. (W49a)	8·50	

Presentation Packs

7.7.71	PO Pack No. 28. 2½p., 3p. (*2 bands*), 5p., 7½p. (*Nos.* W13/14, W19, W24)	2·00	
29.5.74	PO Pack No. 63. 3p. (1 centre band), 3½p. (2 bands) or (1 centre band), 5½p. (2 bands) or (1 centre band), 8p. (Nos. W15, W16 or W17, W20 or W21, W25). The 4½p. (No. W18) was added later	2·25	

20.10.76	PO Pack No. 86. 6½p., 8½p., 10p. (2 bands), 11p. (Nos. W22, W26, W28, W31)	1·40	
28.10.81	PO Pack No. 129c. 7p., 9p., 10½p., 12p. (photo), 13½p., 15p. (photo), 11½p., 14p. grey-blue, 18p. dp violet, 22p. blue (Nos. W23, W27, W30, W32/5, W39, W46, W54)	6·00	
3.8.83	PO Pack No. 3. 10p. (1 centre band), 12½p., 16p., 20½p., 26p. rosine, 28p. dp violet-blue (Nos. W29, W37, W43, W53, W61, W63)	14·00	
23.10.84	PO Pack No. 7. 10p. (1 centre band), 13p., 16p., 17p. grey-blue, 22p. yellow-green, 26p. rosine, 28p. dp violet-blue, 31p. (Nos. W29, W38, W43a, W44, W55, W61, W63, W65)	12·00	
3.3.87	PO Pack No. 11. 12p. (litho), 13p., 17p. grey-blue, 18p. dp olive-grey, 22p. yellow-green, 26p. rosine, 28p. dp violet-blue, 31p. (Nos. W36, W38, W44, W47, W55, W61a, W63a, W65)	15·00	

Presentation Packs containing stamps of Northern Ireland, Scotland and Wales are listed after those for Northern Ireland.

(Des Jeffery Matthews after plaster cast by Arnold Machin. Litho Questa)

1993 (7 Dec)**–96.** Chalk-surfaced paper. Perf 15×14 (with one elliptical hole in each vertical side).

W70	W **4**	19p. bistre (1 centre band)	60	60
W71		19p. bistre (1 band at right) (25.4.95)	1·90	1·90
W72		20p. bright green (1 centre band) (23.7.96)	1·00	1·00
W73		25p. red (2 bands)	75	75
W74		26p. red-brown (2 bands) (23.7.96)	1·20	1·20
W75		30p. deep olive-grey (2 bands)	80	80
W76		37p. bright mauve (2 bands) (23.7.96)	1·60	1·60
W77		41p. grey-brown (2 bands)	1·40	1·40
W78		63p. light emerald (2 bands) (23.7.96)	4·00	4·00

No. W71 only comes from booklets.

First Day Covers

7.12.93	19p., 25p., 30p., 41p. (W70, W73, W75, W77)	3·75	
23.7.96	20p., 26p., 37p., 63p., (W72, W74, W76, W78)	6·00	

For Presentation Packs containing stamps of Northern Ireland, Scotland and Wales see after No. NI85 of Northern Ireland.

W **5** Without "p"

(Gravure Walsall (20p., 26p. (No. W80a), 63p.),
Harrison or Walsall (26p. (No. W80), 37p.))

1997 (1 July)**–98.** Chalk-surfaced paper. Perf 14 (No. W79a) or 15×14 (others) (both with one elliptical hole in each vertical side).

W79	W **5**	20p. bright green (1 centre band)	80	80
W79a		20p. bright green (1 side band at right) (13.10.98)	3·25	3·25
W80		26p. chestnut (2 bands)	1·40	1·40
		a. Perf 14 (13.10.98)	3·25	3·25
W81		37p. bright mauve (2 bands)	1·80	1·80
W82		63p. light emerald (2 bands)	4·00	4·00

Nos. W79a and W80a were only issued in booklets.
The Harrison printings of Nos. W80/1 come from booklet pane No. NI81al.

First Day Cover

1.7.97	20p., 26p., 37p., 63p. (W79, W80/2)	6·00	

Presentation Pack

1.7.97	PO Pack No. 39. 20p., 26p., 37p., 63p. (Nos. W79, W80/2)	12·00	

W **6** Leek

W **7** Welsh dragon

W **8** Daffodil

W **9** Prince of Wales' Feathers

(Des David Petersen (Leek), Toby & Gideon Petersen (Welsh dragon), Ieuan Rees (Daffodil), Rhiannon Evans (Prince of Wales' Feathers). Adapted Tutssels. Gravure De La Rue or Walsall (2nd, 1st), De La Rue (68p.), Walsall (others))

1999 (8 June)–**2002**. One phosphor band (2nd) or two phosphor bands (others). Perf 14 (No. W83a) or 15×14 (others) (both with one elliptical hole in each vertical side).

W83	W **6**	(2nd) Leek (1 centre band)......................	1·25	1·25
W83a		(2nd) Leek (1 band at right) (P 14) (18.9.00)..	2·50	2·50
		al. Booklet pane. No. 2124d and W83a, each×4, with centre label and margins all round	10·00	
W84	W **7**	(1st) Welsh dragon..............................	1·75	1·75
W85	W **8**	(E) Daffodil..	2·10	2·10
W86	W **9**	64p. Prince of Wales' Feathers....................	6·00	6·00
W87		65p. Prince of Wales' Feathers (25.4.00)..	2·75	2·75
W88		65p. Prince of Wales' Feathers (4.7.02)	2·50	2·50

Presentation Pack (PO Pack No. 46)
(2nd, 1st, E, 64p.) (*Nos*. W83, W84/6).. 9·00
Presentation Pack (PO Pack No. 51) (65p.) (*No.* W87))........ 10·00
Presentation Pack (PO Pack No. 56)
(2nd, 1st, E, 65p.) (*Nos*. W83, W84/5, W87)........................ 16·00
PHQ Cards (set of 4) (D13) (*Nos.* W83, W84/6) .... 10·00

Nos. W83, W84 and W85 were initially sold at 19p., 26p. and 30p., the latter representing the basic European airmail rate.

New printings of Nos. W83 and W84, produced by De La Rue instead of Walsall, were issued on 28 May 2003 and 4 March 2003. Stamps from these printings do not differ from those produced by Walsall.

No. W83a comes from the £7 Treasury of Trees booklet (No.DX26).

For combined presentation pack for all four Regions, see under England.

First Day Covers

8.6.99	2nd (*centre band*), 1st, E, 64p. (W83, W84/6)		
	Philatelic Bureau	3·00	
	Cardiff	3·25	
25.4.00	65p. (W87) Philatelic Bureau	3·00	
	Cardiff	3·50	
18.9.00	Treasury of Trees *se-tenant* pane 1st (*Millennium*), 2nd (2124d, W83a) Philatelic Bureau	5·00	
	Llangernyw, Abergele..	5·00	
4.7.02	68p. (W88) Tallents House (Type K) (*see Introduction*)	2·50	
	Cardiff	2·50	

W **10**

(Des Jeffery Matthews. Gravure Walsall)

2000 (15 Feb). Type W **4** redrawn with *1af/st* face value as Type W **10**. Two phosphor bands. Perf 14 (with one elliptical hole in each vertical side).

W97	W **10**	(1st) bright orange-red	2·10	2·10

No. W97 was only issued in £7·50 stamp booklets (No. DX24).

2003 (14 Oct)–**17**. As Nos. W83, W84/5 and W88, and new values, but with white borders. One centre phosphor band (2nd) or two phosphor bands (others). Perf 15×14 (with one elliptical hole in each vertical side).

(a) (Gravure Walsall or De La Rue (42p.) or De La Rue (others))

W98	W **6**	(2nd) Leek	1·10	1·10
W99	W **7**	(1st) Welsh dragon	1·60	1·60
W100	W **8**	(E) Daffodil..	2·25	2·25
W101		40p. Daffodil (11.5.04)........................	1·40	1·40
W102		42p. Daffodil (5.4.05)..........................	2·00	2·00
W103		44p. Daffodil (28.3.06)........................	1·60	1·60
W104		48p. Daffodil (27.3.07)........................	1·10	1·10
W105		50p. Daffodil (1.4.08)..........................	1·40	1·40
W106		56p. Daffodil (31.3.09)........................	1·50	1·50
W107		60p. Daffodil (30.3.10)........................	1·70	1·70
W108	W **9**	68p. Prince of Wales' Feathers.............	1·60	1·60
W109		72p. Prince of Wales' Feathers (28.3.06).	1·60	1·60
W110		78p. Prince of Wales' Feathers (27.3.07).	2·00	2·00
W111		81p. Prince of Wales' Feathers (1.4.08)..	2·25	2·25
W112		90p. Prince of Wales' Feathers (31.3.09).	2·40	2·40
W113		97p. Prince of Wales' Feathers (30.3.10).	2·50	2·50

(b) Litho Enschedé, De La Rue or ISP Cartor (1st) or ISP Cartor (others)

W121	W **6**	(2nd) Leek (1.13)...................................	1·40	1·40
W122	W **7**	(1st) Welsh dragon (20.9.07)	1·60	1·60
W123	W **8**	68p. Daffodil (29.3.11)........................	1·75	1·75
W124		87p Daffodil (25.4.12).........................	2·25	2·25
W125		88p. Daffodil (27.3.13)........................	2·25	2·25
W126		97p. Daffodil (26.3.14)........................	2·50	2·50
W127		£1 Daffodil (24.3.15)............................	2·50	2·50
W128		£1·05 Daffodil (22.3.16).......................	2·75	2·75
W129	W **9**	£1·10 Prince of Wales' Feathers (29.3.11).	2·50	2·50

W134		£1·28 Prince of Wales' Feathers (25.4.12).	2·75	2·75
W135		£1·33 Prince of Wales' Feathers (24.3.15).	2·75	2·75

Presentation Pack (PO Pack No. 65) (*Nos.* W98/100, W108)... 5·00
PHQ Cards (set of 4) (D26) (*Nos.* W98/100, W108)........... 5·00

The Walsall printing of No. W102 was issued on 5 April 2005 and the De La Rue on 24 May 2005.

Stamps as Nos. W110/11 but printed in lithography were only issued within **MS**2796 (W110) or **MS**2886 (W111).

No. W122 was first issued in £7·66 stamp booklets, No. DX40 printed by Enschedè, then on 29 September 2008 in £9·72 booklets (DX43) printed by De La Rue and on 26 February 2009 in **MS**W147. It was issued in sheets printed by ISP Cartor in January 2013.

A design as No. W122 but self-adhesive was issued on 1 March 2007 in sheets of 20, each stamp accompanied by a *se-tenant* label showing a Welsh scene (LS37). These sheets were printed in lithography by Cartor, perforated 15×14 without the elliptical holes, and sold at £6·55 each. They were also available with personalised photographs on the labels at £14·95 from Royal Mail in Edinburgh.

Stamps as Nos. EN30, NI95, S131 and W122 but self-adhesive were issued on 29 September 2008 in sheets of 20 containing five of each design with *se-tenant* labels (LS49).

First Day Covers

14.10.03	2nd, 1st, E, 68p. (W98/100, W108)		
	Tallents House (Type K) (see Introduction)	3·25	
	Cardiff..	3·25	
11.5.04	40p. (W101) Tallents House (Type K)................	1·75	
	Cardiff..	1·75	
5.4.05	42p. (W102) Tallents House (Type K)................	2·00	
	Cardiff..	2·00	
28.3.06	44p., 72p. (W103, W109) Tallents House (Type K)	3·25	
	Cardiff..	3·25	
27.3.07	48p., 78p. (W104, W110) Tallents House (Type K)	3·50	
	Cardiff..	3·50	
1.4.08	50p., 81p. (W105, W111) Tallents House (Type K)	3·75	
	Cardiff..	3·75	
31.3.09	56p., 90p. (W106, W112) Tallents House (Type K)	4·00	
	Cardiff..	4·00	
30.3.10	60p., 97p. (W107, W113) Tallents House (Type K)	4·00	
	Cardiff..	4·00	
29.3.11	68p., £1·10 (W123, W129) Tallents House (Type K)......	4·25	
	Cardiff..	4·25	
25.4.12	87p. £1·28 (W124, W134) Tallents House (Type K)......	5·00	
	Cardiff..	5·00	
27.3.13	88p. (W125) Tallents House (Type K)................	2·25	
	Cardiff..	2·25	
26.3.14	97p. (W126) Tallents House (Type K)................	2·50	
	Cardiff..	2·50	
24.3.15	£1, £1·33 (W127, W135) Tallents House (Type K)........	5·25	
	Cardiff..	5·25	
22.3.16	£1·05 (W128) Tallents House (Type K)................	2·75	
	Cardiff..	2·75	

W **10a** (Illustration reduced.)

(Des Silk Pearce. Gravure De La Rue)

2006 (1 Mar). *Opening of New Welsh Assembly Building, Cardiff*. Sheet 123×70 mm. One centre phosphor band (2nd) or two phosphor bands (others). Perf 15×14 (with one elliptical hole in each vertical side).

MSW143 W **10a** Nos. W98, W99×2 and W108×2........		4·50	4·50

First Day Cover (Tallents House) .... 4·75
First Day Cover (Cardiff).. 4·75

(Litho De La Rue)

2008 (29 Sept). *50th Anniversary of the Country Definitives*. As Nos. W1, W3 and W5 (definitives of 1958) but inscribed 1st. Two phosphor bands. Perf 15×14½ (with one elliptical hole in each vertical side).

W144	W **1**	(1st) deep lilac..	1·60	1·60
		l. Booklet pane. Nos. W144/6 and W122×3................................	7·00	
W145	W **3**	(1st) green..	1·60	1·60
W146	W **2**	(1st) deep claret.......................................	1·60	1·60

Nos. W144/6 come from £9·72 booklets, No. DX43.

DATHLU CYMRU · CELEBRATING WALES

W **11** *(Illustration reduced.)*

(Des Clare Melinsky and Silk Pearce. Litho De La Rue)

2009 (26 Feb). *Celebrating Wales.* Sheet 123×70 mm. Two phosphor bands. Perf 15×14 (with one elliptical hole in each vertical side) (1st) or 14½×14 (81p.).

MSW147 W **11** (1st) Red dragon; (1st) No. W122; 81p.
St David; 81p. National Assembly for Wales, Cardiff..	4·25	4·25
First Day Cover (Tallents House)		5·25
First Day Cover (St Davids)		5·25
Presentation Pack (P.O. Pack No. 424)	5·00	
PHQ Cards (set of 5) (CGB4)	1·50	8·00

MSW147 was on sale at post offices throughout the UK.
The five PHQ cards show the four individual stamps and the complete miniature sheet.
The 1st class Red dragon stamp from **MS**W147 but self-adhesive were issued on 1 March 2010 in sheets of 20 with *se-tenant* labels showing Welsh Castles, No. LS71. These sheets were printed in lithography by ISP Cartor and sold for £8·35 each.
Miniature sheet collection containing Nos. **MS**EN50, **MS**NI152, **MS**S153 and **MS**W147 in a folder was available from 6 March 2009, sold at £31·95.

W **12** Red dragon

Des Peter Crowther (illustrations) and Silk Pierce.
Litho ISP Cartor or Enschedé)

2013 (9 May). *Wales Flag.* Two phosphor bands. Perf 14½×14 (with one elliptical hole in each vertical side).

W148 W **12** (1st) Red dragon .... 4·00 4·00
No. W148 was issued in £11·11 Football Heroes booklets, No. DY7 (see booklet pane No. U3010*a*), £13·97 Classic Locomotives booklets, No. DY9 (see booklet pane No. U3011*b*) and £16·49 Centenary of the First World War (3rd issue), No. DY18 (booklet pane 3717*a*).

W **13** Leek

W **14** Welsh dragon

W **15** Daffodil

W **16** Prince of Wales' Feathers

(Des David Petersen (Leek), Toby & Gideon Petersen (Welsh dragon), Ieuan Rees (Daffodil), Rhiannon Evans (Prince of Wales' Feathers). Adapted Tutssels. Gravure De La Rue)

2017 (21 Mar)–**2018**. As previous set but with value indicated in revised typeface. One centre band (2nd) or two phosphor bands. Perf 15×14 (with one elliptical hole in each vertical side).
W149	W **13**	(2nd) Leek (20.3.18)	1·00	75
W150	W **14**	(1st) Welsh dragon (20.3.18)	1·25	75
W151	W **15**	£1·17 Daffodil (21.3.17)	2·75	2·75
W152		£1·25 Daffodil (20.3.18)	2·75	2·75
W157	W **16**	£1·40 Prince of Wales' Feathers (21.3.17)	2·75	2·75
W158		£1·45 Prince of Wales' Feathers (20.3.18)	3·25	3·25

Numbers have been left for possible additions to the above definitive series.

First Day Covers
21.3.17	£1·17, £1·40 (W151, W157) Tallents House (Type K)	5·75
	Cardiff	5·75
20.3.18	2nd, 1st, £1·25, £1·45. (W149/50, W152, W158)	
	Tallents House (Type K)	9·00
	Cardiff	9·00

V. GUERNSEY

War Occupation Issues

BISECTS. On 24 December 1940 authority was given, by Post Office notice, that prepayment of penny postage could be effected by using half a British 2d. stamp, diagonally bisected. Such stamps were first used on 27 December 1940.
The 2d. stamps generally available were those of the Postal Centenary issue, 1940 (SG 482) and the first colour of the King George VI issue (SG 465). These are listed under Nos. 482a and 465b. A number of the 2d. King George V, 1912–22, and of the King George V photogravure stamp (SG 442) which were in the hands of philatelists, were also bisected and used.

1

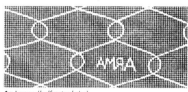

1a Loops *(half actual size)*

(Des E W Vaudin. Typo Guernsey Press Co Ltd)

1941–44. Rouletted.

(a) White paper. No wmk.
1	**1**	½d. light green (7.4.41)	6·00	3·50
		a. Emerald-green (6.41)	6·50	3·50
		b. Bluish green (11.41)	35·00	15·00
		c. Bright green (2.42)	25·00	12·00
		d. Dull green (9.42)	5·00	3·50
		e. Olive-green (2.43)	45·00	25·00
		f. Pale yellowish green (7.43 and later) (shades)	5·00	3·50
		g. Imperf (pair)	£250	
		h. Imperf between (horizontal pair)	£800	
		i. Imperf between (vertical pair)	£950	
2		1d. scarlet (18.2.41)	3·25	2·00
		a. Pale vermilion (7.43)	5·00	2·00
		b. Carmine (1943)	3·50	2·00
		c. Imperf (pair)	£200	90·00
		d. Imperf between (horizontal pair)....	£800	
		da. Imperf vertical (centre stamp of horizontal strip of 3)		
		e. Imperf between (vertical pair)	£950	
		f. Printed double (scarlet shade)	£150	
3		2½d. ultramarine (12.4.44)	18·00	15·00
		a. Pale ultramarine (7.44)	15·00	10·00
		b. Imperf (pair)	£550	
		c. Imperf between (horizontal pair)....	£1250	
Set of 3			15·00	14·00

First Day Covers
18.2.41	1d.	15·00
7.4.41	½d.	10·00
12.4.44	2½d.	20·00

*(b) Dark bluish French bank-note paper. W **1a** (sideways).*
4	**1**	½d. bright green (11.3.42)	32·00	25·00
5		1d. scarlet (9.4.42)	18·00	25·00

First Day Covers
11.3.42	½d.	£325
9.4.42	1d.	£125

The dates given for the shades of Nos. 1/3 are the months in which they were printed as indicated on the printer's imprints. Others are issue dates.

2

3

(Des Eric A Piprell. Portrait by Dorothy Wilding Ltd.
Photo Harrison & Sons)

1958 (18 Aug)–**67**. *W* **179** of Great Britain. Perf 15×14.

6	**2**	2½d. rose-red (8.6.64)	40	40
7	**3**	3d. deep lilac	30	30
		p. One centre phosphor band		
		(24.5.67)	30	30
8		4d. ultramarine (7.2.66)	40	40
		p. Two phosphor bands (24.10.67)	20	20
Set of 3 (cheapest)			1·00	1·00

First Day Covers

18.8.58	3d.		20·00
8.6.64	2½d.		30·00
7.2.66	4d.		8·00

For No. 7 in Presentation Pack, see Regional Issues below Wales No. W6.

1968–69. No wmk. Chalk-surfaced paper. PVA gum*. One centre phosphor band (Nos. 10/11) or two phosphor bands (others). Perf 15×14.

9	**3**	4d. pale ultramarine (16.4.68)	20	20
		Ey. Phosphor omitted	50·00	
10		4d. olive-sepia (4.9.68)	20	20
		Ey. Phosphor omitted	50·00	
11		4d. bright vermilion (26.2.69)	20	20
12		5d. royal blue (4.9.68)	30	30
Set of 4			80	80

First Day Cover

4.9.68	4d., 5d.	3·00

No. 9 was not issued in Guernsey until 22 April.

* PVA Gum. See note after No. 722 of Great Britain.

VI. ISLE OF MAN

Although specifically issued for use in the Isle of Man, these issues were also valid for use throughout Great Britain.

    1    **2**

(Des John Hobson Nicholson. Portrait by Dorothy Wilding Ltd.
Photo Harrison)

1958 (18 Aug)–**68**. *W* **179**. Perf 15×14.

1	**1**	2½d. carmine-red (8.6.64)	70	70
2	**2**	3d. deep lilac	50	50
		a. Chalk-surfaced paper (17.5.63)	6·50	6·50
		p. One centre phosphor band		
		(27.6.68)	20	20
3		4d. ultramarine (7.2.66)	1·00	1·00
		p. Two phosphor bands (5.7.67)	30	30
Set of 3 (cheapest)			1·00	1·00

First Day Covers

18.8.58	3d		32·00
8.6.64	2½d		45·00
7.2.66	4d		15·00

No. 2a was released in London sometime after 17 May 1963, this being the date of issue in Douglas.

For No. 2 in Presentation Pack, see Regional Issues below Wales No. W6.

1968–69. No wmk. Chalk-surfaced paper. PVA gum. One centre phosphor band (Nos. 5/6) or two phosphor bands (others). Perf 15×14.

4	**2**	4d. blue (24.6.68)	25	25
5		4d. olive-sepia (4.9.68)	30	30
		Ey. Phosphor omitted	25·00	
6		4d. bright vermilion (26.2.69)	45	45
7		5d. royal blue (4.9.68)	45	45
		Ey. Phosphor omitted	£175	
Set of 4			1·25	1·25

First Day Cover

4.9.68	4d., 5d.	4·00

3

(Des Jeffery Matthews. Portrait after plaster cast by Arnold Machin.
Photo Harrison)

1971 (7 July). *Decimal Currency*. Chalk-surfaced paper. One centre phosphor band (2½p.) or two phosphor bands (others). Perf 15×14.

8	**3**	2½p. bright magenta	30	30
		Ey. Phosphor omitted	£1500	
9		3p. ultramarine	30	30
10		5p. reddish violet	70	70
		Ey. Phosphor omitted	£275	
11		7½p. chestnut	80	80
Set of 4			1·80	1·80
Presentation Pack (P.O. Pack No 30)			2·50	

First Day Cover

7.7.71	2½p., 3p., 5p., 7½p.	3·50

All values exist with PVA gum on ordinary cream paper and the 2½p. and 3p. also on fluorescent white paper.

Nos. 8/11 and current stamps of Great Britain were withdrawn from sale on the island from 5 July 1973 when the independent postal administration was established but remained valid for use there for a time. They also remained on sale at the Philatelic Sales counters in the United Kingdom until 4 July 1974.

VII. JERSEY

War Occupation Issues

5

(Des Major Norman Victor Lacey Rybot. Typo Evening Post, Jersey)

1941–43. White paper (thin to thick). No wmk. Perf 11.

1	**5**	½d. bright green (29.1.42)	8·00	6·00
		a. Imperf between (vertical pair)	£900	
		b. Imperf between (horizontal pair)	£800	
		c. Imperf (pair)	£300	
		d. On greyish paper (1.43)	12·00	12·00
2		1d. scarlet (1.4.41)	8·00	5·00
		a. Imperf between (vertical pair)	£900	
		b. Imperf between (horizontal pair)	£800	
		c. Imperf (pair)	£325	
		d. On chalk-surfaced paper	55·00	48·00
		e. On greyish paper (1.43)	14·00	14·00

First Day Covers

1.4.41	1d.		8·00
29.1.42	½d.		7·50

6 Old Jersey Farm    **7** Portelet Bay

8 Corbière Lighthouse    **9** Elizabeth Castle

10 Mont Orgueil castle    **11** Gathering vraic (seaweed)

(Des Edmund Blampied. Eng H Cortot.
Typo French Govt Ptg Works, Paris)

1943–44. No wmk. Perf 13½.

3	**6**	½d. green (1.6.43)	12·00	12·00
		a. Rough, grey paper (6.10.43)	15·00	14·00
4	**7**	1d. scarlet (1.6.43)	3·00	50
		a. On newsprint (28.2.44)	3·50	75
5	**8**	1½d. brown (8.6.43)	8·00	5·75
6	**9**	2d. orange-yellow (8.6.43)	7·50	2·00

7	**10**	2½d. blue (29 June)............................	3·00	1·00
		a. On newsprint (25.2.44)	1·00	1·75
		ba. Thin paper*............................	£225	
8	**11**	3d. violet (29.6.43)........................	3·00	2·75
Set of 6			30·00	21·00
First Day Covers (3)				36·00
Set of 6 Gutter Pairs...			80·00	

* On No. 7ba the design shows clearly through the back of the stamp.

12   **13**

(Des. Edmund Blampied (T **12**), W Gardner (T **13**).
Portrait by Dorothy Wilding Ltd. Photo Harrison & Sons)

1958 (18 Aug)–**67.** *W* **179** of Great Britain. Perf 15×14.

9	**12**	2½d. carmine-red (8.6.64)	45	45
		a. Imperf three sides..................	£3250	
10	**13**	3d. deep lilac.............................	30	30
		p. One centre phosphor band		
		(9.6.67).................................	20	20
11		4d. ultramarine (7.2.66)	25	25
		p. Two phosphor bands (5.9.67).......	20	20
Set of 3 (cheapest)			80	80

First Day Covers

18.8.58	3d		20·00
8.6.64	2½d..		30·00
7.2.66	4d		10·00

For No. 10 in Presentation Pack, see Regional Issues below Wales No. W6.

1968–69. No wmk. Chalk-surfaced paper. PVA gum*. One centre phosphor band (4d. values) or two phosphor bands (5d.). Perf 15×14.

12	**13**	4d. olive-sepia (4.9.68)	20	20
		Ey. Phosphor omitted....................	£1100	
13		4d. bright vermilion (26.2.69)	20	20
14		5d. royal blue (4.9.68)	20	20
Set of 3			50	50

First Day Cover

4.9.68	4d., 5d.	3·00

* PVA Gum. See note after No. 722 of Great Britain.

PERFORATIONS. All postage due stamps to No. D101 are perf 14×15.
WATERMARK. The watermark always appears sideways and this is the "normal" listed in this Catalogue for Nos. D1/D68. Varieties occur as follows. The point of identification is which way the top of the crown points, but (where they occur) the disposition of the letters needs to be noted also. The meaning of the terms is given below: (1) as described and illustrated in the Catalogue, i.e. as read through the front of the stamp, and (2) what is seen during watermark detection when the stamp is face down and the back is under examination.

Watermark	Crown pointing	Letters reading
(1) As described		
Sideways	left	upwards
Sideways-inverted	right	downwards
Sideways and reversed	left	downwards, back to front
Sideways-inverted and reversed	right	upwards, back to front
(2) As detected (stamp face down)		
Sideways	right	upwards, back to front
Sideways-inverted	left	downwards, back to front
Sideways and reversed	right	downwards
Sideways-inverted and reversed	left	upward

D 1   D 2

(Des G Eve. Typo Somerset House (early trial printings of ½d., 1d., 2d. and 5d.; all printings of 1s.) or Harrison (later printings of all values except 1s.))

1914 (20 Apr)–**22.** *W* **100** (Simple Cypher) (sideways).

			Unmtd mint	Mtd mint	Used
D1	D **1**	½d. emerald.............................	1·50	50	25
		Wi. Watermark sideways-inverted................................	5·00	2·00	2·00
		Wj. Watermark sideways and reversed.............................	30·00	18·00	20·00
		Wk. Watermark sideways-inverted and reversed......			20·00
		s. Overprinted "SPECIMEN"...		45·00	
D2		1d. carmine.............................	1·50	50	25
		a. Pale carmine.........................	1·50	75	50
		Wi. Watermark sideways-inverted................................	5·00	2·00	2·00
		Wj. Watermark sideways and reversed.............................			20·00
		Wk. Watermark sideways-inverted and reversed......	30·00	18·00	20·00
		s. Overprinted "SPECIMEN"..		45·00	
D3		1½d. chestnut (1922)	£150	48·00	20·00
		Wi. Watermark sideways-inverted................................	£190	70·00	24·00
		s. Overprinted "SPECIMEN"..		75·00	
D4		2d. agate...............................	1·50	50	25
		Wi. Watermark sideways-inverted................................	7·00	3·75	3·75
		Wk. Watermark sideways-inverted and reversed......	28·00	18·00	18·00
		s. Overprinted "SPECIMEN"..		40·00	
D5		3d. violet (1918).......................	28·00	9·00	75
		a. Bluish violet.........................	28·00	10·00	2·75
		Wi. Watermark sideways-inverted................................	80·00	40·00	40·00
		Wk. Watermark sideways-inverted and reversed......			
		s. Overprinted "SPECIMEN"..		45·00	
D6		4d. dull grey-green (12.20)	£300	£150	50·00
		Wi. Watermark sideways-inverted................................	£150	40·00	5·00
		s. Overprinted "SPECIMEN"..		45·00	
D7		5d. brownish cinnamon.........	23·00	7·00	3·50
		Wi. Watermark sideways-inverted................................	45·00	20·00	20·00
		s. Overprinted "SPECIMEN"..		45·00	
D8		1s. bright blue (1915)............	£150	40·00	5·00
		a. Deep bright blue	£150	40·00	5·00

	Wi. Watermark sideways-inverted		£150	40·00	40·00
	Wk. Watermark sideways-inverted and reversed				
	s. Overprinted "SPECIMEN".			45·00	
Set of 8		£450	£130	32·00	

Stamps from the above issue are known bisected and used for half their face value at the following sorting offices:

1d. Barrhead (1922), Bristol (1918), Cowes (1923), Elgin (1921), Kidlington (1922, 1923), Kilburn, London NW (1923), Malvern (1915), Palmers Green, London N (1922), Plaistow, London E (1916), River, Dover (1922), Rock Ferry, Birkenhead (1915, 1918), St Ouens, Jersey (1924), Salford, Manchester (1914), South Tottenham, London N (1921), Warminster (1922), Wavertree, Liverpool (1921), Whitchurch (1922), Winton, Bournemouth (1921), Wood Green, London N (1921)

2d. Anerley, London SE (1921), Bethnal Green, London E (1918), Christchurch (1921), Didcot (1919), Ealing, London W (1921), Hythe, Southampton (1923), Kirkwall (1921), Ledbury (1922), Malvern (1921, 1923), Sheffield (1921), Shipley (1922), Streatham, London SW (1921), Victoria Docks & North Woolwich (1921), West Kensington, London W (1921, 1922)

3d. Malvern (trisected and used for 1d.) (1921), Warminster (1922)

(Typo Waterlow)

1924. As 1914–22, but on thick chalk-surfaced paper.

D9	D **1**	1d. carmine	10·00	6·00	6·00
		Wi. Watermark sideways-inverted			

(Typo Waterlow and (from 1934) Harrison)

1924–31. W 111 (Block Cypher) sideways.

D10	D **1**	½d. emerald (6.25)	2·50	1·25	75
		Wi. Watermark sideways-inverted	10·00	5·00	2·50
		s. Overprinted "SPECIMEN"		45·00	
D11		1d. carmine (4.25)	2·50	60	25
		Wi. Watermark sideways-inverted	—	—	30·00
		s. Overprinted "SPECIMEN"		55·00	
D12		1½d. chestnut (10.24)	£160	48·00	22·00
		Wi. Watermark sideways-inverted	—	—	75·00
		s. Overprinted "SPECIMEN"		55·00	
D13		2d. agate (7.24)	9·00	1·00	25
		Wi. Watermark sideways-inverted	—	—	30·00
		s. Overprinted "SPECIMEN"		45·00	
D14		3d. dull violet (10.24)	15·00	1·50	25
		a. Printed on gummed side	£150	£125	†
		bWi. Watermark sideways-inverted	—	—	40·00
		bs. Overprinted "SPECIMEN"		55·00	
		c. Experimental paper W **111a**	£175	95·00	95·00
D15		4d. dull grey-green (10.24)	70·00	15·00	4·25
		Wi. Watermark sideways-inverted	£100	40·00	40·00
		s. Overprinted "SPECIMEN"		55·00	
D16		5d. brownish cinnamon (1.31)	£175	65·00	45·00
D17		1s. deep blue (9.24)	60·00	8·50	50
		Wi. Watermark sideways-inverted			
		s. Overprinted "SPECIMEN"		55·00	
D18	D **2**	2s.6d. purple/*yellow* (5.24)	£275	85·00	1·75
		Wi. Watermark sideways-inverted	£750	—	90·00
		s. Overprinted "SPECIMEN"		55·00	
Set of 9		£725	£200	70·00	

Stamps from the above issue are known bisected and used for half their face value at the following sorting offices:

1d. Ashton under Lyne (1932), Hastings (1930), Penryn, Cornwall (1928), Shenfield (1926), Wimbledon, London SW (1925)

2d. Perranwell Station (1932)

1936–37. W 125 (E 8 R) sideways.

D19	D **1**	½d. emerald (6.37)	15·00	10·50	
D20		1d. carmine (5.37)	2·00	1·75	
D21		2d. agate (5.37)	15·00	12·00	
D22		3d. dull violet (3.37)	2·00	2·00	
		s. Overprinted "SPECIMEN"			
D23		4d. dull grey-green (12.36)	65·00	35·00	
		s. Overprinted "SPECIMEN"			
D24		5d. brownish cinnamon (11.36)	90·00	30·00	
		a. Yellow-brown (1937)	40·00	28·00	
		s. Overprinted "SPECIMEN"			
D25		1s. deep blue (12.36)	25·00	8·50	
		s. Overprinted "SPECIMEN"			
D26	D **2**	2s.6d. purple/*yellow* (5.37)	£325	12·00	
Set of 8		£450	£100		

The 1d. of the above issue is known bisected and used for half its face value at the following sorting office:

1d. Solihull (1937)

1937–38. W 127 (G VI R) sideways.

D27	D **1**	½d. emerald (5.38)	13·00	3·75	
D28		1d. carmine (5.38)	3·00	50	
		Wi. Watermark sideways-inverted	£150		
D29		2d. agate (5.38)	2·75	30	
		Wi. Watermark sideways-inverted	£150		
D30		3d. violet (12.37)	11·00	30	
		Wi. Watermark sideways-inverted	£150		
D31		4d. dull grey-green (9.37)	£110	10·00	
		Wi. Watermark sideways-inverted	£300		
D32		5d. yellow-brown (11.38)	17·00	75	
		Wi. Watermark sideways-inverted	£150		
D33		1s. deep blue (10.37)	80·00	75	
		Wi. Watermark sideways-inverted	£150		
D34	D **2**	2s.6d. purple/*yellow* (9.38)	85·00	1·25	
Set of 8		£290	16·00		

The 2d. from the above issue is known bisected and used for half its face value at the following sorting offices:

2d. Boreham Wood (1951), Camberley (1951), Harpenden (1951, 1954), St Albans (1951)

DATES OF ISSUE. The dates for Nos. D35/68 are those on which stamps were first issued by the Supplies Department to postmasters.

1951–54. Colours changed and new value (1½d.). W 127 (G VI R) sideways.

D35	D **1**	½d. yellow-orange (18.9.51)	3·50	3·50	
		a. Bright orange (5.54)	55·00		
D36		1d. violet-blue (6.6.51)	1·50	75	
		Wi. Watermark sideways-inverted	£140	£140	
D37		1½d. green (11.2.52)	2·00	2·00	
		Wi. Watermark sideways-inverted	£140	£140	
D38		4d. blue (14.8.51)	50·00	22·00	
		Wi. Watermark sideways inverted	†	£1000	
D39		1s. ochre (6.12.51)	28·00	5·25	
		Wi. Watermark sideways-inverted	£2800		
Set of 5		75·00	30·00		

The 1d. of the above issue is known bisected and used for half its face value at the following sorting offices:

1d. Camberley (1954), Capel, Dorking (1952)

1954–55. W 153 (Tudor Crown) sideways.

D40	D **1**	½d. bright orange (8.6.55)	7·00	5·25	
		Wi. Watermark sideways-inverted	£150	£150	
D41		2d. agate (28.7.55)	26·00	23·00	
		Wi. Watermark sideways-inverted			
D42		3d. violet (4.5.55)	75·00	60·00	
D43		4d. blue (14.7.55)	26·00	32·00	
		a. Imperf (pair)	£250		
D44		5d. yellow-brown (19.5.55)	20·00	20·00	
D45	D **2**	2s.6d. purple/*yellow* (11.54)	£150	5·75	
		Wi. Watermark sideways-inverted			
Set of 6		£250	£130		

1955–57. W 165 (St Edward's Crown) sideways.

D46	D **1**	½d. bright orange (16.7.56)	2·75	3·25	
		Wi. Watermark sideways-inverted	85·00		
D47		1d. violet-blue (7.6.56)	5·00	1·50	
D48		1½d. green (13.2.56)	8·50	7·00	
		Wi. Watermark sideways-inverted	85·00		
D49		2d. agate (22.5.56)	45·00	3·50	
D50		3d. violet (5.3.56)	6·00	1·50	
		Wi. Watermark sideways-inverted	£100		
D51		4d. blue (24.4.56)	25·00	6·00	
		Wi. Watermark sideways-inverted	£175		
D52		5d. brown-ochre (23.3.56)	26·00	20·00	
D53		1s. ochre (22.11.55)	65·00	2·25	
		Wi. Watermark sideways-inverted			
D54	D **2**	2s.6d. purple/*yellow* (28.6.57)	£200	8·25	
		Wi. Watermark sideways-inverted			
D55		5s. scarlet/*yellow* (25.11.55)	£150	32·00	
		Wi. Watermark sideways-inverted		£375	
Set of 10		£475	75·00		

Stamps from the above issue are known bisected and used for half their face value at the following sorting offices:

1d. Beswick, Manchester (1958), Huddersfield (1956), London SE (1957)

2d. Eynsham, Oxford (1956), Garelochhead, Helensburgh (1956), Harpenden (1956), Hull (1956), Kingston on Thames (1956), Leicester Square, London WC (1956), London WC (1956)

3d. London SE (1957) 4d. Poplar, London E (1958)

1959–63. W 179 (Multiple Crowns) sideways.

D56	D **1**	½d. bright orange (18.10.61)	15	1·25	
D57		1d. violet-blue (9.5.60)	15	50	
		Wi. Watermark sideways-inverted	£125		
D58		1½d. green (5.10.60)	2·50	2·50	
D59		2d. agate (14.9.59)	1·10	50	
		Wi. Watermark sideways-inverted	£200		

D60		3d. violet (24.3.59)	30	30
		Wi. Watermark sideways-inverted...........	85·00	85·00
D61		4d. blue (17.12.59)	30	30
		Wi. Watermark sideways-inverted...........	£300	
D62		5d. yellow-brown (6.11.61)	45	60
		Wi. Watermark sideways-inverted...........	5·00	6·00
D63		6d. purple (29.3.62)	50	30
		Wi. Watermark sideways-inverted...........	£400	£400
D64		1s. ochre (11.4.60)	90	30
		Wi. Watermark sideways-inverted...........	75·00	75·00
D65	D 2	2s.6d. purple/*yellow* (11.5.61)	3·00	50
		Wi. Watermark sideways-inverted...........	15·00	15·00
D66		5s. scarlet/*yellow* (8.5.61)	8·25	1·00
		Wi. Watermark sideways-inverted...........	25·00	25·00
D67		10s. blue/*yellow* (2.9.63)	11·50	5·75
		Wi. Watermark sideways-inverted...........	40·00	25·00
D68		£1 black/*yellow* (2.9.63)	45·00	8·25
Set of 13			65·00	20·00

Whiter paper. The note after No. 586 also applies to Postage Due stamps.

Stamps from the above issue are known bisected and used for half their face value at the following sorting offices:
1d. Chieveley, Newbury (1962, 1963), Henlan, Llandyssil (1961), Mayfield (1962), St Albans (1964)
2d. Doncaster (?)

1968–69. Typo. No wmk. Chalk-surfaced paper.

D69	D 1	2d. agate (11.4.68)	75	1·00
		Ev. PVA gum (26.11.68)	75	
D70		3d. violet (9.9.68)	1·00	1·00
D71		4d. blue (6.5.68)	1·00	1·00
		Ev. PVA gum	£2250	
D72		5d. orange-brown (3.1.69)	8·00	11·00
D73		6d. purple (9.9.68)	2·25	1·75
D74		1s. ochre (19.11.68)	4·00	2·50
Set of 6			15·00	16·00

The 2d. and 4d. exist with gum arabic and PVA gum; the remainder with PVA gum only.

Stamps from the above issue are known bisected and used for half their face value at the following sorting offices:
4d. Northampton (1970)
6d. Kilburn, London NW (1968)

1968–69. Photo. No wmk. Chalk-surfaced paper. PVA gum.

D75	D 1	4d. blue (12.6.69)...	7·00	6·75
D76		8d. red (3.10.68)	50	1·00

Nos. D75/6 are smaller, 21½x17½ mm.

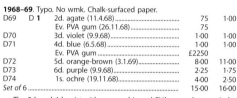

D 3   D 4

(Des Jeffery Matthews. Photo Harrison)

1970 (17 June)–**75**. *Decimal Currency.* Chalk-surfaced paper.

D77	D 3	½p. turquoise-blue (15.2.71)	15	2·50
D78		1p. deep reddish purple (15.2.71)	15	15
D79		2p. myrtle-green (15.2.71)............................	20	15
D80		3p. ultramarine (15.2.71)..............................	20	15
D81		4p. yellow-brown (15.2.71)...........................	25	15
D82		5p. violet (15.2.71)	25	15
D83		7p. red-brown (21.8.74).................................	35	1·00
D84	D 4	10p. carmine...	30	30
D85		11p. slate-green (18.6.75)..............................	50	1·00
D86		20p. olive-brown..	60	25
D87		50p. ultramarine..	2·00	1·25
D88		£1 black...	4·00	1·00
D89		£5 orange-yellow and black (2.4.73)....	25·00	1·50
Set of 13			30·00	7·75

Presentation Pack (PO Pack No. 36)
(*Nos.* D77/82, D84, D86/8 (3.11.71) .... 28·00

Presentation Pack (PO Pack No. 93)
(*Nos.* D77/88) (30.3.77).. 9·00

Later printings were on fluorescent white paper, some with dextrin added to the PVA gum (see notes after X1058).

The 2p. from the above issue is known bisected and used for half its face value at Exeter (1977).

D 5   D 6

(Des Sedley Place Design Ltd. Photo Harrison)

1982 (9 June). Chalk-surfaced paper.

D90	D 5	1p. lake	10	30
D91		2p. bright blue	30	30
D92		3p. deep mauve	15	30
D93		4p. deep blue	15	25
D94		5p. sepia	20	25
D95	D 6	10p. light brown	30	40
D96		20p. olive-green	50	60
D97		25p. deep greenish blue	80	90
D98		50p. grey-black	1·75	1·75
D99		£1 red...	3·00	1·25
D100		£2 turquoise-blue	5·00	4·25
D101		£5 dull orange..	10·00	2·25
Set of 12			19·00	10·00
Set of 12 Gutter Pairs			38·00	
Presentation Pack (P.O. Pack No.135)			24·00	

D 7

(Des Sedley Place Design Ltd. Litho Questa)

1994 (15 Feb). Perf 15×14 (with one elliptical hole in each vertical side).

D102	D 7	1p. red, yellow and black	10	75
D103		2p. magenta, purple and black	10	75
D104		5p. yellow, red-brown and black............	15	50
D105		10p. yellow, emerald and black	30	75
D106		20p. blue-green, violet and black	75	1·50
D107		25p. cerise, rosine and black	1·50	2·00
D108		£1 violet, magenta and black..................	7·00	7·00
D109		£1·20 greenish blue, blue-green and black	8·00	8·00
D110		£5 greenish black, blue-green and black	20·00	20·00
Set of 9			35·00	35·00
First Day Cover..				45·00
Presentation Pack (P.O. Pack No.32)............................			35·00	

Special First Day of Issue Postmarks

London EC3..45·00

Following changes in the method of collecting money due on unpaid or underpaid mail the use of postage due stamps was restricted from April 1995 to mail addressed to business customers and to Customs/V.A.T. charges levied by the Royal Mail on behalf of the Customs and Excise. The use of postage due stamps ceased on 28 January 2000.

D 5   D 6

PRICES. Prices in the used column are for stamps with genuine postal cancellations dated from the time when they were authorised for use as postage stamps. Beware of stamps with fiscal cancellations removed and fraudulent postmarks applied.

VALIDITY. The 1d. surface-printed stamps were authorised for postal use from 1 June 1881 and at the same time the 1d. postage issue, No. 166, was declared valid for fiscal purposes. The 3d. and 6d. values together with the embossed issues were declared valid for postal purposes by another Act effective from 1 January 1883.

SURFACE–PRINTED ISSUES
(Typo Thomas De La Rue & Co.)

F **1** Rectangular Buckle   F **2**

F **3** Octagonal Buckle   F **4**

F **5** Double-lined Anchor   F **6** Single-lined Anchor

1853–57. Perf 15½×15.

*(a) Wmk F **5** (inverted) (1853–55).*

			Unused	Used	Used on cover
F1	F **1**	1d. light blue (10.10.53)	50·00	65·00	£225
		Wi. Watermark upright	£180		
		Wj. Watermark reversed*	£180		
F2	F **2**	1d. ochre (10.53)	£130	£160	£600
		a. Tête-bêche (in block of four)	£22000		
		Wi. Watermark upright			
F3	F **3**	1d. pale turquoise-blue (12.53)	45·00	60·00	£350
F4		1d. light blue/*blue* (12.53)	90·00	95·00	£550
		Wi. Watermark upright	£160	£225	
F5	F **4**	1d. reddish lilac/*blue glazed paper* (25.3.55)	£130	£160	£450
		Wi. Watermark upright	£200	£300	

*Watermark reversed: with the stamp upright and viewed from the front the cable finishes to the right of the base of the anchor shaft.
Only one example is known of No. F2a outside the National Postal Museum and the Royal Collection.

*(b) Wmk F **6** (1856–57).*

F6	F **4**	1d. reddish lilac (*shades*)	12·00	9·50	£180
		Wi. Watermark inverted	£160		
		Wj. Watermark reversed	£180		
		s. Overprinted "SPECIMEN" (2)	£170		
F7		1d. reddish lilac/*bluish* (*shades*) (1857)	12·00	9·50	£180
		Wj. Watermark reversed	£180		

INLAND REVENUE

(F **7**)

1860 (3 Apr). No. F7 overprinted with Type F **7,** in red.

F8	F **4**	1d. dull reddish lilac/*blue*	£950	£725	£1500
		Wj. Wmk reversed			

BLUE PAPER. In the following issues we no longer distinguish between bluish and white paper. There is a range of papers from white or greyish to bluish.

F **8**   F **9**

F **10**

1860–67. Bluish to white paper. Perf 15½×15.

*(a) Wmk F **6** (1860).*

F9	F **8**	1d. reddish lilac (5.60)	14·00	18·00	£180
		Wi. Watermark inverted	£130		
		s. Overprinted "SPECIMEN" (2)	£180		
F10	F **9**	3d. reddish lilac (6.60)	£550	£340	£550
		s. Overprinted "SPECIMEN" (2)	£240		
F11	F **10**	6d. reddish lilac (10.60)	£220	£220	£450
		Wi. Watermark inverted	£275	£220	
		Wj. Watermark reversed	£275	£220	
		s. Overprinted "SPECIMEN" (2)	£220		

*(b) W **40**. (Anchor 16 mm high) (1864).*

F12	F **8**	1d. pale reddish lilac (11.64)	12·00	14·00	£180
		Wi. Watermark inverted			
F13	F **9**	3d. pale reddish lilac	£275	£210	£550
		s. Overprinted "SPECIMEN" (9)	£220		
F14	F **10**	6d. pale reddish lilac	£240	£210	£550
		Wi. Watermark inverted	£360		

*(c) W **40** (Anchor 18 mm high) (1867).*

F15	F **8**	1d. reddish lilac	25·00	27·00	£275
F16	F **9**	3d. reddish lilac	£120	£120	£450
		s. Overprinted "SPECIMEN" (9, 10)	£190		
F17	F **10**	6d. reddish lilac	£110	95·00	£300
		s. Overprinted "SPECIMEN" (9, 10)	£190		

For stamps perf 14, see Nos. F24/7.

F **11**   F **12**

Four Dies of Type F 12

Round "O" (Dies 1 to 3)

Oval "O" (Die 4)

Small corner ornaments (Dies 1 and 2)

Medium corner ornaments (Die 3)

Large corner ornaments (Die 4)

Four lines of shading In left-hand ribbon (Die 1)

Two lines of shading in left-hand ribbon (Die 2)

Three lines of shading In left-hand ribbon (Die 3)

Heavy shading in both ribbons (Die 4)

Band of crown shaded (Dies 1 and 2)

Band of crown unshaded (Die 3)

Band of crown unshaded at front only (Die 4)

Die 1: Round "O" in "ONE"
Small corner ornaments
Four lines of shading in left-hand ribbon
Band of crown shaded
Die 2: Round "O" in "ONE"
Small corner ornaments
Two lines of shading in left-hand ribbon
Band of crown shaded
Die 3: Round "O" in "ONE"
Medium corner ornaments
Three lines of shading in left-hand ribbon
Band of crown unshaded
Die 4: Oval "O" in "ONE"
Large corner ornaments
Heavy shading in both ribbons
Band of crown unshaded at front only

1867–81. White to bluish paper. Perf 14.

*(a) W **47** (Small Anchor).*

F18	F **11**	1d. purple (1.9.67)	22·00	24·00	£140
		Wi. Watermark inverted	£130		
F19	F **12**	1d. purple (Die I) (6.68)	7·50	9·00	£140
		s. Overprinted "SPECIMEN" (6, 9, 10)	60·00		
		Wi. Watermark inverted	90·00		
F20		1d. purple (Die 2) (6.76)	27·00	22·00	£300
		s. Overprinted "SPECIMEN" (9)	£110		
F21		1d. purple (Die 3) (3.77)	14·00	18·00	£220
		s. Overprinted "SPECIMEN" (9)	90·00		
F22		1d. purple (Die 4) (7.78)	8·50	10·00	£120

*(b) W **48** (Orb).*

F23	F **12**	1d. purple (Die 4) (1.81)	8·50	5·00	£110
		Wi. Watermark inverted	£130		

1881. White to bluish paper. Perf 14.

*(a) W **40** (Anchor 18 mm high) (Jan).*

F24	F **9**	3d. reddish lilac	£850	£525	£1000
F25	F **10**	6d. reddish lilac	£400	£225	£450

*(b) W **40** (Anchor 20 mm high) (May).*

F26	3d. reddish lilac	£625	£425	£700
	s. Overprinted "SPECIMEN" (9)	£340		
F27	6d. reddish lilac	£360	£210	£450
	s. Overprinted "SPECIMEN" (9)	£300		

ISSUES EMBOSSED IN COLOUR

(Made at Somerset House)

The embossed stamps were struck from dies not appropriated to any special purpose on paper which had the words "INLAND REVENUE" previously printed, and thus became available for payment of any duties for which no special stamps had been provided.

The die letters are included in the embossed designs and holes were drilled for the insertion of plugs showing figures indicating dates of striking.

F **13**   F **14**

(F **15**)

1860 (3 Apr)–**71**. Types F **13/14** and similar types embossed on bluish paper. No wmk. Imperf.

F28	2d. pink (Die A) (1.1.71)		£775
	s. Overprinted "SPECIMEN" (2, 9)		£210
F29	3d. pink (Die C)		£210
	a. Tête-bêche (vertical pair)		£1700
F30	3d. pink (Die D)		£775
F31	6d. pink (Die T)		
F32	6d. pink (Die U)		£400
	a. Tête-bêche (vertical pair)		
F33	9d. pink (Die C) (1.1.71)		£1000
	s. Overprinted "SPECIMEN" (2, 9)		£210
F34	1s. pink (Die E) (28.6.61)		£775
	a. Tête-bêche (vertical pair)		
F35	1s. pink (Die F) (28.6.61)		£300
	a. Tête-bêche (vertical pair)		£1200
	s. Overprinted "SPECIMEN" (2, 9)		£210
F36	2s. pink (Die K) (6.8.61)		£775
F37	2s.6d. pink (Die N) (28.6.61)		
F38	2s.6d. pink (Die O) (28.6.61)		£400
	s. Overprinted "SPECIMEN" (2, 9)		£210

1871 (Aug). *As last but perf 12½.*

F39	2d. pink (Die A)		£500
	a. Tête-bêche (vertical pair)		
	s. Overprinted "SPECIMEN" (9)		£120
F42	9d. pink (Die C)		£1200
	s. Overprinted "SPECIMEN" (9)		£210
F43	1s. pink (Die E)		£775
F44	1s. pink (Die F)		£700
	s. Overprinted "SPECIMEN" (9)		£195
F45	2s.6d. pink (Die O)		£400
	s. Overprinted "SPECIMEN" (9)		£195

1874 (Nov). Type F **15** embossed on white paper. Underprint, in green. W **47** (Small Anchor). Perf 12½.

F48	1s. vermilion (Die F)		£775

1875 (Nov)–**80**. Types F **13/15** and similar but colour changed and underprint as F **15**. On white or bluish paper. Perf 12½.

F50	2d. vermilion (Die A) (1880)		£600
	s. Overprinted "SPECIMEN" (9)		£210
F51	9d. vermilion (Die C) (1876)		£775
	s. Overprinted "SPECIMEN" (9, 10)		£210
F52	1s. vermilion (Die E)		£500
	s. Overprinted "SPECIMEN" (9, 10)		£210
F53	1s. vermilion (Die F)		£1200
F54	2s.6d. vermilion (Die O) (1878)		£500
	s. Overprinted "SPECIMEN" (9)		£210

1882 (Oct). *As last but W **48** (Orbs).*

F55	2d. vermilion (Die A)		†
	s. Overprinted "SPECIMEN" (9)		£230
F56	9d. vermilion (Die C)		†
	s. Overprinted "SPECIMEN" (9)		£230
F57	1s. vermilion (Die E)		†
	s. Overprinted "SPECIMEN" (9)		£230
F58	2s.6d. vermilion (Die O)	£1000	£775
	s. Overprinted "SPECIMEN" (9)		£230

Although specimen overprints of Nos. F55/7 are known they were never issued.

The sale of Inland Revenue stamps up to the 2s. value ceased from 30 December 1882 and stocks were called in and destroyed. The 2s.6d. value remained on sale until 2 July 1883 when it was replaced by the 2s.6d. "Postage & Revenue" stamps. Inland Revenue stamps still in the hands of the public continued to be accepted for revenue and postal purposes.

Post Office Stamp Booklets

The following listing covers all booklets sold by post offices from 1904.

All major variations of contents and cover are included, but minor changes to the covers and differences on the interleaves have been ignored.

From 1913 each booklet carried an edition number, linked to an internal Post Office system of identification which divided the various booklets into series. In 1943 these edition numbers were replaced by edition dates. No attempt has been made to list separate edition numbers for booklets prior to 1943, although notes giving their extent are provided for each booklet. Edition dates from August 1943 are listed separately and exist for all £.s.d. and most Decimal Stitched booklets (except for the 1s. booklets, the 2s. booklets (N1/3), the 5s. "Philympia" booklets (No. HP34), the £1 "Stamps for Cooks'" booklet (No. ZP1) and the Decimal Sponsored booklets). They are those found printed upon the booklets, either on the outer back cover or on the white leaves.

Note that the date of issue may not coincide with the edition date given on the booklet, thus, No. DW1, issued on 13 November 1974, has an edition date of "SEPT 1974".

ERRORS OF MAKE-UP of booklets exist but we do not list them here. More detailed listings can be found in the 2nd, 3rd and 4th volumes of the *Great Britain Specialised Catalogue*.

ILLUSTRATIONS. The illustrations of the covers are ¾ size except where otherwise stated. Those in Queen Elizabeth II Decimal Sections C to H are ⅔ size, except where otherwise stated.

> **PRICES** quoted are for complete booklets containing stamps with "average" perforations (i.e. full perforations on two edges of the pane only). Booklets containing panes with complete perforations are worth more.

KING EDWARD VII

2s. Booklets

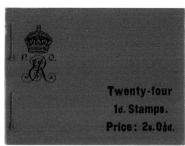

BA **1**

1904 (Mar). *Red* cover printed in black as Type BA **1**. Pages of six stamps: 24×1d. *Wmk* Imperial Crown (No. 219).
BA1 .... £500

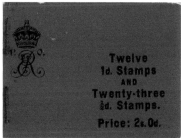

BA **2**

1906 (June). *Red* cover printed in black as Type BA **2**. As before but make-up changed to include 12×1d. and 23×½d. and label showing one green cross (Nos. 217 and 219).
BA2 .... £2200

1907 (Aug). *Red* cover printed in black as Type BA **2**. Make-up changed to include 18×1d. and 11×½d. and label showing one green cross (Nos. 217 and 219).
BA3 .... £3100

1908 (Aug). As before, but interleaves used for post office adverts printed in red.
BA4 .... £3400

1909 (Aug). As before, but interleaves used for trade advert printed in green.
BA5 .... £2700

BA **6**

1911 (June). Red cover printed in black as Type BA **2** but showing a larger Post Office cypher on cover. As before, but containing stamps by Harrison & Sons (Nos. 267 and 272).
BA6 .... £2800

KING GEORGE V

2s. Booklets

BB **1**

1911 (Aug). Red cover printed in black as Type BA **2** showing King George V cypher. Pages of six stamps: 18×1d. and 12×½d. *Wmk* Crown (Nos. 325, 329) Die 1B.
BB1 .... £1600

BB **2**

1912 (Apr). As before, but red cover printed in black as Type BB **2**.
BB2 .... £1900

1912 (Sept). As before, but *wmk* Simple Cypher (Nos. 334, 336) Die 1B.
BB3 .... £1300

BB **5**

1912 (Nov). As before, but red cover printed in black as Type BB **5** but without edition number.
BB4 .... £1600

1913 (Jan). As before, but red cover printed in black as Type BB **5**.
BB5 Edition numbers 8 or 9 .... £1300

1913 (Apr). As before, but 1912–22 *wmk* Simple Cypher (Nos. 351, 357).
BB6 Edition numbers 10 to 35 .... £1300

1915 (Nov). As before, except lower panel of front cover which was changed to show *New rates of postage*.
BB7 Edition numbers 36 to 42 .... £1600

1916 (May). As before, but interleave adverts printed in black instead of green.
BB8 Edition numbers 43 to 45 .... £2000

1916 (July). As before, but orange cover printed in black as Type BB **5**.
BB9 Edition numbers 46 to 64 .... £1500

BB **10**

1917 (Sept). As before, but orange cover printed in black as Type BB **10**.
BB10 Edition numbers 65 to 81 .... £1350

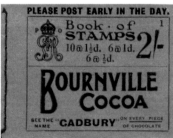

BB **11**

1924 (Feb). Blue cover printed in black as Type BB **11**. Pages of six stamps: 10×1½d. (first completed by two perforated labels), 6×1d. and 6×½d. 1912–22 *wmk* Simple Cypher (Nos. 351, 357, 362).
BB11 Edition numbers 1 or 2 .... £2600

1924 (Mar). As before, but 1924–26 *wmk* Block Cypher (Nos. 418/20).
BB12 Edition numbers 3 to 102 & 108 to 254 .... £900

BB **13**

1929 (May). *Postal Union Congress issue.* Cover of special design as Type BB **13** printed in blue on buff as before but containing stamps of the PUC issue (Nos. 434/6).
BB13 Edition numbers 103 to 107 .... £500

1934 (Feb). Blue cover printed in black as Type BB **11**, but containing stamps with Block Cypher *wmk* printed by Harrison & Sons (Nos. 418/20).
BB14 Edition numbers 255 to 287 .... £1100

1935 (Jan). As before, but containing stamps of the photogravure issue (intermediate format) with the *se-tenant* advertisements printed in brown (Nos. 439/41).
BB15 Edition numbers 288 to 297 .... £2700

BB **16**

1935 (May). *Silver Jubilee issue.* Larger size cover printed in blue on buff as Type BB **16** and containing pages of four stamps with no *se-tenant* advertisements: 12×1½d., 4×1d. and 4×½d. (Nos. 453/5).
BB16 Edition numbers 298 to 304 .... 90·00

1935 (July). As No. BB **15**, but containing stamps of the photogravure (small format) issue with *se-tenant* advertisements printed in black (Nos. 439/41).
BB17 Edition numbers 305 to 353 .... £600

3s. Booklets

BB **19**

1918 (Oct). Orange cover printed in black as Type BB **19**. Pages of six stamps: 12×1½d., 12×1d. and 12×½d. 1912–22 *wmk* Simple Cypher (Nos. 351, 357, 362).
BB18 Edition numbers 1 to 11 .... £1850

1919 (July). As before, but make-up altered to contain 18×1½d., 6×1d. and 6×½d.

BB19   Edition numbers 12 to 26 .... £1850

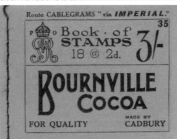

BB **20**

1921 (April). Experimental booklet bound in blue covers as Type BB **20,** containing pages of six stamps: 18×2d. (Die I) (No. 368).
BB20   Edition numbers 35 and part 37 .... £2400
1921 (Dec). As before, but containing 2d. (Die II) (No. 370).
BB21   Edition numbers 12, 13 and part 37 .... £2400

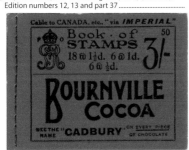

BB **22**

1922 (May). Scarlet cover printed in black as Type BB **22.** Pages of six stamps: 18×1½d., 6×1d. and 6×½d. (Nos. 351,357**,** 362).
BB22   Edition numbers 19, 20, 22, 23 and 25 to 54 .... £2400

BB **23**

1922 (June). Experimental booklet as Edition numbers 12 and 13 bound in blue covers as Type BB **23,** containing pages of six stamps: 24×1½d. (No. 362).
BB23   Edition numbers 21 or 24 .... £2400
1924 (Feb). Scarlet cover printed in black as Type BB **22,** but containing stamps with Block Cypher *wmk*, printed by Waterlow & Sons (No. 418/20).
BB24   Edition numbers 55 to 167 & 173 to 273 .... £550
1929 (May). *Postal Union Congress issue.* Cover of special design as Type BB **13** printed in red on buff as before but containing stamps of the PUC issue (Nos. 434/6).
BB25   Edition numbers 168 to 172 .... £450
1934 (Mar). Scarlet cover printed in black as Type BB **22,** but containing stamps with the Block Cypher *wmk* printed by Harrison & Sons (Nos. 418/20).
BB26   Edition numbers 274 to 288 .... £650
1935 (Jan). As No. BB **29,** but containing stamps of the photogravure issue (intermediate format).
BB27   Edition numbers 289 to 293 .... £2100
1935 (May). *Silver Jubilee* issue. Larger size cover printed in red on buff as Type BB **16** and containing pages of four stamps: 20×1½d., 4×1d. and 4×½d. (Nos. 453/5).
BB28   Edition numbers 294 to 297 .... 90·00
1935 (July). As No. BB **26,** but containing stamps of the photogravure issue (small format) (Nos. 439/41).
BB29   Edition numbers 298 to 319 .... £550

3s.6d. Booklets

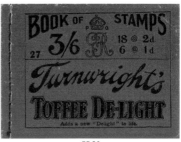

BB **30**

1920 (July). Orange cover printed in black as Type BB **30,** containing pages of six stamps: 18×2d. and 6×1d. (Nos. 357, 368).
BB30   Edition numbers 27 to 32 .... £2200

BB **31**

1921 (Jan). Orange-red cover printed in black as Type BB **31,** as before but make-up changed to include stamps of 1912–22 issue with the Simple Cypher *wmk*: 12×2d. (Die I), 6×1½d., 6×1d. and 6×½d. (Nos. 351, 357, 362, 368).
BB31   Edition numbers 33, 34, 36 & 38 .... £2200
1921 (July). As BB **31** including stamps of the 1912-22 issue with Simple Cypher *wmk*: 12×2d. (Die I or II), 6×1½d., 6×1d. and 6×½d. (Nos. 351, 357, 362, 368 or 370).
BB32   Edition numbers 1 to 11, 14 to 18 .... £2200

5s. Booklets

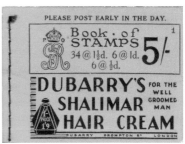

BB **33**

1931 (Aug). Green cover printed in black as Type BB **33.** Pages of six stamps: 34×1½d., 6×1d. and 6×½d. The first 1½d. pane completed by two *se-tenant* advertisements. Printed by Waterlow & Sons on paper with Block Cypher *wmk* (Nos. 418/20).
BB33   Edition number 1 .... £6250

1932 (June). As before, but buff cover printed in black.
BB34   Edition numbers 2 to 6 .... £5250

1934 (July). As before, but containing stamps with Block Cypher *wmk* printed by Harrison & Sons (Nos. 418/20).
BB35   Edition numbers 7 or 8 .... £2200

1935 (Feb). As before, but containing stamps of the photogravure issue (intermediate format) with *se-tenant* advertisements printed in brown (Nos. 439/41).
BB36   Edition number 9 .... £6250

1935 (July). As before, but containing stamps of the photogravure issue (small format) with *se-tenant* advertisements printed in black (Nos. 439/41).
BB37   Edition numbers 10 to 15 .... £650

6d. Booklet

1936. Buff unglazed cover without inscription containing 4×1½d. stamps, in panes of two (No. 459).

BC1   Edition numbers 354 to 385.. 65·00

2s. Booklet

BC **2**

1936 (Oct). Blue cover printed in black as Type BC **2**, containing pages of six stamps: 10×1½d., 6×1d. & 6×½d. (Nos. 457/9).

BC2   Edition numbers 354 to 385... £140

3s. Booklet

1936 (Nov). As No. BB **29**, except for the K.E.VIII cypher on the cover but without "P" and "O" on either side of the crown, and containing Nos. 457/9.

BC3   Edition numbers 320 to 332... £120

5s. Booklet

1937 (Mar). As No. BB **37**, but with the K.E.VIII cypher on the cover and containing Nos. 457/9.

BC4   Edition numbers 16 or 17... £275

6d. Booklets

1938 (Jan). As No. BC **1**, but containing stamps in the original dark colours. Buff cover without inscription (No. 464).

BD1   .... 75·00

1938 (Feb). As before, but pink unprinted cover and make-up changed to contain 2×1½d., 2×1d. and 2×½d. in the original dark colours (Nos. 462/4).

BD2   .... £300

1940 (June). Pale green unprinted cover and make-up changed to include two panes of four stamps with *wmk* sideways. Stamps in original dark colours with binding margin either at the top or bottom of the pane: 4×1d., 4×½d. (Nos. 462a/3a).

BD3   .... £150

1s. Booklets with Panes of 2

1947 (Dec). Cream cover, unglazed and without inscription containing panes of two stamps in pale shades, all with *wmk* normal. Panes of two stamps: 4×½d., 4×1d. and 4×1½d. (Nos. 485/7).

BD4   .... 28·00

1951 (May). As before, but containing stamps in changed colours (Nos. 503/5).

BD5   .... 28·00

1s. Booklets with Panes of 4

1948. Cream cover as before, but make-up changed to contain 4×1½d., 4×1d. and 4×½d. in panes of four of the pale shades with *wmk* normal (Nos. 485/7).

BD6   .... £9000

1951 (May). As before, but stamps in new colours all *wmk* normal, margins at either top or at the bottom. (Nos. 503/5).

BD7   .... 50·00

BD **8**

1952 (Dec). Cream cover printed in black as Type BD **8**. Make-up as before but with *wmk* either upright or inverted and margins only at the top (Nos. 503/5).

BD8   .... 25·00

BD **10**

1954. As before but cover showing GPO emblem with St Edward's crown and oval frame as Type BD **10** (Nos. 503/5).

BD10   .... 35·00

2s. Booklets

BD **11**

1937 (Aug). Blue cover printed in black as Type BB **11**, but with K.G. VI cypher on the cover and containing stamps in the original dark colours. Panes of six stamps: 10×1½d., 6×1d. and 6×½d. The first 1½d. pane completed by two *se-tenant* advertisements. (Nos. 462/4).

BD11   Edition numbers 386 to 412... £1100

BD **12**

1938 (Mar). Blue cover printed in black as Type BD **12** (Nos. 462/4).

BD12   Edition numbers 413 to 508... £1100

2s.6d. Booklets

BD **13**

1940 (June). Scarlet cover printed in black as Type BD **13**, containing panes of six stamps in original dark colours: 6×2½d., 6×2d. and 6×½d. (Nos. 462, 465/6).

BD13   Edition numbers 1 to 8 (part)... £1700

1940 (Sept). As before, but blue cover printed in black as Type BD **13**.

BD14   Edition numbers 8 (part) to 13.. £1700

BD **15**

1940 (Oct). As before, but with green cover printed in black as Type BD **15** (Nos. 462, 465/6).

BD15   Edition numbers 14 to 94.. £975

1942 (Mar). As before, but containing stamps in pale shades (Nos. 485, 488/9).

BD16   Edition numbers 95 to 146 (Part).................................... £975

1942 (Oct). Composition as before, but with unglazed green covers.

BD17   Edition numbers 146 (Part) to 214 .... £975

Type **A** Circular GPO Cypher

1943 (Aug). As before, but green cover printed in black as Type A, with different contents details (Nos. 485, 488/9).

BD18   Edition dates August 1943 to February 1951 .... 95·00

(1) AUG 1943 ....£110	(45) MAY 1947 ....£150
(2) OCT 1943 ....£150	(46) JUNE 1947 ....£150
(3) NOV 1943 ....£180	(47) JULY 1947 ....£150
(4) DEC 1943 ....£170	(48) AUG 1947 ....£150
(5) JAN 1944 ....£160	(49) SEPT 1947 ....£150
(6) FEB 1944............£160	(50) OCT 1947 ....£150
(7) MAR 1944...........£160	(51) NOV 1947 ....£150
(8) APR 1944............£160	(52) DEC 1947 ....£150
(9) MAY 1944 ....£160	(53) JAN 1948.............£180
(10) JUNE 1944 ....£160	(54) FEB 1948.............£150
(11) JULY 1944 ....£160	(55) MAR 1948............£150
(12) AUG 1944 ....£160	(56) APR 1948.............£150
(13) SEPT 1944 ....£160	(57) MAY 1948............£150
(14) OCT 1944 ....£160	(58) JUNE 1948 ....£150
(15) NOV 1944..........£160	(59) JULY 1948 ....£150
(16) DEC 1944 ....£150	(60) AUG 1948 ....£150
(17) JAN 1945...........£160	(61) OCT 1948 ....£140
(18) FEB 1945............£160	(62) NOV 1948...........£140
(19) MAR 1945...........£160	(63) DEC 1948 ....£140
(20) APR 1945............£160	(64) JAN 1949.............£140
(21) MAY 1945 ....£160	(65) FEB 1949.............£150
(22) JUNE 1945 ....£160	(66) MAR 1949............£150
(23) JULY 1945 ....£160	(67) APR 1949.............£150
(24) AUG 1945 ....£160	(68) MAY 1949............£150
(25) SEPT 1945 ....£160	(69) JUNE 1949 ....£150
(26) OCT 1945 ....£160	(70) JULY 1949 ....£150
(27) NOV 1945..........£160	(71) AUG 1949 ....£150
(28) DEC 1945 ....£160	(72) OCT 1949 ....£150
(29) JAN 1946...........£150	(73) NOV 1949...........£150
(30) FEB 1946............£150	(74) DEC 1949 ....£150
(31) MAR 1946...........£150	(75) JAN 1950.............£120
(32) APR 1946............£150	(76) FEB 1950.............£120
(33) MAY 1946 ....£150	(77) MAR 1950............£120
(34) JUNE 1946 ....£150	(78) APR 1950.............£120
(35) JULY 1946 ....£150	(79) MAY 1950............£120
(36) AUG 1946 ....£150	(80) JUNE 1950 ....£120
(37) SEPT 1946 ....£150	(81) JULY 1950 ....95·00
(38) OCT 1946 ....£400	(82) AUG 1950 ....95·00
(39) NOV 1946..........£150	(83) SEPT 1950 ....95·00
(40) DEC 1946 ....£150	(84) OCT 1950 ....95·00
(41) JAN 1947...........£150	(85) NOV 1950...........95·00
(42) FEB 1947............£150	(86) DEC 1950 ....95·00
(43) MAR 1947...........£150	(87) JAN 1951.............95·00
(44) APR 1947............£150	(88) FEB 1951.............95·00

1951 (May). As before, but containing stamps in the new colours (Nos. 503, 506/7).

BD19   Edition dates May 1951 to February 1952........................... 55·00

(1) MAY 1951 ....55·00	(6) OCT 1951.......................55·00
(2) JUNE 1951 ....75·00	(7) NOV 1951 ....55·00
(3) JULY 1951 ....£200	(8) DEC 1951 ....55·00
(4) AUG 1951 ....55·00	(9) JAN 1952.......................55·00
(5) SEPT 1951 ....£175	(10) FEB 1952......................55·00

1952 (Mar). As before, but make-up changed to contain: 6×2½d., 6×1½d., 3×1d. and 6×½d. The 1d. pane was completed by three perforated labels in the lower row inscribed *MINIMUM INLAND PRINTED PAPER RATE 1½d.* (Nos. 503/5, 507).

BD20   Edition dates March 1952 to May 1953 .... 50·00

(1) MAR 1952 ....50·00	(9) NOV 1952......................50·00
(2) APR 1952.......................55·00	(10) DEC 1952.....................50·00
(3) MAY 1952 ....50·00	(11) JAN 1953......................50·00
(4) JUNE 1952......................50·00	(12) FEB 1953......................50·00
(5) JULY 1952 ....55·00	(13) MAR 1953.....................50·00
(6) AUG 1952 ....50·00	(14) APR 1953......................50·00
(7) SEPT 1952......................50·00	(15) MAY 1953......................55·00
(8) OCT 1952.......................50·00	

3s. Booklets

BD **21**

1937 (Aug). Scarlet cover printed black as Type BD **21**, containing pages of six stamps: 18×1½d., 6×1d. & 6×½d. in the original dark colours (Nos. 462/4).

BD21   Edition numbers 333 to 343 .... £1900

BD **22**

1938 (April). As before, but scarlet cover printed in black as Type BD **22** (Nos. 462/4).

BD22   Edition numbers 344 to 377 .... £1900

5s. Booklets

1937 (Aug). Buff cover printed in black as Type BB **33,** containing stamps of the new reign in the original dark colours. Pages of six stamps: 34×1½d., 6×1d. and 6×½d. The first 1½d. pane completed by two *se-tenant* advertisements. (Nos. 462/4).

BD23   Edition numbers 18 to 20... £2000

BD **24**

1938 (May). As before, but with redesigned front cover showing GPO emblem as Type BD **24** instead of royal cypher.
BD24   Edition numbers 21 to 29.. £2000

1940 (July). As before, but make-up changed to contain: 18×2½d., 6×2d. and 6×½d. in the original dark colours (Nos. 462, 465/6).
BD25   Edition numbers 1 to 16 (part).. £2000

1942 (Mar). As before, but containing stamps in pale shades (Nos. 485, 488/9).
BD26   Edition numbers 16 (part) to 36.. £2000

1943 (Sept). As before, but buff cover printed in black as Type A (see No. BD **18**, 2s·6d.) (Nos. 485, 488/9).
BD28   Edition dates September 1943 to December 1950............ £130

(1) SEPT 1943.................. £160	(26) JUNE 1947 .... £180
(2) OCT 1943.................... £230	(27) AUG 1947 .... £180
(3) NOV 1943.................... £180	(28) OCT 1947 .... £180
(4) DEC 1943.................... £230	(29) NOV 1947 .... £180
(5) FEB 1944.................... £190	(30) FEB 1948 .... £180
(6) MAR 1944.................... £190	(31) APR 1948 .... £180
(7) AUG 1944.................... £190	(32) JUNE 1948 .... £180
(8) OCT 1944.................... £190	(33) JULY 1948 .... £180
(9) NOV 1944.................... £190	(34) AUG 1948 .... £180
(10) JAN 1945.................... £190	(35) OCT 1948 .... £180
(11) FEB 1945.................... £200	(36) DEC 1948 .... £200
(12) APR 1945.................... £200	(37) FEB 1949 .... £200
(13) JUNE 1945.................. £200	(38) APR 1949 .... £200
(14) AUG 1945.................. £200	(39) JUNE 1949 .... £190
(15) OCT 1945.................... £200	(40) AUG 1949 .... £190
(16) DEC 1945.................... £200	(41) SEPT 1949 .... £190
(17) JAN 1946.................... £200	(42) OCT 1949 .... £190
(18) MAR 1946.................. £180	(43) DEC 1949 .... £190
(19) MAY 1946.................. £180	(44) FEB 1950 .... £130
(20) JUNE 1946.................. £180	(45) APR 1950 .... £130
(21) AUG 1946.................. £180	(46) JUNE 1950 .... £130
(22) OCT 1946.................... £180	(47) AUG 1950 .... £130
(23) DEC 1946.................... £180	(48) OCT 1950 .... £130
(24) FEB 1947.................... £180	(49) DEC 1950 .... £130
(25) APR 1947.................... £180	

BD **29**

1944 (Apr). As before, but buff cover printed in black as Type BD **29** (Nos. 485, 488/9).
BD29   Edition dates April or June 1944.................................... £5250

(1) APR 1944 .... £5250	(2) JUNE 1944................... £5250

1951 (May). As before, but buff cover changed back to Type A (see No. BD **18**, 2s·6d.) and containing stamps in the new colours (Nos. 503, 506/7).
BD30   Edition dates May 1951 to January 1952....................... 65·00

(1) MAY 1951 .... 65·00	(4) NOV 1951 .... 65·00
(2) JULY 1951..................... 65·00	(5) JAN 1952 .... 65·00
(3) SEPT 1951..................... 65·00	

1952 (Mar). As before, make-up changed to contain: 18×2½d., 6×1½d., 3×1d. and 6×½d. The 1d. pane was completed by three perforated labels in the lower row inscribed *"MINIMUM INLAND PRINTED PAPER RATE 1½d."* (Nos. 503/5, 507).
BD31   Edition dates March to November 1952.......................... 55·00

(1) MAR 1952..................... 55·00	(4) SEPT 1952.................... 55·00
(2) MAY 1952..................... 55·00	(5) NOV 1952.................... 55·00
(3) JULY 1952..................... 55·00	

1953 (Jan). As before, but make-up changed again to include the 2d. value and containing: 12×2½d., 6×2d., 6×1½d., 6×1d. and 6×½d. (Nos. 503/7).
BD32   Edition dates January or March 1953.............................. 65·00

(1) JAN 1953 .... 65·00	(2) MAR 1953 .... 65·00

QUEEN ELIZABETH II

I. £.s.d. Booklets, 1953–70.

TYPES OF BOOKLET COVER WITH GPO CYPHER

Type **A** Circular GPO Cypher
(See illustration above No. BD18)

Type **B** Oval Type GPO Cypher

Type **C** New GPO Cypher (small)

Type **D** New GPO Cypher (large)

1s. Booklets

1953 (2 Sept)–**59**.
I. White unprinted cover. Pages of two stamps: 4×1½d., 4×1d., 4×½d. For use in experimental "D" machines.
    A. Wmk Tudor Crown (Nos. 515/17) EE
E1   No date... 5·00
    B. Wmk St Edward's Crown (Nos. 540/2)
E2   No date (11.57)... 40·00
II. White printed cover as Type B. Pages of four stamps: 4×1½d. 4×1d., 4×1½d. For use in "E" machines.
    A. Wmk Tudor Crown (Nos. 515/17)
K1   No date (22.7.54).. 8·00
    B. Wmk St Edward's Crown (Nos. 540/2)
K2   No date (5.7.56)... 5·00
    C. Wmk Crowns (Nos. 570/2)
K3   No date (13.8.59).. 5·00

2s. Booklets

1959 (22 Apr)–**65**. Pages of four stamps: 4×3d., 4×1½d., 4×1d., 4×½d.
    I. Salmon cover as Type B. Wmk. St Edward's Crown (Nos. 540/2 and 545).
N1   No date... 6·00
    II. Salmon cover as Type C. Wmk Crowns (Nos. 570/2 and 575).
N2   No date (2.11.60)... 6·50
    III. Lemon cover as Type C. Wmk Crowns (Nos. 570/2 and 575).
N3   No date (2.61)... 6·50
    IV. Lemon cover as Type C. Wmk Crowns (sideways) (Nos. 570a, 571a, 572b, 575a) or phosphor (Nos. 610a, 611a, 612a, 615b).
N4   APR 1961... 32·00
    p. With phosphor bands .... 55·00
N5   SEPT 1961.. 50·00

N6	JAN 1962	45·00
N7	APR 1962	55·00
N8	JULY 1962	50·00
	p. With phosphor bands	90·00
N9	NOV 1962	70·00
	p. With phosphor bands	90·00
N10	JAN 1963	55·00
	p. With phosphor bands	£180
N11	MAR 1963	55·00
N12	JUNE 1963	55·00
	p. With phosphor bands	75·00
N13	AUG 1963	55·00
	p. With phosphor bands	£100
N14	OCT 1963	55·00
	p. With phosphor bands	£140
N15	FEB 1964	55·00
	p. With phosphor bands	95·00
N16	JUNE 1964	55·00
	p. With phosphor bands	£120
N17	AUG 1964	80·00
	p. With phosphor bands	£120
N18	OCT 1964	55·00
	p. With phosphor bands	70·00
N19	DEC 1964	65·00
	p. With phosphor bands	70·00
N20	APR 1965	55·00
		65·00

1965 (16 Aug)–**67**. New Composition. Pages of four stamps: 4×4d. and pane of 2×1d. and 2×3d. arranged *se-tenant* horiz. Orange-yellow cover as Type **C** printed in black. *Wmk* Crowns (sideways) (Nos. 571a, 575a and 576ab) or phosphor (Nos. 611a, 615d or 615dEa (one side phosphor band) and 616ab).

N21	JULY 1965	3·50
	p. With phosphor bands	12·00
N22	OCT 1965	3·75
	p. With phosphor bands	12·00
N23	JAN 1966	6·25
	p. With phosphor bands	16·00
N24	APR 1966	6·25
	p. With phosphor bands	8·00
N25	JULY 1966	7·50
	p. With phosphor bands	£150
N26	OCT 1966	6·00
	p. With phosphor bands	10·00
N27	JAN 1967	8·00
	p. With phosphor bands	5·00
N28p	APR 1967. With phosphor bands	6·00
N29p	JULY 1967. With phosphor bands	4·00
N30p	OCT 1967. With phosphor bands	4·00

In the *se-tenant* pane the 3d. appears at left or right to facilitate the application of phosphor bands.

The following illustration shows how the *se-tenant* stamps with one phosphor band on 3d. were printed and the arrows indicate where the guillotine fell. The result gives 1d. stamps with two bands and the 3d. stamps with one band either at left or right.

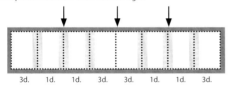

3d.   1d.   1d.   3d.   3d.   1d.   1d.   3d.

1967 (Nov)–**68**. Composition and cover as Nos. N21/30. *Wmk* Crowns (sideways) (Nos. 611a, 615b (two phosphor bands) and 616ab).

N31p	JAN 1968	4·00
N32p	MAR 1968	4·50

2s. Booklets with Machin type stamps

1968 (6 Apr–Aug). Orange-yellow cover as Type C. Pages of four stamps: 4×4d. and pane of 2×1d. and 2×3d. arranged *se-tenant* horiz. PVA gum (Nos. 724, 730, 731Ev).

NP27	MAY 1968	1·20
NP28	JULY 1968	1·00
NP29	AUG 1968	3·75

1968 (16 Sept)–**70**. Grey cover as Type C. New Composition. 4d. stamps only comprising page of 4×4d. with two phosphor bands (No. 731Ev) and page of 2×4d. with one centre phosphor band (No. 732) *se-tenant* with two printed labels.

NP30	SEPT 1968	75
NP31	JAN 1969	£250

Same composition but all six 4d. stamps have one centre phosphor band (No. 732).

NP31a	SEPT 1968	£600
NP32	NOV 1968	80
NP33	JAN 1969	75

Same composition but change to 4d. bright vermilion with one centre phosphor band (No. 733).

NP34	MAR 1969	1·10

NP35	MAY 1969	1·25
NP36	JULY 1969	1·75
NP37	SEPT 1969	1·50
NP38	NOV 1969	1·25
NP39	JAN 1970	2·00
NP40	MAR 1970	2·00
NP41	MAY 1970	2·00
NP42	JULY 1970	2·00
NP43	AUG 1970	2·00
NP44	OCT 1970	2·00
NP45	DEC 1970	2·00

2s. Booklets for Holiday Resorts

1963 (15 July)–**64**.
I. Lemon cover as Type C printed in red. New composition. Pages of four stamps: two of 4×2½d. and one of 3×1½d. and 1×2½d. arranged se-tenant. Chalky paper. Wmk Crowns (Nos. 570k and 574k).

NR1	No date, black stitching	4·00
	a. White stitching (3.9.63)	4·00

II. Lemon cover as Type C printed in red. Composition changed again. Pages of four stamps 2×½d. and 2×2½d. arranged sideways, vertically se-tenant. Wmk Crowns (sideways) (No. 570n×4).

NR2	1964 (1.7.64)	1·50

2s. Booklet for Christmas Cards

1965 (6 Dec). Orange-yellow cover as Type **C** printed in red. Two panes of 4×3d. arranged sideways. *Wmk* Crowns (sideways) (No. 575a).

NX1	1965	1·00

2s.6d. Booklets

Green cover. Pages of six stamps: 6×2½d., 6×1½d., 3×1d. (page completed by three perforated labels), 6×½d.
LABELS. The wording printed on the labels differs as follows:
"PPR" = "MINIMUM INLAND PRINTED PAPER RATE 1½d."
Two types exist:
    A. Printed in photogravure, 17 mm high.
    B. Typographed, 15 mm high.
"Shorthand" = "SHORTHAND IN 1 WEEK" (covering all three labels).
"Post Early" = "PLEASE POST EARLY IN THE DAY".
"PAP" = "PACK YOUR PARCELS SECURELY" (1st label)
    "ADDRESS YOUR LETTERS CORRECTLY" (2nd label),
    "AND POST EARLY IN THE DAY" (3rd label).

1953–54. Composite booklets containing stamps of King George VI and Queen Elizabeth II.

A. K.G.VI ½d. and 1d. (Nos. 503/4) and Q.E.II 1½d. and 2½d. (Nos. 517 and 519b). Cover as Type A. No interleaving pages.

F1	MAY 1953 (PPR 17 mm)	25·00
F2	JUNE 1953 (PPR 17 mm)	30·00
F3	JULY 1953 (PPR 17 mm)	35·00
F4	AUG 1953 (PPR 17 mm)	32·00

B. Same composition but with addition of two interleaving pages, one at each end. Cover as Type A.

F5	SEPT 1953 (PPR 17 mm)	£250
F6	SEPT 1953 (PPR 15 mm)	135·00

C. Same composition and with interleaving pages but with cover as Type B.

F7	OCT 1953 (PPR 17 mm)	50·00
F8	OCT 1953 (PPR 15 mm)	£150
F9	NOV 1953 (PPR 17 mm)	60·00
F10	NOV 1953 (PPR 15 mm)	£250
F11	DEC 1953 (PPR 17 mm)	55·00
F12	JAN 1954 (Shorthand)	75·00
F13	FEB 1954 (Shorthand)	85·00

D. New composition: K.G.VI 1d. (No. 504) and Q.E.II ½d., 1½d. and 2½d. (Nos. 515, 517 and 519b).

F14	MAR 1954 (PPR 17 mm)	£650
F14a	MAR 1954 (Shorthand)	

1954–57. Booklets containing only Queen Elizabeth II stamps. All covers as Type **B**.

A. Wmk Tudor Crown (Nos. 515/17 and 519b).

F15	MAR 1954 (PPR 15 mm)	£325
F16	APR 1954 (Post Early)	65·00
F17	MAY 1954 (Post Early)	65·00
F18	JUNE 1954 (Post Early)	65·00
F19	JULY 1954 (Post Early)	65·00
F20	AUG 1954 (Post Early)	65·00
F21	SEPT 1954 (Post Early)	65·00
F22	OCT 1954 (Post Early)	50·00
F23	NOV 1954 (Post Early)	50·00
F24	DEC 1954 (Post Early)	50·00

B. Same composition but with interleaving pages between each pane of stamps.

F25	JAN 1955 (Post Early)	75·00
F26	JAN 1955 (PAP)	£200
F27	FEB 1955 (PAP)	50·00
F28	MAR 1955 (PAP)	50·00
F29	APR 1955 (PAP)	50·00
F30	MAY 1955 (PAP)	65·00
F31	JUNE 1955 (PAP)	50·00
F32	JULY 1955 (PAP)	50·00
F33	AUG 1955 (PAP)	50·00

C. *Mixed watermarks. Wmk Tudor Crown (Nos. 515/17 and 519b) and wmk St Edward's Crown (Nos. 540/2 and 544b) in various combinations.*

F34	SEPT 1955 (PAP) .... *From*	60·00

2s·6d. booklets dated AUGUST, OCTOBER, NOVEMBER and DECEMBER 1955, JANUARY, MAY and JUNE 1956 exist both as listed and with the two watermarks mixed. There are so many different combinations that we do not list them separately, but when in stock selections can be submitted. The SEPTEMBER 1955 booklet (No. F34) only exists in composite form.

D. *Wmk St Edward's Crown (Nos. 540/2 and 544b).*

F35	OCT 1955 (PAP)	35·00
F36	NOV 1955 (PAP)	35·00
F37	DEC 1955 (PAP)	35·00
F38	JAN 1956 (PAP)	35·00
F39	FEB 1956 (PAP)	35·00
F40	MAR 1956 (PAP)	35·00
F41	APR 1956 (PAP)	45·00
F42	MAY 1956 (PAP)	35·00
F43	JUNE 1956 (PAP)	35·00
F44	JULY 1956 (PAP)	35·00
F45	AUG 1956 (PAP)	25·00
F46	SEPT 1956 (PAP)	45·00
F47	OCT 1956 (PAP)	35·00
F48	NOV 1956 (PAP)	35·00
F49	DEC 1956 (PAP)	35·00
F50	JAN 1957 (PAP)	35·00
F51	FEB 1957 (PAP)	35·00
F52	MAR 1957 (PAP)	35·00

E. *Same wmk but new composition. Pages of six stamps: 6×2½d. (No. 544b), 6×2d. (No. 543b) and 6×½d. (No. 540).*

F53	APR 1957	35·00
F54	MAY 1957	35·00
F55	JUNE 1957	30·00
F56	JULY 1957	30·00
F57	AUG 1957	30·00
F58	SEPT 1957	30·00
F59	OCT 1957	30·00
F60	NOV 1957	25·00
F61	DEC 1957	45·00

3s. Booklets

1958–65. Pages of six stamps: 6×3d., 6×1½d., 6×1d., 6×½d.

I. Red cover as Type **B**.

A. *Wmk St Edward's Crown (Nos. 540/2 and 545).*

M1	JAN 1958	28·00
M2	FEB 1958	38·00
M3	MAR 1958	30·00
M4	APR 1958	28·00
M5	MAY 1958	28·00
M6	JUNE 1958	28·00
M7	JULY 1958	30·00
M8	AUG 1958	32·00
M9	NOV 1958	32·00

The 3s. booklets dated NOVEMBER 1958, DECEMBER 1958 and JANUARY 1959 exist both as listed and with mixed St Edward's Crown and Crowns watermarks.

B. *Wmk Crowns (Nos. 570/2 and 575) or graphite lines (Nos. 587/9 and 592).*

M10	DEC 1958	35·00
M11	JAN 1959	35·00
M12	FEB 1959	35·00
M13	AUG 1959	40·00
	g. With graphite lines	£250
M14	SEPT 1959	40·00
	g. With graphite lines	£325

II. Brick-red cover as Type **C**. *Wmk Crowns (Nos. 570/2 and 575), graphite lines (Nos. 587/9 and 592) or phosphor (Nos. 610/12 and 615).*

M15	OCT 1959	35·00
	g. With graphite lines	£350
M16	NOV 1959	35·00
M17	DEC 1959	35·00
M18	JAN 1960	35·00
M19	FEB 1960	50·00
	g. With graphite lines	£325
M20	MAR 1960	50·00
	g. With graphite lines	£375
M21	APR 1960	45·00
	g. With graphite lines	£325
M22	MAY 1960	60·00
M23	JUNE 1960	60·00
M24	JULY 1960	50·00
M25	AUG 1960	45·00
	p. With phosphor bands	75·00
M26	SEPT 1960	50·00
M27	OCT 1960	50·00
M28	NOV 1960	38·00
	p. With phosphor bands	75·00

III. Brick-red cover as Type **D**. *Wmk Crowns (Nos. 570/2 and 575) or phosphor (Nos. 610/12 and 615).*

M29	DEC 1960	48·00

	p. With phosphor bands	75·00
M30	JAN 1961	60·00
M31	FEB 1961	60·00
M32	MAR 1961	60·00
M33	APR 1961	60·00
	p. With phosphor bands	75·00
M34	MAY 1961	60·00
M35	JUNE 1961	60·00
M36	JULY 1961	55·00
	p. With phosphor bands	75·00
M37	AUG 1961	60·00
	p. With phosphor bands	75·00
M38	SEPT 1961	60·00
	p. With phosphor bands	85·00
M39	OCT 1961	60·00
	p. With phosphor bands	£100
M40	NOV 1961	60·00
M41	DEC 1961	60·00
M42	JAN 1962	60·00
M43	FEB 1962	60·00
	p. With phosphor bands	£100
M44	MAR 1962	50·00
	p. With phosphor bands	£100
M45	APR 1962	60·00
	p. With phosphor bands	£100
M46	MAY 1962	60·00
	p. With phosphor bands	£100
M47	JUNE 1962	60·00
	p. With phosphor bands	£100
M48	JULY 1962	60·00
M49	AUG 1962	60·00
	p. With phosphor bands	90·00
M50	SEPT 1962	55·00
	p. With phosphor bands	£100
M51	OCT 1962	70·00
	p. With phosphor bands	£100
M52	NOV 1962	70·00
	p. With phosphor bands	£100
M53	DEC 1962	70·00
	p. With phosphor bands	£100
M54	JAN 1963	70·00
M55	FEB 1963	70·00
	p. With phosphor bands	£100
M56	MAR 1963	70·00
	p. With phosphor bands	£100
M57	APR 1963	70·00
	p. With phosphor bands	£100
M58	MAY 1963	70·00
	p. With phosphor bands	£500
M59	JUNE 1963	75·00
	p. With phosphor bands	70·00
M60	JULY 1963	60·00
	p. With phosphor bands	£100
M61	AUG 1963	70·00
	p. With phosphor bands	£100
M62	SEPT 1963	70·00
M63	OCT 1963	80·00
M64	NOV 1963	70·00
	p. With phosphor bands	£100
M65	DEC 1963	85·00
	p. With phosphor bands	£200
M66	JAN 1964	80·00
	p. With phosphor bands	75·00
M67	MAR 1964	80·00
	p. With phosphor bands	£100
M68	MAY 1964	80·00
	p. With phosphor bands	£120
M69	JULY 1964	60·00
	p. With phosphor bands	£100
M70	SEPT 1964	60·00
	p. With phosphor bands	£100
M71	NOV 1964	45·00
	p. With phosphor bands	55·00
M72	JAN 1965	45·00
	p. With phosphor bands	70·00
M73	MAR 1965	35·00
	p. With phosphor bands	65·00
M74	MAY 1965	60·00
	p. With phosphor bands	£100

3s.9d. Booklets

1953–57. Red cover as Type B. Pages of six stamps: 18×2½d.

A. *Wmk Tudor Crown (No. 519b)*

G1	NOV 1953	40·00
G2	JAN 1954	60·00
G3	MAR 1954	40·00
G4	DEC 1954	40·00
G5	FEB 1955	40·00
G6	APR 1955	40·00
G7	JUNE 1955	40·00
G8	AUG 1955	40·00
G9	OCT 1955	40·00

G10	DEC 1955	40·00

3s·9d. booklets dated OCTOBER and DECEMBER 1955 exist both as listed and with the two watermarks mixed.

B. Wmk St Edward's Crown (No. 544b). Same composition but with interleaving pages between each pane of stamps.

G12	FEB 1956	30·00
G13	APR 1956	30·00
G14	JUNE 1956	30·00
G15	AUG 1956	30·00
G16	OCT 1956	30·00
G17	DEC 1956	30·00
G18	FEB 1957	30·00
G19	APR 1957	30·00
G20	JUNE 1957	17·00
G21	AUG 1957	40·00

4s.6d. Booklets

1957–65. Pages of six stamps: 18×3d.

I. Purple cover as Type B.

A. Wmk St Edward's Crown (No. 545).

L1	OCT 1957	30·00
L2	DEC 1957	30·00
L3	FEB 1958	35·00
L4	APR 1958	30·00
L5	JUNE 1958	32·00
L6	OCT 1958	30·00
L7	DEC 1958	30·00

B. Wmk Crowns (No. 575).

L8	DEC 1958	£130

II. Purple cover as Type C. Wmk Crowns (No. 575) or graphite lines (No. 592)

L9	FEB 1959	35·00
L10	JUNE 1959	40·00
L11	AUG 1959	30·00
	g. With graphite lines	45·00
L12	OCT 1959	45·00
L13	DEC 1959	35·00

III. Violet cover as Type C. Wmk Crowns (No. 575), graphite lines (No. 592) or phosphor (No. 615).

L14	FEB 1959	£100
L15	APR 1959	35·00
	g. With graphite lines	30·00
L16	JUNE 1959	60·00
	g. With graphite lines	30·00
L17	DEC 1959	60·00
L18	FEB 1960	35·00
	g. With graphite lines	60·00
L19	APR 1960	35·00
	g. With graphite lines	35·00
L20	JUNE 1960	40·00
L21	AUG 1960	40·00
	p. With phosphor bands	60·00
L22	OCT 1960	55·00

IV. Violet cover as Type D. Wmk Crowns (No. 575) or phosphor (No. 615).

L23	DEC 1960	75·00
L24	FEB 1961	75·00
	p. With phosphor bands	50·00
L25	APR 1961	50·00
	p. With phosphor bands	45·00
L26	JUNE 1961	75·00
L27	AUG 1961	70·00
	p. With phosphor bands	80·00
L28	OCT 1961	70·00
	p. With phosphor bands	60·00
L29	DEC 1961	70·00
	p. With phosphor bands	40·00
L30	FEB 1962	65·00
L31	APR 1962	75·00
	p. With phosphor bands	80·00
L32	JUNE 1962	80·00
	p. With phosphor bands	90·00
L33	AUG 1962	60·00
	p. With phosphor bands	90·00
L34	OCT 1962	60·00
	p. With phosphor bands	£275
L35	DEC 1962	70·00
	p. With phosphor bands	80·00
L36	FEB 1963	70·00
	p. With phosphor bands	80·00
L37	APR 1963	70·00
	p. With phosphor bands	55·00
L38	JUNE 1963	70·00
	p. With phosphor bands	55·00
L39	AUG 1963	80·00
	p. With phosphor bands	65·00
L40	OCT 1963	75·00
	p. With phosphor bands	£100
L41	NOV 1963	80·00
	p. With phosphor bands	65·00
L42	DEC 1963	75·00
	p. With phosphor bands	£300

L43	JAN 1964	£125
L44	FEB 1964	80·00
	p. With phosphor bands	55·00
L45	MAR 1964	£125
	p. With phosphor bands	£180
L46	APR 1964	£125
	p. With phosphor bands	65·00
L47	MAY 1964	80·00
	p. With phosphor bands	£100
L48	JUNE 1964	80·00
	p. With phosphor bands	£100
L49	JULY 1964	80·00
	p. With phosphor bands	65·00
L50	AUG 1964	80·00
	p. With phosphor bands	55·00
L51	SEPT 1964	80·00
	p. With phosphor bands	65·00
L52	OCT 1964	80·00
	p. With phosphor bands	£100
L53	NOV 1964	80·00
	p. With phosphor bands	65·00
L54	DEC 1964	80·00
	p. With phosphor bands	65·00
L55	JAN 1965	70·00
	p. With phosphor bands	60·00
L56	FEB 1965	60·00
	p. With phosphor bands	80·00
L57	MAR 1965	35·00
	p. With phosphor bands	£500
L58	APR 1965	55·00

1965 (26 July)–**67**. New composition. Pages of six stamps: 12×1d. Slate-blue cover as Type D. *Wmk Crowns (Nos. 571 and 576a) or phosphor (Nos. 611 and 616a).*

L59	JULY 1965	30·00
	p. With phosphor bands	32·00
L60	SEPT 1965	30·00
	p. With phosphor bands	32·00
L61	NOV 1965	30·00
	p. With phosphor bands	35·00
L62	JAN 1966	35·00
	p. With phosphor bands	32·00
L63	MAR 1966	30·00
	p. With phosphor bands	30·00
L64	JAN 1967	40·00
	p. With phosphor bands	30·00
L65	MAR 1967	70·00
	p. With phosphor bands	25·00
L66p	MAY 1967. With phosphor bands	15·00
L67p	JULY 1967. With phosphor bands	25·00
L68p	SEPT 1967. With phosphor bands	20·00
L69p	NOV 1967. With phosphor bands	15·00
L70p	JAN 1968. With phosphor bands	15·00
L71p	MAR 1968. With phosphor bands	10·00

4s.6d. Booklets with Machin type stamps

1968–70. Slate-blue cover as Type D. Pages of six stamps: 12×4d., 6×1d. PVA gum (Nos. 724, 731Ev).

LP45	MAY 1968	4·00

LP **46** Ships Series with GPO Cypher

(Des S. Rose)

*Blue cover as Type LP **46**. Ships Series. Composition as last.*

LP46	JULY 1968 (*Cutty Sark*)	70

Same composition but changed to 4d. with one centre phosphor band (No. 732).

LP47	SEPT 1968 (*Golden Hind*)	70
LP48	NOV 1968 (*Discovery*)	70

Same composition but changed to 4d. bright vermilion with one centre phosphor band (No. 733).

LP49	JAN 1969 (*Queen Elizabeth 2*)	90
LP50	MAR 1969 (*Sirius*)	2·00
LP51	MAY 1969 (*Sirius*)	1·25
LP52	JULY 1969 (*Dreadnought*)	1·25
LP53	SEPT 1969 (*Dreadnought*)	5·00

LP54	NOV 1969 (*Mauretania*)	1·50
LP55	JAN 1970 (*Mauretania*)	5·00
LP56	MAR 1970 (*Victory*)	1·50
LP57	MAY 1970 (*Victory*)	5·00

LP **58** Ships Series with Post Office Corporation Crown Symbol

(Des S. Rose)

*As last but cover changed to Type LP **58**.*

LP58	AUG 1970 (*Sovereign of the Seas*)	4·50
LP59	OCT 1970 (*Sovereign of the Seas*)	5·00

5s. Booklets

1953–57. Buff cover. Pages of six stamps. 12×2½d., 6×2d., 6×1½d., 6×1d., 6×½d.

I. Composite booklets containing stamps of King George VI and Queen Elizabeth II.

A. *K.G.VI ½d., 1d. and 2d. (Nos. 503/4 and 506) and Q.E.II 1½d. and 2½d. (Nos. 517 and 519b). Cover as Type **A**. No interleaving pages.*

H1	MAY 1953	45·00
H2	JULY 1953	50·00

B. *Same composition but with addition of two interleaving pages, one at each end. Cover as Type **A**.*

H3	SEPT 1953	65·00

C. *Same composition and with interleaving pages but cover as Type **B**.*

H4	NOV 1953	50·00
H5	JAN 1954	65·00

D. *New composition: K.G.VI 1d. and 2d. (Nos. 504 and 506) and Q.E.II ½d., 1½d.and 2½d. (Nos. 515, 517 and 519b).*

H6	MAR 1954	£1000

E. *New composition: K.G.VI 2d. (No. 506) and Q.E.II ½d. 1d., 1½d. and 2½d. (Nos. 515/17 and 519b).*

H7	MAR 1954	£275

*II. Booklets containing only Queen Elizabeth II stamps. Buff cover as Type **B**. Two interleaving pages as before.*

A. *Wmk Tudor Crown (Nos. 515/18 and 519b).*

H8	MAR 1954	£225
H9	MAY 1954	£125
H10	JULY 1954	£135
H11	SEPT 1954	95·00
H12	NOV 1954	£125

B. *Same composition but with interleaving pages between each pane of stamps.*

H13	JAN 1955	95·00
H14	MAR 1955	75·00
H15	MAY 1955	80·00
H16	JULY 1955	£125

C. *Wmk St Edward's Crown (Nos. 540/3 and 544b).*

H17	SEPT 1955	40·00
H18	NOV 1955	42·00
H19	JAN 1956	45·00
H20	MAR 1956	55·00
H21	MAY 1956	48·00
H22	JULY 1956	45·00
H23	SEPT 1956	48·00
H24	NOV 1956	48·00
H25	JAN 1957	55·00

5s. booklets dated SEPTEMBER and NOVEMBER 1955 and JANUARY 1956 exist both as listed and with the two watermarks mixed. There are so many different combinations that we do not list them separately, but when in stock selections can be submitted.

D. *Same watermark. Introduction of 2d. light red-brown (No. 543b) in place of No. 543.*

H26	JAN 1957	48·00
H27	MAR 1957	65·00
H28	MAY 1957	50·00
H29	JULY 1957	40·00
H30	SEPT 1957	40·00
H31	NOV 1957	40·00

1958–65. E. New composition. Pages of six stamps: 12×3d. (No. 545), 6×2½d. (No. 544b), 6×1d. (No. 541), 6×½d. (No. 540). *Wmk* St Edward's Crown.

H32	JAN 1958	40·00
H33	MAR 1958	40·00
H34	MAY 1958	42·00
H35	JULY 1958 (11.58)	28·00
H36	NOV 1958	28·00

5s. booklets dated JULY 1958, NOVEMBER 1958 and JANUARY 1959 exist with mixed watermarks.

F. *Blue cover as Type **C**. Wmk Crowns (Nos. 570/1, 574/5), graphite lines (Nos. 587/8 and 591/2) or phosphor (Nos. 610/11, 614 and 615).*

H37	JAN 1959	35·00
H38	MAR 1959	45·00
H39	JULY 1959	42·00
	g. With graphite lines	£135
H40	SEPT 1959	45·00
H41	NOV 1959	45·00
H42	JAN 1960	45·00
H43	MAR 1960	45·00
	g. With graphite lines	£170
H44	MAY 1960	50·00
H45	JULY 1960	55·00
H46	SEPT 1960	80·00
	g. With graphite lines	£170
	p. With phosphor bands	£120
H47	NOV 1960	60·00

G. *As last but blue cover as Type **D**. Same composition.*
I. Phosphor has two bands on 2½d. (No. 614).

H48	JAN 1961	60·00
H49	MAR 1961	60·00
	p. With phosphor bands	£160
H50	MAY 1961	60·00
H51	JULY 1961	95·00
	p. With phosphor bands	£175
H52	SEPT 1961	60·00
	p. With phosphor bands	£225
H53	NOV 1961	60·00
H54	JAN 1962	95·00
	p. With phosphor bands	£225

II. As last but phosphor has one band on 2½d. (No. 614a).

H55	MAR 1962	85·00
	p. With phosphor bands	£180
H56	MAY 1962	60·00
	p. With phosphor bands	£200
H57	JULY 1962	95·00
	p. With phosphor bands	£180
H58	SEPT 1962	90·00
	p. With phosphor bands	£250
H59	NOV 1962	90·00
	p. With phosphor bands	£250
H60	JAN 1963	60·00
	p. With phosphor bands	£600
H61	MAR 1963	60·00
	p. With phosphor bands	£250
H62	MAY 1963	80·00
	p. With phosphor bands	£250
H63	JULY 1963	95·00
	p. With phosphor bands	£175
H64	SEPT 1963	60·00
	p. With phosphor bands	£250
H65	NOV 1963	60·00
	p. With phosphor bands	£250
H66	JAN 1964	60·00
	p. With phosphor bands	£120
H67	MAR 1964	60·00
	p. With phosphor bands	£120
H68	MAY 1964	95·00
	p. With phosphor bands	£225
H69	JULY 1964	95·00
	p. With phosphor bands	£200
H70	SEPT 1964	60·00
	p. With phosphor bands	£200
H71	NOV 1964	85·00
	p. With phosphor bands	£120
H72	JAN 1965	50·00
	p. With phosphor bands	£120
H73	MAR 1965	48·00
	p. With phosphor bands	£225
H74	MAY 1965	45·00
	p. With phosphor bands	£140

5s. Booklets with Machin type stamps

HP **26** English Homes Series with GPO Cypher

(Des S. Rose)

1968 (27 Nov)–**70**. Cinnamon cover as Type HP **26** (*English Homes Series*). Pages of six stamps: 12×5d. (No. 735).

HP26	DEC 1968 (Ightham Mote)	2·00
HP27	FEB 1969 (Little Moreton Hall)	2·00
HP28	APR 1969 (Long Melford Hall)	2·00
HP29	JUNE 1969 (Long Melford Hall)	2·00
HP30	AUG 1969 (Long Melford Hall)	5·00

HP **31** English Homes Series with Post Office Corporation Crown Symbol

(Des S. Rose)

As last but cover changed to Type HP **31**.

HP31	OCT 1969 (Mompesson House)	2·25
HP32	DEC 1969 (Mompesson House)	2·50
HP33	FEB 1970 (Cumberland Terrace)	2·25

HP **34**

(Des P. Gauld)

As last but cover changed to Type HP **34** (special edition to advertise Philympia International Philatelic Exhibition, London, September 1970).

HP34	(no date) (3.3.70)	2·25

As last but cover changed to Type HP **31**.

HP35	JUNE 1970 (The Vineyard, Saffron Walden)	2·50
HP36	AUG 1970 (The Vineyard, Saffron Walden)	3·25
HP37	OCT 1970 (Mereworth Castle)	3·25
HP38	DEC 1970 (Mereworth Castle)	3·25

6s. Booklets

1965 (21 June)–**67**. Claret cover as Type *D*. Wmk Crowns (No. 576a) or phosphor (No. 616a). Pages of six stamps: 18×4d.

Q1	JUNE 1965	45·00
	p. With phosphor bands	45·00
Q2	JULY 1965	45·00
	p. With phosphor bands	45·00
Q3	AUG 1965	80·00
	p. With phosphor bands	80·00
Q4	SEPT 1965	60·00

	p. With phosphor bands	60·00
Q5	OCT 1965	90·00
	p. With phosphor bands	90·00
Q6	NOV 1965	90·00
	p. With phosphor bands	90·00
Q7	DEC 1965	90·00
	p. With phosphor bands	£100
Q8	JAN 1966	90·00
	p. With phosphor bands	90·00
Q9	FEB 1966	90·00
	p. With phosphor bands	90·00
Q10	MAR 1966	90·00
	p. With phosphor bands	£100
Q11	APR 1966	90·00
	p. With phosphor bands	£200
Q12	MAY 1966	90·00
	p. With phosphor bands	£100
Q13	JUNE 1966	90·00
	p. With phosphor bands	90·00
Q14	JULY 1966	90·00
	p. With phosphor bands	90·00
Q15	AUG 1966	90·00
	p. With phosphor bands	£250
Q16	SEPT 1966	55·00
	p. With phosphor bands	55·00
Q17	OCT 1966	£100
	p. With phosphor bands	£175
Q18	NOV 1966	75·00
	p. With phosphor bands	45·00
Q19	DEC 1966	45·00
	p. With phosphor bands	80·00
Q20	JAN 1967	90·00
	p. With phosphor bands	90·00
Q21	FEB 1967	90·00
	p. With phosphor bands	50·00
Q22	MAR 1967	60·00
	p. With phosphor bands	50·00
Q23	APR 1967	45·00
	p. With phosphor bands	50·00
Q24p	MAY 1967. With phosphor bands	40·00
Q25p	JUNE 1967. With phosphor bands	40·00
Q26p	JULY 1967. With phosphor bands	£100
Q27p	AUG 1967. With phosphor bands	75·00

6s. Booklets with Machin type stamps

1967–70. Claret cover as Type **D**. Pages of six stamps: 18×4d. Two phosphor bands. Gum arabic (No. 731).

QP28	SEPT 1967	50·00
QP29	OCT 1967	60·00
QP30	NOV 1967	50·00
QP31	DEC 1967	50·00
QP32	JAN 1968	48·00
QP33	FEB 1968 (No. 731Ea)	48·00
QP34	MAR 1968 (No. 731Ea)	48·00
QP35	APR 1968 (No. 731Ea)	35·00
QP36	MAY 1968 (No. 731Ea)	18·00

Change to PVA gum (No. 731Ev).

QP37	MAY 1968	£450

QP **38** Birds Series with GPO Cypher

(Des S. Rose)

Orange-red cover as Type QP **38** (*Birds Series*). Same composition. Two phosphor bands. PVA gum (No. 731Ev).

QP38	JUNE 1968 (Kingfisher) (4.6.68)	2·00
QP39	JULY 1968 (Kingfisher)	10·00
QP40	AUG 1968 (Peregrine Falcon)	2·00

Change to one centre phosphor band (No. 732).

QP41	SEPT 1968 (Peregrine Falcon) (16.9.68)	1·40
QP42	OCT 1968 (Pied Woodpecker)	2·00
QP43	NOV 1968 (Pied Woodpecker)	1·50
QP44	DEC 1968 (Great Crested Grebe)	1·50
QP45	JAN 1969 (Barn Owl)	2·75

Change to 4d. bright vermilion with one centre phosphor band (No. 733).

QP46	FEB 1969 (Barn Owl) (20.2.69)	3·50
QP47	MAR 1969 (Jay)	2·50

QP48   MAY 1969 (Jay) .... 3·25
QP49   JULY 1969 (Puffin) .... 2·50
QP50   SEPT 1969 (Puffin) .... 5·00

QP **51** Birds Series with Post Office Corporation
Crown Symbol

(Des S. Rose)

As last but cover changed to Type QP **51**.
QP51   NOV 1969 (Cormorant) .... 3·25
QP52   JAN 1970 (Cormorant) .... 3·75
QP53   APR 1970 (Wren) .... 3·00
QP54   AUG 1970 (Golden Eagle) .... 3·00
QP55   OCT 1970 (Golden Eagle) .... 3·00

10s. Booklets

1961 (10 Apr–Oct). Green cover as Type D. Pages of six stamps: 30×3d.,
6×2d., 6×1½d., 6×1d., 6×½d. *Wmk* Crowns (Nos. 570/3 and 575).
X1   No date £150
X2   OCT 1961 .... £300

1962–64. New Composition. Pages of six stamps: 30×3d., 6×2½d.,
6×1½d., 6×1d. (Nos. 571/2 and 574/5).
X3   APR 1962 .... £130
X4   AUG 1962 .... £180
X5   MAR 1963 .... £275
X6   JULY 1963 .... £180
X7   DEC 1963 .... £160
X8   JULY 1964 .... £130
X9   DEC 1964 .... £600

1965 (23 Aug)–**66**. Ochre cover as Type D. Pages of six stamps: 24×4d.,
6×3d., 6×1d. *Wmk* Crowns (Nos. 571, 575, 576a).
X10   AUG 1965 .... 40·00
X11   DEC 1965 .... 80·00
X12   FEB 1966 .... 65·00
X13   AUG 1966 .... 40·00
X14   NOV 1966 .... 38·00

1967–68. Ochre cover as Type D. Pages of six stamps: 24×4d.,
6×3d., 6×1d. *Wmk* Crowns (Nos. 611, 615c (one side phosphor
band), 616a).
X15p   FEB 1967 .... 10·00

Composition as No. X15p. *Wmk* Crowns (*Nos.* 611, 615e (*one centre
phosphor band*), 616a).
X16p   AUG 1967 .... 7·00
X17p   FEB 1968 .... 8·00

10s. Booklets with Machin type stamps

XP **4** Explorers Series with GPO Cypher

(Des S. Rose)

1968 (25 Mar–Aug). Bright purple cover as Type XP **4** (*Explorers Series*).
Pages of six stamps: 24×4d., 6×3d., 6×1d. PVA gum (Nos. 724,
729Ev, 731Ev).
XP4   MAY 1968 (Livingstone) .... 4·50
XP5   AUG 1968 (Livingstone) .... 4·50

1968 (16 Sept)–**70**. Yellow-green covers as Type XP **4** (*Explorers Series*) New
composition. Pages of six stamps: 12×5d. (with two phosphor bands),
12×4d. (with one centre phosphor band) and pane comprising 4×1d.
se-tenant with vert pair of 4d. (each with one centre phosphor band).
PVA gum (Nos. 725, 732 and 735).
XP6   SEPT 1968 (Scott) .... 3·00

*Change to 4d. bright vermilion (one centre band) but se-tenant pane
comprises 1d. with two phosphor bands and 4d. with one left side
phosphor band (Nos. 724 and 733/4).*
XP7   FEB 1969 (Mary Kingsley) (6.1.69) .... 2·50
XP8   MAY 1969 (Mary Kingsley) .... 3·25
XP9   AUG 1969 (Shackleton) .... 3·50
XP10   NOV 1969 (Shackleton) .... 5·00

XP **11** Explorers Series with Post Office Corporation
Crown Symbol

(Des S. Rose)

As last but cover changed to Type XP **11**.
XP11   FEB 1970 (Frobisher) .... 5·00
XP12   NOV 1970 (Captain Cook) .... 6·00

£1 Booklet with Machin type stamps

ZP **1**

1969 (1 Dec). *Stamps for Cooks* Type ZP **1** (150×72 mm) with full colour
pictorial cover showing 'Baked, Stuffed Haddock'. Contains 12 recipes
on interleaving pages and on *se-tenant* labels attached to booklet
panes. PVA gum. Stapled.
ZP1   £1 containing panes of fifteen stamps (5×3): 15×5d.
(No. 735), 30×4d. (No. 733) and pane comprising 6×4d.
(three each of Nos. 734 and 734Eb) *se-tenant* with
6×1d. (No. 724) and 3×5d. (No. 735) £325
ZP1a   As last but booklet is sewn with thread instead of
being stapled .... 6·50

II. Decimal Booklets, 1971 onwards.

A. Stitched Booklets.

The 25p., 30p., 35p., 45p. and 50p. booklets have pictorial covers
(except for the 35p. and 45p.) without the design inscription. This was
no longer necessary as the designs and background information were
given on the inside of the front cover. Each series was numbered.

10p. Booklets

DN **46** British Pillar Box Series
(Des R. Maddox)

1971 (15 Feb–1 June). *British Pillar Box Series*. Orange yellow cover as
Type DN **46**. Pages of four stamps: 2×2p. *se-tenant* vertically with
2×½p. and 2×1p. *se-tenant* vertically with 2×1½p. (Nos. X841I
and X844I).
DN46   FEB 1971 (No. 1 1855 type) .... 1·30
DN47   APR 1971 (No. 1 1855 type) (19.3.71) .... 1·00

DN48 JUNE 1971 (No. 2 1856 type) (1.6.71) .... 1·75
In No. DN47 the pillar box is slightly reduced in size.

1971 (14 July)–**74**. *British Pillar Box Series* continued. Orange-yellow cover as Type DN **46**. Contents unchanged but panes are *se-tenant* horizontally (Nos. X841la and X844m).

DN49 AUG 1971 (No. 2 1856 type) (14.7.71) .... 1·50
DN50 OCT 1971 (No. 3 1857–9 type) (27.8.71) .... 1·50
DN51 DEC 1971 (No. 3 1857–9 type) (6.10.71) .... 2·25
DN52 FEB 1972 (No. 4 1866–79 type) (8.12.71) .... 2·25
DN53 APR 1972 (No. 4 1866–79 type) (24.2.72) .... 1·75
DN54 JUNE 1972 (No. 5 1899 type) (12.4.72) .... 1·25
DN55 AUG 1972 (No. 5 1899 type) (8.6.72) .... 1·50
DN56 OCT 1972 (No. 6 1968 type) (2.8.72) .... 1·50
DN57 DEC 1972 (No. 6 1968 type) (30.10.72) .... 1·50
DN58 FEB 1973 (No. 7 1936 type) (5.1.73) .... 1·50
DN59 APR 1973 (No. 7 1936 type) (2.4.73) .... 5·00
DN60 JUNE 1973 (No. 8 1952 type) (18.4.73) .... 2·00
DN61 AUG 1973 (No. 8 1952 type) (4.7.73) .... 10·00
DN62 OCT 1973 (No. 9 1973 type) (16.8.73) .... 1·75
DN63 DEC 1973 (No. 9 1973 type) (12.11.73) .... 2·00
DN64 FEB 1974 (No. 9 1973 type) (17.12.73) .... 2·25
DN65 APR 1974 (No. 10 1974 type) (22.2.74) .... 1·50
DN66 JUNE 1974 (No. 10 1974 type) (23.4.74) .... 1·50

DN **67** Postal Uniforms Series

(Des C. Abbott)

1974 (23 July)–**76**. *Postal Uniforms Series.* Orange-yellow cover as Type DN **67**. Contents unchanged.

DN67 AUG 1974 (No. 1 1793 type) .... 1·00
DN68 OCT 1974 (No. 1 1793 type) (27.8.74) .... 1·00
DN69 DEC 1974 (No. 2 1837 type) (25.10.74) .... 1·00
DN70 FEB 1975 (No. 2 1837 type) (12.12.74) .... 1·00
DN71 APR 1975 (No. 3 1855 type) (26.3.75) .... 1·00
DN72 JUNE 1975 (No. 3 1855 type) (21.5.75) .... 1·00
DN73 AUG 1975 (No. 3 1855 type) (27.6.75) .... 1·00
DN74 OCT 1975 (No. 3 1855 type) (3.10.75) 50
DN75 JAN 1976 (No. 3 1855 type) (16.3.76) 50

25p. Booklets

DH **39** Veteran Transport Series

(Des D. Gentleman)

1971 (15 Feb). *Veteran Transport Series.* Dull purple cover as Type DH **39**. Pages of six stamps: 5×2½p. with one printed label, 4×2½p. with two printed labels, 5×½p. with one printed label (Nos. X841m and X851l/m).

DH39 FEB 1971 (No. 1 Knife-board omnibus) .... 3·00

DH **40**

1971 (19 Mar). Issued to publicise the National Postal Museum Exhibition of *80 Years of British Stamp Booklets*. Dull purple cover as Type DH **40**.

DH40 APR 1971. .... 3·50

1971 (11 June)–**73**. Dull purple cover as Type DH **39**. *Veteran Transport Series* continued.

DH41 JUNE 1971 (No. 2 B-type omnibus) .... 3·25
DH42 AUG 1971 (No. 2 B-type omnibus) (17.9.71) .... 8·00
DH43 OCT 1971 (No. 3 Showman's Engine) (22.11.71) .... 8·00
DH44 FEB 1972 (No. 4 Mail Van) (23.12.71) .... 4·50
DH45 APR 1972 (No. 4 Mail Van) (13.3.72) .... 5·50
DH46 JUNE 1972 (No. 5 Motor Wagonette) (24.4.72) .... 4·00
DH47 AUG 1972 (No. 5 Motor Wagonette) (14.6.72) .... 8·00
DH48 OCT 1972 (No. 6 Taxi Cab) (17.7.72) .... 6·00
DH49 DEC 1972 (No. 6 Taxi Cab) (19.10.72) .... 8·00
DH50 DEC 1972 "Issue S" (No. 6 Taxi Cab) (6.11.72) .... 4·50
DH51 FEB 1973 (No. 7 Electric Tramcar) (26.2.73) .... 6·00
Nos. DH42/51 contain panes showing the perforations omitted between the label and the binding margin.

DH **52**

1973 (7 June). Dull mauve cover as Type DH **52**.

DH52 JUNE 1973. .... 6·00
No. DH52 contains panes showing the perforations omitted between the label and the binding margin.

30p. Booklets

DQ **56** British Birds Series

(Des H. Titcombe)

1971 (15 Feb). *British Birds Series.* Bright purple cover as Type DQ **56**. Pages of six stamps: 2 panes of 5×3p. with one printed label (No. X855l).

DQ56 FEB 1971 (No. 1 Curlew) .... 2·75

1971 (19 Mar). Bright purple cover as Type DH **40**.

DQ57 APR 1971. .... 3·75

1971 (26 May)–**73**. Bright purple cover as Type DQ **56**. *British Birds Series* continued.

DQ58 JUNE 1971 (No. 2 Lapwing) .... 3·75
DQ59 AUG 1971 (No. 2 Lapwing) (23.7.71) .... 3·75
DQ60 OCT 1971 (No. 3 Robin) (1.10.71) .... 3·75
DQ61 DEC 1971 (No. 3 Robin) (10.11.71) .... 4·50
DQ62 FEB 1972 (No. 4 Pied Wagtail) (21.12.71) .... 3·75
DQ63 APR 1972 (No. 4 Pied Wagtail) (9.2.72) .... 3·75
DQ64 JUNE 1972 (No. 5 Kestrel) (12.4.72) .... 3·75
DQ65 AUG 1972 (No. 5 Kestrel) (8.6.72) .... 3·75
DQ66 OCT 1972 (No. 6 Black Grouse) (31.7.72) .... 4·25

DQ67   DEC 1972 (No. 6 Black Grouse) (30.10.72).............................   4·25
DQ68   DEC 1972 "Issue S" (No. 6 Black Grouse) (6.12.72)..............   4·25
DQ69   FEB 1973 (No. 7 Skylark) (29.1.73)..   4·00
DQ70   APR 1973 (No. 7 Skylark) (2.4.73)...   3·50
DQ71   JUNE 1973 (No. 8 Oyster-catcher) (8.5.73)...........................   4·00
DQ72   AUG 1973 (No. 8 Oyster-catcher) (7.6.73).............................   5·50
DQ72a   As DQ72 but buff cover (10.8.73)*..   4·50
    Nos. DQ59/72a contain panes showing the perforations omitted
between the label and the binding margin.*No. DQ 72a was printed
with a buff cover because of a shortage of the original purple-
coloured card.

1974 (30 Jan). Red cover similar to Type DH **52**. Make-up as before
    but containing panes of 5×3p. (1 centre band) (No. X856) with
    blank label.
DQ73   SPRING 1974..   3·00

1974 (2 June). Red cover similar to Type DT **9**. Make-up as before.
DQ74   JUNE 1974...   4·00

35p. Booklets

DP **1** British Coins Series

(Des P Gauld)

1973 (12 Dec)–74. *British Coins Series*. Blue cover as Type DP **1**. Pages of
    six stamps: 2 pages of 5×3½p. with one blank label (No. X858Eb).
DP1   AUTUMN 1973 (No. 1 Cuthred's Penny).....................................   2·25
DP2   APR 1974 (No. 1 Cuthred's Penny) (10.4.74)..........................   4·00
DP3   JUNE 1974 (No. 2 Silver Groat) (4.7.74)..................................   2·50

1974 (23 Oct). Blue cover as Type DT **9**. Make-up as before but with
    No. X859.
DP4   SEPT 1974..   2·50

45p. Booklets

1974 (9 Oct–26 Nov). *British Coins Series* continued. Yellow-brown cover
    as Type DP **1**. Pages of six stamps: 2 pages of 5×4½p. (No. X865)
    with one blank label.
DS1   SEPT 1974 (No. 3 Elizabeth Gold Crown) ....   3·00
DS2   DEC 1974 (No. 3 Elizabeth Gold Crown) (1.11.74)............   3·00
DS2a   As DS2 but orange-brown cover (26.11.74)*.......................   20·00
    *No. DS2a was printed with an orange-brown cover because of a
shortage of the original yellow-brown card.

50p. Booklets

DT **1**

(Des Rosalie Southall)

1971 (15 Feb)–72. *British Flowers Series*. Turquoise-green cover as Type
    DT **1**. Pages of six stamps: 6×3p., 4×3p. *se-tenant* horizontally with
    2×2½p. (side band), 5×2½p. (centre band) with one printed label
    and 5×½p. with one printed label (Nos. X841m, X851l, X852l and
    X855×6).
DT1   FEB 1971 (No. 1 Large Bindweed) ....   5·00
DT2   MAY 1971 (No. 2 Primrose) (2.4.3.71).......................................   6·00
DT3   AUG 1971 (No. 3 Honeysuckle) (28.6.71).................................   6·00
DT4   NOV 1971 (No. 4 Hop) (17.9.71)...   6·25
DT5   FEB 1972 (No. 5 Common Violet) (23.12.71)* ....   6·25
DT6   MAY 1972 (No. 6 Lords-and-Ladies) (13.3.72).......................   6·25
DT7   AUG 1972 (No. 7 Wood Anemone) (31.5.72).........................   6·25
DT8   NOV 1972 (No. 8 Deadly Nightshade) (15.9.72)................   5·25

    Nos. DT4/8 contain panes showing the perforations omitted
between the label and the binding margin.
    *Although generally released on 24 December, this booklet was
put on sale at the London E.C.1 Philatelic Counter and also at one
other Philatelic Counter on 23 December.

DT **9**

1973 (19 Jan–June). Turquoise-green cover as Type DT **9**.
DT9   FEB 1973...   5·25
DT10   APR 1973 (26.2.73)..   7·00
DT11   MAY 1973 (2.4.73)..   6·75
DT12   AUG 1973 (14.6.73)...   10·50

1973 (14 Nov)–**74**. Moss-green cover similar to Type DT **9**. Pages of six
    stamps: 2 pages of 5×3½p. with one blank label (No. X858Eb) and
    1 page of 5×3p. (centre band) and one blank label (No. X856).
DT13   AUTUMN 1973..   4·50
DT14   MAR 1974 (18.2.74)..   3·50

85p. Booklet

1974 (13 Nov). Purple cover similar to Type DT **9**.
DW1   Containing 3 pages of 5×4½p. (No. X865) with one
    blank label and 1 page of 5×3½p. (No. X859) with one
    blank label...   6·25
    No. DW1 is dated "SEPT 1974".

Sponsored and "Prestige" Booklets

DX **1**

(Des J. Wallis)

1972 (24 May). *The Story of Wedgwood*. Full colour pictorial cover, Type DX **1**
    (150×72 mm). Containing information and illustrations on interleaving
    panes and on *se-tenant* label attached to booklet panes.
DX1   £1 containing Nos. X841o/p, X851n and X855n booklet
    panes ....   60·00
    Price quoted for No. DX1 is for examples showing the ½p. 1 side
band, No. X842, (in pane No. X841p) with full perforations. Examples
of the booklet with this ½p. value showing trimmed perforations are
priced at £15.

ILLUSTRATIONS. Sponsored and "Prestige" booklet covers from No.
DX2 are illustrated at one-third linear size *unless otherwise stated*.

DX **2**

(Des J. Wallis)

1980 (16 Apr). *The Story of Wedgwood*. ^{MULTI}_{COLOUR} cover, Type DX **2**
    (163×97 mm) showing painting *'Josiah Wedgwood and his Family'* by
    George Stubbs. Booklet contains text and illustrations on the labels
    attached to panes and on interleaving pages.
DX2   £3 containing booklet panes Nos. X849n, X849o, X888l
    and X895l...   3·75
    No. DX2 is inscribed "January 1980".

DX **3**

(Des B. Dedman)

1982 (19 May). *Story of Stanley Gibbons.* |MULTI COLOUR cover, Type DX **3** (163×97 mm) showing early envelope design on front and stamp album with text on back. Booklet contains text and illustrations on labels attached to panes and on interleaving pages.

DX3 £4 containing booklet panes Nos. X849p, X899m and
X907l/m.. 5·00

No. DX3 is inscribed "February 1982".

DX **4**

(Des B. West)

1983 (14 Sept). *Story of the Royal Mint.* |MULTI COLOUR cover, Type DX **4** (163×97 mm) showing current coins, die and tools. Booklet contains text and illustrations on labels attached to panes and on interleaving pages.

DX4 £4 containing booklet panes Nos. X899m×2, X930b and
X949l .... 5·00

DX **5**

(Des P. Miles)

1984 (4 Sept). *The Story of our Christian Heritage.* |MULTI COLOUR cover, Type DX **5** (163×97 mm) showing mosaic of Christ from Hinton St Mary Roman villa. Booklet contains text and illustrations on labels attached to panes and on interleaving pages.

DX5 £4 containing booklet panes Nos. X886bl, X901m×2 and
X952l .... 13·00

DX **6**

(Des D. Driver)

1985 (8 Jan). *Story of The Times (newspaper).* |MULTI COLOUR cover, Type DX **6** (163×95 mm) showing Waiting for *The Times* (painting by Haydon). Booklet contains text and illustrations on labels attached to panes and on interleaving pages.

DX6 £5 containing booklet panes Nos. X864l, X900l, X952l and
X952m .... 8·50

DX **7**

(Des Trickett and Webb Ltd)

1986 (18 Mar). *The Story of British Rail.* |MULTI COLOUR cover, Type DX **7** (162×95 mm) showing diesel locomotive. Booklet contains text and illustrations on labels attached to panes and on interleaving pages.

DX7 £5 containing booklet panes Nos. X896l, X897m, X952l
and X952m.. 10·00

DX **8**

(Des Aitken Blakeley Designers)

1987 (3 Mar). *The Story of P & O.* |MULTI COLOUR cover, Type DX **8** (162×95 mm) showing the *'William Fawcett'.* Booklet contains text and illustrations on labels attached to panes and on interleaving pages.

DX8 £5 containing booklet panes Nos. X847m, X900l, X900m
and X955l .... 10·00

DX **9**

(Des The Partners)

1988 (9 Feb). *The Story of the Financial Times (newspaper).* |MULTI COLOUR cover, Type DX **9** (162×97 mm). Booklet contains text and illustrations on labels attached to the panes and on interleaving pages.

DX9 £5 containing booklet panes Nos. X1005l, X1006l, X1009l
and X1009m .... 16·00

DX **10**

(Des Tayburn)

1989 (21 Mar). *The Scots Connection.* |MULTI COLOUR cover, Type DX **10** (162×97 mm). Booklet contains text and illustrations on labels attached to the panes and on interleaving pages.

DX10 £5 containing booklet panes Nos. S54l, S55l, S62l and
S62m .... 10·00

DX **11**

(Des D. Driver)

1990 (20 Mar). *London Life.* |MULTI COLOUR cover, Type DX **11** (162×97 mm). Booklet contains text and illustrations on labels attached to the panes and on interleaving pages.

DX11 £5 containing booklet panes Nos. X906m, 1469n×2 and 1493a .... 12·50

DX **12**

(Des Trickett and Webb Ltd)

1991 (19 Mar). *Alias Agatha Christie.* |MULTI COLOUR cover, Type DX **12** (162×97 mm). Booklet contains text and illustrations on labels attached to the panes and on interleaving pages.

DX12 £6 containing booklet panes Nos. X1008l×2, X1016l and X1016m.. 9·00

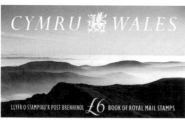

DX **13**

(Des G. Evernden and J. Gibbs)

1992 (25 Feb). *Cymru–Wales.* |MULTI COLOUR cover, Type DX **13** (162×97 mm). Booklet contains text and illustrations on labels attached to the panes and on interleaving pages.

DX13 £6 Containing booklet panes Nos. 1591a, W48a, W49a and W59a.. 9·00

DX **14**

(Des The Partners)

1992 (27 Oct). *Birth Centenary of J. R. R. Tolkien* (author). |MULTI COLOUR cover, Type DX **14** (162×97 mm). Booklet contains text and illustrations on labels attached to the panes and on interleaving pages.

DX14 £6 containing booklet panes Nos. X1011/2l and X1017l×2 .... 9·00

DX **15**

(Des The Partners)

1993 (10 Aug). *The Story of Beatrix Potter.* |MULTI COLOUR cover, Type DX **15** (162×97 mm). Booklet contains text and illustrations on labels attached to the panes and on interleaving pages.

DX15 £5.64, containing booklet panes Nos. X1012m, 1451al, 1649b and NI48l... 12·00

Although inscribed "£6·00" No. DX 15 was sold at the face value of its contents, £5·64.

DX **16**

(Des Carroll, Dempsey and Thirkell Ltd)

1994 (26 July). *Northern Ireland.* |MULTI COLOUR cover, Type DX **16** (162×97 mm). Booklet contains text and illustrations on labels attached to the panes and on interleaving pages.

DX16 £6.04, containing booklet panes Nos. Y1766l, 1812a and NI70a/b, together with a 35p. postal stationery air card... 11·00

DX **17**

(Des The Partners)

1995 (25 Apr). *Centenary of the National Trust.* |MULTI COLOUR cover, Type DX **17** (162×97 mm). Booklet contains text and illustrations on labels attached to the panes and on interleaving pages.

DX17 £6 containing booklet panes Nos. Y1767l, Y1771l, 1869a and NI70d.. 10·00

DX **18**

(Des Why Not Associates)

1996 (14 May). *European Football Championship.* |MULTI COLOUR cover, Type DX **18** (162×97 mm). Booklet contains text and illustrations on labels attached to the panes and on interleaving pages.

DX18 £6·48, containing booklet panes Nos. Y1775l, 1925a, 1926a and 1927a .... 8·50

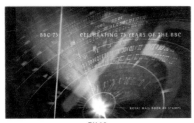

DX **19**

(Des H. Brown)

1997 (23 Sept). *75th Anniversary of the B.B.C.* |MULTI COLOUR cover, Type DX **19** (162×97 mm). Booklet contains text and illustrations on labels attached to the panes and on interleaving pages.
DX19 £6·15, containing booklet panes Nos. Y1686l, 1940ab, 1668l and NI81al .... 10·00

DX **20**

(Des Dew Gibbons Design Group)

1998 (10 Mar). *The Wilding Definitives.* Black and gold cover, Type DX **20** (162×96 mm). Booklet contains text and illustrations on labels attached to the panes and on interleaving pages.
DX20 £7·49, containing booklet panes Nos. 2031b/c and 2032a/b .... 11·00
  Folder containing DX20, DX22, DX24 and **MS**2147 *cancelled on presentation card*... £150

DX **21**

(Des Roundel Design Group)

1998 (13 Oct). *Breaking Barriers.* British Speed Record Holders. |MULTI COLOUR cover, Type DX **21** (161×96 mm). Booklet contains text and illustrations on labels attached to the panes and on interleaving pages.
DX21 £6·16, containing booklet panes Nos. 1665l, Y1676al, 2059ac and NI80al... 18·00

(Des Dew Gibbons Design Group)

1999 (16 Feb). *Profile on Print.* |MULTI COLOUR cover as Type DX **20** (162×96 mm). Booklet contains text and illustrations on labels attached to the panes and on interleaving pages.
DX22 £7·54, containing booklet panes Nos. 1667l, 1671n and 2077l/9l .... 22·00

DX **23**

(Des Silk Pearce)

1999 (21 Sept). *World Changers.* |MULTI COLOUR cover as Type DX **23** (163×96 mm). Booklet contains text and illustrations on labels attached to the panes and on interleaving pages.

DX23 £6·99, containing booklet panes Nos. Y1667n, 2072ab, 2080a, 2103ba and 2104ab... 14·00

(Des Dew Gibbons Design Group)

2000 (15 Feb). *Special by Design.* |MULTI COLOUR cover as Type DX **20** (162×96 mm). Booklet contains text and illustrations on labels attached to the panes and on interleaving pages.
DX24 £7·50, containing booklet panes Nos. Y1683l, 2124dl, 2133l and NI88al .... 20·00

DX **25**

(Des J. Gibbs)

2000 (4 Aug). *Queen Elizabeth the Queen Mother's 100th Birthday.* Brownish grey and grey cover as Type DX **25** (162×96 mm). Booklet contains text and illustrations on labels attached to the panes and on interleaving pages.
DX25 £7·03, containing booklet panes Nos. 2124bm, 2160a, **MS**2161a and S94a .... 15·00

DX **26**

(Des Roundel Design Group)

2000 (18 Sept). *A Treasury of Trees.* Slate-green and bright green cover as Type DX **26** (162×95 mm). Booklet contains text and illustrations on panes and interleaving pages.
DX26 £7 containing booklet panes Nos. 2155a, 2156a, 2158a, 2159a and W83al .... 17·00

DX **27**

(Des D. Davis)

2001 (22 Oct). *Unseen and Unheard.* Centenary of Royal Navy Submarine Service. Black, greenish yellow, new blue and red cover as Type DX **27** (162×97 mm). Booklet contains text and illustrations on labels attached to the panes and on interleaving pages.
DX27 £6·76, containing booklet panes Nos. 2202ab, 2203ab, **MS**2206a and S95a .... 18·00

DX **28**

(Des GBH)

2002 (6 Feb). *A Gracious Accession*. Golden Jubilee of Queen Elizabeth II. |MULTI COLOUR cover as Type DX **28** (161×96 mm). Booklet contains text and illustrations on labels attached to the panes and interleaving pages.

DX28   £7·29, containing booklet panes Nos. 1664n, 2253b/4b
and 2258b .... 20·00

DX **29**

(Des CDT Design)

2002 (24 Sept). *Across the Universe*. |MULTI COLOUR cover as Type DX **29** (164×95 mm). Booklet contains text and illustrations on labels attached to the panes and interleaving pages. Stitched.

DX29   £6·83, containing booklet panes Nos. 1668m, 2126ac,
MS2315a and EN1b .... 19·00

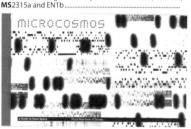

DX **30**

(Des CDT Design)

2003 (25 Feb). *Microcosmos*. 50th Anniv of Discovery of DNA. |MULTI COLOUR cover as Type DX **30** (164×95 mm). Booklet contains text and illustrations on labels attached to the panes and interleaving pages. Stitched.

DX30   £6·99, containing booklet panes Nos. 1668m, 2343a,
2345a and NI89a .... 20·00

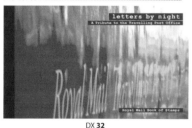

DX **31**

(Des GBH)

2003 (2 June). *A Perfect Coronation*. 50th Anniv of Coronation. |MULTI COLOUR cover as Type DX **31** (161×96 mm). Booklet contains text and illustrations on the panes and on interleaving pages.

DX31   £7·46, containing booklet panes Nos. 1664o, 2368b/9b
and 2378a .... 32·00

DX **32**

(Des Kate Stephens)

2004 (16 Mar). *Letters by Night A Tribute to the Travelling Post Office*. |MULTI COLOUR cover as Type DX **32** (164×95 mm). Booklet contains text and illustrations on labels attached to the panes and on interleaving pages. Stitched.

DX32   £7·44, containing booklet panes Nos. 1668o, 2392a,
2418a and S109l.. 15·00

DX **33**

(Des John and Orna Designs)

2004 (25 May). *The Glory of the Garden*. Bicentenary of the Royal Horticultural Society. |MULTI COLOUR cover as Type DX **33** (162×96 mm). Booklet contains text and illustrations on labels attached to the panes and interleaving pages. Stitched.

DX33   £7·23, containing booklet panes Nos. 1668p, 2456a,
2457a and 2463a .... 19·00

DX **34**

(Des Morgan Radcliffe)

2005 (24 Feb). *The Brontë Sisters*. 150th Death Anniversary of Charlotte Brontë. |MULTI COLOUR cover as Type DX **34** (162×96 mm). Booklet contains text and illustrations on panes and interleaving pages. Stitched.

DX34   £7·43, containing booklet panes Nos. 1664p, EN6l, 2518a
and 2520a.. 15·00

DX **35** White Ensign

(Des Webb & Webb)

2005 (18 Oct). *Bicentenary of the Battle of Trafalgar*. Black, scarlet and ultramarine cover as Type DX **35** (162×96 mm). Booklet contains text and illustrations on labels attached to the panes and interleaving pages. Stitched.

DX35   £7·26 containing booklet panes Nos. 1668q, 2574b/5b
and 2581a.. 14·00

DX **36** Plaque showing Clifton Suspension Bridge

(Des Hat-trick Design)

2006 (23 Feb). *Birth Bicentenary of Isambard Kingdom Brunel*. Grey and grey-black cover as Type DX **36** (162×96 mm). Booklet contains text and illustrations on panes and interleaving pages. Stitched.

DX36   £7·40 containing booklet panes Nos. 1668r, 2607a/8a
and 2610a .... 14·00

DX **37**

(Des Atelier Works)

2006 (21 Sept). *150th Anniversary of the Victoria Cross.* Blackish-brown and gold cover as Type DX **37** (162×96 mm). Booklet contains text and illustrations on panes and interleaving pages. Stitched.

DX37 £7·44 containing booklet panes Nos. 2651a, 2659b, 2660b and 2666a .... 14·00

DX **38**

(Des R. Warren-Fisher)

2007 (1 Mar). *World of Invention.* Black, olive-grey and grey cover as Type DX **38** (162×95 mm). Booklet contains text and illustrations on panes and interleaving pages. Stitched.

DX38 £7·49 containing booklet panes Nos. S109m, Y1670l and 2721a/b .... 15·00

DX **39**

(Des R. Warren-Fisher)

2007 (5 June). *The Machin The Making of a Masterpiece.* |MULTI COLOUR cover as Type DX **39** (165×96 mm). Booklet contains text and illustrations on panes and interleaving pages. Stitched.

DX39 £7·66 containing booklet panes Nos. Y1668l, Y1744l, 2650a and 2741a.. 15·00

DX **40** Soldiers of 1854

(Des Atelier Works)

2007 (20 Sept). *British Army Uniforms.* |MULTI COLOUR cover as Type DX **40** (164×96 mm). Booklet contains text and illustrations on panes and interleaving pages. Stitched.

DX40 £7·66 containing booklet panes Nos. Y1667o, 2774b, 2777b and EN30l .... 14·00

DX **41** Typewriter and Casino Royale

(Des GBH)

2008 (8 Jan). *Ian Fleming's James Bond.* |MULTI COLOUR cover as Type DX **41** (164×96 mm). Booklet contains text and illustrations on panes and interleaving pages. Stitched.

DX41 £7·40 containing booklet panes Nos. 1672l, 2797a/8a and 2805a .... 16·00

DX **42** RAF Badge

(Des Silk Pearce)

2008 (18 Sept). *Pilot to Plane.* RAF Uniforms. Black on light blue cover as Type DX **42** (162×96 mm). Booklet contains text and illustrations on panes and interleaving pages. Stitched.

DX42 £7·15 containing booklet panes Nos. 1670l, 2862b, 2865b and 2868a.. 15·00

DX **43** Symbols of Northern Ireland, Scotland and Wales

(Des Sedley Place)

2008 (29 Sept). *50th Anniversaryersary of the Country Definitives.* |MULTI COLOUR cover as Type DX **43** (162×96 mm). Booklet contains text and illustrations on panes and interleaving pages. Stitched.

DX43 £9·72 containing booklet panes Nos. NI154I/m, S154I and W144I... 20·00

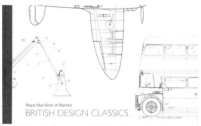

DX **44** Graphic Drawings of Spitfire, Anglepoise Lamp and Routemaster Bus

(Des HGV)

2009 (13 Jan). *British Design Classics.* |MULTI COLOUR cover as Type DX **44** (162×96 mm). Booklet contains text and illustrations on panes and interleaving pages. Stitched.

DX44 £7·68 containing booklet panes Nos. Y1769I, 2887b, 2888a and 2891a .... 20·00

DX **45** Charles Darwin

(Des Howard Brown)

2009 (12 Feb). *Birth Bicentenary of Charles Darwin.* |MULTI COLOUR cover as Type DX **45** (162×96 mm). Booklet contains text and illustrations on panes and interleaving pages. Stitched.

DX45 £7·75 containing booklet panes Nos. Y1762I, **MS**2904a, 2905a and 2906a .... 35·00

DX **46** Proof Sheet of Penny Black Stamps

(Des Silk Pearce)

2009 (18 Aug). *Treasures of the Archive.* Clear cover showing illustrated pane as Type DX **46** (162×96 mm). Booklet contains text and illustrations on panes and interleaving pages. Stitched.

DX46 £8·18 containing booklet panes Nos. Y1770I, 2950a, 2955a and 2957a .... 14·00

DX **47** Officers, Marines and Seamen on Deck

(Des Webb and Webb Design Ltd)

2009 (17 Sept). *Royal Navy Uniforms.* |MULTI COLOUR cover as Type DX **47** (163×96 mm). Booklet contains text and illustrations on panes and interleaving pages. Stitched.

DX47 £7·93 containing booklet panes Nos. Y1761I, 2964b, 2967b and 2970a .... 14·00

DX **48** Vinyl Disc

(Des True North)

2010 (7 Jan). *Classic Album Covers.* Black and pale blue cover as Type DX **48** (162×96 mm). Booklet contains text and illustrations on panes and interleaving pages. Stitched.

DX48 £8·06 containing booklet panes Nos. Y1765I, Y1773I, 3009a and 3015a .... 28·00

DX **49** Diagram and Signatures

(Des Russell Warren-Fisher)

2010 (25 Feb). *350th Anniversaryersary of the Royal Society.* |MULTI COLOUR cover as Type DX **49** (162×96 mm). Booklet contains text and illustrations on panes and interleaving pages. Stitched.

DX49 £7·72 containing booklet panes Nos. Y1774I, 3026b, 3027a and 3029a .... 15·00

DX **50**

(Des Silk Pearce)

2010 (8 May). *Centenary of Accession of King George V.* Deep carmine and cream cover, 162×97 mm, as Type DX **50**. Booklet contains text and illustrations on panes and interleaving pages. Stitched.

DX50 £11·15 containing booklet panes Nos. U2917a, 3066a/7a and 3070a .... 18·00

DX **51**

(Des Why Not Associates)

2010 (13 May). *Britain Alone* Grey, black and stone cover, 163×96 mm, as Type DX **51**. Booklet contains text and illustrations on panes and interleaving pages. Stitched.

DX51   £9·76 containing booklet panes Nos. Y1763l, 3074a, 3076a and 3082a ....   15·00

DX **52** Wildlife

(Des Russell Warren-Fisher)

2011 (22 Mar). *50th Anniversaryersaryersary of the WWF.* |MULTI COLOUR| cover, 162×96 mm, as Type DX **52**. Booklet contains text and illustrations on panes and interleaving pages. Stitched.

DX52   £9·05 containing booklet panes Nos. Y1764l, 3162b, 3164b and **MS**3172a ....   22·00

PREMIUM BOOKLETS: From the issue of the 'Morris and Co' booklet, Royal Mail introduced an additional cost, over and above the face value of the stamps contained within them. They are separately numbered in a new series, commencing DY1.

DY **1** "Flora" (wallpaper pattern by William Morris), 1891

(Des Kate Stephens)

2011 (5 May). *150th Anniversaryersaryersary of Morris and Company* (designers and manufacturers of textiles, wallpaper and furniture). |MULTI COLOUR| cover as Type DY **1** (162×96 mm). Booklet contains text and illustrations on panes and interleaving pages. Stitched.

DY1   £9·99 containing booklet panes Nos. U3057a, 3181a/2a and 3186ab...   15·00

The contents of No. DY1 have a face value of £9·04.

DY **2** Poster for First UK Aerial Mail, Hendon Aerodrome, 1911

(Des Robert Maude and Sarah Davies)

2011 (9 Sept). *Centenary of the First United Kingdom Aerial Post.* Black and grey cover as Type DY **2** (161×96 mm). Booklet contains text and illustrations on panes and interleaving pages. Stitched.

DY2   £9·97 containing booklet panes Nos. Y1763m, 3216a, 3217a and 3221a ....   40·00

The contents of No. DY2 have a face value of £9·02.

DY **3** Bookshelf

(Des Magpie Studio)

2012 (10 Jan). *Roald Dahl's Children's Stories.* |MULTI COLOUR| cover as Type DY **3** (163×96 mm). Booklet contains text and illustrations on panes and interleaving pages. Stitched.

DY3   £11·47 containing booklet panes Nos. Y1668m, 3254a, 3255a and 3260a...   15·00

The contents of No. DY3 have a face value of £10·52.

DY **4**

(Des Russell Warren-Fisher)

2012 (31 May). *Diamond Jubilee.* Ultramarine, black and silver cover as Type DY **4** (162×96 mm). Booklet contains text and illustrations on panes and interleaving pages. Stitched.

DY4 £12·77 containing booklet panes Nos. B3319b, B3320b, B3322b and 3279a ....   16·50

The contents of No. DY4 have a face value of £11·84.

DY **5**

(Des True North)

2012 (27 July). *Olympic and Paralympic Games, London.* 'Keeping the Flame Alive'. |MULTI COLOUR| cover, 162×96 mm, as Type DY **5**. Booklet contains text and illustrations on panes and interleaving pages. Stitched.

DY5 £10·71 booklet containing panes Nos. 2982b, 2983b, 2984b and 3337a ....   35·00

The contents of No. DY5 have a face value of £9·76.

DY **6**

(Des GBH)

2013 (26 Mar). *50th Anniversary of Doctor Who* (TV programme). |MULTI COLOUR cover, 163×96 mm, as Type DY **6**. Booklet contains text and illustrations on panes and interleaving pages. Stitched.

DY6 £13·77 containing booklet panes Nos. U3072a, 3437b, 3440b, 3444b and **MS**3451a.. 22·00

The contents of No. DY6 have a face value of £12·82.

DY **7** Gordon Banks, John Barnes, Bobby Moore, Kevin Keegan and George Best

(Des True North)

2013 (9 May). *Football Heroes.* |MULTI COLOUR cover as Type DY **7** (163×96 mm). Booklet contains text and illustrations on panes and interleaving pages. Stitched.

DY7 £11·11 containing booklet panes Nos. U3070a/71a, 3479a and 3484a.. 22·00

No. DY7 was issued in a souvenir foil wrapper.

The contents of No. DY7 have a face value of £10·56.

DY **8** Merchant Ensign

(Des Russell Warren-Fisher)

2013 (19 Sept). *Merchant Navy.* |MULTI COLOUR cover, as Type DY **8** (163×96 mm). Booklet contains text and illustrations on panes and interleaving pages. Stitched.

DY8 £11·19 booklet containing panes Nos. U3073a, 3519a, 3522a and 3525a.. 16·00

The contents of No. DY8 have a face value of £10·24.

DY **9** Southern Railway Class M7 No. 53 on the Great Central Railway, 2012

(Des Delaney Design Consultants)

2014 (20 Feb). *Classic Locomotives of the United Kingdom.* Black, grey and gold cover, 163×96 mm, as Type DY **9**. Booklet contains text and illustrations on panes and interleaving pages. Stitched.

DY9 £13·97 containing booklet panes Nos. U3071b, 3570a, 3571a, 3572a and 3573a.. 18·00

The contents of No. DY9 have a face value of £13·02.

DY **10**

(Des So Design Consultants)

2014 (15 Apr). *Buckingham Palace, London.* |MULTI COLOUR cover as Type DY **10** (162×96 mm). Booklet contains text and illustrations on panes and interleaving pages. Stitched.

DY10 £11·39 containing booklet panes Nos. U3074a, 3589ba, 3591ba and 3597a.. 15·00

The contents of No. DY10 have a face value of £10·44.

DY **11**

(Des Hat-trick Design)

2014 (28 Jul). *Centenary of the First World War* (1st issue). |MULTI COLOUR cover, 163×96 mm, as Type DY **11**. Booklet contains text and illustrations on panes and interleaving pages. Stitched.

DY11 £11·30 booklet containing panes Nos. U3074b, U3082a, 3626b and 3629b.. 15·00

The contents of No. DY11 have a face value of £10·35

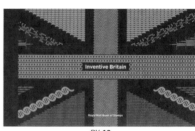

DY **12**

(Des Supple Studio)

2015 (19 Feb). *Inventive Britain* Black and silver cover, 162×96 mm, as Type DY **12**. Booklet contains text and illustrations on panes and interleaving pages. Stitched.

DY12 £14·60 containing booklet panes Nos. U3070b, 3679b/c and 3681b.. 20·00

The contents of No. DY12 have a face value of £13·67.

DY **13** 11th Battalion, 3rd Brigade, Australian Imperial Force on Great Pyramid of Khufu, 1915 and Worker at National Shell Filling Factory, Chilwell, Nottinghamshire

(Des hat-trick design)

2015 (14 May). *Centenary of the First World War* (2nd issue). |MULTI COLOUR| cover, 162×96 mm, as Type DY **13**. Booklet contains text and illustrations on panes and interleaving pages. Stitched.

DY13 £13·96 booklet containing panes Nos. 2776b, U3070c, 3711a and 3714a.. 20·00

The contents of No. DY13 have a face value of £11·68.

DY **14** Arthur Wellesley, First Duke of Wellington, the Emperor Napoleon and Battle of Waterloo

(Des Webb & Webb Design Ltd)

2015 (18 June). *Bicentenary of the Battle of Waterloo.* |MULTI COLOUR| cover as Type DY **14** (161×96 mm). Booklet contains text and illustrations on panes and interleaving pages. Stitched.

DY14 £14·47 containing booklet panes Nos. U3072b, 3724a/5a and 3730a.. 24·00

The contents of No. DY14 have a face value of £13·52.

DY **15** Starfighters

(Des Interabang)

2015 (17 Dec). *The Making of Star Wars – The British Story.* |MULTI COLOUR| cover as Type DY **15** (163×95 mm). Booklet contains text and illustrations on panes and interleaving pages. Stitched.

DY15 £16·99 containing booklet panes Nos. U3095a, 3758b, 3759b, 3780a and 3783a.................................... 24·00

The contents of No. DY15 have a face value of £16·20.

No. DY15 was issued to coincide with the UK release of *Star Wars: The Force Awakens.*

DY **16** Cancelled Penny Red

(Des Atelier Works)

2016 (18 Feb). *500 Years of Royal Mail.* |MULTI COLOUR| cover, 163×96 mm, as Type DY **16**. Booklet contains text and illustrations on panes and interleaving pages. Stitched.

DY16 £16·36 containing booklet panes Nos. 3795a, 3796a, 3802a and 3807a.. 22·00

The contents of No. DY16 have a face value of £15·41.

DY **17** Queen Elizabeth II on State Visit to Germany, June 2015

(Des Kate Stephens)

2016 (21 Apr). *90th Birthday of Queen Elizabeth II.* |MULTI COLOUR| cover, 161×95 mm, as Type DY **17**. Booklet contains text and illustrations on panes and interleaving pages. Stitched.

DY17 £15·11 containing booklet panes Nos. U3097a, 3826b, 3829b and MS3832b.. 35·00

The contents of No. DY17 have a face value of £14·16.

DY **18** William Leefe Robinson (awarded Victoria Cross) and Infantry Attack, Battle of the Somme

(Des hat-trick design)

2016 (21 Jun). *Centenary of the First World War* (3rd issue). |MULTI COLOUR| cover, 161×95 mm, as Type DY **18**. Booklet contains text and illustrations on panes and interleaving pages. Stitched.

DY18 £16·49 booklet containing panes Nos. 3717a, 3838a, 3841a and 3844a.. 24·00

The contents of No. DY 18 have a face value of £15·54.

DY **19** Beatrix Potter with Spaniel Spot, Rabbit Benjamin Bouncer and Two Pekingese Dogs/

(Des Webb & Webb Design Ltd)

2016 (28 July). *The Tale of Beatrix Potter.* |MULTI COLOUR| cover, 162×96 mm, as Type DY **19**. Booklet contains text and illustrations on panes and interleaving pages. Stitched.

DY19 £15·37 containing booklet panes Nos. U3072d, 3856b, 3857b and 3864a.. 24·00

The contents of No. DY19 have a face value of £14·42.

DY **20** Windsor Castle: from the River Thames (Richard Willis)

(Des Silk Pearce)

2017 (15 Feb). *Windsor Castle.* |MULTI|COLOUR cover, 162×96 mm, as Type DY **20**. Booklet contains text and illustrations on panes and interleaving pages. Stitched.
DY20   £14.58 containing booklet panes Nos. U3071c, 3920b, 3921b and 3928a 22.00
   The contents of No. DY20 have a face value of £13.63.

DY **21** Machin Definitives

(Des Godfrey Design)

2017 (5 June). *50th Anniversary of the Machin Definitive.* |MULTI|COLOUR cover, 162×96 mm, as Type DY **21**. Booklet contains text and illustrations on panes and interleaving pages. Stitched.
DY21   £15.59 containing booklet panes Nos. 3958a, 3961a, 3966ba, Y1667p and 1668sb... 22.00
   The contents of No. DY21 have a face value of £14.64

DY **22** Women's Land Army member competing in All England Girls' Farming Competition, Bishops Stortford, Hertfordshire, 1917 and Australian Troops crossing duckboard track through remains of Chateau Wood during Third Battle of Ypres (Passchendaele), 29 October 1917

(Des Hat-trick Design)

2017 (31 July). *Centenary of the First World War* (4th issue). Grey and gold cover, 162×96 mm, as Type DY **22**. Booklet contains text and illustrations on panes and interleaving pages. Stitched.
DY22   £15.41 containing booklet panes Nos. 2883b, 3717b, 3983a and 3986a 24.00
   The contents of No. DY22 have a face value of £14.46.

DY**23** Filming Rey (Daisy Ridley) and BB-8 in Desert near Abu Dhabi

(Des Interabang)

2017 (14 Dec). *Star Wars*: The Making of the Droids, Aliens and Creatures. |MULTI|COLOUR cover, 162×96 mm, as Type DY **23**. Booklet contains text and illustrations on panes and interleaving pages. Stitched.
DY23   £15.99 Containing booklet panes Nos. U3095b, 3759c, 3762b and 4008b.. 24.00
   The contents of No. DY23 have a face value of £14.32.

DY **24** Game of Thrones

(Des GBH)

2018 (23 Jan). *Game of Thrones.* |MULTI|COLOUR cover, 162×96 mm, as Type DY **24**. Booklet contains text and illustrations on panes and interleaving pages. Stitched.
DY 24   £13.95 containing booklet panes Nos. 4033b, 4036b, 4045a and U3072e... 22.00
   The contents of No. DY24 have a face value of £12.99

DY **25** RAF Roundel and Centenary Emblem

(Des Common Curiosity)

2018 (20 Mar). *Centenary of the RAF* (Royal Air Force). |MULTI|COLOUR cover, 163×96 mm, as Type DY **25**. Booklet contains text and illustrations on panes and interleaving pages. Stitched.
DY25   £18.69 containing booklet panes Nos. U3071e, 4058b, 4059b, 4067a and 4070a... 27.00
   The contents of No. DY25 have a face value of £18.54

B. Folded Booklets.

NOTE: All panes are attached to the covers by the selvedge. Inscribed dates are those shown with the printer's imprint.

Illustrations for 10p., 50p., £1 and £2 booklets are ¾ size; others are ²/₃ size.

10p. Booklets

FA **1**

1976 (10 Mar)–**77**. Cover as Type FA **1** printed in dull rose on very pale lavender. Containing booklet pane No. X841r.

FA1	NOV 1975	45
FA2	MAR 1976 (9.6.76)	60
FA3	JUNE 1977 (13.6.77)	40

FA **4**

(Des N. Battershill)

1978 (8 Feb)–**79**. *Farm Buildings Series.* Bistre-brown and turquoise-blue covers as Type FA **4**, containing booklet pane No. X843m.

FA4	Design No. 1, Oast Houses	35
FA5	Design No. 2, Buildings in Ulster (3.5.78)	40
FA6	Design No. 3, Buildings in Yorkshire (9.8.78)	35
FA7	Design No. 4, Buildings in Wales (25.10.78)	35
FA8	Design No. 5, Buildings in Scotland (10.1.79)	35
FA9	Design No. 6, Buildings in Sussex (4.4.79)	35

Nos. FA4/5 are inscribed "January 1978", FA6 "July 1978", FA7 "October 1978", FA8 "December 1978" and FA9 "March 1979".

FA **10**

(Des Hamper and Purssell)

1979 (17 Oct)–**80**. *London 1980 International Stamp Exhibition.* Red and blue cover as Type FA **10** showing Post Office exhibition stand and containing booklet pane No. X845l.

FA10	Inscr "August 1979"	30
FA11	Inscr "January 1980" (12.1.80)	35

50p. Booklets

All booklets were sold at the cover price of 50p. although some contain stamps to a greater value.

FB **1**

1977 (26 Jan). Cover as Type FB **1** printed in maroon and pale blue.

FB1A	Containing booklet pane X841s	1·50

FB1B   Containing booklet pane X841sa .... 1·50

1977 (13 June). Cover as Type FB **1**. Printed in chestnut and stone.

FB2A	Containing booklet pane X844n	2·50
FB2B	Containing booklet pane X844na	1·50

Nos. FB1A and FB1B are inscribed "March 1976" and FB2A and FB2B "June 1977".

FB **3**

(Des J. Ireland)

1978 (8 Feb)–**79**. *Commercial Vehicles Series.* Olive-yellow and grey covers as Type FB **3.** A. Containing booklet pane No. X844n. B. Containing booklet pane No. X844na.

		A	B
FB3	Design No. 1, Clement Talbot van	2·75	1·70
FB4	Design No. 2, Austin taxi (3.5.78)	2·65	1·50
FB5	Design No. 3, Morris Royal Mail van (9.8.78)	2·65	1·50
FB6	Design No. 4, Guy Electric dustcart (25.10.78)	3·75	1·50
FB7	Design No. 5, Albion van (10.1.79)	4·00	3·75
FB8	Design No. 6, Leyland fire engine (4.4.79)	3·75	3·75

Nos. FB3/4 are inscribed "January 1978", FB5 "July 1978", FB6 "October 1978", FB7 "December 1978" and FB8 "March 1978".

1979 (28 Aug). Contents changed. A. Containing booklet pane No. X849l. B. Containing booklet pane No. X849la.

		A	B
FB9	Design No. 6, Leyland fire engine	1·60	1·60

No. FB9 is inscribed "August 1979".

FB **10**

(Des B. Smith)

1979 (3 Oct)–**81**. *Veteran Cars Series.* Orange-red and reddish lilac covers as Type FB **10**. A. Containing booklet pane No. X849l. B. Containing booklet pane No. X849la.

		A	B
FB10	Design No. 1, 1907 Rolls-Royce Silver Ghost	1·50	1·50

No. FB10 is inscribed "August 1979".

Contents changed. A. Containing booklet pane No. X849m. B. Containing booklet pane No. X849ma.

		A	B
FB11	Design No. 2, 1908 Grand Prix Austin (4.2.80)	1·50	1·50
FB12	Design No. 3, 1903–5 Vauxhall (25.6.80)	1·50	1·50
FB13	Design No. 4, 1897–1900 Daimler (24.9.80)	1·45	1·45

No. FB11 is inscribed "January 1980", No. FB 12 "May 1980" and No. FB 13 "July 1980".

Contents changed. A. Containing No. X841t. B. Containing No.X841ta.

		A	B
FB14	Design No. 5, 1896 Lanchester (26.1.81)	1·45	1·45
FB15	Design No. 6, 1913 Bull-nose Morris (18.3.81)	1·75	1·75

Nos. FB14/15 are inscribed "January 1981".

FB **16**

(Des R. Downer)

1981 (6 May)–**82**. *Follies Series.* Brown and orange-brown covers as Type FB **16**. A. Containing No. X841t. B. Containing No. X841ta.

		A	B
FB16	Design No. 1, Mugdock Castle, Stirlingshire	1·50	1·50

No. FB16 is inscribed "January 1981".

Contents changed. A. Containing No. X854l. B. Containing No. X854la.

		A	B
FB17	Design No. 1, Mugdock Castle, Stirlingshire (26.8.81)	4·25	7·00
FB18	Design No. 2, Mow Cop Castle, Cheshire–Staffs border (30.9.81)	4·25	4·25

Nos. FB17/18 are inscribed "January 1981".

Contents changed. A. Containing No. X841u. B. Containing No. X841ua.

		A	B
FB19	Design No. 3, Paxton's Tower, Llanarthney, Dyfed (1.2.82)	1·75	1·75
FB20	Design No. 4, Temple of the Winds, Mount Stewart, Northern Ireland (6.5.82)	1·75	1·75
FB21	Design No. 5, Temple of the Sun, Stourhead, Wilts (11.8.82)	1·00	1·75
FB22	Design No. 6, Water Garden, Cliveden, Bucks (6.10.82)	1·75	1·75

Nos. FB19/22 are inscribed "February 1982".

FB **23**

(Des H. Titcombe)

1983 (16 Feb–26 Oct). *Rare Farm Animals Series.* Bright green and black covers as Type FB **23**. A. Containing booklet pane No. X841ul. B. Containing booklet pane No. X841ua.

		A	B
FB23	Design No. 1, Bagot Goat	1·75	2·00

Contents changed. Containing No. X845n.

FB24	Design No. 2, Gloucester Old Spot Pig (5.4.83)	3·50	
	b. Corrected rate	12·00	
FB25	Design No. 3, Toulouse Goose (27.7.83)	3·75	
FB26	Design No. 4, Orkney Sheep (26.10.83)	3·75	

No. FB23 is inscribed "February 1982" and Nos. FB24/6 "April 1983". The corrected rate reads, "36p. for 200g" instead of "37p. for 200g".

FB **27**

(Des P. Morter)

1984 (3 Sept)–**85**. *Orchids Series.* Yellow-green and lilac covers as Type FB **27**. Containing booklet pane No. X845p.

FB27	Design No. 1, *Dendrobium nobile* and *Miltonia* hybrid	2·50
FB28	Design No. 2, *Cypripedium calceolus* and *Ophrys apifera* (15.1.85)	2·50
FB29	Design No. 3, *Bifrenaria* and *Vanda tricolor* (23.4.85)	2·50
FB30	Design No. 4, *Cymbidium* and *Arpophyllum* (23.7.85)	2·50

Nos. FB27/30 are inscribed "September 1984".

50p
Royal Mail Stamps
Three at 17p

Type FB **31**

(Des M. Thierens Design)

1985 (4 Nov). Cover as Type FB **31** printed in black and bright scarlet. Containing booklet pane No. X909l.

FB31	Pillar box design	2·75

No. FB **31** is inscribed "November 1985".

FB **32**

(Des P. Morter)

1986 (20 May–12 Aug). *Pond Life Series.* Dull blue and emerald covers as Type FB **32**. Containing booklet pane No. X909l.

FB32	Design No. 1, Emperor Dragonfly, Four spotted Libellula and Yellow Flag	1·75
FB33	Design No. 2. Common Frog, Fennel-leaved Pondweed and Long-stalked Pondweed (29.7.86)	2·25
	a. Containing booklet pane No. X909Ela (12.8.86)	2·15

Nos. FB32/33a are inscribed "November 1985".

FB **34**

(Des N. Battershill)

1986 (29 July). *Roman Britain Series.* Brown-ochre and Indian red cover as Type FB **34**. Containing booklet pane No. X845q.

FB34	Design No. 1, Hadrian's Wall	6·50

No. FB34 is inscribed "November 1985".

1986 (20 Oct)–**87**.*Pond Life Series* continued. Dull blue and emerald covers as Type FB **32**. Containing booklet pane No. X845s.

FB35	Design No. 3, Moorhen and Little Grebe	3·50
FB36	Design No. 4, Giant Pond and Great Ramshorn Snails (27.1.87)	3·50

No. FB36 is inscribed "October 1986".

1986 (20 Oct)–**87**. *Roman Britain Series* continued. Brown ochre and Indian red covers as Type FB **34**. Containing booklet pane No. X847l.

FB37	Design No. 2, Roman Theatre of Verulamium, St Albans	2·25
FB38	Design No. 3, Portchester Castle, Hampshire (27.1.87)	2·40

No. FB38 is inscribed "October 1986".

FB **39**

(Des Patricia Howes)

1987 (14 Apr)–**88**. *Bicentenary of Marylebone Cricket Club Series* Brown and dull ultramarine covers as Type FB **39**. Containing booklet pane No. X847l.

FB39	Design No. 1, Father Time weather vane	1·75
FB40	Design No. 2, Ashes urn and embroidered velvet bag (14.7.87)	1·75
FB41	Design No. 3, Lord's Pavilion and wrought iron decoration on roof (29.9.87)	1·75
FB42	Design No. 4, England team badge and new stand at Lord's (26.1.88)	1·75

Nos. FB39/42 are inscribed "October 1986".

FB 43

(Des G. Evernden)

1987 (14 Apr)–**88**. *Botanical Gardens Series.* Covers as Type FB **43**. Containing booklet panes No. X845s (FB43/**4**) or X845sa (FB45/**6**).

FB43	Design No. 1 (cover in ultramarine and rosered), Rhododendron "Elizabeth", Bodnant......................	3·25
FB44	Design No. 2 (cover in deep ultramarine and cobalt), Gentiana sino-ornata, Edinburgh (14.7.87)............................	3·25
FB45	Design No. 3 (cover in dull ultramarine and orange-yellow), Lilium auratum and "Mount Stuart" (incorrect inscr) (29.9.87)...	1·65
	a. With corrected spelling "Mount Stewart" (30.10.87)	2·00
FB46	Design No. 4 (cover in dull ultramarine and yellow-orange), Strelitzia reginae, Kew (26.1.88)........................	2·00

Nos. FB43/6 are inscribed "October 1986".
The panes from Nos. FB45/6 have imperforate vertical sides.

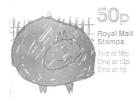

FB 47

1988 (12 Apr–5 July). *London Zoo. Children's Drawings Series.* Covers as Type FB **47**.

FB47	Pigs design (cover in black and rose) containing booklet pane No. X847l...	2·00
FB48	Birds design (cover in black and yellow) containing booklet pane No. X845sa..	2·00
FB49	Elephants design (cover in black and grey) containing booklet pane No. X847l (5.7.88)................................	2·00

Nos. FB47/9 are inscribed "October 1986". The pane from No. FB48 has imperforate vertical sides.

FB 50

(Des P. Morter)

1988 (5 July). *Marine Life Series.* Blue and orange-brown cover as Type FB **50**. Containing booklet pane No. X845sa.

FB50	Design No. 1, Parasitic Anemone on Common Whelk Shell and Umbrella Jellyfish..	2·00

No. FB50 is inscribed "October 1986" and has the vertical sides of the pane imperforate.

FB 51

(Des Lynda Gray)

1988 (5 Sept)–**89**. *Gilbert and Sullivan Operas Series.* Black and red covers as Type FB **51**. Containing booklet pane No. X904l.

FB51	Design No. 1, The *Yeomen of the Guard*..................................	5·00
FB52	Design No. 2, *The Pirates of Penzance* (24.1.89)....................	5·00
FB53	Design No. 3, *The Mikado* (25.4.89)..	5·00

1989 (18 July). *Marine Life Series* continued. Blue and orange brown cover as Type FB **50**. Containing booklet pane No. X904l.

FB54	Design No. 2, Common Hermit Crab, Bladder Wrack and Laver Spire Shell..	5·00

For Design No. 3, see £1 Booklet No. FH17.

FB 55

(Des P. Hutton)

1989 (2 Oct)–**90**. *Aircraft Series.* Turquoise-green and light brown covers as Type FB **55**. Containing booklet pane No. X906l.

FB55	Design No. 1, HP42, Armstrong Whitworth Atalanta and de Havilland Dragon Rapide..	7·50

No. FB55 was incorrectly inscribed "Atalanta".

As before, but containing Penny Black Anniversary booklet pane No. 1468l.

FB56	Design No. 2, Vickers Viscount 806 and de Havilland Comet 4 (30.1.90)	10·00

1990 (4 Sept)–**91**. *Aircraft Series* continued. Turquoise-green and light brown covers as Type FB **55**. Containing booklet pane No. X911l.

FB57	Design No. 3, BAC 1-11 and VC10..	10·00
FB58	Design No. 4, BAe ATP, BAe 146 and Aérospatiale–BAC Concorde (25.6.91)..	10·00

FB 59

(Des A. Drummond)

1991 (10 Sept)–**92**. *Archaeology Series.* Covers as Type FB **59**. Containing booklet pane No. X925m.

FB59	Design No. 1 (cover in bright blue and lake brown), Sir Arthur Evans at Knossos, Crete...................................	1·75
	a. Corrected rate (10.91)...	2·00
FB60	Design No. 2 (cover in bright blue and yellow), Howard Carter in the Tomb of Tutankhamun (21.1.92)......................	1·75
FB61	Design No. 3 (cover in bright blue and yellow), Sir Austen Layard at Assyrian site (28.4.92)	1·35
FB62	Design No. 4 (cover in new blue and yellow), Sir Flinders Petrie surveying the Pyramids and temples of Giza (28.7.92)	1·75

On the inside front cover of No. FB59 the inland letter rates are shown as 1st class 24, 35, 43, 51p. and 2nd class 18, 28, 33, 39p. These were corrected on No. FB59a to read: 1st class 24, 36, 45, 54p. and 2nd class 18, 28, 34, 41p.

FB 63

(Des J. Matthews)

1992 (22 Sept). *1000th Anniv of Appointment of Sheriffs.* Dull blue and scarlet cover as Type FB **63**. Containing booklet pane No. X925m.

FB63	Design showing Crest, with Helm and Mantling, and Badge of The Shrievalty Association	1·60

FB **64**

(Des M. Newton)

1993 (9 Feb–6 July). *Postal History Series.* Covers as Type FB **64**. Containing booklet pane No. X925m.

FB64 Design No. 1 (cover in grey-green and greyblack), Airmail postmarks.. 1·50

FB65 Design No. 2 (cover in dull orange and black), Ship mail postmarks (6.4.93)... 1·50

FB66 Design No. 3 (cover in blue and grey-black), Registered mail postmarks (6.7.93)... 1·50

1993 (1 Nov). *Postal History Series* continued. Rose-red and grey-black cover as Type FB **64** containing booklet pane No. Y1689l.

FB67 Design No. 4, "Paid" postmarks.................................. 1·50

FB **68**

(Des A. Davidson)

1994 (25 Jan–6 Sept). *Coaching Inns Series.* Covers as Type FB **68**. Containing booklet pane No. Y1689l.

FB68 Design No. 1 (cover in myrtle-green and pale myrtle-green), "Swan with Two Necks"................................ 1·50

FB69 Design No. 2 (cover in sepia and buff), "Bull and Mouth" (26.4.94) .... 1·50

FB70 Design No. 3 (cover in reddish brown and cinnamon), "Golden Cross" (6.6.94) .... 1·50

FB71 Design No. 4 (cover in black and slate-blue), "Pheasant Inn", Wiltshire (6.9.94) .... 1·50

FB **72**

(Des D. Davis)

1995 (7 Feb–4 Apr). *Sea Charts Series.* Rosine and black covers as Type FB **72,** containing booklet pane No. Y1689l.

FB72 Design No. 1, John o' Groats, 1800 .... 1·50

FB73 Design No. 2, Land's End, 1808 (4.4.95) .... 1·50

1995 (6 June–4 Sept). *Sea Charts Series* continued. Rosine and black covers as Type FB **72,** containing booklet pane No. Y1690l.

FB74 Design No. 3, St David's Head, 1812 .... 2·00

FB75 Design No. 4, Giant's Causeway, 1828 (4.9.95) ...... 2·00

65p. Booklet

1976 (14 July). Cover as Type FB **1,** but larger (90×49 mm). Printed in turquoise-blue and pale buff. A. Selvedge at left. B. Selvedge at right.

	A	B
FC1 Containing ten 6½p. (No. X872)	10·00	5·25

No. FC1 is inscribed "March 1976".

70p. Booklets

1977 (13 June). Cover as Type FB **1,** but larger (90×49 mm). Printed in purple-brown and dull rose. A. Selvedge at left. B. Selvedge at right.

	A	B
FD1 Containing ten 7p. (No. X875)	4·00	4·00

No. FD1 is inscribed "June 1977".

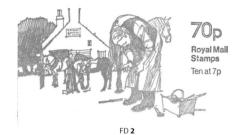

FD **2**

(Des E. Stemp)

1978 (8 Feb)–**79**. *Country Crafts Series.* Grey-green and red brown covers as Type FD **2** (90×49 mm). Containing ten 7p. (No. X875). A. Selvedge at left. B. Selvedge at right.

	A	B
FD2 Design No. 1, Horse-shoeing	35·00	3·00
FD3 Design No. 2, Thatching (3.5.78)	£175	3·00
FD4 Design No. 3, Dry-stone-walling (9.8.78)	£165	3·00
FD5 Design No. 4, Wheel-making (25.10.78)	5·75	4·00
FD6 Design No. 5, Wattle fence-making (10.1.79)	12·00	4·00

Nos. FD2/3 are inscribed "January 1978", FD4 "July 1978", FD5 "October 1978" and FD6 "December 1978".

FD **7**

(Des F. Wegner)

1979 (5 Feb). *Official opening of Derby Mechanised Letter Office.* Pale yellow-green and lilac cover as Type FD **7** (90×49 mm). Containing ten 7p. (No. X875). A. Selvedge at left. B. Selvedge at right.

	A	B
FD7 Kedleston Hall	5·50	5·50

No. FD7 is inscribed "December 1978".

On sale only in the Derby Head Post Office area to promote postcode publicity and also at the Philatelic Bureau and philatelic sales counters.

1979 (4 Apr). *Country Crafts Series* continued. Grey-green and red-brown covers as Type FD **2** (90×49 mm). containing ten 70p. (No. 875) A. Selvedge at left. B. Selvedge at right.

	A	B
FD8 Design No. 6, Basket-making	6·00	3·00

No. FD8 is inscribed "March 1979".

80p. Booklet

FE **1**

(Des P. Hutton)

1979 (3 Oct). *Military Aircraft Series.* Blue and grey cover as Type FE **1** (90×49 mm). Containing ten 8p. (No. X879**)** attached by the selvedge. A. Selvedge at left. B. Selvedge at right.

		A	B
FE1	Design No. 1, BE2B, 1914, & Vickers Gun Bus, 1915	2·25	2·25

No. FE1 is inscribed "August 1979".

85p. Booklet

1976 (14 July). Cover as Type FB **1** but larger (90×49 mm). Printed in light yellow-olive and brownish grey. A. Selvedge at left. B. Selvedge at right.

		A	B
FF1	Containing ten 8½p. (No. X881)	5·50	7·50

No. FF1 is inscribed "March 1976".

90p. Booklets

1977 (13 June). Cover as Type FB **1,** but larger (90×49 mm). Printed in deep grey-blue and cobalt. A. Selvedge at left. B. Selvedge at right.

		A	B
FG1	Containing ten 9p. (No. X883)	3·50	5·50

No. FG1 is inscribed "June 1977".

FG **2**

(Des R. Maddox)

1978 (8 Feb)—**79**. *British Canals Series.* Yellow-olive and new blue covers as Type FG **2** (90×49 mm). Containing ten 9p. (No. X883). A. Selvedge at left. B. Selvedge at right.

		A	B
FG2	Design No. 1, Grand Union	22·00	4·00
FG3	Design No. 2, Llangollen (3.5.78)	3·00	£325
FG4	Design No. 3, Kennet & Avon (9.8.78)	10·00	7·50
FG5	Design No. 4, Caledonian (25.10.78)	4·25	3·50
FG6	Design No. 5, Regents (10.1.79)	10·00	6·25

Nos. FG2/3 are inscribed "January 1978", FG4 "July 1978", FG5 October 1978" and FG6 "December 1978".

(Des F. Wegner)

1979 (5 Feb). *Official Opening of Derby Mechanised Letter Office.* Violet-blue and rose cover as Type FD **7** (90×49 mm). Containing ten 9p. (No. X883). A. Selvedge at left. B. Selvedge at right.

		A	B
FG7	Tramway Museum, Crich	7·00	7·00

No. FG7 is inscribed "December 1978".

On sale only in the Derby Head Post Office area to promote postcode publicity and also at the Philatelic Bureau and philatelic sales counters.

1979 (4 Apr). *British Canals Series* continued. Yellow-olive and new blue cover as Type FG 2 containing ten 9p. (No. X883). A. Selvedge at left. B. Selvedge at right.

		A	B
FG8	Design No. 6, Leeds & Liverpool	3·00	3·00

No. FG8 is inscribed "March 1979".

£1 Booklets

All booklets were sold at the cover price of £1 although some contain stamps to a greater value.

FH **1**

(Des N. Battershill)

1979 (3 Oct). *Industrial Archaeology Series.* Red and green cover as Type FH **1** (90×49 mm). Containing ten 10p. (No. X887). A. Selvedge at left. B. Selvedge at right.

		A	B
FH1	Design No. 1, Ironbridge, Telford, Salop	2·50	2·50

No. FH1 is inscribed "August 1979".

1980 (4 Feb—24 Sept). *Military Aircraft Series* continued. Blue and grey covers as Type FE **1** (90×49 mm). Containing ten 10p. (No. X888). A. Selvedge at left. B. Selvedge at right.

		A	B
FH2	Design No. 2, Sopwith Camel & Vickers Vimy	2·50	2·50
FH3	Design No. 3, Hawker Hart* & Handley Page Heyford (25.6.80)	3·50	3·50
FH4	Design No. 4, Hurricane & Wellington (24.9.80)	2·50	2·50

No FH2 is inscribed "January 1980", No. FH3 "May 1980" and No. FH4 "July 1980".
* On the booklet cover the aircraft is wrongly identified as a Hawker Fury.

FH **5**

(Des M. Newton and S. Paine)

1986 (29 July)–**87**. *Musical Instruments Series.* Scarlet and black covers as Type FH **5**. Containing six 17p. (X952).

FH5	Design No 1, Violin		3·00

No. FH5 is inscribed "November 1985".
Contents changed. Containing No. X901n.

FH6	Design No. 2, French horn (20.10.86)		3·00
FH7	Design No. 3, Bass clarinet (27.1.87)		3·00

No. FH7 is inscribed "October 1986".

FH **8**

(Des A. Davidson)

1987 (14 Apr)–**88**. *Sherlock Holmes Series.* Bright scarlet and grey-black covers as Type FH **8**. Containing booklet pane No. X901n (FH8/**9**) or X901na (FH10/11).

FH8	Design No. 1, *A Study in Scarlet*		3·00
FH9	Design No. 2, *The Hound of the Baskervilles* (14.7.87)		3·00
FH10	Design No. 3, *The Adventure of the Speckled Band* (29.9.87)		3·00
FH11	Design No. 4, *The Final Problem* (26.1.88)		2·75

Nos. FH8/11 are inscribed "October 1986".
The panes from Nos. FH10/11 have imperforate vertical sides.

1988 (12 Apr). *London Zoo. Children's Drawings Series.* Cover as Type FB **47** in black and brown. Containing booklet pane No. X901na.

FH12	Bears design		3·00

No. FH12 is inscribed "October 1986" and has the vertical sides of the pane imperforate.

FH **13**

(Des Liz Moyes)

1988 (5 July)–**89**. *Charles Dickens Series* Orange-red and maroon covers as Type FH **13**.

FH13	Designs No. 1, *Oliver Twist,* containing booklet pane No. X901na		3·75
FH14	Design No. 2, *Nicholas Nickleby,* containing booklet pane No. X904m (5.9.88)		3·75
FH15	Design No. 3, *David Copperfield,* containing booklet pane No. X904m (24.1.89)		3·75

FH16   Design No. 4, *Great Expectations*, containing booklet pane
No. X1051I (25.4.89)... 8·50
No. FH13 is inscribed "October 1986" and No. FH16 "September 1988", Nos. FH13/16 have the vertical sides of the pane imperforate.
1989 (18 July). *Marine Life Series* continued. Cover as Type FB **50** in turquoise-green and scarlet. Containing booklet pane No. X904m.
FH17   Design No. 3, Edible Sea Urchin, Common Starfish and
Common Shore Crab... 3·75
No. FH17 has the vertical edges of the pane imperforate.

FH **18**

(Des J. Sancha)

1989 (2 Oct)–**90**. *Mills Series*. Grey-black and grey-green matt card cover as Type FH **18**.
FH18   Design No. 1, Wicken Fen, Ely containing booklet pane
No. X960I... 4·00
As Type FH **18** but glossy card cover containing Penny Black Anniversary booklet pane No. 1476I printed in litho by Walsall.
FH19   Design No. 1 (cover in bottle-green and pale green),
Wicken Fen, Ely (30.1.90)... 9·50
No. FH19 was an experimental printing to test a new cover material. This appears glossy when compared with Nos. FH18 and FH20.
As Type FH **18** but changed to matt card cover containing Penny Black Anniversary booklet pane No. 1469I printed in photo by Harrison.
FH20   Design No. 1 (cover in grey-black and bright green), Click
Mill, Dounby, Orkney (30.1.90)... 6·00
1990 (4 Sept)–**91**. *Mills Series* continued. Covers as Type FH **18**. Containing booklet pane No. X911m.
FH21   Design No. 3 (cover printed in light blue and buff) Jack
and Jill Mills, Clayton, Sussex... 3·00
FH22   Design No. 4 (cover printed in dull blue and bright yellow-
green). Howell Mill, Llanddeusant, Anglesey (25.6.91)...... 3·00
Nos. FH18/22 have the vertical edges of the pane imperforate.

FH **23**

(Des J. Gibbs)

1991 (10 Sept)–**92**. *150th Anniv of Punch Magazine*. Magenta and grey-black covers as Type FH **23** containing booklet pane No. X927I.
FH23   Design No. 1, Illustrations by Richard Doyle and Hoffnung 2·00
      a. Corrected rate (10.91)... 2·00
FH24   Design No. 2, Illustrations by Sir John Tenniel and Eric
Burgin (21.1.92).. 2·00
FH25   Design No. 3, Illustrations by Sir John Tenniel and Anton
(28.4.92).. 2·00
FH26   Design No. 4, Illustrations by Sir John Tenniel and
Hewison (28.7.92)... 2·00
Nos. FH23/6 have the vertical edges of the pane imperforate.
No. FH23a has corrected letter rates as No. FB59a.

(Des J. Matthews)

1992 (22 Sept). *1000th Anniv of Appointment of Sheriffs*. Scarlet and dull blue cover as Type FB **63** containing booklet pane No. X927I.
FH27   Design as Type FB63 but elements in reverse order........... 2·00
No. FH27 has the vertical edges of the pane imperforate.

FH **28**
(Des J. Lawrence)

1993 (9 Feb–6 July). *Educational Institutions Series*. Covers as Type FH **28** containing booklet pane No. X1050I printed in litho by Walsall.

FH28   Design No. 1 (cover in lake-brown and light blue),
University of Wales.. 4·00
FH29   Design No. 2 (cover in deep dull green and lemon), St
Hilda's College, Oxford (6.4.93).. 4·00
FH30   Design No. 3 (cover in purple-brown and flesh),
Marlborough College, Wiltshire (6.7.93)............................ 4·00

1993 (1 Nov). *Educational Institutions Series* continued. Deep bluish green and lilac cover as Type FH **28** containing four 25p. (No. Y1775) printed in litho by Walsall.
FH31   Design No. 4, Free Church of Scotland College, Edinburgh 3·75

FH **32**

(Des H. Brockway)

1994 (25 Jan). *20th-century Prime Ministers Series*. Brown and pale brown cover as Type FH **32** containing four 25p. (No. Y1775) printed in litho by Walsall.
FH32   Design No. 1, Herbert Asquith....................................... 1·75

(Des H. Brockway)

1994 (26 Apr–6 Sept). *20th-century Prime Ministers Series* continued. Covers as Type FH **32**. Containing four 25p. (No. Y1689) printed in photo by Harrison.
FH33   Design No. 2 (cover in sepia and buff),
David Lloyd-George .... 1·75
FH34   Design No. 3 (cover in greenish blue and pale blue),
Winston Churchill (6.6.94) .... 1·75
FH35   Design No. 4 (cover in black and yellow-olive),
Clement Attlee (6.9.94) .... 1·75

FH **36**

(Des L. Thomas)

1995 (7 Feb–4 Apr). *50th Anniversary of End of Second World War*. Covers as Type FH **36** containing four 25p. (No. Y1689) printed in photo by Harrison.
FH36   Design No. 1 (cover in brown-olive and brownish black),
Violette Szabo (S.O.E. agent) .... 1·75
FH37   Design No. 2 (cover in red-brown and black), Dame Vera
Lynn (entertainer) (4.4.95).. 1·75

1995 (16 May–4 Sept). 50th Anniversary of End of Second World War Series continued. Covers as Type FH **36** containing four 25p. (No. Y1690) printed in photo by Harrison.
FH38   Design No. 3 (cover in black and steel-blue), R. J. Mitchell
(designer of Spitfire).. 1·75
FH39   Design No. 4 (cover in grey-green and black), Archibald
McIndoe (plastic surgeon) (4.9.95)................................... 2·00

FH **40**

1996 (16 Jan). |MULTI COLOUR| laminated cover as Type FH **40**. Stamps printed in litho by Questa.
FH40   Containing four 25p. stamps (No. Y1775) .... 4·00
For an initial test period No. FH40 was only available from machines at twelve post offices, five in London and seven in Scotland, in addition to philatelic outlets. Stocks were distributed nationally from May 1996.

1996 (8 July)–**97**. |MULTI COLOUR| laminated cover as Type FH **40**. Stamps printed in litho by Questa.

FH41 Containing booklet pane of No. Y1760l .... 3·75
    a. Corrected rate (4.2.97).. 3·50
    b. Inland rate table at right .... 3·50
    No. FH41 was reissued on 4 February 1997 showing the 200g second class rate on the inside cover altered from 47p. to 45p. A further printing issued 5 May 1998 was without the overseas postage rate table.

1998 (1 Dec). |MULTI COLOUR| laminated cover as Type FH **40**. Stamps printed in gravure by Questa.

FH42 Containing booklet pane of No. Y1667l .... 20·00

1999 (26 Apr). |MULTI COLOUR| laminated cover as Type FH **40**. Stamps printed in gravure by Questa.

FH43 Containing booklet pane of No. Y1667m .... 6·00

2000 (27 Apr)–**01**. |MULTI COLOUR| laminated cover as Type FH **40**. Stamps printed in gravure by Questa.

FH44 Containing booklet pane of No. 1664l..................................... 6·75
    a. Containing booklet pane No. 1664la (17.4.01)................ 7·00

£1.15 Booklets

1981 (26 Jan–18 Mar). *Military Aircraft Series* continued. Blue and grey covers as Type FE **1** (90×49 mm). Containing ten 11½p. (No. X893). A. Selvedge at left. B. Selvedge at right.

		A	B
FI1	Design No. 5, Spitfire & Lancaster...........................	3·00	3·00
FI2	Design No. 6, Lightning & Vulcan (18.3.81)	3·25	3·00

Nos. FI1/2 are inscribed "January 1981".

FI **3**
(Des R. Maddox)

1981 (6 May–30 Sept). *Museums Series.* Blue and turquoise green covers as Type FI **3** (90×49 mm). Containing ten 11½p. (No. X893). A. Selvedge at left. B. Selvedge at right.

		A	B
FI3	Design No. 1, Natural History Museum (British Museum), London	3·00	3·00
FI4	Design No. 2, National Museum of Antiquities of Scotland (30.9.81)	3·00	3·00

Nos. FI3/4 are inscribed "January 1981".

£1.20 Booklets

1980 (4 Feb–24 Sept). *Industrial Archaeology Series* continued. Red and green covers as Type FH **1** (90×49 mm). Containing ten 12p. (No. X943). A. Selvedge at left. B. Selvedge at right.

		A	B
FJ1	Design No. 2, Beetle Mill, Ireland	3·00	3·00
FJ2	Design No. 3, Tin Mines, Cornwall (25.6.80)	3·00	4·00
FJ3	Design No. 4, Bottle Kilns, Gladstone, Stoke-on-Trent (24.9.80)	3·00	3·25

No. FJ1 is inscribed "January 1980", No. FJ2 "May 1980" and No. FJ3 "July 1980".

1986 (14 Jan). Pillar box *Write Now* cover as Type FB **31** (90×49 mm), printed in yellow-green and pale red. Containing ten 12p. (No. X896). A. Selvedge at left. B. Selvedge at right.

		A	B
FJ4	"Write Now" (Pillar box design) (no imprint date)	4·50	4·50

FJ **5**
(Des R. Maddox)

1986 (29 Apr). *National Gallery* cover as Type FJ **5** (90×49 mm), printed in magenta and blue-green. Containing ten 12p. (No. X896). A. Selvedge at left. B. Selvedge at right.

		A	B
FJ5	National Gallery design....................................	4·25	4·25

No. FJ5 is inscribed "November 1985".

FJ **6**
(Des Trickett and Webb Ltd)

1986 (29 July). *Handwriting* cover as Type FJ **6** (90×49 mm), printed in bright orange and bright blue. Containing ten 12p. (No. X896). A. Selvedge at left. B. Selvedge at right.

		A	B
FJ6	"Maybe"...	4·25	4·25

No. FJ6 is inscribed "November 1985".

£1.25 Booklets

1982 (1 Feb–6 Oct). *Museums Series* continued. Blue and turquoise-green covers as Type FI **3** (90×49 mm). Containing ten 12½p. (No. X898). A. Selvedge at left. B. Selvedge at right.

		A	B
FK1	Design No. 3, Ashmolean Museum, Oxford...........	2·75	2·75
FK2	Design No. 4, National Museum of Wales, Cardiff (6.5.82)	2·75	2·75
FK3	Design No. 5, Ulster Museum, Belfast (11.8.82)	2·75	2·75
FK4	Design No. 6, Castle Museum, York (6.10.82)........	2·75	2·75

Nos. FK1/4 are inscribed "February 1982".

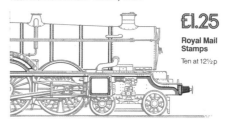

FK **5**
(Des S. Paine)

1983 (16 Feb–26 Oct). *Railway Engines Series.* Red and blue-green covers as Type FK **5** (90×49 mm). Containing ten 12½p. (No. X898). A. Selvedge at left. B. Selvedge at right.

		A	B
FK5	Design No. 1, GWR *Isambard Kingdom Brunel*	4·00	4·00
FK6	Design No. 2, LMS Class 4P Passenger Tank Engine (5.4.83)	4·75	4·75
	a. Corrected rate	80·00	£125
FK7	Design No. 3, LNER *Mallard* (27.7.83).....................	4·00	4·00
FK8	Design No. 4, SR/BR *Clan Line* (26.10.83)	4·00	4·00

No. FK5 is inscribed "February 1982" and Nos. FK6/8 "April 1983". The corrected rate reads "36p. for 200g" instead of "37p. for 200g".

£1.30 Booklets

FL **1**
(Des J. Gibbs)

1981 (6 May–30 Sept). *Postal History Series.* Covers as Type FL **1** (90×49 mm). Containing No. X894l. A. Selvedge at left. B. Selvedge at right.

		A	B
FL1	Design No. 1, Penny Black (red & black cover)	3·75	2·75
FL2	Design No. 2, The Downey Head, 1911 (red and green cover) (20.9.81)	4·75	16·00

No. FL1 is inscribed "April 1981" and No. FL2 "September 1981".

FL **3**

(Des J. Thirsk)

1984 (3 Sept)–**85**. *Trams Series.* Yellow-orange and purple covers as Type FL **3** (90×49 mm). Containing ten 13p. (No. X900). A. Selvedge at left. B. Selvedge at right.

		A	B
FL3	Design No. 1, Swansea/Mumbles Railway Car No. 3	2·75	2·75
FL4	Design No. 2, Glasgow Car No. 927 and Car No. 1194 (15.1.85)	3·25	3·25
FL5	Design No. 3, Car No. 717, Blackpool (23.4.85)	3·25	3·00
FL6	Design No. 4, Car No. 120 and "D" Class Car, London (23.7.85)	2·75	2·75

Nos. FL3/6 are inscribed "September 1984".

FL **7**

(Des Anne Morrow)

1986 (20 Oct). *Books for Children.* Cover as Type FL **7** (90×49 mm) printed in rose-red and lemon. Containing ten 13p. (No. X900). A. Selvedge at left. B. Selvedge at right.

		A	B
FL7	Teddy bears design	2·75	2·75

FL **8**

(Des Trickett and Webb Ltd)

1987 (27 Jan). *Keep in Touch* cover as Type FL **8** (90×49 mm), printed in light green and bright blue. Containing ten 13p. (No. X900). A. Selvedge at left. B. Selvedge at right.

		A	B
FL8	Handclasp and envelope design	2·75	2·75

No. FL8 is inscribed "October 1986".

FL **9**

(Des Hannah Firmin)

1987 (14 Apr). *Ideas for your Garden* Cover as Type FL **9** (90×49 mm) printed in bistre and orange-brown. Containing ten 13p. stamps (No. X900). A. Selvedge at left. B. Selvedge at right.

		A	B
FL9	Conservatory design	2·75	2·75

No. FL9 is inscribed "October 1986".

FL **10**

(Des Trickett and Webb Ltd)

1987 (14 July). *Brighter Writer.* Cover as Type FL **10** (90×49 mm) printed in orange and bright reddish violet. Containing ten 13p. stamps (No. X900). A. Selvedge at left. B. Selvedge at right.

		A	B
FL10	Flower design	2·75	2·75

No. FL10 is inscribed "October 1986".

FL **11**

(Des E. Stemp)

1987 (29 Sept). *Jolly Postman* Cover as Type FL **11** (90×49 mm) *printed in pale blue and deep blue. Containing ten 13p. stamps (No. X900). A. Selvedge at left. B. Selvedge at right.*

		A	B
FL11	Boy drawing design	2·80	2·80

No. FL11 is inscribed "October 1986".

FL **12**

(Des E. Hughes)

1988 (26 Jan). *Bicentenary of Linnean Society.* Cover as Type FL **12** (90×49 mm) printed in blue and claret. Containing ten 13p. stamps (No. X900). A. Selvedge at left. B. Selvedge at right.

		A	B
FL12	Mermaid, fish and insect (from "Hortus Sanitatis", 1497)	3·40	3·40

No. FL12 is inscribed "October 1986".

FL **13**

1988 (12 Apr). *Recipe Cards.* Cover as Type FL **13** (90×49 mm) printed in brown and green. Containing ten 13p. stamps (No. X900). A. Selvedge at left. B. Selvedge at right.

	A	B
FL13 Vegetables design	2·75	2·75

No. FL13 is inscribed "October 1986".

FL **14**

(Des Trickett and Webb Ltd)

1988 (5 July). *Children's Parties* Cover as Type FL **14** (90×49 mm) printed in blue-green and bright purple. Containing ten 13p. stamps (No. X900). A. Selvedge at left. B. Selvedge at right.

	A	B
FL14 Balloons and streamers design	2·75	2·75

No. FL14 is inscribed "October 1986".

£1.40 Booklets

1981 (26 Jan–18 Mar). *Industrial Archaeology Series* continued. Red and green covers as Type FH **1** (90×49 mm). Containing ten 14p. (No. X946). A. Selvedge at left. B. Selvedge at right.

	A	B
FM1 Design No. 5, Preston Mill, Scotland	2·75	3·00
FM2 Design No. 6, Talyllyn Railway, Tywyn (18.3.81)	3·00	2·75

Nos. FM1/2 are inscribed "January 1981".

FM **3**

(Des E. Stemp)

1981 (6 May–30 Sept). *19th-century Women's Costume Series.* Claret and blue covers as Type FM **3** (90×49 mm). Containing ten 14p. (No. X946). A. Selvedge at left. B. Selvedge at right.

	A	B
FM3 Design No. 1, Costume, 1800–15	2·75	2·75
FM4 Design No. 2, Costume, 1815–30 (30.9.81)	2·75	2·75

Nos. FM3/4 are inscribed "January 1981".

FM **5**

(Des A. Drummond)

1988 (5 Sept). *Pocket Planner* Cover as Type FM **5** (90×49 mm) printed in grey-black and yellow. Containing ten 14p. stamps (No. X903). A. Selvedge at left. B. Selvedge at right.

	A	B
FM5 "Legal Charge" design	2·75	2·75

FM **6**

(Des Debbie Cook)

1989 (24 Jan). *150th Anniv of Fox Talbot's Report on the Photographic Process to Royal Society.* Cover as Type FM **6** (90×49 mm) printed in reddish orange and black. Containing ten 14p. stamps (No. X903). A. Selvedge at left. B. Selvedge at right.

	A	B
FM6 Photographs and darkroom equipment	2·80	2·80

No. FM6 is inscribed "September 1988".

£1.43 Booklets

1982 (1 Feb–6 May). *Postal History Series* continued. Covers as Type FL **1** (90×49 mm). Containing No. X899I. A. Selvedge at left. B. Selvedge at right.

	A	B
FN1 Design No. 3, James Chalmers (postal reformer) (orange and turquoise-blue cover)	3·00	3·00
FN2 Design No. 4, Edmund Dulac (stamp designer) (brown and red cover) (6.5.82)	3·00	3·00

FN **3**

(Des J. Gardner)

1982 (12 July). *Holiday Postcard Stamp Book* Purple and turquoise-blue cover as Type FN **3** (90×49 mm). Containing No. X899I. A. Selvedge at left. B. Selvedge at right.

	A	B
FN3 *Golden Hinde* on front, postcard voucher on back	3·00	3·00

1982 (21 July)–**83**. *Postal History Series* continued. Covers as Type FL **1** (90×49 mm). Containing No. X899I. A. Selvedge at left. B. Selvedge at right.

	A	B
FN4 Design No. 5, "Forces Postal Service" (grey and violet cover)	3·00	3·00
FN5 Design No. 6, The £5 Orange (orange and black cover) (6.10.82)	3·00	3·00
FN6 Design No. 7, Postmark History (bright scarlet and deep dull blue cover) (16.2.83)	3·00	3·00

No. FN1 is inscribed "February 1982". FN2/3 "May 1982", FN4 "July 1982", FN5 "October 1982", FN6 "November 1982".

For booklet No. FS2 with cover price of £1·45, see £1·60 booklets.

£1.46 Booklets

1983 (5 Apr–26 Oct). *Postal History Series* continued. Covers as Type FL **1** (90×49 mm). A. Containing No. X899n. B. Containing No. X899na.

		A	B
FO1	Design No. 8, Seahorse High Values (blue and green cover)	5·50	5·50
	a. Corrected rate	48·00	15·00
FO2	Design No. 9, Parcel Post Centenary (turquoise-blue and carmine cover) (27.7.83)	4·75	4·75
FO3	Design No. 10, Silver Jubilee of Regional Stamps (dull green & reddish violet cover) (26.10.83)	4·75	4·75

No. FO1 is inscribed "March 1983", No. FO2 "May 1983" and No. FO3 "June 1983".
The corrected rate reads "36p. for 200g" instead of "37p. for 200g".

£1.50 Booklets

1986 (14 Jan). *Pillar box Write Now* cover as Type FB **31** (90×49 mm), printed in ultramarine and red. A. Containing No. X897l. B. Containing No. X897la.

		A	B
FP1	"Write Now" (Pillar box design)	3·50	3·50

No. FP1 shows no imprint date.

1986 (29 Apr). *National Gallery* cover as Type FJ **5** (90×49 mm), printed in violet and vermilion. A. Containing No. X897l. B. Containing No. X897la.

		A	B
FP2	National Gallery design	3·50	3·50

No. FP2 is inscribed "November 1985".

1986 (29 July). *Handwriting* cover as Type FJ **6** (90×49 mm), printed in blue-green and bright blue. A. Containing No. X897l. B. Containing No. X897la.

		A	B
FP3	"No"	3·50	3·50

No. FP3 is inscribed "November 1985".

£1.54 Booklets

1984 (3 Sept)–**85**. *Postal History Series* continued. Covers as Type FL **1** (90×49 mm). A. Containing No. X901l. B. Containing No. X901la.

		A	B
FQ1	Design No. 11, Old and new Postage Dues (reddish purple and pale blue cover)	3·00	3·00
FQ2	Design No. 12, Queen Victoria embossed stamps (yellow-green and blue-cover) (15.1.85)	3·00	3·00
FQ3	Design No. 13, Queen Victoria surface printed stamps (blue-green and carmine cover) (23.4.85)	3·00	3·00
FQ4	Design No. 14, 17th-century mounted and foot messengers (deep brown & orange-red cover) (23.7.85)	3·00	3·00

No. FQ1 is inscribed "July 1984" and Nos. FQ2/4 are inscribed "September 1984".

£1.55 Booklets

1982 (1 Feb–6 Oct). *19th-century Women's Costume Series* continued. Claret and blue covers as Type FM **3** (90×49 mm). Containing ten 15½p. (No. X948). A. Selvedge at left. B. Selvedge at right.

		A	B
FR1	Design No. 3, Costume, 1830–50	2·80	2·80
FR2	Design No. 4, Costume, 1850–60 (6.5.82)	2·80	2·80
FR3	Design No. 5, Costume, 1860–80 (11.8.82)	3·00	3·00
FR4	Design No. 6, Costume, 1880–1900 (6.10.82)	2·80	2·80

Nos. FR1/4 are inscribed "February 1982".

£1.60 Booklets

FS **1**

(Des Carol Walklin)

1983 (5 Apr). *Birthday Box* Design. Magenta and red-orange cover as Type FS **1** (90×49 mm). Depicting birthday cake and associated items. A. Selvedge at left. B. Selvedge at right.

		A	B
FS1	Containing ten 16p. stamps (No. X949) (no imprint date)	3·50	3·50
	a. Rates altered and "February 1983" imprint date	60·00	90·00

The converted rate reads "36p. for 200g." instead of 37p. for 200g.".

FS **2**

(Des R. Maddox)

1983 (10 Aug). *British Countryside Series*. Special Discount Booklet (sold at £1.45). Greenish blue and ultramarine cover as Type FS **2** (90×49 mm). Containing ten 16p. stamps (No. X949Eu). A. Selvedge at left. B. Selvedge at right.

		A	B
FS2	Design No. 1, Lyme Regis, Dorset	4·75	4·75

Stamps from No. FS2 show a double-lined "D" printed in blue on the reverse over the gum.
No. FS2 is inscribed "April 1983".

1983 (21 Sept). *British Countryside Series* continued. Dull green on violet cover as Type FS **2** (90×49 mm). Containing ten 16p. stamps (No. X949). A. Selvedge at left. B. Selvedge at right.

		A	B
FS3	Design No. 2, Arlington Row, Bibury, Gloucestershire	3·00	3·00

No. FS3 is inscribed "April 1983".

FS **4**

(Des M. Newton)

1984 (14 Feb). *Write it* Design. Vermilion and ultramarine cover as Type FS **4** (90×49 mm). Containing ten 16p. stamps (No. X949). A. Selvedge at left. B. Selvedge at right.

		A	B
FS4	Fountain pen	3·50	3·50

No. FS4 is inscribed "April 1983".

£1.70 Booklets

FT **1**

1984 (3 Sept). *Social Letter Writing Series*. Rose and deep claret cover as Type FT **1** (90×49 mm). Containing ten 17p. (No. X952). A. Selvedge at left. B. Selvedge at right.

		A	B
FT1	Design No. 1, "Love Letters"	3·50	3·50

No. FT1 is inscribed "September 1984".

1985 (5 Mar). *Social Letter Writing* continued. Special Discount Booklet (sold at £1·55). Turquoise-blue and deep claret cover as Type FT **1** (90×49 mm). Containing ten 17p. (No. X952Eu). A. Selvedge at left. B. Selvedge at right.

		A	B
FT2	Design No. 2, "Letters abroad"	3·50	3·50

Stamps from No. FT2 show a double-lined "D" printed in blue on the reverse over the gum.
No. FT2 is inscribed "September 1984".

1985 (9 Apr). *Social Letter Writing Series* continued. Bright blue and deep claret cover as Type FT **1** (90×49 mm). Containing ten 17p. (No. X952). A. Selvedge at left. B. Selvedge at right.

		A	B
FT3	Design No. 3, "Fan letters"......................................	3·20	3·20

No. FT3 is inscribed "September 1984".

£1.53

Royal Mail Stamps

Ten at 17p

Free Stamp

10 for the price of 9

FT **4**

(Des B. Smith)

1985 (30 July). *350 Years of Royal Mail Public Postal Service* Special Discount Booklet (sold at £1·53). Cover Type FT **4** (90×60 mm), printed in rosine and bright blue. Containing ten 17p. (No. 1290Eu) with selvedge at top.

FT4	Datapost Service design..	3·75

The stamps from this booklet show double-lined letters "D" printed on the reverse over the gum.

No. FT4 is inscribed "September 1984".

1985 (8 Oct)–**86**. *Social Letter Writing Series* continued. Black and bright scarlet cover as Type FT **1** (90×49 mm). Containing ten 17p. (No. X952). A. Selvedge at left. B. Selvedge at right.

		A	B
FT5	Design No. 4, "Write Now" (Pillar box)	3·25	3·25
	a. Revised rates (2nd class (60g) 12p.) (1.86)........	24·00	16·00

1986 (29 Apr). *National Gallery.* Cover as Type FJ **5** (90×49 mm), printed in blue-green and blue. Containing ten 17p. (No. X952). A. Selvedge at left. B. Selvedge at right.

		A	B
FT6	National Gallery design.......................................	3·50	3·50

No. FT6 is inscribed "November 1985".

1986 (29 July). *Handwriting.* Cover as Type FJ **6** (90×49 mm) printed in red and bright blue. Containing ten 17p. (No. X952). A. Selvedge at left. B. Selvedge at right.

		A	B
FT7	"Yes"...	3·50	3·50

No. FT7 is inscribed "November 1985".

£1.80 Booklets

1986 (20 Oct). *Books for Children.* New blue and orange-brown cover as Type FL **7**. Containing ten 18p. (No. X955). A. Selvedge at left. B. Selvedge at right.

		A	B
FU1	Rabbits design...	3·75	3·75

1987 (27 Jan). *Keep in Touch.* Cover as Type FL **8** printed in magenta and bright blue. Containing ten 18p. (No. X955). A. Selvedge at left. B. Selvedge at right.

		A	B
FU2	Handclasp and envelope design	3·75	3·75

No. FU2 is inscribed "October 1986".

1987 (14 Apr). *Ideas for your Garden Claret and brown-olive cover as Type FL* **9** (90×49 mm). Containing ten 18p. stamps (No. X955). A. Selvedge at left. B. Selvedge at right.

		A	B
FU3	Garden path design...	3·75	5·00

No. FU3 is inscribed "October 1986".

1987 (14 July). *Brighter Writer* Turquoise-green and reddish orange cover as Type FL **10** (90×49 mm). Containing ten 18p. stamps (No. X955). A. Selvedge at left. B. Selvedge at right.

		A	B
FU4	Berries and leaves design.....................................	3·75	3·75

No. FU4 is inscribed "October 1986".

1987 (29 Sept). *Jolly Postman.* Cover as Type FL **11** (90×49 mm) printed in deep blue and claret. Containing ten 18p. stamps (No. X955). A. Selvedge at left. B. Selvedge at right.

		A	B
FU5	Girl drawing design...	3·75	3·75

No. FU5 is inscribed "October 1986".

1988 (26 Jan). *Bicentenary of Linnean Society.* Cover as Type FL **12** (90×49 mm) printed in dull yellow-green and dull claret. Containing ten 18p. stamps (No. X955). A. Selvedge at left. B. Selvedge at right.

		A	B
FU6	Wolf and birds (from "Hortus Sanitatis", 1497)	3·75	3·75
	a. Inside cover text for FL12.......................................	95·00	95·00

No. FU6 is inscribed "October 1986".

The inside cover text for FU6a has the special offer of the £1·30 booklet, No. FL12 (four 13p. stamps).

1988 (12 Apr). *Recipe Cards.* Cover as Type FL **13** (90×49 mm) printed in claret and Indian red. Containing ten 18p. stamps (No. X955). A. Selvedge at left. B. Selvedge at right.

		A	B
FU7	Fruits, pudding and jam design	3·75	3·75

No. FU7 is inscribed "October 1986".

1988 (5 July). *Children's Parties* Cover as Type FL **14** (90×49 mm) printed in violet and rosine. Containing ten 18p. stamps (No. X955). A. Selvedge at left. B. Selvedge at right.

		A	B
FU8	Balloons and party hats design................................	3·75	3·75

No. FU8 is inscribed "October 1986".

£1.90 Booklets

1988 (5 Sept). *Pocket Planner* Cover as Type FM **5** (90×49 mm) printed in yellow-green and magenta. Containing ten 19p. stamps (No. X956). A. Selvedge at left. B. Selvedge at right.

		A	B
FV1	"Marriage Act" design...	4·50	4·50

1989 (24 Jan). *150th Anniversary of Fox Talbot's Report on the Photographic Process to Royal Society.* Cover as Type FM **6** (90×49 mm) printed in emerald and black. Containing ten 19p. stamps (No. X956). A. Selvedge at left. B. Selvedge at right.

		A	B
FV2	Fox Talbot with camera and Lacock Abbey............	4·50	4·50

No. FV2 is inscribed "September 1988".

£2 Booklets

£2

Royal Mail Stamps

Eight at 25p

FW **1**

(Des Debbie Cook)

1993 (1 Nov)–**94**. *Postal Vehicles Series.* Covers as Type FW **1**. Containing eight 25p. (No. Y1689).

FW1	Design No. 1 (cover in dull vermilion and deep blue), Motorised cycle-carrier	3·25
FW2	Design No. 2 (cover in green and deep violet-blue), Experimental motor-mail van (26.4.94).................	3·25
FW3	Design No. 3 (cover in red and black), Experimental electric mail van, 1932 (6.9.94)	3·25

£2

Royal Mail Stamps

Eight at 25p

FW **3**

(Des The Four Hundred)

1995 (7 Feb–4 Apr). *Birth Bicentenary of Sir Rowland Hill.* Covers as Type FW **3**. Containing eight 25p. (No. Y1689).

FW4	Design No. 1 (cover in purple and new blue), Rowland Hill as director of London and Brighton Railway Company	3·25
FW5	Design No. 2 (cover in deep mauve and greenish blue), Rowland Hill and Hazlewood School (4.4.95)	3·25

1995 (6 June–4 Sept). *Birth Bicentenary of Sir Rowland Hill Series* continued. Covers as Type FW **3**. Containing eight 25p. (No. Y1690).

FW6	Design No. 3 (cover in deep blue-green and dull orange), Rowland Hill as Secretary to the Post Office........................	3·50
FW7	Design No. 4 (cover in red-brown and orange), Uniform Penny Postage petition and Mulready envelope (4.9.95).	3·50

1996 (16 Jan). MULTI COLOUR laminated cover as Type FH **40**. Stamps printed in litho by Questa.

FW8	Containing eight 25p. stamps (No. Y1775)............................	3·75

For an initial test period No. FW 8 was only available from machines at twelve post offices, five in London and seven in Scotland, in addition to philatelic outlets. Stocks were distributed nationally from May 1996.

1996 (8 July)–**97**. ⏐MULTI COLOUR laminated cover as Type FH **40**. Stamps printed in litho by Questa.
FW9   Containing booklet pane of No. Y1772l .... 3·75
    a. Corrected rate (4.2.97).. 3·75
    b. Inland rate table inside at right (5.5.98)......................... 3·75
    No. FW9 was reissued on 4 February 1997 showing the 200g second class rate on the inside cover altered from 47p. to 45p. A further printing issued 5 May 1998 was without the overseas postage rate table.

1998 (1 Dec). ⏐MULTI COLOUR laminated cover as Type FH **40**. Stamps printed in gravure by Questa.
FW10   Containing booklet pane of No. Y1685l .... 20·00

1999 (26 Apr). ⏐MULTI COLOUR laminated cover as Type FH **40**. Stamps printed in gravure by Questa.
FW11   Containing booklet pane of No. Y1682l .... 6·50

2000 (27 Apr). ⏐MULTI COLOUR laminated cover as Type FH **40**. Stamps printed in gravure by Questa.
FW12   Containing booklet pane of No. 1664m .... 6·25

Christmas Booklets

FX **1**

(Des J. Matthews)

1978 (15 Nov). *Christmas Greetings*. Cover Type FX **1** (90×49 mm). Printed in rose-red and sage-green.
FX1   £1.60, containing booklet pane No. X875l............................. 2·50
    No. FX1 is inscribed "August 1978".

FX **2**

(Des P. Sharland)

1979 (14 Nov). *Christmas Greetings*. Red and green cover as Type FX **2** (90×49 mm), showing Christmas cracker.
FX2   £1.80, containing booklet pane No. X879l .... 3·00
    No. FX2 is inscribed "October 1979".

FX **3**

(Des E. Fraser)

1980 (12 Nov). *Christmas*. Red and blue cover as Type FX **3** (90×49 mm), showing Nativity scene.
FX3   £2·20, containing booklet pane No. X888m .... 3·25
    No. FX3 is inscribed "September 1980".

FX **4**

(Des W. Sanderson)

1981 (11 Nov). *Christmas*. Red and blue cover as Type FX **4**, (90×49 mm), showing skating scene.
FX4   £2·55, containing booklet pane No. X893l .... 4·25
    No. FX4 is inscribed "January 1981".

FX **5**

(Des A. Davidson)

1982 (10 Nov). *Christmas*. Red and green cover as Type FX **5** (90×49 mm), showing Christmas Mummers.
FX5   £2·50, containing booklet pane No. X898l.............................. 5·00
    No. FX5 is inscribed "February 1982" and was sold at a discount of 30p. off the face value of the stamps.
    Each stamp in the pane has a blue star printed on the reverse over the gum.

FX **6**

(Des Barbara Brown)

1983 (9 Nov). *Christmas*. Brown-lilac and yellow cover as Type FX **6** (90×49 mm), showing pantomime scenes.
FX6   £2·20, containing twenty 12½p. (No. X898Ev) .... 4·50
    No. FX6 is inscribed "April 1983" and was sold at a discount of 30p. off the face value of the stamps.
    Each stamp in the pane has a double-lined blue star printed on the reverse over the gum.

FX **7**

(Des Yvonne Gilbert)

1984 (20 Nov). *Christmas*. Light brown and red-orange cover as Type FX 7 (90×60 mm), showing Nativity scene.
FX7   £2·30, containing twenty 13p. (No. 1267Eu).......................... 5·00

No. FX7 is inscribed "September 1984" and was sold at a discount of 30p. off the face value of the stamps.

The stamps from this booklet show double-lined blue stars printed on the reverse over the gum.

FX **8**

(Des A. George)

1985 (19 Nov). *Christmas.* Bright blue and rose cover as Type FX **8** (90×60 mm), showing The Pantomime.

FX8   £2·40, containing twenty 12p. (No. 1303Eu)......................... 4·50

The stamps from this booklet show double-lined blue stars printed on the reverse over the gum.

FX **9**

(Des Lynda Gray)

1986 (2 Dec). *Christmas.* Red and dull blue-green cover as Type FX **9** (90×49 mm), showing Shetland Yule cakes. A. Selvedge at left. B. Selvedge at right.

	A	B
FX9 £1·20, containing ten 13p. (No. X900Eu)	4·50	8·00

No. FX9 is inscribed "October 1986" and was sold at a discount of 10p. off the face value of the stamps.

Each stamp in the pane has a blue star printed on the reverse over the gum.

For 1990 and later Christmas stamps, see Barcode Booklets Section G.

£1.90 Greetings Booklet

FY **1**

(Des L. Moberly)

1989 (31 Jan). *Greetings Stamps.* Multi Colour cover as Type FY **1** (89×60 mm). Containing booklet pane No. 1423a, including twelve special greetings labels in a block (3×4) at right, attached by the selvedge.

FY1   Greetings design .... 24·00

No. FY1 is inscribed "September 1988".

The cover of No. FY **1** shows an overall pattern of elements taken from the stamp designs. Due to the method of production the position of these elements varies from cover to cover.

For Greetings stamps in Barcode booklets, see Barcode Booklets Section F.

III. BARCODE BOOKLETS

These booklets are listed in 11 sections.

SECTION C. G numbers containing Machin stamps with face values

SECTION D. H numbers containing Machin NVI stamps

SECTION E. J numbers containing Machin Penny Black Anniversary stamps

SECTION F. KX numbers containing Greetings stamps

SECTION G. LX numbers containing Christmas stamps

SECTION H. M numbers containing self-adhesive NVI definitive stamps

SECTION I. N numbers containing self-adhesive definitive stamps with face values

SECTION J. PM numbers containing both special and definitive self-adhesive NVI stamps

SECTION K. Q numbers containing NVI "Smilers" stamps in definitive size

SECTION L. R numbers containing stamps with value indicator at upper left

SECTION M. SA numbers containing NVI "Smilers" stamps and definitive stamps.

These are produced for sale in both post offices and commercial outlets.

NOTE: All panes are attached to the covers by the selvedge. Barcode booklet covers are illustrated at two-thirds linear size *unless otherwise stated.*

C. Barcode Booklets containing Machin stamps with values shown as Type 367.

COVERS. These are all printed in scarlet, lemon and black with the barcode on the reverse. Type GA **1** has a clear "window" to view the contents. Type GB **3** is shorter and has a stamp illustration printed on the cover to replace the "window". These illustrations show an oblique white line across the bottom right-hand corner of the "stamp". Unless otherwise stated all covers were printed by Harrison.

From early 1997 the printer of each booklet is identified by a small capital letter below the barcode on the outside back cover.

52p. Booklet

GA **1**

1987 (4 Aug). Laminated cover Type GA **1** (75×60 mm).
GA1   Containing booklet pane No. X900n .... 2·25
    No. GA1 is inscribed "20 October 1986".

56p. Booklets

1988 (23 Aug). Laminated cover as Type GA **1** (75×56 mm).
GB1   Containing booklet pane No. X903l .... 3·50
1988 (11 Oct). Laminated cover as Type GA **1** (75×56 mm) printed by Walsall.
GB2   Containing booklet pane No. X903l .... 5·25

GB **3** Large Crown

1988 (11 Oct). Laminated cover as Type GB **3** (75×48 mm) with stamp printed on the cover in deep blue.
GB3   Containing booklet pane No. X903n .... 4·00
    No. GB3 is inscribed "5 September 1988" and has the horizontal edges of the pane imperforate.

1989 (24 Jan). Laminated cover as Type GB **3** (75×48 mm) with stamp printed on the cover in deep blue by Walsall.
GB4   Containing booklet pane No. X903q .... 20·00
    No. GB4 is inscribed "5 September 1988" and has the three edges of the pane imperforate.

72p. Booklet

1987 (4 Aug). Laminated cover as Type GA **1** (75×60 mm).
GC1   Containing booklet pane No. X955m .... 2·25
    No. GC1 is inscribed "20 October 1986".

76p. Booklets

1988 (23 Aug). Laminated cover as Type GA **1** (75×56 mm).
GD1   Containing booklet pane No. X956l .... 4·00

1988 (11 Oct). Laminated cover as Type GA **1** (75×56 mm) printed by Walsall.
GD2   Containing booklet pane No. X956l .... 4·25

1988 (11 Oct). Laminated cover as Type GB **3** (75×48 mm) with stamp printed on the cover in bright orange-red.
GD3   Containing booklet pane No. X956n .... 5·00
    No. GD3 is inscribed "5 September 1988" and has the horizontal edges of the pane imperforate.

1989 (24 Jan). Laminated cover as Type GB **3** (75×48 mm) with stamp printed on the cover in bright orange-red by Walsall.
GD4   Containing booklet pane No. X956q .... 20·00
    No. GD4 is inscribed "5 September 1988" and has the three edges of the pane imperforate.

78p. Booklet

GD **4a** (As Type GM **1** but without "4")

1992 (28 July). MULTI COLOUR laminated cover as Type GD **4**a (75×49 mm) with stamp printed on the cover in bright mauve by Walsall.
GD4a   Containing two 39p. stamps (No. X1058)
    (pane No. X1058l with right-hand vert pair removed) and pane of 4 air mail labels .... 2·00
    Stamps in No. GD4a have top or bottom edge imperforate. Booklet No. GD4a was produced in connection with a Kellogg's Bran Flakes promotion.

£1.04 Booklet

1987 (4 Aug). Laminated cover as Type GA **1** (75×60 mm).
GE1   Containing booklet pane No. X971bl .... 10·00
    No. GE1 is inscribed "20 October 1986".

£1.08 Booklets

1988 (23 Aug). Laminated cover as Type GA **1** (75×56 mm).
GF1   Containing booklet pane No. X973l .... 8·00
    a. Postage rates omitted from inside back cover .... 20·00

1988 (11 Oct). Laminated cover as Type GB **3** (75×48 mm) with stamp printed on the cover in chestnut.
GF2   Containing booklet pane No. X973m .... 30·00
    No. GF2 is inscribed "5 September 1988" and has the horizontal edges of the pane imperforate.

£1.16 Booklets

GG **1** Redrawn Crown

1989 (2 Oct). Laminated cover as Type GG **1** (75×48 mm) with stamp printed on the cover in deep mauve by Walsall.

GG1   Containing booklet pane No. X1054l .... 12·00
    No. GG1 has three edges of the pane imperforate.

1990 (17 Apr). Laminated cover as Type GG **1** (75×48 mm) with stamp printed on the cover in deep mauve by Walsall.

GG2   Containing booklet pane No. X1055l .... 12·00
    No. GG2 has three edges of the pane imperforate.

£1.20 Booklets

GGA **1** ("BY AIR MAIL *par avion*" at bottom left)

1998 (5 May). |MULTI COLOUR laminated cover as Type GGA **1** (75×50 mm) with stamps printed on cover in olive-grey by Walsall. Inscr For items up to 20g" on yellow tab at right.

GGA1   Containing four 30p. (gravure) (No. Y1694) and a pane of 4 air mail labels .... 2·25

GGA **2** "Create a card Design"

1998 (3 Aug). |MULTI COLOUR laminated cover as Type GGA **2** (75×50 mm) printed by Walsall. Inscr See inside for offer details" on yellow tab at right.

GGA2   Containing four 30p. (gravure) (No. Y1694) and a pane of 4 air mail labels .... 2·25
    This booklet was not placed on philatelic sale until 7 September 1998.

£1.24 Booklet

GH **1** Crown on White

1990 (17 Sept). |MULTI COLOUR laminated cover as Type GH **1** (75×49 mm) with stamp printed on the cover in ultramarine by Walsall.

GH1   Containing booklet pane No. X1056l .... 4·00
    No. GH1 has the horizontal edges of the pane imperforate.

£1.30 Booklet

1987 (4 Aug). Laminated cover as Type GA **1** (98×60 mm).

GI1   Containing booklet pane No. X900o .... 3·50
    No. GI1 is inscribed "20 October 1986".

£1.32 Booklet

GJ **1**

1991 (16 Sept)–**92**. |MULTI COLOUR laminated cover as Type GJ **1** (75×49 mm) with stamp printed on the cover in light emerald by Walsall. Inscr For letters up to 10g" on yellow strip at right.

GJ1   Containing booklet pane No. X1057l and a pane of 4 air mail labels .... 3·50
    a. Inscr "For Worldwide Postcards" on yellow strip (8.9.92)   7·00
    Nos. GJ1/a have the horizontal edges of the pane imperforate.

£1.40 Booklets

1988 (23 Aug). Laminated cover as Type GA **1** (97×56 mm).

GK1   Containing booklet pane No. X903m .... 8·50

1988 (11 Oct). Laminated cover as Type GA **1** (97×56 mm) printed by Questa.

GK2   Containing ten 14p. (No. X1007) .... 8·50

1988 (11 Oct). Laminated cover as Type GB **3** (75×48 mm) with stamp printed on the cover in deep blue.

GK3   Containing booklet pane No. X903p .... 5·50
    No. GK3 is inscribed "5 September 1988" and has horizontal edges of the pane imperforate.

1988 (11 Oct). Laminated cover as Type GB **3** (75×48 mm) with stamp printed on the cover in deep blue by Questa.

GK4   Containing ten 14p. (No. X1007) .... 10·00

1993 (1 Nov). Laminated cover as Type GJ **1** (76×50 mm) with stamp printed on the cover in yellow by Walsall. Inscribed "For Worldwide Postcards" on yellow tab at right.

GK5   Containing four 35p. (No. Y1778) and a pane of 4 air mail labels .... 3·25

Type GK **6** (without diagonal white line across corners of stamps)

1995 (16 May). |MULTI COLOUR laminated cover as Type GK **6** (75×48 mm) with stamps printed on the cover in yellow by Walsall.

GK6   Containing four 35p. (No. Y1778) and a pane of 4 air mail labels .... 3·25

1996 (19 Mar). |MULTI COLOUR laminated cover as Type GK **6** (75×48 mm) without *International* and showing Olympic symbols on the back. Stamps printed on the cover in yellow by Walsall.

GK7   Containing four 35p. (No. Y1778) and a pane of 4 air mail labels .... 3·50

£1.48 Booklets

GL **1** ("Worldwide Postcard Stamps" ranged left without diagonal white lines across corner of stamps)

1996 (8 July). |MULTI COLOUR laminated cover as Type GL **1** (75×48 mm) showing Olympic symbols on the back. Stamps printed on the cover in bright mauve by Walsall. Inscribed For Worldwide Postcards on yellow tab at right.

GL1   Containing four 37p. (No. Y1779) and a pane of 4 air mail labels .... 5·25

1997 (4 Feb). |MULTI COLOUR| laminated cover as Type GL **1** (75×48 mm) without Olympic symbols on the back. Stamps printed on the cover in bright mauve by Walsall. Inscribed *For Worldwide Postcards* on yellow tab at right.
GL2   Containing four 37p. (No. Y1779) and a pane of 4 air mail labels .... 5·25

GL **3**

1997 (26 Aug)–**98**. |MULTI COLOUR| laminated cover as Type GL **3** (75×48 mm) printed by Walsall. Inscribed *For Worldwide Postcards* on yellow tab at right.
GL3   Containing four 37p. (gravure) (No. Y1703) and a pane of 4 new design air mail labels .... 3·50
         a. Showing validity notice on inside backcover (5.5.98).... 3·50
    No. GL3 has the postage rate table on the inside back cover.

1998 (3 Aug). |MULTI COLOUR| laminated cover as Type GGA **2** (Create a card design) (75×50 mm) printed by Walsall.
GL4   Containing four 37p. (gravure) (No. Y1703) and a pane of 4 air mail labels .... 5·00
    This booklet was not placed on philatelic sale until 7 September 1998.

£1.52 Booklet

1999 (26 Apr). |MULTI COLOUR| laminated cover as Type GGA **1** (76×50 mm) with stamps printed on cover in ultramarine by Walsall. Inscr *For Worldwide Postcards* on yellow tab at right.
GLA1   Containing four 38p. (gravure) (No. Y1707) and a pane of 4 air mail labels .... 3·25

£1.56 Booklet

GM **1**

1991 (16 Sept). |MULTI COLOUR| laminated cover as Type GM **1** (75×49 mm) with stamp printed on the cover in bright mauve by Walsall.
GM1   Containing booklet pane No. X1058l and a pane of 4 air mail labels .... 5·75
    No. GM1 has the horizontal edges of the pane imperforate.

£1.60 Booklet

2000 (27 Apr). |MULTI COLOUR| laminated cover as Type GGA **1** (76×50 mm) with stamps printed on cover in deep azure by Walsall. Inscr *For Worldwide Postcards* on yellow tab at right.
GMA1   Containing four 40p. (gravure) (No. Y1710) and a pane of 4 air mail labels .... 4·00

£1.64 Worldwide Air Mail Stamps Booklets

1993 (1 Nov). Laminated cover as Type GM **1** (76×50 mm) with stamp printed on the cover in drab by Walsall. Inscribed *For letters up to 10g* on yellow tab at right.
GN1   Containing four 41p. (No. Y1780) and a pane of 4 air mail labels .... 3·00

1995 (16 May). |MULTI COLOUR| laminated cover as Type GK **6** (75×48 mm) with stamps printed on the cover in drab by Walsall. Inscribed *For items up to 10g* on yellow tab at right.
GN2   Containing four 41p. (No. Y1780) and a pane of 4 air mail labels .... 3·00

1996 (19 Mar). |MULTI COLOUR| laminated cover as Type GK **6** (75×48 mm) without *International* and showing Olympic symbols on the back. Stamps printed on the cover in drab by Walsall. Inscribed *For items up to 10g* on yellow tab at right.
GN3   Containing four 41p. (No. Y1780) and a pane of 4 air mail labels .... 3·00

£1.80 Booklet

1987 (4 Aug). Laminated cover as Type GA **1** (98×60 mm).
GO1   Containing booklet pane No. X955n .... 4·75
    No. GO1 is inscribed "20 October 1986".

£1.90 Booklets

1988 (23 Aug). Laminated cover as Type GA **1** (97×56 mm).
GP1   Containing booklet pane No. X956m .... 6·50

1988 (11 Oct). Laminated cover as Type GA **1** (97×56 mm) printed by Questa.
GP2   Containing ten 19p. (No. X1013) .... 12·50

1988 (11 Oct). Laminated cover as Type GB **3** (75×48 mm) with stamp printed on the cover in bright orange-red.
GP3   Containing booklet pane No. X956o .... 6·50
    No. GP 3 is inscribed "5 September 1988" and has the horizontal edges of the pane imperforate.

1988 (11 Oct). Laminated cover as Type GB **3** (75×48 mm) with stamp printed on the cover in bright orange-red by Questa.
GP4   Containing ten 19p. (No. X1013) .... 12·50

£2.40 Booklets

1994 (9 Aug). Laminated cover as Type GM **1** (75×49 mm) with stamp printed on the cover in dull blue-grey by Walsall. Inscribed *items up to 20g* on yellow tab at right.
GQ1   Containing four 60p. (No. Y1784) and a pane of 4 air mail labels .... 4·50

GQ **2**

1994 (4 Oct). Laminated cover as Type GQ **2** (75×49 mm) with stamp printed on the cover in dull blue-grey by Walsall.
GQ2   Containing four 60p. (No. Y1784) and a pane of 4 air mail plus 4 "Seasons Greetings" labels .... 4·75

1995 (16 May). Laminated cover as Type GK **6** (75×48 mm) with stamps printed on the cover in dull blue-grey by Walsall. Inscribed *For items up to 20g* on yellow tab at right.
GQ3   Containing four 60p. (No. Y1784) and a pane of 4 air mail labels .... 4·75

1996 (19 Mar). |MULTI COLOUR| laminated cover as Type GK **6** (75×48 mm) without *International* and showing Olympic symbols on the back. Stamps printed on the cover in dull grey blue by Walsall. Inscribed *For items up to 20g* on yellow tab at right.
GQ4   Containing four 60p. (No. Y1784) and a pane of 4 air mail labels .... 4·75

£2.52 Booklets

1996 (8 July). |MULTI COLOUR| laminated cover as Type GL **1** (75×48 mm) but inscr *Worldwide Airmail Stamps* and showing Olympic symbols on the back. Stamps printed on the cover in light emerald by Walsall. Inscribed *For items up to 20g* on yellow tab at right.
GR1   Containing four 63p. (No. Y1787) and a pane of 4 air mail labels .... 8·00

1997 (4 Feb). |MULTI COLOUR| laminated cover as Type GL **1** (75×48 mm) without Olympic symbols on the back. Stamps printed on the cover in light emerald by Walsall. Inscribed *For items up to 20g* on yellow tab at right.
GR2   Containing four 63p. (No. Y1787) and a pane of 4 air mail labels .... 8·00

1997 (26 Aug). |MULTI COLOUR| laminated cover as Type GL **1** (75×48 mm). Stamps printed on the cover in light emerald by Walsall. Inscribed *For items up to 20g* on yellow tab at right.
GR3   Containing four 63p. (gravure) (No. Y1732) and a pane of 4 air mail labels .... 5·00

1998 (5 May). |MULTI COLOUR| laminated cover as Type GGA **1** (75×50 mm). Stamps printed on the cover in light emerald by Walsall. Inscribed *For items up to 20g* on yellow tab at right.
GR4   Containing four 63p. (gravure) (No. Y1732) and a pane of 4 new design air mail labels .... 5·00

£2.56 Booklets

1999 (26 Apr). |MULTI COLOUR| laminated cover as Type GGA **1** (75×50 mm). Stamps printed on cover in turquoise-green by Walsall. Inscribed *For items up to 20g* on yellow tab at right.

GS1   Containing four 64p. (gravure) (No. Y1733) and a pane of 4 air mail labels .... 5·25

£2.60 Booklet

2000 (27 Apr). |MULTI COLOUR| laminated cover as Type GGA **1** (76×50 mm) with stamps printed on cover in greenish blue by Walsall. Inscr *For items up to 20g* on yellow tab at right.

GT1   Containing four 65p. (gravure) (No. Y1734) and a pane of 4 air mail labels .... 6·00

D. Barcode Booklets containing No Value Indicated stamps with barcodes on the back cover.

Panes of four 2nd Class stamps.

HA **1** Redrawn Crown (small)

1989 (22 Aug). Laminated cover as Type HA **1** (75×48 mm) with stamp printed on the cover in bright blue by Walsall.

HA1   (56p) Containing booklet pane No. 1449b .... 4·25
    No. HA1 has three edges of the pane imperforate.

1989 (28 Nov). Laminated cover as Type HA **1** (75×48 mm) with stamp printed on the cover in bright blue by Walsall containing stamps printed in gravure by Harrison.

HA2   (60p) Containing booklet pane No. 1445b .... 24·00
    No. HA2 has three edges of the pane imperforate.

HA **3** Crown on white

1990 (7 Aug). |MULTI COLOUR| laminated cover as Type HA **3** (75×48 mm) with stamp printed on the cover in deep blue by Walsall.

HA3   (60p) Containing booklet pane No. 1515a .... 3·50
    No. HA3 has the horizontal edges of the pane imperforate.

1991 (6 Aug). |MULTI COLOUR| laminated cover as Type HA **3** (75×48 mm) with stamp printed on the cover in bright blue by Walsall (25.9.92). Barcode in black.

HA4   (68p) Containing booklet pane No. 1449c .... 3·50
    a. Barcode printed in blue .... 3·50
    No. HA4 has the horizontal edges of the pane imperforate and exists with the barcode printed in either black or blue.

HA **5** Olympic Symbols

1992 (21 Jan). |MULTI COLOUR| laminated cover as Type HA **5** (75×48 mm) with stamp printed on the cover in bright blue by Walsall.

HA5   (72p) Containing booklet pane No. 1449c .... 3·75
    No. HA5 has the horizontal edges of the pane imperforate.

PERFORATIONS. Booklets from No. HA6 show perforations on all edges of the pane.

1993 (6 Apr). |MULTI COLOUR| laminated cover as Type HA **3** (75×48 mm) with stamp printed on the cover in bright blue by Walsall.

HA6   (72p) Containing four 2nd Class stamps (No. 1670) .... 3·25
    No. HA6 was re-issued on 6 December 1994 showing the inscriptions on the inside of the cover re-arranged.

1993 (7 Sept). |MULTI COLOUR| laminated cover as Type HA **3** (75×48 mm) with stamp printed on the cover in bright blue by Harrison.

HA7   (72p) Containing four 2nd Class stamps (No. 1664) .... 3·25

Type HA **8** ("Second Class Stamps" centred) (with diagonal white line across corners of stamps)

1995 (10 Jan). |MULTI COLOUR| laminated cover as Type HA **8** (75×48 mm) with stamps printed on the cover in bright blue by Harrison.

HA8   (76p) Containing four 2nd Class stamps (No. 1664) .... 3·25

1995 (12 Dec). |MULTI COLOUR| laminated cover as Type HA **8** (75×48 mm) with stamps printed on the cover in bright blue by Walsall, but without *Pull Open* inscription on yellow tab.

HA9   (76p) Containing four 2nd Class stamps (No. 1670) .... 3·25
    No. HA9 was initially sold at 76p, which was increased to 80p. from 8.7.96.

1996 (6 Feb). |MULTI COLOUR| laminated cover as Type HA **8** (75×48 mm) but without *Pull Open* inscription on yellow tab and showing Olympic symbols on the back. Stamps printed on the cover in bright blue by Walsall.

HA10   (76p) Containing four 2nd Class stamps (No. 1670)........... 3·25

NOTE: From No. HA11 onwards, the printer of each booklet is identified by a small capital letter below the barcode on the outside back cover.

HA **11** ("Second Class Stamps" ranged left) (without diagonal white line across corners of stamps)

1997 (4 Feb). |MULTI COLOUR| laminated cover as Type HA **11** (75×48 mm). Stamps printed on the cover in bright blue by Walsall.

HA11 (80p) Containing four 2nd Class stamps (No. 1670) .... 3·25

1997 (26 Aug). |MULTI COLOUR| laminated cover as Type HA **11** (75×48 mm). Stamps printed on the cover in bright blue by Walsall.

HA12 (80p) Containing four 2nd Class stamps (gravure)   3·25
    (No. 1664) ....
    No. HA12 was re-issued on 5 May 1998 showing the positions of the imprint and the post code notice transposed, and again on 14 March 2000 with changed telephone number and added website address.

Panes of four 1st Class stamps

1989 (22 Aug). Laminated cover as Type HA **1** (75×48 mm) with stamp printed on the cover in brownish black by Walsall.

HB1 (76p) Containing booklet pane No. 1450a .... 4·75

No. HB1 has three edges of the pane imperforate.

No. HB1 was initially sold at 76p., which was increased to 80p. from 2.10.89.

1989 (5 Dec). Laminated cover as Type HA **1** (75×48 mm) with stamp printed on the cover in brownish black by Walsall containing stamps printed in photo by Harrison.

HB2 (80p) Containing booklet pane No. 1447b .... 25·00

No. HB2 has three edges of the pane imperforate.

1990 (7 Aug). |MULTI COLOUR| laminated cover as Type HA **3** (75×48 mm) with stamp printed on the cover in bright orange-red by Walsall (22.9.92). Barcode in black.

HB3 (80p) Containing booklet pane No. 1516a .... 4·00
   a. Containing pane No. 1516ca .... 10·00
   b. Barcode in blue .... 4·00

No. HB3 has the horizontal edges of the pane imperforate.

1992 (21 Jan). |MULTI COLOUR| laminated cover as Type HA **5** (75×48 mm) with stamp printed on the cover in bright orange-red by Walsall.

HB4 (96p) Containing booklet pane No. 1516a .... 4·00

No. HB4 has the horizontal edges of the pane imperforate.

PERFORATIONS. Booklets from No. HB5 show perforations on all edges of the pane.

1993 (6 Apr). |MULTI COLOUR| laminated cover as Type HA **3** (75×48 mm) with stamp printed on the cover in bright orange-red by Harrison.

HB5 (96p) Containing four 1st Class stamps (No. 1666) .... 4·00

1993 (17 Aug). |MULTI COLOUR| laminated cover as Type HA **3** (76×50 mm) with stamp printed on the cover in bright orange-red by Walsall.

HB6 (96p) Containing four 1st Class stamps (No. 1671) .... 4·00

No. HB6 was reissued on 1 November 1993 with changes to the inside-cover text.

1994 (27 July). |MULTI COLOUR| laminated cover as Type HA **3** (76×50 mm) with stamp printed on the cover in bright orange-red by Questa.

HB7 (£1·00) Containing booklet pane No. 1671l which includes a label commemorating the 300th anniv of the Bank of England .... 5·50

1995 (10 Jan). |MULTI COLOUR| laminated cover as Type HA **8** (75×48 mm) with stamps printed on the cover in bright orange-red by Walsall.

HB8 (£1·00) Containing four 1st Class stamps (No. 1671) .... 4·00

1995 (16 May). |MULTI COLOUR| laminated cover as Type HA **8** (75×48 mm) with stamps printed on the cover in bright orange-red by Walsall.

HB9 (£1·00) Containing booklet pane No. 1671la which includes a label commemorating the birth centenary of R. J. Mitchell (designer of Spitfire) .... 4·25

1996 (6 Feb–Aug). |MULTI COLOUR| laminated cover as Type HA **8** (75×48 mm) showing Olympic symbols on the back. Stamps printed on the cover in bright orange-red by Walsall.

HB10 (£1·00) Containing four 1st Class stamps (No. 1671) .... 4·00
   a. Without diagonal white line across corners of stamps (Aug) £125

1996 (16 Apr). |MULTI COLOUR| laminated cover as Type HA **11** (75×48 mm) with stamps printed on the cover in bright orange-red by Walsall. Inscribed Commemorative Label Inside" on yellow tab at right.

HB11 (£1·00) Containing booklet pane No. 1671la (includes label commemorating the 70th birthday of Queen Elizabeth II) 4·00

NOTE: From No. HB12 onwards, the printer of each booklet (with the exception of No. HB19) is identified by a small capital letter below the barcode on the outside back cover.

1997 (4 Feb). |MULTI COLOUR| laminated cover as Type HA **11** (75×48 mm). Stamps printed on the cover in bright orange-red by Walsall.

HB12 (£1·04) Containing four 1st Class stamps (No. 1671) .... 4·00

1997 (12 Feb). |MULTI COLOUR| laminated cover as Type HA **11** (75×48 mm). Stamps printed on the cover in bright orange-red by Walsall. Inscribed 'Special Label Inside on yellow tab at right'.

HB13 (£1·04) Containing booklet pane No. 1671la (includes label commemorating Hong Kong '97 international stamp exhibition) .... 4·50

1997 (26 Aug). |MULTI COLOUR| laminated cover as Type HA **11** (75×48 mm). Stamps printed on the cover in bright orange-red by Walsall.

HB14 (£1·04) Containing four 1st Class stamps (gravure) 5·00
(No. 1667) ....

No. HB14 was re-issued on 5 May 1998 showing the positions of the imprint and the post code notice transposed, on 16 March 1999 with "Please note that the First Class rate is no longer valid to Europe" added to inside back cover and again on 14 March 2000 with changed telephone number and added website address.

1997 (21 Oct). |MULTI COLOUR| laminated cover as Type HA **11** (75×48 mm). Stamps printed on the cover in bright orange-red by Walsall. Inscribed "Commemorative Label Inside" on yellow tab at right.

HB15 (£1·04) Containing booklet pane No. 1671la (litho) (includes label commemorating Commonwealth Heads of Government Meeting, Edinburgh) .... 6·25

1998 (14 Nov). |MULTI COLOUR| laminated cover as Type HA **11** (75×48 mm). Stamps printed on the cover in bright orange-red by Walsall. Inscribed *Commemorative Label Inside* on yellow tab at right.

HB16 (£1·04) Containing booklet pane No. 1671la (litho) (includes label commemorating 50th birthday of the Prince of Wales) .... 4·75

1999 (12 May). |MULTI COLOUR| laminated cover as Type HA **11** (75×48 mm). Stamps printed on the cover in bright orange-red by Walsall. Inscribed *Commemorative Label Inside* on yellow tab at right.

HB17 (£1·04) Containing booklet pane No. 1667m (gravure) (includes label commemorating 50th anniv of Berlin Airlift) .... 5·25

1999 (1 Oct). |MULTI COLOUR| laminated cover as Type HA **11** (76×50 mm). Stamps printed on the cover in bright orange-red by Walsall. Inscribed *Commemorative Label Inside* on yellow tab at right.

HB18 (£1·04) Containing booklet pane No. 1667m (gravure) (includes label commemorating Rugby World Cup) .... 4·50

2000 (21 Mar). |MULTI COLOUR| laminated cover as Type HA **11** (75×48 mm). Stamps printed on the cover in olive-brown by Walsall with Postman Pat. Inscribed *Postman Pat Label Inside* on yellow tab at right.

HB19 (£1·04) Containing booklet pane No. 2124bl (gravure) (includes label commemorating "Stamp Show 2000", Earls Court) .... 4·50

2000 (4 Apr). *Opening of National Botanic Garden of Wales.* |MULTI COLOUR| laminated cover as Type HA **11** (75×48 mm). Stamps printed on the cover in olive-brown by Walsall. Inscribed *Botanic Garden Label Inside* on yellow tab at right.

HB20 (£1·04) Containing booklet pane No. 2124bl .... 4·50

Panes of eight 1st Class stamps plus pane of 2 Millennium commemoratives

HBA **1**

1999 (12 May). |MULTI COLOUR| laminated cover as Type HBA **1** (76×50 mm) showing Millennium and Machin stamps printed by Walsall.

HBA1 (£2·60) Containing booklet pane No. 2085a and eight 1st Class stamps (gravure) (No. 1667) .... 8·50

1999 (21 Sept). |MULTI COLOUR| laminated cover as Type HBA **1** (76×50 mm) showing Millennium and Machin stamps printed by Walsall.

HBA2 (£2·60) Containing booklet pane No. 2108a and eight 1st Class stamps (gravure) (No. 1667) .... 8·50

2000 (26 May). |MULTI COLOUR| laminated cover as Type HBA **1** (76×50 mm) showing Millennium and Machin stamps printed by Walsall.

HBA3 (£2·70) Containing booklet pane No. 2126ab and eight 1st Class stamps (gravure) (No. 2124) .... 9·00

2000 (18 Sept). |MULTI COLOUR| laminated cover as Type HBA **1** (76×50 mm) showing Millennium and Machin stamps printed by Walsall.

HBA4 (£2·70) Containing booklet pane No. 2153a and eight 1st Class stamps (gravure) (No. 2124) .... 9·00

Panes of ten 2nd Class stamps

1989 (22 Aug–2 Oct). Laminated cover as Type HA **1** (75×48 mm) with stamp printed on the cover in bright blue by Harrison.

HC1 (£1·40) Containing booklet pane No. 1445a .... 9·00
   a. Inside cover with new rates (2 Oct) .... 9·50

Nos. HC1/a have the horizontal edges of the pane imperforate.

1989 (19 Sept). Laminated cover as Type HA **1** (75×48 mm) with stamp printed on the cover in bright blue by Questa.

HC2 (£1·40) Containing ten 2nd Class stamps (No. 1451) .... 8·50

No. HC2 has perforations on all edges of the pane.

1990 (7 Aug). |MULTI COLOUR| laminated cover as Type HA **3** (75×48 mm) with stamp printed on the cover in deep blue by Harrison.

HC3 (£1·50) Containing booklet pane No. 1511a .... 9·50

No. HC3 has the horizontal edges of the pane imperforate.

1990 (7 Aug). |MULTI COLOUR| laminated cover as Type HA **3** (75×48 mm) with stamp printed on the cover in deep blue by Questa.

HC4 (£1·50) Containing ten 2nd Class stamps (No. 1513) .... 10·00

No. HC4 has perforations on all edges of the pane.

1990 (7 Aug). |MULTI COLOUR| laminated cover as Type HA **3** (75×48 mm) with stamp printed on the cover in deep blue by Walsall.

HC5 (£1·50) Containing booklet pane No. 1515b .... 7·50

No. HC5 has the horizontal edges of the pane imperforate.

1991 (6 Aug). |MULTI COLOUR| laminated cover as Type HA **3** (75×48 mm) with stamp printed on the cover in bright blue by Questa. Barcode in black.

HC6	(£1·70) Containing ten 2nd Class stamps (No. 1451)	7·50
	a. Barcode printed in blue (22.9.92)..	7·50

No. HC6 has perforations on all edges of the pane. No. HC6a was sold at £1·80.

1991 (6 Aug). |MULTI COLOUR| laminated cover as Type HA **3** (75×48 mm) with stamp printed on the cover in bright blue by Walsall. Barcode in black.

HC7	(£1·70) Containing booklet pane No. 1449d	7·50
	a. Barcode printed in blue (22.9.92)..	7·50

No. HC7 has the horizontal edges of the pane imperforate. No. HC7a was sold at £1·80.

1992 (21 Jan). |MULTI COLOUR| laminated cover as Type HA **5** (75×48 mm) with stamp printed on the cover in bright blue by Walsall.

HC8	(£1·80) Containing booklet pane No. 1449d	7·50

No. HC8 has the horizontal edges of the pane imperforate.

1992 (31 Mar). |MULTI COLOUR| laminated cover as Type HA **5** (75×48 mm) with stamp printed on the cover in bright blue by Questa.

HC9	(£1·80) Containing ten 2nd Class stamps (No. 1451)	7·75

No. HC9 has perforations on all edges of the pane.

1992 (22 Sept). |MULTI COLOUR| laminated cover as Type HA **3** (75×48 mm) with stamp printed on the cover in bright blue by Harrison.

HC10	(£1·80) Containing booklet pane No. 1445a	7·50

No. HC10 has the horizontal edges of the pane imperforate.

PERFORATIONS. Booklets from No. HC11 show perforations on all edges of the pane.

1993 (6 Apr). |MULTI COLOUR| laminated cover as Type HA **3** (75×48 mm) with stamp printed on the cover in bright blue by Questa.

HC11	(£1·80) Containing ten 2nd Class stamps (No. 1670)	7·50

No. HC11 was re-issued on 17 August 1993 showing changes to the text on the inside of the cover and again on 6 September 1994 showing further changes.

1993 (1 Nov). |MULTI COLOUR| laminated cover as Type HA **3** (75×48 mm) with stamp printed on the cover in bright blue by Walsall.

HC12	(£1·90) Containing ten 2nd Class stamps (No. 1670)	8·00

1995 (10 Jan). |MULTI COLOUR| laminated cover as Type HA **8** (75×48 mm) with stamps printed on the cover in bright blue by Questa.

HC13	(£1·90) Containing ten 2nd Class stamps (No. 1670)	8·00

1995 (12 Dec). |MULTI COLOUR| laminated cover as Type HA **8** (75×48 mm) with stamps printed on cover in bright blue by Harrison.

HC14	(£1·90) Containing ten 2nd Class stamps (No. 1664)	7·50

1996 (6 Feb). |MULTI COLOUR| laminated cover as Type HA **8** (75×48 mm) showing Olympic symbols on the back. Stamps printed on the cover in bright blue by Harrison.

HC15	(£1·90) Containing ten 2nd Class stamps (No. 1664)..........	7·50

1996 (6 Feb). |MULTI COLOUR| laminated cover as Type HA **8** (75×48 mm) showing Olympic symbols on the back. Stamps printed on the cover in bright blue by Questa.

HC16	(£1·90) Containing ten 2nd Class stamps (No. 1670)	8·50

NOTE: From No. HC17 onwards, the printer of each booklet is identified by a small capital letter below the barcode on the outside back cover.

1996 (6 Aug). |MULTI COLOUR| laminated cover as Type HA **8** (75×48 mm) but with diagonal white lines across corners of stamps, showing Olympic symbols on the back. Stamps printed on the cover in bright blue by Harrison.

HC17	(£2·00) Containing ten 2nd Class stamps (No. 1664)	7·50

1996 (6 Aug). |MULTI COLOUR| laminated cover as Type HA **11** (75×48 mm) showing Olympic symbols on the back. Stamps printed on the cover in bright blue by Questa.

HC18	(£2·00) Containing ten 2nd Class stamps (No. 1670)	8·00

1997 (4 Feb). |MULTI COLOUR| laminated cover as Type HA **11** (75×48 mm). Stamps printed on the cover in bright blue by Harrison.

HC19	(£2·00) Containing ten 2nd Class stamps (No. 1664)..........	7·50

1997 (4 Feb). |MULTI COLOUR| laminated cover as Type HA **11** (75×48 mm). Stamps printed on the cover in bright blue by Questa.

HC20	(£2·00) Containing ten 2nd Class stamps (No. 1670)	7·50

No. HC20 was re-issued on 5 May 1998 showing the positions of the imprint and the post code notice transposed.

1998 (5 May). |MULTI COLOUR| laminated cover as Type HA **11** (75×48 mm). Stamps printed on the cover in bright blue by De La Rue.

HC21	(£2·00) Containing ten 2nd Class stamps (No. 1664)	7·50

1998 (1 Dec). |MULTI COLOUR| laminated cover as Type HA **11** (75×48 mm). Stamps printed on the cover in bright blue by Questa.

HC22	(£2·00) Containing ten 2nd Class stamps (No. 1664a) (gravure)	9·50

No. HC22 was re-issued on 14 March 2000 with changed telephone number and added website address.

Panes of ten 1st Class stamps

1989 (22 Aug–2 Oct). Laminated cover as Type HA **1** (75×48 mm) with stamp printed on the cover in brownish black by Harrison.

HD1	(£1·90) Containing booklet pane No. 1447a	11·00
	a. Inside cover with new rates (2 Oct)	11·00

Nos. HD1/a have the horizontal edges of the pane imperforate. No. HD1a was sold at £2.

1989 (19 Sept). Laminated cover as Type HA **1** (75×48 mm) with stamp printed on the cover in brownish black by Questa.

HD2	(£1·90) Containing ten 1st Class stamps (No. 1452)	13·00

No. HD2 has perforations on all edges of the pane.

1990 (7 Aug). |MULTI COLOUR| laminated cover as Type HA **3** (75×48 mm) with stamp printed on the cover in bright orange-red by Harrison. Barcode in black.

HD3	(£2·00) Containing booklet pane No. 1512a	9·00
	b. Barcode printed in blue (22.9.92)..	9·25

No. HD3 has the horizontal edges of the pane imperforate.

1990 (7 Aug). |MULTI COLOUR| laminated cover as Type HA **3** (75×48 mm) with stamp printed on the cover in bright orange-red by Questa. Barcode in black.

HD4	(£2·00) Containing ten 1st Class stamps (No. 1514)	9·00
	b. Barcode printed in blue (22.9.92)..	9·75

No. HD4 has perforations on all edges of the pane.

1990 (7 Aug). |MULTI COLOUR| laminated cover as Type HA **3** (75×48 mm) with stamp printed on the cover in bright orange-red by Walsall. Barcode in black.

HD5	(£2·00) Containing booklet pane No. 1516b	9·00
	c. Barcode printed in blue (22.9.92)..	9·25

No. HD5 has the horizontal edges of the pane imperforate.

1992 (21 Jan). |MULTI COLOUR| laminated cover as Type HA **5** (75×48 mm) with stamp printed on the cover in bright orange-red by Harrison.

HD6	(£2·40) Containing booklet pane No. 1512a..........................	9·50

No. HD6 has the horizontal edges of the pane imperforate.

1992 (21 Jan). |MULTI COLOUR| laminated cover as Type HA **5** (75×48 mm) with stamp printed on the cover in bright orange-red by Walsall.

HD7	(£2·40) Containing booklet pane No. 1516b	9·00

No. HD7 has the horizontal edges of the pane imperforate.

1993 (9 Feb). |MULTI COLOUR| laminated cover as Type HA **3** (77×44 mm) with advertisement for Greetings Booklet on reverse showing Rupert Bear as in Type KX **5**. Stamp printed on the cover in bright orange-red by Walsall.

HD8	(£2·40) Containing booklet pane No. 1516b	9·00

No. HD8 has the horizontal edges of the pane imperforate.

PERFORATIONS. Booklets from No. HD9 show perforations on all edges of the pane.

1993 (6 Apr). |MULTI COLOUR| laminated cover as Type HA **3** (75×48 mm) with stamp printed on the cover in bright orange-red by Harrison.

HD9	(£2·40) Containing ten 1st Class stamps (No. 1666)	9·00

No. HD9 was re-issued on 17 August 1993 showing changes to the text on the inside of the covers.

1993 (6 Apr). |MULTI COLOUR| laminated cover as Type HA **3** (75×48 mm) with stamp printed on the cover in bright orange-red by Walsall.

HD10	(£2·40) Containing ten 1st Class stamps (No. 1671)	9·00

No. HD10 was re-issued on 17 August 1993 showing changes to the text on the inside of the covers.

1993 (1 Nov). *Laminated cover as Type HA **3** (75×50 mm) with stamp printed on the cover in bright orange-red by Questa.*

HD11	(£2·50) Containing ten 1st Class stamps (No. 1671)	9·00

No. HD11 was re-issued on 4 October 1994 showing changes to the text on the inside of the cover.

1993 (1 Nov). Laminated cover as Type HA **3** (75×50 mm) with advertisement for Greetings Booklet on reverse showing Rupert Bear as in Type KX **5**. Stamp printed on the cover in bright orange-red by Walsall.

HD12	(£2·50) Containing ten 1st Class stamps (No. 1671)	9·50

1994 (22 Feb). |MULTI COLOUR| laminated cover as Type HA **3** (75×48 mm) with stamp printed on the cover in bright orange-red by Walsall. Inscribed *FREE POSTCARDS* on yellow tab at right.

HD13	(£2·50) Containing ten 1st Class stamps (No. 1671) and additional page giving details of Greetings Stamps postcard offer	9·00

1994 (1 July). |MULTI COLOUR| laminated covers as Type HA **3** (76×50 mm) with advertisement for Greetings Booklet on reverse showing Rupert Bear as in Type KX **5**. Stamp printed on the cover in bright orange-red by Walsall. Inscribed *OPEN NOW Chance to win a kite* on yellow tab at right.

HD14	(£2·50) Containing ten 1st Class stamps (No. 1671) with "Better luck next time." etc on inside back cover	9·00
HD15	(£2·50) Containing ten 1st Class stamps (No. 1671) with "You've Won!" etc on inside back cover	9·00

Nos. HD14/15 were initially only available from branches of W.H. Smith and Son. They were issued in connection with a competition in which the prizes were Paddington Bear kites. The booklets were not available from Royal Mail philatelic outlets until 4 October 1994.

HD **16**

HD **31**

1994 (20 Sept). |MULTI COLOUR laminated covers as Type HD **16** (76×50 mm) printed by Walsall. Inscribed *ORDER YOURS INSIDE* on yellow tab at right.

HD16 (£2·50) Containing ten 1st Class stamps (No. 1671) with "DO NOT OPEN UNTIL....."on front cover .... 9·00

HD17 (£2·50) Containing ten 1st Class stamps (No. 1671) with "KEEP IN TOUCH" on front cover .... 9·00

HD18 (£2·50) Containing ten 1st Class stamps (No. 1671) with "HAPPY BIRTHDAY" on front cover .... 9·00

HD19 (£2·50) Containing ten 1st Class stamps (No. 1671) with "What's Happenin'?" on front cover .... 9·00

1995 (10 Jan). |MULTI COLOUR laminated cover as Type HD **8** (75×48 mm) with stamps printed on the cover in bright orange-red by Harrison.

HD20 (£2·50) Containing ten 1st Class stamps (No. 1666) .... 9·50

1995 (10 Jan). |MULTI COLOUR laminated cover as Type HD **8** (75×48 mm) with stamps printed on the cover in bright orange-red by Questa.

HD21 (£2·50) Containing ten 1st Class stamps (No. 1671) .... 9·25

1995 (10 Jan). |MULTI COLOUR laminated cover as Type HD **8** (75×48 mm) with stamps printed on the cover in bright orange-red by Walsall.

HD22 (£2·50) Containing ten 1st Class stamps (No. 1671) .... 9·25

HD **23**

1995 (14 Feb). |MULTI COLOUR laminated cover as Type HD **23** (76×50 mm) showing card, Thorntons chocolates and box, printed by Walsall. Inscribed DETAILS INSIDE" on yellow tab at right.

HD23 (£2·50) Containing ten 1st Class stamps (No. 1671) .... 9·25

1995 (4 Apr). |MULTI COLOUR laminated cover as Type HD **8** (76×48 mm) with stamps printed on cover in bright orange-red by Harrison.

HD24 (£2·50) Containing ten 1st Class stamps (No. 1667)............ 9·25

1995 (24 Apr). |MULTI COLOUR laminated cover as Type HD **8** (75×48 mm) with stamps printed on cover in bright orange-red by Walsall. Inscribed *W H Smith Special Offer* on yellow tab at right.

HD25 (£2·50) Containing ten 1st Class stamps (No. 1671) .... 9·25
No. HD25 was initially only available from W. H. Smith branches and offered 50p. off the purchase of own brand stationery. The booklet was not placed on philatelic sale until 3 October 1995.

1995 (26 June). |MULTI COLOUR laminated cover as Type HA **8** (76×48 mm) with stamps printed on cover in bright orange red by Questa. Inscribed *Sainsbury's Promotion* on yellow tab at right.

HD26 (£2·50) Containing ten 1st Class stamps (No. 1671) .... 9·25
No. HD26 was initially only available from Sainsbury's branches and offered the chance to win a year's free shopping. The booklet was not placed on philatelic sale until 5 September 1995.

1995 (4 Sept). |MULTI COLOUR laminated cover as Type HD **23** (76×48 mm) showing ceramic figures of Benjy Bear and Harry Hedgehog, printed by Harrison.

HD27 (£2·50) Containing ten 1st Class stamps (No. 1667) .... 9·25

1996 (6 Feb). |MULTI COLOUR laminated cover as Type HA **8** (76×48 mm) showing Olympic symbols on the back. Stamps printed on the cover in bright orange-red by Walsall.

HD28 (£2·50) Containing ten 1st Class stamps (No. 1671)............ 9·25

1996 (19 Feb). |MULTI COLOUR laminated cover as Type HD **23** (76×48 mm) showing Walt Disney World, printed by Harrison.

HD29 (£2·50) Containing ten 1st Class stamps (No. 1667) .... 9·25

1996 (19 Mar). |MULTI COLOUR laminated cover as Type HA **8** (76×48 mm) showing Olympic symbols on the back, printed by Harrison.

HD30 (£2·50) Containing ten 1st Class stamps (No. 1667) .... 9·50

1996 (13 May). |MULTI COLOUR laminated covers as Type HD **31** (76×48 mm) showing woman lighting Olympic torch, printed by Harrison, with each booklet showing a scratchcard on the reverse based on different Olympic events.

HD31 (£2·50) Containing ten 1st Class stamps (No. 1667) .... 9·00 (Shot Put)..

HD32 (£2·50) Containing ten 1st Class stamps (No. 1667) .... 9·00 (Hurdles) ....

HD33 (£2·50) Containing ten 1st Class stamps (No. 1667) .... 9·00 (Archery)..

NOTE: From No. HD34 onwards, the printer of each booklet is identified by a small capital letter below the barcode on the outside back cover.

1996 (15 July). |MULTI COLOUR laminated cover as Type HA **11** (76×48 mm) showing Olympic symbols on the back. Stamps printed on the cover in bright orange-red by Walsall. Inscribed *WHSmith Offer Inside* on yellow tab at right.

HD34 (£2·60) Containing ten 1st Class stamps (No. 1671) .... 9·00
No. HD34 was initially only available from branches of W. H. Smith and Sons. It was issued in connection with a special offer of AA/OS Leisure Guides. The booklets were not available from Royal Mail philatelic outlets until 17 September 1996.

1996 (6 Aug). |MULTI COLOUR laminated cover as Type HA **11** (76×48 mm), but with diagonal white line across corners of stamps and showing Olympic symbols on the back. Stamps printed on the cover in bright orange-red by Harrison.

HD35 (£2·60) Containing ten 1st Class stamps (No. 1667) .... 9·50

1996 (6 Aug). |MULTI COLOUR laminated cover as Type HA **11** (76×48 mm) showing Olympic symbols on the back. Stamps printed on the cover in bright orange-red by Walsall.

HD36 (£2·60) Containing ten 1st Class stamps (No. 1671) .... 9·00

1996 (9 Sept). |MULTI COLOUR laminated cover as Type HD **31** (76×48 mm) showing iced cakes on front and back, printed by Walsall. Inscribed *OPEN FOR DETAILS* on yellow tab at right.

HD37 (£2·60) Containing ten 1st Class stamps (No. 1671) .... 9·00

1996 (7 Oct). |MULTI COLOUR laminated cover as Type HA **11** (76×48 mm) showing Olympic symbols on the back. Stamps printed on cover in bright orange-red by Walsall. Inscribed *Offer Inside* on yellow tab at right.

HD38 (£2·60) Containing ten 1st Class stamps (No. 1671) .... 9·00
No. HD38 was initially only available from ASDA stores and offered £1 off greetings cards. The booklet was not placed on philatelic sale until 13 January 1997.

1997 (4 Feb). |MULTI COLOUR laminated cover as Type HA **11** (76×48 mm). Stamps printed on the cover in bright orange-red by Harrison.

HD 39 (£2·60) Containing ten 1st Class stamps (No. 1667) .... 9·00

1997 (4 Feb). |MULTI COLOUR laminated cover as Type HA **11** (76×48 mm). Stamps printed on the cover in bright orange-red by Walsall.

HD40 (£2·60) Containing ten 1st Class stamps (No. 1671) .... 9·00

1997 (21 Apr). *Royal Golden Wedding.* |MULTI COLOUR laminated cover as Type HA **11** (76×48 mm). Stamps printed on the cover in gold by Harrison.

HD41 (£2·60) Containing ten 1st Class stamps (No. 1668) .... 9·00

1997 (21 Apr). *Royal Golden Wedding.* |MULTI COLOUR laminated cover as Type HA **11** (76×48 mm). Stamps printed on the cover in gold by Walsall.

HD42 (£2·60) Containing ten 1st Class stamps (No. 1668) .... 9·50

1997 (15 Sept). |MULTI COLOUR laminated cover as Type HD **31** (76×48 mm) showing a tropical beach scene printed by Harrison. Inscr *FIRST CLASS TRAVEL* on front, and *OPEN FOR DETAILS* on yellow tab at right.

HD43 (£2·60) Containing ten 1st Class stamps (No. 1668) .... 9·00

1997 (8 Nov). |MULTI COLOUR| laminated cover as Type HA **11** (76×48 mm). Stamps printed on the cover in bright orange-red by Walsall.

HD44 (£2·60) Containing ten 1st Class stamps (gravure) .... 9·00
(No. 1667) ....

No. HD44 was re-issued on 5 May 1998 showing the positions of the imprint, which was now vertical, and the post code notice transposed and again on 16 March 1999 with "Please note that the First Class rate is no longer valid to Europe" added to inside back cover.

HD **45**

1998 (2 Feb). |MULTI COLOUR| laminated cover as Type HD **45** (76×48 mm) showing Disney illustration printed by De La Rue, with a scratch card on the reverse. Inscr *See reverse for Scratch and Win* on yellow tab at right.

HD45 (£2·60) Containing ten 1st Class stamps (gravure) .... 9·00
(No. 1667) ....

HD **46**

1998 (27 Apr). |MULTI COLOUR| laminated cover as Type HD **46** (76×48 mm) showing Peugeot 106 printed by De La Rue. Inscr *WIN A PEUGEOT 106* on yellow tab at right.

HD46 (£2·60) Containing ten 1st Class stamps (gravure) .... 9·00
(No. 1667) ....

No. HD46 was not placed on philatelic sale until 23 June 1998.

1998 (5 May). |MULTI COLOUR| laminated cover as Type HA **11** (76×48 mm). Stamps printed on the cover in bright orange-red by De La Rue.

HD47 (£2·60) Containing ten 1st Class stamps (gravure) .... 9·00
(No. 1667) ....

1998 (1 July). |MULTI COLOUR| laminated cover as Type HD **46** (76×48 mm) showing JVC Camcorder printed by De La Rue. Inscr *WIN A JVC CAMCORDER* on yellow tab at right.

HD48 (£2·60) Containing ten 1st Class stamps (gravure) .... 9·00
(No. 1667) ....

No. HD48 was not placed on philatelic sale until 27 August 1998.

1998 (3 Aug). |MULTI COLOUR| laminated cover as Type GGA **2** (76×48 mm) inscr (*Create a card design*), printed by De La Rue.

HD49 (£2·60) Containing ten 1st Class stamps (gravure) .... 9·00
(No. 1667) ....

No. HD49 was not placed on philatelic sale until 7 September 1998.

1998 (7 Sept). |MULTI COLOUR| laminated cover as Type HA **11** (75×49 mm), with stamps printed on the cover in bright orange-red by Questa.

HD50 (£2·60) Containing ten 1st Class stamps (litho) .... 9·00
(No. 1671) ....

1998 (1 Dec). |MULTI COLOUR| laminated cover as Type HA **11** (75×48 mm). Stamps printed on the cover in bright orange-red by Questa.

HD51 (£2·60) Containing ten 1st Class stamps (gravure) .... 12·00
(No. 1667a) ....

No. HD51 was re-issued on 16 March 1999 with "Please note that the First Class rate is no longer valid to Europe" added to inside back cover.

2000 (6 Jan). |MULTI COLOUR| laminated cover as Type HA **11** (75×48 mm). Millennium definitives printed on the cover in olive-brown by Questa.

HD52 (£2·60) Containing ten 1st Class stamps (gravure) .... 9·00
(No. 2124d) ....

No. HD52 was re-issued on 14 March 2000 with a changed telephone number on the inside back cover.

2000 (6 Jan). |MULTI COLOUR| laminated cover as Type HA **11** (75×48 mm). Millennium definitives printed on the cover in olive-brown by Walsall.

HD53 (£2·60) Containing ten 1st Class stamps (gravure) .... 10·00
(No. 2124) ....

No. HD53 was was re-issued on 14 March 2000 with a changed telephone number on the inside back cover.

Panes of four European Air Mail stamps

HF **1**

1999 (19 Jan). |MULTI COLOUR| laminated cover as Type HF **1** (75×50 mm). Stamps printed on the cover in deep blue by Walsall. Inscr *For items up to 20g* on yellow tab at right.

HF1 (£1·20) Containing four European Air Mail stamps (No. 1669) and pane of four air mail labels .... 6·00

No. HF1 was re-issued on 27 April 2000 showing an amended Customer Services telephone number on the inside back cover.

E. Barcode Booklets containing Penny Black Anniversary stamps with barcodes on back cover.

60p. Booklet

JA **1**

1990 (30 Jan). Laminated cover as Type JA **1** (75×48 mm) showing Penny Black Anniversary stamp in bright blue. Containing booklet pane No. 1475l, printed in litho by Walsall.

JA1 Containing booklet pane No. 1475l .... 3·75

No. JA1 has three edges of the pane imperforate.

80p. Booklets

1990 (30 Jan). Laminated cover as Type JA **1** (75×48 mm) showing Penny Black Anniversary stamp in brownish black and cream. Containing booklet pane No. 1476m, printed in litho by Walsall.

JB1 Containing booklet pane No. 1476m .... 5·00

No. JB1 has three edges of the pane imperforate.

1990 (17 Apr). Laminated cover as Type JA **1** (75×48 mm) showing Penny Black Anniversary stamp printed on the cover in brownish black by Walsall. Containing stamps printed in photo by Harrison.

JB2 Containing booklet pane No. 1469r .... 4·50

No. JB2 has three edges of the pane imperforate.

£1.50 Booklets

1990 (30 Jan). Laminated cover as Type JA **1** (75×48 mm) showing Penny Black Anniversary stamp in bright blue. Containing booklet pane No. 1467l printed in photo by Harrison.

JC1 Containing booklet pane No. 1467l .... 5·50

No. JC1 has the horizontal edges of the pane imperforate.

1990 (17 Apr). Laminated cover as Type JA **1** (75×48 mm) showing Penny Black Anniversary stamp printed on the cover in bright blue, printed in litho by Questa.

JC2 Containing ten 15p. (No. 1477) .... 10·00

1990 (12 June). Laminated cover as Type JA **1** (75×48 mm) showing Penny Black Anniversary stamp in bright blue. Containing booklet pane No. 1475m, printed in litho by Walsall.

JC3 Containing booklet pane No. 1475m .... 6·25

No. JC3 has three edges of the pane imperforate.

£2 Booklets

1990 (30 Jan). Laminated cover as Type JA **1** (75×48 mm) showing Penny Black Anniversary stamp in brownish black and cream. Containing booklet pane. No. 1469m, printed in photo by Harrison.

JD1 Containing booklet pane No. 1469m .... 6·25

No. JD1 has the horizontal edges of the pane imperforate.

1990 (17 Apr). Laminated cover as Type JA **1** (75×48 mm) showing Penny Black Anniversary stamp printed on the cover in brownish black, printed in litho by Questa.

JD2   Containing ten 20p. (No. 1478) .... 12·00

1990 (12 June). Laminated cover as Type JA **1** (75×48 mm) showing Penny Black Anniversary stamp in brownish black and cream. Containing booklet pane No. 1476n, printed in litho by Walsall.

JD3   Containing booklet pane No. 1476n .... 9·00
    No. JD3 has three edges of the pane imperforate.

F. Barcode Booklets containing Greetings stamps with barcodes on the back cover.

For first greetings booklet, issued 31 January 1989, see FY1 in section B.

£2 Greetings Booklet

KX **1** (Illustration reduced. Actual size 135×85 mm)

(Des Michael Peters and Partners)

1990 (6 Feb). *Greetings Stamps.* Cover printed in scarlet, lemon and black as Type KX **1** (135×85 mm) by Harrison. Containing booklet pane No. 1483a, and a separate sheet of 12 greetings labels.

KX1   "Smile" design cut-out showing stamps inside .... 13·50

Greetings Booklets containing No Value Indicated stamps

KX **2**

(Des T. Meeuwissen)

1991 (5 Feb). *Greetings Stamps.* |MULTI COLOUR| laminated cover as Type KX **2** (95×69 mm) by Harrison. Containing booklet pane No. 1536a, including twelve special greetings labels in a block (3×4) at right, attached by the selvedge.

KX2   (£2·20) "Good Luck" charms design .... 9·00

KX **3**

(Des Michael Peters and Partners)

1991 (26 Mar). *Greetings Stamps.* |MULTI COLOUR| laminated cover as Type KX **3** (95×69 mm) by Harrison. Containing booklet pane No. 1550a, including twelve special greetings labels in a block (3×4) at right, attached by the selvedge.

KX3   (£2·20) Laughing pillar box design .... 9·00
    a. Amended text to inside back cover (3.3.92) .... 9·00
    The note on the inside back cover of No. KX3 is headed "Greetings Stamps". In No. KX3a there is no heading but details of the validity of the stamps to European destinations have been added.

KX **4**

(Des Trickett and Webb)

1992 (28 Jan). *Greetings Stamps.* |MULTI COLOUR| laminated cover as Type KX **4** (95×69 mm) by Harrison. Containing booklet pane No. 1592a, including twelve special greetings labels in a block (3×4) at right, attached by selvedge.

KX4   (£2·40) Pressed Flowers design .... 9·00

KX **5**

(Des Newell and Sorrell)

1993 (2 Feb). *Greetings Stamps.* |MULTI COLOUR| laminated cover as Type KX **5** (96×60 mm) by Harrison. Containing booklet pane No. 1644a and pane of twenty special greetings labels in a block (5×4), both panes attached by a common gutter margin.

KX5   (£2·40) Children's Characters design .... 9·00
    No. KX5 was re-issued on 15 June 1993 with "Thompson" corrected to "Thomson" (bottom line at left) and on 17 August 1993 with "Sorell" corrected to "Sorrell".

KX **6**

(Des Newell and Sorrell)

1994 (1 Feb). *Greetings Stamps.* |MULTI COLOUR cover as Type KX **6** (96×60 mm) by Harrison. Containing booklet pane No. 1800a and pane of twenty special greetings labels in a block (5×4), both panes attached by a common gutter margin.

KX6　(£2·50) Children's Characters design .... 9·00

KX **7**

(Des Newell and Sorrell)

1995 (21 Mar)–**96**. *Greetings Stamps.* |MULTI COLOUR cover as Type KX **7** (96×60 mm) by Walsall. Containing booklet pane No. 1858a and pane of twenty special greetings labels in a block (5×4), both panes attached by a common gutter margin. Inscr *Pull Open* on yellow strip at right.

KX7　(£2·50) Clown design .... 9·00
　　　a. No inscr on yellow strip (5.2.96) .... 10·00

KX **8**

(Des M. Wolff)

1996 (26 Feb–11 Nov). *Greetings Stamps.* |MULTI COLOUR cover as Type KX **8** (96×60 mm) by Walsall. Containing booklet pane No. 1905a and pane of twenty special greetings labels in a block (5×4), both panes attached by a common gutter margin.

KX8　(£2·50) "MORE! LOVE" design .... 8·50
　　　a. Containing pane No. 1905pa (11 Nov) .... 24·00

No. KX8a shows a redesigned inside front cover which omits references to 1996 dates.

KX **9**

(Des Tutssels)

1997 (6 Jan). *Greetings Stamps. 19th-century Flower Paintings.* |MULTI COLOUR cover as Type KX **9** (96×61 mm) by Walsall. Containing booklet pane No. 1955a and pane of twenty special greetings labels in a block (5×4), both panes attached by a common gutter margin.

KX9　(£2·60) *Gentiana acaulis* design .... 9·00

No. KX9 was re-issued on 16 March 1999 with "Please note that the First Class rate is no longer valid to Europe" added to inside front cover.

1997 (3 Feb). *Greetings Stamps. 19th-century Flower Paintings.* |MULTI COLOUR cover as Type KX **9** (96×61 mm) *by Walsall* but with box inscribed *WIN A BEAUTIFUL BOUQUET INSTANTLY?* printed in yellow on red over the flower on the front and with a scratch card on the inside back cover. Inscribed *Open now – See if you've won* on yellow tab at right. Containing booklet pane No. 1955a and pane of twenty special greetings labels in a block (5×4), both panes attached by a common gutter margin.

KX10　(£2·60) *Gentiana acaulis* design .... 9·00

KX **11**

(Des Tutssels)

1998 (5 Jan). *Greetings Stamps. 19th-century Flower Paintings.* |MULTI COLOUR cover as Type KX **11** (96×61 mm) *by Walsall.* Inscribed *See reverse for special offer* on yellow tab at right. Containing booklet pane No. 1955a and pane of twenty special greetings labels in a block (5×4), both attached by a common gutter margin.

KX11　(£2·60) Chocolate design .... 9·00

1998 (3 Aug). *Greetings Stamps. 19th-century Flower Paintings.* |MULTI COLOUR cover as Type GGA **2** (88×61 mm) printed by Walsall. Containing booklet pane No. 1955a and pane of twenty special greetings labels in a block (5×4), both attached by a common gutter margin.

KX12　(£2·60) "Create a card" design .... 9·50

No. KX12 was not placed on philatelic sale until 7 September 1998.

G. Barcode Booklets containing Christmas stamps with barcode on the back.

LX **1**

(Des A. Davidson)

1990 (13 Nov). Christmas. |MULTI COLOUR laminated cover as Type LX **1** (96×60 mm) by Harrison. Containing booklet pane No. 1526b, attached by the selvedge.

LX1   £3·40, Snowman design .... 5·50

1991 (12 Nov). |MULTI COLOUR laminated cover as Type LX **1,** but 95×70 mm by Harrison. Containing booklet pane No. 1582b attached by the selvedge.

LX2   £3·60, Holly design .... 5·75

LX **3**

(Des Karen Murray)

1992 (10 Nov). |MULTI COLOUR laminated cover as Type LX **3** (95×70 mm) by Harrison. Containing booklet pane No. 1634a attached by the selvedge.

LX3   £3·60, Santa Claus and Reindeer design .... 5·75

1993 (9 Nov). |MULTI COLOUR laminated covers as Type LX **3,** but 95×60 mm by Harrison, each showing Santa Claus and Reindeer. Panes attached by selvedge.

LX4   £2·50, containing ten 25p. stamps (No. 1791) .... 5·00
LX5   £3·80, containing twenty 19p. stamps (No. 1790) .... 6·00

No. LX4 was only available from Post Offices in the Central T.V. area and from philatelic outlets.

LX **6**

(Des Yvonne Gilbert)

1994 (1 Nov). |MULTI COLOUR laminated covers as Type LX **6** (95×60 mm) by Harrison, showing different Nativity Play props. Panes attached by selvedge.

LX6   £2·50, containing ten 25p. stamps (No. 1844) .... 4·00
LX7   £3·80, containing twenty 19p. stamps (No. 1843) .... 5·50

LX **8**

(Des K. Lilly)

1995 (30 Oct). |MULTI COLOUR laminated covers as Type LX **8** (95×60 mm) by Harrison, showing Robins as depicted on the contents. Panes attached by selvedge.

LX8   £2·40, containing four 60p. stamps (No. 1900) plus 4 air mail labels .... 3·80
LX9   £2·50, containing ten 25p. stamps (No. 1897) .... 3·80
LX10   £3·80, containing twenty 19p. stamps (No. 1896) .... 6·00

LX **11**

1996 (28 Oct). |MULTI COLOUR laminated covers as Type LX **11** (95×60 mm) by Harrison, showing scenes from the Nativity as depicted on the contents. Panes attached by selvedge.

LX11   (£2·60) Containing ten 1st Class stamps (No. 1951)............   9·00
LX12   (£4·00) Containing twenty 2nd Class stamps (No. 1950) .   12·50

LX **13**

1997 (27 Oct). |MULTI COLOUR laminated covers as Type LX **13** (95×60 mm) by Harrison, showing Father Christmas and crackers as depicted on the contents. Panes attached by selvedge.

LX13   (£2·60) Containing ten 1st Class stamps (No. 2007) ....   9·00
LX14   (£4·00) Containing twenty 2nd Class stamps (No. 2006) .   12·50

LX **15**

1998 (2 Nov). |MULTI COLOUR red laminated covers as Type LX **15** (95×60 mm) by De La Rue, showing angels as depicted on the contents. Panes attached by selvedge.

LX15   £2·60 booklet containing ten 26p. stamps (No. 2065) ......   4·25
LX16   £4 booklet containing twenty 20p. stamps (No. 2064) .....   6·25

LX **17**

1999 (2 Nov). |MULTI |COLOUR laminated covers as Type LX **17** (95×70 mm) by De La Rue, showing designs as depicted on the contents. Panes attached by selvedge.

LX17 £2·60 booklet containing ten 26p. stamps (No. 2116) .... 4·25
LX18 £3·80 booklet containing twenty 19p. stamps (No. 2115) 6·00

LX **19**

2000 (7 Nov). |MULTI |COLOUR laminated covers as Type LX **19** (96×70 mm by De La Rue), showing designs as depicted on the contents. Inscribed *Season's Greetings* on yellow tab at right. Panes attached by selvedge.

LX19 £2·70, containing ten 1st Class stamps (No. 2171) .... 9·00
LX20 £3·80, containing twenty 2nd Class stamps (No. 2170) .... 12·00

2001 (6 Nov). Self-adhesive booklet containing Nos. 2238a and 2239a, each with a multicoloured header label showing barcode and Royal Mail emblem and further label at foot with telephone numbers, folded to form booklets 119×81 mm by De La Rue.

LX21 £3·24, booklet containing twelve 1st Class stamps (No. 2239a)... 11·00
LX22 £4·56, booklet containing twenty-four 2nd Class stamps (No. 2238a)... 16·00
Nos. LX21/2 show the surplus self-adhesive paper around each stamp retained.

2002 (5 Nov). Self-adhesive booklet containing Nos. 2321a and 2322a, each with a multicoloured header label showing barcode and Royal Mail emblem and further label at foot with telephone numbers, folded to form booklets 106×72 mm by De La Rue.

LX23 £3·24, booklet containing twelve 1st Class stamps (No. 2322a)... 11·00
LX24 £4·56, booklet containing twenty-four 2nd Class stamps (No. 2321a).. 16·00
No. LX23 was sealed into a cellophane packet which also contained a Lord of the Rings game card.
Nos. LX23/4 show the surplus self-adhesive paper around each stamp retained.

2003 (4 Nov). Self-adhesive booklet containing Nos. 2410a and 2411a, each with a multicoloured header label showing barcode and Royal Mail emblem and further label at foot with telephone numbers, folded to form booklets 106×71 *mm* by De La Rue.

LX25 £3·36, booklet containing twelve 1st Class stamps (No. 2411a)... 11·00
LX26 £4·80, booklet containing twenty-four 2nd Class stamps (No. 2410a)... 16·00
Nos. LX25/6 have the surplus self-adhesive paper around each stamp removed.

2004 (2 Nov). Self-adhesive booklet containing Nos. 2495a and 2496a, each with a multicoloured header label showing barcode and Royal Mail emblem and further label at foot with contact information, folded to form booklets 105×71 mm by De La Rue.

LX27 £3·36 booklet containing twelve 1st Class stamps (No. 2496a) .... 12·00
LX28 £5·04 booklet containing twenty-four 2nd Class stamps (No. 2495a)... 16·00
Nos. LX27/8 have the surplus self-adhesive paper around each stamp removed.

2005 (1 Nov). Self-adhesive booklet containing Nos. 2582a and 2583a, each with a multicoloured header label showing barcode and Royal Mail emblem and further label at foot with contact information, folded to form booklets 106×71 mm by De La Rue.

LX29 £3·60 booklet containing twelve 1st Class stamps (No. 2583a) .... 10·50
LX30 £5·04 booklet containing twenty-four 2nd Class stamps (No. 2582a)... 16·00
Nos. LX29/30 have the surplus self-adhesive paper around each stamp removed.

LX **31**

2006 (7 Nov). Covers as Type LX **31** (75×57 mm) by De La Rue. Self-adhesive.

LX31 £2·76 booklet containing twelve 2nd Class stamps (No. 2678a) (Type LX **31**)... 9·00
LX32 £3·84 booklet containing twelve 1st Class stamps (No. 2679a) (red cover inscr "12×1st") .... 11·00
Nos. LX31/2 have the surplus self-adhesive paper around each stamp removed.

2007 (6 Nov). Covers as Type LX **31** (75×57 mm) by De La Rue. Self-adhesive.

LX33 £2·88 booklet containing twelve 2nd Class stamps (No. 2789a) (Type LX **31**)... 9·00
LX34 £4·08 booklet containing twelve 1st Class stamps (No. 2790a) (red cover inscr '12×1st')................................ 11·00
Nos. LX33/4 have the surplus self-adhesive paper around each stamp removed.

2008 (4 Nov). Covers as Type LX **31** (75×57 mm) by De La Rue. Self-adhesive.

LX35 £3·24 booklet containing twelve 2nd Class stamps (No. 2876a) (Type LX **31**)... 9·00
 a. "Oh YES it is!" along right-hand edge of pane............. 9·00
LX36 £4·32 booklet containing twelve 1st Class stamps (No. 2877a) (red cover inscr "12×1st")................................ 11·00
 a. "It's behind you!" along right-hand edge of pane .... 11·00
Nos. LX35/6 have the surplus self-adhesive paper around each stamp removed.
No. LX35 is inscr "Oh NO it isn't!" and No. LX36 "Abracadabra!", both along the right-hand edges of the booklet panes.

2009 (3 Nov). *Christmas. Covers* as Type LX **31** (75×57 mm) by De La Rue. Self-adhesive.

LX37 £3·60 booklet containing twelve 2nd class stamps (No. 2991a) (Type LX 31)... 9·00
LX38 £4·68 booklet containing twelve 1st class stamps (No. 2992a) (red cover inscr '12×1st')................................ 10·50
Nos. LX37/8 have the surplus self-adhesive paper around each stamp removed.

LX **39** Wallace and Gromit posting Christmas Cards

2010 (2 Nov). *Christmas.* |MULTI COLOUR covers as Type LX **39** (74×58 mm) by De La Rue. Self-adhesive.
LX39   £3·84 booklet containing twelve 2nd class stamps
(No. 3128a) (Type LX**39**)................................... 9·00
LX40   £4·92 booklet containing twelve 1st class stamps
(No. 3129a) (cover as Type LX **39** but red background).. 10·50
Nos. LX39/40 have the surplus self-adhesive paper around each stamp removed.

2011 (8 Nov). *Christmas. 400th Anniversary of the King James Bible.* |MULTI COLOUR covers as Type LX **31** (74×58 mm) by Walsall. Self-adhesive.
LX41   (£4·32) booklet containing twelve 2nd class stamps
(No. 3242a) (Type LX **31**)............................... 9·00
LX42   (£5·52) booklet containing twelve 1st class stamps
(No. 3243a) (cover as Type LX **31** but red background).. 10·25
Nos. LX41/2 have the surplus self-adhesive paper around each stamp removed.

2012 (6 Nov). *Christmas.* Illustrations by Axel Scheffler. |MULTI COLOUR covers as Type LX **31** (74×58 mm) by Walsall. Self-adhesive.
LX43   (£6) booklet containing twelve 2nd class stamps
(No. 3415a) (Type LX **31**)............................... 9·00
LX44   (£7·20) booklet containing twelve 1st class stamps
(No. 3416a) (cover as Type LX **31** but red background).. 10·25

2013 (5 Nov). *Christmas.* |MULTI COLOUR covers as Type LX **31** (89×66 mm) by Walsall. Self-adhesive.
LX45   (£6) booklet containing twelve 2nd class stamps
(No. 3542a) (as Type LX **31**).......................... 9·00
LX46   (£7·20) booklet containing twelve 1st class stamps
(No. 3543a) (as Type LX **31** but red background).. 10·25

2014 (4 Nov). *Christmas.* |MULTI COLOUR covers as Type LX **31** (74×58 mm) by Walsall. Self-adhesive.
LX47   (£6·36) booklet containing twelve 2nd class stamps
(No. 3650a) (as Type LX **31**).......................... 10·25
LX48   (£7·44) booklet containing twelve 1st class stamps
(No. 3651a) (as Type LX **31** but red background).. 13·00

2015 (3 Nov). *Christmas.* |MULTI COLOUR covers as Type LX **31** (89×65 mm) by Walsall. Self-adhesive.
LX49   (£6·48) booklet containing twelve 2nd class stamps
(No. 3771a) (as Type LX **31**)........................... 9·00
LX50   (£7·56) booklet containing twelve 1st class stamps (No. 3772a) (as Type LX **31** but red cover inscr '12×1st') .... 10·25

2016 (8 Nov). *Christmas.* |MULTI COLOUR covers as Type LX **31** (89×65 mm) by Walsall. Self-adhesive.
LX51   (£6·60) booklet containing twelve 2nd class stamp
(No. 3903a) (as Type LX **31**)........................... 9·25
LX52   (£7·68) booklet containing twelve 1st class stamps
(No. 3904a) (as Type LX **31** but red cover inscr '12×1st'). 10·50

LX **53**

2017 (7 Nov). *Christmas.* |MULTI COLOUR covers as Type LX 53 (89×65 mm). Self-adhesive.
LX53   (£6.72) booklet containing twelve 2nd class stamps
(No. 4019a) (Type LX **53**)............................... 9.75
LX54   (£6.72) booklet containing twelve 2nd class stamps
(No. 4019b) (Type LX **53**)............................... 9.75
LX55   (£7.80) booklet containing twelve 1st class stamps
(No. 4020a) (as Type LX **53** but red cover inscr '12×1st').   10.75
LX56   (£7.80) booklet containing twelve 1st class stamps
(No. 4021a) (as Type LX **53** but red cover inscr '12×1st').   10.75
Nos. LX54 and LX56 were described as 'Reserve stock' by Royal Mail and, initially, were only available from Tallents House.

H. Self-adhesive Barcode Booklets containing No Value Indicated stamps.

NOTES. All booklets in this section show the surplus self-adhesive paper around each stamp retained, unless otherwise stated.
Booklets which are omitted from the listings here e.g. MB8d, are only differentiated by the year codes on the stamps or other features outside the scope of this catalogue. They are however, listed in the appropriate volume of the *Great Britain Specialised Catalogue.*

Containing six 2nd class stamps.

MA **1**

2001 (29 Jan). |MULTI COLOUR laminated cover as Type MA **1** (74×56 mm). Stamps printed on the cover in bright blue by Walsall.
MA1   (£1·14) Containing six 2nd Class self-adhesive stamps
(No. 2039)... 5·00
No. MA1 was re-issued on 1 August 2001 showing "Cod Post" added to the "Ffôn Testun" inscription on the back cover.
No. MA1 exists imperforate.

Containing six 1st Class stamps

2001 (29 Jan). |MULTI COLOUR laminated cover as Type MA **1** (74×56 mm). Stamps printed on the cover in bright orange-red by Walsall.
MB1   (£1·62) Containing six 1st Class self-adhesive stamps
(No. 2040)... 5·25
No. MB1 was re-issued on 1 August 2001 showing "Cod Post" added to the "Ffôn Testun" inscription on the back cover.

MB **2**

2001 (29 Jan). |MULTI COLOUR laminated cover as Type MB **2** (74×56 mm). Stamps printed on the cover in bright orange-red with portrait of Queen Victoria by Walsall.
MB2   (£1·62) Containing No. 2040l (includes label
commemorating death centenary of Queen Victoria).... 11·50

MB **3**

2002 (5 June). Gold laminated cover as Type MB **3** (74×56 mm) by Questa.
MB3 (£1·62) Containing six 1st Class self-adhesive stamps
(No. 2295)... 5·25
No. MB3 was sold at £1·62. It shows the surplus self-adhesive paper around each stamp removed and a single notch at top right.

2002 (5 June) – **2008**. Gold laminated cover as Type MB **3** (74×56 mm) by Walsall.
MB4 (£1·62) Containing six 1st Class self-adhesive stamps
(No. 2295)... 6·00
a. (£1·68) Inside cover with Smilers advertisement
(27.1.05) .... 6·50
b. (£1·92) Back cover with added text about new
pricing structure (25.4.06) .... 8·00
c. (£2·04) Inside cover with "To find the correct
postcodes for your mail" notice (5.6.07) .... 5·25
d. (£2·04) Inside cover with commemorative
inscription for Machin Anniversary (5.6.07).................... 5·25
e. (£2·04) Inside cover with Harry Potter stamps
advertisement (28.8.07) .... 5·25
f. (£2·04) Inside cover with postcode text in English
and Welsh (20.9.07)... 6·00
g. (£2·16) Inside cover with *Carry On* stamps
advertisement (10.6.08)... 5·25
No. MB4 shows the surplus self-adhesive paper around each stamp removed and a single notch at top right.
No. MB4 was re-issued on 27 January 2005 (MB4a) with a Smilers advertisement (showing No. 2262 and photograph of baby) on the inside front cover. It was re-issued again on 26 July 2005 with a different Smilers advertisement (showing No. 2261 and photograph of bride).
No. MB4a was available from Tallents House from 27 January 2005, and from general post offices from 22 March 2005.
No. MB4b does not have Smilers advertisement.
The added text on the back cover of No. MB4b reads "Valid for items up to 60g before 21 August 2006. Under new pricing structure from 21 August 2006 – valid for postal items up to: 240 mm Long; 165 mm Wide; 5 mm Thick; 100g Weight."
The text on the back cover of Nos. MB4c/g reads "Valid for items up to: 240 mm Long 165 mm Wide 5 mm Thick 100g Weight".
No. MB4d has Arnold Machin's signature along the right-hand edge of the booklet pane.
No. MB4g has characters from *Carry On* films illustrated along the right-hand edge of the booklet pane.

2002 (4 July). [MULTI COLOUR] laminated cover as Type MA **1** (74×56 mm) with stamps printed on the cover in bright orange-red by Questa.
MB5 (£1·62) Containing six 1st Class self-adhesive stamps
(No. 2040)... 5·50
No. MB5 was sold at £1·62.

MB **6** ("The Real Network" added below logo)

2003 (27 Mar). Gold cover with multicoloured emblem as Type MB **6** (74×56 mm) by Walsall.
MB6 (£1·62) Containing six 1st Class self-adhesive stamps
(No. 2295)... 5·50
No. MB6 shows the surplus self-adhesive paper around each stamp removed and has a single notch at top right.
No. MB6 exists imperforate.

MB **7** (Supporting London 2012)

2004 (15 June). *London's bid to host Olympic Games, 2012.* Gold cover with multicoloured emblem as Type MB **7** (74×56 mm) by Walsall.
MB7 (£1·68) Containing six 1st Class self-adhesive stamps
(No. 2295)... 6·75
No. MB7 has the surplus self-adhesive paper around each stamp removed and a single notch at top right.

Containing six 1st Class Olympic and Paralympic Games stamps (MB9/10) or "Security Machins"

2009 (31 Mar)–**11**. Gold cover with multicoloured emblem as Type MB **3** (74×57 mm) by Walsall.
MB8 (£2·16) Containing six 1st Class self-adhesive stamps
(No. U2985) (code "MSIL" without year code)................... 15·00
a. (£2·34) Containing No. U3019 (code "MSIL" with year
code) (26.1.10)... 10·00
b. (£2·34) Containing No. U3019 (code "MSIL" with
year code). Inside cover with inscription and emblem
for London 2010 Festival of Stamps (30.3.10).................. 7·75
c. (£2·46) Containing No. U3019 (code "MSIL" with year
code) (19.8.10)... 6·00
e. (£2·76) Containing No. U3019 (code "MSIL" with
year code). Inside front cover advertising the 2012
special stamp programme. Back cover with FSC logo
(25.10.11).. 11·50
No. MB8 has the surplus self-adhesive paper around each stamp removed and a single small notch at top right.
The e-mail address on the inside front cover of No. MB8 reads 'www.royalmail.com/Postcodes4free'.
No. MB8a has a lower case 'p' in this email address 'www.royalmail.com/postcodes4free'.
No. MB8b has 'LONDON 2010 FESTIVAL OF STAMPS' along the right hand edge of the booklet pane.
No. MB8/b are inscribed "Walsall Security Printers, UK" along the left hand edge of the back cover. This was removed for MB8c/e.
No. MB8d is outside the scope of this catalogue.
Year codes for MB8a/b are "MA10", for MB8c "MA10" and "M11L" and for MB8e "M11L".

London 2012 Olympic and Paralympic Games

MB **9**

2012 (5 Jan). *Olympic and Paralympic Games, London.* |MULTI COLOUR| cover, (75×58 mm), as Type MB **9** by Walsall. Self-adhesive.

MB9 (£2·76) Containing booklet pane No. 3250a with Paralympic Games stamp at top left........................ 7·00

MB10 (£2·76) Containing booklet pane No. 3250a with Olympic Games stamp at top left.......................... 7·00

No. MB9/10 have the surplus self-adhesive paper around each stamp removed and a single small notch at top right.

The inside cover of No. MB9 is inscribed 'London's vision is to reach young people all around the world, to connect them with the inspirational power of the Games, so that they are inspired to choose sport'.

The inside cover of No. MB10 is inscribed "Key dates for London 2012" and dates.

MB **11**

2012 (1 Oct). *Diamond Jubilee.* Slate-blue cover with multicoloured emblem as Type MB **11** (74×57 mm) by Walsall.

MB11 (£3·60) Containing six 1st Class self-adhesive stamps (No. U3275, code "MSND") .... 8·00

No. MB11 has the self-adhesive paper around each stamp removed and a single small notch at the top right.

MB **12**

2013 (3 Jan). Red cover with multicoloured emblem as Type MB **12** (74×57 mm) by Walsall.

MB12 (£3·60) Containing six 1st Class self-adhesive stamps (No. U3024, code "MSIL") .... 7·00

No. MB12 has the surplus self-adhesive paper around each stamp removed and a single small notch at top right.

No. MB12 reissued on 31 July 2014 with the Royal Mail telephone numbers on the back cover changed from 08457 740 740 and 08456 000 606 to 03457 740 740 and 03456 000 606. The price shown for MB12 is with the changed telephone number. With 08 telephone number £10.00

Year codes for MB12 are "M12L", "M13L" or "M14L", and with changed telephone numbers "M14L" or "M15L".

2015 (6 May). *175th Anniversary of the Penny Black.* Red cover with multi-coloured emblem as Type MB **12** (75×57 mm) by ISP Walsall.

MB13 (£3·78) Containing six 1st Class self-adhesive stamps (No. 3709) .... 10·00

No. MB13 has the self-adhesive paper around each stamp removed and a single small notch at the top right.

MB **14**

2015 (9 Sept). *Long to Reign Over Us.* Lilac cover with multicoloured emblem as Type MB **14** (74×58 mm) by ISP Walsall.

MB14 (£3·78) Containing six 1st Class self-adhesive stamps (No. U3745, code 'REIGS')................................ 7·00

No. MB14 has the self-adhesive paper around each stamp removed and a single small notch at the top right.

Year code for MB14 is "015R".

2016. *Long to Reign Over Us.* Lilac cover with multicoloured emblem as Type MB **14** (74×58 mm) by ISP Walsall. Repeating 'ROYALMAIL' wording (Type PB-Up) printed on the front of the self-adhesive backing paper

MB15 (£3·78) Containing six 1st Class self-adhesive stamps (No. U3745, code "REIGS") .... 13·00

No. MB15 has the self-adhesive paper around each stamp removed and a single small notch at the top right.

Year codes for MB15 are "015R" or "016R".

2016 (18 Feb). *175th Anniversary of the Penny Red.* Red cover with multicoloured emblem as Type MB **12** (74×57 mm) by ISP Walsall.

MB16 (£3·78) Containing six 1st Class self-adhesive stamps (No. 3806)................................ 7·00

No. MB16 has the self-adhesive paper around each stamp removed and a single small notch at the top right-hand edge

6 × 1st *Long to Reign Over Us* retail booklets with self-adhesive Security Machins, with source code and year code. Printed in gravure by ISP Walsall. With lilac covers as noted below. Front of the self-adhesive backing paper plain, or with repeating 'ROYALMAIL' wording as noted.

Booklet	Stamp	Booklet description	Backing paper type	Source/year code	
MB14	U3745 1st bright lilac	Lilac cover (Type MB**14**)	Plain	'REIGS''015R'	7.00
MB15	U3745 1st bright lilac	Lilac cover (Type MB**14**)	Type PB-Up	'REIGS''015R'	—
			Type PB-Up	'REIGS''016R'	13.00

MB **17**

2016 (28 July). |MULTI COLOUR| cover as Type MB **17** (74×57 mm) by ISP Walsall. Repeating 'ROYALMAIL' wording (Type PB-Up) printed on the front of the self-adhesive backing paper.
MB17 (£3·84) Containing six 1st Class self-adhesive stamps
(No. U3024, code 'MSIL') 6.75
No. MB17 has the surplus self-adhesive paper around each stamp removed and a single small notch at the top right.
Year code for MB17 is "M16L".

MB **18**

2016 (20 Oct). |MULTI COLOUR| cover as Type MB **18** (74×57 mm) by ISP Walsall. Repeating 'ROYALMAIL' wording printed on the front of the self-adhesive backing paper.
MB18 (£3·84) Containing six 1st Class self-adhesive stamps
(No. U3028, code 'MSIL') (Type PB-Up) .... 7·00
a. With alternate pairs of lines in background text inverted (Type PB-Ls/sL) .... 10·00

No. MB18 has the surplus self-adhesive paper around each stamp removed and a single small notch at the top right-hand edge.
MB18a exists with the large 'ROYALMAIL' lettering above the small and with the small above the large in the alternate pairs of lines in the background text.
Year code for MB18 is "M16L", and for MB18a "M16L" or "M17L".

MB **19**

2017 (5 June). *The Machin Definitive: 50th Anniversary*. Red cover with multicoloured emblem as Type MB **19** (74×57 mm) by ISP Walsall. Repeating 'ROYALMAIL' wording (Type PB-Up) printed on the front of the self-adhesive backing paper.
MB19 (£3·90) Containing six 1st Class self-adhesive stamps
(No. U3028, code MSIL) 6.50
No. MB19 has the surplus self-adhesive paper around each stamp removed and a single small notch at the top right-hand edge.
No. MB19 has the 'ROYALMAIL' printed backing paper upright (Type PB-Up).
Year code for MB19 is "M17L".

2018 (23 Jan). *Game of Thrones*. Red cover with multicoloured emblem as Type MB **19** (74×57 mm) by ISP Walsall. Repeating 'ROYALMAIL' wording printed on the front of the self-adhesive backing paper, with alternate pairs of lines inverted.
MB20 (£3·90) Containing six 1st Class self-adhesive stamps
(No. 4044a) 6.50
No. MB20 has the surplus self-adhesive paper around each stamp removed and a single small notch at the top right-hand edge.
MB20 has the large 'ROYALMAIL' lettering above the small (Type PB-Ls) in the alternate pairs of lines in the background text.

Containing ten 2nd Class stamps

2001 (29 Jan). |MULTI COLOUR| laminated cover as Type MA **1** (74×56 mm). Stamps printed on the cover in bright blue by Questa.
MC1 (£1·90) Containing ten 2nd Class self-adhesive stamps
(No. 2039) .... 7·50
No. MC1 was intended for use in stamp machines.

Containing ten 1st Class stamps

2001 (29 Jan). |MULTI COLOUR| laminated cover as Type MA **1** (74×56 mm). Stamps printed on the cover in bright orange-red by Questa.
MD1 (£2·70) Containing ten 1st Class self-adhesive stamps
(No. 2040) .... 9·00
No. MD1 was intended for use in stamp machines.

---

6 × 1st retail booklets with self-adhesive Security Machins, with source code (top right), with year code.
Printed in gravure by ISP Walsall. With covers as noted below.
Repeating 'ROYALMAIL' wording printed on the front of the self-adhesive backing paper.
Stamps vermilion or bright scarlet.

Booklet	Stamp	Booklet description	Backing paper type	Source/year code	
MB17	U3024 1st vermilion	Padlock cover, traditional style typeface on outside cover (sharp edges to value indicator) (Type MB**17**)	Type PB-Up	'MSIL' 'M16L'	6.75
MB18	U3028 1st bright scarlet	Padlock cover, new corporate style typeface on outside cover (rounded edges to value indicator) (Type MB**18**), as issued on 20 October 2016	Type PB-Up	'MSIL' 'M16L'	7.00
MB18a	U3028 1st bright scarlet	Cover as MB18	Type PB-Ls/sL	'MSIL' 'M16L'	13.00
			Type PB-Ls/sL	'MSIL' 'M17L'	10.00

Note. The repeating 'ROYALMAIL' wording that is printed on the front of the backing paper where alternate pairs of lines are inverted can exist in two versions, with Large lettering above small (Type PB-Ls), and with small lettering above Large (Type PB-sL). For further information see the notes to the tables listing source and year-code combinations which follow the Security Machin listing. Where a booklet is known with both Type PB-Ls and Type PB-sL the price quoted is for the cheaper of the two versions, whichever that is. Type PB-Up are noted and priced separately.

Containing 12 2nd Class stamps

2001 (29 Jan). |MULTI COLOUR| laminated cover as Type MA **1** (74×56 mm). Stamps printed on the cover in bright blue by Questa.
ME1 (£2·28) Containing twelve 2nd Class self-adhesive
stamps (No. 2039)... 8·50
No. ME1 was re-issued on 1 August 2001 showing "Cod Post" added to the "Ffôn Testun" inscription on the back cover.

ME **2**

2002 (4 July). |MULTI COLOUR| laminated cover as Type ME **2** (74×57 mm) printed by Questa with the surplus self-adhesive paper around each stamp removed.
ME2 (£2·28) Containing twelve 2nd Class self-adhesive
stamps (No. 2039)... 9·00
No. ME2 shows the surplus self-adhesive paper around each stamp removed and two notches at top right.

ME **3** ("The Real Network" added below logo)
2003 (27 Mar). Blue cover with multicoloured emblem as Type ME **3** (74×57 mm) by Walsall.
ME3 (£2·28) Containing twelve 2nd Class self-adhesive
stamps (No. 2039)... 9·00
No. ME3 shows the surplus self-adhesive paper around each stamp removed and has two notches at top right.

2004 (15 June).-07 Blue cover with multicoloured emblem as Type ME **2** (74×56 mm) by Walsall.

ME4 (£2·52) Containing twelve 2nd Class self-adhesive
stamps (No. 2039)... 9·00
a. (£2·76) Back cover with added text about new
pricing structure (25.4.06) .... 9·50
b. (£2·88) Back cover with text about validity (5.6.07) ... 9·50
No. ME4 has the surplus self-adhesive paper around each stamp removed and has two notches at top right.
The back cover of No. ME4a has added text as No. MB4b.
The back cover of No. ME4b has text as No. MB4c/d.

Containing 12 2nd Class "Security Machins"

2009 (31 Mar)–**11**. Blue cover with multicoloured emblem as Type ME **2** (74×57 mm) by Walsall.
ME5 (£3·24) Containing twelve 2nd Class self-adhesive
stamps (No. U2981, code "MTIL" without year code)....... 12·50
a. (£3·60) Ditto but containing No. U3013 (code "MTIL"
with year code) (2.10)... 60·00
b. (£3·84) Ditto but with printer's imprint removed
(19.8.10).. 12·50
c. (£4·32) Ditto but with FSC logo added (25.10.11)....... 13·00
No. ME5 has the surplus self-adhesive paper around each stamp removed and has two small notches at top right.
No. ME5/a are inscribed "Walsall Security Printers Limited, UK" along the left-hand edge of the back cover. This was removed for MB5b/c.
No. ME5c was re-issued on 31 July 2014 with the telephone numbers on the back cover charged from 08 to 03 numbers as for MB12. The price shown for ME5c is with either the 08 or 03 telephone numbers.
Year code for ME5a is "MA10", for ME5b "MA10" or "M11L" and for ME5c "M11L" , "M12L", "M13L" or "M14L", and for ME5c with changed telephone numbers "M14L" or "M15L".

2016. Blue cover with multicoloured emblem as Type ME 2 (74×57 mm) by Walsall. 'Repeating 'ROYALMAIL' wording (Type PB-Up) printed on the front of the self-adhesive backing paper
ME6 (£6·48) Containing twelve 2nd Class self-adhesive stamps
(No. U3013, code "MTIL" with year code)..................................... 12·50
No. ME6 was originally sold at £6·48. It has the surplus self-adhesive paper around each stamp removed and has two small notches at top right.
Year codes for ME6 are "M15L" or "M16L"

ME **7**

2016 (20 Oct). Blue cover with multicoloured emblem as Type ME **7** (74×57 mm) by Walsall. Repeating 'ROYALMAIL' wording printed on the front of the self-adhesive backing paper.
ME7 (£6·60) Containing twelve 2nd Class self-adhesive
stamps (No. U3013 code "MTIL") (Type PB-Up).................... 12.00

---

12 × 2nd retail booklets with self-adhesive Security Machins, with source code (top right), with year code.
Printed in gravure by ISP Walsall. With blue covers as noted below
Repeating 'ROYALMAIL' wording printed on the front of the self-adhesive backing paper.

Booklet	Stamp	Booklet description	Backing paper type	Source/year code	
ME6	U3013 2nd bright blue	Traditional style typeface on outside cover (sharp edges to value indicator) (Type ME2)	Type PB-Up	'MTIL''M15L'	60.00
			Type PB-Up	'MTIL''M16L'	12.50
ME7	U3013 2nd bright blue	New corporate style typeface on outside cover (rounded edges to value indicator) (Type ME7), as issued on 20 October 2016	Type PB-Up	'MTIL''M16L'	12.00
ME7a	U3013 2nd bright blue	Cover as ME7	Type PB-sL	'MTIL''M16L'	13.75
			Type PB-Ls/sL	'MTIL''M17L'	13.00

Note. The repeating 'ROYALMAIL' wording that is printed on the front of the backing paper where alternate pairs of lines are inverted can exist in two versions, with Large lettering above small (Type PB-Ls), and with small lettering above Large (Type PB-sL). For further information see the notes to the tables listing source and year-code combinations which follow the Security Machin listing. Where a booklet is known with both Type PB-Ls and Type PB-sL the price quoted is for the cheaper of the two versions, whichever that is. Type PB-Up are noted and priced separately.

a. With alternate pairs of lines in the background text
inverted (Type PB-Ls/sL)... 13.00
No. ME7 has the surplus self-adhesive paper around each stamp removed and has two small notches at top right.
No. ME7a exists with the large 'ROYALMAIL' lettering above the small and with small above the large in the alternate pairs of lines in the background text.
Year code for ME7 is "M16L", and for ME7a is "M16L" or "M17L".

Containing 12 1st Class stamps

2001 (29 Jan). |MULTI COLOUR laminated covers as Type MA **1** (74×56 mm).
Stamps printed on the covers in bright orange-red by Questa (No. MF1) or Walsall (No. MF2).
MF1   (£3·24) Containing twelve 1st Class self-adhesive
stamps (No. 2040) (Questa).. 11·00
MF2   Containing twelve 1st Class self-adhesive stamps
(No. 2040) (Walsall)... 11·00
Nos. MF1/2 were re-issued on 1 August 2001 showing "Cod Post" added to the "Ffôn Testun" inscription on the back covers.

2002 (5 June)–**07**. Gold laminated cover as Type MB **3** (74×56 mm)
by Walsall.
MF3   (£3·24) Containing twelve 1st Class self-adhesive
stamps (No. 2295)... 11·00
a. (£3·84) Back cover with added text about new
pricing structure (25.4.06).. 11·50
b. (£4·08) Back cover with text about validity (5.6.07) ... 11·00
No. MF3 shows the surplus self-adhesive paper around each stamp removed and a single notch at the top right hand edge to facilitate identification by the blind.
The back cover of No. MF3a has added text as No. MB4b.
The back cover of No. MF3b has text as No. MB4c/d.

2003 (27 Mar). Gold cover with multicoloured emblem as Type ME **3**
(74×57 mm) by Walsall.
MF4   (£3·24) Containing twelve 1st Class self-adhesive
stamps (No. 2295)... 11·00
No. MF4 shows the surplus self-adhesive paper around each stamp removed and has a single notch at top right.

Containing 12 1st Class "Security" Machins

2009 (31 Mar)–**11**. Gold cover with multicoloured emblem as Type MB **3**
(74×57 mm) by Walsall.
MF5   (£4·32) Containing twelve 1st Class self-adhesive
stamps (No. U2986, code "MTIL" without year code)....... 12·50
a. (£4·68) Ditto but with printer's imprint removed
(15.12.09)... 14·00
b. (£4·68) Ditto but containing No. U3020, code "MTIL"
with year code (.2.10)... 20·00
c. (£5·52) Ditto but with FSC logo added (25.10.11)....... 14·00
No. MF5 has the surplus self-adhesive paper around each stamp removed and has a single small notch at top right.
No. MF5 is inscribed "Walsall Security Printers Limited, UK" along the left hand edge of the back cover. This was removed for MF5a/c.
Year codes for MF5b are "MA10" and "M11L" and for MF5c "M11L" and "M12L".

2012 (6 Feb). *Diamond Jubilee.* Slate-blue cover with multicoloured
emblem as Type MB **11** (74×57 mm) by Walsall.
MF6   (£5·52) Containing twelve 1st class self-adhesive
stamps (No. U3272, code "MTND")............................. 11·00
No. MF6 has the surplus self-adhesive paper around each stamp removed and a single notch at the top right

2013 (3 Jan). Red cover with multicoloured emblem as Type MB **12**
(74×57 mm) by Walsall.
MF7   (£7·20) Containing twelve 1st Class self-adhesive stamps
(No. U3025, code "MTIL").. 12·00

No. MF7 has the surplus self-adhesive paper around each stamp removed and a single small notch at top right.
No. MF7 was re-issued on 31 July 2014 with the telephone numbers on the back cover charged from 08 to 03 numbers as for MB12. The price shown for MF7 is with the changed telephone number. With 08 telephone number £17.00
Year codes for MF7 are "M12L", "M13L" and "M14L", and with changed telephone numbers "M14L" or "M15L".

2016. Red cover with multicoloured emblem as Type MB **12** (74×57
mm) by Walsall. Repeating 'ROYALMAIL' wording (Type PB-Up)
printed on the front of the self-adhesive backing paper
MF8   (£7·56) Containing twelve 1st Class self-adhesive stamps
(No. U3025, code "MTIL")... 15·00
No. MF8 has the surplus self-adhesive paper around each stamp removed and a single small notch at top right
Year codes for MF8 are "M15L" or "M16L".

2016 (20 Oct). Red cover with multicoloured emblem as Type ME **7**
(74×57 mm) by ISP Walsall. Repeating 'ROYALMAIL' wording printed
on the front of the self-adhesive backing paper.
MF9   (£7·68) Containing twelve 1st Class self-adhesive
stamps (No. U3029, code "MTIL") (Type PB-Up) .... 13·00
a. With alternate pairs of lines in the background text
inverted (Type PB-Ls/sL)... 15·00
No. MF9 has the surplus self-adhesive paper around each stamp removed and a single small notch at top right.
No. MF9a exists with the large 'ROYALMAIL' lettering above the small and with the small above the large in the alternate pairs of lines in the background text
Year code for MF9 is "M16L", and for MF9a is "M16L" or "M17L".

Containing 20 1st Class stamps

MG **1**

1993 (19 Oct). |MULTI COLOUR *cover as Type* MG **1** (91×77 mm).
MG1   (£4·80) Containing booklet pane No. 1789a...................... 15·00

Containing six E stamps

2002 (4 July). |MULTI COLOUR laminated cover as Type ME **2** (74×57 mm) printed
by Walsall with the surplus self-adhesive paper around each stamp
removed.
MH1   (£2·22) Containing six E stamps (No. 2296) and six Air
Mail labels... 10·00

---

12 × 1st retail booklets with self-adhesive Security Machins, with source code (top right), with year code.
Printed in gravure by ISP Walsall. With red covers as noted below.
Repeating 'ROYALMAIL' wording printed on the front of the self-adhesive backing paper.
Stamps vermilion or bright scarlet.

Booklet	Stamp	Booklet description	Backing paper type	Source/year code	
MF8	U3025 1st vermilion	Traditional style typeface on outside cover (sharp edges to value indicator) (Type MB**12**)	Type PB-Up	'MTIL' 'M15L'	35.00
			Type PB-Up	'MTIL' 'M16L'	15.00
MF9	U3029 1st bright scarlet	New corporate style typeface on outside cover (rounded edges to value indicator) (Type ME**7**), as issued on 20 October 2016	Type PB-Up	'MTIL' 'M16L'	13.00
MF9a	U3029 1st bright scarlet	Cover as MF9	Type PB-Ls/sL	'MTIL' 'M16L'	15.00
			Type PB-Ls/sL	'MTIL' 'M17L'	15.00

Note. The repeating 'ROYALMAIL' wording that is printed on the front of the backing paper where alternate pairs of lines are inverted can exist in two versions, with Large lettering above small (Type PB-Ls), and with small lettering above Large (Type PB-sL). For further information see the notes to the tables listing source and year-code combinations which follow the Security Machin listing. Where a booklet is known with both Type PB-Ls and Type PB-sL the price quoted is for the cheaper of the two versions, whichever that is. Type PB-Up are noted and priced separately.

No. MH1 shows the surplus self-adhesive paper around each stamp removed.

2003 (28 May). |MULTI COLOUR| cover as Type MB **6** (74×57 mm with *The Real Network* added below logo) printed by Walsall with the surplus self-adhesive paper around each stamp removed.

MH2 (£2·28) Containing six E stamps (No. 2296) and six Air Mail labels .... 10·00

Containing four Europe stamps

All booklets in this section show the surplus self-adhesive paper around each stamp removed.

MI **1** ("The Real Network" below logo)

2003 (27 Mar). Ultramarine cover with multicoloured emblem as Type MI **1** (74×57 mm) by Walsall.

MI1 (£2·08) Containing four Europe 40g self-adhesive stamps (No. 2358) and four Air Mail labels .... 8·75

MI **2**

2004 (15 June). Ultramarine cover with multicoloured emblem as Type MI **2** (74×57 mm) by Walsall.

MI2 (£2·28) Containing four Europe up to 40 grams self-adhesive stamps (No. 2358) and four Air Mail labels ...... 8·75

2010 (30 Mar). Deep green cover with multicoloured emblem as Type MI **2** (74×57 mm) by Walsall.

MI3 (£2·24) Containing four Europe up to 20 grams self-adhesive stamps (No. 2357b) and four Air Mail labels ... 7·50

Containing four Worldwide stamps

All booklets in this section show the surplus self-adhesive paper around each stamp removed.

2003 (27 Mar). Red cover with multicoloured emblem as Type MI **1** (74×57 mm) by Walsall.

MJ1 (£4·48) Containing four Worldwide up to 40 grams self-adhesive stamps (No. 2359) and four Air Mail labels .... 11·75

2004 (15 June). Red cover with multicoloured emblem as Type MI **2** (74×57 mm) by Walsall.

MJ2 (£4·48) Containing four Worldwide up to 40 grams self-adhesive stamps (No. 2359) and four Air Mail labels .... 11·75

2010 (30 Mar). Deep mauve cover with multicoloured emblem as Type MI **2** (74×57 mm) by Walsall.

MJ3 (£3·60) Containing four Worldwide up to 20 grams self-adhesive stamps (No. 2358a) and four Air Mail labels .... 7·75

Containing four Worldwide postcard stamps

All booklets in this section have the surplus self-adhesive paper around each stamp removed.

2004 (1 Apr). Grey-black cover with multicoloured emblem as Type MI **2** (74×57 mm) by Walsall.

MJA1 (£1·72) Containing four Worldwide postcard self-adhesive stamps (No. 2357a) and four Air Mail labels ... 7·50

I. Self-adhesive. Barcode Booklets containing stamps with face values.

NOTE. All booklets in this section show the surplus self-adhesive paper around each stamp removed.

£2·52 Booklets

2002 (4 July). |MULTI COLOUR| laminated cover as Type ME **2** (74×57 mm) printed by Walsall with the surplus self-adhesive paper around each stamp removed.

NA1 Containing six 42p. stamps (No. 2297) and six Air Mail labels .... 25·00

2003 (28 May). |MULTI COLOUR| cover as Type MB **6** (74×57 mm with "*The Real Network*" added below logo) printed by Walsall.

NA2 Containing six 42p. stamps (No. 2297) and six Air Mail labels .... 22·50

£4·08 Booklets

2002 (4 July). |MULTI COLOUR| laminated cover as Type ME **2** (74×57 mm) printed by Walsall with the surplus self-adhesive paper around each stamp removed.

NB1 Containing six 68p. stamps (No. 2298) and six Air Mail labels .... 26·00

2003 (28 May). |MULTI COLOUR| cover as Type MB **6** (74×57 mm with *The Real Network* added below logo) printed by Walsall.

NB2 Containing six 68p. stamps (No. 2298) and six Air Mail labels .. 26·00

J. Self-adhesive Barcode Booklets containing No Value Indicated Special or Occasions issues, with Definitive stamps.

NOTE. *All booklets in this section show the surplus self-adhesive paper around each stamp retained, unless otherwise stated.*

PM **1**

2001 (13 Feb). *Cats and Dogs.* |MULTI COLOUR| cover as Type PM **1** (84×64 mm). Printed by Walsall.

PM1 (£3·24) booklet containing pane pane of twelve 1st stamps (No. 2187b) .... 25·00

PM **2**

2001 (17 Apr). *Centenary of Royal Navy Submarine Service.* |MULTI COLOUR| cover as Type PM **2** (75×57 mm). Printed by Questa.

PM2 (£1·62) booklet containing pane No. 2207a .... 70·00

2001 (4 Sept). *Punch and Judy Show Puppets.* |MULTI COLOUR| cover as Type PM **2** (74×57 mm). Printed by Questa.

PM3 (£1·62) booklet containing pane No. 2230a .... 15·00

2001 (22 Oct). *Flags and Ensigns.* |MULTI COLOUR| cover as Type PM **2** (74×57 mm). Printed by Questa.

PM4 (£1·62) booklet containing pane No. 2208a .... 15·00

2002 (2 May). *50th Anniversary of Passenger Jet Aviation. Airliners.* |MULTI COLOUR cover as Type PM **2** (74×57 mm). Printed by Questa.
PM5   (£1·62) booklet containing pane No. 2290a........................   6·25

2002 (21 May). *World Cup Football Championship, Japan and Korea.* |MULTI COLOUR cover as Type PM **2** (74×57 mm). Printed by Walsall.
PM6   (£1·62) booklet containing pane No. 2293a........................   6·25

PM **7**

2002 (10 Sept). *Bridges of London.* Gold cover with multicoloured emblem and stamp illustration as Type PM **7** (74×57 mm). Printed by Questa.
PM7   (£1·62) booklet containing pane No. 2314a........................   7·00
No. PM7 shows the surplus self-adhesive paper around each stamp removed and a single notch at top right.

2003 (4 Mar). *Occasions* Greetings Stamps. Gold cover with multicoloured emblem and stamp illustration as Type PM **7** (74×57 mm). Printed by Questa.
PM8   (£1·62) booklet containing pane No. 2264ab......................   7·50
No. PM8 shows the surplus self-adhesive paper around each stamp removed and a single notch at top right.

PM **9** ("The Real Network" added below logo)

2003 (29 Apr). *Extreme Endeavours.* Gold cover with multicoloured emblem and stamp illustration as Type PM **9** (74×57 mm). Printed by De La Rue.
PM9   (£1·62) booklet containing pane No. 2366a........................   7·50
No. PM9 shows the surplus self-adhesive paper around each stamp removed and has a single notch at top right.

2003 (15 July). *A British Journey: Scotland.* Gold cover with multicoloured emblem and stamp illustration as Type PM **9** (74×57 mm). Printed by De La Rue.
PM10   (£1·68) booklet containing pane No. 2391a........................   8·00
No. PM10 has the self-adhesive paper removed from each stamp removed and has a single notch at top right.

2003 (18 Sept). *Classic Transport Toys.* Gold cover with multicoloured emblem and stamp illustration as Type PM **7** (74×57 mm). Printed by De La Rue.
PM11   (£1·68) booklet containing pane No. 2403a........................   6·75
No. PM11 shows the surplus self-adhesive paper around each stamp removed and has a single notch at top right.

2004 (16 Mar). *A British Journey: Northern Ireland.* Gold cover with multicoloured emblem and stamp illustration as Type PM **7** (74×57 mm). Printed by De La Rue.
PM12   (£1·68) booklet containing pane No. 2445a........................   6·75
No. PM12 shows the surplus self-adhesive paper around each stamp removed and has a single notch at top right.

2004 (13 Apr). *Ocean Liners.* Gold cover with multicoloured emblem and stamp illustration as Type PM **7** (74×57 mm). Printed by De La Rue.
PM13   (£1·68) booklet containing pane No. 2455a........................   6·75
No. PM13 has the self-adhesive paper around each stamp removed and has a single notch at top right.

2004 (15 June). *A British Journey: Wales.* Gold cover with multicoloured emblem and stamp illustration as Type PM **7** (74×57 mm). Printed by De La Rue.
PM14   (£1·68) booklet containing pane No. 2472a........................   6·75
No. PM14 has the self-adhesive paper around each stamp removed and has a single notch at top right.

PM **15**

2008 (13 May). *Beside the Seaside.* Red cover with multicoloured emblem (74×57 mm) as Type PM **15**. Printed by Walsall.
PM15   (£2·16) booklet containing pane No. 2848a........................   6·75
No. PM15 has the self-adhesive paper removed from around the 1st class gold stamps only and has a single notch at top right.

Booklets containing "Security" Machins

Unless otherwise stated all 1st Class Machin stamps are coded "MCIL" and for PM16–PM21 without year codes. The self-adhesive backing paper is removed from around the Machin stamps and the booklets have a single notch at top right.

PM36 contains four definitive-size Tardis stamps in place of the usual Machin design.

2009 (10 Mar). *Design Classics 1* (Telephone Kiosk and Routemaster Bus). Red cover with multicoloured emblem as Type PM **15** (74×57 mm). Printed by Walsall.
PM16   (£2·16) booklet containing pane No. 2911a........................   5·75

2009 (21 Apr). *Design Classics 2* (Mini). Red cover with multicoloured emblem as Type PM **15** (74×57 mm). Printed by Walsall.
PM17   (£2·34) booklet containing pane No. 2913a........................   5·75

2009 (21 May). *50th Anniversary of NAFAS* (National Association of Flower Arrangement Societies). Red cover with multicoloured emblem as Type PM **15** (74×57 mm). Printed by Walsall.
PM18   (£2·34) booklet containing pane No. 2942a........................   10.00

2009 (18 Aug). *Design Classics 3* (Concorde). Red cover with multicoloured emblem as Type PM **15** (74×57 mm). Printed by Walsall.
PM19   (£2·34) booklet containing pane No. 2914a........................   5·75

2009 (17 Sept). *Design Classics 4* (Miniskirt). Red cover with multicoloured emblem as Type PM **15** (74×57 mm). Printed by Walsall.
PM20   (£2·34) booklet containing pane No. 2915a........................   5·75

2010 (7 Jan). *Olympic and Paralympic Games, London (2012) 1 (Judo and Archery).* Red cover with multicoloured emblem as Type PM **15** (74×57 mm). Printed by Walsall.
PM21   (£2·34) booklet containing pane No. 3020a........................   5·75

2010 (25 Feb). *Olympic and Paralympic Games, London (2012) 2 (Track and Basketball).* Red cover with multicoloured emblem as Type PM **15** (74×57 mm). Printed by Walsall.
PM22   (£2·34) booklet containing pane No. 3022a........................   5·75
The year code for U3016 is "MA10".

2010 (15 June). *Mammals.* Red cover with multicoloured emblem as Type PM **15** (74×57 mm). Printed by Walsall.
PM23   (£2·46) booklet containing pane No. 3095a........................   10·75
Year code for No. U3016 is "MA10".

2010 (27 July). *Olympic and Paralympic Games, London (2012) 3 (Rowing and Tennis).* Red cover with multicoloured emblem as Type PM **15** (74×57 mm). Printed by Walsall.
PM24   (£2·46) booklet containing pane No. 3107a........................   5·75
Year code for No. U3016 is "MA10".

2010 (15 Sept). *British Design Classics 5* (Spitfire). Red cover with multicoloured emblem as Type PM **15** (74×57 mm). Printed by Walsall.
PM25   (£2·46) booklet containing pane No. 2915ba......................   5·75
Year code for No. U3016 is "MA10".

2010 (12 Oct). *Olympic and Paralympic Games, London (2012) 4 (Football and Cycling).* Red cover with multicoloured emblem as Type PM **15** (74×57 mm). Printed by Walsall.
PM26   (£2·46) booklet containing pane No. 3108ab....................   5·75
Year code for No. U3016 is "MA10".

2011 (11 Jan). *F.A.B. The Genius of Gerry Anderson'* Red cover with multicoloured emblem as Type PM **15** (74×57 mm). Printed by Walsall.

PM27 (£2·46) booklet containing pane No. 3143a.......................... 5·75
    Year code for No. U3016 is "M11L".

2011 (24 Feb). *50th Anniversary of the British Heart Foundation*. Red cover with multicoloured emblems as Type PM **15** (74×57 mm). Printed by Walsall.

PM28 (£2·46) booklet containing pane No. 3153a.......................... 5·75
    Year code for No. U3016 is "M11L".

2011 (14 Jun). *Thomas the Tank Engine*. Red cover with multicoloured emblem (74×57 mm) as Type PM **15**. Printed by Walsall.

PM29 (£2·76) booklet containing pane No. 3194a.......................... 5·75
    Year code for No. U3016 is "M11L".

2011 (27 July). *Olympic and Paralympic Games*, London (**2012**) 5 (Wheelchair Rugby and Sailing). Red cover with multicoloured emblem as Type PM **15** (74×57 mm). Printed by Walsall.

PM30 (£2·76) booklet containing pane No. 3205a.......................... 5·50
    Year code for No. U3016 is "M11L".

2011 (23 Aug). *Classic Locomotives of England*. Red cover with multicoloured emblem as Type PM **15** (74×57 mm). Printed by Walsall.

PM31 (£2·76) booklet containing pane No. 3215a.......................... 5·75
    Year code for No. U3016 is "M11L".

2011 (15 Sept). *Olympic and Paralympic Games, London (2012) 6* (Gymnastics and Fencing). Red cover with multicoloured emblem as Type PM **15** (74×57 mm). Printed by Walsall.

PM32 (£2·76) booklet containing pane No. 3206ab .... 5·50
    Year code for No. U3016 is "M11L".

2012 (31 May). *Diamond Jubilee*. Red cover with multicoloured emblem (74×57 mm) as Type PM **15**. Printed by Walsall.

PM33 (£3·60) booklet containing pane No. 3327a.......................... 6·00
    The 1st class slate-blue stamps (No. U3274) are coded 'MCND'.

2012 (27 Sept). *Classic Locomotives of Scotland*. Red cover with multicoloured emblem as Type PM 15 (74×57 mm). Printed by Walsall.

PM34 (£3·60) booklet containing pane No. 3407a.......................... 5·75
    The 1st class slate-blue stamps (No. U3274) are coded 'MCND'.

2013 (9 Jan). *150th Anniversary of the London Underground*. Red cover with multicoloured emblem as Type PM **15** (74×57 mm). Printed by Walsall.

PM35 (£3·60) booklet containing pane No. 3430a.......................... 6·75
    Year code for No. U3022 to "M12L".

2013 (26 Mar). *50th Anniversary of Doctor Who* (TV programme). Red cover with multicoloured emblem as Type PM **15** (74×57 mm). Printed by Walsall. Self-adhesive.

PM36 (£3·60) booklet containing No. 3448a.......................... 14·00

2013 (9 May). *Football Heroes*. Red cover with multicoloured emblem (74×57 mm) as Type PM **15**. Printed by Walsall .

PM37 (£3·60) booklet containing pane No. 3475a.......................... 10·00
    Year code for No. U3022 is "M13L".

2013 (18 Jun). *Classic Locomotives of Northern Ireland*. Red cover with multicoloured emblem as Type PM **15** (75×58 mm). Printed by Walsall.

PM38 (£3·60) booklet containing pane No. 3497a.......................... 5·75
    Year code for No. U3022 is "M13L".

2013 (11 July). *Butterflies*. Red cover with multicoloured emblem as Type PM **15** (74×57 mm) Printed by Walsall.

PM39 (£3·60) booklet containing pane No. 3509a.......................... 6·00
    Year code for No. U3022 is "M13L".

2013 (19 Sept). *Royal Mail Transport: By Land and Sea*. Red cover with multicoloured emblem as Type PM **15** (74×58 mm). Printed by Walsall.

PM40 (£3·60) booklet containing pane No. 3530a.......................... 14·00
    Year code for No. U3022 is "M13L".

2014 (20 Feb). *Football Heroes*. Red cover with multicoloured emblem (74×57 mm) as Type PM **15**. Printed by Walsall.

PM41 (£3·60) booklet containing pane No. 3477a.......................... 10·00
    Year code for No. U3022 is "M13L".

2014 (15 Apr). *Buckingham Palace, London*. Red cover with multicoloured emblem (74×57 mm) as Type PM **15**. Printed by Walsall.

PM42 (£3·72) booklet containing pane No. 3595a.......................... 5·50
    Year code for No. U3022 is "M14L".

2014 (17 July). *Commonwealth Games, Glasgow*. Red cover with multicoloured emblem as Type PM **15** (74×57 mm). Printed by Walsall.

PM43 (£3·72) booklet containing pane No. 3625a.......................... 5·50
    Year code for No. U3022 is "M14L".

2014 (18 Aug). *Sustainable and Threatened Fish*. Red cover with multicoloured emblem as Type PM **15** (74×57 mm). Printed by Walsall.

PM44 (£3·72) booklet containing pane No. 3632a.......................... 5·50
    Year code for No. U3022 is "M14L".

2014 (18 Sep). *Classic Locomotives of Wales*. Red cover with multicoloured emblem as Type PM **15** (74×57 mm). Printed by Walsall.

PM45 (£3·72) booklet containing pane No. 3634a.......................... 5·50
    Year code for No. U3022 is "M14L".

2015 (6 Jan). *Alice in Wonderland*. Red cover with multicoloured emblem as Type PM **15** (74×57 mm). Printed by ISP Walsall.

PM46 (£3·72) booklet containing pane No. 3668a.......................... 12·00
    Year code for No. U3022 is "M15L".

2015 (1 Apr). *Comedy Greats*. Red cover with multicoloured emblem as Type PM **15** (74×57 mm). Printed by ISP Walsall.

PM47 (£3·78) booklet containing pane No. 3707a.......................... 9·00
    Year code for No. U3022 is "M15L".

2015 (18 Aug). *Bees*. Red cover with multicoloured emblem as Type PM **15** (74×57 mm). Printed by ISP Walsall.

PM48 (£3·78) booklet containing pane No. 3743a.......................... 5·75
    Year code fo No. U3022 is "M15L".

2015 (18 Sept). *Rugby World up*. Re cover with multicoloured emblem as Type PM **15** (74×57 mm). Printed by ISP Walsall.

PM49 (£3·78) booklet containing pane No. 3756a.......................... 6·50
    Year code for No. U3746 is "015R".

'ROYALMAIL' printed backing paper. From No. PM50 all booklets in this section have repeating undulating 'ROYALMAIL' background in two sizes of grey text printed on the front of the backing paper. On Nos. PM50/56 the text is upright (Type PB-Up); from PM57 alternate pairs of lines are inverted (Type PB-Ls/sL).

2016 (21 Apr-9 Jun). *90thBirthday of Queen Elizabeth II*. Red covers with multicoloured emblem as Type PM **15** (74×57 mm). Printed by ISP Walsall.

PM50 (£3·84) booklet containing pane No. 3833a.......................... 5·75
PM51 (£3·84) booklet containing pane No. 3835a.......................... 5·75
    Year code for No. U3746 is "016R".

2016 (28 July). *150th Birth Anniversary of Beatrix Potter*. Red cover with multicoloured emblem as Type PM **15** (74×56 mm). Printed by ISP Walsall.

PM52 (£3·84) booklet containing pane No. 3862a.......................... 5·75
    Year code for No. U3746 is "016R".

2016 (16 Aug). *Landscape Gardens*. Red cover with multicoloured emblem as Type PM **15** (74×57 mm). Printed by ISP Walsall.

PM53 (£3·84) booklet containing pane No. 3877a.......................... 5·75
    Year code for No. U3746 is "016R".

PM **54**

2016 (20 Oct). *Mr. Men and Little Miss* (children's books by Roger Hargreaves). Red cover with multicoloured emblem as Type PM **54** (74×57 mm). Printed by ISP Walsall.

PM54 (£3·84) booklet containing pane No. 3901a.......................... 5·75
    Year code for No. U3027 is "M16L".

2017 (15 Feb). *Windsor Castle*. Red cover with multicoloured emblem as Type PM **54** (74×57 mm). Printed by ISP Walsall.

PM55 (£3·84) booklet containing pane No. 3926a.......................... 5·75
    Year code for No. U3027 is "M17L".

2017 (14 Mar). *David Bowie* (1947-2016, singer, songwriter and actor) *Commemoration*. Red cover with multicoloured emblem as Type PM **54** (74×57 mm). Printed by ISP Walsall.

PM56 (£3·84) booklet containing pane No. 3934a.......................... 5·75
    Year code for No. U3027 is "M17L".

2017 (12 Oct). *Star Wars*. Red covers with MULTI COLOUR emblems as Type PM **54** (74×57 mm). Printed by ISP Walsall.

PM57 (£3·90) booklet containing pane No. 4015a.......................... 6.00
PM58 (£3·90) booklet containing pane No. 4017a.......................... 6.00
    Year code for No. U3027 is "M17L".

2018 (20 Mar). *Centenary of the RAF* (Royal Air Force). Red cover with multicoloured emblem as Type PM **54** (74×57 mm). Printed by ISP Walsall.

PM59 (£3·90) booklet containing pane No. 4065a.......................... 5·75
    Year code for No. U3027 is "M18L".

K. Self-adhesive Barcode Booklets containing No Value Indicated "Smilers" stamps in definitive size.

Containing six "Smilers" stamps

NOTE. Nos. QA1–4and QB1 have the self-adhesive paper around each stamp removed and have a single notch at top right.

QA **1**

2005 (4 Oct). Gold cover with multicoloured emblem as Type QA **1** (74×56 mm) by Walsall.
QA1   (£1·80) booklet containing No. 2567a.................................... 9·00

QA **2**

2006 (17 July). Gold cover with multicoloured emblem as Type QA **2** (74×56 mm) by Walsall.
QA2   (£1·92) booklet containing No. 2567a .... 10·00

2006 (17 Oct). Gold cover with multicoloured emblem as Type QA **1** (74×56 mm) by Walsall.
QA3   (£1·92) containing No. 2672a .... 6·25

2008 (28 Feb). Gold cover with multicoloured emblem as Type QA **2** (74×56 mm) by Walsall.
QA4   (£2·04) booklet containing No. 2819a................................. 30·00

Containing 12 "Smilers" stamps

2015 (20 Jan). Red cover with multicoloured emblem as Type MB **12** (74×57 mm).
QB1   (£7·44) booklet containing No. 3670a.................................. 17·50

L. Self-adhesive Barcode Booklets containing stamps with value indicator at upper left.

Containing four 2nd Class Large stamps

RA **1**

2006 (15 Aug). Blue cover with multicoloured emblem as Type RA **1** (74×57 mm) by Walsall.
RA1   (£1·48) Containing four 2nd Class Large self-adhesive
        stamps (No. 2656) .... 5·00
No. RA1 has the surplus self-adhesive paper around each stamp removed and two notches at top right for identification by the blind.

Containing four 2nd Class Large "Security" stamps

2009 (31 Mar)–**11**. Blue cover with multicoloured emblem as Type RA **1** (74×57 mm) by Walsall.
RA2   (£1·68) Containing four 2nd Class Large self-adhesive
        stamps (No. U2988 code "FOYAL" without year code) .... 7·50
    a. (£2·04) Ditto but containing No. U3032 (code "MFIL"
        with year code) (8.5.10) .... 60·00
    b. (£2·04) Ditto but with printer's imprint removed
        (22.3.11) .... 5·75
    c. (£2·32) Ditto but with FSC logo added (25.10.11) .... 5·50
No. RA2 has the surplus self-adhesive paper around each stamp removed and two large notches at top right.
Nos. RA2/a are inscribed "Walsall Security Printers Limited, UK" along the left-hand edge of the back cover. This was removed from Nos. RA2b/c.
No. RA2c was reissued on 31 July 2014 with the telephone numbers on the back cover charged from 08 to 03 numbers as for MB12. The price shown for RA2c is with either the 08 or 03 telephone numbers.
Year code for RA2a is "MA10", for RA2b "MA11" and for RA2c "MA11", "MA12", "MA13" or "MA14", and with changed telephone numbers "MA14" or "MA15".

2016. Blue cover with multicoloured emblem as Type RA **1** (74×57 mm) by ISP Walsall. Repeating 'ROYALMAIL' wording (Type PB-Up) printed on the front of the self-adhesive backing paper.
RA3   (£3·00) Containing four 2nd Class Large self-adhesive
        stamps (No. U3032 code "MFIL") .... 12·00
No. RA3 has the surplus self-adhesive paper around each stamp removed and two large notches at top right.
Year code for RA3 is "M16L".

---

4 x 2nd Large retail booklets with self-adhesive Security Machins, with source code (in front of hair), with year code. Printed in gravure by IPS Walsall. With blue covers as noted below.
Repeating 'ROYALMAIL' wording printed on the front of the self-adhesive backing paper.

Booklet	Stamp	Booklet description	Backing paper type	Source/year code	
RA3	U3032 2nd bright blue	Traditional style typeface on outside cover (sharp edges to value indicator) (Type RA**1**)	Type PB-Up	'MFIL''M16L'	12.00
RA4	U3032 2nd bright blue	New corporate style typeface on outside cover (rounded edges to value indicator) (Type RA**4**), as issued on 20 October 2016	Type PB-Up	'MFIL''M16L'	10.00
RA4a	U3032 2nd bright blue	Cover as RA4	Type PB-Ls	'MFIL''M17L'	10.00

Note. The repeating 'ROYALMAIL' wording that is printed on the front of the backing paper where alternate pairs of lines are inverted can exist in two versions, with Large lettering above small (Type PB-Ls), and with small lettering above Large (Type PB-sL). For further information see the notes to the tables listing source and year-code combinations which follow the Security Machin listing. Where a booklet is known with both Type PB-Ls and Type PB-sL the price quoted is for the cheaper of the two versions, whichever that is. Type PB-Up are noted and priced separately.

RA **4**

2016 (20 Oct). Blue cover with multicoloured emblem as Type RA **4** (74×56 mm) by ISP Walsall. Repeating 'ROYALMAIL' wording printed on the front of the self-adhesive backing paper

RA4   (£3·00) Containing four 2nd Class Large self-adhesive
stamps (No. U3032 code "MFIL") (Type PB-Up)..................... 10.00
  a. With alternate pairs of lines in the background text
  inverted (Type PB-Ls) 10.00
  No. RA4 has the surplus self-adhesive paper around each stamp removed and two large notches at top right.
  No. RA4a exists only with the large 'ROYALMAIL' lettering above the small.
  Year code for RA4 is "M16L", and for RA4a is "M17L".

Containing four 1st Class Large stamps

RB **1**

2006 (15 Aug). Gold cover with multicoloured emblem as Type RB **1** (74×57 mm) by Walsall.

RB1   (£1·76) Containing four 1st Class Large self-adhesive
stamps (No. 2657) .... 6·50
  No. RB1 has the surplus self-adhesive paper around each stamp removed and a single large notch at top right.

Containing four 1st Class Large "Security" stamps

2009 (31 Mar).–11 Gold cover with multicoloured emblem as Type RB **1** (74×57 mm) by Walsall.

RB2   (£2·08) Containing four 1st Class Large self-adhesive
stamps (No. U2990 code "FOYAL" without year code) ....   11·00
  a. (£2·62) Ditto but containing No. U3035 (code "MFIL"
  with year code) (8.5.10) ....   20·00
  b. (£2·62) Ditto but with printer's imprint removed
  (22.3.11) ....   7·25
  c. (£3·00) Ditto but with FSC logo added (25.10.11) ....   7·25
  No. RB2 has the surplus self-adhesive paper around each stamp removed and a single large notch at top right.
  No. RB2/a are inscribed "Walsall Security Printers Limited, UK" along the left-hand edge of the back cover. This was removed for RB2b/c.
  Year code for RB2a is "MA10" and for RB2b/c "MA11".

2012 (25 Apr). *Diamond Jubilee.* Slate-blue cover with multicoloured emblem as Type RB **1** (74×57 mm) by Walsall.

RB3 (£3·00) Containing four 1st Class Large self-adhesive
stamps (No. U3277, code "JUBILFE") ....   7·00
  No. RB3 has the surplus self-adhesive paper around each stamp removed and a single large notch at top right.

RB **4**

2013 (3 Jan). Red cover with multicoloured emblem as Type RB **4** (74×57 mm) by Walsall.

RB4 (£3·60) Containing four 1st Class Large self-adhesive
stamps (No. U3037, code "MFIL") ....   7·00
  No. RB4 has the surplus self-adhesive paper around each stamp removed and a single large notch at top right.
  No. RB4 was reissued on 31 July 2014 with the telephone numbers on the back cover charged from 08 to 03 numbers as for MB12. The price shown for RB4 is with either the 08 or 03 telephone numbers.
  Year codes for RB4 are "MA12", "MA13" or "MA14", and with changed telephone numbers "MA14" or "MA15".

2016. Red cover with multicoloured emblem as Type RB **4** (74×57 mm) by ISP Walsall. 'Repeating 'ROYALMAIL' wording (Type PB-Up) printed on the front of the self-adhesive backing paper

RB5   (£3·80) Containing four 1st Class Large self-adhesive
stamps (No. U3037, code "MFIL") ....   12·00
  No. RB5 has the surplus self-adhesive paper around each stamp removed and a single large notch at top right.
  Year code for RB5 is "MA15" or "M16L"

**4 x 1st Large retail booklets with self-adhesive Security Machins, with source code (in front of hair), with year code.
Printed in gravure by ISP Walsall. With red covers as noted below.
Repeating 'ROYALMAIL' wording printed on the front of the self-adhesive backing paper.
Stamps vermilion or bright scarlet.**

Booklet	Stamp	Booklet description	Backing paper type	Source/year code	
RB5	U3037 1st vermilion	Traditional style typeface on outside cover (sharp edges to value indicator) (Type RB4)	Type PB-Up Type PB-Up	'MFIL'MA15' 'MFIL'M16L'	12.00 13.00
RB6	U3039 1st bright scarlet	New corporate style typeface on outside cover (rounded edges to value indicator) (Type RB6), as issued on 20 October 2016	Type PB-Up	'MFIL'M16L'	10.00
RB6a	U3039 1st bright scarlet	Cover as RB6	Type PB-Ls/sL	'MFIL'M17L'	10.50

Note. The repeating 'ROYALMAIL' wording that is printed on the front of the backing paper where alternate pairs of lines are inverted can exist in two versions, with Large lettering above small (Type PB-Ls), and with small lettering above Large (Type PB-sL). For further information see the notes to the tables listing source and year-code combinations which follow the Security Machin listing. Where a booklet is known with both Type PB-Ls and Type PB-sL the price quoted is for the cheaper of the two versions, whichever that is. Type PB-Up are noted and priced separately.

RB **6**

2016 (20 Oct). Red cover with multicoloured emblem as Type RB **6** (74×57 mm). Printed by ISP Walsall. Repeating 'ROYALMAIL' wording printed on the front of the self-adhesive backing paper.

RB6   (£3·84) Containing four 1st Class Large self-adhesive stamps (No. U3039, code "MFIL") (Type PB-Up)................... 10.00
      a. With alternate pairs of lines in the background text inverted (Type PB-Ls/sL)............................... 10.50

No. RB6 has the surplus self-adhesive paper around each stamp removed and a single large notch at top right.

No. RB6a exists with the large 'ROYALMAIL' lettering above the small and with the small above the large in the alternate pairs of lines in the background text

Year code for RB6 is "M16L", and for RB6a is "M17L".

Containing six "Pricing in Proportion" 1st class stamps
2006 (12 Sept)–**2007**. Gold cover with multicoloured emblem as Type MB **3** (74×57 mm) by Walsall.

RC1   (£1·92) Containing six 1st Class self-adhesive stamps (No. 2655) .... 5·50
      a. Inside cover with "don't just send a stamp" advertisement (2.10.06) .... 7·00
      b. Inside cover with "To find the correct postcodes for your mail" notice (1.2.07) .... 5·50

Nos. RC1/b have the surplus self-adhesive backing paper around each stamp removed and a notch at top right.

Containing 12 "Pricing in Proportion" 2nd class stamps
2006 (12 Sept). Blue cover with multicoloured emblem as Type MB **3** (74×57 mm) by Walsall.

RD1   (£2·76) Containing twelve 2nd Class self-adhesive stamps (No. 2654) .... 9·00

Nos. RD1 has the surplus self-adhesive paper around each stamp removed and two notches at top right.

Containing 12 "Pricing in Proportion" 1st class stamps
2006 (12 Sept). Gold cover with multicoloured emblem as Type MB **3** (74×57 mm) by Walsall.

RE1   (£3·84) Containing twelve 1st Class self-adhesive stamps (No. 2655) .... 11·00

No. RE1 has the surplus self-adhesive paper around each stamp removed and a notch at top right.

M. Self-adhesive Barcode Booklets containing No Value Indicated "Smilers" stamps in definitive size, with Definitive stamps.

NOTE. Nos. SA1 and SA2 have the surplus self-adhesive paper around each stamp removed and a notch at top right.

2007 (16 Jan). Gold cover with multicoloured emblem as Type MB **3** (74×57 mm) by Walsall.

SA1   (£1·92) booklet containing No. 2693a .... 17·50

2008 (15 Jan). Gold cover with multicoloured emblem as Type MB **3** (74×57 mm) by Walsall.

SA2   (£2·04) booklet containing No. 2693b .... 16·00

POST OFFICE LABEL SHEETS

At the Stamp Show 2000 International Stamp Exhibition visitors could purchase sheets of 10 × 1st class stamps in the "Smiles" designs (as Nos. 1550/9), each stamp having a *se-tenant* label on which the exhibition visitor's picture was printed, the photographs being taken in a booth at the exhibition.

For those unable to visit the exhibition, the same sheet could be purchased from the Philatelic Bureau and from Post Office philatelic outlets with a "Stamp Show 2000" label in place of the photograph.

For Christmas 2000, sheets of 20 × 19p stamps in the "Robin in Pillar Box" design (as No. 1896) or 10 × 1st class "Father Christmas with Cracker" design (as No. 2007) were available through the Philatelic Bureau, with *se-tenant* labels as part of a "customised" service, purchasers supplying their own photographs for reproduction on the *se-tenant* label.

This service has continued under the name "Smilers", after the initial set of stamp designs employed, and was also made available at photo-booths at selected post offices. Corporate label panes, allowing commercial and charitable organisations to have their logo or message reproduced on the *se-tenant* labels were made available through the Bureau from 2000.

Label sheets have continued to be offered with a standard greeting or message. These "Generic Smilers" have been available from the Philatelic Bureau or from philatelic outlets.

As "personalised", "corporate" and "generic" label sheets could only be purchased at a premium over the face value of the stamps within them, they are not given full listing in this catalogue; neither are individual stamps (with or without their *se-tenant* label), some of which are identifiable as having come from Label Sheets, due to perforation, phosphor or printing differences.

The list which follows comprises the "generic" sheets only. Differences between the stamp in the Label Sheets and those of the standard issues are given under the respective listings in this catalogue.

An asterisk (*) in the listing indicates a difference in process, phosphor or perforation from the original design.

Smilers

LS **1**

2000 (22 May). *The Stamp Show 2000*. Type LS **1**. Gravure Questa. Original selling price £2·95. Perf 15×14.

LS1	10×(1st) "Smiles" stamps, as Nos. 1550/9 and attached labels	22·00

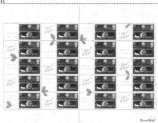

LS **2**

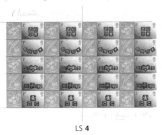

LS **3**

2000 (3 Oct)–**01**. *Christmas*. Types LS **2** and LS **3**. Gravure Questa. Original selling price £3·99 (LS 2/2a) and £2·95 (LS 3/a). Perf 15×14.

LS2	20×19p. "Robin in Pillar Box" stamps, as No. 1896 and attached labels (Imprint "Post Office 2000")	£125
	a. Imprint "Consignia 2001" (9.10.01)	£600

LS3	10×(1st) "Father Christmas with Cracker" stamps, as No. 2007 and attached labels (Imprint "Post Office 2000")	£125
	a. Imprint "Consignia 2001" (9.10.01)	£600

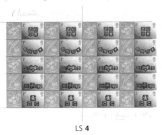

LS **4**

2001 (5 June). *Occasions*. Type LS **4**. Litho* Questa. Original selling price £5·95. Perf 14×14½.

LS4	20×(1st) "Occasions" stamps as Nos. 2182/6 in four vertical columns of five with attached labels	35·00

2001 (3 July). *Smiles* As Type LS **1** but with greetings shown in attached labels. Litho* Questa. Original selling price £2·95. Perf 14½×14*.

LS5	10×(1st) "Smiles" stamps, as Nos. 1550/9 and attached labels	£160

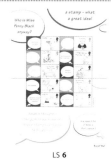

LS **6**

2001 (18 Dec). *Greetings Cartoons* Type LS **6**. Litho Questa. Original selling price £2·95. Two phosphor bands. Perf 14½×14 (without* elliptical holes).

LS6	10×(1st) Greetings Cartoons, as Nos. 1905p/14p and attached labels	28·00

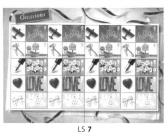

LS **7**

2002 (23 Apr). *Occasions* Stamps. Type LS **7**. Litho Questa. Original selling price £5·95. Perf 14*.

LS7	20×(1st) "Occasions" stamps as Nos. 2260/4 in four vertical columns of five with attached labels	58·00

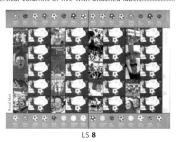

LS **8**

2002 (21 May). *Football World Cup*. Type LS **8**. Litho* Questa. Original selling price £5·95. Perf 14½×14.

LS8	20×(1st) as bottom right quarter of flag stamp in **MS**2292 and attached labels	21·00

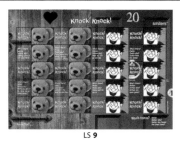

LS **9**

2002 (1 Oct). *Smiles* Type LS **9**. Litho* Questa. Original selling price
£5·95. Perf 15×14.
LS9   10×(1st) "Teddy Bear" and 10 × (1st) Dennis the
        Menace, as Nos. 1550/1, each with attached labels....... 26·00

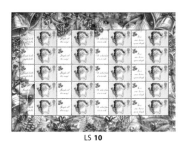

LS **10**

2002 (1 Oct). *Christmas.* Type LS **10**. Litho* Questa. Original selling price
£5·95. Perf 14½×14*.
LS10   20×(1st) "Father Christmas with Cracker", as No. 2007,
         with attached greetings labels .... 18·00

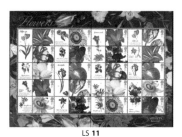

LS **11**

2003 (21 Jan). *Flower Paintings.* Type LS **11**. Litho Questa. Original selling price £5·95. Perf 14½×14 (without* elliptical holes).
LS11   20×(1st) Flowers Greetings Stamps, as Nos. 1955/64
         (two of each design) with floral labels attached .... 27·00

LS **12**

2003 (4 Feb). *Occasions.* Type LS **12**. Litho Questa. Original selling price
£5·95. Perf 14½×14.
LS12   20×(1st) "Tick box" Occasions stamps, as Nos. 2337/42
         (four of Nos. 2338 and 2340 and 3 each of the others)
         with attached labels... 20·00
         a. "Multiple Choice" in green.
    "Multiple Choice" at top left of sheet is generally in red. LS12a is
believed to have come from trial sheets which were put on sale in
error.

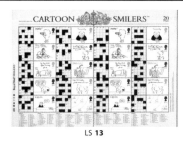

LS **13**

2003 (29 July). *Crossword Cartoons.* Type LS **13**. Litho Questa. Original
selling price £6·15. Two phosphor bands. Perf 14½×14 (without*
elliptical holes).
LS13   20×(1st) Cartoons as Nos. 1905p/14p with "Crossword"
         labels attached.. 18·00

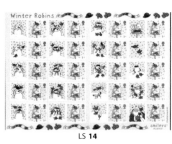

LS **14**

2003 (30 Sept). *Christmas. Winter Robins.* Type LS **14**. Litho* De La Rue.
Original selling price £6·15. Perf 14½.
LS14   20×(1st) Winter Robins, self-adhesive, as No. 2239
         with labels alongside .... 18·00

LS **15**

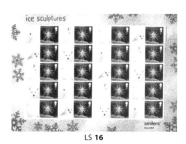

LS **16**

2003 (4 Nov). *Christmas.* Types LS **15** and LS **16**. Litho* De La Rue.
Original selling prices £4·20 (2nd) and £6·15 (1st). Perf 14½×14.
LS15   20×(2nd) Ice Sculptures, self-adhesive, as No. 2410
         with labels showing ice sculptures of polar fauna
         alongside.. 20·00
LS16   20×(1st) Ice Sculptures, self-adhesive, as No. 2411
         with labels showing photographs of polar fauna
         alongside.. 20·00

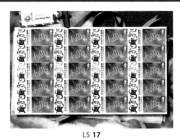

LS **17**

2004 (30 Jan). *Hong Kong Stamp Expo.* Litho Walsall. Original selling price £6·15. Perf 14½.

LS17   20×(1st) "Hello" greetings stamps, as No. 2262 with labels alongside... 17·00

LS **21**

2004 (2 Nov). *Christmas.* Type LS **21**. Litho* De La Rue. Original selling price £5·40. Perf 14½×14.

LS21   10×(2nd) and 10×(1st) "Father Christmas", self-adhesive, as Nos. 2495/6 with attached labels.................. 17·00

LS **18**

2004 (3 Feb). *Occasions Entertaining Envelopes* Type LS **18**. Litho De La Rue. Original selling price £6·15. Perf 14½×14.

LS18   20×(1st) "Entertaining Envelopes" greetings stamps, as Nos. 2424/8 (four of each design) with attached labels   17·50

LS **22**

2005 (11 Jan). *Farm Animals.* Type LS **22**. Litho* Walsall. Original selling price £6·15. Perf 14½.

LS22   20×(1st) Farm Animals, as Nos. 2502/11 with attached labels... 18·00

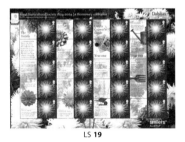

LS **19**

2004 (25 May). *Royal Horticultural Society.* Type LS **19**. Litho* Walsall. Original selling price £6·15. Perf 14½.

LS19   20×(1st) Dahlia, as No. 2457 with attached labels........... 17·50

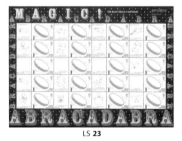

LS **23**

2005 (15 Mar). *Centenary of the Magic Circle.* Type LS **23**. Litho* Walsall. Original selling price £6·15. Perf 14½×14.

LS23   20×(1st) Spinning Coin, as No. 2525 with attached labels... 17·00

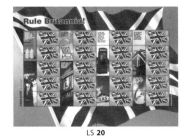

LS **20**

2004 (27 July). *Rule Britannia.* Type LS **20**. Litho* Walsall. Original selling price £6·15. Perf 14½.

LS20   20×(1st) Union Flag, as Type **1517** with attached labels... 17·50

LS **24**

2005 (21 Apr). *Pacific Explorer 2005 World Stamp Expo.* Type LS **24**. Litho Walsall. Original selling price £6·55. Perf 14*.

LS24   20×(1st) "Hello" greetings stamps, as No. 2262 with attached labels.. 17·00

LS **25**

2005 (21 June). *The White Ensign.* Type LS **25**. Litho* Cartor. Original selling price £6·55. Perf 14½.
LS25   20×(1st) White Ensign stamps, as Type **1516** with
attached labels.. 17·00

LS **26**

2005 (15 Sept). *Classic ITV.* Type LS **26**. Litho Walsall. Original selling price £6·55. Perf 14½×14.
LS26   20×(1st) Emmerdale stamps, as No. 2562 with
attached labels.. 17·00
The original printing of LS26 contained errors in some of the labels and was withdrawn prior to issue.

LS **27**

2005 (1 Nov). *Christmas. Christmas Robins.* Type LS **27**. Litho* Cartor. Original selling price £5·60. Perf 14½.
LS27   10×(2nd) and 10×(1st) Robins, self-adhesive, as
Nos. 2238/9 with attached labels .... 17·00

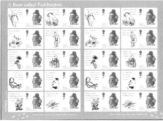

LS **28**

2006 (10 Jan). *A Bear called Paddington.* Type LS **28**. Litho Cartor. Original selling price £6·55. Perf 14½.
LS28   20×(1st) Paddington Bear, self-adhesive*, as No. 2592
with attached labels.. 17·50

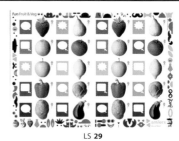

LS **29**

2006 (7 Mar). *Fun Fruit and Veg.* Type LS **29**. Litho Cartor. Original selling price £6·55. Perf 14½×14.
LS29   20×(1st) Fruit and Vegetables stamps, self-adhesive as
Nos. 2348/57 with attached labels............................. 17·50

LS **30**

2006 (25 May). *Washington 2006 International Stamp Exhibition.* Type LS **30**. Litho Cartor. Original selling price £6·95. Perf 14*.
LS30   20×(1st) "Hello" greetings stamps, as No. 2262 with
attached labels.. 17·00

LS **31**

2006 (6 June). *World Cup Football Championship, Germany. World Cup Winners* Type LS **31**. Litho Cartor. Original selling price £6·95. Perf 14½.
LS31   20×(1st) England footballer (1966) stamps, as No. 2628
with attached labels .... 17·50

LS **32**

2006 (4 July). *For Life's Special Moments.* Type LS **32**. Litho* Cartor. Original selling price £6·95. Perf 15×14.
LS32   20×(1st) "Smilers" stamps self-adhesive as Nos. 2567/72
(four of Nos. 2568/9 and 3 each of the others) with
attached labels.. 17·00

LS **33**

2006 (17 Oct). *Extra Special Moments*. Type LS **33**. Litho* Cartor. Original selling price £6·95. Perf 15×14.
LS33   20×(1st) "Smilers" stamps self-adhesive as Nos. 2672/7 (four of Nos. 2672 and 2677, 3 each of the others) with attached labels .... 17·00

LS **34**

2006 (7 Nov). *Christmas*. Type LS **34**. Litho* Cartor. Original selling price £6. Perf 15×14.
LS34   10×(2nd) and 10×(1st) Christmas self-adhesive as Nos. 2678/9 with attached labels .... 17·00

LS **35**

2006 (9 Nov). *We Will Remember Them*. Type LS **35**. Litho* Cartor. Original selling price £6·95. Perf 14½.
LS35   20×(1st) Poppies on barbed wire stems stamps as Type **1941** with attached labels .... 17·00

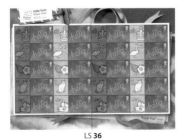

LS **36**

2006 (14 Nov). Belgica 2006 International Stamp Exhibition, Brussels. Type LS **36**. Litho Cartor. Original selling price £6·95. Perf 14*.
LS36   20×(1st) "Hello" greetings stamps, No. 2262 with attached labels .... 17·00

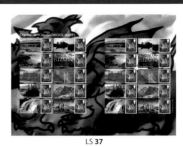

LS **37**

2007 (1 Mar). *Glorious Wales*. Type LS **37**. Litho Cartor. Original selling price £6·95. Perf 15×14 (without* elliptical holes).
LS37   20×(1st) Wales stamps, self-adhesive*, as No. W122 with attached labels .... 16·00

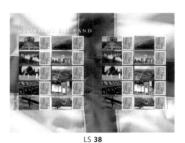

LS **38**

2007 (23 Apr). *Glorious England* . Type LS **38**. Litho Cartor. Original selling price £7·35. Perf 15×14 (without* elliptical holes).
LS38   20×(1st) England stamps, self-adhesive* as No. EN30 with attached labels .... 17·00
On labels from the original printing "Isle of Wight" was incorrectly spelled "Isle of White". These were recalled before issue but some were released in error. (*Price £650*)

LS **39**

2007 (17 May). *Memories of Wembley Stadium*. Type LS **39**. Litho* Cartor. Original selling price £7·35. Perf 14½×14.
LS39   20×(1st) stamps as No. 2291 but without "WORLD CUP 2002" inscription with attached labels .... 17·00

LS **40**

2007 (5 June). *40th Anniversary of the First Machin Definitives*. Type LS **40**. Litho Cartor. Original selling price £7·35. Phosphor frame*. Perf 14½.
LS40   20×(1st) stamps as Type **1984** with attached labels .... 18·00

LS 41

2007 (17 July). *Harry Potter.* Type LS **41**. Litho Walsall. Original selling price £7·35. Perf 15×14.
LS41   20×(1st) stamps as within **MS**2757 but self-adhesive*, four of each design with attached labels .... 16·50

LS 42

2007 (6 Nov). *Christmas.* Type LS **42**. Litho* Cartor. Original selling price £8·30. Perf 15×14.
LS42   8×(2nd), 8×(1st) and 4×78p. Christmas self-adhesive as Nos. 2789/90 and 2793 with attached labels .... 17·25

LS 43

2007 (8 Nov). *Letters from the Front.* Type LS **43**. Litho Cartor. Original selling price £7·35. Perf 14½.
LS43   20×(1st) Soldiers in poppy flower stamps as Type **2038** with attached labels... 16·50

LS 44

2007 (30 Nov). *Glorious Scotland.* Type LS **44**. Litho Cartor. Original selling price £7·35. Perf 15×14 (*without** elliptical holes).
LS44   20×(1st) Scotland stamps, self-adhesive*, as No. S131 with attached labels.. 17·00

LS 45

2008 (15 Jan). *I wrote to say?.* Type LS **45**. Litho* Cartor. Original selling price £7·35. Perf 15×14 (with one elliptical hole in each vert side*).
LS45   20×(1st) "Smilers" stamps self-adhesive as Nos. 2568/70 (eight of No. 2569, 6 each of Nos. 2568 and 2570) with attached circular labels................................ 17·00

LS 46

2008 (11 Mar). *Glorious Northern Ireland.* Type LS **46**. Litho Cartor. Original selling price £7·35. Perf 15×14 (*without** elliptical holes).
LS46   20×(1st) Northern Ireland stamps, self-adhesive*, as No. NI95 with attached labels....................................... 17·00

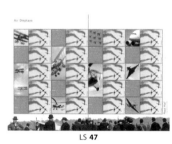

LS 47

2008 (17 July). *Air Displays.* Type LS **47**. Litho Cartor. Original selling price £7·75. Perf 14½×14.
LS47   20 ×(1st) Red Arrows stamps as No. 2855 with attached labels.. 17·00

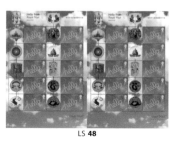

LS 48

2008 (5 Aug). *Beijing 2008 Olympic Expo.* Type LS **48**. Litho Cartor. Original selling price £7·75. Perf 14*.
LS48   20 (1st) "Hello" greetings stamps No. 2262 with attached labels.. 17·00

LS **49**

2008 (29 Sept). *Glorious United Kingdom*. Type LS **49**. Litho Cartor. Original selling price £7·75. Perf 15×14 (with one elliptical hole in each vertical side).
LS49   5 ×1st England, 5×1st Northern Ireland, 5×1st
      Scotland and 5×1st Wales stamps, self-adhesive*, as
      Nos. EN30, NI95, S131 and W122 with attached labels .   18·00

LS **50**

LS **51**

LS **52**

LS **53**

2008 (28 Oct). *Smilers for Kids* (1st series). Types LS **50/3**. Litho Cartor. Original selling price £7·95 each. Perf 15×14 (with one elliptical hole on each vertical side).
LS50   (1st) ×20 New Baby stamps as No. 2672* with
      attached circular Peter Rabbit labels....................................   90·00
LS51   (1st) ×20 Sunflower stamps No. 2820 with attached
      circular Almond Blossom fairy labels.....................................   90·00
LS52   (1st) ×20 Balloons stamps No. 2822 with attached
      circular Mr. Men labels ....   90·00

LS53   (1st) ×20 Balloons stamps No. 2822 with attached
      circular Noddy labels..   90·00
      No. LS50 contains stamps as No. 2672 but perforated with one
      elliptical hole on each vertical side.
      Sheets as Nos. LS50/3 but containing ten stamps and ten labels
      were sold in packs at £7·95 per pack.

LS **54**

2008 (4 Nov). *Christmas*. Type LS **54**. Litho* Cartor. Original selling price £8·85. Perf 15×14.
LS54   8×(2nd), 8×(1st) and 4×81p. Christmas self-adhesive
      as Nos. 2876/7 and 2881 with attached labels..................   17·50

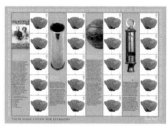

LS **55**

2008 (6 Nov). *We Will Remember*. Type LS **55**. Litho Cartor. Original selling price £7·75. Perf 14½.
LS55   20 ×(1st) Soldier's face in poppy flower stamps as
      No. 2885 with attached labels ....   17·00

LS **56**

2009 (13 Jan). *Design Classics*. Type LS **56**. Litho Cartor. Original selling price £7·75. Perf 14×14½*.
LS56   20×(1st) Mini stamps as No. 2889 with attached
      labels...   17·00

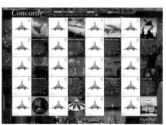

LS **57**

2009 (2 Mar). *40th Anniversary of the First Flight of Concorde*. Type LS **57**. Litho Cartor. Original selling price £7·75. Perf 14×14½*.
LS57   20×(1st) Concorde stamps as No. 2891 ....   16·50

LS **58**

2009 (17 Mar). *Castles of Northern Ireland*. Type LS **58**. Litho Cartor.
Original selling price £7·74. Perf 15×14 (with one elliptical hole in
each vertical side).
LS58   20×(1st) Northern Ireland stamps, self-adhesive*, as
      No. NI95 with attached labels.............................. 17·00

LS **59**

2009 (23 Apr). *Castles of England*. Type LS **59**. Litho Cartor. Original
selling price £8·35. Perf 15×14 (with one elliptical hole in each
vertical side).
LS59   20×(1st) As St. George's flag stamp from **MS**EN50 but
      self-adhesive* with attached labels................... 17·00

LS **60**

LS **61**

LS **62**

LS **63**

2009 (30 Apr). *Smilers for Kids* (2nd series). Types LS **60/3**. Litho Cartor.
Original selling price £8·50 each. Perf 15×14 (with one elliptical
hole in each vertical side).
LS60   20×(1st) "Hello" stamps as No. 2819 with attached
      circular Jeremy Fisher labels .... 90·00
LS61   20×(1st) Sunflower stamps as No. 2820 with attached
      circular Wild Cherry fairy labels.......................... 90·00
LS62   20×(1st) Balloons stamps as No. 2822 with attached
      circular LIttle Miss Sunshine labels.................... 90·00
LS63   20×(1st) Balloons stamps as No. 2822 with attached
      circular Big Ears labels.. 90·00
    Sheets as Nos. LS60/3 but containing ten stamps and ten labels
were sold in packs at £7·95 per pack.

LS **64**

2009 (3 Aug). *Thaipex 09 International Stamp Exhibition, Bangkok*.
Type LS **64**. Litho Cartor. Original selling price £8·35. Perf 14*.
LS64   20×(1st) "Hello" greetings stamps as No. 2262 with
      attached labels... 17·00

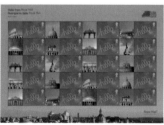

LS **65**

2009 (18 Aug). *Post Boxes*. Type LS **65**. Litho Cartor. Original selling
price £8·35. Perf 14.
LS65   20×(1st) Letter box stamps as No. 2950 with attached
      labels.. 17·00

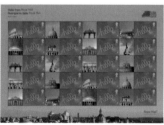

LS **66**

2009 (21 Oct). *Italia 2009 International Stamp Exhibition, Rome*. Type
LS **66**. Litho Cartor. Original selling price £8·35. Perf 14*.
LS66   20×(1st) "Hello" greetings stamps as No. 2262 with
      attached labels... 17·50

LS **67**

2009 (3 Nov). *Christmas.* Type LS **67**. Litho Cartor. Original selling price £9. Perf 14½×14 (with one elliptical hole in each vertical side).
LS67 8×(2nd), 8×(1st), 2×56p. and 2×90p. Christmas self-adhesive as Nos. 2991/2, 2994 and 2996.............................. 20·00

LS **68**

2009 (30 Nov). *Castles of Scotland.* Type LS **68**. Litho Cartor. Original selling price £8·35. Perf 15×14 (with one elliptical hole in each vertical side).
LS68 20×(1st) As Scottish flag stamp from **MS**S153 but self-adhesive with attached labels .... 17·00

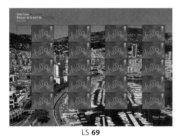

LS **69**

2009 (4 Dec). *MonacoPhil 2009 International Stamp Exhibition, Monaco.* Type LS **69**. Litho Cartor. Original selling price £8·35. Perf 14*.
LS69 20×(1st) "Hello" greetings stamps as No. 2262 with attached labels... 17·00

LS **70**

2010 (26 Jan). *For all occasions .* Type LS **70**. Litho Cartor. Original selling price £9·70. Perf 14½×14 (with one elliptical hole in each vertical side).
LS70 16×(1st), 2×(Europe up to 20 grams) and 2×(Worldwide up to 20 grams) stamps as within **MS**3024 but self-adhesive* two of each design with attached labels... 30·00

LS **71**

2010 (1 Mar). *Castles of Wales.* Type LS **71**. Litho Cartor. Original selling price £8. Perf 15×14 (with one elliptical hole in each vertical side).
LS71 20×(1st) As Red Dragon stamp from **MS**W147 but self-adhesive* with attached labels .... 17·00

LS **72**

2010 (8 May). *London 2010 Festival of Stamps.* Type LS **72**. Litho Cartor. Original selling price £8·50. Die-cut Perf 15×14 (with one elliptical hole in each vertical side).
LS72 20×(1st) "Hello" greetings stamps as No. 2819 with attached labels... 17·00

LS **73**

2010 (8 May). *Keep Smiling 10 Years of Smilers* Type LS **73**. Litho Cartor. Original selling price £10. Die-cut Perf 15×14 (with one elliptical hole in each vertical side).
LS73 3× No. 2821 (1st) Union Jack, one each of Nos. 2572 (1st) Robin in pillar box, 2674 (1st) THANK YOU, 2693 (1st) LOVE, 2822 (1st) Balloons, 2823 (1st) Fireworks and also 4×(1st) Birthday cake, 4×(1st) Birthday present, 2×(Europe up to 20 grams) and 2×(Worldwide up to 20 grams) stamps as within **MS**3024 but self-adhesive* with attached labels.. 50·00

2010 (15 Sept). *70th Anniversary of the Battle of Britain.* Type LS **74**. Litho Cartor. Original selling price £8·50. Perf 14×14½.
LS74 20×(1st) Spitfire stamps as No. 2887 with attached labels... 17·00

LS **74**

LS **75**

2010 (2 Nov). *Christmas.* Type LS **75**. Litho Cartor. Original selling price £9·30. Perf 14½×14 (with one elliptical hole in each vertical side).
LS75   8×(2nd), 8×(1st), 2×60p. and 2×97p. Christmas self-
             adhesive as Nos. 3128/34.. 18·50

LS **76**

2011 (12 Feb). *Indipex International Stamp Exhibition,* New Delhi. Type LS **76**. Litho Cartor. Original selling price £8·50. Perf 15×14 (with one elliptical hole in each vertical side).
LS76   20×(1st) Union Jack self-adhesive stamps as No. 2821
             with attached labels................................. 17·50

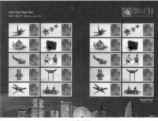

LS **77**

2011 (28 July). *Philanippon '11 World Stamp Exhibition, Yokohama.* Type LS **77**. Litho Cartor. Original selling price £9·50. Die-cut perf 15×14 (with one elliptical hole in each vertical side).
LS77   20×(1st) "Hello" self-adhesive greetings stamps as
             No. 2819 with attached labels showing
             origami models....................................... 17·50

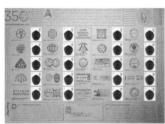

LS **78**

2011 (15 Sept). *350th Anniversary of the Postmark.* Type LS **78**. Litho Cartor. Original selling price £9·50. Die-cut perf 14½×14 (with one elliptical hole in each vertical side).
LS78   20×(1st) Recreation of Crown seal stamps as within
             MS3024 but self-adhesive with attached
             labels showing postmarks .... 17·00

LS **79**

2011 (8 Nov). *Christmas. 400th Anniversary of the King James Bible.* Type LS **79**. Litho. Original selling price £10·45. Die-cut perf 14½×14 (with one elliptical hole in each vertical side).
LS79   8×(2nd) 8×(1st), 2×68p. and 2×£1·10 Christmas
             self-adhesive stamps as Nos. 3242/8 with
             attached labels showing verses from the
             King James Bible....................... 30·00

LS **80**

2012 (20 Jan). *Lunar New Year. Year of the Dragon.* Type LS **80**. Litho Cartor. Original selling price £9·50. Die-cut perf 15×14 (with one elliptical hole in each vertical side).
LS80   20×(1st) Fireworks self-adhesive greetings stamps as
             No. 2823 with attached labels .... 20·00

LS **81**

2012 (18 June). *Indonesia 2012 International Stamp Exhibition, Jakarta.* Type LS **81**. Litho. Original selling price £12·50. Die-cut perf 15×14 (with one elliptical hole in each vertical side).
LS81   20×(1st) "Hello" self-adhesive greetings stamps as No.
             2819 with attached labels showing images
             of Indonesia .... 17·00

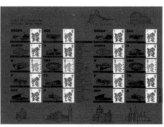

LS **82**

2012 (27 June). *Olympic and Paralympic Games, London. Games Venues.* Type LS **82**. Litho Cartor. Die-cut perf 14½×14 (with one elliptical hole in each vertical side).

LS82   8×(1st) Olympic Games, 8×1st Paralympic Games, 2×Worldwide up to 20g Olympic Games and 2×Worldwide up to 20g Paralympic Games as Nos. 3250/3 with attached labels showing Games venues... 90·00

LS **83**

2012 (6 Nov). *Christmas.* Illustrations by Axel Scheffler. Type LS **83**. Litho. Original selling price £13·10. Die-cut perf 14½×14 (with one elliptical hole in each vertical side).

LS83   8×(2nd), 8×1st, 2×87p. and 2×£1·28 Christmas self-adhesive as Nos. 3415/16, 3418 and 3420 ...... 18·50

LS **84**

2013 (7 Feb). *Lunar New Year. Year of the Snake.* Type LS **84**. Litho Cartor. Original selling price £12·50. Die-cut perf 15×14 (with one elliptical hole in each vertical side).

LS84   20×(1st) Fireworks stamps as No. 2823 with attached labels showing Chinese decorations .... 18·50

LS **85**

2013 (26 Mar). *50th Anniversary of Doctor Who* (TV programme). Type LS **85**. Litho Cartor. Original selling price £12. Die-cut perf 14½×14 (with one elliptical hole in each vertical side).

LS85   20×(1st) TARDIS stamps as No. 3449 with attached labels showing Cybermen, Daleks, Silurians, Sontarans and The Master .... 20·00

LS **86**

2013 (10 May). *Australia 2013 World Stamp Exhibition, Melbourne.* Type LS **86**. Litho* Cartor. Original selling price £12·50. Die-cut perf 15×14 (with one elliptical hole in each vertical side)

LS86 20×1st Hello self-adhesive greetings stamps as No. 2819 with attached labels showing images of Melbourne...................... 18·50

LS **87**

2013 (2 Aug). *Bangkok 2013 World Stamp Exhibition, Thailand.* Type LS **87**. Litho* Cartor. Original selling price £12·50. Die-cut perf 15×14 (with one elliptical hole in each vertical side).

LS87 20 x 1st Hello self-adhesive greetings stamps as No. 2819 with attached labels showing images of Thailand........................... 18·50

LS **88**

2013 (5 Nov). *Christmas. Madonna and Child Paintings.* Type LS **88**. Litho* ISP Cartor. Original selling price £13·62. Die-cut perf 14½×15 (with one elliptical hole in each vertical side*).

LS88 8×(2nd), 8×(1st), 2×88p. and one each of £1·28 and £1·88 Christmas self-adhesive as Nos. 3542/3, 3545 and 3547/8 with attached labels... 32·00

LS **89**

2013 (10 Dec). *Lunar New Year. Year of the Horse.* Type LS **89**. Litho* ISP Cartor. Original selling price £12·50. Die-cut perf 15×14 (with one elliptical hole in each vertical side).

LS89 20×1st Fireworks stamps as No. 2823 with attached labels   18·50

LS **90**

2014 (4 Nov). *Christmas.* Illustrations by Andrew Bannecker. Type LS **90**. Litho* ISP Cartor. Original selling price £15·20. Die-cut perf 14½×15 (with one elliptical hole in each vertical side*).

LS90   8×(2nd), 8×(1st), 2×£1·28 and 2×£1·47 Christmas self-adhesive as Nos. 3650/1 and 3654/5 with attached labels .... 20·00

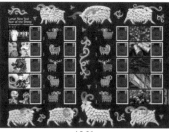

LS **91**

2014 (19 Nov). *Lunar New Year. Year of the Ram.* Type LS **91**. Litho* ISP Cartor. Original selling price £12·90. Die-cut perf 15×14 (with one elliptical hole in each vertical side).
LS91   20×1st Fireworks stamps as No. 2823 with attached labels .... 18·50

LS **92**

2014 (1 Dec). *Kuala Lumpur 2014 World Stamp Exhibition, Malaysia.* Type LS **92**. Litho* ISP Cartor. Original selling price £12·90. Die-cut perf 15×14 (with one elliptical hole in each vertical side).
LS92   20×1st Hello self-adhesive greetings stamps as No. 2819 with attached labels showing images of Malaysia .... 18·50

LS **93**

2015 (20 Jan). *Smilers.* Type LS **93**. Litho* ISP Cartor. Original selling price £12·90. Die-cut perf 14½×14 (with one elliptical hole in each vertical side*).
LS93   20×1st Smilers stamps self-adhesive as Nos. 3670/7 (3×Nos. 3670, 3672/3 and 3675, 2× Nos. 3671, 3674 and 3676/7) with attached labels £185

LS **94**

2015 (6 May). *175th Anniversary of the Penny Black.* Type LS **94**. Litho* ISP Cartor. Original selling price £12·90. Die-cut perf 14½×14 (with one elliptical hole in each vert side*).
LS94   10×1st Penny Black and 10×1st Two Pence Blue (as within MS3710) self-adhesive with attached labels 65.00

LS **95**

2015 (13 May). *Europhilex London 2015 Exhibition.* Type LS **95**. Litho* ISP Cartor. Original selling price £12·90. Die-cut perf 15×14 (with one elliptical hole in each vert side).
LS95   20×1st "Hello" self-adhesive greetings stamps as No. 2819 with attached labels 19.00

LS **96**

2015 (20 Oct). *Star Wars. Heroes and Villains.* Type LS **96**. Litho ISP Cartor. Original selling price £6.80. Die-cut perf 14½.*
LS96   10×1st *Star Wars* stamps as Nos. 3758/9, each ×3, and as Nos. 3761/2, each×2, but self-adhesive 11.00

LS **97**

2015 (3 Nov). *Christmas.* Type LS **97**. Litho* ISP Cartor. Original selling price £15.96. Die-cut perf 14½×15 (with one elliptical hole in each vert side*).
LS97   8x(2nd), 8x(1st) and one each of £1, £1.33, £1.52 and £2.25 Christmas self-adhesive as Nos. 3771/2 and 3775/8 with attached labels 22.00

LS **98**

2015 (9 Nov). *Lunar New Year. Year of the Monkey.* Type LS **98**. Litho* ISP Cartor. Original selling price £13.10. Die-cut perf 15×14 (with one elliptical hole in each vert side).

LS98   20×1st Fireworks self-adhesive greetings stamps as No. 2823 with attached labels... 18.50

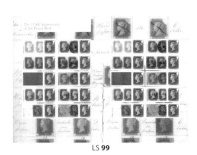

LS **99**

2016 (18 Feb). *175th Anniversary of the Penny Red.* Type LS **99**. Litho ISP Cartor. Original selling price £13.10. Die-cut perf 14½×14 (with one elliptical hole in each vert side).

LS99   20×1st Penny Red self-adhesive stamps as No. 3806 with attached labels 19.00

LS **100**

2016 (28 May). *New York World Stamp Show.* Type LS **100**. Original selling price £13.30. Litho* ISP Cartor. Die-cut perf 15×14 (with one elliptical hole in each vert side).

LS100   20×1st Hello self-adhesive greetings stamps as No. 2819 with attached labels.................................... 19.00

LS **101**

2016 (20 Oct). *Mr. Men and Little Miss* (children's books by Roger Hargreaves). Type LS **101**. Original selling price £6.90. Litho ISP Cartor. Die-cut perf 14½.

LS101   10×1st Mr. Men and Little Miss stamps as Nos. 3891/900 but self-adhesive.. 11.00

LS **102**

2016 (8 Nov). *Christmas.* Type LS **102**. Original selling price £16.21. Litho ISP Cartor. Die-cut perf 14½×15 (with one elliptical hole in each vert side*).

LS102   8×(2nd), 8×(1st) and one each of £1.05, £1.33, £1.52 and £2.25 Christmas self-adhesive as Nos. 3903/10 with attached labels.. 22.50

LS **103**

2016 (8 Nov). *Celebrating 50 Years of Christmas Stamps.* Type LS **103**. Original selling price £12.40. Litho ISP Cartor. Die-cut perf 14½×15 (with one elliptical hole in each vert side*).

LS103   8×(2nd) and 8×(1st) Christmas self-adhesive stamps as Nos. 3903/4 with attached labels................................ 17.00

LS **104**

2016 (15 Nov). *Lunar New Year. Year of the Rooster.* Type LS **104**. Original selling price £13.30. Litho* ISP Cartor.

LS104   20×1st Fireworks self-adhesive greetings stamps as No. 2823 with attached labels.................................... 18.50

LS **105**

2017 (24 May). *Finlandia 2017* European Stamp Exhibition, Tampere. Type LS **105**. Original selling price £13.50. Litho ISP Cartor. Die-cut perf 15×14 (with one elliptical hole in each vert side).

LS105   20 ×1st Hello self-adhesive greetings stamps as No. 2819 with attached labels.................................... 20.00

LS **106**

2017 (7 Nov). *Christmas*. Type LS **106**. Original selling price £16.40. Litho ISP Cartor. Die-cut perf 14½×15 (with one elliptical hole in each vert side).

LS106   8×(2nd), 8×(1st) and one each of £1.17, £1.40, £1.57 and £2.27 Christmas self-adhesive stamps as Nos. 4019/20 and 4023/6 with attached labels 25.00

LS **107**

2017 (7 Nov). *Christmas*. Type LS **107**. Original selling price £12.60. Litho ISP Cartor. Die-cut perf 14½×15 (with one elliptical hole in each vert side).

LS 107   8×(2nd) and 8×(1st) Christmas self-adhesive stamps as Nos. 4028/9 with attached labels 19.00

LS **108**

2017 (16 Nov). *Lunar New Year. Year of the Dog*. Type LS **108**. Original selling price £13.50. Litho ISP Cartor. Die-cut perf 15×14 (with one elliptical hole in each vert side).

LS108   10×1st Fireworks self-adhesive greetings stamps as No. 2823 with attached labels 20.00

The following Royal Mail commemorative sheets were sold at a significant premium over the face value of the stamps:

1.4.2008   *100 Years of the Territorial Army*. 10×1st Union Flag stamps with labels

24.7.2008   *The London 1908 Olympic Games*. 10×1st Union Flag stamps with labels

14.11.2008   *60th Birthday of Prince Charles*. 10×1st Wales self-adhesive stamps with labels

21.7.2009   *40th Anniversary of Moon Landing*. 10×1st Union Flag stamps with labels

18.9.2009   *Big Ben* 10×1st Union Flag stamps with labels

7.10.2009   *800th Anniversary of the University of Cambridge*. 10×1st Fireworks stamps (as Type **1993**) with labels

22.10.2009   *Olympic and Paralympic Games* (I). "The Journey Begins" 10×1st as Types **2192/2201** with labels

18.5.2010   *Halley's Comet* 10×1st Union Flag stamps with labels

8.7.2010   *Grand Prix* 10×1st Union Flag stamps with labels

27.7.2010   *Olympic and Paralympic Games* (II). "One Aim" 10×1st as Types **2290/9** with labels

10.8.2010   *10th Anniversary of the London Eye*. 10×1st Union Flag stamps with labels

28.10.2010   *Remembrance: The National Memorial Arboretum*. 10×1st Poppies on Barbed Wire Stem stamps (as Type **2112**)

30.3.2011   *50th Anniversary of the E Type Jaguar*. 10×1st Union Flag stamps with labels

10.6.2011   *90th Birthday of Prince Philip*. 10×1st self-adhesive Union Flag stamps with labels

27.7.2011   *Olympic and Paralympic Games* (III). "High Hopes". 10×1st as Types **2383/92** with labels

10.4.2012   *Centenary of the Sinking of the Titanic*. 10×1st As Crown seal stamp from **MS**3024 with labels

1.5.2012   *50th Anniversary of the First James Bond Film*. 10×1st Union Flag stamps with labels

5.10.2012   *40th Anniversary of the Last Goon Show*. 10×1st Union Flag stamps with labels

8.11.2012   *150th Anniversary of Notts County Football Club*. 10×1st Fireworks stamps with labels

16.4.2013   *60th Anniversary of Launch of Royal Yacht Britannia*. 10×1st Union Flag stamps with labels

1.5.2013   *Birth Bicentenary of David Livingstone* (explorer and medical missionary) 10×1st Scottish Flag stamps (as within **MS**S153) and labels

19.9.2013   *150th Birth Anniversary of Bertram Mackennal* 10×1st As Crown Seal stamps from MS3024 with labels

25.2.2014   *Middlesex County Cricket Club* 10×1st Fireworks stamps with labels

25.3.2014   *By Sea, By Land. 350th Anniversary of the Royal Marines* 10x1st Union Flag stamps with labels

16.10.2014   *50th Anniversary of Donald Campbell's Water and Land Speed Records*. 10×1st Union Flag with labels

11.11.2014   *Christmas Truce*. 10×1st Poppies on Barbed Wire Stems stamps as Type **2588** with labels

18.3.2015   *The Post Office Rifles during the Great War*. 10×1st Union Flag stamps with labels

24.4.2015   *Birth Bicentenary of Anthony Trollope*. 10×1st Union Flag stamps with labels

20.8.2015   *The Gurkhas Celebrating 200 Years of Service 1815-2015*. 10×1st Union Flag stamps with labels

17.9.2015   *Animals of the First World War 1914-1918*. 10×1st Union Flag stamps with labels

12.1.2016   *The Duke of Edinburgh's Award Diamond Anniversary* 10×1st Union Flag stamps with labels

25.4.2016   *ANZAC*. 10×1st Poppies on Barbed Wire Stems stamps as Type **2588** with labels

14.10.2016   *950th Anniversary of the Battle of Hastings*. 10×1st England Flag stamps as Type EN **6** with labels

13.6.2017   *HRH The Princess Royal Thirtieth Anniversary*. 10×Union Flag stamps with labels

30.6.2017   *Canada Celebrating 150 Years*. 10×1st Fireworks stamps with labels

13.9.2017   *Opening of The Postal Museum*. 10×1st (4 Penny Black as T **2848**, 3 Two Pence Blue as T **2938**, 3 Penny Red as T **2937**) all with labels

1.6.2018   *150th Anniversary of the Trades Union Congress*. 10×1st Royalty Seal stamps with labels

continued

Looking for that
Elusive Stamp?

Get in touch with our team

Great Britain Department: email gb@stanleygibbons.com or phone 020 7557 4464
Commonwealth Department: email amansi@stanleygibbons.com or phone 020 7557 4455

BY APPOINTMENT TO
HER MAJESTY THE QUEEN
PHILATELISTS
STANLEY GIBBONS LTD
LONDON

STANLEY GIBBONS
LONDON 1856

STANLEY GIBBONS 399 STRAND LONDON WC2R 0LX | WWW.STANLEYGIBBONS.COM

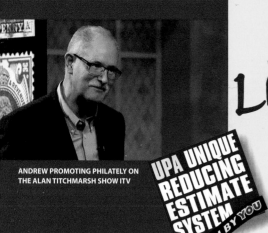

ANDREW PROMOTING PHILATELY ON THE ALAN TITCHMARSH SHOW ITV

UPA UNIQUE REDUCING ESTIMATE SYSTEM DRIVEN BY YOU

Literally **The** that Every is

Dear Colleague,
For the first time, in this open letter, I'm going to give you the thinking, the 'mindset' if you will, of how and why my stamp auction thrives where others do not...

As many of you will attest. At certain 'peak' times in our auction 'cycle,' I personally answer the telephone to callers. It's a wonderfully enjoyable and rewarding thing for me to do, because, you kindly inform me of your likes and dislikes, about us, and other auctions that you may have dealt with before discovering U P A...

One of the most common 'threads' that I have learnt from You, and from other Dealers and Auctioneers, is simply 'how does U P A do it?' How is it that we have become the largest Stamp Auction in the UK and almost the largest globally? How can we afford to expend more upon advertising worldwide than most dealers sell in a year? Simply put: How can we afford to offer more and charge less – indeed – how can we afford to offer more and charge you no extra w-h-a-t-s-o-e-v-e-r ??

The fundamental reason why is because, unlike others, everything we do is Driven by You.. Over the course of the past 18 years I have discovered that combining this 'bottom-up' thinking with offering **simply MASSIVE Philatelic Choice** – permits us to offer you a Unique Collector-Driven Stamp Auction Experience. Think about it: whilst the rest of our philatelic industry works 'top-down' – issuing diktats, regulation, charges and fees, and few guarantees – ever increasingly we throw these off encouraged by more and more collectors joining us, who crucially continue to participate in auction after auction... rewarding us by their loyalty, enriching their collections... enabling us, in turn, to reward them.

...So that, when you inform us that You don't like 'X' (extra shipping and insurance charges), and You dislike 'Y' (paying credit card charges) and you positively abhor paying 'Z' – up to 25% buyer's premiums... (particularly when you may realise that you are possibly or probably paying a buyer's premium upon that dealer's own stamps that they are selling to You)... we take that valuable knowledge you've imparted and 'dial' it back into our auction system, not purely for your benefit BUT for our mutual benefit because over the 18 years that U P A has been auctioning I have discovered that if we have enough participating bidders in our auctions we can offer you a **radically superior service and a radically different deal than others**...

1st £55 FREE WINNINGS

I SUPPORT NO BP
Shield Yourself & Save
SUPPORT NO BUYER'S PREMIUM
DRIVEN BY YOU

NO SURCHARGE
MasterCard
DRIVEN BY YOU

NEW ✓ POST-FREE UPA Loyalty Bonus
DRIVEN BY YOU

Discover the Difference

UNIVERSAL PHILATELIC AUCTIONS SINCE 1958

Philately Understood

Difference is thing we Do Driven by You...

To me it is logical that when you configure your auction to really give collectors what they seek, mixing in a unique reducing-estimate-auction system, blended with hundreds and thousands of simply massive philatelic choice – these are the reasons why more Collectors bid in my U P A auctions than any other auction in the UK and almost all others globally. Consider that each U P A auction adds up to 250 different new bidders when most stamp auctions only have a few hundred bidders TOTAL – the SCALE of Your SUPPORT permits us to 'square' the circle so that, hopefully, we can offer collectors like you *True Philatelic VAL-YOU for Money...*

How can you help? Simply by participating regularly in our auctions permits us to give back, producing the most expensive and the best post-free auction catalogues you may ever receive whilst staying in business. Your continued support is powering our new Loyalty Post-Free System. So, all that I would respectfully ask and encourage you to do – is join the 2,184 different Collectors and Dealers from 58 different countries worldwide, who participated in my last auction U P A #69, creating new philatelic world records of participation and in some cases of realisations – whilst an astonishing 90% of bidders were successful... and those lots that remained unsold carried forward at *ever decreasing estimate and reserve* thereby creating the nucleus of this auction with a 'sprinkling' of more than 8,000 new lots of absolutely extraordinary NEW material... whereby, ultimately collectors like You determine values, not catalogues...

My wife and I, and members of our super Team, wish you Happy Hunting and great Philatelic Fun. With thanks for Your continued support. Please do tell your Philatelic Friends. They'll receive the best Philatelic Thank You for joining us and you'll be rewarded too!

To Collect Your NEXT £20 20,000± lot Auction Catalogue FREE Request Yours NOW

IT'S SO EASY – START NOW

Andrew McGavin, Managing Director
Universal Philatelic Auctions UPA,

TIPS OF THE TRADE
Your *Expert* Guide to Stamp Collecting
Volume 1
✓How to buy: How to Sell
✓Catalogue Value: common misconceptions
✓How to insure reasonably
✓Which Accessories do you really need?
And Much Much More...

£55 OFF
1st UPA STAMP AUCTIONS PURCHASES

£55 OFF: Do You Qualify?
INSIDE: See pages 15/16 →

REQUEST MY 'TIPS OF THE TRADE' FREE BOOKLET

UNIVERSAL PHILATELIC AUCTIONS (GB-CONC)
4 The Old Coalyard, West End Northleach, Glos. GL54 3HE UK
Tel: 01451 861111 • Fax: 01451 861297

BY APPOINTMENT TO
HER MAJESTY THE QUEEN
PHILATELISTS
STANLEY GIBBONS LTD
LONDON

STANLEY GIBBONS
LONDON 1856

WINDSOR ALBUMS
in line with the Great Britain Concise catalogue

Windsor albums are the only ones to provide stamp descriptions on the left hand page and spaces for mounting on the right. Updated with annual supplements, the Windsor albums run in line with the Stanley Gibbons Great Britain Concise catalogue. Windsor leaves fit both the 22 ring Sovereign binder and the Windsor Popular Springback binder.

Leaf dimensions: 247 × 281mm.
Leaf colour: cream.
Album colour: ● ●

HANDMADE

This handmade Album is the only one country to come with black mounts.

WINDSOR ALBUM

Please add RED or GRN after the codes listed below to specify which colour you wish to order eg. R5240RED

	Album		Album with Mounts		Leaves		Leaves with mounts	
Vol. 1 Album (1840-1952)	R5240	£65	R5240HL	£159	R5248	£44.95	R5248HL	£139
Vol. 2 Album (1952-1970)	R5241	£65	R5241HL	£159	R5249	£44.95	R5249HL	£139
Vol. 3 Album (1970-1985)	R5242	£65	R5242HL	£159	R5250	£44.95	R5250HL	£139
Vol. 4 Album (1986-1995)	R5243	£65	R5243HL	£159	R5251	£44.95	R5251HL	£139
Vol. 5 Album (1996-2003)	R5244	£65	R5244HL	£159	R5252	£44.95	R5252HL	£139
Vol. 6 Album (2004-2009)	R5245	£65	R5245HL	£159	R5253	£44.95	R5253HL	£139
Vol. 7 Album (2010-2012)	R5227	£65	R5227HL	£159	R5227	£44.95	R5227HL	£139
Vol. 8 Album (2013-2015)	R5224	£65	R5224HL	£159	R5224	£44.95	R5224HL	£139
Vol. 9 Album (2016)	R5900	£65	R5900HL	£115	R5223-16	£44.95	R5223-16HL	£84.95
Vol. 1-9 Album Set	R5240(SO)	£499.95	R5240(SO)HL	£1220	R5248(SO)	£340	R5248HL(SO)	£1040
	SAVE £85.05		SAVE £167		SAVE £64.55		SAVE £156.95	

Binder Only R3210 £33.95 Blank Leaves (per 25) R0322 £9.95 Windsor Slipcase R0335 £22.95

Gold Foil Windsor Spine Labels R7559SL £2.25